Foundations of **Physics**

Tom Hsu, Ph.D.

Teacher's Guide

First Edition
CPO Science
Peabody, Massachusetts 01960

About the Author

Dr. Thomas C. Hsu is a nationally recognized innovator in science and math education and the founder of CPO Science (formerly Cambridge Physics Outlet). He holds a Ph.D. in Applied Plasma Physics from the Massachusetts Institute of Technology (MIT), and has taught students from elementary, secondary and college levels across the nation. He was nominated for MIT's Goodwin medal for excellence in teaching and has received numerous awards from various state agencies for his work to improve science education. Tom has personally worked with more than 12,000 K-12 teachers and administrators and is well known as a consultant, workshop leader and developer of curriculum and equipment for inquiry-based learning in science and math. With CPO Science, Tom has published textbooks in physical science, integrated science, Earth and space science, and also written fifteen curriculum Investigation guides that accompany CPO Science equipment. Along with the CPO Science team, Tom is always active, developing innovative new tools for teaching and learning science, including an inquiry-based chemistry text.

Foundations of Physics Teacher's Guide
Copyright © 2004 CPO Science
ISBN 1-58892-061-5
2 3 4 5 6 7 8 9 - QWE - 08 07 06

CPO Science
26 Howley Street
Peabody, MA 01960
(800) 932-5227
http://www.cposcience.com

Printed and bound in the United States of America

ynda Pennell – Educational Products, Executive Vice esident

A., English, M.Ed., Administration, Reading Disabilities, ortheastern University; CAGS Media, University of assachusetts, Boston

ationally known in high school restructuring and for tegrating academic and career education. Served as the rector of an urban school with 17 years teaching/ Iministrative experience.

homas Narro – Product Design, Senior Vice President

S., Mechanical engineering, Rensselaer Polytechnic Institute

ccomplished design and manufacturing engineer; xperienced consultant in corporate reengineering and dustrial-environmental acoustics.

cott Eddleman – Curriculum Manager

S., Biology, Southern Illinois University; M.Ed., Harvard niversity

aught for 13 years in urban and rural settings; nationally nown as trainer of inquiry-based science and mathematics roject-based instruction; curriculum development onsultant.

tacy Kissel – Physics Teacher, Brookline High School, rookline, Massachusetts

ight years teaching experience physics, math and ategrated science.

risty Beauvais – Physics Teacher, Concord-Carlisle egional High School, Concord, Massachusetts

ix years teaching experience in physics and chemistry.

Ir. Darren Garnier – Research Physicist, Columbia niversity/MIT

xtensive experience with experiment design. Developed oftware and applications for the CPO Data Collector.

CPO Science Development Team

Laine Ives – Curriculum Writer

B.A., English, Gordon College; graduate work, biology, Cornell University, Wheelock College

Experience teaching middle and high school, here and abroad; expertise in developing middle school curriculum and hands-on activities.

Mary Beth Abel Hughes – Curriculum Writer

B.S., Marine biology, College of Charleston; M.S., Biological sciences, University of Rhode Island

Taught science and math at an innovative high school; expertise in scientific research and inquiry-based teaching methods and curiculum development.

Sonja Taylor – Curriculum Writer

B.S., Chemistry, Stephen F. Austin State University

Taught chemistry and biology for four years. Exptertise in teaching with inquiry and technology.

Bruce Holloway – Senior Creative Designer

Pratt Institute, N.Y.; Boston Museum School of Fine Arts

Expertise in product design, advertising, and three-dimensional exhibit design. Commissioned for the New Hampshire Duck Stamp for 1999 and 2003.

Science Content Consultants

Dr. David Guerra – Associate Professor, Department Chair Physics, St. Anselm College, Manchester, New Hampshire

Fourteen years college teaching experience. Research laser development and applications.

David Bliss – Physics Teacher, Mohawk Central High School, New York, New York

Thirty-two years teaching experience.

Polly Crisman – Graphic Designer and Illustrator

B.F.A., University of New Hampshire

Graphic artist with expertise in advertising and marketing design, freelance illustrating, and caricature art.

Patsy DeCoster – Staff Development and Service Director

B.S., Biology/Secondary education, Grove City College; M.Ed., Tufts University

Curriculum and professional development specialist. Taught science for 12 years. National inquiry-based science presenter.

Erik Benton – Professional Development Specialist

B.F.A., University of Massachusetts

Taught for 8 years in public and private schools, focusing on inquiry and experiential learning environments.

Matt Lombard – Photographing and Marketing

B.S., Salem State College

Oversees all marketing activities for CPO Science. Expertise in equipment photography and catalog design.

Susan Gioia – Education Office Administrator

Oversees all the details necessary to keep the education product team working smoothly.

Thomas C. Altman – Physics Teacher, Oswego High School, New York, New York

Twenty-one years teaching experience, NSTA Award winner, and inventor of Altman Holography Method.

Dr. Mitch Crosswait – Nuclear Engineer/Physicist, United States Government , Alexandria, VA.

Research scientist and technology analyst. Evaluates programs for their technical merit and advises government on science and technology.

Technical Consultants

Tracy Morrow – Framework expert, technical editing programs, and training of staff.

Julie Dalton – Senior Copy Editor, Journalist, sports writer and former English teacher.

James Travers – Graphic designer, animator, and artist.

Mary Ann Erickson – Indexing/Glossary, Technic Writing and Engineering.

Science Content Reviewers

Dr. Jeff Schechter

Physicist
Boston, Massachusetts

Beverly T. Cannon

Physics Teacher
Highland Park High School
Dallas, Texas

Betsy Nahas

Physics Teacher
Chelmsford High School
Westford, Massachusetts

Bruce Ward

Nuclear Medical Technician
Boston, Massachusetts

Dr. Michael Saulnier

Physicist
Boston, Massachusetts

Lebee Meehan

Physicist
National Aeronautics and Space Administration
Houston, Texas

Dr. Manos Chaniotakis

Physicist
Massachusetts Institute of Technology
Cambridge, Massachusetts

CPO Science Equipment and Instrumentation

Greg Krekorian – Production manager

Roger Barous – Machinist

John Erickson – Electrical engineer

Nick Loy – Electrical engineer

George Silva – Electrical engineer/software

Dr. Darren Garnier – Physicist/software

Jim Hall – Electrical engineer

Shawn Greene – Electronics specialist

Kathryn Gavin – Quality specialist

David Zucker – Industrial engineer

The CPO Science Program

It was Albert Einstein who said, *"It is nothing short of a miracle that the modern methods of instruction have not yet entirely strangled the holy curiosity of inquiry."* The great 20th-century scientist, thinker and theorist was a strong believer in learning by discovery and exploration. The method of learning by memorization of complex facts or rote learning Einstein considered "a very grave mistake to think that the enjoyment of seeing and searching can be promoted by means of coercion and a sense of duty."

"The whole of science is nothing more than a refinement of everyday thinking."

Albert Einstein

The CPO Foundations of Physics Program is created around the premise that science is a process of exploration and discovery of ideas and that this new knowledge connects and enhances our lives. The program is presented and sequenced in a way that moves the student through an inquiry-based learning approach. For example, each Investigation begins with a key question that forms the foundation for the learning in the Investigation. In many sections, students complete experiments and hands-on activities before reading and conceptualizing ideas in the student text. Throughout all the instruction, probing questions stimulate exploration, discovery, the quest for data to prove theories, and the need to communicate findings to others.

Scope and sequence

Unlike other textbooks that match content to National Science Education Standards, the CPO Science Program was written directly to state standards. The standards form the benchmark criteria from which each science topic, specific content requirement, and science process was developed. The program provides numerous opportunities for students, teachers, and schools to meet the standards and the state testing requirements. Matching the standards to CPO Unit topics ensures that students will receive the highest quality science instruction to the depth and breadth necessary to meet teaching needs.

On request, CPO Science staff will provide you with your state correlation; many correlations also can be found on the CPO Science website. The correlation document demonstrates the alignment between your standards and the Foundations of Physics Program. The index lists page numbers from the CPO Student Edition and Investigation Lab Manual where examples of specific correlations are found. The Physics Scope and Sequence chart found on the following pages demonstrates the careful consideration and detailed content match between the Student Edition and its accompanying Investigations. These charts can be reviewed as a quick reference to the teaching and learning objectives covered in this program.

Meeting all students' needs

Learning science through investigation is an active process allowing students to gain abstract conceptual knowledge. Most students learn best when reading is enhanced by doing. The CPO Physics Program combines strong, in-depth coverage of physics content with abundant hands-on learning activities in order to meet the variety of learning styles. Real-world examples and application sections provide students the authenticity that validates their connection to the science content. Teaching tips are found in the teacher's guide for providing further information, skill development, and practice problems.

The Multilevel Classroom of Today

The Foundations of Physics Program has been designed to meet the challenge of bringing in-depth, accurate science to all students. To teach in depth science concepts and skills, the design of the Student Edition reflects the use of instructional aids and strategies to meet that diversity of student need. Careful consideration has been taken to include reading, mathematics, and learning techniques that help all students grasp science concepts and skills.

Reading and concept-learning strategies

Main idea indicators — Main idea indicators appear in the left margin of each paragraph in the Student Edition to help students find information and understand the main concepts in the instruction. Students can use the indicators in the following ways:

- Read all the main idea indicators before reading the section text as a whole.
- List the important points of the section.
- Create outlines and concept maps.
- Find answers to questions by skimming and scanning the indicators for a quick review.

Highlighted vocabulary — As in any discipline or occupation, people must understand the subject's terminology and know how to use it correctly. Terms, units of measurement, and concepts are highlighted in blue so that students may easily identify key words that are important to learn in understanding physics content.

Bold highlighted points — Important scientific concepts, formulas, and laws appear in larger, bold print. Blue type is used to label the variables and further explain the concepts. These statements identify the most important learning points and what to review when studying.

Math and formula identification — Math is integrated throughout the text, with many example problems and a sequence of steps outlining how to solve the problems. Formulas are clearly marked, with each variable clearly labeled.

Building problem-solving skills by using key questions

Asking questions before starting an activity focuses students on what they will learn during the experiment or reading. Each Investigation begins with a key question that students need to answer. Students build problem-solving and critical thinking skills as they tackle each Investigation question. The following is a suggested sequence to use for deciphering questions:

- Have the student reread the question.
- Underline the action words and explain what is being asked.
- Identify the important words (usually vocabulary words).
- Have the students rewrite the question in their own words.
- Help students decide what they will need to know in order to answer the question.

Reading illustrations and graphics for science concepts

Some students learn best through visual clues and illustrations. Others need the dual support of text and visual clues in order to comprehend science concepts and theories. Our student text and Investigations manual have numerous content-rich illustrations, charts, tables, and graphics. Suggestions for using the visual clues include:

- Give students enough time to analyze the graphics and illustrations. Decoding the meaning of a visual is like reading text.
- Ask the students to explain verbally what they see in the graphic and what is being demonstrated.
- Teach students to read data tables and graphs so that they understand how to organize and represent data. Numerous examples and questions requiring completion of tables are presented with explanations.
- Have students organize into teams, then illustrate a concept or create graphics for the section. Other team members decide which concept or section is to be illustrated.

Reading, understanding, and using math formulas

Formulas help students describe relationships between quantities. After students understand the basis for formulas and how they represent relationships, they can use them as tools for solving problems or predicting outcomes. We emphasize understanding relationships rather than simply memorizing formulas. All formulas are in bold type and the variables are clearly labeled.

- Math formulas are connected to the data-collection process during hands-on activities. The formulas are all in the context of the Investigation; as a result, students apply math formulas to actual science experiences.
- Important math formulas are highlighted, written in large print, and also explained in the text.
- Example problems illustrate how to use the formula and how it can be applied to other situations. Students' learning of the formulas is reinforced throughout the Student Edition and in the assessment sections.
- Only the most relevant math formulas are presented in the text and explained in depth.
- A reference section in the Investigation manual contains an easy-to-read table of all the formulas in the program.

Expressing learning in a variety of ways

Students learn differently and use various avenues for expressing their knowledge. In the review questions at the end of each chapter in the Student Edition, students are asked to answer questions. These questions are presented in different difficulty levels. They allow students to express their knowledge and demonstrate their learning in several modalities. Question formats include matching vocabulary and definitions, designing an experiment, researching information, giving other examples, writing short answers, drawing diagrams, using a diagram to answer a question, comparing and contrasting, true and false, and finding information through the Internet.

Evaluation and Assessment

"It is not the answe that enlightens but th question."

Eugene Ionesc

The CPO Science Program is committed to presenting material in a variety of ways to meet the diversity of student learning styles. Students learn in a combination of modalities and demonstrate understanding through a variety of modes. A combination of evaluation methods is available to ensure multilevel and diverse opportunities. A variety of methods is necessary in order for students to demonstrate science content knowledge, application skills, performance abilities, and scientific process and problem-solving skills to the best of their ability. Below are descriptions of the different evaluations.

Review and practice — formative assessment

Review questions, found at the end of each chapter, evaluate student progress on key chapter objectives. These questions provide students wit opportunities to practice vocabulary, apply concept knowledge, use computational ability, and solve problems. Review questions also provid students practice in using formulas and math. Skill and Practice Worksheets, provided for additional practice in problem solving and applyin conceptual knowledge, are ideal for use as homework assignments. These worksheets are provided for every chapter in the text and are foun on the Teacher Support CD.

Assessing broader knowledge with assessment questions — summative assessment

The assessment questions have been carefully designed to test all the important topics covered in a unit. Included in the questions are example of graphs, charts, and computational information needed to answer questions and demonstrate application skills. The assessment questions ar on the ExamView® CD and consist of multiple-choice and multiformat questions that can be used to build your own exams and question designed to meet the unit content. These questions are designed to reflect typical standardized test questions. Exposure and practice i answering multiple-choice-type and short-answer questions has proved helpful to students in formal standardized testing situations. There ar over 1,200 questions on the ExamView® CD. The Examview® booklet includes the questions along with their level of difficulty and th answer.

Learning and applying skills — performance assessment

Being able to justify conclusions based on active experimentation and data collection is a powerful skill in today's technological worl Performance assessment measures how well a student can solve problems and demonstrate understanding through application. Th Foundations of Physics Program builds the self-confidence students need in order to tackle problems through the use of investigation.

Each Investigation begins with a key question that students answer at the end of the hands-on activity. These activities allow the teacher t observe students' ability to think and work through a lab process. Investigations rely on team participation to solve the key questions an problems. Students are continuously exposed to a systematic problem-solving method that encourages observation, collection of data, an justification of findings.

Safety

Safety is highlighted throughout the CPO Science Program by the use of safety icons and safety tips in the Investigations. The Investigations activities and experiments have been written to reduce safety concerns in the laboratory. The equipment required for the Investigations is very stable and easy to use and manage. All the chemistry-related Investigations use supplies and chemicals that can be purchased readily in a grocery or hardware store. Although this does not mean that these supplies are nontoxic, you will be able to dispose easily of most of these chemicals. In cases where you are concerned about safety and proper use or disposal, we strongly recommend that you obtain the Materials Safety Data Sheets (MSDS) for the chemicals. These are easily obtained by calling the manufacturer of the product.

The CPO Science Program introduces students to basic safety using a Safety Skill Builder worksheet (see the Skill and Practice Worksheets that come with the Ancillaries). This skill builder includes basic safety information, a quiz that can be administered to the students after you have covered safety in the laboratory, and a student safety contract. Use the skill builder as a guide for your lesson and fill in any information and guidelines that are particular to your classroom and school. Safety is such a crucial concern when working in a laboratory environment that having students sign a contract may emphasize that safety in the science lab is everyone's responsibility. We recommend devoting an entire lesson to safety in the classroom and laboratory.

Units and Measurement

The CPO Science Program was designed to prepare students to be successful in any career, not just academia. Students need to be fluent with scientific skills in any system of units prevalent in the workplace. Virtually all engineering and industrial careers require proficiency in both English and metric units. Even metric measures are not standardized. Research scientists use two varieties of metric: meter-kilogram-second (MKS) for physics and centimeter-gram-second (CGS) for chemistry. Ocean and air transportation industries use nautical miles. Medicine uses both Fahrenheit and Celsius temperature scales. Astronomers use light-years. The message to take from this diversity is that students need to learn and practice science in several systems of units because they will encounter different systems outside the classroom.

Because of their extensive practical use, English units are presented in the Student Edition and Investigations, however metric units are emphasized throughout the text. The use of English units was done to connect the student's common experience and also to provide a bridge between the systems. Almost all concepts are presented in metric units, with an occasional reference to other systems when appropriate. All of the assessments use only metric units, which is common practice for standardized tests. It is our opinion that a basic high school science education should be focused on developing practical quantitative reasoning, problem solving, and observational skills. By presenting a mixture of units as they occur in the real world, we help prepare students for success in any endeavor that requires scientific thinking, such as business, industry, or education, as well as for further study in science.

Organization of the Program

The CPO Science Program has four components: Student Edition, Investigations, Teacher's Guide, and Equipment. These components interweave and reinforce inquiry-based learning, hands-on discovery, and grasping science concepts through reading. Abstract concepts and skill development opportunities are presented in a variety of ways to address many and diverse learning styles. Enhancing the readings are clear, accurate illustrations that reinforce the learning of abstract concepts. By the end of each section, students have completed a hands-on experiment, answered essential questions, completed a reading to master the science content, and also have read an application of how the science is used in the real world.

The one-volume Teacher's Guide provides information, answers, and teaching tips. Ancillary teaching tools also include three CD-ROMs containing student answer sheets for the Investigations, color teaching tools, the entire student text on an electronic book file, and the ExamView® question builder.

"Hear and yo forget; see and yo remember; do an you understand."

Confuci

Student Text

The basic organizational structure of the student text is the unit. There are nine units, each one broken into topic chapters containing three content-specific sections. The unit themes covered in the Foundations of Physics Program were chosen for their relevance to CPO's commitment to provide in-depth coverage of science concepts. The glossary and index have been designed so students can quickly skim for page numbers and definitions. Each student chapter contains pertinent content and skill-development reading with numerous illustrations for reading support. Each chapter contains an extensive review question section that evaluates the student's progress in areas such as vocabulary development, concept understanding, computation skills, and problems. Special features of the Student Edition:

- **Chapter page:** This introductory page presents the important objectives of the student reading, including pertinent vocabulary.
- **Side heading outlines:** Developing literacy skills in math and reading is stressed throughout the instruction. Left-margin side heading highlight the main ideas in the text and help the student grasp reading concepts through skimming, scanning, and key-word identification.
- **Highlighted vocabulary:** Science vocabulary mastery is paramount for science concept understanding. Science vocabulary can be highly technical and abundant. Vocabulary words are highlighted for easy identification and defined in a variety of ways.
- **Numerous visual teaching tools:** The Student Edition contains graphics, charts, illustrations, and data tables supporting abstract conceptual learning. These teaching tools reinforce instruction and aid in visual representation of material necessary for addressing the broad range of learning styles. The visuals are precise in content and presentation and reflect CPO's commitment to accuracy, science content excellence, and inquiry-based instruction.
- **Formulas:** The most important formulas and laws are highlighted and in bold type, with each variable labeled.
- **Math:** The use of math is integrated in the physics instruction. Numerous problems are presented for student practice, each containing the steps for solving the problems.

Investigations

The Investigations are the heart of the CPO Science Program. We believe that most students learn best and are motivated to learn through direct experience and exploration activities. Key questions focus the student on the main points of the concept to be learned and what they should be able to answer after the experiment. There is one Investigation for each student reading section. The student reading and Investigation closely compliment the science instruction and reinforce the same principles.

Each Investigation is introduced with a key question that the students will be able to answer after completing the hands-on activity. Students are also given learning goals for each Investigation and a short informational piece to get them thinking about the content of the Investigation. Student answer sheets are found on the Teaching Tools CD-ROM. The answer sheets contain more space for writing and larger tables and graphs. The teacher can print and duplicate the sheets for students' use.

Investigations are usually completed before the accompanying student reading chapter. The CPO philosophy is based on the premise that through discovery, the students will begin to understand science concepts and build on them with new skill development. The student readings strengthen the students' knowledge of theory and aid their understanding. For certain Investigations, the student reading must be done first so that students have the basic knowledge necessary to complete the Investigation. Whether a chapter should be read before or after an Investigation is explained under the reading synopsis heading in the teacher's guide pages for each section.

"The greatest tragedy of Science: the slaying of a beautiful hypothesis by an ugly fact."

Thomas Huxley

Special features

- **Data collection, graphing, and the scientific process:** These skills are emphasized and reinforced throughout the program and students are frequently encouraged to practice these skills as self-learners.
- **Lesson planning page:** The information you need to know to teach and conduct the Investigation is available in the teacher's guide section pages. The learning goals and questions, equipment setup, consumable materials list, teaching sequence, and a synopsis of the student reading are all found on the lesson introduction pages.
- **Icons:** Throughout the Investigations, icons are used to point out safety requirements and to reference the unit that is being presented. The unit icons are the same as for the accompanying material.
- **Explanation:** Further content information and explanation is sometimes given to the student in the Investigation to assist in its completion and to present background skill knowledge.
- **Equipment:** Specialized equipment has been designed to accompany the teaching of the Investigations. The equipment is durable and provides consistent and accurate results. The equipment pictured in the Investigation is the same as the equipment the student is using to complete the hands-on activity. Student text illustrations also show the same equipment used for experimentation.

Teacher's guides

The teacher's guides are constructed around the same premise as the student instructional materials: inquiry-based learning. The guides include a sample demonstration lesson for each Investigation, written as a dialogue between the teacher and the class. These samples demonstrate how to teach the Investigation using inquiry-based teaching and student group discovery. The sample demonstration is only one example of teaching the Investigation with possible student responses. Teaching tips, the accompanying student section synopsis, and teaching strategies are also included.

The first two pages of each teacher's guide section contain a clear, concise overview of the Investigation. It is our belief that a quick guide is useful in outlining the learning objectives, setting up the Investigation, and mapping the sequence of the Investigation procedures. These pages contain a brief synopsis of the student reading, a review of the leading question, the learning objectives, and a clear equipment and consumable materials list. Detailed equipment setup instructions are included in an Equipment Setup Booklet that comes with each physics equipment kit.

The Investigation lesson pages present a sample teaching scenario written as a dialog between the teacher and class. The dialogs present actual lessons taught from the teacher's point of view, as well as possible student responses. The dialogs provide excellent support for teachers who are new to the subject area, as they identify possible student misconceptions and highlight important learning content. The dialogs provide teaching tips such as:

- What to put on the chalkboard.
- How to teach by questioning.
- What reactions the students may have and how to respond.
- Interesting stories to make connections between key concepts and everyday life.
- Computational information and more problems.

On the facing page of the dialog is a miniature Investigation page and the answers for the Investigation. The dialog and Investigation page have corresponding reference numbers to aid in matching the dialog to the Investigation.

Teacher's guides contents

The teacher's guide contains an explanation of the program, scope and sequence charts, the summaries and dialogs for each chapter, a miniature Investigation page and accompanying answers, and a list of consumable materials. Answers for the review questions in the student text are also included.

> *"The most important thing in science is not so much to obtain new facts as to discover new ways to think about them."*
>
> William Bragg

The Teacher's Guide Investigation Overview Pages

The teacher's guide for each Investigation begins with the overview pages. The overview pages correspond to each section of the Student Edition and each Investigation in the CPO Science Program. These pages review the instructional components, beginning with a summary of what the students will learn in the Investigation. Included are a synopsis of the reading, pertinent vocabulary from the Investigation, learning goals, and the key and leading questions that students will be able to answer after completing the Investigation. It is important to note that below the heading for the reading synopsis, there is a suggested sequence for teaching the student section and the Investigation. The student reading section frequently follows completion of the hands-on Investigation. In some sections, the student reading must be completed first in order for students to assimilate the skills and concepts required to complete the Investigations.

The second page outlines the equipment and material needed, preparation considerations, skill sheets, and the sequence of teaching steps.

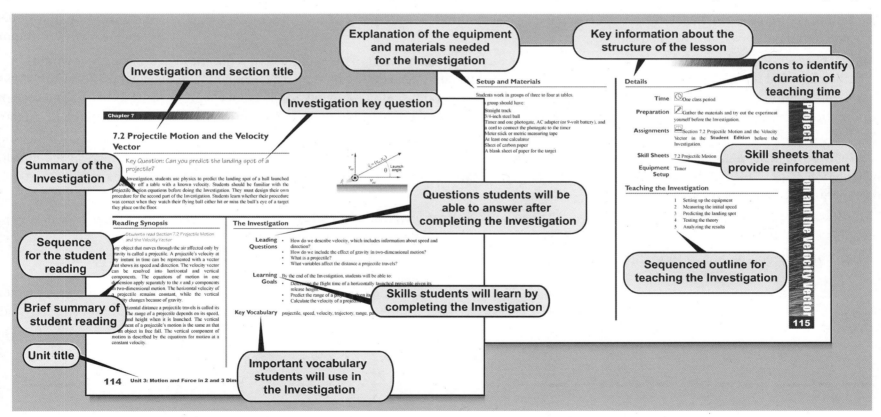

Teacher's Guide Demonstration Lessons

Each teacher's guide demonstration lesson contains an outline of the lesson, a "sample dialog," and teaching strategies and tips. These pages also include the Investigation and sample answers to the activity. In the facing-page format, you can review the sample dialog between the teacher and students, the Investigation page, and sample data and answers. All the information you will need to teach the Investigation is easily skimmed in this format.

Below are features of the dialog, Investigation answer page, and sidebar teacher notes.

Outline: This section contains an at-a-glance sequence of steps that a teacher can skim. It is a quick guide to what is taught in the Investigation and notes on the Investigation.

Inv.: In this column the teacher will find a reference number that matches the parts of the Investigation page. These corresponding numbers guide you to the part discussed in the dialog.

Dialog: This section is presented as an exchange between the teacher and the class. This sample lesson outlines what the teacher would actually say to the class and typical responses from the students. Helpful teaching ideas and tips such as: "Students will need access to water," "Group supervision is important at this point" are included. The teacher's directions and comments to the students are printed in black, and responses and directions are in blue text. It is our hope that teachers will review the dialog before presenting the Investigations to the class, both as a supportive tool and to help clarify the goals and important points of each Investigation.

Investigation: This is a miniaturized Investigation page that is referenced in the dialog. The teacher can refer to the numbers at the left of the Investigation page and match them to the opposite page as numbers under the "Inv" column. These numbers indicate what part of the Investigation the dialog is referring to.

Example answers and data: Sample student data, answers to Investigation questions, and graphs are found in the right-hand sidebar area. The data and some of the reflective answers are only examples of data and responses that could be given by the students.

Sidebar notes: Teaching tips, information, and more reinforcement ideas for students are also found in the right-hand sidebar area.

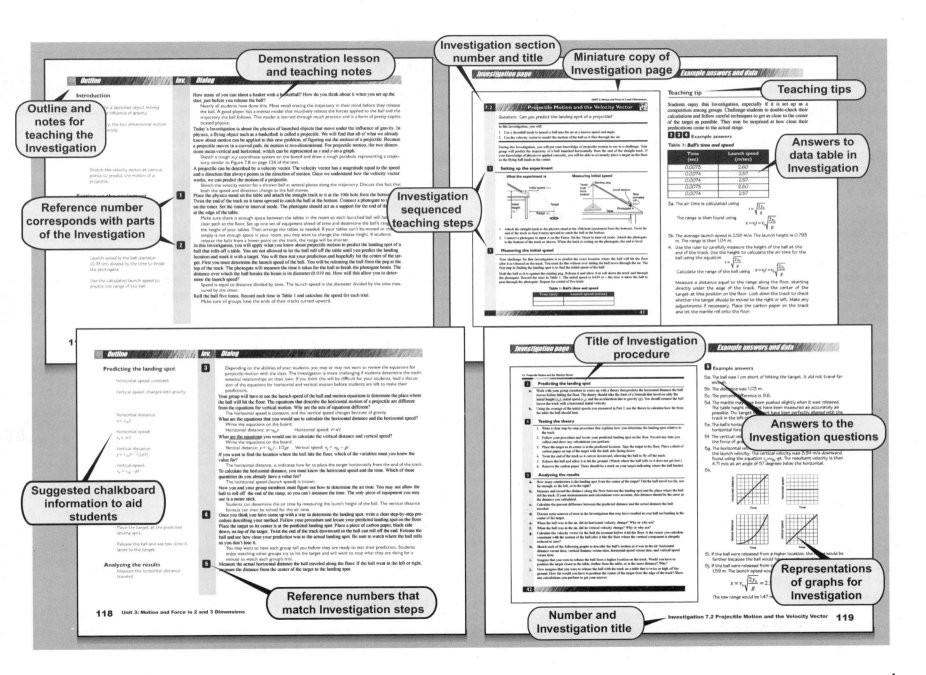

Demonstration lesson and teaching notes

Investigation section number and title

Miniature copy of Investigation page

Outline and notes for teaching the Investigation

Teaching tips

Answers to data table in Investigation

Reference number corresponds with parts of the Investigation

Investigation sequenced teaching steps

Title of Investigation procedure

Suggested chalkboard information to aid students

Answers to the Investigation questions

Reference numbers that match Investigation steps

Representations of graphs for Investigation

Number and Investigation title

Scope and Sequence

The way in which concepts are sequenced and presented to the student is critical to the teaching and learning process. The CPO Science Program is based upon inquiry and discovery teaching approaches. As a result, the Investigations, hands-on activities, are frequently completed before reading the accompanying section in the student text. Both teaching tools are closely aligned and reinforce the same concepts. The Scope and Sequence Charts identify how the Student Edition and Investigations are aligned and highlights the learning goals, major science skills and needed equipment/materials taught in the Unit. These charts are a quick reference to what concepts students will be learning and the sequence and duration for the instruction. A class period is assumed to be 45 minutes.

2.1 Distance and Length

Learning Goals	Reading Synopsis	Materials and Setup
• Estimate metric lengths and distances. • Make measurements using significant digits correctly. • Measure surface area and volume of various shapes. **Key question:** How do we accurately communicate length and distance? **Leading questions:** • How large are a meter, kilometer, millimeter, or centimeter relative to the size of familiar objects? • What kinds of situations require precise measurements? • What are significant digits?	All measurements are made up of two parts: a quantity and a unit. There are two common systems to measure length, the English system and the metric (also called SI) system. Scientists most often use metric units, but both systems are used in everyday life. The English system uses inches, feet, yards, and miles to measure length. The metric system uses millimeters, centimeters, meters, and kilometers. Converting between metric system units is easy because they are based on powers of 10. You can use conversion factors to convert English system units to metric system units. It is often important to know the surface area or volume of an object. Surface area is measured in square units, while volume is measured in cubic units. When converting one surface area from one unit to another, the conversion factor is applied twice. **Sequence:** Students complete the reading after the Investigation.	• Meter stick and/or metric ruler • Calculator • Pencil with eraser • Paper clip • Street map of local area (used by students to estimate distance from school to home) • 2 sheets of heavy paper, such as construction paper • A compass for drawing circles • Scissors • Tape • 1 liter of sand • A one-liter soda bottle **Duration:** One class period

2.2 Time

Learning Goals	Reading Synopsis	Materials and Setup
• Use electronic timing equipment and photogates. • Use units of time in calculations and conversions. • Correctly apply the terms accuracy, precision, and resolution to scientific instruments and measurements. **Key question:** How do we measure and describe time? **Leading questions:** • Why are accurate measurements of time necessary? • How do we describe how close a measurement is to the true value we are trying to measure?	There are two related meanings for "time." One is to specify a particular moment such as 2:30 p.m. Another is to describe a quantity of time, such as 30 seconds. Time is measured in several related units: years, hours, minutes, seconds, etc. Time intervals appearing in physics calculations must be converted to seconds. Physical phenomena occur on a wide range of time scales from shorter than 10^{-18} seconds (light to cross an atom) to 10^{17} seconds (age of the universe). Many key physics concepts are based on how certain quantities change with time, such as position. Accuracy and precision are important to consider when doing experiments. Accuracy describes how close a measurement is to the true value. Precision describes how small a difference can be reliably distinguished by a measurement. **Sequence:** Students complete the reading after the Investigation.	• Timer with photogates, AC adapter (or 9-volt battery), and cords to connect the photogates to the timer **Duration:** One class period

2.3 Mass, Matter, and the Atom

Learning Goals	Reading Synopsis	Materials and Setup
• Give an example of an object with a mass of one kilogram. • Describe and measure the mass of objects in kilograms. • Write and read numbers in scientific notation. **Key question:** How is mass described? **Leading questions:** • What is mass? • How big is a kilogram? • How do you write very large and very small numbers?	Mass is a measure of the amount of matter contained in an object. Mass creates weight and inertia. Mass is measured in grams and kilograms. Objects of concern to physics have ranges of mass from smaller than a single electron (10^{-31} kg) to bigger than the Milky Way galaxy (10^{40} kg). Very small numbers are represented in scientific notation. A review of scientific notation is presented. Ordinary matter is made of tiny particles called atoms. There are 92 types of atoms in normal matter, one type for each of the 92 naturally occurring elements. Atoms in familiar matter are usually combined in molecules and mixtures. The atoms in a solid are packed and bonded together. Atoms in a liquid are slightly farther apart (ordinarily) and loosely bonded so they can move. Atoms in a gas are much farther apart and free to move independently. **Sequence:** Students complete the reading after the Investigation.	Each group should have: • Electronic scale or triple-beam balance • Bathroom scale • Scientific calculator • 1-liter bottle of water (full) You will need several objects to serve as examples of mass. The objects listed in the Investigation are: • Pencil • Cement block • Paper clip Other objects will also work. **Duration:** One class period

3.1 Speed

Learning Goals	Reading Synopsis	Materials and Setup
• Calculate the speed of a ball rolling down a ramp. • Describe measurements that allow the speed of any moving object. • Compare speeds in different units. • Solve one-step problems involving speed, distance, and time. **Key question:** What is speed and how is it measured? **Leading questions:** • What is the definition of speed? • How do you calculate the speed of an object? • How can the relationship between speed, distance, and time be used to find any one of the three variables if the other two variables are known?	Speed is the ratio of distance traveled divided by the time it takes to travel the distance. Units of speed are length over time. Metric examples are m/sec and cm/sec. A common example is mph. The formula for speed is $v = d/t$, where d is the distance traveled and t is the time taken. This formula may be rearranged to calculate any of the three variables from the other two. A four-step problem-solving technique is described and illustrated. 1 Identify what you are asked to find. 2 Identify what information you are given. 3 Identify any relationships that involve the information asked for or the information given. These might include formulas, conversion factors, etc. 4 Use the relationships to solve the problem. **Sequence:** Students complete the reading after the Investigation.	• Straight track with a threaded knob • 3/4-inch steel ball • Timer with photogates, AC adapter (or 9-volt battery), and cords to connect the photogates to the timer • Physics stand • Metric and English rulers **Duration:** One class period

3.2 Observations of Motion

Learning Goals	Reading Synopsis	Materials and Setup
• Determine the speed of a ball at different points as it rolls down the track. • Identify the variables that influence the speed of the ball. • Design an experiment that controls some variables while others are monitored • Make a speed versus position graph from collected data. • predict the speed of the ball at any point from the speed vs position graph. **Key question:** Can you predict the speed of a ball rolling down a ramp? **Leading questions:** • What are variables and why are they so important in collecting data • What is a graphical model? • How do you recognize a cause-and-effect relationship from experimental data?	Models are an important part of science. Models allow you to predict what will happen based on knowledge of how changes in one variable affect other variables. Models are built from data. Data is collected in experiments. An experiment should be well designed to properly interpret the data that is generated. The experimental variable is allowed to change while the control variables are kept constant. The procedure is a record of all the experimental techniques used. Two useful forms of models are graphs and formulas. Graphs represent data in pictures that are easy to understand compared to a list of numbers. Graphs provide evidence of cause-and-effect relationships, and also show the form of relationship between two variables, called the dependent variable and the independent variable. Graphs can also be used to make predictions when one of the two variables is known. **Sequence:** Students complete the reading after the Investigation.	• Straight track with a threaded knob • 3/4-inch steel ball • Timer with photogates, AC adapter (or 9-volt battery), and cords to connect the photogates to the timer • Physics stand • Graph paper • Metric and English rulers **Duration:** One class period

3.3 Analyzing Motion with Graphs

Learning Goals	Reading Synopsis	Materials and Setup
• Set up a situation with constant speed motion. • Model constant speed motion with a position versus time graph. • Calculate speed from the slope of the position versus time graph. • Use the speed versus time graph to calculate the distance traveled. **Key question:** How do you model motion? **Leading questions:** • What can be learned from the position vs time graph? • What can be learned from the speed vs time graph? • What are the relationships between speed vs time and position vs time graphs? • Calculate distance an object has traveled when you know the speed vs time graph?	The chapter begins by explaining the distinction between position and distance. Consistent with Unit 1, all analyses are restricted to one dimension. This chapter discusses the speed versus time and position versus time graphs and the relationship between the two. The interpretation of slope is explained with examples. The slope of the position versus time graph is the speed. The calculus technique of area under a graph is used to show how distance can be calculated from the speed versus time graph. Distance is equal to area on a speed versus time graph. This technique is used to show that the distance traveled during accelerated motion is one-half the product of the maximum speed multiplied by the time taken to reach the maximum speed (starting from rest). This result is important to deriving the equations for motion in one dimension developed in the subsequent chapter. **Sequence:** Students complete the reading after the Investigation.	• Straight track with a threaded knob • Cardboard shims to raise and lower the end of the track • 3/4-inch steel ball • Timer with photogates, AC adapter (or 9-volt battery), and cords to connect the photogates to the timer • Physics stand • Graph paper • Meter stick **Duration:** One class period

4.1 Acceleration

Learning Goals	Reading Synopsis	Materials and Setup
• Observe how accelerated motion appears on graphs. • Determine the acceleration of a ball through a calculation using speed and time. • Determine the acceleration of a ball using the slope of a graph. **Key question:** How is the speed of the ball changing? **Leading questions:** • How do you define acceleration? • How are acceleration and speed different? • How is acceleration measured and calculated? • How does acceleration relate to the speed versus time graph?	The definition of acceleration is the rate of change in the speed of an object. Acceleration may be calculated by dividing the change in speed by the time interval over which the change occurs. Units of acceleration are m/sec^2. Acceleration may be positive or negative compared to speed. Speed and acceleration are not the same. Constant speed means zero acceleration. Constant acceleration means the speed increases by the same amount in equal time intervals. An object may momentarily have zero speed, but non-zero acceleration. The speed versus time graph for accelerated motion is a straight line which is not horizontal, but makes an angle with the x-axis. Acceleration is the slope of the line on the speed versus time graph. This definition is mathematically equivalent to calculating acceleration as the change in speed divided by the change in time. **Sequence:** Students complete the reading after the Investigation.	• Straight track ramp • Two photogates • Timer with photogates, AC adapter (or 9-volt battery), and cords to connect the photogates to the timer • Physics stand • Graph paper **Duration:** One class period

4.2 A Model for Accelerated Motion

Learning Goals	Reading Synopsis	Materials and Setup
• Use the equations for uniform accelerated motion to calculate the speed or position of a moving object when given the initial velocity, acceleration, and time. • Identify acceleration and initial speed from the speed versus time graph. • Describe the meaning of each of the terms in the two equations that make up the model for uniformly accelerated motion. **Key question:** How do we describe and predict accelerated motion? **Leading questions:** • How do we predict where an accelerated object will be at a future time? • Is there a formula that describes accelerated motion like $d = vt$ describes motion at constant speed? • How do you get from a graph to formula?	Acceleration can be defined and calculated as $\Delta v/\Delta t$ or $(v_2 - v_1)/(t_2 - t_1)$. These equations can be rearranged to give $v = v_0 + at$. This is a model which describes the speed of an object under constant acceleration. The distance traveled by an object in uniformly accelerated motion is $1/2\ at^2$ when the objects starts at rest. This is derived from the area of a triangle on the speed versus time graph. The formula is generalized to include initial speed and position to give $x = x_0 + v_0t + {}^1/_2at^2$. A model for uniformly accelerated motion includes two equations, one for speed and one for position. Together, the two equations link position, time, speed, and acceleration. Problem solving techniques are presented. **Sequence:** Students complete the reading after the Investigation.	• Straight track and marble • Timer with photogates, AC adapter (or 9-volt battery), and cords to connect the photogates to the timer • Graph paper **Duration:** One class period

4.3 Free Fall and the Acceleration due to Gravity

Learning Goals	Reading Synopsis	Materials and Setup
• Describe a method for measuring the acceleration due to gravity. • Use the equation that relates distance, time, and acceleration of an object in free fall. • Suggest ideas for measuring the acceleration due to gravity more accurately. **Key question:** How do you measure the acceleration of a falling object? **Leading questions:** • What is free fall? • How does gravity affect the speed of a falling object? • How can the acceleration due to gravity be measured? • How close does a real object in free fall come to accelerating at the theoretical value of 9.8 m/sec^2?	An object is in free fall if it is moving only under the influence of gravity. The symbol g is used to represent the acceleration due to gravity. Freely falling objects accelerate at the rate of 9.8 m/sec^2 on Earth. The value of g depends on the distance from the center of Earth The motion of an object in free fall can be described using the equations for speed and position. The value of g is substituted for the acceleration, a. The speed of an object that is dropped or thrown downward will increase by 9.8 m/sec each second. The speed of an object thrown upward will decrease by 9.8 m/sec each second. The acceleration due to gravity does not depend on the mass of the object that is falling. Objects do accelerate differently when influenced by friction from air resistance. The maximum speed at which an object can fall when limited by air resistance is called the terminal speed. **Sequence:** Students complete the reading before the Investigation.	• Timer with photogates, AC adapter (or 9-volt battery), and cords to connect the photogates to the timer • Plastic ball • Steel ball • Physics stand • String with steel ball on end (from colliding pendulum exp.) • Meter stick • Calculator **Duration:** One class period

5.1 The First Law: Force and Inertia

Learning Goals	Reading Synopsis	Materials and Setup
• Use Newton's first law to explain why an object at rest tends to stay at rest if no forces are exerted. • Use Newton's first law to describe the motion of an object moving with no unbalanced forces acting on it. • Explain the effect of an unbalanced force on the motion of an object. **Key question:** How does the first law apply to objects at rest and in motion? **Leading questions:** • What property of matter tends to keep a moving object moving and resist the motion of an object at rest? • What must be done to change the motion of a moving object or start an object moving if it is at rest?	A force is a push or pull or any action that has the ability to change an object's state of motion. Forces can be created by many different processes, but all forces have the potential ability to change the motion of an object. Newton's first law states that all objects tend to keep doing what they are doing. Inertia is the term used to describe the ability of an object to resist a change in its state of motion. Newton's first law is sometimes called the law of inertia. The amount of inertia an object has depends on its mass. More massive objects have more inertia. An unbalanced force is required to change an object's motion. Objects with more mass, and therefore more inertia, require more force to change their state of motion. **Sequence:** Students complete the reading before the Investigation.	• Straight track with a threaded knob • 3/4-inch steel ball • Timer with photogates, AC adapter (or 9-volt battery), and cords to connect the photogates to the timer • Physics stand • Metric and English rulers • Calculator • Blocks, books, or other objects to support the free end of the track • Cardboard shims of different thicknesses **Duration:** One class period

5.2 The Second Law: Force, Mass, and Acceleration

Learning Goals	Reading Synopsis	Materials and Setup

Learning Goals

- Use the second law to calculate force, mass, or acceleration when two of the three variables are known.
- Qualitatively describe the relationship between acceleeleration,mass and force.
- Use the second law to determine unknown forces from experimental measurements of motion and mass.

Key question:
What is the relationship between force, mass, and acceleration?

Leading questions:
- How is force measured and described in the metric and English systems?
- What is the exact relationship between inertia (mass), force, and motion?
- Can we predict the motion of objects from the forces acting on them?
- If an object is not moving, what does that tell us about the forces acting it?

Reading Synopsis

If you apply more force to an object, it has proportionally greater acceleration. If the mass of the object is increased, and the force is kept constant, the acceleration diminishes proportionally. Newton's second law states that the acceleration of an object is equal to the net force applied divided by the mass of the object. In the metric system, the unit of force, the newton, is defined by mass and acceleration. In the English system, the unit of force is the pound (lb.).

The concept of net force is presented. The application of the second law is presented with several example problems. Acceleration is determined when force and mass are known. Force is determined when mass and acceleration are known. A condition of zero acceleration implies that the net force is zero (equilibrium). Positive and negative numbers are used to indicate the direction of a force.

Sequence: Students complete the reading before the Investigation.

Materials and Setup

- Ultimate pulleys set
- 2.5- and 5-N spring scales
- Physics stand
- Timer with photogates, AC adapter (or 9-volt battery) and cords to connect the photogates to the timer
- Electronic scale or triple-beam balance to measure mass
- Calculator

Duration: One class period

5.3 The Third Law: Action and Reaction

Learning Goals	Reading Synopsis	Materials and Setup
• Draw a diagram showing an action-reaction pair of forces. • Determine the reaction force when given an action force. • Describe how Newton's third law affects the motion of objects. **Key question:** Can you identify action-reaction pairs? **Leading questions:** • How do forces affect objects? • What happens when one object pushes on another object? • What proof is there that action and reaction forces exist? • How do action -reaction forces affect objects involved with their interaction?	"For every action there is an equal and opposite reaction." This statement is known as Newton's third law and it affects our everyday lives even when we are sitting perfectly still in a chair or lying on the ground. Forces are explained in terms of action-reaction pairs. Anytime there is a force pushing on something there is another force of equal strength pushing back in the opposite direction. While Newton's first and second laws apply to single objects, the third law involves pairs of objects. Each object in the pair feels the affects of one of the action-reaction forces. It does not matter which is the action force and which is the reaction force. The important thing is to understand that they are equal and opposite counterparts and to recognize which force acts on which object in the pair. Locomotion is the act of moving and any machine or animal that moves depends on Newton's third law to do so. The human body uses the third law constantly and the study of how is called biomechanics. **Sequence:** Students complete the reading after the Investigation.	• Plain, white copy paper or sketch paper for making diagrams • Pencils • Colored pencils (optional) • No other equipment or materials are required **Duration:** One class period

6.1 Mass, Weight and Gravity

Learning Goals	Reading Synopsis	Materials and Setup
• Analyze the forces acting on an object to determine its acceleration. • Predict the time it takes an object to move a given distance if the acceleration and initial speed are known. **Key question:** What is speed and how is it measured? **Leading questions:** • How is the net force acting on an object related to its acceleration? • How are an object's speed and acceleration related?	Mass is a measure of the amount of matter an object contains. An object's mass remains the same whether the object is on Earth, Mars, or any other location. Weight is the force of gravity on an object. The weight of an object depends on its mass and the strength of gravity in the place where the object is located. The weight of an object is its mass in kilograms multiplied by g, which has a value of 9.8 N/kg on the Earth's surface. The value of g changes depending on where in the universe you are, such as what planet you are on. An object is weightless when it feels no force from gravity. One way to become weightless is to get far away from any source of gravity such as planets and stars. A second way to become weightless is to be in free fall. Weight and mass are not the same. Using mass in a formula that requires weight (or vice-versa) will result in the wrong answer. **Sequence:** Students complete the reading before the Investigation.	• Ultimate pulleys set • Physics stand • Timer and one photogate, AC adapter (or 9-volt battery), and cords to connect the photogate to the timer • Electronic scale or triple-beam balance **Duration:** One class period

6.2 Friction

Learning Goals	Reading Synopsis	Materials and Setup
• Distinguish between static and sliding friction. • Measure friction forces. • Explain the factors that determine the magnitude of the force of friction between surfaces. • Calculate the coefficients of static and sliding friction from experimental measurements. **Key question:** How can we describe and model friction? **Leading questions:** • What is friction? • How is friction described and modeled? • Are there different types of friction? • When is friction not desirable and what can we do to reduce it in these cases?	Friction is a resistive force that always works against the motion that produces it. The force of friction between two surfaces sliding past each other is approximately proportional to the force squeezing the surfaces together. The coefficient of sliding friction is the proportionality constant relating the friction force to the normal force and is usually between zero and one, depending on the surfaces that create the friction. Static friction describes the force that exists between two surfaces that are not moving but would be if friction were not present. The force of static friction is not one definite value but can vary up to a maximum value. If this maximum is exceeded, the objects will start to slide. The coefficient of static friction is almost always greater than the coefficient of sliding friction. Friction has both beneficial and detrimental aspects. Friction is necessary for tires to have traction, brakes to work, and for walking. Friction also causes wear and inefficiency. Devices such as lubricants and bearings are designed to reduce friction. **Sequence:** Students complete the reading after the Investigation.	• Friction block • 2.5- and 5-N spring scales • Assortment of weights to place on top of friction block • Calculator • Electronic scale or triple-beam balance (one per class is acceptable) Optional: Other types of surfaces such as sandpaper, wood, glass, carpet, or plastic on which to slide the friction block. **Duration:** One class period

6.3 Equilibrium of Forces and Hooke's Law

Learning Goals	Reading Synopsis	Materials and Setup
• Calculate the force exerted by extension and compression springs when given the spring constant and deformation. • Calculate the deformation of a spring when given the spring constant and applied force. • Build a force-measuring scale from a spring. • Explain how Hooke's law solves the paradox of how inanimate objects "know" how much reaction force to exert to satisfy Newton's third law. **Key question:** How do you predict the force on a spring? **Leading questions:** • Describe equilibrium and give examples. • How can you tell how much force a spring will exert if it is stretched or compressed?	Equilibrium exists when the net force is zero. Objects in equilibrium experience no change in motion (no acceleration). A free body diagram replaces all interactions between an object and its surroundings by forces. A common application of equilibrium and free body diagrams is to find an unknown force when equilibrium exists and some forces are known. Hooke's law describes the forces created by springs, rubber bands, and other objects that stretch. According to Hooke's law the strength of the force exerted by a spring is the spring constant times the length the spring is extended or compressed ($F = -kx$). The negative sign indicates that the force created by the spring is in the opposite direction to the extension or compression. The spring-like behavior of all materials is what creates the forces between inanimate objects that "know" how to make the forces exactly equal and opposite. **Sequence:** Students complete the reading after the Investigation.	• Ultimate pulleys set (in particular, the compression and extension springs and washers will be used) • Physics stand • Graph paper • Meter stick **Duration:** One class period

xix

7.1 Vectors and Direction

Learning Goals	Reading Synopsis	Materials and Setup

Learning Goals

- Write displacement vectors in Cartesian and polar coordinates.
- Convert vectors between Cartesian and polar coordinates.
- Represent a sequence of vectors to scale on a map.
- Use vectors to give very precise directions.
- Use vectors and a compass to construct a geometrically accurate map showing the position of an object.

Key question:
How do we accurately communicate length and distance?

Leading questions:
- Why are vectors important?
- How are vectors added or subtracted?
- How can a complex movement with many turns be represented?
- How do you use a compass?

Reading Synopsis

A scalar is a quantity that can be described by a single value, with units. A vector is a quantity that requires at least two values and includes information about magnitude and direction. The displacement vector has units of length and describes a movement relative to a coordinate system. The position vector describes the location of an object relative to a coordinate system.

Two dimensional vectors can be represented in (x, y) components (Cartesian) or in (r, θ) components (polar). Vectors are added or subtracted by adding or subtracting components. A triangle and trigonometry are used to find the components of a vector in one coordinate system from the components in another coordinate system. The Pythagorean theorem ($c^2 = a^2 + b^2$) is used to find the magnitude of a vector from the x and y components. The section reviews the use of calculators to determine the trigonometric functions and their inverses.

Sequence: Students complete the reading after the Investigation.

Materials and Setup

- Navigational compass
- Meter stick
- Protractor
- Graph paper

Duration: One class period

7.2 Projectile Motion and the Velocity Vector

Learning Goals	Reading Synopsis	Materials and Setup
• Determine the flight time of a horizontally launched projectile given its release height. • Predict the range of a projectile given its launch speed and flight time. • Calculate the velocity of a projectile after it is in the air for a specified time. **Key question:** Can you predict the landing spot of a projectile? **Leading questions:** • How do we describe velocity, which includes information about speed and direction? • How do we include the effect of gravity in two-dimensional motion? • What is a projectile? • What variables affect the distance a projectile travels?	Any object that moves through the air affected only by gravity is called a projectile. A projectile's velocity at any instant in time can be represented with a vector that shows its speed and direction. The velocity vector can be resolved into horizontal and vertical components. The equations of motion in one dimension apply separately to the x and y components in two-dimensional motion. The horizontal velocity of a projectile remains constant, while the vertical velocity changes because of gravity. The horizontal distance a projectile travels is called its range. The range of a projectile depends on its speed, angle, and height when it is launched. The vertical component of a projectile's motion is the same as that of an object in free fall. The vertical component of motion is described by the equations for motion at a constant velocity. **Sequence:** Students complete the reading before the Investigation.	• Straight track • 3/4-inch steel ball • Timer and one photogate, AC adapter (or 9-volt battery), and a cord to connect the photogate to the timer • Meter stick or metric measuring tape • At least one calculator • Sheet of carbon paper • A blank sheet of paper for the target **Duration:** One class period

7.3 Forces in Two Dimensions

Learning Goals	Reading Synopsis	Materials and Setup
• Resolve a force vector into its components. • Calculate the net force on an object. **Key question:** How do forces balance in two dimensions? **Leading questions:** • What is meant by the term net force? • What does it mean to say an object is in equilibrium? • How can you find the components of a force? • How do forces combine?	A force vector can be used to indicate the strength and direction in which a force is acting. A force vector can be specified with polar coordinates or x-y components. The magnitude of a vector stated as two components can be found with the Pythagorean theorem. If an object is in equilibrium, all of the forces acting on it are balanced and the net force is zero. If forces act in two dimensions, the net force in the x-direction is zero, and the net force in the y-direction is zero. Forces act in two dimensions on an object located on an inclined plane or ramp. The surface exerts a force on the object that is perpendicular to the slope. The force of gravity and friction also act on the object. Its acceleration can be found by resolving all of the forces into components, summing the components, finding the net force, and using Newton's second law. **Sequence:** Students complete the reading before the Investigation.	• Graph paper • 5 N, 10 N, and 20 N spring scales • Three 25-centimeter pieces of string • Circular ring such as a metal key ring • Scientific calculator with trigonometry functions **Duration:** One class period

8.1 Motion in Circles

Learning Goals	Reading Synopsis	Materials and Setup
• Create circular motion and relate it to linear motion. • Measure angular speed in radians per second. • Perform calculations with linear speed and angular speed including converting between the two when the radius is known. **Key question:** How do you describe circular motion? **Leading questions:** • How is circular motion different from linear motion? • What is angular speed? • How are linear speed and angular speed related? • How is angular speed calculated?	Objects in circular motion rotate or revolve around an imaginary line called the axis. The angular speed is the rate at which an object revolves or rotates. Angular speed is measured in revolutions per minute (rpm) or radians per second. Most physics problems use angular speed in radians per second. A radian is the angle defined by an arc equal in length to the radius of a circle, about 57.3 degrees. The linear speed of a rolling object is related to its angular speed via the relationship $v = \omega r$. This relationship comes from the geometric fact that a rolling object moves a distance equal to one circumference in each rotation. Instruments such as speedometers and odometers derive the linear speed of a car or bicycle from the angular speed of the wheels. **Sequence:** Students complete the reading after the Investigation.	• Ultimate pulleys set • Physics stand • Timer and one photogate, AC adapter (or 9-volt battery), and a cord to connect the photogate to the timer • Ball (preferably a basketball) • Masking tape • Permanent markers **Duration:** One class period

8.2 Centripetal Force

Learning Goals	Reading Synopsis	Materials and Setup
• Describe why there is a minimum height at which the ball must be started before it will make it around the circular loop. • Describe and sketch the balance of forces at the top of the loop using the concepts of centripetal force, normal force, and weight. • Use the formula for centripetal force to solve problems when given three of four variables (speed, radius, mass, force) **Key question:** Why does a roller-coaster stay on track upside down on a loop? **Leading questions:** • What keeps a roller coaster on the track (even upside down) when it goes around a loop? • How are velocity, radius, and centripetal force related? • How does changing an object's mass affect centripetal force?	Centripetal force is any force that causes an object to move in a circular path. Centripetal force always points toward the center of rotation. If the centripetal force causing an object to move in a circle is removed, the object travels in a straight line as predicted by Newton's first law. The centripetal force required to cause an object of mass (m) to move in a circle of radius, r is given by about formula $F_c = mv^2/r$. If the centripetal force is increased, the radius of curvature decreases, and vice versa. Centripetal acceleration is the radially inward acceleration experienced by an object moving in a circular path. Centripetal acceleration is caused by centripetal force. The centripetal acceleration depends only on the speed of the object and the radius of the circular path according to the equation $a_c = v^2/r$. Centrifugal force is not truly a force but an effect caused by an object's inertia. **Sequence:** Students complete the reading after the Investigation.	• Loop track • Physics stand • Steel ball • Plastic ball • Timer with photogates, AC adapter (or 9-volt battery), and cords to connect the photogates to the timer **Duration:** One class period

8.3 Universal Gravitation and Orbital Motion

Learning Goals	Reading Synopsis	Materials and Setup
• Use Newton's law of universal gravitation to calculate the gravitational force of attraction between various objects. • Use Newton's law of universal gravitation to calculate the strength of gravity for different planets in the universe. **Key question:** How strong is gravity in other places in the universe? **Leading questions:** • How does gravity affect objects? • How can we calculate the force of gravity between objects? • How would gravity be different on different planets in our solar system?	One of the most important sources of centripetal force is gravity. The force of gravity always acts toward the center of a spherical object such as a planet. Gravity keeps the planets moving in their orbits and you firmly attached to Earth's surface. The law of universal gravitation describes the force of gravity between two objects of mass m_1 and m_2 separated by a distance r. The force between the objects is given by $F = G\, m_1 m_2/r$, where G is the gravitational constant which is the same everywhere in the universe ($G = 6.67 \times 10^{-11}$ N·m^2/kg^2). A satellite is an object bound by gravity to another object such as a planet or star. An orbit is the path followed by a satellite around another object under the influence of gravity. The orbits of most planets are nearly circular while the orbits of comets are highly elliptical. **Sequence:** Students complete the reading after the Investigation.	• Calculator and paper • Access to data on the planets from the Investigation book or a similar source. • Access to a balance for measuring the mass of a few small items. **Duration:** One class period

9.1 Torque

Learning Goals	Reading Synopsis	Materials and Setup
• Calculate torque in units of newton-meters (N-m). • Measure torque by measuring force and distance. • Apply balanced and unbalanced torque to an object. • Create rotational equilibrium by balancing torques. • Draw a diagram showing the torques acting on a system. **Key question:** How does force create rotation? **Leading questions:** • What action changes rotational motion in a similar way as force affects linear motion? • How is torque determined? • How is torque related to the direction of a force? • Can an object be at rest and still have torque acting on it?	Force is the action that creates changes in linear motion. For rotational motion, the same force can cause very different results. For rotational motion, the torque is what is most directly related to the motion, not the force. This section is about torque and the relationship between torque and rotational motion. A torque is required to rotate an object and is the rotational equivalent of force. Torque is created when the line of action of a force does not pass through the center of rotation. Torque is calculated by multiplying the length of the lever arm by the magnitude of the force. If more than one torque acts on an object, the torques are combined to determine the net torque. Rotational equilibrium exists when the net torque on an object is zero. Common units of torque are the newton-meter (metric) and the foot-pound (English). **Sequence:** Students complete the reading after the Investigation.	• Ultimate pulleys set (using the 1-meter length of string) • Physics stand • Electronic scale or triple-beam balance (one per class) **Duration:** One class period

xxiii

9.2 Center of Mass

Learning Goals	Reading Synopsis	Materials and Setup
• Locate an object's center of mass. • Explain how the position of an object's center of mass is related to its ability to balance. **Key question:** How do objects balance? **Leading questions:** • What is meant by the terms center of mass and center of gravity? • How can we find an object's center of mass or center of gravity? • How is center of gravity related to balance?	The center of mass of an object is the average position of all the particles that make up its mass. An object naturally tends to spin about its center of mass. An object's center of gravity is the average position of the object's weight. The center of gravity and center of mass of an object are located at the same place as long as the acceleration due to gravity is the same at all points on the object. This is the case for nearly all objects, so the terms center of mass and center of gravity are usually interchangeable. If an object is suspended from one point at its edge, its center of gravity will always fall in the line below the suspension point. If an object is suspended from two or more points, the center of mass can be found by tracing the line below each point and finding the point where the lines intersect. For an object to balance, its center of gravity must be above its area of support. The larger the area of support, the less likely an object is to topple over. **Sequence:** Students complete the reading after the Investigation.	• Piece of cardboard or thick paper • Scissors • Hole punch (hand-held) • Piece of string at least as long as the largest dimension of the cardboard • Washers or other mass to hang at the end of the string (you may use the washers from the ultimate pulleys se • Five identical books, dominos, or blocks for stacking • Metric ruler • Graph paper • Chair **Duration:** One class period

9.3 Rotational Inertia

Learning Goals	Reading Synopsis	Materials and Setup
• Calculate the moment of inertia for point masses. • Explain how moment of inertia, torque, and angular acceleration are related. • Calculate angular acceleration if the change in angular speed and the time are known. **Key question:** Does mass resist rotation the way it resists acceleration? **Leading questions:** • What is rotational inertia? • On which properties of an object does rotational inertia depend? • What is required for an object to rotate? • How does Newton's second law apply to rotating objects?	Rotational inertia is the term used to describe an object's resistance to a change in its rotational motion. An object's rotational inertia depends on its mass and the way the mass is distributed. When an object's mass is concentrated near its axis of rotation, the object is easy to spin. When the mass is far from the axis of rotation, the object is difficult to spin. Newton's second law can be applied to rotational motion and relates torque, rotational inertia, and angular acceleration. Angular acceleration is the rate at which angular speed changes. It is directly proportional to torque and inversely proportional to rotational inertia. The rotational inertia of a point mass is equal to mr^2, where m is the object's mass and r is the radius of the motion. When an object is not a point mass, the average value of mr^2 is calculated. The result of this calculation is called its moment of inertia. **Sequence:** Students complete the reading before the Investigation.	• Ultimate pulleys set (use the 1 meter length of string) • Physics stand • Timer and one photogate, AC adapte (or 9-volt battery), and cords to connect the photogates to the timer • Electronic scale or triple-beam balance **Duration:** One class period

10.1 Machines and Mechanical Advantage

Learning Goals

- Build a simple block and tackle machine using ropes and pulleys.
- Measure the input and output forces of simple machines.
- Calculate the mechanical advantage of the block and tackle.
- Describe any machine conceptually in terms of input, output, and mechanical advantage.

Key question:
How do simple machines work?

Leading questions:
- What is a machine and why is it useful?
- How do we describe action of a machine?
- What is mechanical advantage?
- How does a lever work?
- What is a block and tackle machine?

Reading Synopsis

Machines can be described in terms of input and output, such as input force and output force. A simple machine has no energy source other than forces applied directly and immediately to the machine and functions with a single movement. Gears, levers, screws, ramps, wheel/axle, rope/pulley are simple machines.

Mechanical advantage is the ratio of output force to input force. The mechanical advantage of a lever is the ratio of lengths of the input and output arms. A lever works by balancing torques. The mechanical advantage of a rope and pulleys is the ratio of the number of strands supporting the load to the number of strands to which force is applied, usually 1. Gears and wheels manipulate torque instead of force. The mechanical advantage of a pair of gears is the ratio of their diameters. The mechanical advantage of a frictionless ramp is the ratio of length to height. A screw works like a rotating ramp.

Sequence: Students complete the reading after the Investigation.

Materials and Setup

- Ultimate pulleys set
- Physics stand
- Spring scales
- Electronic scale, or triple-beam balance
- Calculator
- Metric ruler

Duration: One class period

10.2 Work

Learning Goals

- Discover what trade-off there must be for a machine to achieve a mechanical advantage greater than 1.
- Calculate the work done by a machine.
- State the relationship between work and energy.
- Calculate work in joules when given force and distance.
- Use arguments based on input and output work to explain the fundamental limitations of simple machines.

Key question:
What are the consequences of multiplying forces in a machine?

Leading questions:
- In physics, "work" has a special definition. What is "work"?
- What is the difference between force and work?
- Is more work involved in moving up three flights of stairs or riding an elevator?

Reading Synopsis

All simple machines obey a rule that states that any advantage in force must be compensated by applying the force over proportionally longer distance. The law involves the physics meaning of work, which is the subject of this section.

Work is done by forces. The amount of work done is equal to the force times the distance over which the force acts, where distance is measured in the direction of the force. Work is the way mechanical systems change the amount of energy they have. When work is done on a system, its energy increases. When a system does work, its energy decreases. The unit of measurement for work is the joule. One joule of work is done by a force of one newton acting over a distance of one meter. Work done against gravity is equal to the weight of an object multiplied by its change in height, no matter what path is taken. Machines are described by input work and output work. The output work of a simple machine can never exceed the input work.

Sequence: Students complete the reading after the Investigation.

Materials and Setup

- Ultimate pulleys set (use the 5 meter length of string)
- Physics stand
- Spring scales
- Metric ruler, meter stick, or metric measuring tape
- Calculator

Duration: One class period

10.3 Energy and Conservation of Energy

Learning Goals	Reading Synopsis	Materials and Setup
• Explain the relationship between speed and height on the loop track using the conservation of energy. • Calculate potential and kinetic energy. • Describe how the law of energy conservation is used to analyze moving systems that include changes in height and speed, such as a ball rolling downhill. **Key question:** How is motion on a track related to energy? **Leading questions:** • What is energy? • Why is energy an important quantity n physics? • How are speed and height on a roller coaster related? • How are energy and motion related? • What does it mean to state that energy is conserved in a system?	Our universe is made up of matter, energy and information. Matter is something that has mass and takes up space. Energy is the ability to make things change. Information describes where everything is and how it fits together. Energy appears in different forms, such as motion and heat. Energy can travel in different ways, such as light, or sound, or electricity. A system that has energy has the ability to do work. This means that anything with energy can produce a force that is capable of acting over a distance. Energy is measured in joules, the same units as work because work is the transfer of energy. Work is the action of making things change. Energy moves though the action of work There are different forms of energy such as mechanical, light, radiant, nuclear, electrical, chemical, thermal, and pressure. Objects that have potential energy do not use the energy until they move. The energy of motion is called kinetic energy. **Sequence:** Students complete the reading before the Investigation.	• Loop track • Physics stand • Steel and plastic balls • Timer and one photogate, AC adapt (or 9-volt battery), and a cord to connect the photogate to the timer • Meter stick or metric measuring tap • Graph paper • Colored pencils **Duration:** One class period

11.1 Efficiency

Learning Goals	Reading Synopsis	Materials and Setup
• Calculate the efficiency of a process when given the input and output energy. • Give at least one example of how efficiency is defined in a mechanical system, a natural system, and a living organism. **Key question:** How efficient is the straight track? **Leading questions:** • What is efficiency? • How are kinetic and potential energy related to efficiency? • What are input and output energy and how are they related to efficiency? • How does the concept of efficiency apply to mechanical technology, to natural systems, and to living things?	A process is any activity that changes things and can be described in terms of input and output. The energy efficiency of a process is the ratio of useful output energy to input energy. All processes can be described by an efficiency including human-built technology and natural systems. Scientists believe that efficiency less than 100% is a characteristic of all natural processes and is the reason time goes forward, not backward. The efficiency of a mechanical system is always less than 100% because friction converts energy to heat or wear. In terms of natural systems efficiency is usually defined separately for each processes that use energy. For example, the Earth absorbs sunlight with an average efficiency of 78%. The other 22% is reflected back into space. The efficiency of biological systems tends to be very low, on the order of 1-10%. **Sequence:** Students complete the reading after the Investigation.	• Straight track • Plastic ball • Steel ball • Physics stand • Timer and one photogate, AC adapte (or 9-volt battery), and cords to connect the photogates to the timer • Mass balance for determining about mass of the steel and plastic balls (1 per class). **Duration:** One class period

11.2 Energy and Power

Learning Goals	Reading Synopsis	Materials and Setup
• Calculate the work done when lifting an object. • Calculate the power output while lifting an object. • Identify the factors that determine the work a person does and his or her power output. • Calculate power in watts. • Describe the difference between energy and power.	Power is the rate at which energy flows or the rate at which work is done. Power can be calculated by dividing the quantity of work or energy by the time. An alternative way to calculate power is to multiply the force by the velocity. The unit in which power is measured is the watt. One watt is equal to one joule per second. The power of machines is sometimes stated in horsepower. One horsepower is equal to 746 watts.	Each group should have: • Timer or stopwatch • Meter stick • Object for lifting such as a small barbell, loaded backpack, brick, or heavy book • Scale to determine the object's weight or mass • Piece of masking tape
Key question: How powerful are you? **Leading questions:** • How do we calculate power? • What is power? • How much power is used by common devices, like a light bulb? • How much power do we produce with our bodies? • What is the source of the output power in living things?	Power is an important consideration in technology, and also applies to living things and systems in nature. An automobile has a power output of more than 100,000 watts. As an example of a natural system, the Earth gets power from the sun's radiant energy. Solar power drives weather patterns on Earth and supports the food chain that begins with green plants. The power developed by animals and plants ranges from 0.0001 watts for an insect to 375,000 watts for a blue whale. Humans typically produce a maximum power of 300 watts. **Sequence:** Students complete the reading after the Investigation.	For the class activity, the class should have: • Three timers or stopwatches • Access to a set of stairs **Duration:** One class period

11.3 Energy Flow in Systems

Learning Goals	Reading Synopsis	Materials and Setup
• Identify transformations where energy changes forms. • Follow sequences in which energy changes forms in technical, natural, and biological systems. • Sketch an energy flow diagram of technical, natural, and biological systems.	Our universe consists of matter and energy organized in systems. In every system, energy flows, creating change. Energy flows almost always involve energy conversions. This chapter presents a few examples of how energy flows in a system.	• Pencils and paper **Duration:** One class period
Key question: Where did the energy go? **Leading questions:** • What happens to the energy in a process? • How can we describe the flow of energy in a process? • What form does energy take in technology, in natural systems, and in living organisms?	One of the first steps to understanding an energy flow is to write down the forms that energy takes. The next step is to diagram the flow of energy from start to finish for all the important processes that take place. The last step is to try to estimate how much energy is involved and what are the efficiencies for each energy conversion. Examples of these steps are given for energy flows in human technology, in natural systems, and in biological systems. **Sequence:** Students complete the reading before the Investigation.	

12.1 Momentum

Learning Goals	Reading Synopsis	Materials and Setup
• Show how collisions between moving objects obey the law of conservation of momentum. • Use momentum conservation to estimate the mass of unknown objects. **Key question:** What are some useful properties of momentum? **Leading questions:** • How can the momentum of an object be measured? • What is the law of conservation of momentum? • How can we use the law of conservation of momentum to predict what will happen when two objects collide?	The momentum of a moving object is its mass multiplied by its velocity. The momentum of an object is a measure of the object's tendency to continue moving at the same speed in the same direction. Momentum is a vector. Kinetic energy also depends on mass and velocity but is not a vector. In an isolated system, momentum is conserved. The total momentum before a collision equals the total momentum after the collision The conservation of momentum is a consequence of the third law. In an elastic collision, the colliding objects separate after the collision and conserve kinetic energy. In an inelastic collision, the objects stick together and do not conserve kinetic energy. Momentum is conserved in both elastic and inelastic collisions. Techniques and examples are presented for solving momentum problems. In two and three dimensions, momentum is conserved separately in each dimension. **Sequence:** Students complete the reading after the Investigation.	• Show how collisions between movin objects obey the law of conservatior of momentum. • Use momentum conservation to estimate the mass of unknown objects. **Duration:** One class period

12.2 Force is the Rate of Change of Momentum

Learning Goals	Reading Synopsis	Materials and Setup
• Observe elastic and inelastic collisions. • Deduce the comparative strength of the forces that act during elastic and inelastic collisions. • Show that the observations are explained if force is the rate of change of momentum. **Key question:** How are force and momentum related? **Leading questions:** • What causes momentum to change? • What is the difference between elastic and inelastic collisions? • How is momentum related to force?	Momentum changes when a net force is applied. The converse is also true. If momentum changes, forces are created. The force is equal to the rate of change of momentum. Airbags and seat belts are two devices that slow down the change of momentum and therefore reduce the force acting on an occupant of a car during a collision. Newtons second law can be written $\vec{F} = m(\Delta \vec{v}/\Delta t)$, or $\vec{F} = \Delta \vec{p}/\Delta t$. The momentum form is useful when analyzing forces that are exerted over a very short time. The impulse is the product of force and time. Impulse has units of newton-seconds. The total impulse exchanged during a collision is equal to the total change in momentum. **Sequence:** Students complete the reading after the Investigation.	• Physics stand • A rubber ball about 5 centimeters in diameter • Soft clay also about 5 centimeters in diameter • A block of wood $5 \times 10 \times 25$ centimeters • Paper clips (two) • String (two meters) • Meter stick **Duration:** One class period

12.3 Angular Momentum

Learning Goals	Reading Synopsis	Materials and Setup
• Observe how angular momentum tends to keep an object rotating at a constant angular speed. • Show that angular momentum depends on both the angular speed and the moment of inertia. **Key question:** How does the first law apply to rotational motion? **Leading questions:** • What is angular momentum? • How is angular momentum related to moment of inertia? • How do you calculate angular momentum? • Is angular momentum a vector like linear momentum? • How can the law of conservation of angular momentum be used to explain the motion of rotating objects?	Angular momentum is the rotational equivalent of linear momentum. The angular momentum of an object comes from the organized motion of each particle of mass around the center of rotation. Angular momentum obeys a conservation law similar to linear momentum. The angular momentum of an object can be changed by torques applied to the object. The angular momentum of an object is its moment of inertia multiplied by its angular velocity. The units of angular momentum are kg-m^2/sec. Angular momentum is a vector; however, the vector points along the axis of rotation and not in the direction of motion. If the angular momentum of a system is changed, the system exerts reaction torques acting in a direction to resist the change. A gyroscope is a device that uses angular momentum to maintain its orientation. **Sequence:** Students complete the reading after the Investigation.	• One flexible straw • String (about one meter long) • Two washers **Duration:** One class period

13.1 Harmonic Motion

Learning Goals	Reading Synopsis	Materials and Setup
• Measure the amplitude and period of a pendulum. • Describe any oscillator in terms of frequency, period, amplitude, and phase. • Learn to read and represent frequency, period, amplitude, and phase on a graph. **Key question:** How do we describe the back and forth motion of a pendulum? **Leading questions:** • How do we describe repetitive motion in physics? • What are some examples of harmonic motion and oscillators? • Why does a pendulum clock need to be wound?	There are two types of motion: linear and harmonic. Harmonic motion repeats itself over and over. A pendulum swinging back and forth is an example of harmonic motion. A cycle is a pattern of motion that repeats over and over. Harmonic motion is a sequence of repeating cycles. A system that exhibits harmonic motion is called an oscillator. A pendulum moving back and forth and a spring bouncing up and down are examples of oscillators. The period of an oscillator is the time it takes to complete one cycle. The frequency of an oscillator is the number of cycles it makes per second. The amplitude of a cycle is the maximum amount the system moves away from equilibrium. Damping is the reduction of amplitude over time due to friction. Harmonic motion graphs show cycles are usually drawn with time on the horizontal axis. Amplitude, period, and frequency can be determined easily from a graph of position versus time. The phase of an oscillator describes where the oscillator is in its cycle. **Sequence:** Students complete the reading after the Investigation.	• Pendulum (use at least 3 steel balls with string attached, two of which should be the same size) • Physics stand • Timer and one photogate, AC adapter (or 9-volt battery), and a cord to connect the photogate to the timer • Calculator • Graph paper **Duration:** One class period

13.2 Why Things Oscillate

Learning Goals	Reading Synopsis	Materials and Setup
• Create an oscillator and measure its period. • Apply the concepts of restoring force and inertia to change the period of an oscillator. **Key question:** What kinds of systems oscillate? **Leading questions:** • Why do some systems have harmonic motion while others do not? • Is it possible to predict when harmonic motion will occur? • Why do systems in harmonic motion tend to have a specific frequency at which they always oscillate? • Is it possible to change the natural frequency of a system? • restoring force relate to equilibrium? • What is inertia? • What is natural frequency?	Harmonic motion occurs throughout nature. Harmonic motion occurs when a system is stable, has restoring forces, and has some property that provides inertia. Systems that exhibit harmonic motion move back and forth around a central or equilibrium position. A system is stable when equilibrium is maintained by restoring forces. A restoring force is any force that always acts to pull the system back toward equilibrium. When disturbed from equilibrium, inertia causes a stable system to overshoot equilibrium. Harmonic motion is the result. Stable systems have a natural frequency at which they tend to oscillate when disturbed. The natural frequency depends on the ratio of the strength of the restoring force compared with the inertia of the system. Strengthening the restoring force increases the natural frequency of a system. Increasing the inertia decreases the natural frequency. **Sequence:** Students complete the reading after the Investigation.	The following are some suggested materials to make a mechanical oscillator: • Rubber bands • String • Elastic bands • Curved tracks • Steel marbles • Wood block • Steel bolt The group also needs the following: • Rulers • Photogate • Stopwatch • Calculator **Duration:** One class period

13.3 Resonance and Energy

Learning Goals	Reading Synopsis	Materials and Setup
• Describe the relationship between resonance, energy and natural frequency. • Describe how to create resonance in a system in harmonic motion. • Represent and recognize resonance on a graph of amplitude versus period or amplitude vs. frequency. **Key question:** What is resonance and why is it important? **Leading questions:** • Is the relationship between force and motion the same for harmonic motion as it is for linear motion? • Why is the natural frequency important? • What is resonance and why is it important to understand? • How does friction effect systems in harmonic motion?	A force that oscillates in strength or direction is called a periodic force. Periodic forces create harmonic motion. The frequency of a periodic force affects the motion as well as the magnitude and direction. Even a small force applied at the natural frequency can produce large amplitude motion (resonance). Resonance occurs when the frequency of a periodic force matches the natural frequency of a system. The amplitude of harmonic motion increases dramatically at resonance. Resonance is common because every system that can oscillate has a natural frequency and most systems have more than one. In resonance, an applied force efficiently transfers energy to the oscillating system. The energy builds up over time. The amplitude of the motion typically increases until a balance is reached between friction (damping) and the applied force. **Sequence:** Students complete the reading after the Investigation.	• Physics stand and base • Pendulum hanger • Wiggler • Timer, AC adapter, 2 telephone wires and 1 photogate • Wave generator and wires • Steel ball on a string (medium-sized ball) • Graph paper • Meter stick **Duration:** One class period

14.1 Waves and Wave Pulses

Learning Goals	Reading Synopsis	Materials and Setup

Learning Goals

- Create wave pulses on an elastic cord.
- Measure the speed at which wave pulses travel.
- Observe how changing conditions can speed up or slow down a wave.
- Describe the difference between the speed of a wave and the speed of a moving object.

Key question:
What is the speed of a wave?

Leading questions:
- What is a wave and what are some examples of waves?
- What do we mean by the speed of a wave?
- How is the speed of a wave influenced by the physical parameters of a system, such as mass or restoring force?

Reading Synopsis

Waves are traveling oscillations that move energy from one place to another. The energy might be in the form of actual motion, or it might be in sound, light, or another form of energy that can support oscillations. When a wave moves across the surface of water, the water itself does not move with the wave. What is moving is the energy of the wave, and a wave can be described as a traveling form of energy.

Waves have cycles, frequency, and amplitude, just like oscillations. They have properties of wavelength and speed. The amplitude of a wave is the largest amount that it moves above or below the equilibrium level. Wavelength is the length of one complete cycle of a wave. For a water wave this would be the distance from one point on one wave to the same point on the next wave, such as from crest to crest or trough to trough.

Waves can be transverse or longitudinal, and these categories of waves are explored and studied in this section.

Sequence: Students complete the reading after the Investigation.

Materials and Setup

- Timer with photogates, AC adapter (or 9-volt battery), and cords to connect the photogates to the timer
- Elastic string (three meters long; use the string that comes with the sound and waves equipment module)
- Tape strong enough to attach the string to a desk or table
- Chair
- A 5-newton spring scale
- Meter stick or tape measure

Duration: One class period

14.2 Motion and Interaction of Waves

Learning Goals	Reading Synopsis	Materials and Setup

Learning Goals

- Create plane and circular waves
- Describe how the shape of a wave affects its propagation.
- Use the concept of diffraction to describe what happens when a wave passes through a slit that is narrow compared to its wavelength.
- Use of the concept of reflection to describe a wave strikes a hard boundary.

Key question:
How do waves move and interact with things?

Leading questions:
- Describe is a two dimensional wave.
- How do waves move through water?
- What are the basic types of two dimensional waves?
- What happens when a wave hits a boundary, such as a wall?
- What happens when a wave passes through an opening?

Reading Synopsis

A wave can be described by a series of high points (crests) and low points (troughs). The shape of a wave crest is called the wave front. Circular waves have circular wave fronts that move outward from the center. Plane waves have straight wave fronts that move in a line perpendicular to the wave front. Waves propagate through continuous media, such as the surface of a pond.

A wave approaching a boundary is an incident wave. Reflection describes how waves bounce off a boundary. Refraction describes how waves bend crossing a boundary. Diffraction describes how waves spread out passing through openings and around edges. Absorption describes the loss of energy as a wave is absorbed by passing through a material.

More than one wave may exist in a space at one time (superposition principle). When two or more waves are present they may combine to make a larger wave (constructive interference) or a smaller wave (destructive interference).

Sequence: Students complete the reading after the Investigation.

Materials and Setup

- Flat tray such as a cookie tray that can be used for making water waves. You may also want to adhere laminated grids on the bottom of the trays.
- Container for transferring water.
- Ruler or other straight edge that can be used to make waves inside the tray.
- Two blocks of wood or plastic that can be used to block a width of the tray except for a small opening.
- Metric ruler
- One gallon of water mixed with one 1-oz. bottle of blue or green food coloring
- Slinky$^{(TM)}$ spring toy to demonstrate transverse and longitudinal waves.

Duration: One class period

14.3 Natural Frequency and Resonance

Learning Goals	Reading Synopsis	Materials and Setup
• Describe how frequency, wavelength, and speed are related. • Recognize and apply the concept of resonance to any system that can vibrate. • Measure the wavelength and frequency for a vibrating string. • Describe and apply methods for changing the natural frequency of a system. **Key question:** How do we make and control waves? **Leading questions:** • How do we make and control waves? • What is resonance? • Is there a relationship between wave properties of frequency, wavelength, and speed? • What is the relationship between waves and energy?	The natural frequency of a wave depends on the wave and also on the boundaries of the system that contains the wave. A standing wave is a wave trapped between boundaries. Resonance in standing waves comes from the interaction of a wave with reflections from the boundaries. The concepts of resonance and natural frequency apply to a huge range of natural and human-made systems that include waves. Most real, three dimensional systems have many natural frequencies, usually one or more fundamentals each with a series of harmonics. The energy in a wave is proportional to frequency and amplitude. Waves can be described by wavelength. The wavelength is the distance between three successive nodes or antinodes. In a one dimensional system like a string, the nodes are points where the string does not move. In two or three dimensional systems the standing wave patterns are more complex and the nodes and antinodes may be curves or surfaces. **Sequence:** Students complete the reading after the Investigation.	• Sound and waves equipment module • Timer with the AC adapter and a cord to connect the sound and waves console to the timer • Physics stand • Meter stick or metric tape measure • Spring scale • Graph paper • At least one calculator **Duration:** Two to three class periods

15.1 Properties of Sound

Learning Goals	Reading Synopsis	Materials and Setup
• Identify the range of frequencies humans can hear. • Identify the qualities of a good experiment. • Design double-blind experiments and explain their importance in discovering scientific information free from bias. • Apply a simple binary decision tree to evaluate the chances of guessing through a multiple-question test. **Key question:** What is sound and how do we hear it? **Leading questions:** • How are experiments on human perception designed and carried out? • How is the reliability of an experimental conclusion assessed? • How can a scientist be confident people are not just guessing the right answers?	Sound is a traveling oscillation of pressure carried by solid, liquid, or gas. Like other waves, sound has properties of frequency, wavelength, amplitude, and speed. Humans hear frequencies between 20 Hz and 20,000 Hz as sounds of different pitch. Most sound contains many frequencies (superposition principle). The loudness of sound is measured in decibels and depends mostly on the amplitude of the wave. The decibel scale is logarithmic; each increase of 20 dB represents a sound wave with 10 times greater amplitude. Sound is created by anything that vibrates with a frequency between 20 Hz and 20,000 Hz. Speakers create sound by using a oscillating electrical signal to drive a vibrating element. A microphone is a device that transforms a sound wave into an electrical signal with the same pattern of oscillation. Each second of a digital sound recording, such as on a CD, stores the oscillating electrical signal as a sequence of 44,100 numbers. Stereo sound includes two separate recordings for the left and right speakers. **Sequence:** Students complete the reading after the Investigation.	• Sound and wave equipment module (speakers and sound and waves console) • Timer with the AC adapter and a cord to connect the sound and waves console to the timer • Graph paper **Duration:** One class period

15.2 Sound Waves

Learning Goals	Reading Synopsis	Materials and Setup
• Use interference to measure the wavelength of a sound wave. • Demonstrate resonance of sound in different systems. **Key question:** Does sound behave like other waves? **Leading questions:** • What happens when more than one frequency of sound is present at the same time? • Are interference and resonance related? • How does the size of an object influence the sound it makes?	The pressure oscillations in a sound wave are very small, typically a few millionths of an atmosphere. Sound travels through matter but cannot travel through the vacuum of space. Like other waves, the speed of sound is equal to frequency multiplied by wavelength. The speed of sound is 343 m/sec at room temperature and pressure. If a sound source is moving relative to an observer, the frequency of the sound heard by the observer may change. This phenomenon is called the Doppler effect. An object is supersonic if it is moving faster than the speed of sound. Enclosed spaces or vibrating objects can support resonance and standing sound waves. Resonance is applied to the construction of musical instruments. Multiple reflection of sound from the walls of a room is called reverberation and is an important criteria for concert halls and auditoriums. Fourier's theorem states that any complex wave can be represented as a sum of single frequency waves. **Sequence:** Students complete the reading before the Investigation.	• Sound and waves equipment module (speakers and sound and waves console) • Timer with the AC adapter and a cord to connect the sound and waves console to the timer • Tuning fork • 3 wine glasses (for each group or for demonstration) • A pitcher or large cup of water for filling the wine glasses **Duration:** One class period

15.3 Sound, Perception, and Music

Learning Goals	Reading Synopsis	Materials and Setup
• Describe how beats create dissonance. • Calculate the frequencies of the 8 notes of the musical scale given the first note. • Describe the frequency relationship between two notes that are an octave apart. • Describe how resonance, frequency, and wavelength are used to create musical instruments that play the correct frequencies of notes. **Key question:** How is musical sound different than other types of sound? **Leading questions:** • What do frequency and wavelength have to do with pitch and the musical scale? • What is an octave? • What creates consonance and dissonance in sound?	The meaning in sound is encoded in how thousands of individual frequencies perceived by the brain change over time. A sonogram is a graphical representation showing how the frequency spectrum changes with time. The sense of hearing comes from the cochlea, a part of the inner ear. Musical sound is a pattern of pitch and rhythm. Pitch describes the frequency of sound and rhythm describes the regular time-pattern in a sound. A musical scale is a collection of frequencies called notes. The 8 notes in the Western musical scale have a simple mathematical relationship based on ratios of frequency. The frequencies of the notes are chosen to minimize dissonance. Dissonance is caused by beats which occur when two frequencies are close together but not exactly the same. Musical sounds contain harmonics as well as the fundamental note. The relative balance between the loudness, attack, and decay of the different harmonics gives each instrument its characteristic sound. **Sequence:** Students complete the reading after the Investigation.	• Sound and Wave generator • Timer • Speakers **Duration:** One class period

16.1 Properties and Sources of Light

Learning Goals	Reading Synopsis	Materials and Setup
• Use simple ray diagrams to show how mirrors, lenses, and prisms cause objects to appear to be where they are not. • Calculate the time it takes light to move ordinary distances. • Use the inverse square law to explain why stars appear dimmer or brighter. • Calculate the intensity of light from the inverse square law when given the power and distance. **Key question:** What are some useful properties of light? **Leading questions:** • What is light and how can we describe the behavior of light? • What are reflection and refraction? • How fast does light move? • Why do far away objects appear dimmer than identical objects that are nearby?	Every time we look at something, light is involved. Light has properties of color, intensity, and power. Electric light is produced by hot material in a incandescent bulb and by atomic processes in a fluorescent bulb. The intensity of light is the amount of energy per second per unit of surface area. The intensity of a point light source diminishes as the inverse square of the distance. Light carries information. Light is used to transmit pictures, sound, or computer data, and other information. Light is a form of energy that travels at 3×10^8 m/sec. Light ordinarily travels in straight lines but can be bent by mirrors or lenses. Reflection describes the bouncing of light from a surface. Refraction describes the bending of light crossing through a surface. **Sequence:** Students complete the reading after the Investigation.	• Light and Optics kit, specifically the mirror and prism • Graph paper • White paper or index cards • Calculator • Ruler **Duration:** One class period

16.2 Color and Vision

Learning Goals	Reading Synopsis	Materials and Setup
• Show that the white light can be made from red, green and blue. • Interpret the rainbow that appears when a light source is viewed through a diffraction grating. • Explain how a color filter makes colored light from white light. **Key question:** How do we see color? **Leading questions:** • How do we perceive color? • How is color created by objects that give off light, such as a TV? • How is color created by objects that reflect light, such as printed pictures or clothes? • How is white light created? • How do we know what colors are in any given light?	Our eyes can see colors from deep red, through yellows, greens, and blues, to deep purple like violet. The order of colors is always the same when white light is separated with a prism: red, orange, yellow, green, blue, indigo and violet. We call the combination of all colors white light. All the colors in the rainbow are actually light of different energies. Moving through the rainbow from red to yellow to blue to violet, the energy of the light increases. Special rod and cone cells in the retina of the eye are sensitive to color and intensity. There are different receptor cells for red, green, and blue light. The brain perceives a variety of color using the RGB additive process. We see mostly reflected light. The CMYK process creates color in reflected light by selective absorption of colors from white light. Green plants reflect green light and absorb red and blue. Color TV's and computer monitors create colored images using thousands of red, green, and blue pixels. **Sequence:** Students complete the reading after the Investigation.	• Light and Optics kit with red, green, and blue lamps, mounted lens, screen table, and laser • Diffraction grating glasses • colored pencils • Paper **Duration:** One class period

16.3 Photons and Atoms

Learning Goals	Reading Synopsis	Materials and Setup
• Described the basic idea behind the photon theory of light • Explain why blue light causes a photo luminescent plastic to blow while red light does not, even when the red light is made brighter than the blue light. **Key question:** How does light fit into the atomic theory of matter? **Leading questions:** • How is light produced? • How do photoluminescent (as in glow-in-the-dark) materials work? • How is light described in the atomic theory of matter? • What color light has the highest energy?	Light energy comes in tiny, discrete bundles called photons. The energy of a photon is proportional to its frequency. Blue photons have a higher energy than red photons Because blue light has a higher frequency than red light. The intensity of light is determined by the number of photons and by the energy of each photon. Equal intensities of red and blue light represent different numbers of photons because blue photons individually carry more energy than red photons. In the atomic theory, each atom interacts with only one photons at a time. The phosphorus atoms in glow-in-the-dark plastic require a minimum energy to absorb light that can be released later as a photo luminescent glow. A white page looks white because the atoms absorb and re-emit photons of all energies equally. Black ink looks black because the atoms absorb all colors of visible photons and emit none. **Sequence:** Students complete the reading after the Investigation.	• Optics board • LEDs: red, green and blue **Duration:** One class period

17.1 Reflection and Refraction

Learning Goals	Reading Synopsis	Materials and Setup
• Trace light rays from a laser using a prism and a mirror to find the angles of incidence. • Measure the index of refraction and observe the critical angle for glass. **Key question:** How do we describe the reflection and refraction of light? **Leading questions:** • How does reflection change the path of light rays? • How does refraction change the path of light rays? • What does the index of refraction tell you about a material? • How is the critical angle affected by the index of refraction?	The study of how light behaves is called optics. Optical devices include lenses, mirrors, cameras, telescopes, and microscopes. A ray diagram uses imaginary lines called light rays to describes how light travels. A normal line is perpendicular to a surface. The law of reflection states that the angle of reflection is equal to the angle of incidence. The index of refraction for a material determines the ability of that material to bend light rays. Snell's law of refraction states that $n_i \sin\theta_i = n_r \sin\theta_r$ where the subscripts i and r refer to the incident and reflected rays. All angles are measured relative to the normal line. Depending on the angle of incidence, light crossing a surface for which $n_i > n_r$ may be reflected instead of refracted. If the angle of incidence is greater than the critical angle, the light is reflected in a process called total internal reflection. The index of refraction typically varies with the color of the light creating a phenomenon called dispersion. Dispersion causes blue light to be bent more than red light in a prism or lens. **Sequence:** Students complete the reading after the Investigation.	• Light and Optics Kit • Mirror • Graph paper • Pencils **Duration:** One class period

17.2 Mirrors, Lenses and Images

Learning Goals	Reading Synopsis	Materials and Setup
• Use the laser beam to trace light rays from a lens to determine its focal length. • Show how ray diagrams are used to predict where images form with lenses and mirrors. **Key question:** How does a lens or mirror form an image? **Leading questions:** • How does a mirror form an image? • What does the focal length of a convex lens indicate about how light rays passing through it will be affected? • How does a convex lens form an image? • What is magnification and how is it calculated?	Objects are real physical entities that give off or reflect light. Images are patterns of light formed where many rays from the same point on an object meet, or appear to meet, in a point. A virtual image is formed when light rays appear to come from a point, like the image in a mirror. A real image is formed when light rays actually come to a point, like the image formed by an overhead projector. The magnification of an image is the ratio of the image's size divided by the object's size. Images may be right side up or inverted. Ray diagrams may be used to determine the location and characteristics of an image. The image formed by a convex lens can be analyzed by tracing three principal rays. A convex (converging) lens forms a real image when the object is beyond the focal length and a virtual image when the object is within the focal length. A diverging lens always forms a virtual image. **Sequence:** Students complete the reading after the Investigation.	• Light and Optics Kit • Graph paper • Ruler • Prism • Mirror • Lasers **Duration:** One class period

17.3 Optical Systems

Learning Goals	Reading Synopsis	Materials and Setup
• Use the principles of geometric optics to predict where images form with lenses. • Use the thin lens formula to predict how and where images are formed by a single convex lens. • Explain chromatic aberration and show how single lenses suffer from this defect. **Key question:** How are the properties of images determine? **Leading questions:** • What is an optical system? • What will a ray tracing diagram tell you about an image? • How are different colors affected by a convex lens? • How can the location of an image formed by a convex lens be predicted?	An optical system is a collection of mirrors, lenses, prisms, or other optical elements that performs a useful function with light. Characteristics of optical systems include location type and magnification of images; amount of light collected; accuracy in sharpness, color, and distortion; ability to change image characteristics; and the ability to record an image. The quality of an image is limited by chromatic aberration, spherical aberration, and diffraction. The thin lens formula is used to determine image and object distances. This formula is an algebraic representation of the geometrical optics approach of tracing rays. Multiple lenses such as in a telescope or telephoto lens allow an optical system to change the size of an image. Multiple lenses can be analyzed in sequence by considering the image formed by one lens as the object for the next lens. **Sequence:** Students complete the reading after the Investigation.	• Light and Optics Kit • Lens • Graph paper **Duration:** One class period

18.1 The Electromagnetic Spectrum

Learning Goals	Reading Synopsis	Materials and Setup
• Research one type of wave that is part of the electromagnetic spectrum. • Prepare a poster containing the information they discover. • Make an oral presentation to share the information with the class. **Key question:** What is the electromagnetic spectrum? **Leading questions:** • What uses do different types of waves have? • How do you use electromagnetic waves in your everyday life?	The electromagnetic spectrum includes visible light and all other forms of electromagnetic radiation. Electromagnetic waves are traveling oscillations in the electromagnetic field. The waves can travel through vacuum. Like other waves, the speed of electromagnetic waves is equal to frequency multiplied by wavelength. In vacuum, electromagnetic waves travel at the speed of light, or 3×10^8 m/sec. Electromagnetic waves travel slower when passing through matter such as light through glass. Radio waves have the lowest energy and longest wavelength of the spectrum. The wavelength of radio waves ranges from a few centimeters to kilometers or longer. Microwaves have higher energy than radio waves. Moving up the spectrum in energy are infrared light, visible light, ultraviolet light, x-rays, and gamma rays. This section presents applications for each category of waves. **Sequence:** Students complete the reading before the Investigation.	• This is a research Investigation, so no equipment is necessary to complete it. • Poster board **Duration:** One class period

18.2 Interference, Diffraction and Polarization

Learning Goals	Reading Synopsis	Materials and Setup
• Observe and explain how a diffraction grating creates a rainbow. • Observe and explain what happens when a laser shines through a diffraction grating. • Explain the interaction of light and polarizers using the wave theory of light. **Key question:** What are some ways light behaves like a wave? **Leading questions:** • What does a diffraction grating do to light passing through it? • How does an interference pattern produced by a diffraction grating support the wave theory of light? • What uses does a spectrometer have? • What does a polarizing filter do to light passing through it?	We say light is a wave because the results of many experiments with light demonstrate properties of waves. Young's double slit experiment is a good example of interference. A diffraction grating creates an interference pattern similar to the double slit. The first order bright spot in a diffraction pattern results from constructed interference that occurs when the grating equation ($\lambda = d\sin\theta$) is satisfied. A spectrometer is a device that measures the wavelength of light. Polarization is a property of transverse waves. The direction of polarization is a vector perpendicular to the direction the wave propagates. The polarization vector of light points in the direction of the electric field of the wave. A polarizer is a material that is sensitive to the polarization of light. One polarization is absorbed. The perpendicular polarization is transmitted, or emitted. Applications of polarizers include sunglasses and LCD computer screens. **Sequence:** Students complete the reading after the Investigation.	• Light and optics kit (laser) • Diffraction grating glasses • Metric ruler • Spectrometer • Two polarizing filters • A large spring or Slinky$^{(TM)}$ spring toy to demonstrate waves. Slinkies$^{(TM)}$ can be plastic or metal. Both types will work. **Duration:** One class period

18.3 Special Relativity

Learning Goals	Reading Synopsis	Materials and Setup
• Explore some consequences of time dilation. • Calculate the equivalence of mass and energy using Einstein's formula $E = mc^2$. **Key question:** What are some of the implications of special relativity? **Leading questions:** • Does time move at the same speed for everyone everywhere? • What is the relationship between frames of reference and time dilation? • How are energy, mass, and the speed of light related? • What does Einstein's mass - energy formula tell us about the potential for possible sources of energy?	The theory of special relativity describes what happens to matter, energy, time, and space when the speed of a moving object becomes close to the speed of light. The speed of light is the same for all observers regardless of their relative motion. This implies that time passes more slowly for a moving observer compared to a stationary observer. Light emitted from a moving source is perceived by a stationary observer at a different frequency from the frequency measured by an observer moving with the light source. Einstein's formula $E = mc^2$ describes the equivalent of mass and energy. Matter cannot exceed or even reach the speed of light. The reason is because energy can be converted to mass instead of speed. The concept of simultaneity is affected by special relativity. Events that are simultaneous to one observer may not be simultaneous to a second observer moving relative to the first observer. **Sequence:** Students complete the reading before the Investigation.	• Calculators • No other equipment is necessary because most of the Investigation centers around students completing calculations. **Duration:** One class period

19.1 Electric Circuits

Learning Goals	Reading Synopsis	Materials and Setup
• Construct simple electric circuits using a battery, bulb, switch and wires. • Draw circuit diagrams using electrical symbols. • Explain the concepts of open, closed, and short circuits. **Key question:** What is an electric circuit? **Leading questions:** • What is electricity? • How does a circuit work? • What are open, closed, and short circuits? • Why doesn't electricity leak from an open circuit?	Electricity refers to the presence of electric current in wires, motors, light bulbs, and other devices. Like water, electric current flows. However, electric current is not normally visible because it flows through solid metal. Electric current flows in circuits and can transmit energy and power. Electric circuits are represented by circuit diagrams. A circuit diagram contains symbols that represent electrical components such as resistor, batteries, and switches. An open circuit has a break that prevents current from flowing. A closed circuit makes a complete path allowing current to flow. A short circuit is a potentially dangerous, low resistance path that may allow too much current to flow. **Sequence:** Students complete the reading after the Investigation.	• Electric circuits kit components: bulb and socket, wires, switch • One C-cell battery **Duration:** One class period

19.2 Current and Voltage

Learning Goals	Reading Synopsis	Materials and Setup
• Measure electrical current with a multimeter. • Compare current in circuits with one or two bulbs. • Measure voltage with a multimeter. • Combine two batteries to increase the voltage in a circuit. **Key question:** How does current move through a circuit? **Leading questions:** • How is electrical current measured? • What is voltage and how is it measured? • What is the function of a battery in a circuit?	Current and voltage are the two most important concepts to understanding electricity. Current is what actually flows through wires, carries energy and does work. Voltage measures the difference in energy between two places in a circuit. Current flows in response to differences in voltage just like water flows in response to differences in height. Current is measured in amperes, or amps. Voltage is measured in volts. One volt means each amp of current carries one watt of power. Both voltage and current can be measured with a multimeter. To measure voltage the leads of the meter are touched to two points in a circuit. The meter measures the voltage difference between the two points. To measure current, the meter must be inserted in the circuit so that the current is forced to flow through it. **Sequence:** Students complete the reading after the Investigation.	• Multimeter with red and black leads • Electric circuits kit components: circuit board, two bulbs and sockets, wires, switch, battery holder • Two C-cell batteries **Duration:** One class period

19.3 Electrical Resistance and Ohm's Law

Learning Goals	Reading Synopsis	Materials and Setup
• • Measure the current when the resistance is changed. • Use the current versus voltage graph to find a relationship between voltage, current, and resistance. • Use Ohm's law to predict voltage, current, or resistance when two of the three variables are known. **Key question:** How are voltage, current, and resistance related? **Leading questions:** • How does a circuit know how much current to use? • What is the relationship between voltage, current, and resistance? • How do you compare and contrast conductors and insulators? • Why won't a 1.5-volt battery light up a 100-watt light bulb?	You can apply the same voltage to different circuits and different amounts of current will flow. The amount of current that flows in a circuit is determined by the resistance of the circuit. The resistance in ohms is the voltage (volts) divided by the current (amps) according to Ohm's law. Every device that uses electrical energy adds resistance to a circuit. The current that flows in a circuit is directly proportional to the voltage and inversely proportional to resistance. Conductors have low resistance and insulators have high resistance. A resistor is an electrical device with a controlled resistance. A variable resistor is called a potentiometer. Potentiometers are used to control or adjust the current and voltage in a circuit. **Sequence:** Students complete the reading after the Investigation.	• Multimeter with red and black leads • Electric circuits kit components: circuit board, potentiometer, switch, battery holder, bulb and socket, 20Ω resistor, wires • One D-cell battery • Graph paper **Duration:** One class period

20.1 Series and Parallel Circuits

Learning Goals	Reading Synopsis	Materials and Setup
• Explain the difference between a series and parallel circuit. • Calculate the total resistance in series and parallel circuits. • Describe what happens to the voltage across to each component in a series circuit. • Give two important advantages parallel circuits have over series circuits. **Key question:** How do series and parallel circuits work? **Leading questions:** • In what ways can electrical components be connected together to make circuits? • What are the rules for how current and voltage behave in a circuit with many components?	Series circuits have only one path for current to flow. The total resistance in a series circuit is the sum of the individual resistances ($R_T = R_1 + R_2 + ...$). The voltage drop across each resistance in a series circuit is calculated using Ohm's law ($V = I \div R$). Parallel circuits have branches and multiple paths for current to flow. Each electrical component in a parallel circuit sees the same voltage. However, because the circuit contains the branches, the current through each component made not to be that same. Adding additional resistances in parallel lowers the total resistance of a parallel circuit. This is because each new resistance adds another independent path for current to flow. For a parallel circuit the total resistance is calculated by $1/R_T = 1/R_1 + 1/R_2 + ...$. **Sequence:** Students complete the reading after the Investigation.	• Multimeter with red and black leads • Two D-cell batteries • Electric circuits kit components: circuit board, potentiometer, switch, two battery holders, three bulbs and sockets, wires **Duration:** One class period

20.2 Analysis of Circuits

Learning Goals	Reading Synopsis	Materials and Setup
• Build a network circuit. • Determine the total resistance of a 3 element resistor network circuit. **Key question:** How do we analyze network circuits? **Leading questions:** • Can circuits only be connected in either series or parallel? • Is there a process for analyzing complicated circuits? • How is a complex circuit designed? • How can the behavior of a complex circuit be understood? • Why is circuit analysis useful?	All circuits work by manipulating currents and voltage. The process of circuit analysis means figuring out what the currents and voltages in a circuit are. there are three basic laws that are the foundation of circuit analysis. Ohm's law relates voltage and current and resistance. Kirchhoff's current laws states that the sum of currents leaving a branch point must be equal to the currents entering the branch point. Kirchhoff's voltage law says the sum of the voltage changes around any loop in a circuit must be zero. Together with the formulas for combining resistors, Ohm's law and Kirchhoff's current and voltage laws are the foundation of circuit analysis. A voltage divider is a commonly used resistor circuit that produces an output voltage that is a fraction of the input voltage. The voltage divider and other examples of network circuits are discussed. **Sequence:** Students complete the reading after the Investigation.	• Multimeter with red and black leads • Two D-cell batteries • Electric circuits kit components: two 5-ohm resistors, one 10-ohm resistor, one 20-ohm resistor, two battery holders, wires, 3 bulbs and sockets **Duration:** One class period

20.3 Electric Power, AC, and DC Electricity

Learning Goals	Reading Synopsis	Materials and Setup
• Explain power in terms of energy and time. • Calculate power in a DC circuit when given the current and voltage. • Rank the amount of power used by various household appliances. • Estimate the cost per month of using a common household appliance. • Use dimensional analysis to show that a kilowatt hour is a unit of energy not a unit of power. **Key question:** How much does electricity cost and what do you pay for? **Leading questions:** • How is the energy and power in electricity measured? • What do we mean when we say that household appliances use electricity? • What do the terms on an electric bill mean? • Which household appliances are costliest to operate?	The watt (W) is a unit of power. Power measures the rate of energy transfer. One joule per second is equal to one watt. A 100-watt light bulb uses 100 joules of energy *every second*. Electrical power in a circuit id the product of voltage and current ($P = VI$). Utility companies charge for a unit of energy called the kilowatt-hour. One kilowatt-hour is 3.6 million joules, which is the equivalent of one kilowatt of power for one hour. A battery supplies and DC power, which means of a positive and stays positive always. Most electricity supplied to homes and businesses is AC rather than DC. In household AC electricity, the voltage on one terminal alternates between +170V and -170V sixty times per second. The average absolute value is 120 volts therefore this type of electricity is known as 120 VAC (120 Volt Alternating Current). Because the voltage and current may be out of phase with each other, power in an AC circuit is usually less than the average voltage times the average current. **Sequence:** Students complete the reading after the Investigation.	• Two or three small appliances labeled with power ratings, such as an iron, toaster oven, electric drill, desk lamp, or hair dryer • Calculators **Duration:** Two class periods; there is a home assignment between the two periods

21.1 Electric Charge

Learning Goals	Reading Synopsis	Materials and Setup
• Charge pieces of tape and observe their interactions with an electroscope. • Identify electric charge as the property of matter responsible for electricity. • List the two forms of electric charge. • Describe the forces electric charges exert on each other. **Key question:** How do electric charges interact? **Leading questions:** • What causes electricity? • What causes electrical current to move in a circuit? • What is moving through the wires of a circuit?	Electric charge is a fundamental property of matter. There are two types of charge we call positive and negative. Like charges repel each other and unlike charges attract. Forces between charges hold the atom together and cause electric current to flow. Electrons carry negative charge and protons carry positive charge. Electric current is moving charge. . In a conductor, many electrons are free to move independently of the atoms they belong to. These electrons carry current. In an insulator, electrons are bound tightly to atoms and are not free to move. Insulators block the flow of electric current. A semiconductor has a few mobile electrons and can carry small amounts of current. We do not ordinarily see charged matter because positive and negative are perfectly balanced leaving zero net charge. We called a material electrically polarized if there is an uneven distribution of positive or negative charge. **Sequence:** Students complete the reading after the Investigation.	• Two rectangles of clay, about 2-by-2-by-4 centimeters • Four flexible straws • Metric ruler • Scotch™ brand magic tape • Small light objects such as pieces of thread and small pieces of paper (optional) • Pairs of materials that can be charged, such as plastic combs rubbed with wool, glass rubbed with wool, and dry wood rubbed with glass (optional) **Duration:** One class period

21.2 Coulomb's Law

Learning Goals	Reading Synopsis	Materials and Setup
• Calculate the electrical force between charged objects. • Compare electrical and gravitational forces. • Calculate the charge on objects if the electrical force between them is known. **Key question:** How strong are electrical forces? **Leading questions:** • What are the types of electrical charges? • How do different types of electrical charges interact? • What determines the strength of the electrical force between charged objects? • What is Coulomb's law?	The electrical force between two charged objects increases if they move closer together or if the amount of either charge increases. Coulomb's law relates the force between charges, their separation distance, and the magnitude of the charges. Electrical forces attract if the charges are opposite and repel if the charges are the same. Electrical forces are very strong, even when only small amounts of charge are present. We do not usually notice the strength of electrical forces because positive and negative charges in matter are not usually separated from each other. The interaction between two charges is transmitted by the electric field. A charge creates an electric field around it. Another charge placed in the field experiences a force ($\vec{F} = q\vec{E}$). Electric field lines can be drawn to show the direction of the electric field. The field lines point from positive to negative, showing the force on a positive test charge. **Sequence:** Students complete the reading before the Investigation.	• Two small balloons, such as those meant to be water balloons • Meter stick • Small ruler or stick • Balance or digital scale • Piece of light string or thread, approximately 50 cm long • Piece of tape **Duration:** One class period

21.3 Capacitors

Learning Goals	Reading Synopsis	Materials and Setup
• Explain how the voltage across a capacitor varies with time as it charges. • Explain how the voltage across a capacitor varies with time as it discharges. • Explain how the current in a circuit with a capacitor changes with time as it charges and discharges. • Explain the relationship between the circuit resistance and the charging rate of a capacitor. **Key question:** How does a capacitor work? **Leading questions:** • What is a capacitor? • What does it mean to say a capacitor is charged? • How can a capacitor become charged?	A capacitor is a device that stores charge. A capacitor can be charged with a battery or other source of current. The voltage across the terminals of a capacitor is proportional to the amount of charge stored and to the capacitance. The capacitance is the ratio of charge stored per volt and depends on the structure of the capacitor and the materials of which it is made. Capacitance is measured in farads. The rate of charging and discharging of a capacitor depends on the current allowed to flow. The greater the current (low resistance) the faster the capacitor charges and discharges. The current and capacitor voltage vary with time. As a capacitor charges, the current decreases and the capacitor voltage increases. As a capacitor discharges, the current and capacitor voltage decrease. The simplest type of capacitor is called a parallel plate capacitor. It is made of two metal plates that are close together. One plate becomes negative and the other positive. **Sequence:** Students complete the reading before the Investigation.	• Multimeter with red and black leads • Two D-cell batteries • Electric circuits kit components: two battery holders, two switches, wires • Circuits RC pack: one 470 μF capacitor, one each of 22kΩ, 47kΩ, and 100 kΩ resistors • Timer with AC adapter (or 9-volt battery) • Graph paper **Duration:** One to two class periods

22.1 Properties of Magnets

Learning Goals	Reading Synopsis	Materials and Setup
• Describe the properties of a permanent magnet. • Describe and measure the forces that magnets exert on each other. • Describe and sketch magnetic fields. **Key question:** How do magnets interact with each other? **Leading questions:** • What are the characteristics common to all magnets? • How far does the magnetic force reach? • How do you tell which direction a magnet will be pushed or pulled when it is near another magnet? • What is magnetic force and how can it be measured? • What is the magnetic field?	If a material is magnetic, it has the ability to exert forces on other magnets or magnetic materials. All magnets have common properties. For example, they always have two opposite "poles," called north and south. If divided, each part of a magnet has both north and south poles—we never see an unpaired north or south pole. When near each other, magnets exert magnetic forces on each other. The forces between magnets depend on the distance between them and the relative orientation of their poles. Two unlike poles attract each other and two like poles repel each other. The strength of the force between magnets decreases rapidly as the distance between the magnets increases. Magnetic forces are carried through a magnetic field, similar to electrical forces. A magnet creates a magnetic field then the field exerts forces on other magnets. Magnetic field lines point from north to south and are drawn to show the shape of the magnetic field in a region. **Sequence:** Students complete the reading after the Investigation.	• 10 ceramic magnets (from the electric motor set) • Navigational compass **Duration:** One class period

22.2 Magnetic Properties of Materials

Learning Goals	Reading Synopsis	Materials and Setup
• Describe how a magnet is used to test between magnetic and nonmagnetic materials. • Describe common magnetic materials. • Describe the effect of nonmagnetic materials on the force between magnets. **Key question:** How do magnets interact with different materials? **Leading questions:** • What materials are affected by magnets? • What do magnetic materials have in common? • If a material is magnetic, how does it interact with a magnet? • How do materials affect the force between two magnets? Does the force change as it passes through materials?	The source of magnetic effects in matter is the motion of electrons. Diamagnetic materials contain equal numbers of electrons spinning in each direction, which results in a net magnetic field of zero. Individual atoms in paramagnetic materials are magnetic, but atoms are randomly arranged so the overall field is zero. Ferromagnetic materials such as iron, nickel, and cobalt are highly magnetic. Individual atoms are magnetic and form groups called magnetic domains. Magnetic domains contain atoms with their fields oriented in the same direction. When placed in an external magnetic field, the domains grow and the object becomes magnetized. Ferromagnetic materials that make good permanent magnets are called hard magnets. Domains in these materials tend to remain aligned. Materials that lose their magnetism quickly are called soft magnets. Both hard and soft magnets can become demagnetized through vibration or with heat. **Sequence:** Students complete the reading after the Investigation.	• Two ceramic magnets (use the magnets from the electric motor set) • An assortment of materials to test, such as a plastic spoon, wooden pencil, steel paper clip, fabric, scissors, aluminum foil, coins, a nail, or chalk **Duration:** One class period

22.3 The Magnetic Field of the Earth

Learning Goals	Reading Synopsis	Materials and Setup
• Explain how a compass works. • Read and use a compass. • Explain how magnetic declination affects a compass. • Identify materials that will affect a compass magnetically. **Key question:** How do we use Earth's magnetic field to tell direction? **Leading questions:** • In which direction does a compass needle point? • What is magnetic declination? • Can any other materials affect a compass?	Like many other planets, Earth has a magnetic field, as if its core contained a huge magnet. Magnetite and lodestone are naturally occurring magnetic rocks. A compass works because a magnetized needle that is free to rotate will align itself with the magnetic field of the Earth. The geographic north pole of the Earth is actually a south magnetic pole. The magnetic field of the Earth comes from the circulation of electric currents deep in the molten iron core of the planet. Over the history of the planet, the magnetic field has reversed itself on average every 500,000 years. The magnetic poles of Earth do not align exactly with the geographic poles. The difference between the orientation of the Earth's magnetic field and the geographic direction of north is called declination. In North America, the declination may be up to 16 degrees, with magnetic north slightly west of geographic north. **Sequence:** Students complete the reading after the Investigation.	• Navigational compass • A magnet (from the electric motor set) • A steel bucket or baking pan **Duration:** One class period

23.1 Electric Current and Magnetism

Learning Goals	Reading Synopsis	Materials and Setup
• Build an electromagnet. • Explain how electric current affects the strength of the magnetic field in an electromagnet. • Compare permanent magnets and electromagnets. **Key question:** Can electric current create a magnet? **Leading questions:** • How it is magnetism created? • Do magnets exert forces on moving currents? • What is the unit of magnetic field and what does it mean? • What is the relationship between current and magnetic field? • Do permanent magnets and electromagnets create the same kind of magnetism or is there a difference?	A wire carrying current creates a magnetic field that circles the wire in a direction given by the right hand rule. Parallel wires carrying current in the same direction attract each other. Parallel wires carrying current in opposite directions repel each other. Atomic-scale electric currents create the magnetism in permanent magnets. Magnetic fields exert forces on moving charges. The force on a moving charge, or current flowing in a wire is perpendicular to both the direction of current and to the direction of the magnetic field. The unit of magnetic field strength is the tesla (T). A magnetic field of one tesla exerts a force of one newton on one meter of wire carrying a current of 1 amp. The direction of the force is given by the right-handed rule. Formulas are presented for the magnetic field near a wire and at the center of a coil. **Sequence:** Students complete the reading after the Investigation.	• Two ceramic magnets (from the electric motor set) • Three meters of magnetic wire, 24 gauge • Sandpaper • Two galvanized nails 7 centimeters long • Electric circuits kit • Two D-cells • The assortment of magnetic and nonmagnetic materials used in Investigation 22.2 • Multimeter with red and black leads • 100 steel paper clips • Graph paper • Pencils • Ruler or straightedge Teacher should have: • A working electromagnet **Duration:** Two class periods

23.2 Electromagnets and the Electric Motor

Learning Goals	Reading Synopsis	Materials and Setup
• Build a working electric motor. • Explain how permanent magnets and electromagnets interact to make a motor spin. • Measure the motor's current and voltage. • Calculate the power used by various motor designs. **Key question:** How does a motor work? **Leading questions:** • How is an electromagnet made? • How does an electric motor work? • How can a motor be designed for optimum performance? • How much electric power does a motor use?	Electromagnets depend on electric current to create their magnetism. The most efficient design for an electromagnet is a coil of wire wrapped around a core of iron or steel. The magnetic field of an electromagnet is proportional to the current and to the number of turns of wire in the coil. An electric motor converts electrical energy to rotating motion. One type of motor has a rotating spindle (the armature) that contains permanent magnets. These permanent magnets are alternately attracted and repelled by stationary electromagnets. Electromagnets are used because they can be switched from north to south by reversing the current through them. The commutator is the part of the motor that switches the electromagnets from attract to repel at the right time to keep the armature spinning. **Sequence:** Students complete the reading after the Investigation.	• Electric motor set with four D-cell batteries • Multimeter with red and black leads In addition, the teacher should have: • Extra D-cell batteries **Duration:** Two class periods

23.3 Induction and the Electric Generator

Learning Goals	Reading Synopsis	Materials and Setup
• Explain how an electric generator works. • Build and test several electric generator designs. • Use Faraday's law of induction to explain why the amount of electricity generated depends on the speed and number of magnets in the generator. **Key question:** How does a generator produce electricity? **Leading questions:** • How is the electricity you use in your home or business created? • How does an electric generator work? • What is the relationship between electricity and magnetism?	A changing magnetic field can generate voltage and create electric current in a coil of wire. Using moving magnets to create electric current is called electromagnetic induction and is the principle behind the electric generator. Faraday's law of induction says the induced voltage (or current) is proportional to the number of turns of wire in a coil and to the rate of change of the magnetic field through the coil. Because the magnetic poles switch back and forth, generators produce alternating current (AC) electricity. This is the type of electricity produced by power plants and used in homes. A transformer is another electrical device based on induction. A transformer changes AC electricity at one voltage to AC electricity at a different voltage keeping the total power constant. Transformers are used to step down high voltage electricity from power transmission lines to 120 VAC electricity used in homes and businesses. **Sequence:** Students complete the reading after the Investigation.	• Electric motor kit with generator coil • Timer with one photogate, AC adapter (or 9-volt battery), and a cord to connect the photogate to the timer • Multimeter with red and black leads • Graph paper In addition, the teacher should have: • Extra rubber bands **Duration:** One to two class periods

24.1 Semiconductors

Learning Goals	Reading Synopsis	Materials and Setup
• Describe the electrical behavior of a diode. • Describe how a diode is different from a resistor in terms of its current and voltage characteristics. **Key question:** What is speed and how is it measured? **Leading questions:** • How are semiconductor electronic devices different from resistors and capacitors? • How is the direction of electric current controlled? • What does a diode do?	Diodes are a basic building block of all electronics. A diode is a one way valve for electric current. A transistor is a control valve for electric current. The conductivity of semiconductor materials lies between conductors and insulators and depends on the number of free charge carriers. An n-type semiconductor is created when a phosphorus impurity is added to silicon. Each phosphorus atom contributes an extra electron to the silicon crystal, increasing its conductivity. A p-type semiconductor is created when atoms of boron are added to silicon. Each boron atom captures an electron from the silicon crystal. The resulting "hole" in the crystal acts like a positive charge which can move and carry current. A p-n junction is formed where n-type and p-type semiconductors meet. The p-n junction is the fundamental operating structure of electronic devices. A p-n junction allows current to flow only in one direction. A diode contains a single p-n junction and a transistor contains two p-n junctions back to back. **Sequence:** Students complete the reading after the Investigation.	• Solderless breadboard • 2 D batteries • An assortment of small 22 gage soli‡ core wires • A small flat bladed screwdriver • A small pair of needle nose plier‡ • A wire stripping tool • Electric Circuits experiment with battery holder and potentiometer. • Two jumper wires with alligator clip‡ to bring 3V and 0V from the Electri‡ Circuits to the breadboard. • Several diodes to test. Rectifier diodes and signal diodes work well. • A multimeter **Duration:** One class period

24.2 Circuits with Diodes and Transistors

Learning Goals	Reading Synopsis	Materials and Setup
• Describe the three terminals of a transistor and their functions. • Describe how to make a transistor work as a switch. • Connect a circuit using a transistor as a switch. **Key question:** What is speed and how is it measured? **Leading questions:** • What is a transistor and what does it do? • How are the electrical characteristics of a transistor different from electrical components such as resistors and capacitors? • How is a transistor used in a circuit?	This section is an introduction to simple circuits using diodes and transistors. A very common diode circuit is a rectifier. A rectifier circuit uses diodes to convert AC electricity into DC. A transistor may be used as an electronic switch. A small voltage or current applied to the base of a transistor causes the collector-emitter resistance to drop from $>100,000\Omega$ to less than 10Ω. A transistor may also be used as an amplifier. An amplifier takes a small signal and multiplies its voltage without changing the time dependent shape of the signal. The section introduces the concept of input and output voltage as applied to electronic circuits. Transistors are also used to construct electronic logic circuits. A logic circuit makes a decision based on evaluation of a number of conditions. An example is given of a three input AND function constructed with three transistors. **Sequence:** Students complete the reading before the Investigation.	• Solderless breadboard • 2 D-batteries • An assortment of small 22 gage soli‡ core wires . • A small flat bladed screwdriver • A small pair of needle nose pliers • A wire stripping tool (or use pre-stripped wire) • Electric Circuits experiment with battery holder and potentiometer. • Two jumper wires with alligator clip‡ • A 1.5 V to 3V DC electric motor • A solar cell of 4-10 cm^2 area. • Several npn transistors to test. • An assortment of resistors with value‡ from 100Ω to 100 kΩ • A multimeter **Duration:** One class period

24.3 Digital Electronics

Learning Goals	Reading Synopsis	Materials and Setup
• Describe how electronic logic functions in terms of circuits and voltages. • Use the AND and OR logical functions to solve a logic problem with 2-4 inputs and one output. • Connect a logic integrated circuit chip into a circuit. **Key question:** What is speed and how is it measured? **Leading questions:** • What is the difference between an analog and a digital circuit? • How can electronic devices like computers evaluate information and make logical decisions? • What is an integrated circuit? • Why is a logic circuit useful?	A signal is a stream of information, often in the form of voltage, current, or light. The information in an analog signal is represented by a continuous value such as a voltage. A digital signal is not continuous, and can only be on or off. Information in a digital (binary) signal is encoded as a sequence of on-off transitions. Several codes exist for representing numbers and letters in binary (ASCII, BCD). Chapters 19-23 have dealt with analog circuits. Analog circuits are built to do a specific function. Computers are digital circuits. Computers are able to do many functions with the same circuit by changing a program. Different programs instruct the electronic hardware to do different functions. Logic circuits are the building block of computers. The four basic logic gates are called AND, OR, NAND, and NOR. An integrated circuit (chip) may contain hundreds or thousands of individual transistors to implement one or more logic functions. **Sequence:** Students complete the reading before the Investigation.	• Solderless breadboard • 3 D-batteries • An assortment of small 22 gage solid core wires • A small flat bladed screwdriver • A small pair of needle nose pliers • A wire stripping tool • Electric Circuits experiment with battery holder and potentiometer. • Two jumper wires with alligator clips • A 1.5 V to 3V DC electric motor • A solar cell of 4-10 cm^2 area. • Several logic integrated circuit • An half dozen 330Ω resistors. These may be 1/8 watt or 1/4 watt size. • A multimeter **Duration:** One class period

25.1 Matter and Atoms

Learning Goals	Reading Synopsis	Materials and Setup
• Explain the observed diversity of matter in terms of elements, compounds, and mixtures. • Describe the properties of a pure element, such as its atomic number, mass, boiling point, melting point • Describe examples of where an element is found, in what types of matter, and in what forms. **Key question:** What are the properties of different elements? **Leading questions:** • Are the diverse forms of matter actually made from a smaller number of basic substances? • How many elements are there? • What makes each elements different • How do elements combine to make different forms of matter?	There is a tremendous variety of matter in the universe. A simple list of matter in the home includes: wood, plastic, glass steel pots, leaves, and even the air. This section begins with three questions for students to think about: What is the smallest piece of matter? Does matter have different forms? and Can one type of matter transform into another type with different properties? Democritus a Greek philosopher proposed that matter is made up of small particles called atoms. In 1803, John Dalton revived the idea of atoms, but lacked proof. Albert Einstein finally proved that matter was made of tiny particles by explaining Brownian motion. These particles of matter are atoms and molecules. A molecule is a group of two or more atoms than are joined. Matter can be made of atoms, molecules, or mixtures of these. Nearly all the matter in the world is made from 92 different elements which are arranged on the periodic table. Each of the 92 elements has a unique type of atom and all atoms of a given element are similar to each other. **Sequence:** Students complete the reading.	• A copy of the periodic table • Access to the library, internet, and/or science resource materials • Poster board • Colored markers • Glue and tape • Any additional supplies for creating the poster such as old magazines, construction paper, and rulers **Duration:** One class period

25.2 Temperature and the Phases of Matter

Learning Goals	Reading Synopsis	Materials and Setup
• Observe and identify phase changes of water from liquid to solid or gas. • State evidence that mass does not change during a phase change. • Demonstrate that phase changes are physical changes because they are reversible. **Key question:** What is temperature? **Leading questions:** • Why can the same substance exist as a solid, liquid, or gas? • How is temperature related to the phase of matter? • How do properties such as density, mass and volume change during phase changes	Temperature is measured in Fahrenheit and Celsius. Thermometers, thermistors, and thermocouples measure temperature. Temperature describes the average kinetic energy of atoms in random motion. It is not possible for objects to be colder than absolute zero (-273°C), the temperature at which the motion of atoms reaches a minimum. The Kelvin temperature scale starts at absolute zero. Ordinary matter exists as solid, liquid, and gas. Solid has the lowest energy per atom, and the lowest temperature. Atoms in the gas phase have the most energy and the highest temperature of the three common phases. Plasma is a fourth phase of matter that occurs at greater than 10,000 K. The melting point is the transition temperature from solid to liquid, and the boiling point is the transition temperature from liquid to gas. Phase changes use or give off energy, even though the temperature does not change. Evaporation and condensation describe phase changes at temperatures other than the melting or boiling point. **Sequence:** Students complete the reading after the Investigation.	• A clear, flexible plastic water bottle with cap (500 mL volume or smaller) • Stove or hot plate • Pan of water with a lid (large enough to submerge two-thirds of the bottle) • Thermometer • A graduate cylinder • A timer or stopwatch • Second pan or bowl with ice water (large enough to submerge two-thirds of the bottle) • Tongs to hold the bottle • Mitts to hold hot material • Safety goggles **Duration:** One class period

25.3 Heat and Thermal Energy

Learning Goals	Reading Synopsis	Materials and Setup
• Explain the connection between temperature, heat, and thermal energy. • Use the specific heat equation to calculate thermal energy. • Explain the meaning of the specific heat of a substance. **Key question:** What is the relationship between heat, temperature, and energy? **Leading questions:** • How much energy does it take to change the temperature of a material? • How is the temperature of a substance related to its thermal energy? • Do the same amounts of different substances at the same temperature have the same thermal energy?	This reading describes heat, thermal energy, and temperature. Temperature measures the random kinetic energy of each atom and is an average measurement of this energy. Thermal energy is the total amount of random kinetic energy for all atoms in a substance. It takes 400 J of thermal energy to heat a cup of coffee to 100°C, but 400,000 J to heat 1,000 cups of coffee to 100°C. Heat is moving thermal energy that flows from high to low temperatures. Units of heat (and thermal energy) are joules, calories, or BTUs (British thermal unit). One calorie equals 4.184 joules. One BTU equals 1,055 joules. The heat equation is used to calculate how much heat it takes to make a temperature change. The equation relates mass, temperature, and specific heat. Specific heat is the quantity of heat it takes to raise the temperature of one kilogram of material by 1°C. Different substances have different specific heats because of differences in the mass of their atoms. The application reading is on the refrigeration cycle. **Sequence:** Students complete the reading after the Investigation.	• Hot water baths at about 50°C with a thermometer and a cup for removing water • A cold water bath with ice cubes at about 0°C with a thermometer and a cup for removing water • Another Celsius thermometer • 15 steel washers held together with a small piece of string or wire (from the ropes and pulleys kit) • A balance • Tongs • Stirring rod • A timer or stop watch • About 300 grams of vegetable oil • Three 16-ounce foam cups • Three 8-ounce plastic cups • Paper towels for cleaning up • Simple calculator **Duration:** One class period

26.1 Heat Conduction

Learning Goals	Reading Synopsis	Materials and Setup
• Describe how thermal energy is transferred by conduction. • List what kinds of materials are thermal conductors or insulators. • Describe a technique for measuring the thermal conductivity of a material. **Key question:** How does heat pass through different materials? **Leading questions:** • How fast does heat flow from one material to another? • Does heat flow differently in different materials? • What property of a material describes its ability to conduct heat? • How does temperature influence the flow of heat?	Thermal energy travels as heat from a material at a higher temperature to a material at a lower temperature. This general process is called heat transfer. One of the three mechanisms of heat transfer is conduction. Conduction is heat transfer by the direct contact of particles of matter. It occurs between two materials at different temperatures when they are touching each other. The atoms in the hotter material have more kinetic energy. This energy is transferred to the cooler material by the collisions of atoms until thermal equilibrium is reached and both materials have the same temperature. Materials that conduct heat easily are called thermal conductors, and those that conduct heat poorly are thermal insulators. Thermal conductors tend to be dense, metallic, and can conduct electricity (due to having free electrons). Thermal insulators tend to be less dense. The degree to which something can conduct heat is measured as a value called thermal conductivity. **Sequence:** Students complete the reading after the Investigation.	• One shallow baking pan • Two thin plastic and foam cups • Four copper nails • One metric ruler • One permanent marker • Two Celsius thermometers • One small pot • One hot plate • One timer or stopwatch • Ring stand • Clamps • Crushed ice and water • Digital or triple beam balance (accuracy to at least 0.1 gram) **Duration:** Two class periods

26.2 Convection

Learning Goals	Reading Synopsis	Materials and Setup
• Describe free and forced convection and give an example of each. • Explain how thermal energy is be transferred by convection. • Describe what causes motion in liquid or gas during free convection. **Key question:** Can moving matter carry thermal energy? **Leading questions:** • When matter moves, such as wind blowing, thermal energy moves with the moving matter. How is this kind of heat transfer described? • Why are fans used to blow air around in heating and cooling? • Why do you stir up a pot when heating it? What does the stirring accomplish?	Convection is a type of heat transfer that occurs only in fluids (liquids and gases). This process of heating occurs because warmer fluids are less dense and rise. Cooler fluids are denser and sink. This temperature-based motion of fluids causes fluid currents and circulation. There are two types of convection: free (natural) and forced. Free convection causes global weather patterns and ocean currents. In cooking, free convection is essential for heating pots of liquid. Free convection occurs when less dense, warm fluid displaces denser cool fluid and vice versa so that fluid circulation results. In forced convection, a mechanical device (like a fan or pump) forces the air or liquid to move. Warm fluids can carry heat to cooler regions. Likewise, forced convection can be used for cooling. Moving cool fluids can take heat from hot regions. Most homes are heated and cooled using a combination of free and forced convection. **Sequence:** Students complete the reading after the Investigation.	• Two clear identical glasses • One colored ice cube • Uncolored ice cubes • Tongs • One Celsius thermometer • Metric ruler • Stirring rod • Hot tap water The teacher needs: • Food coloring • Access to a freezer • Six or more ice cube trays for making ice cubes **Duration:** One class period

26.3 Radiant Heat

Learning Goals	Reading Synopsis	Materials and Setup
• Explain how sunlight carries heat. • Describe how the spectrum of light emitted by hot objects changes with their temperature. • Describe the properties that make an object a good absorber or emitter? **Key question:** How does heat from the sun get to Earth? **Leading questions:** • How do we describe the heat we receive from the sun as light? • What is the source of thermal radiation? • How is heat transfer by radiation different from conduction and convection?	Radiation is heat transfer by electromagnetic radiation that occurs in the presence or absence of matter. Radiation is the only way that heat can travel through space (a vacuum) from the sun to Earth. Heat transfer by convection and conduction occurs only in the presence of matter. Objects emit radiation according to their thermal properties or internal energy. radiation is in the form of visible light or invisible forms of light such as infrared or ultraviolet. A color-temperature relationship exists for objects that emit visible light. For example, the temperature of stars is determined by their spectral diagrams. Warm stars have peaks of blue in their spectral diagrams, while cold stars have peaks of red. Radiation is reflected or absorbed by varying degrees from objects. Objects that are good reflectors are shiny and metallic, or light colored. Good absorbers are dark colored. Objects can re-emit heat by radiation, conduction, or convection. **Sequence:** Students complete the reading after the Investigation.	• Two 8.5" x 11" pieces of cardboard • Double sided tape • One Celsius thermometer • One incandescent lamp with a dimmer switch • One spectrometer • Scissors • Glue • Aluminum foil • Metric ruler • Pencil • Timer or stopwatch • Thermometer **Duration:** Two class periods

27.1 Properties of Solids

Learning Goals	Reading Synopsis	Materials and Setup
• Describe the terms stress and strain as applied to the strength of a material. • Measure the tensile strength of a material. • Explain the relationship between force, strength, and stress. **Key question:** How do you measure the strength of a solid material? **Leading questions:** • How is the strength of a material described and measured? • How are things designed so they do not break? • Rubber is a solid but is stretchy. Steel is a solid that does not seem to stretch at all. How is the "stretchiness" of a solid material described and measured? • How do we describe the fact that the size of solid objects changes when their temperature changes? • What types of solid materials exist?	Solids have a definite shape and volume. The atoms or molecules of a solid occupy fixed positions, therefore, solids do not flow. The density of common solids ranges from 100 kg/m^3 (cork) to 21,000 kg/m^3 (platinum). Not all solid materials have equal strength. Stress is force per unit area. The breaking strength of a material is the maximum amount of stress the material can take before it breaks, or bends irreversibly. Solid materials deform (strain) under stress. The strain is the percent change in a linear dimension. Hooke's law for solids says the strain equals the applied stress multiplied by the modulus of elasticity. Solid materials also expand and contract with changes in temperature. The coefficient of thermal expansion describes how much a material changes in any linear dimension per degree change in temperature. A wide range of mechanical properties exist in solids. For example, the tensile strength is very different for plastic, wood, aluminum, and steel. **Sequence:** Students complete the reading after the Investigation.	• Modeling clay (one cup) • Metric ruler • One 5-Newton spring scale • Graph paper • Packaging tape • Calculator **Duration:** One class period

27.2 Properties of Liquids and Fluids

Learning Goals	Reading Synopsis	Materials and Setup
Students review Bernoulli's equation. They use a simple demonstration to show that as air speed increases, the air pressure decreases. They build their own device to measure the pressure difference when air flows from a larger to smaller diameter tube. They use their pressure measurements to calculate the speed of the air in large and small tubes. **Key question:** • What are some implications of Bernoulli's equation? **Leading questions:** • How are stress and pressure alike? How are they different? • How do aircraft wings generate lift? • If air is flowing through a pipe that has a reduction in diameter, what happens to the speed of the air? What happens to the air pressure?	Buoyancy is an important property of fluids. An object submerged in a fluid feels a buoyant force equal to the weight of the liquid displaced by an object. Pressure is created when force is applied to a fluid. PRessure acts in all directions and is measured in force per unit area. The metric unit N/m, the pascal. Gravity is one cause of pressure because fluids have weight. Dense fluids (water) create more pressure than light fluids (air) at the same depth. PRessure in a fluid is still fluid is equal to density times gravitational acceleration times depth. Fluids flow because of difference in pressure. Moving fluids because of difference in pressure. Moving fluids have different speed in different places. The law of conversation of energy applies to fluids. The total energy of small mass of fluid is equal to its potential energy from gravity plus potential energy from pressure plus kinetic energy. This is know as Bernoulli's equation.	• Plastic straw with flexible "elbow" • 30by3 inch sticky note • 8-inch length of 3/4 pvc pipe with pre-drilled holes • 8-inch length of 1/2-inch pvc pipe with pre-drilled hole • coupling to join the two pipes • 0.5-meter length of 1/4-inch clear flexible plastic tubing • red food coloring • water • paper cup • clear tape • two meter sticks **Duration:** One class period

27.3 Properties of Gases

Learning Goals	Reading Synopsis	Materials and Setup
• Describe experimental evidence that gas contains mass. • Explain why changing the pressure of a fixed volume of gas changes its mass. • Describe what happens to mass and pressure of a fixed volume of gas when its temperature is reduced. **Key question:** How much matter is in a gas? **Leading questions:** • What proof exists that a gas such as air has mass? • What is the relationship between pressure and mass? • How can you describe the relationship between mass, density and pressure in a gas?	Gases are fluids because like liquids, they can change shape and flow when force is applied. However, while liquids and solids undergo only small density changes, the density of a gas can vary greatly because gases easily expand and contract. Buoyant forces apply to gases as well as liquids. A helium balloon, for example, floats because it weighs less than the air it displaces. Boyle's law explains that at constant temperature, the pressure of a gas is inversely proportional to its volume. If you double the pressure, the volume is halved. Charles' law states that the pressure of a gas is directly proportional to temperature when volume and mass are constant. If you double the temperature, the pressure is doubled as well. The ideal gas law, $PV=mRT$, relates pressure, volume, and temperature of a gas in one equation. R is a constant unique to each gas, and m is mass in kg. **Sequence:** Students complete the reading after the Investigation.	• 100-milliliter graduated cylinder • Water source • Bottle cap with valve stem attached (• Good quality tire pressure gauge with dial readout • Electronic balance • Calculator • Graph paper • Bucket of ice water Optional material for lesson extension: • 10-milliliter oral syringe commonly used to dispense liquid cough syrup • Petroleum jelly • Candle • Kitchen matches **Duration:** One class period

28.1 The Nucleus and Structure of the Atom

Learning Goals	Reading Synopsis	Materials and Setup
• Describe the structure of the atom. • Identify what makes elements different from each other. • Recognize the differences between stable and unstable isotopes. **Key question:** What is inside an atom? **Leading questions:** • What makes atoms of one element different from atoms of another element? • What is inside an atom? • What is radioactivity and how does it relate to the structure of the atom?	The atom is made from three basic particles: electrons, protons, and neutrons. The protons and neutrons have 99.97 percent of the mass and are in the nucleus. The electrons are outside the nucleus and define the size of an atom. All of the elements are made from different combinations of protons, neutrons, and electrons. The atomic number is the number of protons in the nucleus. The periodic table shows the elements in order of increasing atomic number. Elements may have several isotopes, which differ from one another in the number of neutrons. The atomic mass is an average including all naturally occurring isotopes of an element. Some isotopes are not stable, and are called radioactive. A nucleus with too many protons is not stable because the electromagnetic repulsion between protons overcomes the attraction of the strong nuclear force. Chemical reactions rearrange atoms into different molecules. Nuclear reactions may change atoms of one element into atoms of a different element. **Sequence:** Students complete the reading after the Investigation.	• Atom building game • Marbles representing subatomic particles that come with the model • A copy of the periodic table that comes with the model **Duration:** One class period

28.2 Electrons and Quantum States

Learning Goals	Reading Synopsis	Materials and Setup
• Describe qualitatively how atoms absorb and emit light. • Model how lasers work, using the Atom Building Game. **Key question:** How do atoms create and interact with light? **Leading questions:** • What is a quantum state? • How do energy levels explain spectral lines? • What is stimulated emission? • How do atoms absorb and emit light?	Quantum theory is the branch of physics that deals with extremely small systems such as an atom. The wavelengths of light given off by particular atoms show discrete spectral lines. For hydrogen the wavelengths of the lines are predicted by the Balmer formula. Neils Bohr proposed that electrons in the atom were limited to having certain energies corresponding to being in discrete *quantum* states. The energy of an electron depends on which quantum state it is in, and the quantum states in an atom are grouped into energy levels. Bohr explained that characteristic spectral lines (that show up when atoms of elements are energized) are produced by electrons moving between different energy levels. Two electrons cannot occupy the same quantum state at the same time. The rows of the periodic table correspond to the number of quantum states in each energy level. The "shape" of quantum states (orbital shapes) of the atoms that make up a molecule determine the ultimate structure of the molecule. **Sequence:** Students complete the reading after the Investigation.	• Atom building game • A copy of the periodic table that comes with the game • For Part 4 of the Investigation, two groups will combine so that they have two atom building games. **Duration:** One class period

8.3 The Quantum Theory

Learning Goals	Reading Synopsis	Materials and Setup
• Show how a vibrating string has similar properties to a quantum system. • Identify the "quantum states" of a vibrating string. • Calculate the energy of a quantum from Planck's constant and the frequency. • Calculate the wavelength of a particle from its mass, speed and Planck's constant.	Quantum theory was invented to explain the photoelectric effect and blackbody radiation, to phenomenon which could not be explained by classical physics. In the quantum theory, matter and energy exist in tiny bundles called quanta. Light, which was previously believed to be a way, was shown to have particle like properties. A particle of light is known as a photon. Matter particles were also shown to have a wave like properties.	• Sound and waves equipment module • Timer with the AC adapter and a cord • Physics stand • Calculator **Duration:** One class period

Key question:
How can a system be quantized?

Leading questions:
- What does it mean that a system is quantized?
- What do quantum numbers mean?
- What does Plank's constant have to do with energy?
- Why don't we see the quantum wavelengths of ordinary objects?

The uncertainty principle places a fundamental limit on how well certain variables such as a position and momentum can simultaneously be measured for the same particle. Quantum theory is based on probability. When systems to get very small, such as inside an atom, it is not possible to predict the exact location or the value of any measurable quantity. The best that can be done is to predict the probability that a quantity will have a specific value. Quantum theory only becomes exact when applied to the average behavior of a very large number of atoms or particles.

Sequence: Students complete the reading after the Investigation.

29.1 Chemistry

Learning Goals	Reading Synopsis	Materials and Setup
• Separate a heterogeneous mixture using their own procedure. • Calculate the percent composition of their sample. • Evaluate their procedure and suggest ways to make it more efficient.	Chemistry is the science of how atoms and elements create the world that we experience. Chemists classify matter into substances and mixtures. A substance is made up of one kind of element or compound. It can't be separated by physical means. Each particle of a substance is like every other. Mixtures contain more than one substance. In a homogeneous mixture, the substances are evenly distributed. In a heterogeneous mixture, different samples may have different amounts of each substance.	• One 100 mL vial containing a mixture of sawdust, colored sand, salt, and iron filings (see preparation instructions below) **Duration:** Two class periods

Key question:
What techniques are used to separate heterogeneous mixtures?

Leading questions:
- Which branches of science and/or industry routinely separate complex mixtures?
- What physical properties of materials may be used to separate a mixture?
- How can you determine percent composition of a sample?

A physical change does not make one substance into another; instead it may change the phase of the substance between solid, liquid, or gas, or change the physical form in another way. Chemical changes turn one substance into a different substance or substances. Chemical changes rearrange atoms into new molecules. A solution is a mixture in which solute molecules move freely among solvent molecules. Solubility tells how much solute will dissolve in a given amount of solvent at a given temperature.

Sequence: Students complete the reading after the Investigation.

29.2 Chemical Bonds

Learning Goals	Reading Synopsis	Materials and Setup
• Build models of atoms showing the arrangement of electrons. • Identify how atoms form chemical bonds • Explain the role of electrons in bonding. **Key question:** Why do atoms form chemical bonds? **Leading questions:** • Why do atoms form molecules? • How do chemical bonds form between atoms? • What are the different types of chemical bonds? • How can you tell what kind of bonds a molecule has?	Almost every atom in the matter you experience is bonded to at least one other atom. For example, the oxygen in the air is not in the form of single atoms, but molecules made from two oxygen atoms bonded together. There are two major types of chemical bonds that form between atoms (ionic, covalent). A chemical bond forms when atoms exchange or share electrons. The electrons that participate in chemical bonds are called valence electrons. Two atoms that are sharing one or more electrons are chemically bonded together. Chemical bonds form because the constituent atoms are able to lower their total energy by being combined in a molecule. In a covalent bond the electrons are shared between atoms. Atoms in the same group of the periodic table have the same number of valence electrons and similar bonding properties. Acids and bases are solutions that contain ions. **Sequence:** Students complete the reading after the Investigation.	• Atom building game • A copy of the periodic table that comes with the game • For Part 4 of the Investigation, two groups will combine so that they ha~~ two atom game boards. **Duration:** One class period

29.3 Chemical Reactions

Learning Goals	Reading Synopsis	Materials and Setup
• Write a balanced equation for a simple chemical reaction with only a few products and reactants. • Use a balanced equation to calculate the quantities of required reactants in grams. • Use a balanced equation to predict the yield of one of the products in a chemical reaction. • Measure the amount of product produced in the reaction and compare predicted yield with actual yield. **Key question:** How can you predict the yield of a chemical reaction? **Leading questions:** • What is a chemical reaction? • How are chemical reactions described? • How can you predict the amount of product in a reaction? • What stops a chemical reaction from continuing?	Chemical reactions rearrange atoms into different molecules. In a chemical reaction, reactants are changed into products. For example, iron and oxygen react to form rust. Through chemical reactions, chemical bonds between atoms in the reactants are broken and re-formed to make new products. Energy is required to break chemical bonds and energy is released when new bonds are formed. In an exothermic reaction, more energy is given off when new bonds are formed than the energy required to break the original bonds. Endothermic reactions are the opposite. A chemical equation is a way of writing a chemical reaction. The chemical equation for a reaction must have the same number of atoms on the reactants side as are found on the products side. A balanced chemical equation tells you how many of each molecule or atom the reaction uses and produces. In a chemical reaction, the total mass of the reactants is always equal to the total mass of the products. **Sequence:** Students complete the reading after the Investigation.	• Electronic scale or triple-beam balance NOTE: The Investigation works bes~~ if the scale is accurate to 0.01 gram. ~~ a 0.1 gram balance is used, have students round their predicted masse~~ to the nearest 0.1 gram. • 250 mL glass beaker • 250 mL plastic beaker • 200 mL of 0.1M hydrochloric acid solution (provided to students in a 500 mL bottle) • 5 strips of magnesium ribbon (approximately 2.0 grams per strip) • Forceps • Thermometer • Calculator **Duration:** One class period

30.1 Radioactivity

Learning Goals	Reading Synopsis	Materials and Setup
• Describe the three different types of radioactive decay (alpha, beta, and gamma decay). • Calculate the fraction of a radioactive sample that remains in its original isotope after an integer number of half lives. • Explain how probability and half life are related concepts.	The nuclei of radioactive atoms are unstable. Over time, radioactive nuclei spontaneously turn into nuclei of other elements, releasing energy and/or particles in the process. Radioactivity occurs because matter tends to move toward lower energy and nuclei may achieve lower energy by reorganizing their protons and neutrons into different nuclei.	• 100 pennies in a jar or paper cup • A tray or box to collect the pennies when they are poured out • Graph paper **Duration:** One class period

Key question:
How do we model radioactivity?

Leading questions:
• What is radioactivity?
• What causes radioactivity?
• What types of radioactivity exist in nature?
• How fast does radioactivity happen?

The three most common forms of radioactivity are alpha, beta, and gamma. In alpha decay the nucleus ejects two protons and two neutrons. In beta decay one neutron becomes a proton, an electron, and a neutrino. In gamma decay the nucleus emits high energy electromagnetic radiation but does not change the number of neutrons or protons.

The half-life is the time it takes for one half the atoms in any sample of radioactive atoms to decay. The half lives of different isotopes vary from fractions of a second to billions of years. Carbon-14 has a half life of 5,700 years.

Sequence: Students complete the reading after the Investigation.

30.2 Radiation

Learning Goals	Reading Synopsis	Materials and Setup
• Calculate radiation intensity and show it diminishes with the inverse square of the distance. • Describe at least three types and sources of radiation experience by the average person. • Describe at least one radiation detector. • Explain the term "dose" in the context of radiation.	Radiation describes the flow of energy through space. Intensity is measured in watts per square meter. The intensity from a point source of radiation diminishes the according to the inverse square law. The inverse square law is a property of geometry.	• Calculator • Access to the Internet or library for research • **Duration:** One class period

Key question:
What are some types and sources of radiation?

Leading questions:
• What is a radiation?
• What types of radiation exist in the environment?
• What types of radiation are created by human technology?
• How is radiation described and measured?
• How does radiation spread out from a source?

Radiation is harmful when it has enough energy to remove electrons from atoms (ionizing radiation). X-rays, gamma rays and ultraviolet light are examples of ionizing radiation. The energy absorbed by living tissue from radiation (dose) is measured in rems.

The two largest sources of ionizing radiation in your environment are background and medical procedures such as x-rays. Background radiation includes cosmic rays (21%), radon gas (20%), natural radioactivity in rocks and soil (57%) and fallout from nuclear weapons testing (2%).

A medical procedure typically results in a dose equal to 10% of the yearly background dose. Medical procedures that use ionizing radiation include x-rays, and CAT scans. A geiger counter is one of many types of radiation detectors.

Sequence: Students complete the reading.

30.3 Nuclear Reactions and Energy

Learning Goals	Reading Synopsis	Materials and Setup

Learning Goals

- Describe the processes of fission and fusion.
- Write the equation for a simple nuclear reaction.
- Describe at least two fundamental differences between nuclear reactions and chemical reactions.

Key question:
How do we describe nuclear reactions?

Leading questions:
- What is a nuclear reaction?
- How are nuclear reactions different from chemical reactions?
- How does the nucleus of an atom change during fission?
- How is a fusion reaction different from a fission reaction?

Reading Synopsis

A nuclear reaction is a process that affects the nucleus of an atom. Radioactive decay is a type of nuclear reaction. Nuclear reactions are represented by equations similar to chemical reactions. Mass may not be conserved in a nuclear reaction because some of the mass is often converted to energy in the reaction.

Nuclear reactions occur when protons and neutrons can lower their total energy by reorganizing into a different nucleus. Fusion reactions combine small nuclei to form larger nuclei. Fission reactions split up large nuclei into smaller nuclei. Nuclear reactions follow rules that allow some reactions and not others. Energy and momentum must be conserved in nuclear reactions, although energy may be in the form of mass. Nuclear reactions create particles other than neutrons, protons, and electrons. Muons, pions, and neutrinos are a few of the other subatomic particles. Each particle of ordinary matter also has a antimatter partner with opposite electric charge.

Sequence: Students complete the reading

Materials and Setup

- Atom building game
- A copy of the periodic table of stable isotopes that comes with the game
- The Nuclear Reaction cards that come with the game

Duration: One class period

CONTENTS

Table of Contents

CONTENTS

CONTENTS

Table of Contents

2.1 Distance and Length

Key Question: How do we accurately communicate length and distance?

In this Investigation, students practice making estimates and review using metric units. They discuss how estimating is important in everyday situations, and how estimating helps scientists to quickly analyze a situation to determine what may have occurred or what will happen. Estimation also allows people to catch calculation errors before they become costly mistakes. Next, students learn how to report measurements using significant digits. Finally, students practice calculating area and volume, converting between English and metric units, and check their work by finding volume experimentally.

BOSTON 50 MILES
NEW YORK 200 MILES

Reading Synopsis

Students read Section 2.1 Distance and Length after the Investigation

All measurements are made up of two parts: a quantity and a unit. There are two common systems to measure length, the English system and the metric (also called SI) system. Scientists most often use metric units, but both systems are used in everyday life.

The English system uses inches, feet, yards, and miles to measure length. The metric system uses millimeters, centimeters, meters, and kilometers. Converting between metric system units is easy because they are based on powers of 10. You can use conversion factors such as those printed on the inside back cover of the Student Edition to convert English system units to metric system units.

It is often important to know the surface area or volume of an object. Surface area is measured in square units, while volume is measured in cubic units. When converting one surface area from one unit to another, the conversion factor is applied twice. To convert volume, the conversion factor is applied three times.

The Investigation

Leading Questions
- When is estimating a useful tool?
- How large are a meter, kilometer, millimeter, or centimeter relative to the size of familiar objects?
- What kinds of situations require precise measurements?
- What are significant digits?

Learning Goals

By the end of the Investigation, students will be able to:
- Estimate metric lengths and distances.
- Make measurements using significant digits correctly.
- Measure surface area and volume of various shapes.

Key Vocabulary

distance, length, English system, metric system, inches, feet, miles, millimeters, centimeters, meters, kilometers, conversion factors, surface area, volume, significant digits

Setup and Materials

Students work in groups of four or five at tables.

Each group should have:

- Meter stick and/or metric ruler
- Calculator
- Pencil with eraser
- Paper clip
- Street map of local area (used by students to estimate distance from school to home)
- 2 sheets of heavy paper, such as construction paper
- A compass for drawing circles
- Scissors
- Tape
- 1 liter of sand
- A one-liter soda bottle

Details

Time ⏱ One class period

Preparation ✎ Students will need meter sticks, but no other preparation is necessary.

Assignments 📖 Section 2.1 Distance and Length in the **Student Edition** after the Investigation.

Skill Sheets 1.1 Solving Equations
2.1 International System of Units
Skill Builder: Significant Digits
Skill Builder: Safety Skills

Teaching the Investigation

1 Introduction
2 Estimating
3 Significant digits and measuring length
4 More about significant digits
5 Analyzing the results
6 Calculating area
7 Calculating volume
8 Volume by experiment

Introduction

English system:
-Miles, yards, feet, inches.

Metric system:
-Kilometer, meter, centimeter, millimeter

Estimating

One centimeter = width of a fingernail

One meter = the distance from your nose to the fingertips of one outstretched arm

Significant digits and measuring length

Metric ruler is marked in 1-millimeter increments. You can estimate to the tenth of a millimeter.

Significant digits - those you are certain of plus one additional digit that can be meaningfully estimated.

Today's Investigation takes a look at English and metric system measurements of distance and length. You will practice estimating with the metric system, calculate area and volume, and do some conversions from the English to metric system. This may be review for many of you, but it certainly is useful in real-life situations. Can anyone tell me about a time you had to convert from English to metric system units, or when it's been useful to be able to estimate metric distances?

Allow students time to share their experiences. Some may have traveled to countries which use metric measurements, or they may have purchased sports equipment or car parts that were sized with metric measurements.

Do you remember hearing about why NASA lost the Mars Climate Orbiter in September 1999?

Students may remember hearing on the news or discussing in class the loss of this $125 million spacecraft. The orbiter incinerated because it came too close to the surface of Mars. The team in charge of the mission failed to convert distance from English units to metric units and as a result the orbiter's path was miscalculated.

Now complete Parts 1 and 2 on your own. Your goal is to gain a sense of metric distances that will allow you to make accurate estimates. These estimates can help you quickly judge if a complicated physics calculation is on target or way off base. If the scientists involved in the Orbiter loss had been better able to estimate metric distances, they might have noticed their calculation couldn't have been right.

Allow students time to complete these exercises independently. Afterward, ask them to answer these kinds of questions:

A centimeter is about the size of _____.

A meter is about the same length as _____.

Students should be able to give an answer that works for them as a general guide. A centimeter may be about the width of one of their fingernails, for example.

You might mention to students that in fabric stores, clerks often estimate that a yard is the distance from your nose to the fingertips of one outstretched arm. While clerks wouldn't use this estimating tool to measure and cut a piece of cloth to sell to a customer, they can use it to quickly get a sense of how much fabric is left on a bolt of cloth. Ask students to come up with a similar means of estimating the size of one meter.

In Part 3, you will be making measurements rather than estimates. Throughout this course, you will be making careful measurements as you carry out Investigations. Accuracy and precision are extremely important for achieving believable, repeatable results. Now take a look at your metric rulers. How precisely can you measure a length with this tool?

Metric rulers are marked in 0.001 meter, or 1-millimeter, increments. Many students will say they are precise to 1millimeter. However, we can estimate one more digit. Lengths measured using this device should be reported to the tenth of a millimeter.

In the lab, we will always report measurements using significant digits. Significant digits are those you are certain of, plus one additional digit that can be meaningfully estimated. If you were using a 10-milliliter graduated cylinder marked off in one-tenth of a milliliter increments, which of these measurements has the correct number of significant digits: 8.1 milliliters, 8.17 milliliters, or 8.175 milliliters?

Students should respond 8.17 milliliters. The .07 is a meaningful estimate.

Now read and complete Part 3 of the Investigation.

2.1 — Distance and Length

Question: How do we accurately communicate length and distance?

In this Investigation, you will:

1. Learn how to estimate length.
2. Learn how to measure and describe lengths using the correct significant figures.

Measurements such as length and distance are part of the alphabet of physics. In this Investigation, you will estimate the lengths of various objects and learn to precisely measure those lengths using the proper number of significant digits.

1 Estimating

The word *estimate* means to make an educated, approximate guess. For example, you might estimate that it takes 20 minutes to drive to the store. Your estimate is likely to be based on experience making the trip, so it is not just a wild guess. The actual time might be off by a few minutes but it is not likely to be off by five or 10 times that 20-minute estimate! Estimating is a very handy tool in physics because it often provides a check on whether an answer could be right or is probably a mistake.

Estimating length requires you to be familiar with the different units of length used in the world. For a given estimate, first decide on an appropriate unit; then try to make the estimate. For example, to estimate your height:

- First choose an appropriate unit. Kilometers are not a good unit to use for a person's height because the value would be a very small fraction, in the range of 0.001-0.002 km. Values this small are hard to estimate. The millimeter is not the best unit either because your height in millimeters would be a very large value, more than 1,000. Large numbers are also hard to estimate.

- The meter is a good unit for estimating height because the average height of a person is between 1 and 2 meters.

a. Look at a meter stick but do not use it to measure anything yet. Imagine holding a meter stick up to your body. Estimate your height in meters.

b. Use the meter stick to measure your height in meters. How far off was your estimate compared with the actual measurement? Express your answer as a percent of your actual height.

2 Estimate lengths and distances in meters

Use your sense of how long a meter is to estimate the following lengths. You may want to do some of the estimations in two steps. For example, estimate the diameter of a pencil eraser in millimeters and convert the value to meters.

a. The length of your classroom.
b. The diameter of your pencil's eraser.
c. The height of your desk or laboratory bench.
d. The length of a paper clip.
e. The distance from where you live to this lab or classroom.

Reading the metric ruler (meter stick)

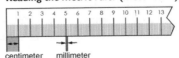

centimeter   millimeter

Teaching tip

Hold a discussion with your students about the importance of being able to estimate distances in both metric and English units. For example, if they want to sign up for a 5- or 10-kilometer charity walk/run, they need to be able to picture how far these distances are. If they are looking for a new area rug for their room, they need to know whether a 3-by-5 foot rug or a 5-by-8 foot rug is needed. Ask your students to come up with other "everyday life" examples where they may not have any measuring tools handy, but need to have a sense of length.

1 2 Example answers

1a. 1.6 meters
1b. 1.588 meters. 1.6 meters= 100.76% of 1.588 meters, so I was 0.76% off.
2a. 5.75 meters
2b. 0.006 meter
2c. 0.75 meter
2d. 0.03 meter
2e. 5,000 meters

More about significant digits

On an electronic balance, the final digit in the measurement is considered to be an estimated digit.

When making calculations with measurement values, round the answer to the correct number of significant digits.

Example: 56.7931 cm² = 56.79 cm²

Analyzing the results

Distances larger than 10 meters are hard to estimate without a reference object of known length.

Calculating area

How many sheets of paper would it take to cover the floor of the classroom?

Calculating volume

Volume by experiment

Sometimes you will use an electronic device for measuring. For example, you may use an electronic balance that reports the mass of an object to 0.1 gram. Can you make a meaningful estimate of the next digit in this case?

No. In fact, students may find that if they put the same object on an electronic balance, they may find that the reported mass changes + or - 0.1 gram. The final digit reported by the balance is considered to be the estimated digit.

In Part 5, you will be asked to make calculations based on measurements. Let's say you used your metric ruler to measure a rectangle that is 10.27 cm wide and 5.53 cm long. How would you find the area of this rectangle? Would someone please make the calculation and report what their calculator says?

The calculator will read 56.7931 square centimeters.

Why would I consider this answer misleading?

It seems to indicate that the measurement was made to a ten-thousandth of a centimeter.

What would be the best answer to write down on your paper, taking significant digits into consideration?

Round the answer to the correct significant digits. In this case, the answer would be 56.79 cm.

4 Part 4 asks you to compare your estimates and your measurements. Which are easier to estimate—small distances or large ones? Why?

Most students will respond that small distances are easier to picture than large ones, and with a small distance there's less room for error. This is true for distances between a centimeter and a few meters. Distances larger than 10 meters are hard to estimate without a reference object of known length. Of course, "small" is relative and small distances can also be hard to estimate. For example, distances that are smaller than a millimeter are hard to estimate because you cannot easily see objects this small.

5 In the next part of the Investigation, you will calculate the area of a piece of paper in square meters, and then estimate the number of sheets it would take to cover the floor of the classroom. There are several approaches you could take to solve this problem, so I expect to see a variety of methods when I collect your papers.

The quickest way to approach the problem is to simply estimate the number of square meters in the classroom and then divide this figure by the size of one sheet of paper. However, this method doesn't take into consideration the shape of the paper and how to cover the floor with the least amount of waste (or overlap). Both methods are shown in the example answers. You may wish to discuss when each method would be most appropriate to use (the first is faster, the second is more accurate).

6 Next, you will do some volume calculations. Complete Part 6 on your own.

Circulate around the room, paying special attention to each group's approach to question 6a. It's crucial that they understand why they can't simply divide 30 centimeters by 10 centimeters to get the correct answer. You may wish to announce that the answer to 6a is NOT 3, so that students continue working until they get the correct solution.

7 Now you will have a chance to compare calculated and experimental values. Follow the directions in Part 7 to construct your own 1,000-cubic-centimeter cylinder. Then you will use sand to determine the volume experimentally.

2.1 Distance and Length

5 **Area**

A standard sheet of paper measures 8.5 × 11 inches.

a. Calculate the area of one side of a sheet of paper in square inches.
b. Convert the length and width measurements from inches to meters.
c. Calculate the area in square meters.
 Hint: The answer is much less than 1 m².
d. Estimate the area of the floor of your lab or classroom.
e. How many sheets of paper would it take to cover the floor of your lab or classroom? Explain how you arrived at your estimate, and show any calculations you made.

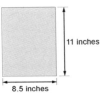

11 inches

8.5 inches

6 **Volume**

A soda bottle is advertised to contain one liter of liquid. One liter is the volume of a cube that measures 10 centimeters on a side. That means there are 1,000 cm³ in one liter (1,000 = 10 × 10 × 10).

a. How many liters fit in a cube that is 30 centimeters on a side?
b. Calculate the volume of a cylinder that has a radius of 4 centimeters and a height of 20 centimeters. The volume of a cylinder is approximately 3.14 × radius × radius × height. This relationship is often written $V = \pi r^2 h$. How many liters fit in this cylinder?

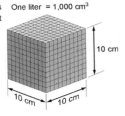

One liter = 1,000 cm³

10 cm

10 cm   10 cm

7 **Volume by experiment**

1. Take a sheet of paper and measure 25.1 centimeters along the long side. Draw a line parallel to the short side as shown in the diagram. Roll the paper into a cylinder and tape it together so the edge lines up with the line at 25.1 centimeters. This cylinder has a radius of 4 centimeters. Cut a paper circle with a radius of 4 centimeters and tape it securely to the bottom of the cylinder.
2. Take a 1 liter soda bottle and fill it with sand to the level the liquid would normally fill.
3. Pour the sand into the cylinder and measure the height it fills.

25.1 cm

Line

Tape

a. Calculate the height of a cylinder that has a radius (r) of 4 centimeters and a volume of 1,000 cm³. (Hint: The volume of a cylinder is $\pi r^2 h$.)
b. How close did 1 liter of sand come to matching the height required to make a volume of 1,000 cm³?

3

3 **4** **5** **6** **7** **Example answers (page two not shown)**

3a. 5.4865 meters (measured with carpenter's measuring tape marked off in millimeters)

3b. 0.70 cm

3c. 76.25 cm

3d. 2.65 cm

3e. 27.65 cm

4a. I was closer on my estimate of the paper clip than on my estimate of the classroom. It's easier for me to visualize small distances accurately. A larger distance leaves more room for error.

4b. Answers will vary. Students who use public transportation may need to skip the second part of this question.

Example answers from Page 3 (not shown)

5a. 93.5 square inches

5b. 11 inches= 0.279 meters; 8.5 inches = 0.216 meters

5c. 0.060 square meters

5d. 4.6 meters x 5.5 meters = 25.3 square meters

5e. Simplest method: 25.3 m² ÷ 0.062 m² = 408 sheets
 More accurate method:
 4.6 m ÷ 0.22 m = 20.9 sheets of paper would fit with the short side of the paper along the short side of the classroom
 5.5 m ÷ 0.28 m = 19.6 sheets of paper would fit the long way down the long side of the classroom.
 21 whole sheets wide × 20 whole sheets long = 420 total sheets. (There would be some overlap along one long side and one short side of the classroom)
 If you turned the paper the opposite way,
 4.6 m ÷0.28 m = 16.4 sheets. 5.5 m ÷ 0.22 m = 25.0 sheets.
 17 whole sheets × 25 whole sheets = 425 total sheets

6a. 27

6b. Volume of cylinder= 1,004.8 square centimeters. One liter plus 4.8 mL would fit into this cylinder

7a. 3.14 × 16 × h = 1,000; h = 1,000÷ 54.4 = 18.4 cm

7b. My sand came up to 18 cm, but a little sand stuck to the inside of the bottle, and I had to estimate exactly where the liquid level usually is.

2.2 Time

Key Question: How do we measure and describe time?

In this Investigation, the students will learn how to use the electronic timer and photogate equipment. By doing a series of inquiry activities, they must deduce the rules by which the timer works from observing what happens as objects move in and out of the two photogates. The Investigation is important for learning to measure and work with time, but is almost more important as a model for learning through experiment rather than being told what will happen. Since inquiry-based investigation is the foundation of the course, this Investigation plays a critical role in establishing the protocol that will be followed in the subsequent Investigations. The concepts of accuracy, resolution, and precision are introduced through time measurements made with photogates and with a stopwatch.

1985   1991   2004

Time

Reading Synopsis

Students read Section 2.2 Time after the Investigation.

There are two related meanings for "time." One is to specify a particular moment such as 2:30 p.m. Another is to describe a quantity of time, such as 30 seconds. Time is measured in several related units: years, hours, minutes, seconds, etc. Time intervals appearing in physics calculations must be converted to seconds.

Physical phenomena occur on a wide range of time scales from shorter than 10^{-18} seconds (light to cross an atom) to 10^{17} seconds (age of the universe). Many key physics concepts are based on how certain quantities change with time, such as position.

Accuracy and precision are important to consider when doing experiments. Accuracy describes how close a measurement is to the true value. Precision describes how small a difference can be reliably distinguished by a measurement.

The Investigation

Leading Questions
- Why are accurate measurements of time necessary?
- How do the timer and photogates work?
- How do we describe how close a measurement is to the true value we are trying to measure?
- How do we describe the difference between an instrument that can measure to 0.0001 seconds and another that can only measure to 0.01 seconds?

Learning Goals

By the end of the Investigation, students will be able to:
- Use electronic timing equipment and photogates.
- Use units of time in calculations and conversions.
- Correctly apply the terms accuracy, precision, and resolution to scientific instruments and measurements.

Key Vocabulary   time interval, precision, accuracy, resolution

Setup and Materials

Students work in groups of four or five at tables.

Each group should have:

- Timer with photogates, AC adapter (or 9-volt battery), and cords to connect the photogates to the timer

Details

Time	🕐 One class period
Preparation	✏️ **Practice using the timer and photogates**
Assignments	📖 Section 2.2 Time in the **Student Edition** after completing the Investigation
Skill Sheets	2.2 Converting Units Skill Builder: Significant Digits
Equipment Setup	Timer and photogates

Teaching the Investigation

1 Introduction
2 Using the timer as a stopwatch
3 The 100-yard dash
4 Mixed units for time
5 Using the photogates
6 Two photogates
7 Accuracy, resolution, and precision

Introduction

Digital photogate - provides time measurements up to one ten-thousandth of a second.

Using the timer as a stopwatch

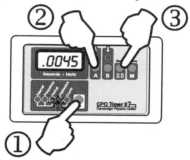

(1) Set the timers in stopwatch mode.
(2) The A button starts and stops time.
(3) The red 0 button resets.

The 100-yard dash

10.00 seconds
10.01 seconds

Is a stopwatch accurate enough to determine the winner of a race?

Mixed units for time

4:23:15.00

means: four hours, 23 minutes, and 15 seconds.

A good part of the usefulness of science is knowing how to predict what will happen next. The word "next" implies the passage of time, and much of our study of physics deals with the way things change in time. A ball rolls down a hill and its motion can be described by where it is at any time after it starts moving. Today's Investigation is about the measurement of time. Many experiments in physics will require us to measure time very precisely, often to one ten-thousandth of a second. A simple stopwatch will not usually be enough. For accurate time measurements we will use a digital photogate timer and today's Investigation is about how this measuring tool works and what its limitations are.

1 Take the timers out, and turn them on. The on-off switch is on the left side. Slide the switch to the on position. The display shows you a number or "CPO." Push the yellow button on the bottom until the light is under the word "stopwatch."

> Students should have timers but no photogates out yet. Everyone should have a battery or be connected via the AC adapter and extension cord.

Push the A button to start time, push A again to stop time, and push the red button to reset.

> Encourage students to try it and walk around the room, prompting people to share and let the entire class try the timer.

Who can get the fastest time? Try pushing the A button twice in a row, and see what you can get. Who can beat one second?

> Encourage students to push the A button twice in a row rapidly. Write the times on the board. Start by asking students if they can get a time shorter than one second. The fastest time should be about 0.1 to 0.2 seconds. Students are often laughing and having fun with this activity.

Where does your time go? Fit it in the list.

> As each group calls out the time, add it to a list on the blackboard.

Here are two runners who did the 100-yard dash. One did the dash in 10.00 seconds, and the other took 10.01 seconds. Who wins?

> The students should respond by saying the 10.00-second runner wins. Emphasize that greater speed means lower time, an inverse relationship.

Suppose we had the best stopwatch in the world. Could we tell the difference between the winner and the loser?

> Prompt the students to look at the times you just put on the board, and conclude the answer is no. The difference is 0.01 seconds, and the best reaction time you will have been able to get will be at least seven times too large (0.07 sec). Human reaction time is about 0.1 seconds, the signal travel time for a nerve from the brain to a muscle. The loss of precision is due to human reaction time.

To make matters most confusing, time is often written in mixed units. A time of four hours, 23 minutes, and 15 seconds is written like this.

> Write 4:23:15.00 on the board as an example.

To use time in physics calculations, the units must all be the same. For most problems and experiments you will want time in seconds. How many seconds are there in 4:23:15.00?

> Review how to calculate the total number of seconds with students.

UNIT I: Measurement and Motion

2.2 Time

Question: How do we measure and describe time?

In this Investigation, you will:

1. Learn to use electronic timing equipment and photogates.
2. Use units of time in calculations and conversions.
3. Investigate the accuracy, precision, and resolution of a scientific instrument.

1 Using the Timer as a stopwatch

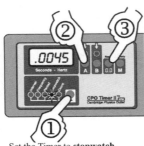

In science, it is often important to know how things change with time. The electronic Timer allows us to make accurate, precise measurements of time. The Timer performs many different functions. The first function to try is **stopwatch**. Use the button (1) to move the light under the word "stopwatch."

A stopwatch measures a **time interval**. The stopwatch is started and stopped with the "A" button (2). The display shows time in seconds up to 60 seconds and then changes to show minutes and seconds for times longer than 1 minute.

1. Set the Timer to **stopwatch**.
2. Start and stop the stopwatch with the "A" button.
3. Reset the stopwatch to zero with the "0" button.

The time it takes a signal to go from your brain to move a muscle is called **reaction time**. Reaction time varies from person to person and can be affected by factors such as fatigue or caffeine intake.

Practice taking measurements with the stopwatch; then estimate the approximate reaction time of an average student.

2 Mixed units for time

Hours Minutes Seconds

Time is often given in mixed units including hours, minutes, and seconds. Mixed units are often written as shown in the diagram above.

a. Arrange the following three time intervals from shortest to longest:

1) 4 hours, 23 minutes and 15 seconds (4:23:15)   2) 250 minutes   3) 16,000 seconds

---

Reaction time and driving

The importance of reaction time is often mentioned when discussing automobile braking to avoid an accident. If a driver is in a situation in which he or she must quickly brake, a fast reaction time can help prevent a collision. Other factors such as the speed at which the car is moving, the effectiveness of the brakes, and the condition of the road are important in determining the distance required to bring the car to a stop.

A driver's reaction time depends on a number of factors. Lack of sleep and the ingestion of alcohol or drugs both can substantially increase reaction time. This is why driving when intoxicated or under the influence of drugs (even certain prescription and over the counter drugs) is so dangerous. Some studies have also shown that reaction time increases with age. Caffeine has been shown to decrease reaction time.

1 2 Example answers

1. Our stopwatch times were between 0.07 and 0.14 seconds. I estimate an approximate average reaction time to be about 0.10 seconds.

2a. 16,000 seconds
    4:23:15.00
    250 minutes

Using the photogates

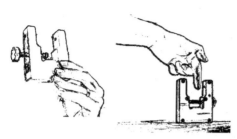

This is a photogate; there are two per timer. Start with one photogate connected to the A input of the timer. Have the students put their finger in the light beam and watch what happens to the timer

Two photogates

A	B	What does it measure?
on	off	Time to pass through A
off	on	????
on	on	????
off	off	????

Put this chart on the board, and have the students do experiments to figure out what the timer shows in each combination of lights.

2   Take one photogate out of the box, and plug it in behind the A button. The photogates have an invisible infrared light beam that goes between the two holes. Once you plug the photogate in, the red status light should go on. The status light should go off when the beam is broken.

> Students should take one photogate and plug it in by connecting a phone cord from the photogate to the socket above the A button. Walk around and check that the students have done this correctly. The red light on the photogate should be on.

Put the timer in interval mode by pressing the mode button at the bottom until the light is under the word "interval." Press the A button to set the display for photogate A. The A light should come on and stay on. Notice that pushing the A button toggles the A light on and off. Take your finger and block the light beam, and describe what happens. What do you do to start and stop the clock now?

> Have the students experiment with the light beam until they can tell you exactly what starts and stops the clock. A good answer is, "Blocking the beam starts the clock and unblocking the beam stops it." An insufficient answer is, "Your finger does it." Getting the entire answer often takes several prompts, such as, "Okay, what stops it?" You can keep up the contest for getting the smallest time interval. Flicking a finger or pencil point through the beam eventually produces a time of 0.0001 seconds. Again, use the board to keep track of the list of times.

If you block the light beam several times in a row, do the times add or do they start from zero each time? Figure out an experiment to test this and show me.

> The point is to introduce the concept of hypothesis and testing the hypothesis by comparing it with experimental evidence. Most students say "add" without thinking about it. Students should see that flicking a finger through the beam repeatedly does not always increase the number. This observation demonstrates that the timer does not add every time the light beam is blocked.

3   Take the other photogate, and plug it in above the B button. Press reset and turn both the A and B lights on. What stops and starts the clock now?

> Students should have both photogates connected with the telephone cords and both A and B lights should be on. The B button toggles the B light just like the A button did for the A light.

There are four combinations of lights:

A on & B off,   A off & B on,   A & B on, and A & B off.

Can you do some experiments to test what starts and stops the timer for each of the four combinations? Hint: We already know what happens when the A light is on.

> The students should play with the photogates and deduce the rules for how it works. Walk around, and makes sure the A and B photogates are some distance apart to avoid confusion.

Make sure that both light beams are not blocked whenever you press reset.

> There is always one student who gets the error display (---). This happens when reset is pressed with one or more light beams blocked. Pressing reset with the light beams unblocked will fix the problem. If not, check the batteries.

What does the timer measure with both lights on? What does it measure with just the B light on?

> Continue to prompt students until they correctly identify the rules. For example, with both lights on, breaking A starts the clock, and breaking B stops it.

2.2 Time

❸ Using the photogates

A photogate uses a light beam to start and stop the Timer. When the Timer is in interval mode, it uses photogates to control the clock.

1. Connect a single photogate to the "A" input with a cord.
2. Select **interval** on the Timer.
3. Push the "A" button and the "A" light should come on and stay on.
4. Try blocking the light beam with your finger and observe what happens to the Timer. Note: The photogate has a reaction time much shorter than your finger. Because it is used for so many measurements, you need to figure out how the photogate and Timer work together. Try your own experiments until you can answer the following questions.

a. Exactly what action do you take to start and stop the Timer. Be very specific in your answer. Someone who has never seen the photogate before should be able to read your answer and know what to do with the light beam to make the Timer start, and what to do to make it stop.

b. If you block the light beam several times in a row, does the Timer add each new measurement to the last one or does it start at zero every time you break the beam? Your answer should provide observations that back up what you say.

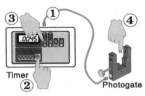

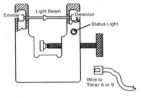

❹ Using the Timer with two photogates

You can connect two photogates to the Timer in interval mode. The second photogate connects behind the "B" light. Notice that the "A" and "B" buttons turn the "A" and "B" lights on and off.

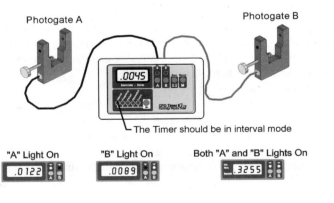

Photogate A   Photogate B

The Timer should be in interval mode

"A" Light On   "B" Light On   Both "A" and "B" Lights On

.0122   .0089   .3255

5

❸ Example answers

3a. Blocking the beam starts the timer. Unblocking the beam stops the timer.

3b. The timer starts at zero every time you break the beam, because the time does not keep getting longer when you block the beam several times in a row.

Two photogates (continued)

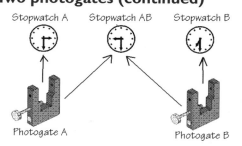

Stopwatch A　　Stopwatch AB　　Stopwatch B

Photogate A　　　　　　Photogate B

Accuracy, resolution, and precision

Resolution: How fine you can read a measurement. Stopwatch is 0.01 sec, photogates are 0.0001 sec.

Accuracy: How close to the truth?

Precision: How repeatable?

3 What happens when both lights are off?

Most students say nothing happens with both lights off. This is not so! Have everyone turn off both the A and B lights, and then press reset. Next have them break both beams, A first then B. Now have them turn the lights back on one at a time. They will see measurements for time A, time B, and time from A to B. The lights tell what the display shows because the timer makes all three possible interval measurements whenever the light beam(s) are broken.

The timer acts like three stopwatches. One measures the time through photogate A. Another measures the time though B. The third measures the time from A to B. The lights tell you which of the three stopwatches you are displaying. All three can be running at the same time!

Draw a diagram on the board similar to the one on the left.

4 The smallest interval an instrument can measure is called its resolution. What is the smallest time you can measure with one photogate? Try flicking something through the beam very quickly.

Have the students flick their finger through the beam with one photogate. How short a time interval can they get? Rubber bands and pencil points are small and have shorter times in the beam. You want to reach 0.0001 seconds, since this is the shortest time they can measure (resolution).

What is the resolution of the timer using the photogates? What was the resolution of the stopwatch?

The resolution is 0.0001 seconds with a photogate and 0.01 seconds in stopwatch mode.

Accuracy describes how close a measurement is to the true value. Suppose you have two measurements from the same experiment. One timer measures 1.02 seconds using stopwatch mode. The second timer has a nearly dead battery and measures 5.0216 seconds using a photogate. Which is more accurate?

This is a tricky question to answer and is designed to make students think about the meaning of accuracy. The word accuracy describes how close a measurement is to the true value.

The stopwatch measurement is probably much closer to the true time, and therefore more accurate, even though a stopwatch measurement has 100 times poorer resolution than a photogate measurement. An instrument which is poorly calibrated or poorly maintained will often have inaccurate results, even when they are displayed to a very high resolution! Do not be fooled by lots of digits on an instrument. If a measurement is critically important, you must know the accuracy of the instrument compared with a reliable reference standard. The National Bureau of Standards maintains many reference instruments that engineers and scientists use to test the accuracy of their own instruments.

Can anyone tell me the meaning of the word precision?

Discuss the relationship between precision, accuracy, and resolution.

Precision is closely related to resolution, and means how repeatable the measurement is. An experiment that is precise reproduces almost the same result every time. If you swing a pendulum through the beam of the photogate 10 times from the same height, you will get 10 time measurements that are within 0.0001 seconds of each other. For our purposes, the precision of a single measurement made with a photogate is the same as the resolution, 0.0001 seconds. The timer can make measurements that are precise to 0.0001 seconds with photogates. The precision is worse than the resolution in stopwatch mode (+/- 0.05 seconds) Why?

The precision of a stopwatch measurement is limited by the reaction time of your finger more than the internal resolution of the timer itself.

2.2 Time

Conduct experiments to determine what stops and starts the stopwatch for each combination of lights. Write your observations as if you were trying to teach someone else how the Timer works.

a. What starts and stops the Timer when *only* the "A" light is on?

b. What starts and stops the Timer when *only* the "B" light is on?

c. What starts and stops the Timer when *both* "A" and "B" lights are on?

d. Does the Timer still make measurements when there are no lights on?

e. What happens if you go though photogate A once and through photogate B multiple times? When answering this question, you might want to think about a race where all the runners start together but you want each runner's individual time for finishing the race.

5 Accuracy, resolution and precision

a. *Resolution* means the smallest interval that can be measured. Try using one photogate to determine the resolution of the Timer. Give your answer in seconds and tell how your observations support your answer.

b. The word *accuracy* refers to how close a measurement is to the true value. Which of the following statements best describes what you know about the accuracy of time measurements made with the photogates? Give a reason for your answer.

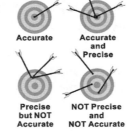

Accurate

Accurate and Precise

Precise but NOT Accurate

NOT Precise and NOT Accurate

   1. The Timer is accurate to 0.001 seconds.

   2. The Timer is accurate to 0.0001 seconds.

   3. It is impossible to know the accuracy without more information on how the Timer determines one second.

   4. A time of 0.0231 seconds is more accurate than a time of 26 seconds.

c. The word *precision* describes how closely repeated measurements of *the same quantity* can be made. When measurements are very precise, they are close to the same value. For example, an ordinary clock (with hands) can determine the time to a precision of about a second. That means many people reading the same clock at the same time will read times that are within a second of each other. It is possible to be precise but not accurate. Which is likely to be more precise: time measurements made with a stopwatch or measurements made with photogates?

6

Example answers

4a. When the A light is on, blocking the beam in photogate A starts the clock, and unblocking the beam in photogate A stops the clock. The timer measures the time it takes for something to travel through photogate A.

4b. When the B light is on, blocking the beam in photogate B starts the clock, and unblocking the beam in photogate B stops the clock. The timer measures the time it takes for something to travel through photogate B.

4c. With the A and B lights on, blocking the beam in photogate A starts the clock and blocking the beam in photogate B stops the clock.

4d. The timer starts and stops even if no lights are on. The timer records the measurements every time the light beam is broken, and the A and B lights show what is being displayed.

4e. Going through photogate A starts the clock. Every time you go through photogate B, it displays the time since you last went through photogate A. If you keep blocking the beam in photogate B, the times keep getting longer. If this were timing a race, all the runners would start the race by going through photogate A and finish by going through photogate B. Each runner's individual time would be displayed as they passed through B.

5a. The resolution is 0.0001 seconds because this is the shortest time you can measure and display.

5b. Choice 3. The timer may show the number 1.0000 seconds, but you don't know how close this really is to a second.

5c. Photogate measurements are more precise because they are not dependent on human reaction time.

2.3 Mass, Matter, and the Atom

Key Question: How is mass described?

This Investigation is designed to build intuitive familiarity with the kilogram as a unit of mass. Mass is a measure of how much matter is present in an object. Students first must estimate the mass of objects in kilograms by comparing them to a 1-liter bottle of water, which has a mass of about 1 kilogram. They then practice using a balance to measure mass. The second half of the Investigation is a review of scientific notation in which students must calculate large and small numbers and represent the number in both decimal (ordinary) notation and in scientific notation.

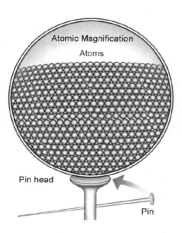

Reading Synopsis

Students read Section 2.3 Mass, Matter, and the Atom after the Investigation.

Mass is a measure of the amount of matter contained in an object. Mass creates weight and inertia. Mass is measured in grams and kilograms. Objects of concern to physics have ranges of mass from smaller than a single electron (10^{-31} kg) to bigger than the Milky Way galaxy (10^{40} kg).

Very small numbers are represented in scientific notation. A review of scientific notation is presented.

Ordinary matter is made of tiny particles called atoms. There are 92 types of atoms in normal matter, one type for each of the 92 naturally occurring elements. Atoms in familiar matter are usually combined in molecules and mixtures. The atoms in a solid are packed and bonded together. Atoms in a liquid are slightly farther apart (ordinarily) and loosely bonded so they can move. Atoms in a gas are much farther apart and free to move independently.

The Investigation

Leading Questions
- What is mass?
- How big is a kilogram?
- How do you write very large and very small numbers?

Learning Goals

By the end of the Investigation, students will be able to:
- Give an example of an object with a mass of one kilogram.
- Describe and measure the mass of objects in kilograms.
- Write and read numbers in scientific notation.

Key Vocabulary

weight, inertia, kilograms, gram, scientific notation, base, power of ten, exponent, atoms, element, molecule, mixtures, plasma

Setup and Materials

Students work in groups of four or five at tables.

Each group should have:

- Electronic scale or triple-beam balance
- Bathroom scale
- Scientific calculator
- 1-liter bottle of water (full)

You will need several objects to serve as examples of mass. The objects listed in the Investigation are:

- Pencil
- Cement block
- Paper clip

Other objects will also work.

Details

Time   One class period

Preparation   Get 1 liter bottles of water to serve as reference masses for one kilogram (1 per group). Lookup the mass of a car you can use for an example.

Assignments   Section 2.3 Mass, Matter, and the Atom in the **Student Edition** after the Investigation.

Skill Sheets   2.3 Scientific Notation

Teaching the Investigation

1   Introduction
2   Estimating mass
3   Estimate the mass of each object
4   Measuring mass
5   Scientific notation
6   Atoms and mass

Introduction

Matter is the "stuff" that everything around you is made of.

Mass - the amount of matter an object contains.

Estimating mass

1

How much mass is there in a textbook?

Pounds are a unit of weight, not a unit of mass.

Pound - a unit of FORCE.

Each kilogram of matter weights 2.2 pounds on Earth's surface.

Kilograms and grams will be used to describe mass.

One gram = mass of one grain of rice.

One kilogram = mass of a one-liter bottle of soda.

Estimate the mass of each object

We use distance and time to describe where things are and how they move. What we need next is to describe how much "stuff" there is in an object. In physics, "stuff" is called a matter and the amount of matter is measured by mass. An object with more mass contains more matter. A small child usually associates the size of an object with the amount of matter it contains. Can anyone give me an example of two objects that are the same size with a different amounts of matter?

An inflated balloon and a bowling ball are about the same size but the bowling ball has much more mass.

Today's Investigation is about mass and the units in which mass is measured. For many of you this will be a review. Even if you already know about mass, in physics we may be dealing with masses much larger and much smaller than any you have probably encountered before.
Who knows a unit of mass? How much mass is there in this book?

Hold up a textbook. Start a discussion on the units of mass. The most common answers are pounds and kilograms or grams.

For most everyday purposes, the weight of an object in pounds is a reasonable measure of its mass. However, the unit of pounds is not a unit of mass. A pound is a unit of force. If I weigh 150 pounds that means my feet push down on the ground with a FORCE of 150 pounds. This force is caused by the gravity of the Earth pulling on my body. Since the force of gravity is proportional to mass, the force of my weight is also proportional to my mass. We can conveniently use weight to describe an object's mass because each kilogram of matter weighs 2.2 pounds on the surface of the Earth. At other places, the force of gravity is not the same as it is on Earth. Two objects with the same mass can have very different weights in pounds.
The proper unit of mass is a kilogram or gram. We will use kilograms and grams to describe mass throughout this course. One gram is the mass of a grain of rice. One kilogram is about the mass of a 1-liter bottle of water. There are 1,000 grams in one kilogram.

Hold up a 1-liter soda bottle. Have students bringing their own 1-liter bottles. You want them to develop an intuitive sense for how much mass is in one kilogram.

Now pick up your book in your other hand. Estimate the mass of your book by comparing its weight to the weight of the bottle. Humans cannot sense mass directly, but we can sense force.

Have students do the comparison and guess at the mass of the textbook. The actual mass of the book is 2.2 kilograms.

The mass of an object is a property of the object and is the same no matter where in the universe the object may be. There are two ways to change the mass of an object. One is easy and one is hard. Can anyone tell me what the two ways are?

The first way is to add or subtract mass by adding or taking off matter from the object. This is simple to understand. The second way is to make the object move at speeds close to the speed of light. As objects reach very high speeds, some of the energy of motion is converted to mass via Einstein's formula $E = mc^2$. This is discussed much later (Chapter 18, Investigation 18.3) in the course.

To get a sense of mass measured in kilograms, I want you to estimate the mass of the objects listed in Part 2 of your Investigation, in kilograms. Think about the amount of matter in each object compared with the amount of matter in the 1-liter bottle of water which has a mass of one kilogram.

Students should make the estimates by discussing the relative size or weight of each object compared with the 1-liter bottle of water. This activity works best if students work in groups.

UNIT I: Measurement and Motion

2.3   Mass, Matter, and the Atom

Question: How is mass described?

In this Investigation, you will:

1. Describe the mass of objects in kilograms.
2. Measure mass and report measurements using scientific notation.

You have investigated length and time. A third fundamental quantity that describes things in the universe is mass. Mass is a measure of how much matter is present in an object. In this Investigation, you will estimate and measure the mass of various objects. You will also review how to represent large and small numbers with scientific notation.

1   Estimating mass

The two most common units for mass are the kilogram and the gram. For easy reference, a 1-liter bottle of soda has a mass of about 1 kilogram; a grain of rice has a mass of about 1 gram. To be precise, one kilogram equals 1,000 grams. In the English system, a *pound* is a unit of *force* (Chapter 5), not a unit of mass.

a. Pick up a full (1 liter) bottle of soda to get a sense of the amount of mass in a kilogram. Next, pick up a book such as your textbook. Use the comparison to estimate the mass of the book in kilograms.

2   Estimate the mass of each object:

The mass of some objects can be estimated (or conveniently measured) directly in kilograms. Others are too large or too small. For a very small object, think about how many it would take to make up 1 kilogram of mass. The mass of a single object is then 1 kg ÷ the number of objects. If you know the weight in pounds, the mass is equal to the number of pounds divided by 2.2 lbs/kg. This conversion works on the surface of Earth where a mass of 1 kg has a weight of 1 lb.

Estimate the mass of the following objects in kilograms:

a. Your pencil.
b. Your shoe.
c. A cement block.
d. Yourself.
e. An automobile.
f. A paper clip.

3   Measuring Mass

You need a very sensitive scale (an electronic scale or triple-beam balance) to measure the mass of an object like a paper clip or a pencil but you need a very sturdy scale (like a bathroom scale) to measure your mass or the mass of a cement block. Learning to choose the right measuring device is an important skill in physics.

a. Use the appropriate measuring device to measure the mass in kilograms of each object listed in Part 2.

7

1a. 0.8 kg

2a. 0.05 kg

2b. 0.5 kg

2c. 10 kg

2d. 45 kg

2e. 1,500 kg

2f. 0.005 kg

3a. Actual masses:

Pencil: 0.02 kg; shoe: 0.7 kg; cement block: 13.5 kg;

myself: 66.2 kg; automobile: too large for our instruments;

paper clip: 0.002 kg.

4   Example answers (shown on page 21)

4a. Answers are:

2a. 8.0×10^{-1} kg   2b. 5.0×10^{-2} kg

2c. 1.0×10^{1} kg   2d. 4.5×10^{1} kg

2e. 1.5×10^{3} kg   2f. 5.0×10^{-3} kg

4b. Answers are:

An atom of hydrogen (1.007 amu):
1.68×10^{-24} g
0.000 000 000 000 000 000 000 001 68 g

An atom of uranium (238.0289 amu):
3.98×10^{-26} g or 3.98×10^{-29} kg
0.000 000 000 000 000 000 000 000 003 98 g

A grain of sand:
between 3.0×10^{-4} g and 1.3×10^{-2} g
between 0.0003 g and .013 g

The space shuttle:
2.04×10^{6} kg   (2.04 million kg)
2,040,000 kg

A professional soccer ball:
43 kg
4.2×10^{-1} kg

The planet Earth:
5.97×10^{24} kg
5 970 000 000 000 000 000 000 000 kg

Measuring mass

Electronic balance - uses a tiny sensor that bends proportional to the force applied.

Triple beam balance - compares the mass of an object with standard masses.

Triple beam balance works on the moon as well as Earth because gravity acts equally on standard masses and the object's mass.

Scientific notation

Scientific notation is a way of writing very large or very small numbers.

Written as two numbers multiplied together. First number is the base and the second number is the exponent (a power of 10).

With numbers larger than zero, the exponent is a positive number.

With numbers smaller than zero, the exponent is a negative number.

Atoms and mass

Matter is made of tiny particles called atoms.

Atoms are so small that one gram of hydrogen contains 6×10^{23} atoms.

3

To measure the mass of an object accurately we use a balance. An electronic balance uses a tiny sensor that bends proportionally to the force applied. That means an electronic balance senses weight, and the computer inside calculates mass using the fact that 1 kilogram weighs 2.2 pounds at the Earth's surface. A triple beam balance works differently. A triple beam balance compares the mass of the object you want to measure with standard masses that you slide on the scale or hang on the end. A triple beam the balance will determine the mass of an object correctly on the moon even where the gravity is different from the Earth, but an electronic balance will not. Can anyone tell me why this is true?

> With a triple beam balance, gravity acts equally on both the standard mass and the mass you want to measure. In the comparison, the strength of gravity cancels out

Use the balance to measure the mass of a few of the objects from Part 2 of the Investigation. How close were your estimates?

> Help students to measure the mass of the objects of some ordinary objects (pencil, paper clip, shoe).
> Typical laboratory balances do not have the capacity to measure a person, a cement block, or an automobile, and possibly not even a shoe.

4

Masses of objects that are important in physics range from exceptionally small to incredibly large. To communicate very large and very small numbers we use scientific notation. In scientific notation a number is written as a product of two numbers multiplied together. The first number is called the base. The second number is a power of 10 called the exponent.

> Work through the example of expressing 75,000 kilograms in scientific notation, given in step 4 of the Investigation. Explain the E key on a calculator (see tip on the right).

To try our hand at a calculation using scientific notation, how many grains of rice have the same mass as a 50,000 kg semitrailer truck? How could we make the calculation?

> Students should recognize that you can divide the mass of a truck (50,000 kg) by the mass of a single grain of rice (0.001 kg). The result is 50,000,000 which can be written 5×10^7 in scientific notation.

Scientific notation is also used to write very small numbers. This works because one over a power of 10 can be written as 10 to a negative power. The number 0.001 is one thousandth, or 1 / 1000. Since the number 1,000 is 10^3 the inverse of 1,000 is 10^{-3}. We can therefore write 0.001 as 1×10^{-3}. What is the number 0.0002 in scientific notation?

> Work this out on the blackboard, showing the students the technique of moving the decimal point one place to the left for each increment of minus one in the exponent.

One of the most interesting discoveries in the last two centuries was that matter is made of very tiny particles called atoms. All of the matter in view, me, and this room are made of extremely tiny atoms. Atoms are so small that we must use a scientific notation to describe almost anything about them, including their size and mass. Atoms are so small that a single gram of hydrogen contains 6×10^{23} atoms. If you were to write this number out in decimal notation that would be a six followed by 23 zeros. In the next part of the Investigation, I want you to look up or calculate the mass of a list of large and small objects. The list is in part for the pop the Investigation.

> Help students working in groups to do the calculations. You may have to refresh their memory on how to get the mass of atoms from the periodic table. Most atomic masses are given in atomic mass units (amu). One amu is 1.66×10^{-27} kg.

2.3 Mass, Matter, and the Atom

4 Scientific notation

Scientific notation is a shorthand method used for expressing extremely large and extremely small numbers. Numbers written in scientific notation are expressed as a product of two numbers: a number between 1 and 10 (called the base) and a power of ten. For example, the number 100 can be written in scientific notation: 100 is 1×10^2 because $10^2 = 100$. If the mass of an airplane is 75,000 kg, how is this written in scientific notation?

- To express 75,000 kg in scientific notation, first identify the base (number between 1 and 10). For the airplane mass, the base is 7.5.

- Next, figure out what power of ten the base needs to be multiplied by to get 75,000. You know that $75,000 = 7.5 \times 10,000$. The number ten thousand (10,000) is a power of ten because $10,000 = 10 \times 10 \times 10 \times 10$, or 10^4. In scientific notation, the mass of the airplane is 7.5×10^4 kg.

Scientific notation also works for numbers less than one. Powers of ten that are *negative* are numbers smaller than one. For example, a quarter has a mass of 0.009 kg, which is smaller than one. The number 0.009 can be broken down into a product of two numbers: 0.009 is equal to 9×0.001. The second number (0.001) is a power of ten. One-thousandth (0.001) can be expressed as $1 \div 1,000$. Since $1,000 = 10^3$, $1 \div 1,000$ is the same as $1 \div 10^3$. Mathematically, $1 \div 10^3$ is written 10^{-3}. The negative exponent means the actual number is one divided by the power of ten. Using scientific notation, the mass of a quarter is 9×10^{-3} kg.

Table 1: Some useful powers of ten

Numbers larger than 1	Numbers smaller than 1	Words for large and small numbers	
$10^1 = 10$	$10^{-9} = 0.000\,000\,001$		
$10^2 = 100$	$10^{-8} = 0.000\,000\,01$		
$10^3 = 1,000$	$10^{-7} = 0.000\,000\,1$	1×10^9	1 billion
$10^4 = 10,000$	$10^{-6} = 0.000\,001$	1×10^6	1 million
$10^5 = 100,000$	$10^{-5} = 0.000\,01$	1×10^3	1 thousand
$10^6 = 1,000,000$	$10^{-4} = 0.000\,1$	1×10^{-3}	1 thousandth
$10^7 = 10,000,000$	$10^{-3} = 0.001$	1×10^{-6}	1 millionth
$10^8 = 100,000,000$	$10^{-2} = 0.01$		
$10^9 = 1,000,000,000$	$10^{-1} = 0.1$		

a. Rewrite your estimates from 2a - 2f using scientific notation.

b. Look up or estimate the mass of each of these objects and write it both using scientific notation and as a decimal (ordinary) number. *It is difficult to write some of the masses as decimal (ordinary) numbers.*

    a   An atom of hydrogen.

    b   An atom of uranium.

    c   A grain of sand.

    d   The space shuttle.

    e   An official professional soccer ball.

    f   The planet Earth.

Scientific notation on a calculator

Many students will need a quick review on how to read or enter numbers in scientific notation on a calculator. Scientific calculators have an exponent key usually labeled with a capital letter E. To enter a number in scientific notation you would enter the base, then press the exponent key and enter the power of ten. For example, to enter the number 5.2×10^6 the sequence of keystrokes is shown below.

The calculator does not display the multiplication sign or the number 10. Calculators usually display the letter E to indicate that the next two-digit number is an exponent of 10. Computer spreadsheets follow the same convention, and the number would be entered 5.2E6.

To enter a number with a negative exponent, the +/- key must be pressed after the E key to tell the calculator that the exponent is negative. For example, to enter 1.6×10^{-19} the sequence of keystrokes is shown below.

The keystrokes: 1 . 6 E ± 1 9   Display: 1.6 E-19

It is also worth reminding students that a negative exponent is NOT a negative number unless the base is also negative. A negative exponent is a number less than one. Some calculators may differ from this standard.

3.1 Speed

Key Question: What is speed and how is it measured?

Understanding the concept and computation of speed is essential. Without this foundation, students will not be able to grasp acceleration, Newton's laws, and other topics that build on knowledge of the relationship between distance, time, and speed. In this Investigation, students precisely measure how fast a ball rolls down a ramp and learn how to calculate speed in different units. They also use the formula for speed to set up physical situations where they control the speed of a moving ball. Speed is controlled by by manipulating the variables that affect the ball's motion, such as the angle of the ramp.

$$\frac{90 \text{ miles}}{1.5 \text{ hours}} = 60 \text{ miles per hour (mph)}$$

Reading Synopsis

Students read Section 3.1 Speed after completing the Investigation

Speed is the ratio of distance traveled divided by the time it takes to travel the distance. Units of speed are length over time. Metric examples are m/sec and cm/sec. A common example is mph.

The formula for speed is $v = d/t$, where d is the distance traveled and t is the time taken. This formula may be rearranged to calculate any of the three variables from the other two.

A four-step problem-solving technique is described and illustrated.

1   Identify what you are asked to find.

2   Identify what information you are given.

3   Identify any relationships that involve the information asked for or the information given. These might include formulas, conversion factors, etc.

4   Use the relationships to solve the problem.

The Investigation

Leading Questions
- What is the definition of speed?
- How do you calculate the speed of an object?
- How can the relationship between speed, distance, and time be used to find any one of the three variables if the other two variables are known?
- Is there a technique for solving physics problems?

Learning Goals

By the end of the Investigation, students will be able to:
- Calculate the speed of a ball rolling down a ramp.
- Describe measurements that allow the speed of any moving object to be determined.
- Compare speeds in different units.
- Solve one-step problems involving speed, distance, and time.

Key Vocabulary   speed, constant speed, distance, time, at rest

---

Setup and Materials

Students work in groups of four or five at tables.

Each group should have:

- Straight track with a threaded knob
- 3/4-inch steel ball
- Timer with photogates, AC adapter (or 9-volt battery), and cords to connect the photogates to the timer
- Physics stand
- Metric and English rulers

Details

Time	One class period
Preparation	Some informal discussion (5 min.) about speed should precede the hands-on part of the Investigation. Go over an example such as working out your speed if you travel 120 miles in two hours.
Assignments	Section 3.1 Speed in the **Student Edition** after completing the Investigation.
Skill Sheets	3.1 Speed Problems
Equipment Setup	Straight track ramp, photogates, and timer

Teaching the Investigation

1   Introduction
2   Setting up
3   Calculating speed
4   Relationships between distance, speed, and time
5   Setting up a controlled speed

Introduction

If you go 120 miles in 2 hours, your speed is 60 miles per hour.

Speed = distance ÷ time

Equation: $v = d/t$

Setting up

Place photogate A and photogate B one foot apart, and record the time it takes to go from A to B.

Calculating speed

How do we calculate speed from the information we have?

Divide the distance travelled (12 inches) by the time it took for the ball to travel from A to B. This is the speed in inches per second.

Calculate the speed in centimeters per second. One inch is equal to 2.54 centimeters.

Which speed is fastest? 6.56 feet per second, or 200 cm/sec?

They are both the same speed!

Today's Investigation is on speed. Can anyone tell me exactly what speed is?

Discuss speed for a few minutes. Try to focus the discussion on being exact. Descriptions such as "how fast something is" are not satisfactory because they lack exactness.

Suppose you go 120 miles and it takes you two hours. What is your speed?

Nearly all students can do this in their heads. The speed is 60 mph.

How did you calculate the answer? Be specific.

Push the students until they recognize that they calculated the speed by dividing the distance traveled by the time taken. They already know a formula for speed, and how to use it! Write the formula down: speed is the distance traveled divided by the time taken, or $v = d/t$.

Attach the ramp to the fifth hole in the stand. Swivel the catcher upward so it catches the ball. Roll the ball down the ramp. Notice you can use the peg to start the ball in the same place every time. How could you precisely measure the speed of the ball as it travels from one point to another on the ramp?

Students should realize that to find a speed, you would have to know how far the ball traveled and how much time it took to travel that distance.

How can we use the photogates and timer to help us precisely measure the speed of the ball as it covers one foot of distance in the middle of the track?

You would place photogate A and B one foot apart, and record the time it takes the ball to travel from A to B.

1 Place photogates A and B one foot apart near the middle of the track. Roll the ball down the track, and record the time it takes to go from A to B. How do we calculate speed from the information we now have?

Prompt for the answer "divide the distance (1 foot) by the time it takes to get from A to B." Note: If you want the entire class to be able to compare data, you should specify exactly where photogate A and B are placed. Also, be sure that all groups have their ramp at the same angle!

Calculate the speed in feet per second. How many feet did the ball go?

The ball went one foot, so the speed is one divided by the time from A to B. Many students will get the division upside down, so coach them along until everyone gets a number between 1 and 10 ft./sec. If the tracks are all at the same angle, and the photogates in similar positions, the speeds should be similar.

Calculate the speed in centimeters per second. Measure the distance between the photogates in centimeters, and you already have the time data.

This time, try to get students to measure the distance. The exact answer is 30.48 cm if the photogates are exactly 12 inches apart. Again, have each group calculate the speeds. The numbers will be larger because one inch per second is equivalent to 2.54 centimeters per second.

Calculate the speed in inches per second. How many inches does the car go?

The students should calculate the speed by figuring 12 inches divided by their times.

Which one of these speeds is fastest: 6.56 feet per second, or 200 cm/sec?

Compare two speeds for the same ramp in ft./sec. and cm/sec. from the actual results on the board.

The students should recognize that they are both the same speed but one has a much bigger number.

Are you telling me 200 is the same speed as 6! How can you say that?

Push the dialog to drive home the concept that "naked numbers" (i.e., without units) have no meaning. Two hundred is the same speed as 6.56 if you are comparing 200 cm/sec and 6.56 ft/sec.

24   **Unit 1: Measurement and Motion**

3.1 **Speed**

Question: What is speed and how is it measured?

In this Investigation, you will:

1. Calculate the speed of a ball rolling down a ramp.
2. Compare speeds in different units.

In this Investigation, you will precisely measure how fast a ball rolls down a ramp and learn how to calculate its speed in different units.

1 **Calculating the speed of the rolling ball**

1. Set up the straight track ramp with two photogates that are 1 foot apart (use a ruler). Measure the distance from the lower edge of one photogate to the lower edge of the next photogate.
2. Measure the distance between photogates in centimeters and record the value in Table 1.
3. Measure the distance between photogates in inches and meters and record these values also.
4. Make sure that the Timer's "A" and "B" lights are both on. Roll the ball down the ramp and measure the time it takes to go from photogate A to photogate B. Record the value in the table under **Time from A to B** *in all four rows* since they are all the same time.

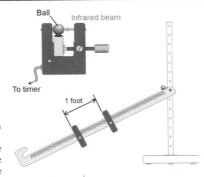
Ball — Infrared beam — To timer — 1 foot

Table 1: Speed, Distance, and Time Data

Distance from A to B	Time from A to B (sec)	Speed
(feet)		(ft/sec)
(centimeters)		(cm/sec)
(inches)		(in/sec)
(meters)		(m/sec)

a. Calculate the speed of the ball in ft/sec, cm/sec, in/sec, and m/sec, and write the results in the table.
b. Which is the fastest speed of the four or are they all the same speed?
c. Is it possible that a speed of 254 and a speed of 100 could be the same speed? Explain your answer, and and state why a speed as "254" is not a very good answer.

Language and units

It is always instructive to work out the same speed calculated in different units. Ask the students how the same quantity can be described by different numbers. Remind them that numbers and units are a language, like French and English are languages. "The dog" in French is *le chien*. Same animal, different language and therefore different representation in letters. One hundred inches per second is the same speed as 254 cm/sec for a similar reason. The two measurements describe the same speed in different languages. Fortunately, translating between units is easier than translating between French and English!

$$\text{speed in feet/sec} = \text{distance in feet} \div \text{time in seconds}$$

$$\text{speed in in/sec} = \text{distance in inches} \div \text{time in seconds}$$

$$\text{speed in cm/sec} = \text{distance in cm} \div \text{time in seconds}$$

1 **Example answers**

Table 1: *Speed, distance, and time data*

Distance from A to B	Time from A to B	Speed
1.00 feet	0.2062	4.85 ft./sec.
30.5 cm	0.2062	148.0 cm/sec.
12.0 in	0.2062	58.2 in/sec.
0.306 m	0.2062	1.48 m/sec.

1a. See Table 1.

1b. They are the same speed.

1c. They could be the same speed. Since 1 inch = 2.54 cm, the speeds 254 cm/sec. and 100 in/sec. are equal values using different distance units. No other combination of units used in this Investigation would work in this case. A speed of 254 is not a very good answer because it does not specify the units being used. 254 cm/sec. and 254 m/sec. are very different speeds and without units, 254 would not be enough information to specify which speed is indicated.

Calculating speed (continued)

A measurement has two parts: a value, and a unit.

Relationships between distance, speed, and time

Average speed - total distance traveled divided by the time it took to travel that distance.

Instantaneous speed - The speed of an object at a given point in time during its trip. The time it takes the ball to travel through one photogate is an approximation of instantaneous speed.

Setting up a controlled speed

Challenge: make the ball move at an average speed of exactly 1.0 meters per second.

A measurement always has two parts, a value and a unit. You cannot understand the value without the unit. This is not just a science question. If I asked you to paint my house for 25, what should you ask me before accepting the job?

> The students should respond "Twenty-five what?"

How about if I said 25 cents? Would that be enough? There is a big difference between 25 cents and 25 dollars or 2,500 dollars. The difference is the units.

2 What sort of speed did you calculate in Part 1 of the Investigation; an average speed or an instantaneous speed? Give an example of when you would calculate this sort of speed in daily life.

> When you divide total distance traveled by the time it took to travel that distance, you are calculating an average speed. This is similar to finding an average speed for an automobile trip. It is an average because it doesn't take into account speed changes, stops, and starts that might occur along the way.

Does the ball travel at a constant speed from photogate A to B, or does the speed change? How could you find the answer to your question?

> Students will probably realize that as the ball travels down the ramp, it speeds up. This is obvious from daily life experience. Thus, the ball is not traveling at a constant speed as it moves down the ramp. Students can find an instantaneous speed at photogate A and photogate B by dividing the diameter of the ball (0.019 m) by the individual A and B times. When comparing these two "instantaneous" speeds, students can see that the ball is moving faster at photogate B. The next Investigation will allow students to explore this concept in depth.

3 In many applications, the speed of a moving object must be carefully controlled. Can you think of any examples?

> Speeds of rotating tool parts and fan blades must be controlled, speed of the moving hands on a clock, speed of conveyer belts on assembly lines, and the speed of paper moving through a copy machine (see example Part 2).

In Part 3 of the Investigation, your challenge is to make the ball move with an **average speed** of exactly 1 meter per second, or as close as you can get.

> This is a great chance for students to apply what they learned about speed in Parts 1 and 2. The guidelines in Part 3 will provide plenty of hints to help students set up a successful experiment. You might want to have students list the measurements they will need to take, and in what order, before you ask them to read Part 3 of the Investigation. The most successful technique is to choose a distance that fits on the track and calculate the time it should take the ball to move between the two photogates. Set the photogates to the chosen distance and have students adjust the angle of the ramp until the time they measure (from A to B) matched the time they calculate if the speed of the ball were 1 m/sec. Give a tolerance that is acceptable for success, such as within 0.0005 seconds.

You may need to adjust the angle by a very small amount to change the speed of the ball. Use the leveling feet on the stand, or put paper under the end of the track.

3.1 Speed

2 Relationships between distance, speed, and time

Speed

Speed (m/sec) $v = \dfrac{d}{t}$ Distance traveled (meters)

Time taken (seconds)

In many applications, the speed of a moving object must be carefully controlled. For example, the speed of the paper moving through a copy machine must be just right or the images do not print correctly on the paper (see diagram at right).

Speed is the ratio of the distance traveled to the time taken. To move an object at a certain speed, you must control both the distance traveled and the time taken. A copy machine has motors and sensors that work together to control the speed of the paper moving through.

Paper moving through a copy machine

Paper moving at the right speed   Paper moving too FAST   Paper moving too SLOW

Image correctly aligned to page   Image prints too low on page   Image prints too high on page

3 Setting up a controlled speed

In the next part of the Investigation, your challenge is to make an object move with a speed of exactly 1 meter per second, or as close as you can get.

1. Start by choosing a distance between the photogates. Make sure your distance can fit on the track.
2. Rearrange the speed formula to calculate the time it must take the ball to get from photogate A to photogate B to make the average speed exactly 1 meter per second.
3. Place the photogates on the track the same distance apart as you chose in step 1.
4. Roll the ball and compare the time it takes to get from A to B with the time you need it to take to make the speed 1 m/sec.
5. Leave the photogates where they are and adjust the ramp until the time it takes to ball to get from A to B is within 0.001 seconds of the time you need it to be. Calculate the actual speed of the ball in m/sec using the actual distance and measured time from the photogates.

Distance between photogates (m):

Required time from A to B (calculated, sec):

Actual time from A to B (measured, sec):

Actual speed (calculated, m/sec):

a. How did you make the time between photogates longer?
b. How did you make the time between photogates shorter?
c. Calculate the percent difference between your measured speed and 1 meter per second.

10

3 Example answers

Distance between photogates (m):

0.1 (8th hole on the stand at 13 cm and 23 cm)

Required time from A to B (calculated, sec.):

0.1000

Actual time from A to B (calculated, sec.):

0.1001

Actual speed (calculated, sec.):

0.9990

3a. There are two ways. Moving the photogates higher up the track while keeping them same distance apart or moving the photogates farther apart will make the time measurement longer.

3b. There are two ways. Moving the photogates lower down the track while keeping them same distance apart or moving the photogates closer together will make the time measurement shorter.

3c. 1.0 m/sec. - 0.999 m/sec. = 0.001

0.001/1.0 = 0.001

0.001 × 100 = 0.1

percent difference = 0.1 %

3.2 Observations of Motion

Key Question: Can you predict the speed of a ball rolling down a ramp?

This Investigation has a dual purpose. The first purpose is to review and reinforce the concept of variables and how they are used in an experiment. The instructor sets up an experiment with a well-known outcome: that steeper angles result in higher speeds. Several variables are intentionally randomized. The students discover that the data does NOT confirm what they know to be true. They then control the variables and see that the data now shows exactly what they expected. For the second part of the investigation, students take data to create a graphical model of speed versus position. Students use their graphs to accurately predict the speed of the ball at any point on the track.

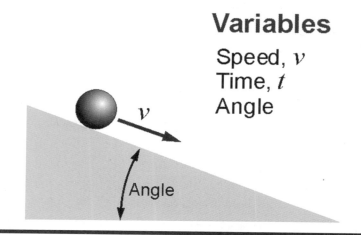

Variables
Speed, v
Time, t
Angle

Reading Synopsis

Students read Section 3.2 Observations of Motion after the Investigation

Models are an important part of science. Models allow you to predict what will happen based on knowledge of how changes in one variable affect other variables. Models are built from data.

Data is collected in experiments. An experiment should be well designed to properly interpret the data that is generated. The experimental variable is allowed to change while the control variables are kept constant. The procedure is a record of all the experimental techniques used.

Two useful forms of models are graphs and formulas. Graphs represent data in pictures that are easy to understand compared to a list of numbers. Graphs provide evidence of cause-and-effect relationships, and also show the form of relationship between two variables, called the dependent variable and the independent variable. Graphs can also be used to make predictions when one of the two variables is known.

The Investigation

Leading Questions
- What are variables and why are they so important in collecting data?
- What is a model and why is it useful?
- What is a graphical model and how does it aid in making predictions?
- How do you recognize a cause-and-effect relationship from experimental data?

Learning Goals

By the end of the Investigation, students will be able to:
- Determine the speed of a ball at different points as it rolls down the track.
- Identify the variables that influence the speed of the ball.
- Design an experiment that controls some variables while others are monitored (experimental variables).
- Make a speed versus position graph from collected data.
- Accurately predict the speed of the ball at any point on the track from the speed versus position graph.

Key Vocabulary

variables, model, initial speed, angle, friction, experimental variable, control variables, trial, experimental technique, procedure, dependent variable, y-axis, x-axis, independent variable, graphic model, graph

Setup and Materials

Students work in groups of four or five at tables.

Each group should have:

- Straight track with a threaded knob
- 3/4-inch steel ball
- Timer with photogates, AC adapter (or 9-volt battery), and cords to connect the photogates to the timer
- Physics stand
- Graph paper
- Metric and English rulers

Details

Time ⏱ One class period

Preparation ✏ You may wish to review the procedures for making a graph, such as scaling the axes, plotting points, etc.

Assignments 📖 Section 3.2 Observations of Motion in the **Student Edition** after the Investigation.

Skill Sheets 3.2 Making Line Graphs
Skill Builder: Graphing Skills

Equipment Setup Straight Track

Teaching the Investigation

1 Introduction
2 Setting up an experiment
3 Eliciting a simple hypothesis
4 Variables in an experiment
5 Doing a controlled experiment
6 Finding the speed of the ball at different points along the track
7 Graphing the results of the experiment
8 Analyzing the data

Introduction

Setting up an experiment

1

How does track angle affect the speed of the ball?

Each group will have a different track angle.

Attach the two photogates somewhere on the track.

Eliciting a simple hypothesis

The ball on the steepest track should have the highest speed, and the shortest time.

In Part I of this Investigation, you will randomize the variables that affect the speed of the ball on the ramp, and students will unknowingly conduct an uncontrolled experiment that will yield results that they do not understand. Students will quickly discover your "tricks" and in so doing they will remember to create controlled experiments in the future.

In the previous Investigation, we discovered how to precisely measure average speed of the ball on the ramp. In the first part of this Investigation, let's see how ramp angle affects the speed of the ball. Each group will have a different ramp angle. Attach two photogates somewhere on the track with photogate A higher than photogate B.

Have each group set their track to a different angle. Allow 2 holes between groups. For example, if you have five groups, choose 2, 4, 6, 8, and 10 as the holes in the stand that each group should use to attach the track. Some students will probably want to know right away where to place the photogates. Tell them "anywhere" as long as photogate A is first. Hopefully, students will place photogates at different places on the ramp, and the distance between photogates will vary from group to group. If students seem to be watching each other and setting up the photogates in similar positions, you will have to sneakily ask some groups to set the photogates in different places, or put them close together. You might even want to quietly give certain groups a steel ball and other groups a plastic ball.

Can you predict which ramp will have the fastest ball?

Students will know intuitively that the ball on the steepest ramp will have the greatest speed, but you are creating a situation where the numbers will not confirm this. Try to put off answering detailed questions, and just ask the students to predict which ramp will have the fastest ball. If groups are particularly adept, suggest that they answer the question as if they were in sixth grade. To set up your "trick" with success, you might need to tell the students that you will not be answering any questions about the procedure until after data has been collected.

Should the fastest ball have the shortest time or the longest time to get from photogate A to B?

The students should recognize that the fastest ball will have the shortest time.

I want everyone to roll the ball down the ramp once, and report to me the time it takes the ball to travel from A to B.

Create a data table on the board, and record the time for each group, starting with the group that has the ramp with the smallest angle, and continuing on through the groups to the one with the greatest angle.

Do these numbers make sense? What happened?

The class should recognize that the distance between the photogates should be the same for each group, and that A and B should be at the same position on each ramp. Also, students will begin to question other variables, such as pushing the ball versus releasing it, which ball was used, etc.

Example answers

1a. Most groups will predict that the steepest ramp will have the fastest ball.

1b. Answers will vary

1c. No, they did not agree. All the measurements took place at different places and different angles.

1d. Yes, a better way would be to place the photogates on the track and keep them there while measuring the time from A to B at several different angles. By comparing the results from the different trials we could see whether increasing the ramp angle makes the ball go faster.

2a. Sample answers:

Table 1: *Variables that affect the time between photogates*

Variable	Variable
Angle of the track/hole used	Distance between photogates
Location of the photogates on the track	Release location of the ball

---

UNIT I: Measurement and Motion

3.2   Observations of Motion

Question: Can you predict the speed of a ball rolling down a ramp?

In this Investigation, you will:

1. Determine the speed of a ball at different points as it rolls down the track.
2. Identify the variables that influence the speed of the ball.
3. Design an experiment that provides good scientific results.
4. Make a speed versus position graph with your collected data.
5. Accurately predict the speed of the ball at any point on the track by using your graph.

1   Setting up an experiment

Different groups will have different angles and different photogate positions.

Set up the track to be sloped like a ramp as instructed. Each group in the class will have a different ramp angle. The angle is determined by which hole in the stand you use to attach the track.

Put two photogates on the track so that you can measure time for the ball. Plug the photogate closest to the top of the track into input A of the Timer and the other photogate into input B.

a. Look around the class and note which hole each group is using for its track. With your group, make a prediction as to which track will have the fastest ball.

b. Roll the ball down the track and record the time it takes to go from photogate A to photogate B.

c. Compare your results with other groups'. Did the times that everyone measured agree with your hypothesis about how the angle of the track would affect the ball's speed? Why or why not?

d. Is there a better way to test whether increasing the ramp angle makes the ball go faster? Explain how you would redo this experiment so the results make sense.

2   Variables in an experiment

Variables are the factors that affect experimental results. In Part 1, each group did the experiment by randomly placing the track at different places. The angle of the track was different for each group. That made it hard to compare results. In an experiment, you have to keep everything the same, and only change one variable at a time. If you change just one variable at a time, you can be confident any changes in the outcome of the experiment are caused by that one variable you changed.

a. What variables may affect the time it takes the ball to get from photogate A to photogate B? Use Table 1 to list all the variables discussed ZZby your group, or by the class.

Table 1: Variables that affect the time between photogates

Variable	Variable

11

Variables in an experiment

Variables in this experiment: distance between photogates, position of photogates, weight of the ball, starting point on the track, start technique, angle of the track, and friction.

Doing a controlled experiment

How will we control the variables?

Each group will vary only the angle of the track. All other variables should remain the same.

Finding the speed of the ball at different points along the track

Where does the ball move the fastest as it travels down the track?

Top?
Middle?
Bottom?

You can find the "instantaneous" speed of the ball by dividing the diameter of the ball (1.9 cm) by the time through one photogate.

2 We are trying to see if changing the ramp angle affects the speed of the ball. What do we need to do to make the experiment a fair test?

> We need to control the variables so all are the same except for the one we are testing (ramp angle).

> The students discovered the variables and now have a first-hand experience of their importance.

What are the variables that could affect the time we measured?

List the variables on the board. They include: distance between photogates, position of the photogates (top, middle, or bottom of ramp), weight of the ball, starting point on the ramp, start technique (push or no push), angle of the ramp (test variable) and friction.

3 Now that we have identified the variables that must be controlled, let's decide as a class how we will control each of the variables.

> Students should indicate that each group will have a different ramp angle, but that all other values will be kept the same. Make sure the entire class puts photogate A at the same position on the ramp, and photogate B at the same position on each ramp. Agree on a release technique, and everyone should use the steel ball, and start the ball against the peg at the top of the ramp.

Conduct the experiment again, controlling all variables except ramp angle, and compare your results with other groups. Do the numbers make sense now?

> Place the times on the board in the same table next to the times you collected in the uncontrolled experiment. The largest ramp angle will have the shortest time, as predicted. Lead the students through he discussion questions in Part 3.

4 Remember in the previous Investigation, when we pointed out that the ball's speed is not constant as it moves down the ramp? Do you think the ball moves fastest at the top, middle, or bottom of the ramp?

> Most students will predict that the ball moves the fastest at the bottom. However, a few students might suggest that it moves faster in the middle, because they are used to experiencing motion as a rider in a car or other vehicle, which hopefully slows down before it comes to a stop!

In previous Investigations of the ball's motion, we have measured average speed as the ball moves from one photogate to another. How can we measure an "instantaneous" speed with the photogates?

> Students should suggest that you could place the photogate at different positions on the ramp, and just record the time it takes the ball to break the beam of one photogate at a time. You can find the speed of the ball at this point on the ramp by dividing the diameter of the ball (1.90 cm) by the time it takes to break the beam of a photogate.

Collect and record position and time data for the ball by placing photogate A at many different positions along the track. Calculate the speed at each of these positions. For ease of comparison, each group should have their ramp at the same angle for this experiment.

> Students should place photogate A at many different positions on the track. It is helpful to vary the positions by the same amount, such as every 5 or 10 centimeters. Six data points is sufficient, but 10 is even better. The trickiest part of this experiment is to make sure that students are calculating the speed correctly (1.90 cm divided by the time at each position). Some students will incorrectly try to divide the position of the photogate by the time.

3.2 Observations of Motion

3 Doing a controlled experiment

In this part of the Investigation, you are going to repeat the time measurements of the ball. The difference is that all the variables are the same for all groups—except the angle of the track. In the table, record the values of the variables you control.

Table 2: Variables and values for a controlled experiment

Variable	Value	Variable	Value

1. Develop a good technique for rolling the ball down the track. You wan to complete at least three trials that are within 0.0005 seconds of one another.
2. Using your new technique and setup, record the time it takes the ball to travel from photogate A to photogate B.

Once you have your new results, compare them with the results of the other groups.

a. Did your times agree with your hypothesis of how they would change with the angle of the track?

b. In one or two sentences describe why this experiment was better or worse than your first experiment. Your answer should discuss the cause-and-effect relationships and variables.

c. It is often easy to confuse cause and effect. When we see something happen, we think up a reason for it happening but we do not always get the right reason. If you drop a piece of paper and a steel weight at the same time, which one hits the ground first? If the paper is flat, the steel weight always hits first. Why does the steel weight hit first? Is it because heavier objects fall faster, or is there another reason? In your answer, give at least one other reason a steel weight might fall faster than a flat sheet of paper.

4 Finding the speed of the ball at different points along the track

Time and distance measurements made with two photogates far apart tell you the *average* speed of the ball. To get more detail on how the speed of the ball changes as it moves, you need to measure the speed with one photogate. Remember, with one photogate the Timer measures the time that the light beam is broken. The track is designed so the light beam crosses the center of the ball. As the ball passes through the photogate, the light beam is broken for the diameter of the ball. The speed of the ball is its diameter (distance traveled) divided by the time it takes to pass through the light beam (time taken). This technique allows you to analyze how the speed of the ball changes because you can measure the speed at a specific place, and can make many measurements over the length of the track.

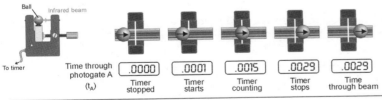

Speed = diameter (1.9 cm) ÷ Time through beam (t_A)

3 Example answers

Table 2: *Variables and values for a controlled experiment*

Variable	Value	Variable	Value
Angle	2, 4, 6, 8, 10	distance between photogates	30.5 cm
release technique	no pushing	mass	steel ball (28 g)
photogate position	25 cm and 55.5 cm	release point	top of ramp
friction	assumed the same		

3a. Yes, the times did agree with the hypothesis.

3b. This experiment was better because the variables were controlled and we were able to see that increasing the angle caused the effect of shorter times and faster speeds.

3c. The steel weight falls faster due to the buoyancy effect. The buoyancy of the paper in the air is the cause, and the effect is it floats slowly down to the ground. The steel weight is not affected as much and falls faster.

Table 3: *Speed, position, and time data*

Position of photogate A from top of track (cm)	Time from photogate A (sec.)	Distance traveled by the ball (1.9 cm)	Speed of the ball (cm/sec.)
10	0.0245	1.9	77.5
20	0.0177	1.9	107
30	0.0141	1.9	135
40	0.0124	1.9	153
50	0.0111	1.9	171

Graphing the results of the experiment

Make a graph of the speed of the ball versus its position on the track.

Independent variable - position of the ball on the track because we moved the photogate to different positions.

Dependent variable - time through the photogate because it depends on the position of the photogate on the track.

Plot independent variable on the x-axis and dependent variable on the y-axis.

Analyzing the data

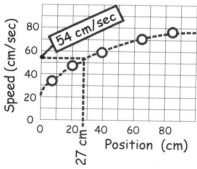

Use your graph to predict the speed of the ball at a position where you did not place the photogate. Make your prediction, test it, and calculate your percent error.

5 It is easier to see data trends when you create a graph. The purpose of this experiment was to see how the speed of the ball changes as it travels down the ramp. Knowing this was our goal, what two variables from your data table should you choose to place on your graph?

Students should see that it is important to graph the speed of the ball versus its position on the ramp. Which of these two variables would be considered the independent variable? Why?

The position of the ball is the independent variable, because we moved the photogate to different positions on the ramp.

Which variable belongs on the *x*-axis, and which variable will we place on the *y*-axis?

The independent variable, position, should be placed on the *x*-axis, and the dependent variable, speed, should be placed on the *y*-axis. Once data points are plotted, students should connect them with a smooth curve. The relationship between speed and position is not linear, and this will spark an interesting discussion. This particular graph is not often addressed in physics books, although it is useful, and lends itself well to data collection with one photogate.

What does your graph show about the speed of the ball?

Students will see that as the ball moves farther and farther down the ramp, the speed increases. The speed, relative to position, increases less and less as the ball moves down the ramp. (If we graphed speed versus time, we would see a linear relationship.) The speed versus position graph is useful for predicting the length of an airport runway. If you know the average speed a particular aircraft must achieve to guarantee liftoff, then you could determine from this type of graph how long the runway would need to be.

6 Your speed versus position graph provides an excellent model for predicting the speed of the ball on the ramp at positions other than those you actually measured. Suppose you did not measure the speed of the ball at the 27.0 cm position. How could you predict the speed at this position?

Students should suggest that they would use their graph to read the speed that corresponds to the 27.0 cm position.

Choose a position on your ramp that you did not actually measure in Part 4. Predict what the speed will be, and write that speed down. Roll the ball down the ramp, record the time, calculate the speed, and compare your measured result with your prediction.

7 This is a powerful part of the experiment. The goal is to show students how carefully collected and graphed data can be used to make accurate predictions.

How close was your prediction? Calculate the percent error.

Most students will have no more than 2 or 3 percent error. For fun, you could give the percent correct as the grade for the lab.

What would you be if you could predict the stock market to this degree of accuracy?

Most students answer "rich" and a few will recognize that you would also likely be under indictment!

Why can't you predict the stock market with 2 percent accuracy?

There are too many variables, and they cannot be controlled—at least, not legally! Despite this fundamental problem, stock analysts make their living doing exactly what the students have been doing: trying to identify cause-and-effect relationships in the data that allow them to make ANY kind of prediction that is based on data.

3.2 Observations of Motion

1. Select between five and 10 locations along the track to measure the speed of the ball. The places should be at regular intervals such as every 10.0 centimeters.
2. At each location record the position of the photogate and the time through the light beam. The distance traveled is the same for every position since it is the diameter of the ball.
3. Calculate the speed of the ball using the diameter (1.9 cm) and the time measurement. Record this value in the table.

Table 3: Speed, position, and time data

Position of photogate A (cm) from top of track	Time from photogate A (sec)	Distance traveled by the ball (1.9 cm)	Speed of the ball (cm/sec)

5 Graphing and analyzing the results

a. Do you notice a trend in your measurements? Does the speed of the ball change as it moves down?
b. Graph the speed of the ball versus its position. Place speed of the ball on the *y*-axis and position of photogate A on the *x*-axis. Add labels to each axis and title the graph.
c. What does the graph show about the speed of the ball?

6 Using your graph to predict the speed of the ball

a. Choose a spot on the track where you *did not* measure the speed of the ball.
b. Use your graph to find the predicted speed of the ball at that position. Record your predicted speed.
c. Use the speed formula to calculate the time it should take the ball to pass through the light beam at the predicted speed. For example, if the ball were going 100 centimeters per second, it would take .0190 seconds to pass through the beam (1.9 cm ÷ 100 cm/sec = .0190 sec).
d. Place the photogate at the spot on the track you chose in step (a) and record the time it takes for the ball to pass through the photogate.
e. How does the predicted time compare with the actual measured time? What does this tell you about your experiment and measurements?

7 Calculating percent error

a. Find the difference between the predicted time and the actual measured time.
   Predicted time – Actual time = Difference
b. Take this difference and divide it by the predicted speed and then multiply by 100.
   (Difference ÷ Predicted time) × 100 = Percent error
c. Use the percent error to calculate percent correct.
   100 – Percent error = Percent correct

13

5 6 7 Example answers

5a. Yes, there is a trend. The speed of the ball increases as it rolls down the ramp. The increases in speed seem to be lessening as the ball rolls down the ramp.

5b. Graph:

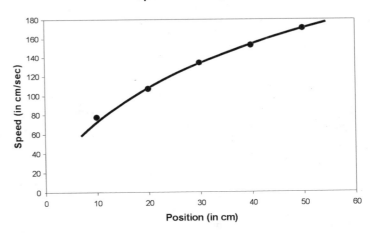

Speed vs. Position

5c. The graph shows that the speed is increasing, but by smaller and smaller amounts as the ball rolls down the track. The graph starts to get less steep and flatten out.

6a. Answers will vary. Example - 25 cm
6b. Prediction: 122cm/sec.
6c. 1.9 cm ÷122 cm/sec. = 0.0156 sec.
6d. Measured time - 0.0155 sec.
6e. The measured time was only 0.0001 sec. different from our prediction. The experiment and the measurements must be correct since our prediction was so accurate.

7a. 0.0156 - 0.0155 = 0.0001
7b. (0.0001/0.0156) x 100 = 0.64 %
7c. 100 - 0.64 = 99.36 %

3.3 Analyzing Motion with Graphs

Key Question: How do you model motion?

In physics, the word position means where something is compared with where it started, including direction. Distance is an interval of length without regard to direction. In this Investigation, students will use graphs to model position versus time and speed versus time for a ball moving with constant speed, or nearly constant speed. They will also be introduced to the idea that area on a graph has physical meaning. The area on the speed versus time graph is the distance traveled. Students will calculate distance from the area on the speed versus time graph and compare it with the actual measured distance.

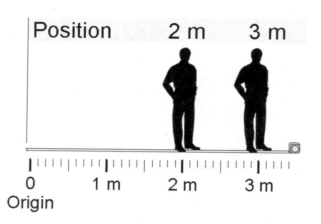

Reading Synopsis

Students read Section 3.3 Analyzing Motion with Graphs after the Investigation.

The chapter begins by explaining the distinction between position and distance. Consistent with Unit 1, all analyses are restricted to one dimension.

This chapter discusses the speed versus time and position versus time graphs and the relationship between the two. The interpretation of slope is explained with examples. The slope of the position versus time graph is the speed. The calculus technique of area under a graph is used to show how distance can be calculated from the speed versus time graph. Distance is equal to area on a speed versus time graph. This technique is used to show that the distance traveled during accelerated motion is one-half the product of the maximum speed multiplied by the time taken to reach the maximum speed (starting from rest). This result is important to deriving the equations for motion in one dimension developed in the subsequent chapter.

The Investigation

Leading Questions
- What can be learned from the position versus time graph?
- What can be learned from the speed versus time graph?
- What are the relationships between the speed versus time and position versus time graphs?
- What is the definition of slope and why is slope important?
- Is there a way to calculate the distance an object has traveled when you know the speed versus time graph?

Learning Goals

By the end of the Investigation, students will be able to:
- Set up a situation with constant speed motion.
- Model constant speed motion with a position versus time graph.
- Calculate speed from the slope of the position versus time graph.
- Use the speed versus time graph to calculate the distance traveled.

Key Vocabulary

position, origin, rate, distance, average speed, instantaneous speed, slope, rise, run

Setup and Materials

Students work in groups of four or five at tables.

Each group should have:

- Straight track with a threaded knob
- Cardboard shims to raise and lower the end of the track
- 3/4-inch steel ball
- Timer with photogates, AC adapter (or 9-volt battery), and cords to connect the photogates to the timer
- Physics stand
- Graph paper
- Meter stick

Details

Time One class period

Preparation You will need to make cardboard shims ahead of time, or have material on hand. Squares of corrugated and ordinary cardboard that are 2×2 inches are ideal. Each group will need four or five of each thickness. You will also need some blocks, books, or other objects to elevate the catcher end of the track about 4 inches.

Assignments Section 3.3 Analyzing Motion with Graphs in the **Student Edition** after the Investigation.

Skill Sheets 3.3A Analyzing Graphs of Motion Without Numbers
3.3B Analyzing Graphs of Motion With Numbers

Equipment Setup Straight track

Teaching the Investigation

1. Introduction
2. Position and distance
3. Setting up the experiment
4. Measuring the motion
5. Recording data in Table 1
6. Graphing and analyzing the data
7. Speed and the slope of a line
8. The speed versus time graph

Introduction

Science helps us predict the future based on observations and experimentation.

Today we will learn to predict the motion of the ball on the ramp.

Position and distance

Position - where you are compared with a reference point

Distance - an interval of length without regard to direction or a starting point

Setting up the experiment

Set the straight track in the lowest hole on the stand.

Set the steel ball in the middle of the track.

Adjust the height of the catcher, or the feet on the physics stand, until the ball can sit in the middle of the track without rolling in either direction.

Attach two photogates about a half-meter apart on the track.

Make the ball move at a constant speed by adjusting the angle of the track until the times in both photogates are the same.

Suppose someone were to ask you the usefulness of learning science. What would be your answer?

This is always a good question to ask a class. The answers vary from passing school, to making a lot of money, to understanding how things work.

Science is the way we predict the future and have reasonable confidence in being right. Science shows us how to observe the world and organize our observations into a form that allows us to predict what will happen next. For example, what would you be if you could accurately predict the weather?

Most students recognize that this would be a valuable skill.

The tools that are used to try to predict the weather were developed by science. Fortunately, the motion of rolling balls on ramps is easier to predict than the weather! This next Investigation will show you two new graphs that look at the motion of the rolling ball. Both graphs demonstrate techniques that you will apply to much of what we do over the rest of the course.

In physics, the word position means where you are compared with a reference point, such as where you started. Distance is an interval of length without regard to direction or starting point. For example, five meters is a distance. Five meters from here in this direction specifies a position.

Walk 5 meters in the classroom to illustrate the point that position is an identification of a point in space relative to an origin.

1 Set the track in the lowest hole of the stand. Find some wooden blocks, paper, or books to prop up the catcher until the track is nearly level. Set the steel ball in the middle of the track. If the ball rolls, then the track is not quite level yet. Adjust the height of the catcher, or the feet on the physics stand, until you can get the ball to sit still when you set it in the middle of the track. If the ball stays without moving, then the track is very close to level.

Students should set up the straight track using the diagram in step 1 of the Investigation for reference. Now attach two photogates about a half-meter apart. Photogate A should be close to the catcher and photogate B should be close to the stand. Release the ball from the top of the little hill near the catcher. Release the ball from the very end of the rubber track using your finger. Try to release it from the same place every time. If the ball is moving at constant speed, what should the times from the photogates be?

Students should answer that the times from the two photogates should be equal if the ball is moving at constant speed. If the track is perfectly level, then the speed at photogate B will be slightly less than the speed at photogate A because friction slows the ball as it moves.

What we want is to make the ball move at constant speed. That means the times at both photogates should be the same. Adjust the angle of the track to make the times the same.

Students should adjust the track to get the photogates to read approximately equal times. If the times are within 0.0002 seconds, it is good enough. If photogate B has the longer time, that means the catcher end of the track must be raised a little to slope the track down by raising photogate A. Students should shim up the catcher end of the track. If photogate A has the longer time, that means the track is sloped too steeply toward photogate B and therefore the catcher end must be lowered a little bit. Small squares of regular and corrugated cardboard make excellent shims for this activity because they provide about the right thicknesses to make adjustments.

UNIT I: Measurement and Motion

3.3   Analyzing Motion with Graphs

Question: *How do you model motion?*

In this Investigation, you will:

1. Set up a situation with constant speed motion.
2. Model the motion with a position versus time graph.
3. Calculate speed from the slope of the position versus time graph.
4. Use the speed versus time graph to calculate the distance traveled.

In physics, the word *position* means where something is compared with where it started, including direction. *Distance* is an interval of length without regard to direction. In this Investigation, you will use graphs to model the position versus time and the speed versus time for a ball moving with constant speed or nearly constant speed.

1   **Setting up the experiment**

1. The ball is going to roll from the catcher to the stand. Attach the track to the lowest hole on the stand as shown in the diagram.

2. Prop the catcher end of the track up on some books to make the track level.

3. Put photogate A near the catcher and photogate B nearer to the stand as shown.

4. Start the ball with one finger, releasing it gently from the start of the rubber track near the catcher. The ball rolls down the small incline and continues on the level part of the track.

5. Adjust the height of the catcher until the time through photogate A and the time through photogate B are within .001 seconds of each other. For example, 0.0262 and 0.0268 are acceptable because the difference is only 0.0006 seconds. Adjust the height using different thicknesses of props under the catcher end of the track.

When the times are equal, the ball is moving at constant speed.

a. Suppose the ball takes a longer time to pass through photogate B compared with photogate A. Should you raise or lower the catcher end to bring the times closer together?

b. After you get the track as level as you can, calculate the speed of the ball as it passes through each photogate. Remember, speed is the diameter (1.9 centimeters) divided by the time through the photogate. How close are the two speeds? Express your answer as a percentage of the speed through photogate A. For example, the speed at B might be 1 percent slower than the speed at A.

Setting up

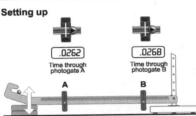

.0262
Time through photogate A

.0268
Time through photogate B

A   B

Adjust the angle of the track until the time through B is within +/- 0.0010 seconds of the time through A

Releasing the ball

1 2 **Example answers**

1a. *Raise the catcher end.*

1b. *Example response: A - 51.6 cm/sec.; B - 51.4 cm/sec*
    51.6 - 51.4 = .2 cm/sec
    0.2/ 51.6 = 0.4%
    The speed at B is 0.4% slower than the speed at A.

Table 1: *Position, speed and time data*

x (cm)	t_{AB} (sec.)	t_A (sec.)	t_B (sec.)	v_A (cm/sec.)	v_B (cm/sec.)
10	0.1639	0.0305	0.0301	62.3	63.1
20	0.3236	0.0303	0.0301	62.7	63.1
30	0.4862	0.0304	0.0302	62.5	62.9
40	0.6444	0.0303	0.0303	62.7	62.7
50	0.8035	0.0304	0.0303	62.5	62.7

14

Measuring the motion

Keep photogate A in one place.

Move photogate B at even intervals such as 10 centimeters.

To calculate the speed of the ball through a photogate, divide the distance (1.9 cm) by the time taken.

t_A = time through photogate A
t_B = time through photogate B
t_{AB} = time from photogate A to photogate B ·

Recording data in Table 1

The position is the distance between photogate A and photogate B.

Graphing and analyzing the data

What should the position versus time graph look like for this experiment?

It should be a straight line that slopes up to the right of the graph.

2 For the first part of the Investigation you want to make a position versus time graph. You will need both photogates for taking data. Set the first photogate (A) as close as you can to the bottom of the hill on the straight section of the track. Do not move photogate A once it is in place.

Students set photogate A.

Photogate B will be moved to different places along the track to observe the motion of the ball. It works best if you move photogate B in even intervals, such as 10 centimeters. How do we calculate the speed of the ball from the time it takes to pass through the photogate?

Students should answer that the speed of the ball is its diameter divided by the time it takes to pass through the photogate. Remind them that the diameter of the ball is 1.9 centimeters. To measure the time through the photogate, either the A light or the B light should be on, but not both.

We also need to measure the time it takes to get from A to B. How do we use the timer to make this measurement?

Students should recall that the timer displays the time from A to B when both the A and B lights are on. Remind them that they can make all three tiny measurements by turning lights on and off without having to roll the ball again. The timer measures t_A, t_B, and t_{AB} for each roll of the ball. The lights select which measurement is displayed.

3 Measure the three times and the position for at least seven or eight places along the track. The position is the distance between photogate A and photogate B. You will have to measure this distance with a meter stick or calculate it by subtracting the measurements on the track.

Students do the experiment and complete Table 1 with their data. You should walk around the room helping students make the measurements and checking that the data and calculations are correct. A common mistake is to calculate speed using the position and the time through a photogate instead of the diameter of the ball. If this happens the speed will be far too great. Another common mistake is to calculate the position incorrectly. The position is the distance between photogate A and photogate B. It is also useful to go through the definition of the variables in Table 1 on the board. At this point in the course, students are still getting used to writing variable names with subscripts.

4 Can anyone describe what the position versus time graph should look like for a ball rolling along the track at constant speed?

Start a discussion. Students should recognize that the graph should slope up to the right, showing that the position of the ball increases with time.

Should the graph be a straight line or a curve?

Discuss the motion. Since the ball has constant speed, the graph should be a straight line. If the ball were speeding up, it would cover each successive distance interval in a shorter amount of time and therefore the position versus time graph would be a curve. When the downhill experiment is done, that experiment will give students a curved position versus time graph.

Use your data to draw the graph of position versus time.

Circulate around the room and help students in drawing this graph. Because the position is defined from photogate A, which is also where $t = 0$, the graph should pass through the origin.

2 **Measuring the motion of the ball**

Running the experiment

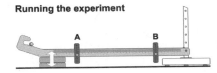

A

.0262

Time through photogate A should remain constant for each trial.

B

.0268

Calculate speed from the time through photogate B

$$v_B = \frac{1.9\ cm}{t_B}$$

The position of the ball changes with time as the ball rolls along the track. The first objective is to make a position versus time graph. You will use both photogates for this experiment.

1. Put photogate A on the level portion of the track near the bottom of the slope on the catcher end. Photogate A should be as close as possible to the 1-meter mark. Do NOT move photogate A once you set it in place. This is be the starting position, which is the position at time $t = 0$.

2. Put photogate B at different positions along the track. It is easiest to graph the data if you move photogate B in even intervals such as every 10 centimeters.

3. Release the ball and record the times from the photogates, as you did in Part 1 of the Investigation. Be careful to release the ball from the same place and use the same technique every time. If you roll the ball twice, your times should differ by less than 0.002 seconds.

4. Take measurements all along the track for each position of photogate B. Record the data in Table 1.

3 **Recording your data in Table 1**

x: **position:** Measure and record the distance from photogate A to photogate B in centimeters.

t_{AB}: **time from A to B:** This is the time it takes the ball to travel from A to B. Record the time from the Timer with both A and B lights on.

t_A: **time through A:** Record the time from the Timer with only the A light on.

t_B: **time through B:** Record the time from the Timer with only the B light on.

v_A: **speed at A:** This is the speed of the ball when it passed through photogate A. Calculate this by dividing the diameter of the ball (1.9 centimeters) by the time through photogate A.

v_B: **speed at B:** This is the speed of the ball when it passed through photogate B. Calculate this by dividing the diameter of the ball (1.9 centimeters) by the time through photogate B.

Table 1: Position, Speed, and Time Data

x (cm)	t_{AB} (sec)	t_A (sec)	t_B (sec)	v_A (cm/sec)	v_B (cm/sec)

15

---

3 **4** **Example answers**

4a. Graph:

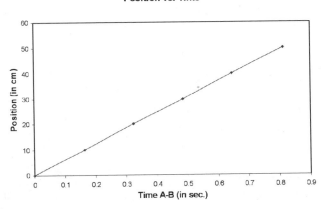

4b. The graph is a straight line.

4c. The slope is constant. This means the speed is increasing steadily (at a constant rate) as the ball rolls down the ramp.

4d. Graph:

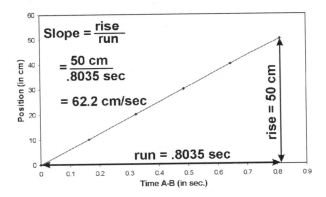

The slope of the line indicates a speed of 62.2 cm/sec. This value is very consistent (within 1%) with the speeds measured during the Investigation.

Speed and the slope of a line

Slope measures the steepness of a line. Slope is calculated by taking the rise (y-axis) divided by the run (x-axis).

Equation for slope:

$m = (y_2 - y_1) \div (x_2 - x_1)$

The slope of the position versus time graph is equal to the speed.

The speed versus time graph

Since the speed of the ball is constant, the speed versus time graph should be a straight line.

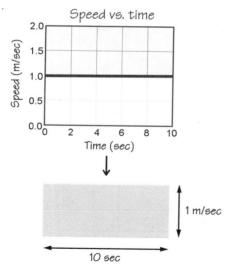

Distance travelled = area:
(10 sec x 1 m/sec) = 10 m

Can anyone recall the definition of slope from math class?

Start a discussion. Slope measures the steepness of a line. Slope is calculated by taking the rise divided by the run. The rise is the change in the vertical axis, or y. The run is the change in the horizontal axis, or x. You can write a formula for slope as $m = (y_2 - y_1) \div (x_2 - x_1)$ where m is the variable often assigned to slope in math courses.

What does the slope mean on the position versus time graph we just drew?

The rise is the change in position. The run is the change in time. Therefore, the slope is the change in position divided by the change in time. This is the definition of speed. This is an important result. The slope of the position versus time graph is the speed.

Calculate the speed of the ball from the slope of the position versus time graph.

Circulate around and help students to make this calculation.

Is there another way to calculate the speed of the ball over the entire distance? How should the speed compare with the speed you derived from the slope of the graph?

The second method for calculating speed is to take the distance between photogates divided by the time from photogate A to photogate B. Have students do this calculation and they should see that it gives the same result as the speed derived from the slope of the position versus time graph.

The next graph we wish to make is the graph of speed versus time. Can anyone suggest what this graph should look like?

The speed of the ball is constant. The graph should be a horizontal line which shows that the speed does not change with time.

Use your data to draw the speed versus time graph for the rolling ball.

Students draw the speed versus time graph.

Let's look at a clever trick we can do with the speed versus time graph. What is the area of a rectangle?

Students should answer that the area of a rectangle is the width times the height.

On the speed versus time graph, the width is the time. What does the height represent?

Height represents the speed of the ball.

Therefore the area on this graph between the line and the x-axis is equal to the time multiplied by the speed. Does anyone remember how to calculate the distance traveled if you know speed and time?

Students may remember that when motion is at constant speed, the distance traveled is the speed multiplied by the time.

That means the area on the speed versus time graph is the distance traveled! This is an important result. Area on the speed versus time graph is distance. When the area is measured between the line that shows the speed and the axis where $y = 0$, the distance is the distance traveled during the time used to calculate the area. Calculate the area of a rectangle on your speed versus time graph. Compare this area with the distance between the two photogates corresponding to the time that you chose.

Students should do the calculation and find that the area under the speed versus time graph is the same as the distance between the two photogates. The only tricky part of the calculation is recognizing that the distance is equal to the distance traveled from photogate A to the position of photogate B corresponding to the time they chose for the width of the rectangle.

3.3 Analyzing Motion with Graphs

4 **Graphing and analyzing your data**

a. Make a position versus time graph using your data. Plot the time from A to B on the *x*-axis and the position from A to B (position of photogate B) on the *y*-axis. At this point, do not connect the data points on the graph. Be sure to label the axes and title the graph.

b. Is the graph a straight line or a curve?

c. Does the graph get steeper as the ball rolls farther, or does the graph keep the same slope the whole way? What does your answer tell you about the speed of the ball at different times as it rolls along the track?

d. Draw a triangle on your graph and determine the rise and run from the triangle (see diagram). Calculate the speed from the slope of the graph. Is the value you get consistent with other speed measurements you have made with the ball and track?

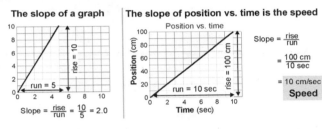

5 **The speed versus time graph**

a. Make a graph of speed versus time. Speed should be the speed at photogate B (v_B) since photogate B was the one that moved. Time should be the time from A to B (t_{AB}). Put speed on the *y*-axis since it is the dependent variable. Time goes on the *x*-axis because it is the independent variable.

b. Describe the graph; does it slope up or down? Is it level or nearly level? Is it a line or a curve?

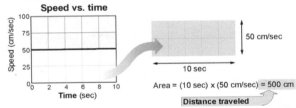

c. Remember, the distance traveled is the product of speed and time. Think about a rectangle drawn on the speed versus time graph. The width of the rectangle is the time. The height of the rectangle is the speed. Since *area* is width × height, the area on the speed versus time graph is the distance traveled.

Pick two times that correspond to measurements that are not right next to each other (see diagram). Draw the rectangle that lies between the *x*-axis, the line showing speed, and the two times you chose. Calculate the area of the rectangle. It should be the same as the distance between the two positions of photogate B.

16

---

5 **Example answers**

5a. Graph:

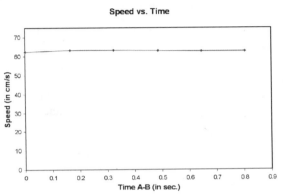

5b. The graph is nearly a level line.

5c. Two times; 0.1639 sec. and 0.4862 sec.
Total time = 0.4862 - 0.1639 = 0.3223 sec.

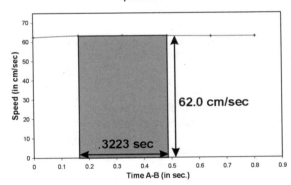

.3223 sec x 62.0 cm/sec = 20.3 cm
Distance traveled

The two speeds are 63.1 cm/sec. and 62.9 cm/sec.; the average of the two is 63.0 cm/sec.

0.3223 sec × 63.0 cm/sec = 20.3 cm

The calculated distance was 20.3 cm and the measured distance was 20.0 cm, a difference of only 1.5%.

4.1 Acceleration

Key Question: How is the speed of the ball changing?

In physics, acceleration is carefully defined. Acceleration is the rate at which speed changes. When a ball rolls down a ramp, it accelerates. The acceleration can be measured in several ways. In this Investigation, students make two different measures of acceleration. In the first experiment, acceleration is determined from photogate measurements of speed at two points and the time interval between the two points. Students calculate acceleration by taking the change in speed divided by the change in time. They observe that the acceleration is the same at different places on the track, even when the speed varies considerably. In the second part of the Investigation, students collect data and determine acceleration from the slope of the speed vs. time graph.

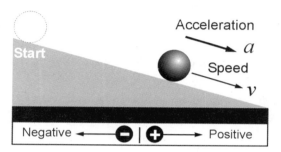

Positive speed and acceleration moving down hill

Reading Synopsis

Students read Section 4.1 Acceleration after the investigation.

The definition of acceleration is the rate of change in the speed of an object. Acceleration may be calculated by dividing the change in speed by the time interval over which the change occurs. Units of acceleration are m/sec^2. Acceleration may be positive or negative compared to speed.

Speed and acceleration are not the same. Constant speed means zero acceleration. Constant acceleration means the speed increases by the same amount in equal time intervals. An object may momentarily have zero speed, but non-zero acceleration.

The speed versus time graph for accelerated motion is a straight line which is not horizontal, but makes an angle with the x-axis. Acceleration is the slope of the line on the speed versus time graph. This definition is mathematically equivalent to calculating acceleration as the change in speed divided by the change in time.

The Investigation

Leading Questions
- How do you define acceleration?
- Where does acceleration fit in a description of motion?
- How are acceleration and speed different?
- How is acceleration measured and calculated?
- How does acceleration relate to the speed versus time graph?

Learning Goals

By the end of the Investigation, students will be able to:
- Observe how accelerated motion appears on graphs.
- Determine the acceleration of a ball through a calculation using speed and time.
- Determine the acceleration of a ball using the slope of a graph.

Key Vocabulary

acceleration, m/sec^2, Change in speed, meters/seconds, delta, constant acceleration, uniform acceleration

Setup and Materials

Students work in groups of four or five at tables.

Each group should have:

- Straight track ramp
- Two photogates
- Timer with photogates, AC adapter (or 9-volt battery), and cords to connect the photogates to the timer
- Physics stand
- Graph paper

Details

Time	⏲ One class period
Preparation	✏ None required
Assignments	📖 Section 4.1 Acceleration in the **Student Edition** after the Investigation.
Skill Sheets	4.1 Acceleration Problems
Equipment Setup	Straight track

Teaching the Investigation

1 Introduction
2 A common example of acceleration
3 Setting up
4 Looking at the data
5 Calculating acceleration from the slope of the line
6 Exploring further

Introduction

Acceleration is the rate of change of velocity.

60 mph - 0 mph/5 sec = 12 mph/sec

A common example of acceleration

Average Car;
60 mph - 0 mph/15 sec = 4 mph/sec
Each second the car's velocity increases by 4 mph.

Race car;
60 mph - 0 mph/5 sec =12 mph/sec
Each second the race car's velocity increases by 12 mph.

Setting up

Each group should keep the same ramp angle throughout the entire investigation.

Photogate A should be about 30 cm from the top of the track.

Place photogate A and photogate B 20 cm apart, and record the time through A, the time through B, and the time it takes to go from A to B.

1

What do you think the word acceleration means? Where is this word used?

> Discuss the meaning of acceleration. Common responses include words like "fast," "quick," "speed," and "power." The real definition of acceleration is the rate of change in velocity. For motion in a straight line, acceleration is the change in speed divided by the time it took for the speed to change.

High acceleration means rapid changes in speed; for example, zero to 60 mph in 5 seconds would be rapid acceleration. Slamming on the brakes and going from 60 to zero in 5 seconds is also rapid acceleration because the speed changes a lot in a short period of time. How would you use the word acceleration to describe the motion you observed in a car?

> This can be a discussion or a writing exercise. Have the students state or write a sentence applying the word acceleration to the motion of a car.

We calculate acceleration as the change in speed divided by the change in time. For example, an average car can go from zero to 60 in about 15 seconds. That means you step on the gas pedal, and 15 seconds later your speedometer reads 60 mph. Your acceleration is equal to the amount your speed changed (60 mph) divided by how long it took for the speed to change (15 seconds). The result is an acceleration of 4 mph per second. Your speed increases by 4 mph every second you hold the pedal to the floor.

A world-class racing car can go from 0 to 60 mph in 5 seconds. The acceleration of this car is 60 mph (the change in speed) divided by 5 seconds, or 12 mph per second. Both cars reach a top speed of 60 mph, but the racing car has higher acceleration.

> Go over the car example on the board.

The units for acceleration are units of speed divided by units of time. With a car the appropriate units are mph/sec since mph is a unit of speed and sec is a unit of time. In physics problems such mixed units are not used because they would lead to problems later when we get to force. When speed is in m/sec and time is in seconds, the units of acceleration work out to be m/sec per sec, which is often written m/sec^2.

> Demonstrate the cancellation of units to get m/sec^2 on the board. Emphasize the meaning of the unit as speed change per second, or m/sec per sec. There is no physical significance to a "square second" like there is to a square centimeter.

Can we measure the acceleration of the ball rolling down the track? What do we need to know? How can we measure the change in speed? How can we measure the change in time?

> Set up an example track as shown in the diagram in step 1 of the Investigation. Discuss how to measure speeds and times with the photogates. Write the equation for calculating the acceleration of the ball: acceleration = (speed at B − speed at A) ÷ time from A to B.

Set up two photogates, and test your new formula for calculating acceleration. To compare the data, everybody set the tracks up to the same hole (choose one). To get a good separation of speeds, keep the two photogates about 20 cm apart, but you can put them anywhere on the track. The data table has places to record your times and to calculate your speeds and acceleration.

> Circulate around the room, and assist any students who are having trouble. After students have made their calculations, have them write their data into the last column of the table. Write a few representative numbers on the board. Does everyone agree with the numbers on the board? If each student does the calculations with the numbers on the board they can check their work.

Teaching tip

While each individual group should keep the same angle throughout the investigation, it is interesting to have half the groups use one angle and the other half use a different angle. This can offer the opportunity to discuss with the class how changing the angle affects the acceleration based on data they collect.

Slight differences in speed and acceleration values seen for ramps with the same angle can often be due to the adjustable feet on the bottom of the wooden physics stand base. By turning the feet, minor height adjustments can be made which is key when performing investigations that require leveling the stand. Tables or lab stations in your classroom that are slightly out of level may also produce slight variations. The variations are subtle and will not affect the overall investigation.

UNIT I: Measurement and Motion

4.1   Acceleration

Question: How is the speed of the ball changing?

In this Investigation, you will:

1. Observe how accelerated motion appears on graphs.
2. Determine the acceleration of a ball through a calculation using distance and time.
3. Determine the acceleration of a ball using the slope of a graph.

What associations or meanings come to your mind when you hear the word *acceleration*? In physics, acceleration has a specific meaning. Acceleration is the rate at which speed changes. A ball accelerates as it rolls down a track. You can tell because the speed changes. In this Investigation, you will measure the acceleration of a ball and learn several techniques for finding acceleration.

 Setting up

To measure acceleration, you will set up the track to measure speed in two places. You can calculate acceleration by dividing the change in speed by the change in time.

1. Set the track up at an angle. Do not change the angle for the rest of the experiments.
2. Put photogate A about 30 centimeters from the top of the track and photogate B another 20-30 centimeters farther down.
3. Set the Timer in interval mode, and roll the ball through the photogates. Use Table 1 to record the three times, t_A, t_B, and t_{AB}.
4. Calculate the speeds at photogate A and B using the time it takes the ball to roll through the light beam in photogates A and B separately (t_A, t_B). Calculate the acceleration by dividing the change in speed by the time it takes the ball to get from photogate A to photogate B (t_{AB}). Record your calculations in Table 1.

$$acceleration = \frac{speed\ at\ B - speed\ at\ A}{time\ from\ A\ to\ B}$$

5. Move both photogates to at least two other places on the track and determine the acceleration again.

Table 1: 4Acceleration Data

	Trial I	Trial 2	Trial 3
t_A: time through A (sec)			
t_B: time through B (sec)			
t_{AB}: time A to B (sec)			
v_A: speed at A (m/sec)			
v_B: speed at B (m/sec)			
a: acceleration (m/sec^2)			

17

 Example data

Table 1: *Acceleration data*

	Trial I	Trial 2	Trial 3
t_A: time through A (sec)	0.0154	0.0154	0.0154
t_B: time through B (sec)	0.0111	0.0093	0.0082
t_{AB}: time A to B (sec)	0.1750	0.2810	0.3746
v_A: speed at A (m/sec)	123.4	123.4	123.4
v_B: speed at B (m/sec)	171.2	204.3	231.7
a: acceleration (m/sec^2)	273.1	287.9	289.1

Looking at the data

Speed vs. Acceleration

Acceleration is the rate at which speed changes.

$$acceleration = \frac{speed\ at\ B - speed\ at\ A}{time\ from\ A\ to\ B}$$

Precision

Time measurements for trials at the same location should vary by no more than 0.002 seconds.

Graphing the data

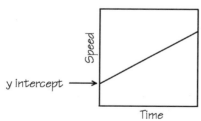

The y intercept is the speed of the ball at photogate A. Students can check their graphs against actual measurements.

2 Try measuring the acceleration at a different place on the ramp. How do the accelerations compare?

> The students should find that the acceleration is the same no matter where on the ramp they measure. This is very different from the speed. The speed changes while the acceleration stays the same.

Suppose you push the ball at the start of the track. What you think that will do to the acceleration farther down?

> Discuss this with students. Point out that once your finger it leaves the ball, it can no longer influence without motion therefore the ball should act as if you had not pushed it as far as acceleration is concerned. Have the students perform the experiment. They will find that the speed at both A and B are higher when the ball is pushed at the start but the acceleration is the same.

This is true because acceleration is the rate at which speed changes. This rate is determined by the angle of the ramp once the ball is rolling free of any other influence except gravity. Can you think of a way to change the acceleration?

> Discuss how changing the angle changes the acceleration because the closer the ramp is to vertical, the more gravity can act to pull the car down.

3
4 For the next part of the investigation we want to look at the speed of the ball at different places along the track. Set photogate A at the top of the track and do not move it for the remainder of the experiment. Photogate A will give us the starting time. Move photogate B to many positions along the track and measure the speed of the ball at each position. Record all of the time, position, and speed data in Table 2.

> Circulate around the room and assist students to make about measurements and recorded the data.

5 Make a graph of speed vs. time. On the vertical axis, plot the speed at photogate B. On the horizontal axis, plot the time from A to B.

> Circulate and help students make the graph of speed vs. time.

The acceleration of the ball can also be calculated from this graph. Remember slope is the ratio of rise over run. The slope of the distance vs. time graph was the speed, since speed is the change in distance divided by the change in time to move the distance. What is the slope of the speed vs. time graph?

> Prompt the students to discuss the application of the slope formula to the speed versus time graph. The graph shows speed on the y-axis and time on the x-axis. The slope of this graph is the change in speed over the change in time, which is the acceleration.

This is an important result: the slope of the speed vs. time graph is the acceleration because slope represents the change in the vertical axis (speed) divided by the change in The horizontal axis (time). What do you notice about the speed vs. time graph? Why do you think the graph looks this way?

> Unlike the distance vs. time graph, the graph should be linear. The graph is a straight line because the acceleration is the same everywhere on the ramp. If the acceleration is the same, the slope must be the same, and this means the graph is a straight line.

What is this point on the graph called? What does it mean for the ball on the ramp? What physical quantity is the *y*-intercept?

> Draw a graph of speed vs. time with a line and point to the y-intercept. Prompt the students until they can tell you the *y*-intercept is the speed of the ball at photogate A. This is because the time from A to B starts (at zero) when the ball rolls through photogate A. It is already rolling, so it has a speed that is not zero.

4.1 Acceleration

2 Looking at the data

a. If you moved the photogates to different places, the speeds for each of the three trials should be different from each other. Are the accelerations different? If so, by how much are they different between the three trials?

b. What would the acceleration be if you pushed the ball at the start? Would you expect it to be greater, less, or about the same compared with the acceleration you measured without pushing? Answer the question and then try it. You can give the ball a small push by rolling lightly with your finger at the start.
NOTE: Measure the acceleration a distance away from the start, so your finger does not get in the way.

c. Propose at least one way to *increase* the acceleration of the ball on the track.

3 The speed versus time graph

The speed of the ball changes with time as the ball rolls along the track. The next objective is to observe the speed versus time graph. You will use both photogates for this experiment.

1. Set photogate A near the top of the track (see diagram). Do NOT move photogate A once you set it. The position of photogate A is the initial position, which is the position at time, $t = 0$.
2. Set photogate B at different positions along the track. It is easiest to graph the data if you move photogate B in even intervals such as every 10 centimeters.
3. Release the ball and record the times from the photogates. You should be careful to release the ball from the same place and use the same technique every time. If you roll the ball twice, your times should differ by less than 0.002 seconds.
4. Take measurements all along the track for each position of photogate B. Record the data in Table 1.

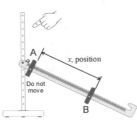

4 Recording position, speed, and time data in Table 2

x: **position:** Measure and record the distance from photogate A to photogate B in centimeters.

t_{AB}: **time from A to B:** This is the time it takes the ball to travel from A to B. Record the time from the Timer with both A and B lights on.

t_A: **time through A:** Record the time from the Timer with only the A light on.

t_B: **time through B:** Record the time from the Timer with only the B light on.

v_A: **speed at A:** This is the speed of the ball when it passes through photogate A. Calculate this by dividing the diameter of the ball (1.9 centimeter) by the time through photogate A.

v_B: **speed at B:** This is the speed of the ball when it passes through photogate B. Calculate this by dividing the diameter of the ball (1.9 cm) by the time through photogate B.

2a. The accelerations are close in value. They vary by at most 26 cm/sec^2 or 9%, and at least 1.2 cm/sec^2 or 0.4%

2b. The acceleration is about the same.

2c. The acceleration of the ball could be increased by increasing the angle of the ramp. (Both reducing air resistance by performing the Investigation in a vacuum and reducing friction between the ball and track would also increase the acceleration of the ball, but only to a very small extent.)

Table 2: *Position, speed, and time data*

x (cm)	t_{AB} (sec)	t_A (sec)	t_B (sec)	v_A (cm/sec)	v_B (cm/sec)
10	0.1160	0.0247	0.0174	76.9	109.2
20	0.1992	0.0247	0.0144	76.9	131.9
30	0.2719	0.0247	0.0124	76.9	153.2
40	0.3347	0.0246	0.0110	77.2	172.7
50	0.3888	0.0245	0.0100	77.5	190.0

Calculating acceleration from the slope of the line

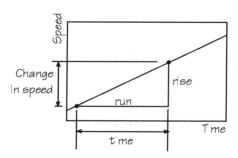

$$\text{slope} = \frac{\text{rise}}{\text{run}} = \frac{\text{change in speed}}{\text{change in time}}$$

$$= \text{acceleration}$$

Exploring further

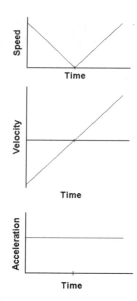

6 I want to look at how much the speed changes in one-tenth of a second. If I look here on the graph and also over here, how much does the speed change?

A straight line means the speed changes equal amounts in equal time intervals anywhere on the graph. Discuss this, and why a curved graph is different. With a curve, the speed might change different amounts in different places on the graph because the slope changes.

Take your data, and draw a big triangle to get the slope. The units for your slope correspond to the units on the y-axis divided by the units on the x-axis.

Circulate and help students draw the triangle and calculate the slope of the graph. The units of the slopes may be centimeters per second per second, or meters per second per second, depending on the distance and time units in which the data was collected.

How does your acceleration from the slope compare with the acceleration you measured earlier?

The accelerations should be similar.

Let's review what we have learned:

- Acceleration is a measure of how rapidly speed changes.
- Acceleration and speed are different quantities with different units.
- Acceleration is calculated as the change in speed divided by the amount of time taken for the speed to change.
- Acceleration is the slope of the speed vs. time graph, since this slope is another way to express the ratio of the change in speed compared with the change in time.

Is it possible to have acceleration but also have a speed of zero?

Start a discussion. Most students will not believe this is possible.

Suppose I start the ball rolling up the ramp with an initial speed by pushing it. Describe its acceleration to me everywhere along the motion.

This is a long discussion. The acceleration is the same no matter if the ball is traveling up or down. When the ball is traveling up its speed is decreasing. To talk about this correctly we need to be able to distinguish upward motion from downward motion. Suppose we assign positive numbers to any variable that points down the ramp. That means any quantity that points up the ramp is negative. When the ball is rolling up its speed decreases with time and its velocity (speed with direction) is negative. A negative velocity with a positive acceleration would result in the velocity getting closer to zero, and that is exactly what we see. The speed of the ball decreases, eventually becoming zero when it reaches its highest point and then increases steadily while it rolls back down. As soon as the ball begins to move down the ramp the velocity becomes positive. In every second, the same positive amount is added to the velocity of the ball. This constant increase in velocity is the value of the acceleration of the ball. Since the velocity increases as it rolls down the ramp we can say that it is a positive acceleration. This is a great way to show that speed is just a value without direction, while velocity and acceleration are values with direction. Can anyone propose an experiment to test whether the acceleration is the same going up or down?

Discuss and design the experiment with the students if you have time. It is a simple experiment to do. The photo gates must be reversed so a is about lower photo gate and be used to hire one. Though Ball is pushed to give it a small initial velocity sufficient to carry it through both photo gates. The tricky part is making sure that photogate A is not too close to the starting region where your finger is still pushing the ball, and B is not too close to the turn-around where the speed changes rapidly.

Table 2: Position, speed, and time data

x (cm)	t_{AB} (sec)	t_A (sec)	t_B (sec)	v_A (cm/sec)	v_B (cm/sec)

5 **Graphing speed versus time**

a. Make a speed versus time graph. Plot the speed at photogate B on the y-axis. Plot the time from A to B on the x-axis.

b. Is your graph a straight line or a curve?

c. The place on the speed versus time graph where the line crosses the y-axis is called the y-intercept. The y-intercept represents something about the ball. What does the y-intercept of your speed versus time graph represent? (Hint: The y-axis is speed.)

d. Does the ball accelerate as it rolls down the track? Justify your answer. Remember that acceleration is defined as a change in speed over time.

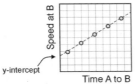

6 **Calculating acceleration from the slope of the line**

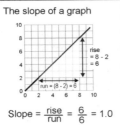

Slope = $\frac{rise}{run}$ = $\frac{6}{6}$ = 1.0

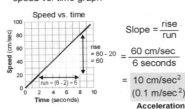

In a speed versus time graph, you are showing the change in speed over time. The slope of the speed versus time graph is equal to the *acceleration* of the ball (diagram above).

a. Using your speed versus time graph, calculate the acceleration of the ball from the slope of the line.

b. How does the acceleration from the slope compare with the acceleration you calculated from the times in Part 1 of the Investigation?

c. Is the acceleration of the ball changing as it moves down the track? Explain your answer using what you know about the slope of a straight line.

5a. Graph:

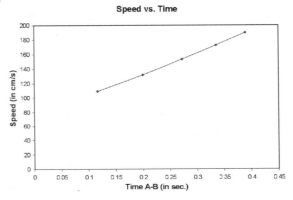

5b. The graph is a straight line.

5c. The y-intercept represents the speed at photogate A, and it matches almost perfectly.

5d. Yes, the ball accelerates. The speed increases over time. Since a change in speed over time is the definition of acceleration, this represents a positive acceleration.

6a. Graph:

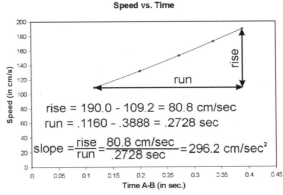

rise = 190.0 - 109.2 = 80.8 cm/sec
run = .1160 - .3888 = .2728 sec
slope = $\frac{rise}{run}$ = $\frac{80.8 \text{ cm/sec}}{.2728 \text{ sec}}$ = 296.2 cm/sec²

6b. The graph's slope is close to the calculated accelerations from Part 1, within 8.4% to 2.3%.

6c. Because the graph is very close to being a straight line, which indicates a constant slope, and the slope of the speed vs. time graph is acceleration, the acceleration seems to be constant.

4.2 A Model for Accelerated Motion

Key Question: How do we describe and predict accelerated motion?

This Investigation develops the analytical model for uniform accelerated motion. A derivation of the equations for uniform accelerated motion in a straight line is developed using area on the speed versus time graph to calculate the distance traveled. Students then measure the speed and position of a ball rolling down a ramp as a function of time. They see that the speed versus time graph is a straight line, described by an equation of the form $y = mx + b$. They deduce the initial speed and acceleration from the graph and then calculate the position of the ball using $x = x_0 + v_0 t + \frac{1}{2}at^2$. They compare the predicted position with the measured position to verify the theory.

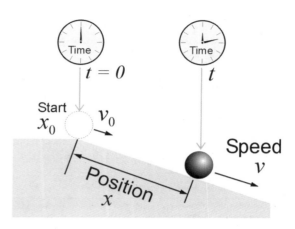

Reading Synopsis

Students read Section 4.2 A Model for Accelerated Motion after the Investigation.

Acceleration can be defined and calculated as $\Delta v/\Delta t$ or $(v_2 - v_1)/(t_2 - t_1)$. These equations can be rearranged to give $v = v_0 + at$. This is a model which describes the speed of an object under constant acceleration.

The distance traveled by an object in uniformly accelerated motion is $\frac{1}{2}at^2$ when the objects starts at rest. This is derived from the area of a triangle on the speed versus time graph. The formula is generalized to include initial speed and position to give $x = x_0 + v_0 t + \frac{1}{2}at^2$.

A model for uniformly accelerated motion includes two equations, one for speed and one for position. Together, the two equations link position, time, speed, and acceleration. Problem solving techniques are presented.

The Investigation

Leading Questions
- How do we predict where an accelerated object will be at a future time?
- Is there a formula that describes accelerated motion like $d = vt$ describes motion at constant speed?
- How do you get from a graph to formula?

Learning Goals

By the end of the Investigation, students will be able to:
- Use the equations for uniform accelerated motion to calculate the speed or position of a moving object when given the initial velocity, acceleration, and time.
- Identify acceleration and initial speed from the speed versus time graph.
- Describe the meaning of each of the terms in the two equations that make up the model for uniformly accelerated motion.

Key Vocabulary term, accelerated motion, model for accelerated motion

Setup and Materials

Students work in groups of four or five at tables. Each group should have:

- Straight track and marble
- Timer with photogates, AC adapter (or 9-volt battery), and cords to connect the photogates to the timer
- Graph paper

Teaching tip: Understanding the equations

The equation for the position of an object in accelerated motion is complex. While a physicist thinks it is easy, to a student it is imposing because there are so many variables, some with subscripts. It is a good exercise to go through the meaning of each variable or term in the equation with your students. The questions I ask are:

1   Q: What does this equation tell us?
    A: The position after time t.

2   Q: What is x_0?
    A: The initial position, when $t = 0$. Note, that x_0 is NOT the position where the motion itself starts. The initial position, x_0 is the position of the moving object at the time when the clock measuring t starts counting. This is an important distinction. In the experiment, x_0 is the position of photogate A since the t_{AB} clock starts when the ball passes photogate A.

3   Q: What is v_0?
    A: The initial speed, which is the speed of the object at the time, $t = 0$. The initial speed, v_0 may NOT be the speed the object has when the motion starts. In the experiment, the motion starts with zero speed at the top of the track, but the clock measuring time does not start until the ball crosses the light beam in photogate A. Therefore, the initial speed is the speed the ball has when it first breaks the light beam in photogate A.

4   Q: If I roll a ball uphill, starting from $x_0 = 0$, tell me which term is positive and which is negative, and why. I choose to define positive as uphill. (draw diagram)
    A: The term $v_0 t$ is positive because it represents the distance traveled uphill if there were no acceleration and the ball kept moving at the same (initial) speed. The term $\frac{1}{2} at^2$ is negative because the acceleration is downhill and the ball must slow down as it rolls.

Details

Time ⏲ One class period

Preparation 🖊 None required

Assignments 📖 Section 4.2 A Model for Accelerated Motion in the **Student Edition** after the Investigation.

Skill Sheets 4.2 Acceleration and Speed-Time Graphs

Teaching the Investigation

1   Introduction
2   The equations for accelerated motion in a line
3   Looking at the variables
4   Doing the experiment
5   Preliminary analysis
6   Testing the equations

Introduction

The equations for accelerated motion in a line

1

How do you calculate the distance a moving object travels while it is being accelerated?

Area of a triangle; A = 1/2 base x height

Distance traveled $d = v_0 t + \frac{1}{2} at$

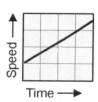

The graph of speed vs. time for an object with initial velocity. To calculate distance traveled we multiply the initial velocity by time and add the result to our first equation of 1/2 at². This adds the rectangular space under the triangle's area geometrically.

In the last few investigations we looked at graphical ways to analyze accelerated motion. We also know how to relate speed, acceleration, and time with a formula, $a = \Delta v / \Delta t$ or $(v_2 - v_1) \div (t_2 - t_1)$. We have another formula to relate speed, time, and distance for constant speed motion, $v = d/t$. Today we are going to put all the pieces together to get a formula which describes accelerated motion and relates all four variables: distance, speed, time, and acceleration.

The piece we are missing is how to calculate the distance a moving object travels while it is being accelerated. Can anyone remember the technique we used to determine the distance traveled from the speed vs. time graph?

> Review with students that technique of calculating the area on a graph. Draw the constant speed graph of speed vs. time as an example. Reminded them that this technique works when the x-axis represents zero speed, so the y-axis starts at zero. The technique does not work when the y-axis does not start at zero.

For accelerated motion starting from rest, the speed vs. time graph makes a triangle like this.

> Draw the speed vs. time graph in the upper diagram of the Investigation Step 1.

What is the area of a triangle?

> Students should know that the area of a triangle is one-half the base times the height.

The base of the triangle is time which we represented with the variable t. The height of the triangle is the speed which we represent with the variable v. The area is therefore $\frac{1}{2}vt$, which is one-half the distance you would have traveled had you gone at a constant speed v for the whole time. Does anyone remember how to relate the speed to the acceleration and time?

> Students should recall that $v = at$ for accelerated motion starting from rest.

We can now modify the formula we just derived to include the acceleration. The distance traveled in motion with constant acceleration that starts from rest is $d = \frac{1}{2} at^2$. We are almost where we want to be now. What happens if the motion starts with initial velocity v_0? What does the graph look like now?

> Sketch the graph which looks like the second graph in step one of the Investigation.

The distance traveled is still the area under the graph only now the area consists of two pieces. One piece is that triangle we just calculated. The second piece is a rectangle which has an area equal to the base times the height, which on our graph is the initial speed multiplied by the time, $d = v_0 t$. The total distance traveled is therefore $d = v_0 t + 1/2 \, at^2$. You can think of this formula in two pieces, or terms as we say in physics. The first term ($v_0 t$) represents the distance traveled at constant initial speed. The second term ($\frac{1}{2} at^2$) represents the additional distance traveled because the speed was increasing due to acceleration. If the acceleration is in a negative direction, then the second term will subtract from the total distance traveled.

> Work out the derivation and explanation of the formula on the board similar to the diagram on the bottom of step one of the Investigation.

To be completely general, we should add one more step. If we wish to describe the position of an object we need to rewrite the distance traveled in terms of the initial and final position. Mathematically we write that the distance traveled, d is the change in position, $x - x_0$, where x_0 is the initial position. Making this substitution into our formula gives us the final result we want. This formula tells us the position of an object which is under constant acceleration a, starting from initial position x_0, with initial speed v_0.

> Write down the final formula on the board: $x = x_0 + v_0 t + \frac{1}{2} at^2$

| 4.2 | **A Model for Accelerated Motion** | |

Question: How do we describe and predict accelerated motion?

In this Investigation, you will:

1. Find and test a theory that predicts the position of the ball from speed, acceleration, and time.

1 The equations for accelerated motion in a line

The speed versus time graph for uniform acceleration looks like the one on the right. The speed starts at zero and increases linearly with time. This is represented by the line $v = at$. The distance traveled (x) is the area of the shaded triangle between the line and the axis ($v = 0$). The area of a triangle is one-half the base times the height, meaning the distance traveled is $x = \frac{1}{2}at^2$.

Uniform Acceleration

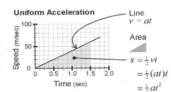

Line $v = at$

Area

$x = \frac{1}{2}vt$
$= \frac{1}{2}(at)t$
$= \frac{1}{2}at^2$

When there is an initial speed, the graph gets an extra rectangle on the bottom, and the equation gets an extra term. The distance traveled is the sum of a rectangle corresponding to constant (initial) speed plus a triangle for the extra distance traveled because of the increasing speed from acceleration.

Uniform Acceleration with Initial Speed

Line $v = v_0 + at$

Area

$x = v_0 t + \frac{1}{2}at^2$

The last thing to consider is position relative to a starting point. The graphs we just analyzed give us the distance traveled. Our position is where we start plus the distance we travel. The general equations for motion in a straight line allow for both an initial position (x_0) and an initial speed (v_0).

Understanding the equations

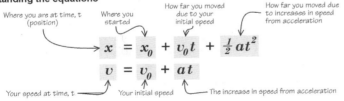

Where you are at time, t (position) | Where you started | How far you moved due to your initial speed | How far you moved due to increases in speed from acceleration

$$x = x_0 + v_0 t + \frac{1}{2}at^2$$

$$v = v_0 + at$$

Your speed at time, t | Your initial speed | The increase in speed from acceleration

20

2 3 Example answers

2a. $\quad x = x_0 + \dfrac{d_b}{t_A}t_{AB} + \dfrac{1}{2}a(t_{AB}^{\ 2}) \qquad v = \dfrac{d_b}{t_A} + at_{AB}$

2b.

$$\dfrac{v - v_0}{t} = a \qquad \dfrac{\dfrac{d_b}{t_B} - \dfrac{d_b}{t_A}}{t_{AB}} = a \qquad a = \dfrac{t_A - t_B}{t_A t_B t_{AB}}d_B$$

Table 1: Experimental data

Initial position (x_0, m)	Position (x, m)	Time A (t_A, sec)	Time B (t_B, sec)	Time A to B (t_{AB}, sec)	Speed B $(v_B, m/sec)$
0.05	0.15	0.0342	0.0202	0.1415	0.94
0.05	0.25	0.0339	0.0156	0.2354	1.22
0.05	0.35	0.0338	0.0132	0.3111	1.44
0.05	0.45	0.0342	0.0116	0.3793	1.64
0.05	0.55	0.0340	0.0104	0.4366	1.83
0.05	0.65	0.0340	0.0097	0.4909	1.96
0.05	0.75	0.0341	0.0089	0.5407	2.13
0.05	0.85	0.0337	0.0084	0.5858	2.26
0.05	0.93	0.0345	0.0080	0.6246	2.38

4a. Graph:

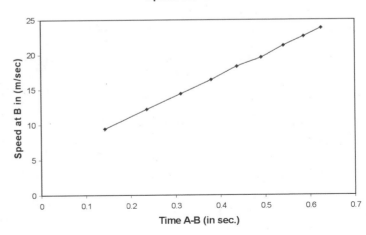

Speed vs. Time

Looking at the variables

Each variable in the acceleration formulas has meaning.

$$v = v_0 + at$$
$$x = x_0 + v_0 t + \tfrac{1}{2} at^2$$

v	Speed (m/sec)	x	Position (m)
v_o	Initial speed (m/sec)	x_o	Initial position (m)
a	Acceleration (m/sec²)	t	Time (sec)

Doing the experiment

Consistent release technique is very important for reliable results.

Preliminary analysis

The straight line formula of y = mx + b matches perfectly with our derived formula of v = at + v₀

The speed vs. time graph should be a straight line because the slope of the line is the acceleration which is constant due to gravity.

2 That was the difficult equation to find. The other one relates speed, initial speed, and acceleration. This one is really just rearranging the definition of acceleration.

Show that $a = (v - v_0) \div t$ can be rearranged to give $v = v_0 + at$.

Now we have a pair of equations that can tell us the speed and position of an object in accelerated motion at any time, t.

Write both equations on the board.

We are going to applying these two formula to the motion of the ball rolling down the track. Set the track at an angle with photogate A near the top. As before, photogate A stays fixed in position and serves as the reference point where $t = 0$. What are the variables x, x_0, v, v_0, and t in terms of the experiment?

Carefully go through the experimental meaning for each of these variables. This should be done slowly and repeated in the hope that most students will grasp the connection between each quantity measured by the real experiment and its corresponding variable. It is excellent practice for learning how to solve physics problems where identifying the information given in the problem is often the most difficult part. The answers are on the right.

Derive a formula for the acceleration that involves only the three times measured by the timer and the diameter of the ball.

You will likely have to assist students with this, even though it comes straight from the definition of acceleration. The result is on the right.

3 Follow the instructions in step 3 and collect data for at least six different positions of photogate B. Record your data and calculations in Table 1.

Students take the data. This data is the same as was taken in the last Investigation. This time however, have all the groups set their tracks at the same angle so you can compare results.

4 Use the data from Table 1 to make the speed vs. time and position vs. time graphs for the ball. Make the scale on the x and y axes start from zero. For the time axis use the time from photogate A to photogate B. Describe what the graphs look like. Which is a line and which is a curve?

The speed vs. time graph should be a straight line and the position vs. time graph should be a curve.

Does anyone remember the equation for a straight line from math class?

A straight line is usually given by the formula **y = mx + b** in math textbooks. Write this formula on the board.

The speed vs. time graph is a straight line therefore should be described by a equation of this form. What we have to do is identify what y, m, x, and b are our the experimental variables. What do the variables y, m, x, and b mean in terms of our speed versus time graph? What is y? What is x?

Y is the speed, v; x is the time t; m is the acceleration, a; and b is the initial speed v_0. Rewrite the equation of the line in variables from the experiment to get $v = at + v_0$, the equation we already have!

This is exactly the equation we already have relating speed, time, and acceleration. Now you see that the equation is not really a law of physics, but a way of saying the speed vs. time graph is a straight line. In fact, the equation does NOT work if the speed vs. time graph is not a straight line. The condition which makes the speed vs. time graph linear is that the acceleration is a constant. The equations we are working with are known as the equations for uniformly accelerated motion. In physics, the word "uniform" is another way to say constant. Uniform acceleration means constant acceleration.

2 **Planning the experiment**

a. Write down the equations for uniform accelerated motion in one dimension using the following variables. Let:
- t be the time since the ball passed through photogate A (t_{AB}).
- x_0 be the position of the ball at time $t = 0$ (at photogate A).
- v_0 be the speed of the ball at time $t = 0$ (speed at photogate A).
- v be the speed at time t (speed at photogate B).
- x be the position of the ball at time t (position of photogate B).
- a be the acceleration of the rolling ball.

b. Derive an equation for the acceleration of the ball in terms of the three times (t_A, t_B, t_{AB}) and the diameter of the ball (d_B). These are all quantities you can measure directly.

3 **Doing the experiment**

1. Set photogate A a few centimeters in front of the ball when the ball is at the start of the track. Photogate A will stay fixed in one place for the whole experiment.
2. Set photogate B down the track from photogate A. You will move photogate B to different positions to make measurements.
3. Move photogate B to at least six different places on the track. Use Table 1 to record the position and time data you measure for each position of photogate B. Your positions should cover the whole track.
4. Calculate the speed of the ball for each position of photogate B. Record the results of your calculations in the last column of Table 1.

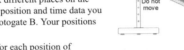

Table 1: Experimental data

Initial position (x_0, m)	Position (x, m)	Time through gate A (t_A, sec)	Time through gate B (t_B, sec)	Time from A to B (t_{AB}, sec)	Speed at gate B (v_B, m/sec)

4 **Example answers**

4b. Graph:

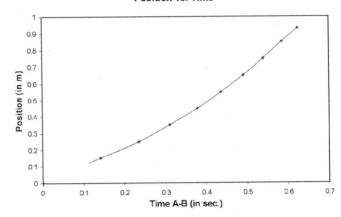

4c. $y = mx + b$ $v = at_{AB} + v_0$

$$v = \frac{\left(\dfrac{d_b}{t_B} - \dfrac{d_b}{t_A}\right)}{t_{AB}} t_{AB} + v_0$$

4d. $V_0 = 5.5$ m/s $a = 2.98$ m/sec^2

$y = v$ $m = a$ $x = t_{AB}$ $b = v_0$

4e. Answers are:

0.25:
$$\frac{\left(\dfrac{d_b}{t_B} - \dfrac{d_b}{t_A}\right)}{t_{AB}} = a \qquad \frac{\left(\dfrac{.019}{.0156} - \dfrac{.019}{.0339}\right)}{.2354} = 3.05 \ \frac{m}{sec^2}$$

0.35:
$$\frac{\left(\dfrac{d_b}{t_B} - \dfrac{d_b}{t_A}\right)}{t_{AB}} = a \qquad \frac{\left(\dfrac{.019}{.0104} - \dfrac{.0--19}{.0340}\right)}{.4366} = 2.98 \ \frac{m}{sec^2}$$

0.45:
$$\frac{\left(\dfrac{d_b}{t_B} - \dfrac{d_b}{t_A}\right)}{t_{AB}} = a \qquad \frac{\left(\dfrac{.019}{.0084} - \dfrac{.019}{.0337}\right)}{.5858} = 2.90 \ \frac{m}{sec^2}$$

Preliminary analysis (continued)

Testing the equations

5

Table 2: Predicted and measured positions

Time (sec)	Pred. pos. (x, m)	Meas. pos. (x, m)
0.1415	0.159	0.15
0.3111	0.367	0.35
0.4909	0.683	0.65
0.5838	0.889	0.85

Use your speed versus time graph to determine the variables v_0 and a. Uses a formula you derived in Part 2b to calculate the acceleration for several data points. Compared the calculated acceleration with the acceleration you determine from the slope of the speed vs. time graph. Which is a more accurate way to measure acceleration?

> The slope is a more accurate measurement because it is based on a straight line that represents all of the data points. A calculation uses only one data point and is therefore subject to more error.

Drawing the best fit line on a graph is a way of representing the average pattern in a set of the data. The average of a set of a data is typically more accurate than any single point.

Once you know the variables v_0 and a, you can calculate where the ball should be on the track at any time. To make the prediction easier, what is x_0?

> The initial position, x_0 is the position of photogate A.

Use of the formula for the position of an object in uniform accelerated motion to calculate the predicted position of the ball at each value of the time from A to B. Write the results of the calculation in Table 2.

> Have students do the calculations. They are using the formula to (essentially) calculate the position of photogate B which they can then compare with the actual position. This type of comparison is how scientific models are evaluated. The theory they are testing is that the motion of the ball on the track is uniform accelerated motion.

Plot the calculated points on the same position vs. time graph as the measurements you made. This time you can connect the dots with a solid curve because of the formula predicts the entire curve. If you need a few more points you may calculate them for some other times in between. How does your calculated theory compared with the actual measured data?

> The comparison should be very close, typically within a few percent. If the curves are different check that students have included the correct initial position. A very accurate graph will even show a consistent offset of 1 cm between predicted and actual positions. The offset comes from the way that time work measures times. The time from A to B is measured from the front edge of the ball. The time through the photogate essentially determines the speed at the center of the ball. That means that speed measurements are out of sync with the time measurements by half the diameter of the ball, a distance of 0.95 centimeters.

A correct physical theory accurately predicts the results of experiment. We used a theory to predict the position vs. time graph, which was an experimental result we could compare with the prediction. What was the theory we were testing in this experiment?

> That the motion of the ball on the track was uniformly accelerated motion.

Is the theory confirmed by experiment?

> Yes.

What would we do if the theory did not agree with the experiment?

> First, carefully repeat the experiment to make sure we had accurate data. Then, if the theory was still not in agreement, we would have to modify the theory.

In science, nature is the ultimate judge of truth. If a theory cannot describe what actually happens then the theory must be incorrect. What happens is real. A theory is a human invention.

4.2 A Model for Accelerated Motion

4 **Preliminary analysis**

a. Use the data from Table 1 to make the speed versus time graph for the ball. Scale the graph so it starts from zero speed and zero time. The time axis (x) should be the time from photogate A to photogate B. The speed axis (y) should be the speed at photogate B.

b. Use the data from Table 1 to make the position versus time graph for the ball. Scale the graph so it starts from zero position and zero time. The time axis (x) should be the time from photogate A to photogate B. The position axis (y) should be the position of photogate B.

c. The equation of a straight line is often given in the form $y = mx + b$. The variable m is the slope and the variable b is the y-intercept. The speed versus time graph should be a straight line; therefore, the equation should apply. Rewrite the equation for a straight line for the speed versus time graph using appropriate variables from the experiment (v, v_0, x, x_0, t_{AB}, and so on). Make a table that shows how y, m, x, and b correspond to the real experimental variables.

d. From your graph of speed versus time, estimate the initial speed and acceleration.

e. Use your formula derived in Part 2b to calculate the acceleration of the ball for a few different measurements. Compare your calculation with the value you estimated from the graph.

5 **Testing the equations**

The equations of uniform accelerated motion provide an accurate model for predicting the position of the ball on the track once you know the initial position, initial speed, and acceleration. However, like most simple models in physics, the equations are only *approximately* true under laboratory conditions. For example, factors such as friction are not included.

a. Calculate the position of the ball from the equations for uniformly accelerated motion. Use Table 2 for the results of your calculations. You need to use the initial speed, initial position, and acceleration you estimated from the speed versus time graph. Do the calculations for the same times (from A to B) as your measured data.

b. Plot the calculation on the same graph as your measured data for position versus time. You can draw the calculation as a solid line on the graph since the equation predicts the entire curve. The experimental data should be left as unconnected dots.

c. How do your measured positions compare with the positions predicted by the equation?

Table 2: Predicted and measured positions

Time (sec)	Predicted position (x, m)	Measured position (x, m)

d. Use the equation for uniform accelerated motion to calculate how long the track would have to be for the ball to reach a speed of 60 miles per hour.

5 **Example answers**

5a. Complete Table 2 using the following equation:

$$x = x_0 + \frac{d_b}{t_A}t_{AB} + \frac{1}{2}a(t_{AB}^2)$$

5b. Graph:

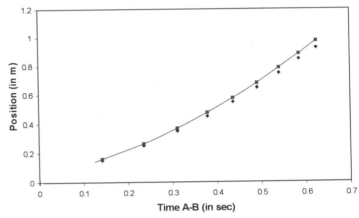

Position and Predicted Position vs. Time

5c. The measured distances are consistently shorter than the predicted distances. The effects of friction and air resistance must have slowed the marble slightly so it didn't move as far down the track as predicted.

5d. 60 mph = 27.8 m/sec, but we'll need to find t_{AB} from 4c,

$y = mx = b$, so $v = at_{AB} + v_0$

$$27.8 = 2.98at_{AB} + 5.5 \qquad 27.8 - 5.5 = 2.98at_{AB}$$

$$\frac{27.8 - 5.5}{2.98} = t_{AB} = 7.5 \text{ sec}$$

With that information we can use the position prediction formula and an average value for t_A from the data table

$$x = x_0 + \frac{d_b}{t_A}t_{AB} + \frac{1}{2}a(t_{AB}^2)$$

$$x = .05 + \frac{019}{.0340}7.5 + \frac{1}{2}2.98(7.5^2)$$

$$x = 88.1 \text{ m}$$

The ramp would have to be 88.1 m long for the ball to reach 60 mph.

4.3 Free Fall and the Acceleration due to Gravity

Key Question: How do you measure the acceleration of a falling object?

Free fall is how physicists describe motion under the influence of gravity only. The acceleration of an object in free fall is not easy to measure accurately with a hand-operated stopwatch. In this Investigation, students use two photogates to measure the time it takes a ball to fall a known distance. The acceleration is estimated by assuming it is constant, so $a = 2y \div t^2$ where y is the drop distance and t is the time of flight. The students then use an iterative calculation to correct for the initial speed of the ball passing through the first photogate. The iterative calculation typically results in an experimentally determined value for g within 1% of the published value of 9.82 m/sec^2.

Reading Synopsis

Students read Section 4.3 Free Fall and the Acceleration due to Gravity before the Investigation.

An object is in free fall if it is moving only under the influence of gravity. The symbol g is used to represent the acceleration due to gravity. Freely falling objects accelerate at the rate of 9.8 m/sec^2 on Earth. The value of g depends on the distance from the center of Earth

The motion of an object in free fall can be described using the equations for speed and position. The value of g is substituted for the acceleration, a. The speed of an object that is dropped or thrown downward will increase by 9.8 m/sec each second. The speed of an object thrown upward will decrease by 9.8 m/sec each second.

The acceleration due to gravity does not depend on the mass of the object that is falling. Objects do accelerate differently when influenced by friction from air resistance. The maximum speed at which an object can fall when limited by air resistance is called the terminal speed.

The Investigation

Leading Questions
- What is free fall?
- How does gravity affect the speed of a falling object?
- How can the acceleration due to gravity be measured?
- How close does a real object in free fall come to accelerating at the theoretical value of 9.8 m/sec^2?

Learning Goals

By the end of the Investigation, students will be able to:
- Describe a method for measuring the acceleration due to gravity.
- Use the equation that relates distance, time, and acceleration of an object in free fall.
- Suggest ideas for measuring the acceleration due to gravity more accurately.

Key Vocabulary gravity, acceleration, free fall, g

Setup and Materials

Students work in groups of three to five at tables.

Each group should have:

- Timer with photogates, AC adapter (or 9-volt battery), and cords to connect the photogates to the timer
- Plastic ball
- Steel ball
- Physics stand
- String with steel ball on end (from colliding pendulum exp.)
- Meter stick
- Calculator

Details

Time   One class period

Preparation   Students should have prior experience using the equation for the distance traveled by an object with constant acceleration.

Assignments   Section 4.3 Free Fall and the Acceleration due to Gravity in the Student Edition before the Investigation

Skill Sheets   4.3 Acceleration due to Gravity

Teaching the Investigation

1   Introduction
2   Setting up the experiment
3   A technique for dropping the ball from the right place
4   Determining g from experiment
5   Analyzing the data
6   Analyzing the data
7   Free fall and mass

Introduction

In this chapter we have been discussing motion with uniform acceleration, that is, motion for which the acceleration stays the same. Can anyone defined what I mean by the term constant acceleration? How does the velocity change under constant acceleration?

> Review the definition of acceleration with students. Constant acceleration means the velocity increases by the same amount every second.

One out of the most important examples of constant acceleration is free fall. In free fall and object tax under the influence of only gravity. If I throw this eraser up into the air, the moment it leaves my hand it is in free fall. That doesn't mean it is falling down! To a physicist, free fall means any motion where the only important force is gravity and the motion is determined completely by the initial velocity and gravity.

> Toss the eraser up into the air to illustrate the point. Free fall does not mean downward motion like the usual definition of the word "falling."

Setting up the experiment

1

In this Investigation, you will be measuring the acceleration of an object in free fall. It is important that you work carefully to get good results. At the end of the Investigation, you will find out how accurate you were. The first step is to level the physics stand. You will be using the string with the steel ball on the end as a plumb line. Place the physics stand on the floor and hold the string in front of its holes. The string should hang straight through the center of the holes and stay the same distance from the pole along its length. If the stand isn't level, adjust its legs by twisting them.

Setup instructions:

1. Level the physics stand using the plumb line.
2. Connect the photogates at the 7th and 17th holes, measured from the bottom. Upper photogate is A and lower is B.
3. Make sure both A and B lights on the timer are lit.

> Demonstrate the use of the plumb line to level the stand. The stand should be level in both the left-right direction and in the front-back direction.

Connect the photogates at the 7th and 17th holes, measured from the bottom. Connect the upper photogate to input A on the timer. Connect the lower photogate to input B. Set your timer to interval mode so it will read the time from photogate A to photogate B. Press buttons A and B so both lights are lit.

A technique for dropping the ball from the right place

2

> While students are connecting the photogates, check to see that they all properly leveled their stands.

Carefully measure the distance between the 7th and 17th holes on the stand. Record the distance in meters.

> Make sure students correctly convert from centimeters to meters. The distance between the holes is exactly 0.50 m.

Measure the distance between the photogates.

Hold the ball so it is just about to break the beam in photogate A then drop it so it falls through both photogates.

One group member should catch the ball at the bottom.

Take a close look at the inside of one of the photogates. You should see two holes facing each other. These holes are where the infrared beam is emitted and detected. Slowly move the plastic ball down through the first photogate and then through the second one. What happens?

> The timer starts when the ball passes through the first photogate and stops when it passes through the second one.

Slowly move the ball through the upper photogate and determine the exact spot where it just starts to break the beam. Hold the ball so it is just about to break the beam and then drop it so it falls through both photogates. One group member should catch it at the bottom. Take several practice runs to perfect your technique. It is important that you drop the ball without pushing it, and that it starts where it is just about to break the beam. It is also necessary to catch the ball at the bottom so it doesn't bounce back up through the bottom photogate.

> Circulate around the room and point out the holes from which the infrared beam is emitted and detected.

UNIT I: Measurement and Motion

4.3 Free Fall and the Acceleration due to Gravity

Question: How dawo you measure the acceleration of a falling object?

In this Investigation, you will:

Measure the time it takes a ball to fall a specific distance.

1. Calculate the acceleration due to gravity.
2. Compare your experimental value of acceleration to the theoretical value.

Gravity causes objects to accelerate as they fall down. In fact, the definition of *down* is "the direction objects fall." An object is in *free fall* if it is moving under the influence of only gravity. For example, when you drop a ball, it is in free fall from the time it leaves your hand until it hits the ground. A ball thrown upward is also in free fall because once it leaves your hand its motion is determined by the influence of gravity. In this Investigation, you will study how gravity affects the motion of objects in free fall. You will measure the time it takes a ball to fall a certain distance. The time measurement will allow you to determine the acceleration due to gravity.

1 Setting up the experiment

1. This Investigation should be done with the physics stand on the floor and with the pole as perfectly vertical as you can make it. Use one of the steel balls on a string to set the pole. Hold the string atop the physics stand and adjust the leveling feet until the string hangs down the center of the pole and maintains a constant distance from the pole.

2. Attach two photogates to the stand so they are at least 0.5 meters apart. Make sure the bottom of the "U" is against the pole.

3. Connect photogates A and B to the Timer so photogate A is above photogate B. Set the Timer to interval mode.

Centered   Parallel

When the pole is vertical, the string is centered and parallel

2 A technique for dropping the ball from the right place

1. Measure and record the distance between the photogates to the nearest millimeter. Use the small dimples on each photogate to make your measurement. These dimples mark the position of the light beam.

2. Examine the photogates and locate the two small rectangular openings where the infrared beam is emitted and detected. Hold the ball so it is above the top photogate, directly in line with the center of the two openings. Slowly move the ball down until it breaks the beam of the photogate and the indicator light on the photogate changes from green to red. It is important that you find the location where the bottom of the ball just starts to break the photogate beam.

3. Once you have found the place where the ball just breaks the beam, hold the ball so that it is slightly above that location. The ball should be out of the beam but as close to the beam as possible. Press the reset button on the Timer. Carefully release the ball *without giving it a push*. Allow it to fall to the bottom of the stand where one group member should catch it.

Dropping the marble from photogate A

23

"g" force and the acceleration of cars

Performance claims for cars and airplanes are often expressed in terms of "g's". An acceleration of 9.8 m/sec^2 is one "g". An acceleration of 19.6 m/sec^2 is 2 g's, and so on. A car accelerating forward at 1 g pushes your body forward with a force equal to your own weight. That is the force you feel pressing you into the seat.

An advertisement for a powerful sports car claims the car can go from zero to 60 miles per hour in four seconds. This claim is all about acceleration. A speed of 60 mph is equal to 26.8 m/sec. The car's average acceleration is 6.7 m/sec^2 (26.8 m/sec ÷ 4 sec). This is about 0.68 g's. If you weighed 100 pounds, you would feel a force of 68 pounds against your back, accelerating you forward with the car (more about this next chapter!).

6.7 m/sec^2

2.2 m/sec^2

1.3 m/sec^2

An average car accelerates from rest to 60 mph in 12 to 20 seconds. At 12 seconds, the acceleration is 2.23 m/sec^2 (0.23 g). At 20 seconds, the acceleration is 1.34 m/sec^2 (0.14 g).

The practical limit for cars is 9.8 m/sec^2. Greater acceleration than this would take a force greater than the force of gravity holding the car down to the road.

Determining g from experiment

3

Explain the theory behind the experiment.

$y = y_0 + v_0 t + 1/2gt^2.$

(equation 1) $\quad g = \dfrac{2h}{t_{AB}^2} - \dfrac{2v_0}{t_{AB}}$

(equation 2) $\quad g = \dfrac{2h}{t_{AB}^2}$

(equation 3) $\quad v_0 = \dfrac{d}{t_A} - \dfrac{gt_A}{2}$

In an iterative calculation, each repetition (iteration) generates a correction that makes the next calculation more accurate.

To get an accurate measure of *g* we are going to measure the time it takes the ball to fall from photogate A to photogate B. We can measure this distance quite accurately, at least to a millimeter. We can use the formula for distance in accelerated motion to calculate the acceleration of gravity from experimental measurements of time a nd distance. What is the equation that relates time, distance, and acceleration for an object in free fall?

The equation is $y = y_0 + v_0 t + 1/2gt^2$. Write this equation on the board.

For convenience, I will choose the positive direction to be down since both speed and acceleration are down. This gets rid of negative signs and makes the calculation easier to follow. Let y = 0 be at the beam of photogate A. Then y = h at the beam of photogate B where h is the distance between photogates.

Draw a quick sketch on the board similar to the diagram in the investigation.

We can solve this equation for g in terms of the time from A to B and the distance between the photogates.

Derived equation 1 on the board being careful to explain the variables with reference to the diagram. We can calculate g only if we can measure everything on the right hand side of the equation. Unfortunately, we cannot measure the initial speed, v_0. The reason we can't measure it is because we need the initial speed at the moment the leading edge of the ball breaks the light beam in photogate A. This is when the timer starts the clock which measures t_{AB}. Our previous technique of finding the initial speed from the ball diameter divided by the time through the beam does not apply in this situation. That calculation gives the speed as the center of the ball passes the beam.

Actually, I am going to show you a clever way to determine the initial velocity however we need to know the value of g first. So the calculation is going to proceed in steps. First, we will assume the initial speed is zero. This makes it easy to calculate a value for g in terms of the things we can measure. Since you dropped the ball very close to the light beam, it is not a bad assumption.

Show how equation 1 becomes equation 2 on the board.

Next we are going to use the value for g to calculate the initial speed from the time it takes the ball to pass through photogate A. When the ball crosses the beam in photogate A, it takes a bit less time than it would if the initial speed were zero. That means t_A is slightly less than it would be if v_0 were zero. We get a formula for the initial speed (v_0) by solving the distance formula again using the diameter (d) of the ball and time t_A, that it takes the ball to pass through the beam in photogate A. These are both quantities we can measure. The result is equation 3.

Sketch the diagram from the investigation and derive equation 3 on the board.

Once we have a value for the initial speed (v_0) we can go back and re-calculate g using equation 1, which is more accurate than equation 2. This is an iterative calculation, which means the calculation is repeated each iteration producing a result more accurate than the last one. The first iteration assumed that $v_0 = 0$. The second iteration calculates g using the value of v_0 determined from the first calculation of g. The second iteration is more accurate than the first iteration because it accounts for the initial speed. The process keeps going. The second calculation of g gives an even better calculation of v_0. In the third iteration the new value for v_0 is used to get an even better value for g. The sequence of calculations gives an improved value of g with every iteration.

The process by which the iterative calculation works is a difficult concept to grasp. You will need to come back to the explanation again later in the experiment as students actually do the calculation.

4.3 Free Fall and the Acceleration due to Gravity

3   Determining g from experiment

It is impossible to drop the ball so it starts *exactly* at the light beam in photogate A. Because the ball drops a small distance before breaking the beam, the ball has a small but unknown initial speed (v_0) at $t = 0$. Remember, $t = 0$ when the edge of the ball just breaks the light beam in photogate A.

To calculate g accurately, we will use a clever technique called *iteration*. Iteration is a process of repeating a calculation that gets more accurate each time. To start the calculation, assume the initial speed is zero when the ball breaks the beam in photogate A. With two photogates, we measure t_{AB}, the time it takes the leading edge of the ball to move from photogate A to photogate B. During this time the ball moves a distance h. Since all the motion is down, it is convenient to make down the positive direction. The equation for distance in free fall is then $y = y_0 + v_0 t + 1/2\, gt^2$. Choose the initial position to be zero ($y_0 = 0$) when the ball first breaks the light beam in photogate A. The distance equation can be solved for the acceleration, g to give equation 1.

We don't know v_0 and have no experimental way to measure it. Therefore, as a first estimate of g, we assume the initial speed is zero ($v_0 = 0$). After making this assumption equation 1 becomes equation 2. Equation 2 includes only variables we can measure in the experiment.

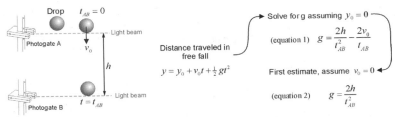

Once we know g however, we DO have a way to experimentally measure v_0. When the ball crosses the beam in photogate A, it takes a bit less time than it would if the initial speed were zero. That means t_A is slightly less than it would be if v_0 were zero. We get a formula for the initial speed (v_0) by solving the distance formula again using the diameter (d) of the ball and time t_A, that it takes the ball to pass through the beam in photogate A. These are both quantities we can measure. The result is equation 3.

Once we have a value for the initial speed (v_0) we can go back and re-calculate g using equation 1, which is more accurate than equation 2. This is the first iteration.

The corrected value of g is then used to make a better calculation of v_0 (second iteration). This new value for v_0 is used to get an even better value for g. The iterative sequence of calculations $g \rightarrow v_0 \rightarrow g \rightarrow v_0 \rightarrow g$ gives an improved value of g with every iteration. With each iteration the difference between the new value and the previous value gets smaller and smaller. You can stop calculating when the difference becomes smaller than the precision to which other quantities are known, such as the distance the beam is blocked by the ball (d), or the height between A and B (h).

24

---

4   Example answers

Table 1: *Time and distance data*

h (m)	t_A (sec)	t_B (sec)	t_{AB} (sec)
0.641	0.0494	0.0024	0.3484
0.641	0.0459	0.0048	0.3427

5   Example answers

Table 2: *Calculation of g*

Iteration	g (m/sec^2)	v_0 (m/sec)	Formula
1	10.9219		equation 2
2		0.1632	equation 3
	9.9689		equation 2
3		0.1852	equation 3
	9.8413		equation 2
4		0.1881	equation 3
	9.8242		equation 2
5		0.1885	equation 3
	9.8219		equation 2

5a

$y = y_0 + v_0 t + \frac{1}{2}gt^2$

$y = h,\quad y_0 = 0,\quad t = t_{AB}$

$h = v_0 t_{AB} + \frac{1}{2}gt_{AB}^2 \quad \rightarrow \quad g = \frac{2h}{t_{AB}^2} - \frac{2v_0}{t_{AB}}$ (equation 1)

When v_0 is zero, equation 1 reduces to equation 2. To get equation 3, assume the ball drops its diameter, d in t_A seconds.

$d = v_0 t_A + \frac{1}{2}gt_A^2 \quad \rightarrow \quad v_0 = \frac{d}{t_A} - \frac{gt_A}{2}$ (equation 3)

5b With each iteration the calculated value for g changes less and less. Between the first and second iterations the value of g changed a lot. Between the fourth and fifth iterations the value hardly changed at all.

Determining g from experiment

4

To measure 'g' accurately you need to measure the three photogate times (t_A, t_B, t_{AB}) and the distance (h) between photogates A and B. On the Timer, turn both the A and B lights on and drop the ball through the photogates. If the Timer did not stop, the ball dropped at an angle and did not break the beam of photogate B. This will happen; simply repeat the trial. In a perfectly straight drop, the whole diameter of the ball breaks the beam in photogate B. Your best data points are those with the largest value for t_B.

Have the students practice a few drops while you circulate around the room and observe them. Because the drop height above the beam will vary with each trial, it is crucial that you have the three time measurements from the same drop of the ball. After each drop, without pressing reset, use the A and B buttons (and lights) to display and record the three times in Table 1. Measure and record the distance between photogates for each trial in case the ball bumps a photogate. You will need to do many trials to get five good data sets.

It is important for students to understand that it is OK to do many trials. It is a quick experiment to do and it is difficult to get a very straight drop. Fortunately, the time through photogate B is a good indicator of the quality of the trial. This is the major data taking activity in the investigation. Assist any groups that have difficulties.

Analyzing the data

5

Choose one row from Table 1 to do the calculation of g. You will get the best result by choosing a row for which the value of t_B is largest, corresponding to the trial with the straightest drop. Use Table 2 to keep track of the calculation working from the first row down. In the first row calculate g using equation 2 which assumes the initial speed is zero. This is the first iteration and the least accurate.

Circulate and see that students make the first calculation. A typical value for g in the first iteration is 10 - 14 m/sec^2.

In the second row of table 2, calculate the initial speed using equation 3. Then use the initial speed to calculate g using equation 1, which is more accurate.

Circulate and assist students to make the second calculation. A typical value for g in the second iteration is 9.7 - 10.1 m/sec^2.

Work your way down through Table 2 alternately calculating v_0 then g. Notice that the values for G. change a lot from the first iteration to the second but the change gets smaller and smaller with each additional iteration.

Students should calculate through five iterations. By the fifth generation the change in the value of g should be much less than 1%.

Repeat the calculation for at least two more sets of data (trials). Calculate the average value for g for all three trials. Calculate the percent difference between your average value and the published value of 9.82 m/sec^2. How does your result compare to the accepted value? If you kept going with more iterations of the calculation would the value of g keep getting more and more accurate?

The values should be within 1-2 percent of the accepted value of g after the fifth iteration. Past a certain limit the calculation will not keep getting more accurate because of other errors in the experiment, such as the actual distance the ball blocks the beam.

Free fall and mass

6

Once you have established an accurate value of g for the steel ball, try the experiment again with the plastic ball. The mass of the plastic ball is only 7 grams compared to 28 grams for the steel ball.

Students should repeat the experiment with the plastic ball and discover that the measured value of g is the same as for the steel ball to within the accuracy of the experiment.

4.3 Free Fall and the Acceleration due to Gravity

4   Measuring data to determine g

To measure 'g' accurately you need to measure the three photogate times (t_A, t_B, t_{AB}) and the distance (h) between photogates A and B.

1. On the Timer, turn both the A and B lights on and drop the ball through the photogates. If the Timer did not stop, the ball dropped at an angle and did not break the beam of photogate B. This will happen; simply repeat the trial. In a perfectly straight drop, the whole diameter of the ball breaks the beam in photogate B. Your best data points are those with the largest value for t_B.

2. Without pressing reset, use the A and B buttons (and lights) to display and record the three times in Table 1. Measure and record the distance between photogates for each trial in case the ball bumps a photogate. You will need to do many trials to get five good data sets.

Table 1: Time and distance data

h (m)	Time, t_A (sec)	Time, t_B (sec)	Time, t_{AB} (sec)

5   Analyzing the data

Choose one row from Table 1 to do the calculation of g. You will get the best result by choosing a row for which the value of t_B is largest, corresponding to the trial with the straightest drop. Use Table 2 to keep track of the calculation working from the first row down.

Table 2: Calculation of g

Iteration	g (m/sec^2)	v_0 (m/sec)	Formula to use
1			equation 2
2			equation 3
			equation 1
3			equation 3
			equation 1

a. Use the formula for distance traveled in free fall to derive equations 1, 2, and 3.

b. Describe how the values for g change in successive iterations of the calculation.

c. Make a graph showing each intermediate value of g on the y-axis and the iteration number on the x-axis. What does the graph show you about the calculation?

d. If you kept going with more iterations of the calculation would the value of g keep getting more and more accurate? Explain why or why not.

e. Repeat the calculation for at least two more sets of data (trials). Calculate the average value for g for all three trials. Calculate the percent difference between your average value and the published value of 9.82 m/sec^2. How does your result compare to the accepted value?

f. Which variable do you think has the largest uncertainty among the quantities you measured in the experiment? Why do you think so?

6   Free fall and mass

1. Repeat the experiment for the plastic ball, which has a much lower mass than the steel ball.

a. How does the value of g compare for the steel and plastic balls

b. Explain any differences you find in part (a) if any.

25

5c.

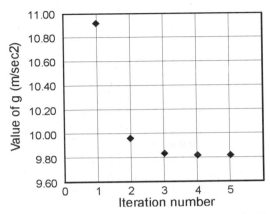

The graph shows that the calculation converges to a value of 9.82 m/sec^2.

5d. Additional calculations would yield smaller corrections to the value of g. Once the corrections get smaller than 0.1% they are no longer significant. Past one part in 1,000 the value of g is limited by the precision to which other variables in the experiment are known.

5e. The values we obtained for three trials were 9.7410, 9.8219, and 9.6954 m/sec^2. The average is 9.746 m./sec^2. This is within 0.7% of the published value of 9.82 m/sec^2.

5f. The uncertainty in the distance is 1 mm in 641, or 0.002%. The uncertainty in t_A is 0.0001 sec in .0459 sec, or .002%. The largest uncertainty is the width of the ball crossing the beam. Since the ball is a sphere, its "width" in the beam varies by 0.5% as the ball moves sideways 1.5 mm in the beam.

6   Example answers

6a. We measured a value of 9.710 m/sec^2 for g using the plastic ball. This is within 0.5% of the value for the steel ball. We conclude that both the steel and plastic balls accelerate at the same rate since the values of g fall within the same range.

6b. The values for g were the same to within the precision of the experiment.

5.1 The First Law: Force and Inertia

Key Question: How does the first law apply to objects at rest and in motion?

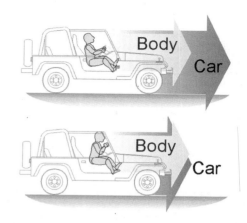

Newton's first law states that all objects want to keep doing what they are doing. An object at rest will remain at rest, and an object in motion will stay in motion at a constant velocity as long as there are no unbalanced forces acting on it. In this Investigation students will use Newton's first law to explain the behavior of a ball with no unbalanced forces acting on it. They will measure the speed of the ball as it rolls along a flat track. They will then provide an unbalanced force by slightly tilting the track and will observe the effect on the speed of the ball. The experimental setup is identical to Investigation 3.3.

Reading Synopsis

Students read Section 5.1 The First Law: Force and Inertia before the Investigation.

A force is a push or pull or any action that has the ability to change an object's state of motion. Forces can be created by many different processes, but all forces have the potential ability to change the motion of an object.

Newton's first law states that all objects tend to keep doing what they are doing. Inertia is the term used to describe the ability of an object to resist a change in its state of motion. Newton's first law is sometimes called the law of inertia. The amount of inertia an object has depends on its mass. More massive objects have more inertia.

An unbalanced force is required to change an object's motion. Objects with more mass, and therefore more inertia, require more force to change their state of motion.

The Investigation

Leading Questions
- What property of matter tends to keep a moving object moving and resist the motion of an object at rest?
- What must be done to change the motion of a moving object or start an object moving if it is at rest?

Learning Goals
By the end of the Investigation, students will be able to:
- Use Newton's first law to explain why an object at rest tends to stay at rest if no forces are exerted.
- Use Newton's first law to describe the motion of an object moving with no unbalanced forces acting on it.
- Explain the effect of an unbalanced force on the motion of an object.

Key Vocabulary
Newton's first law, mass, inertia, force, speed, acceleration

Setup and Materials

Students work in groups of three to five at tables.

Each group should have:

- Straight track with a threaded knob
- 3/4-inch steel ball
- Timer with photogates, AC adapter (or 9-volt battery), and cords to connect the photogates to the timer
- Physics stand
- Metric and English rulers
- Calculator
- Blocks, books, or other objects to support the free end of the track
- Cardboard shims of different thicknesses

Details

Time One class period

Preparation Students should have prior experience using the timer and photogates.

Assignments Section 5.1 The First Law: Force and Inertia in the **Student Text** before the Investigation

Skill Sheets 5.1 Isaac Newton

Teaching the Investigation

1. Introduction
2. Setting up the experiment
3. Reflecting on Newton's first law
4. Creating constant speed motion
5. Collecting data on the first law
6. Analyzing the data

Introduction

Newton's first law

An unbalanced force is required to change an object's motion.

Mass is a measure of an object's inertia.

Setting up the experiment

1

Attach the photogate A at the 75 cm mark and photogate B at the 35 cm mark.

Make the straight track level.

Reflecting on Newton's first law

2

When the ball is at rest, the forces acting on it are balanced.

A question about friction

Slightly sloping the track allows the force of gravity to offset the frictional force.

In this Investigation we will be studying Newton's first law. What does the first law say?

Prompt a discussion on the different ways the first law can be stated. Some possibilities are an object at rest will tend to remain at rest, and an object in motion will tend to remain in motion; objects tend to keep doing what they are already doing; objects have inertia and resist changes in their motion.

What is required for an object to change its state of motion or its state of having no motion?

An unbalanced force is needed. If students simply answer "force" then discuss the difference between a force and an unbalanced force.

Do all objects have the same ability to remain in their state of motion?

No. This ability depends on an object's inertia. An object with more inertia has a greater tendency to remain in its state of motion. Mass is a measure of an object's inertia.

1 Attach the straight track to the physics stand at the bottom hole. Then attach one photogate to the track at the 35 cm mark and the other photogate at the 75 cm mark. Attach the 75 cm photogate to the timer at plug A. Attach the 35 cm photogate to the timer at plug B.

Make sure students do not mix up the two photogate plugs.

Make your track level by propping up the catcher end. You may use the cardboard shims to adjust the height of the catcher until the track is level. When you think your track is perfectly level, place the steel ball in the center of it. The ball should remain at rest.

Circulate and assist students in getting their tracks level. This may take some time.

2 Now we will use Newton's first law to explain why the ball is sitting still. Write Newton's first law in your own words. Think about the ball. If it is not moving, what do we know about the forces on it?

The forces are all balanced. If students answer that there are no forces acting on the ball, discuss the two forces that are definitely present, the force of gravity and the force of the track pushing up on the ball. Friction may also be present.

The ball is at rest now. But what if we were to make it move by giving it a little push? What would its motion be like?

It should move at a constant speed if there are no unbalanced forces to speed it up or slow it down.

Give the ball a little push and allow it to roll along the track. Does its speed seem to change? If its speed is not constant adjust the level of the track until the speed appears constant.

Why did you have to slope the track a little to make the ball roll at constant speed?

Students should recognize that there is some small amount of friction. Sloping the track allows for a little force from gravity to offset the force of friction. When the ball rolls at constant speed, the net force is truly zero, indicating that the force of friction is balanced by the force of gravity. You may wish to discuss the idea of friction since it has not yet been formally introduced. Friction is caused by motion and results in a force that always acts to reduce motion.

Teaching tips

The most difficult part of the Investigation is leveling the track. Students can use books or notebooks to get the track nearly level, but the fine adjustment takes patience. If you have a supply of scrap paper, give each group a small stack to use for the fine adjustment of the slope. Just a single sheet of paper under the edge of the track can make the difference.

2 **Example answers**

2a. An object at rest stays at rest, and an object in motion stays in motion at a constant velocity unless acted on by an unbalanced force.

2b. All of the forces are balanced. The forces include the force of gravity (the ball's weight) and the normal force.

2c. If all of the forces are balanced, the object will move at a constant speed according to Newton's first law.

2d. It moves at a constant speed.

UNIT 2: Motion and Force in One Dimension

5.1 | **The First Law: Force and Inertia**

Question: How does the first law apply to objects at rest and in motion?

In this Investigation, you will:

1. Identify the forces acting on a ball at rest.
2. Analyze the motion of a ball moving at constant speed.
3. Use Newton's first law to explain the behavior of objects at rest and in motion.

Newton's first law states that objects tend to keep doing what they are doing unless acted on by an unbalanced force. This law applies to both objects at rest and objects in motion. In this Investigation, you will use the straight track to apply Newton's first law to describe the behavior of a rolling ball.

1 **Setting up the experiment**

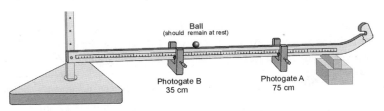

Ball
(should remain at rest)

Photogate B
35 cm

Photogate A
75 cm

1. Attach the straight track to the lowest hole on the stand. Turn the free end of the track so it curves upward to catch the ball.
2. Attach photogates A and B to the Timer. Set the Timer to interval mode. Clamp photogate A to the straight track at approximately the 75 centimeter mark and photogate B at approximately the 35 centimeter mark.
3. Place books, binders, or other objects under the free end of the track so the track appears to be level. Use the steel ball to test whether the track is level. The ball should be able to sit on the track without rolling.

2 **Reflecting on Newton's first law**

a. State Newton's first law in your own words.
b. Place the steel ball in the center of the track so it stays at rest. What do you know about the forces on the ball? Identify the forces acting on it.
c. If an object is moving and there are no unbalanced forces acting on it, does its speed increase, decrease, or remain the same? Explain.
d. Push the ball with your finger and let it roll along the track. Does it appear to speed up or slow down? If so, you may wish to adjust the level of the track so that the ball seems to roll with constant speed.

26

Investigation 5.1 The First Law: Force and Inertia **71**

Creating constant speed motion

Adjust the level of the track so the A and B photogate times are within 0.0005 seconds of each other.

Collecting data on the first law

Record the time for the ball to pass through each photogate and the time from A to B with a level track, then record the times with the track at a slight incline.

The speed of the ball through a photogate is the time through the photogate divided by the distance (1.9 cm).

The acceleration of the ball is the change in speed between the photogates divided by the time between A and B.

Analyzing the data

· *The forces acting on the ball are balanced when it rolls on the level track.*

Tilting the track causes an unbalanced force on the ball that causes its motion to change.

3 Set the timer to interval mode. Place the ball at the top of the hill at the free end of the track. Release the ball and let it roll through the photogates. Read the time the ball takes to pass through each individual photogate. How should these times compare if the ball is moving at a constant speed?

If the ball moves at a constant speed, it will take the same time to pass through each photogate so the two times should be the same.

If your two times are not equal you should adjust your track. You want to get the two times to be within 0.0005 seconds of each other. It may take several adjustments for the times to be within 0.0005 seconds.

Encourage students to be patient when adjusting the tracks.

4 Once you have gotten your track completely adjusted, release the ball from the end of the track. This will be the reference position of the track. Record the time for the ball to pass through each photogate (t_A and t_B) and the time from A to B (t_{AB}) in Table 1. Then calculate the speed of the ball at each photogate and the acceleration. Use the ball's diameter, 1.9 cm, as the distance when calculating the speed.

Check to see that the two photogate times for each group are within 0.0005 seconds.

Now raise the free end of the track 3 or 4 mm. This will slant the track a small amount so the ball is rolling down a slight hill. How do you think the two photogate times will compare now?

The times should be different because the ball will be accelerating. Time A should be greater than time B.

Release the ball from the curved end of the track. Record the times in Table 1. Calculate the speeds and acceleration. Now lower the free end of the track so it is 3 or 4 mm below its previous reference position. This means you should lower it 6 or 8 mm from where it is now. How do you think this will affect the photogate times?

Now the ball will be slowing down as it rolls along the track. Time A should be less than time B.

Release your ball and record the times in Table 1. Calculate the speeds and the acceleration.

5 Were there any forces acting on the ball when it rolled along the level track?

Yes. The force of gravity and the force of the track pushing up on the ball were present. However, there were no unbalanced forces.

How can Newton's first law be used to explain the motion of the ball rolling on a level track?

The ball rolled at a constant speed because there were no unbalanced forces acting on it. It kept on doing what it was already doing due to its inertia.

How did tilting the track affect its motion? How can the first law be used to explain what happened?

The ball did not move at a constant speed when the track was tilted. When the end of the track was raised, the ball's speed increased and its acceleration was positive. When the end of the track was lowered, the ball's speed decreased and its acceleration was negative. There was an unbalanced force acting on the ball that caused its motion to change.

5.1 The First Law: Force and Inertia

3 Creating constant speed motion

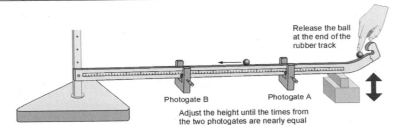

Release the ball
at the end of the
rubber track

Photogate B   Photogate A

Adjust the height until the times from
the two photogates are nearly equal

a. Release the ball from the hill at the free end of the track. Allow it to roll through both of the photogates. If there are no unbalanced forces acting on the ball, how should the time it takes to pass through photogate A (t_A) compare with the time it takes to pass through photogate B (t_B)? Explain.

b. Read t_A and t_B on your Timer. How do the two values compare? What does this tell you about the speed of the ball as it rolls along the track? Continue to adjust the track until t_A and t_B are 0.0005 seconds apart or less. This takes repeated trials, so do not get discouraged.

4 Collecting data on the first law

Use the photogates to measure the speed and acceleration of the ball when the track is level.

1. Use Table 1 to record position and time data from the photogates. Calculate the acceleration using the difference in speed between photogates A and B ($v_B - v_A$) and the time between A and B (t_{AB}).

2. Raise the start of the track (with the hill) about 3 or 4 millimeters above its level position and repeat the measurements and calculations with the track sloped slightly downhill.

3. Lower the start of the track (with the hill) about 3 or 4 millimeters below its level position and repeat the measurements and calculations with the track sloped slightly uphill.

Table 1: Time and speed data

Photogate A			Photogate B			Time t_{AB} (sec)	Accel. (cm/sec²)
Position (cm)	Time t_A (sec)	Speed (cm/sec)	Position (cm)	Time t_B (sec)	Speed (cm/sec)		

5 Analyzing the data

a. Were any forces acting on the ball as it rolled along the level track? Identify the forces. Explain how Newton's first law is applied to describe the motion you observed.

b. What changes occur in the forces acting on the ball when the track is tilted slightly up or down? Explain how the first law is applied to describe the observed motion in the case of uphill or downhill slope.

27

3 4 5 Example answers

3a. The time for the ball to pass through photogate A should be the same as the time for it to pass through photogate B. If the ball moves at a constant speed, it will take the same amount of time to move the same distance.

3b. The two values are only 0.0003 seconds apart. The values are close enough to say that the ball is moving at a constant speed.

Photogate A			Photogate B			Time t_{AB} (sec)	Accel. (cm/sec²)
Pos. (cm)	Time t_A (sec)	Speed (cm/sec)	Pos. (cm)	Time t_B (sec)	Speed (cm/sec)		
75	0.0368	51.6	35	0.0368	51.6	0.7614	0
75	0.0368	51.6	35	0.0352	54.0	0.7453	3.22
75	0.0417	45.6	35	0.0446	42.6	0.8941	-3.36

5a. The forces acting on the ball were the force of gravity, the normal force, and a small amount of friction.

5b. The ball does not roll at a constant speed when the track is tilted. The forces must not all be balanced because the ball does not have a constant speed.

5.2 The Second Law: Force, Mass, and Acceleration

Key Question: What is the relationship between force, mass, and acceleration?

It takes force to get an object moving and more force to make it stop. If you think about the words "get moving" or "stop," you realize that force is linked to acceleration because both phrases imply changes in motion. This Investigation explores the relationship between force, mass, and acceleration. Students will construct an Atwood's machine and use the second law to determine the tension acting in a moving string. This tension force cannot be measured with a spring scale because things are in motion.

$$m = 5,000 \text{ kg}$$
$$a = 5 \text{ m/sec}^2$$

Reading Synopsis

Students read Section 5.2 The Second Law: Force, Mass, and Acceleration before the Investigation.

If you apply more force to an object, it has proportionally greater acceleration. If the mass of the object is increased, and the force is kept constant, the acceleration diminishes proportionally. Newton's second law states that the acceleration of an object is equal to the net force applied divided by the mass of the object. In the metric system, the unit of force, the newton, is defined by mass and acceleration. In the English system, the unit of force is the pound (lb.).

The concept of net force is presented. The application of the second law is presented with several example problems. Acceleration is determined when force and mass are known. Force is determined when mass and acceleration are known. A condition of zero acceleration implies that the net force is zero (equilibrium). Positive and negative numbers are used to indicate the direction of a force.

The Investigation

Leading Questions
- How is force measured and described in the metric and English systems?
- What is the exact relationship between force and motion?
- What is the exact relationship between inertia (mass), force, and motion?
- Can we determine forces by looking at the motion of objects?
- Can we predict the motion of objects from the forces acting on them?
- If an object is not moving, what does that tell us about the forces acting on the object?

Learning Goals

By the end of the Investigation, students will be able to:
- Use the second law to calculate force, mass, or acceleration when two of the three variables are known.
- Qualitatively describe the relationship between acceleration, mass, and force.
- Use the condition of zero acceleration to determine an unknown force.
- Use the second law to determine unknown forces from experimental measurements of motion and mass.

Key Vocabulary   Newton's second law, newton, pound, net force, static, dynamic, equilibrium

Setup and Materials

Students work in groups of four or five at tables.

Each group should have:

- Ultimate pulleys set
- 2.5- and 5-N spring scales
- Physics stand
- Timer with photogates, AC adapter (or 9-volt battery) and cords to connect the photogates to the timer
- Electronic scale or triple-beam balance to measure mass
- Calculator

Details

Time ⏱ One class period

Preparation ✎ Students should be familiar with acceleration and the formulas for accelerated motion from the previous chapter.

Assignments 📖 Section 5.2 The Second Law: Force, Mass, and Acceleration in the **Student Edition** before the Investigation.

Skill Sheets 5.2 Newton's Second Law

Equipment Setup Ultimate Pulleys

Teaching the Investigation

1 Introduction
2 The Atwood's machine
3 Setting up the experiment
4 Analyzing the system
5 Finding the tension in the string
6 Measuring force and mass
7 Thinking about force
8 Measuring the acceleration

Introduction

Newton's second law

The Atwood's machine

An Atwood's machine illustrates a system that is not in equilibrium because of a net force acting on it.

Setting up the experiment

1

2

When the hangers are let go, what kind of motion do the two masses have?

What is the cause of the motion?

Analyzing the system

The equation for Newton's second law:
$F = ma$

1 newton = 1 kg-m/sec^2

What forces are acting on the mass going up?

What is the net force?

Newton's second law is one of the most useful relationships in all of physics. The second law tells you how an object's motion will change if you know its mass and the forces acting on it. The second law also tells you how much force you need to apply to an object to create a specific change in its motion. Today's Investigation will use a clever device called an Atwood's machine to explore an application of the second law.

An Atwood's machine is a pulley with a string over it. Each end of the string has a different mass attached. When you let the string go, one mass rises and the other mass falls.

> Set up an Atwood's machine with the pulley in front of the class and demonstrate.

Why does one mass rise while the other mass falls?

> Start a discussion. The system is not in equilibrium because one mass is larger than the other and therefore there is a net force acting.

To do the Investigation we are going to use the pulley and spindle. Attach the spindle in the top hole of the physics stand. Slide the pulley on the shaft, followed by several of the 1-inch-long plastic spacers. To hold everything together, slide the short length of tubing onto the end of the shaft as a stop. Leave a little room on the shaft so everything can spin without much friction.

> Students set up the apparatus as shown in the diagram in step 1.

Put a nut and 5-10 washers on one of the white plastic threaded rods. You will use the rod to hang weight from the pulley. Attach a nut and washers to a second rod to make another mass hanger with a different mass from the first one.

> Students assemble 2 weight hangers to the ends of the string.

Loop the string over the pulley. Pull the lower mass hanger down until it hits the base of the stand. Let the hangers go and observe the motion of the two masses. What sort of motion do you observe and what is the cause of that motion?

> Students should observe that the motion is accelerated because the speed changes. The cause of the acceleration is the unbalanced force caused by the excess mass on one hanger.

Acceleration is caused by unbalanced force. According to Newton's second law, the acceleration of an object is equal to the net force acting on the object divided by the mass of the object. In fact, the metric definition of force is based on mass and acceleration. A force of 1 newton is exactly the force required to create an acceleration of 1 meter per second squared for a 1 kilogram object.

> Write the definition of force on the board: $1 N = 1$ kg-m/sec^2, or $F = ma$. Point out that this is a different, but equivalent, arrangement of the same relationship, $a = F \div m$.

I should be able to predict the acceleration of one of the moving masses if I know the mass and the forces that are acting. Pick the mass that is going up; this is the lighter of the two hangers. We will call this mass m_1. Can someone tell me what forces are acting on mass m_1?

> Start a discussion. Gravity creates a way for force to pull down. Label this force F_1. The strain pulls upward with another force. Label this force T, for tension. Draw the diagram in the center of step 2 of the Investigation.

What is the net force?

> The net force is $T - F_1$. Remind students that positive means upward forces and negative means downward forces.

A challenge

Many devices use acceleration to measure the mass of an object. Very often the technique employed is to cause something to vibrate. A vibration is a rapid back-and-forth motion that results in similarly rapid acceleration. If the mass of an object changes, its acceleration changes and the frequency of vibration changes. Electronic devices can easily be made that are very responsive to small changes in frequency. As a result, this technique is used to measure very small amounts of mass quickly, such as the mass of a single drop of water.

Challenge students to measure the mass of a single steel washer by making acceleration measurements. To do this they will first have to calibrate the apparatus for the effects of friction. This means measuring the acceleration for a known mass of washers on both sides of the pulley. Once the system is calibrated, a single washer added to one of the hangers will result in a measurable change in acceleration. The change in acceleration can be used to determine the mass.

The sensitivity of the technique depends on the accuracy with which acceleration can be measured. Two factors are important: the repeatability of triggering the stopwatch with a finger, and the resolution of the stopwatch (0.01 sec). Have the students measure the repeatability of their timing measurements. If the timing is repeatable to within 5 percent, then the acceleration may also be accurate to 5 percent if there are no other significant sources of error. To determine the effect of limited time resolution, have the students estimate the difference in acceleration that would result from a time measurement being +/- 0.1 seconds from its nominal value.

5.2 The Second Law: Force, Mass, and Acceleration

Question: What is the relationship between force, mass, and acceleration?

In this Investigation, you will:

1. Change the force acting on a mass and observe its acceleration.
2. Derive Newton's second law of motion from experimental results.

It takes force to get an object moving and more force to make it stop. If you think about the words "get moving" or "stop," you realize that force is linked to acceleration because both phrases imply changes in motion. This Investigation explores the relationship between force, mass, and acceleration.

1 **Setting up the experiment**

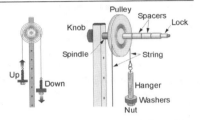

1. Attach the spindle to the top hole in the stand using a threaded knob.
2. Find the pulley that is labeled "sec/cm." Slide the pulley onto the spindle. Use plastic spacers and the stopper to keep the pulley from sliding off the spindle.
3. Attach the threaded plastic hangers to the string. Place 5 - 10 washers onto one of the hangers. Put a greater number of washers on the second hanger.
4. Loop the string over the pulley so that the first hanger (with less mass) is sitting on the base of the stand. When you release the second hanger, the first will rise as the second one falls.
5. Changing the washers allows you to change the mass and/or force acting on the system.

2 **Analyzing the system to find the tension in the string**

The system of two masses connected by a string over a pulley is called an Atwood's machine. How much force is applied by the string when the masses are moving? The string tension is hard to measure directly because things are moving. Fortunately, the second law can be used to find this force.

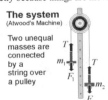

The system
(Atwood's Machine)

Two unequal masses are connected by a string over a pulley

Find the net force

m_1 Net force $F = T - F_1$

Apply the second law using net force

$$a_1 = \frac{T - F_1}{m_1}$$

Solve for the string tension *(T)*

$$T = m_1 a_1 - F_1$$

To analyze the forces, consider mass, m_1. The forces that act on m_1 are weight (F_1) and tension in the string (T). The net force is the string tension minus the weight ($T - F_1$). If we assume the pulley has no mass or friction, the second law is applied to show that the force in the string must be $T = m_1 a_1 - F_1$.

28

Finding the tension in the string

The acceleration of mass m_1 is the net force divided by the mass:
$a_1 = (T - F_1) \div m_1$

The tension in the string:
$T = m_1 a_1 - F_1$

Measuring force and mass

Thinking about force

Arranging the size of the forces:
$F_1 < T < F_2$

Measuring the acceleration

The acceleration of mass m_1:
$a = 2x \div t^2$

x: the distance traveled by m_1
t: the time it takes for the mass to move from top to bottom

Calculate the acceleration of mass m_1 from the measured time and distance. Use the measured mass (m_1) and weight (F_1) and the calculated acceleration to determine the tension of the string (T).

2 What is the acceleration of mass m_1?

Students should answer that the acceleration is equal to the net force divided by the mass, or $a_1 = (T - F_1) \div m_1$. The subscript 1 refers to all quantities that apply to mass m_1. The tension, T, has no subscript because it acts on both masses.

We can measure the force from the weight easily with a spring scale. But how do we measure the tension force in the string?

Discuss with students that this force is hard to measure because things are moving. The force in the string is different when the heavier mass is at rest on the base of the physics stand.

Newton's second law actually gives us a prescription for how to find the string tension. We just have to rearrange the formula we just wrote for acceleration. The string tension is equal to $m_1 a_1$ minus F_1.

Using simple algebra, solve on the board. Discuss that it must be true if the second law is true.

If the string tension were equal to the weight (F_1), the mass m_1 would not move at all. If the string tension was less than the weight, then mass m_1 would move down. We observe that mass m_1 moves upward; therefore, the string tension must be greater than the weight, $T > F_1$.

3 The next step in the Investigation is to measure the masses and forces.

Students should use a balance to measure masses m_1 and m_2. They should use a carefully calibrated spring scale to measure the weight forces F_1 and F_2.

4 There are three forces acting in the system: the string tension, and the two weight forces, F_1 and F_2. How should these forces be arranged from smallest to largest?

Discuss that the net force on m_2 must be down; therefore, $F_2 > T$. We already know that $T > F_1$; therefore, the arrangement of the three forces is $F_1 < T < F_2$.

5 We are now going to do an experiment to determine the tension in the string and test our hypothesis. The acceleration of m_1 should be constant since the force is constant. Can anyone describe what the speed versus. time graph looks like for constant acceleration?

Sketch the graph on the board. The graph should look like the diagram in Part 5.

What is the distance traveled on a speed versus time graph?

Review that area on a speed versus time graph is equal to distance traveled.

That means that the distance traveled by m_1 must be given by the formula $x = \frac{1}{2} at^2$. If we solve this formula for the acceleration, we find $a = 2x \div t^2$.

Solve this derivation on the board.

Experimentally, we can measure the distance traveled (x) and the time it takes (t) for the mass to move over its full range of motion from top to bottom. Use a meter stick to measure how far m_1 falls from its highest point, when mass m_2 is at rest on the base of the stand. Record this in Table 2 as the distance. Use the stopwatch function of the timer to measure the time interval between releasing mass m_2 and the instant that mass m_1 hits the bottom of the stand. Record this time in Table 2. Use the formula we just derived to calculate the acceleration from the time and distance. Use the relationship we derived from the second law to determine the string tension in newtons.

Students should take at least three trials that produce consistent data and use the average time to calculate the acceleration and string tension. Students should find that the calculated string tension is indeed greater than the weight of mass m_1 and less than the weight of mass m_2.

5.2 The Second Law: Force, Mass, and Acceleration

3 Measure forces and masses

The string carries force between the two masses. Because the string is flexible, the force is the same everywhere. This means that any place you cut the string, the force is the same. The force comes from gravity pulling on the two masses.

Measure forces F_1 and F_2

1. Measure the mass of each hanger, including washers.
2. Use a spring scale to measure the force of gravity pulling on each mass. Be sure to calibrate the spring scale by adjusting the pointer to zero when there is no mass attached. Record the mass, force, and number of washers in Table 1.

F

Table 1: Force and mass data

	No. of washers	Mass (kg)	Force (N)
Mass #1		$m_1 =$	$F_1 =$
Mass #2		$m_2 =$	$F_2 =$

4 Thinking about force

a. Which way do the masses move? Does m_1 rise or fall? Does m_2 rise or fall?

b. The three forces acting are T, F_1, and F_2. Based on your answers to (4a) above, arrange these forces in order from smallest to largest. Explain what physical reasoning you used to arrange the forces.

5 Measuring the acceleration

If you assume the acceleration of the system is constant, the acceleration can be determined from the distance traveled by the hangers and the time it takes them to move. The diagram shows a graph of uniform accelerated motion. The distance traveled is the area on the graph that is one-half the base times the height of the shaded triangle. Solving the equation for the acceleration gives the result that $a = 2x \div t^2$. The distance (x) and the total time (t) are measured in the experiment.

$v = at$

Speed

Time t

1. Use the Timer in stopwatch mode. Start the stopwatch when you release the lighter mass and stop it when the heavier mass hits the base of the stand. Record the measurement in Table 2.
2. Use a meter stick to measure the distance that the heavier mass travels, that is, between where it starts and the base of the stand. Record the measurement in Table 2.
3. Calculate the acceleration using the equation $a = 2x \div t^2$. Use the calculated acceleration to determine the tension force in the string (T). Do at least three trials.

Table 2: Distance, time, and acceleration data

Time (sec)	Distance (m)	Acceleration (m/sec²)	String tension (N)

a. Does the strength of the tension force in the experiment agree with your prediction from Part 4?

b. If the pulley created a friction force, would the tension force in the string be larger, smaller, or stay about the same? (This is tricky because you need to consider the sides of the string separately.)

29

3 4 5 Example answers

Table 1: Force and mass data

	No. of washers	Mass (kg)	Force (N)
Mass #1	5	$m_1 = 0.104$ kg	$F_1 = 1.02$ N
Mass #2	7	$m_2 = 0.127$ kg	$F_2 = 1.24$ N

4a. The heavier (more massive) mass will fall, and the lighter one will rise. m_1 will rise, and m_2 will fall.

4b. In order from smallest to largest: F_1, T, F_2. When set in motion, m_1 will rise, so T has to be greater than F_1, and m_2 will fall, so T has to be less than F_2.

Table 2: Distance, time, and acceleration data

Time (sec)	Distance (m)	Acceleration (m/sec²)	String tension (N)
1.23	0.69	0.91	1.11
1.27	0.69	0.86	1.11

5a. Their answer depends on their prediction.

5b. The acceleration would be smaller; friction slows things down. However, the masses have not changed. Looking at the heavier side, since the acceleration is smaller, the tension must increase. On the lighter side, the tension must decrease to result in a smaller acceleration.

5.3 The Third Law: Action and Reaction

Key Question: Can you identify action-reaction forces?

Newton's third law deals with action-reaction pairs. We rely on this law when we walk, place an item on a table, push a shopping cart or travel in a car. Examples and demonstrations of Newton's third law are everywhere in our lives yet the subtle way it affects us can often be overlooked without careful analysis to what is actually taking place. In this investigation students examine common events and situations they are familiar with to discover how action-reaction pairs interact. By describing in their own words and diagramming with simple sketches students explore the properties and implications of Newton's third law.

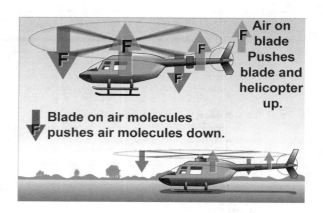

Air on blade Pushes blade and helicopter up.

Blade on air molecules pushes air molecules down.

Reading Synopsis

Students read Section 5.3 The Third Law: Action and Reaction after the investigation.

"For every action there is an equal and opposite reaction." This statement is known as Newton's third law and it affects our everyday lives even when we are sitting perfectly still in a chair or lying on the ground. Forces are explained in terms of action-reaction pairs. Anytime there is a force pushing on something there is another force of equal strength pushing back in the opposite direction.

While Newton's first and second laws apply to single objects, the third law involves pairs of objects. Each object in the pair feels the affects of one of the action-reaction forces. It does not matter which is the action force and which is the reaction force. The important thing is to understand that they are equal and opposite counterparts and to recognize which force acts on which object in the pair.

Locomotion is the act of moving and any machine or animal that moves depends on Newton's third law to do so. The human body uses the third law constantly and the study of how is called biomechanics.

The Investigation

Leading Questions
- How do forces affect objects?
- What happens when one object pushes on another object?
- What proof is there that action and reaction forces exist?
- How do action -reaction forces affect objects involved with their interaction?

Learning Goals
By the end of the Investigation, students will be able to:
- Draw a diagram showing an action-reaction pair of forces.
- Determine the reaction force when given an action force.
- Describe how Newton's third law affects the motion of objects.

Key Vocabulary
force, Newton's third law, action, reaction

Setup and Materials

Students work in groups of four or five at tables.

Each student or group should have:

- Plain, white copy paper or sketch paper for making diagrams
- Pencils
- Colored pencils (optional)
- No other equipment or materials are required

Details

Time One class period

Preparation You may wish to think of some action-reaction pairs in your lab or classroom that you can use as examples for discussion.

Assignments Section 5.3 The Third Law: Action and Reaction in the **Student Edition** after the investigation

Teaching the Investigation

1　Introduction

2　Identifying action-reaction pairs

3　Identifying action-reaction pairs in your life

4　Why don't equal and opposite forces cancel each other out?

5　Thinking deeper about the third law

Introduction

Newton's first and second laws of motion deal with single objects and the forces that act on them.

Newton's third law deals with pairs of objects and the interactions between them.

The third law applies to action/reaction pairs.

The two forces in an action/reaction pair always point in exactly opposite directions.

Action/reaction forces do not cancel each other out because they act on different objects.

If equal and opposite forces act on a single object, no motion will occur.

Newton's first and second laws of motion deal with *single* objects and the motion that results from forces that act on them. Newton's third law of motion pertains to *pairs* of objects and the interactions between them. The important thing to remember about Newton's third law is that it *always* applies to two objects. In fact, an isolated force can *never* be created without its twin prescribed by the second law. If I throw this eraser, I apply a force to it. Call that the action force. I feel the eraser against my hand, resisting my action force through its inertia. That means the eraser exerts a force back against my hand, which is what I feel. This is the reaction force. The action is me acting on the eraser. The reaction is the eraser acting back against my hand. Suppose Joe is pulling a heavy wagon. What is the action/reaction pair in this scenario?

> Joe exerts a force on the wagon, and the wagon exerts an equal and opposite force on Joe. Joe feels the handle of the wagon against his hand, that is the reaction force.

It is obvious that Joe exerts a force on the wagon, but why is it true that the wagon exerts an equal and opposite force on Joe? It is one of the rules of the universe. If object A exerts a force on object B, object B exerts an equal and opposite force on object A - the pair of forces occur simultaneously as part of an interaction. Which one we call the action and which one we define as the reaction makes no difference. Practically speaking, you know that the wagon must exert a force on Joe, because imagine how it feels on your arm to pull a heavy wagon; it sometimes feels as though the wagon is pulling on you, and it is, because it is automatically part of a force pair that is created as soon as you grab the handle and start pulling.

If Joe and the wagon exert equal and opposite forces on each other, isn't it true that the forces cancel out and no movement will ever occur?

> This is a common misconception that is easily cleared up by stressing (and repeating) that action and reaction forces act on different objects so they do not cancel out. Forces cancel when they act on the same object. If action/reaction forces DID cancel out, there would be no motion in the universe at all!

Explain why Joe is able to pull the wagon.

> The force the wagon exerts on Joe is equal and opposite to Joe's force on the wagon, but Joe is joined to the earth by flat shoes, while the wagon is free to roll on its wheels. Joe is able to push off of the earth and provide a net force to get the wagon rolling.

What is the action/reaction force pair for you sitting on a chair?

> This can take thought. You weight pulls down toward the center of the Earth. The reaction to the weight force is the attraction of your body's mass pulling back on the Earth. Another action-reaction pair occurs where your bottom meets the seat. The seat exerts a force up against your bottom that keeps you from going through the chair. Your bottom is compressed as a result and acts with an equal and opposite force against the chair.

The net force on YOU is zero because the force of the chair against you bottom cancels with the force of gravity pulling you toward the center of the Earth. These forces are NOT an action-reaction pair because they act on the same object, you. They are opposite in direction however, but are not equal unless your feet are off the floor. If your feet are on the floor, some of your weight creates another action-reaction pair between your shoes and the floor.

Example answers

1b sketch:

5.3　The Third Law: Action and Reaction

Question: Can you identify action-reaction forces?

In this Investigation, you will:

1.　Identify action-reaction forces in several given situations.
2.　Identify action-reaction forces in several of your daily activities.
3.　Learn why action-reaction forces do not cancel each other out.

Newton's first and second laws of motion discuss *single* objects and the forces that act on them. Newton's third law of motion discusses *pairs* of objects and the interactions between them. Newton's third law states that "For every action there is an equal and opposite reaction." The third law tells us that forces *always* come in pairs. The forces in an *action-reaction pair* are equal in strength and opposite in direction. In this Investigation, you will identify the action-reaction pairs of forces that are present in a variety of situations.

1　Identifying action-reaction pairs

Each force in an action-reaction pair acts on a different object. The clearest way to identify the forces is to draw a free body diagram. In the free body diagram, an object is isolated from all other objects. Any interaction between the object and other objects such as the floor is represented by a force. Often, it is possible to identify the forces that must be present for the object to have the motion, or lack of motion, that is observed.

Suppose a person is sitting in a chair on the floor and you are asked to identify the forces. The diagram below shows two action-reaction pairs involving the person, the chair, and the floor. Physically, it does not matter which you label the action and which is the reaction. The important thing is that the forces in a pair are equal in strength, opposite in direction, and act on opposite objects.

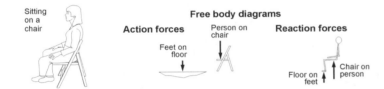

For each of the situations described below, sketch the situation and identify at least one pair of forces that make up an action-reaction pair.

a.　A can of soda sitting on a table.
b.　A skateboarder pushing off the ground.
c.　A swimmer moving through the water.
d.　A runner pushing off from a starting block.
e.　A boater paddling through the water.

Reaction, ground pushing on you

Action, you pushing on ground

1e sketch:

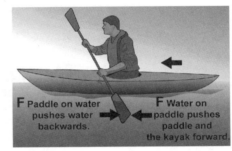

F Paddle on water pushes water backwards.　　F Water on paddle pushes paddle and the kayak forward.

2a through c:

Weekly activity	Action/reaction pair
Ride in a car	The wheels push down on the ground and the ground pushes back on the wheels
Walk to class	My feet push on the ground and the ground pushes back to hold me up
Watch television	I push down in the seat and the seat pushes back up
Bounce a basketball	The ball pushes on the floor and the floor pushes back on the ball
Carry a backpack	The backpack pulls on my shoulders and my shoulders pull on the backpack

Identifying action-reaction pairs

1

In the first part of this investigation, you will be sketching the action/reaction force pairs for five different situations. The important thing to remember when sketching these free body diagrams is that the forces in a pair are equal in strength, opposite in direction, and act on opposite objects.

Circulate among the student groups and help students to correctly identify force pairs in their diagrams.

Identifying action-reaction pairs in your life

2

In Part 2 of the Investigation, you will come up with five different daily life situations of your own, and again draw free body diagrams showing the action/reaction force pairs.

Students may need some suggestions for selecting appropriate situations. It helps to have students think of cases in which one object exerts a force on another as in a swimmer stroking against the water, a baseball hitting a bat, a gymnast jumping on a trampoline, or a person knocking on a door.

Why don't equal and opposite forces cancel each other out?

3

Remember our discussion about how action/reaction force pairs never cancel each other out? In the third part of this Investigation, you will draw a series of free body diagrams to prove this fact.

Action/reaction pairs act on different objects. No single object has both members of an action/reaction pair acting on it.

At this point in the study of Newton's third law, students will be very comfortable with drawing action/reaction force pair diagrams. This activity will further drive home the key to Newton's third law: action/reaction forces are equal in size and opposite in direction, but since they act on different objects, they do not cancel each other out. Students will see this clearly when they study each object in their diagram—none of the objects have both members of any force pair acting on it!

Thinking deeper about the third law

4

This has been a thorough study of how Newton's third law of motion applies to the world around us. Now we are going to take our understanding one step further. Many important results in science are deduced by carefully thinking about what would happen if the opposite, or a different law were true. What would happen if Newton's third law stated that for every action force, there is a reaction force that is only one-half as strong as the action force?

What would happen if Newton's third law were changed so that for every action force, there was a reaction force only one-half as strong as the action force?

This is meant to be a class discussion question since many students are not used to thinking in this way. For example, suppose the upward force of the chair on your bottom were twice as great as the force of your bottom against the chair. You would accelerate up since the force of the chair against you is twice as big as you weight! This is a problem because you do NOT go flying up from the chair all by yourself. However, the worst problem is that anything that makes the action and reaction forces unequal breaks the symmetry between action and reaction. If the forces are different then it matters which is which and there is really no physical reason why the force of your bottom on the chair should be the action force instead of the reaction. Symmetry in physics is a very important concept. If there is no physical reason for calling one force the action and one the reaction, then there can be no physical difference attached to the labels. The only way for this to be true is for both forces to be equal in magnitude and opposite in direction. Students can go back to the situations that were diagrammed in parts 1, 2, and 3 to show what effects, if any, this strange law would have on the world around us.

2 Identifying action-reaction pairs in your life

a. List five specific activities you do on a weekly basis. For example, if you are on the tennis team, you might list "hitting a tennis ball" as one activity.

b. Make a free body diagram of each activity.

c. For each activity, identify at least one pair of forces that are an action-reaction pair.

3 Why don't equal and opposite forces cancel each other out?

It is easy to get confused about action-reaction forces. People often ask, "Why don't they cancel each other out?" The reason is that the action and reaction forces act on *different* objects. Prove that action-reaction forces never act on the same object by doing the following:

a. Create a sketch showing your calculator sitting on top of your textbook which is sitting on top of your desk which is standing on the tile floor.

b. Identify the forces that serve as the action-reaction forces and draw them in your sketch.

c. Now draw a free body diagram that shows each object by itself (the calculator, the textbook, the table, the tile floor, and Earth) and uses arrows to represent the forces acting on each particular object.

d. Look at the forces on any one object. That object *does not* have both forces from any single action-reaction pair acting on it. Is this true for all of the objects? (This is the key to Newton's third law: The action-reaction forces are equal in size and opposite in direction but since they act on different objects, they do not cancel each other out.)

4 Thinking deeper about the third law

Many important results in science are deduced by carefully thinking about what would happen if the opposite, or a different law, were true. For example, imagine if Newton's third law of motion was a law made by the government. Also, imagine there is going to be a vote tomorrow on whether to keep Newton's third law as it is or change the third law so every action force creates a reaction force that is always *one-half* as strong as the action force. Think up one strange scenario that might happen if forces obeyed a law in which the reaction force is opposite in direction and one-half as strong as the action force. You may wish to do this as a project jointly with your group.

What would happen if this were true?

LAW
WE THE PEOPLE DO HEREBY DECLARE THAT THE REACTION TO ANY ACTION FORCE SHALL BE OPPOSITE IN DIRECTION AND ONE HALF IN STRENGTH.

2 3 4 Example answers

2b,c sketch:

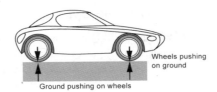

Wheels pushing on ground

Ground pushing on wheels

2b,c sketch

Basketball pushing on floor

Floor pushing on basketball

3a.

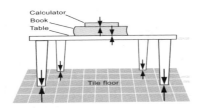

Calculator
Book
Table

Tile floor

3c.

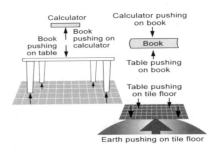

Calculator

Calculator pushing on book

Book pushing on table

Book pushing on calculator

Book

Table pushing on book

Table pushing on tile floor

Earth pushing on tile floor

3d. None of the objects have both forces from an action/reaction pair acting on it.

4. If the reaction force was halved, you would have to double your effort to get the same response as if the reaction was full strength. For example, if you were walking across the floor, it would feel as if you were walking in soft sand or snow because the floor would not be pushing as strongly against your foot.

6.1 Mass, Weight and Gravity

Key Question: What is speed and how is it measured?

In this Investigation, students build an Atwood's machine consisting of two unequal hanging masses connected over a pulley. They analyze the system and use Newton's second law to predict the acceleration. Based on the acceleration, they then predict how long it will take the masses to move a measure distance. The students use a stopwatch to test their predictions.

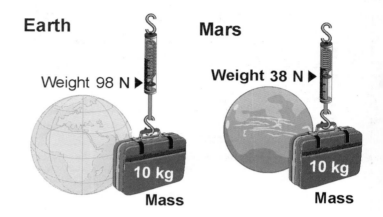

Earth Weight 98 N ▶ 10 kg Mass

Mars Weight 38 N ▶ 10 kg Mass

Reading Synopsis

Students read Section 6.1 Mass, Weight and Gravity before the Investigation.

Mass is a measure of the amount of matter an object contains. An object's mass remains the same whether the object is on Earth, Mars, or any other location. Weight is the force of gravity on an object. The weight of an object depends on its mass and the strength of gravity in the place where the object is located.

The weight of an object is its mass in kilograms multiplied by g, which has a value of 9.8 N/kg on the Earth's surface. The value of g changes depending on where in the universe you are, such as what planet you are on.

An object is weightless when it feels no force from gravity. One way to become weightless is to get far away from any source of gravity such as planets and stars. A second way to become weightless is to be in free fall.

Weight and mass are not the same. Using mass in a formula that requires weight (or vice-versa) will result in the wrong answer.

The Investigation

Leading Questions
- How is the net force acting on an object related to its acceleration?
- How are an object's speed and acceleration related?

Learning Goals
By the end of the Investigation, students will be able to:
- Analyze the forces acting on an object to determine its acceleration.
- Predict the time it takes an object to move a given distance if the acceleration and initial speed are known.

Key Vocabulary Newton's second law, force, tension, acceleration, speed

Setup and Materials

Students work in groups of three to four at tables.

Each group should have:

- Ultimate pulleys set
- Physics stand
- Timer and one photogate, AC adapter (or 9-volt battery), and cords to connect the photogate to the timer
- Electronic scale or triple-beam balance

Details

Time	One class period
Preparation	Students should be familiar with the calculation of net forces and with Newton's second law
Assignments	Section 6.1 Mass, Weight and Gravity in the **Student Text** before the Investigation
Skill Sheets	6.1 Mass and Weight
Equipment Setup	Ultimate Pulleys

Teaching the Investigation

1　Introduction
2　Setting up the experiment
3　Analyzing the system to find the acceleration
4　A hypothesis that can be tested
5　Testing the hypothesis
6　Analyzing the data

Introduction

You have already heard from me that objects of different mass fall at the same rate. Of course, this assumes that there is no friction. As long as friction can be ignored, objects fall at the same rate because the increased force of gravity that comes from increased mass is exactly counteracted by the increase of inertia. Remember, inertia makes objects harder to accelerate. Today's investigation is about weight, which uses the force exerted by gravity on objects with mass. The weight of an object is a force and on the surface of the Earth this force has a strength of 9.8 N/kg. In terms of the second law, acceleration is force divided by mass. The force of gravity acting on an object is its mass times the strength of gravity, g. If we replace the force in the second law with the weight, we see that the mass cancels from the top and bottom.

> Showed that a = F/m reduces to a = g when F = mg.

Today we are going to do an experiment that tests the hypothesis that weight acts like any other force and that the weight of an object is mg where g = 9.8 N/kg.

Setting up the experiment

1 Attach the spindle to the top of the physics stand. Place the pulley on the spindle and use the spacers and stopper to keep the pulley in place. Place the string around the pulley and connect the hangers to each end of the string. One of the hangers should be just below the pulley when the other is sitting at the bottom of the stand.

> Check each group's setup to make sure the pulley and hangers are correctly attached.

Place unequal numbers of washers on the hangers. Adjust the numbers of washers until the heavier mass takes at least five seconds to fall from the top to the bottom of the stand when released.

> If the hangers have equal weights, it is possible to make one fall by giving it a slight push. Make sure all groups have unequal numbers of washers on their hangers so the heavier one will fall when released.

Analyzing the system to find the acceleration

2 This setup is called an Atwood machine. How do you think it may be useful?

> The machine makes it easier to lift a heavy object. One of the weights acts as a counterweight.

You will be analyzing the forces on the system to determine the acceleration. First we will identify the forces acting on each of the hangers.

> Draw a sketch of each hanger on the board. Each hanger has two forces—weight and tension—acting on it Draw vectors to indicate each force.

What is the net force on each hanger?

> The net force is the difference between the tension and the weight. If the positive direction is defined as upward, the net force is *T – mg*.

How can we use Newton's second law to determine the acceleration of each hanger?

> The net force on each hanger is equal to its mass multiplied by its acceleration. Write the equation for each on the board. Then equate the net force on each hanger to its mass multiplied by its acceleration to derive *T – mg = ma*.

How did the accelerations of the hangers compare? How did the directions of the net forces compare?

> The accelerations are equal in magnitude but opposite in direction.

How did the directions of the net forces compare? How are the directions of the net forces and accelerations related?

> The heavier hanger has a downward net force and a downward acceleration. Its weight is greater than the tension. The lighter hanger has an upward net force and an upward acceleration. The tension is greater than the weight.

Hanger 1

$\text{Net } F = T_1 - m_1 g$
$\text{Net } F = m_1 a_1$
Equating the two: $\quad T_1 - m_1 g = m_1 a_1$

Hanger 2

$\text{Net } F = T_2 - m_2 g$
$\text{Net } F = m_2 a_2$
Equating the two: $\quad T_2 - m_2 g = m_2 a_2$

Two meanings for g

Many textbooks write the equation for weight as $F = mg$ then define g as 9.8 m/sec^2. While this is common practice, it is somewhat confusing and not technically correct. An object at rest has an acceleration of zero yet it has a weight which is not zero. In Chapter 4, students learned that the symbol "g" stands for the acceleration of gravity in free fall, which is 9.8 m/sec^2. In this Investigation they are being introduced to another meaning for g, and that is the strength of gravity at the Earth's surface, which is 9.8 N/kg. Technically, this number represents the magnitude of the gravitational field at the surface of the Earth. Each kilogram of mass feels a force of 9.8 newtons from the Earth's gravity.

In Chapter 4, we discussed objects that were in free fall being accelerated by the force of gravity. Here, we are discussing the force of gravity acting on all objects, whether they are accelerating or not. When calculating weight, it is more natural to discuss gravity in N/kg instead of m/sec^2. This is because objects may not be in motion but they still have weight. The two meanings for g are equivalent in calculations since a force of 9.8 N acting on a mass of 1 kg produces an acceleration of 9.8 m/sec^2.

However, the two meanings for g are not conceptually identical. On careful reflection, why should same property (mass) that resists acceleration also determine an object's interaction with gravity? What has gravity got to do with acceleration? You can have acceleration described by $a = F/m$ in the complete absence of gravity. Einstein was convinced that it was not a coincidence. The value of g for both interpretations was a clue telling Einstein that somehow, gravity and motion were related. Einstein's theory of general relativity (Chapter 31) solves the paradox by explaining gravity as a curvature of space itself that is caused by mass. The force we label "gravity" arises when we reconcile the requirements of Newton's first and second law with the "straight" path objects take through curved space.

6.1 Mass, Weight and Gravity

Question: What is the relationship between mass and weight?

In this Investigation, you will:

1. Develop a model that predicts the acceleration of a system in which only weight forces are important.
2. Test the model by measuring the acceleration of the system.

1 Setting up the experiment

1. Set up the experiment as shown in the diagram using one pulley. Slide the pulley onto the spindle. Use plastic spacers and the stopper to keep the pulley from sliding off the spindle.
2. Attach unequal masses to the two hangers and loop the string over the pulley. The experiment works best if the heavier side has 2 or 3 more washers than the lighter side.

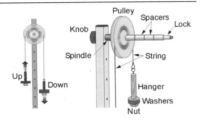

2 Analyzing the system to find the acceleration

From a previous Investigation, you know that the acceleration of the masses comes from the difference in weight between m_1 and m_2. Using the second law ($F = ma$), the diagram below shows how to calculate the accelerations of m_1 and m_2 in terms of the masses and the strength of gravity, g.

The system
(Atwood's Machine)

Forces include the tension (T) and the weights (m_1g, m_2g)

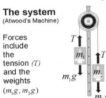

Find the accelerations

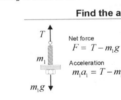

Net force
$F = T - m_1g$
Acceleration
$m_1a_1 = T - m_1g$

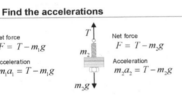

Net force
$F = T - m_2g$
Acceleration
$m_2a_2 = T - m_2g$

Because the masses are connected by the string, when one accelerates up (+), the other accelerates down (-) with the same acceleration. Mathematically, this means $a_2 = -a_1$. If we substitute $-a_1$ for a_2 in the equation for the acceleration of m_2, we get two equations for the tension (T) in the string. Since the string is the same string on both sides, the tension must be equal for m_1 and m_2. The result is an equation that contains only one unknown, the acceleration, a_1. Every other variable is known or can be determined in the experiment.

From acceleration of m_1
$T = m_1a_1 + m_1g$

From acceleration of m_2
$T = -m_2a_1 + m_2g$

The tension (T) is the same, therefore
$m_1a_1 + m_1g = -m_2a_1 + m_2g$

32

Let $T_2=T_1$ and $a_2=-a_1$

Hanger 1: $T_1-m_1g = m_1a_1$
$T_1=m_1a_1+m_1g$

Hanger 2: $T_1m_2g = m_2(-a_1)$
$T_1=-m_2a_1+m_2g$

Equate: $m_1a_1+m_1g=-m_2a_1+m_2g$

A hypothesis that can be tested

$m_1a+m_1g=-m_2a+m_2g$

$m_1a+m_2a=m_2g-m_1g$

$a(m_1+m_2)=m_2g-m_1g$

$a=(m_2g-m_1g)/(m_1+m_2)$

Testing the hypothesis

Analyzing the data

[3]

[4]

[5]

How does the tension in the string on the right compare with the tension on the left?

> The tensions are equal. (The tensions will not be exactly equal if the pulley has significant mass or friction. However, the tensions in this case are virtually equal and the analysis of unequal tensions is beyond the scope of this Investigation.)

Knowing that the two tensions are equal and the accelerations are equal and opposite, we can write an equation that will allow us to find the acceleration without having to know the tension.

> Give students some time to work on finding the equation. Then work through the solution on the board. Solve the equation for each pulley for the tension. Eliminate a_2 by letting it equal $-a_1$. Then set the two equations equal to each other, eliminating T. Acceleration is the only unknown quantity left.

Using the equation we derived, we can predict the acceleration of the hangers if we know their masses. Rearrange the equation to solve for the acceleration.

> Work through the solution on the board. The final result is $a = (m_2g-m_1g)/(m_1+m_2)$.

Now think about how acceleration is related to distance and time. What equation allows us to calculate the distance something moves during accelerated motion?

> Review the equation $x = x_0 + v_0t + 1/2\ at^2$.

Consider the falling mass on the Atwood's machine. We know the acceleration because we just calculated it. How long should it take the hanger to fall from its highest position to its lowest?

> Demonstrate the apparatus dropping one hanger as described in the investigation.

If the initial speed and position are both zero, the time should be the square root of two times the height divided by the acceleration.

> Work this out on the board.

This is a prediction we can test! According to our analysis we can predict how long it should take for the hanger to fall a given distance.

Follow the procedure in step four of the Investigation. Use a pad to stop the hanger from crashing down and making dents in the base of the stand. A ratio of 7 to 5 washers gives good results, as does any combination with 2 - 3 washers difference. Remember to measure the height from the bottom of the hanger to the top of the pad as shown in the diagram in step 4. Record at least 5 times and take an average. You should NOT look at the Timer when you are taking a measurement so you don't subconsciously stop the Timer at your predicted time.

> Circulate and assist students to do the experiment.

Calculate the average of all the times. What kind of variability is in the measurements? What does this tell you about the sensitivity of the experiment?

> Human reaction time is around 0.1 seconds so you should expect to see times that vary by this amount. The experiment can only prove or disprove the hypothesis to within +/- 0.1 seconds, because of the variability in the reaction time.

How does your measured time compare with your predicted time? Why might the values not be exactly equal? Can you make the experiment more accurate?

> Typical results agree with predictions to within +/- 0.2 seconds or 5-8 %. The values might differ slightly due to friction in the pulley. The experiment could be improved by using one configuration to estimate the friction in the pulley, then changing the balance of washers (keeping total mass the same) and correcting for the force of friction.

3

3   A hypothesis that can be tested

According to the theory of the last section, if we know the masses and (g), we can determine the acceleration. If we know the acceleration, we should be able to predict the speed at any time during the motion.

a. Rearrange the last equation to get a formula for the acceleration, a_1.

b. Use the equations for uniformly accelerated motion to derive a formula that gives the time (t) it takes to fall a height (h) after the masses start moving. You may assume zero initial speed.

The formula you get in (b) is actually a hypothesis that the experiment can test to see if the theory is correct. Note that we made some assumptions to arrive at this hypothesis. The assumptions are that there is no friction and that the pulley has no mass.

1. Measure the mass of each hanger (m_1 and m_2) and record the results in Table 1.
2. Use a small square of cardboard or a dry sponge as a pad to protect the base of the stand from the falling mass. Bring the heavier hanger up until the lighter hanger is resting on the base of the stand. Measure the height the hanger falls from the highest point to the lowest.
3. Calculate the predicted time in seconds it should take the hanger to fall using the formula you derived in part (b) above.

Table 1: Mass and Speed		
m_1	Washers	
	mass (kg)	
m_2	Washers	
	mass (kg)	
Calculated acceleration (a)		
Measured height (h)		
Predicted Time (t)		

4   Testing the hypothesis

1. Bring the heavier hanger up until the lighter one is resting on the base of the stand. Release the heavier hangar and let it fall.
2. Use the stopwatch function of the Timer to measure the time it takes the heavier hangar to fall through the height, h that you measured in step 3.
3. Do several trials to get an average time.

5   Analyzing the data

a. Discuss the accuracy and precision of the experiment. How much variability was there in the times you measured? What does that tell you about how well your experiment is able to test your hypothesis?

b. Compare the predicted time with the measured time. Does your experiment confirm your hypothesis? How does your answer to question (a) above affect the conclusion of the experiment (whether the hypothesis is confirmed)?

c. What factors might account for any difference between measurement and prediction?

d. Can you think of a way to make the experiment a more sensitive test of your hypothesis by accounting for any of the factors you identified in part (c)?

33

3

a. $a = (m_2 - m_1) \div (m_2 + m_1)$

b. $t = \sqrt{\dfrac{2h}{a}}$

4

Table 1: Mass and Speed		
m_1	Washers	5
	mass (kg)	0.104
m_2	Washers	7
	mass (kg)	0.127
Calculated acceleration (a)		
0.976 m/sec^2		
Measured height (h)		
0.775 m		
Predicted Time (t)		
1.26 sec		

5

a. We observed times of 1.39, 1.32, 1.46, 1.41, and 1.52 seconds. The average is 1.42 seconds. The highest and lowest times are 0.1 seconds away from the average. This variability tells us that the experiment can only test our hypothesis to within 0.1 seconds.

b. The predicted time is 1.26 seconds, which is 0.16 seconds less than the measured time. The difference is 11%. The difference is larger than the variability in the experiment, therefore we conclude that the hypothesis cannot be completely correct.

c. Friction was ignored.

d. We could use the results to calculate a force of friction, then do the experiment over with the same total number of washers, but a different balance on left and right. Since the total mass is the same, the frictional force should be the same in both cases. In the second experiment we could subtract out the force of friction before calculating the acceleration.

6.2 Friction

Key Question: How can we describe and model friction?

Sliding friction is a resistive force that works against the motion of two surfaces that are sliding relative to each other. Static friction exists when an object might move but does not move due to the force of friction. The coefficients of sliding and static friction relate the friction force to the force pressing two surfaces together. In this Investigation, students measure friction forces and determine the coefficients of static and sliding friction for two different surfaces sliding on a smooth tabletop.

Reading Synopsis

Students read Section 6.2 Friction after the Investigation.

Friction is a resistive force that always works against the motion that produces it. The force of friction between two surfaces sliding past each other is approximately proportional to the force squeezing the surfaces together. The coefficient of sliding friction is the proportionality constant relating the friction force to the normal force and is usually between zero and one, depending on the surfaces that create the friction.

Static friction describes the force that exists between two surfaces that are not moving but would be if friction were not present. The force of static friction is not one definite value but can vary up to a maximum value. If this maximum is exceeded, the objects will start to slide. The coefficient of static friction is almost always greater than the coefficient of sliding friction.

Friction has both beneficial and detrimental aspects. Friction is necessary for tires to have traction, brakes to work, and for walking. Friction also causes wear and inefficiency. Devices such as lubricants and bearings are designed to reduce friction.

The Investigation

Leading Questions
- What is friction?
- How is friction described and modeled?
- Are there different types of friction?
- How is friction useful to us in our everyday lives?
- When is friction not desirable and what can we do to reduce it in these cases?

Learning Goals

By the end of the Investigation, students will be able to:
- Distinguish between static and sliding friction.
- Measure friction forces.
- Explain the factors that determine the magnitude of the force of friction between surfaces.
- Calculate the coefficients of static and sliding friction from experimental measurements.

Key Vocabulary

force, friction, static friction, sliding friction, coefficient of friction, normal force

Setup and Materials

Students work in groups of three to five at tables.

Each group should have:

- Friction block
- 2.5- and 5-N spring scales
- Assortment of weights to place on top of friction block
- Calculator
- Electronic scale or triple-beam balance (one per class is acceptable)

Optional: Other types of surfaces such as sandpaper, wood, glass, carpet, or plastic on which to slide the friction block.

Details

Time   One class period

Preparation   Students should be familiar with the use of spring scales to measure forces.

Assignments   Section 6.2 Friction in the **Student Text** after the Investigation

Skill Sheets   6.2 Friction

Teaching the Investigation

1   Introduction
2   Static friction
3   Examining the data
4   Sliding friction
5   Comparing static and sliding friction
6   Friction between other surfaces

Introduction

Friction is a force that resists motion.

If I start sliding this eraser along the desk, why doesn't it keep moving after I stop pushing? According to the first law, an object should continue along in the same motion it has once all forces have been removed. Is the first law wrong?

Discuss the situation until someone points out that all forces have NOT been removed. The force of friction still exists.

What is friction?

Students may have varied ideas about what friction is. Lead them to the fact that friction is a force that resists motion.

Can friction be present when objects are moving, when objects are at rest, or both?

Friction can be present both when objects are moving and when objects are at rest.

Static friction

1

Static friction is the resistive force that is present when an object is not moving.

Static friction is the name given to friction that is present when an object is not moving. For example, if I push on this desk and it does not move, static friction keeps the desk from moving.

Press horizontally on a desk with a small force so it does not move.

What if I push harder and the desk still does not move? What's happening to the static friction force?

Act like you are exerting a strong force on the desk. Students should realize that the friction force is greater now. The friction force must be equal and opposite your pushing force because the desk does not move.

Can you use one of Newton's laws to explain what is happening?

Newton's first law states that an object at rest will stay at rest unless there is an unbalanced force acting on it. Newton's second law states that the acceleration is proportional to the net force. There is no acceleration, so the net force is zero.

If I push hard enough, I can get the desk to move. Why do you think this happens?

There is a maximum amount of friction force that can be present. Once the pushing force is greater than the maximum friction force, the desk moves.

Measure the maximum static friction force by finding the largest force the block can resist without moving.

In the first part of the Investigation, you will be measuring the static friction force on a block. Calibrate your spring scales so they read zero. Then measure the weight of the friction block and record it in Table 1. Now place your block on the table so the felt side is facing down. The spring scale should be attached to the block in a way that allows you to see the force readings on the scale. Keep the scale horizontal and pull on the block so it is just on the verge of moving. You want to find the maximum amount of force the block can resist without moving. This is equal to the maximum static friction force. Record this force in Table 1.

Make sure students hold the spring scales horizontally, not on a diagonal. Also check to see that each group is reading the force in newtons rather than the kilogram measurement on the spring scale.

Now you will be adding weight to the top of the block. Measure the weight you will be adding and record it in Table 1. Place the weight on top of the block and measure the maximum force the block can resist without moving. Repeat this for at least four different amounts of added weight.

Circulate among the groups to ensure that they are properly following the procedure.

Calculate the total weight that was pulled in each trial. Then divide the friction force by the total weight and record this ratio as a decimal in the table. It should be a value less than one.

Some students will divide the wrong way. If any ratios come out to be larger than one, students have made this mistake.

6.2 Friction

Question: How can we describe and model friction?

In this Investigation, you will:

1. Measure forces of static friction and sliding friction.
2. Calculate the coefficients of static and sliding friction.
3. Compare static and sliding friction forces.

Friction is a resistive force that works against the motion that produces it. You encounter friction every day. Without friction, cars wouldn't move, you couldn't write with a pencil, and you would have difficulty staying on your chair. In this Investigation, you will study two types of friction: static friction and sliding friction.

1 **Static friction**

Static friction is present when you try to push or pull on an object and it does *not* move. The first part of the Investigation explores static friction.

The force of static friction between an object and a surface is not a constant value. Instead, the force is equal and opposite to the net force applied to the object up to a maximum value. If the applied force is increased beyond the maximum static friction force, the object starts moving. To measure static friction, you determine the *maximum* force that can be applied to an object *before* it starts moving.

You will use a spring scale to measure forces. First, make sure your scale is calibrated to zero. To get the most accurate readings, use the lowest value spring scale that measures the force without exceeding the limit of the scale. For example, use a 2.5-newton scale when measuring forces between 0 and 2.5 newtons. Use a 5-newton scale to measure forces between 2.5 and 5 newtons.

1. Measure the mass of the friction block and record it in Table 1. Calculate the weight by multiplying by *g* (9.8 N/kg)

Measuring the force of static friction

Spring scale — Friction block

Record the force just *before* the block moves

2. Place the block on the table with the felt side facing down. Attach a spring scale so the newton markings are facing upward.
3. Gently pull on the scale until the block is on the verge of moving. You want to carefully find the greatest amount of force the block can resist *without* sliding. This is equal to the maximum static friction force. Record this as the friction force in Table 1.
4. Divide the friction force by the total weight and record the resulting ratio as a decimal value in the last column of Table 1.
5. Add weight to the block and repeat the experiment for at least four different weights.

Table 1: Static friction data

Mass (kg)	Weight (N)	Friction force (N)	Ratio

Friction in our lives

It is interesting to think about how much we rely on friction in our everyday lives. We could not walk, drive a car, sit on a chair, hold a cup, or write with a pencil if it were not for friction. You might have students imagine what it would be like to wake up one day and find that friction did not exist.

Many products we buy are made of materials that are chosen specifically for the amount of friction they provide. Sneakers and tires contain rubber that has a high coefficient of friction against concrete. Frying pans are coated with a material that prevents food from sticking. Shoelaces, string, and rope made of cotton stay tied better than those made of nylon because the friction is greater. Have students brainstorm a list of products for which friction is important.

1 **Example answers**

Table 1: *Sliding Friction Data*

Mass (kg)	Weight (N)	Friction force (N)	Ratio
0.106	1.04	0.25	0.240
0.288	2.82	0.75	.248
0.481	4.71	1.15	0.244
0.677	6.63	1.65	0.249

Examining the data

The static friction force increases proportionally as the weight being pulled increases.

The coefficient of static friction is the ratio of the friction force to the total weight.

Sliding friction

Sliding friction is caused by irregularities in the surfaces when two surfaces move across each other.

Measure the sliding friction by finding the force required to pull the block at a slow constant speed.

Comparing static and sliding friction

The coefficient of static friction is larger than the coefficient of sliding friction.

Friction between other surfaces

2

What happened to the friction force as the weight that was being pulled increased?

The friction force increased proportionally.

Why do you think there was this type of relationship between the friction force and the weight that was being pulled?

The heavier the block, the greater the force squeezing the block to the table.

The ratio you calculated is called the coefficient of static friction. How did your different values of the ratio compare?

All of the values within a single group should be very similar. Discuss the fact that there may be slight differences, but that overall the values are close to each other. Compare the values between different groups. They should be similar if all of the groups worked on the same type of tabletop. If there were differences, discuss possible reasons.

Do you think the results of this experiment would have been different if you had placed the block on a rougher surface?

The friction force would be greater, and the coefficient of friction would have been greater.

3

Friction is also present when objects are moving. If you slide the block across the table, you will feel the force of sliding friction between the felt and the table. This force keeps the block from moving as fast as it would if there were no friction. How do you think we can measure this type of friction?

Students will have varied answers. Discuss Newton's first law. A moving object will keep moving at a constant speed if there is no unbalanced force on it. If the block is pulled at a constant speed, the pulling force must balance the friction force.

Now you will measure the force of sliding friction. To do this, pull your block across the table at a slow constant speed. You will have to read the force on the scale while you are pulling the block. It may take some practice to keep the block's speed constant and to read the scale accurately. Then you will place weight on top of the block as you did in Part 1. Repeat this for at least four different amounts of added weight. Calculate the coefficient of sliding friction for each trial.

Make sure students are pulling the blocks at a slow constant speed.

4

What happened to the friction force as the weight of the block increased?

The force increased proportionally.

How does the coefficient of sliding friction compare with the coefficient of static friction?

The coefficient of static friction should be larger. It takes more force to break surfaces loose from each other than it does to keep them sliding once they are already moving.

5

If time allows, have students determine the coefficients of static and sliding friction for other combinations of surfaces.

2 | Examining the data

a. What happened to the friction force as the weight of the pulled objects increased?

b. Discuss a possible explanation for the relationship.

c. The ratio of the friction force to the weight of the pulled objects is called the *coefficient of static friction*. Was there a trend among these values or were they all roughly equal?

d. What effect would placing the block on a rougher surface (such as sandpaper) have on the coefficient of static friction?

3 | Sliding friction

Measuring the force of sliding friction

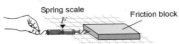

Spring scale   Friction block

Record the force it takes to drag the block slowly at constant speed

1. Repeat the experiment from Part 1 except this time measure the friction force as you slowly slide the block along at constant speed. Record the masses, weights, and forces in Table 2.

2. Calculate the ratio of force ÷ weight and enter the result in the last column of Table 2.

Table 2: Sliding Friction Data

Mass (kg)	Weight (N)	Friction force (N)	Ratio

4 | Comparing static and sliding friction

a. What happened to the friction force as the weight of the pulled objects increased in Table 2?

b. Is the relationship between the friction force and the total weight in Table 2 similar to the relationship in Table 1?

c. The ratio of the sliding friction force to the total weight is called the *coefficient of sliding friction*. Compare the coefficient of sliding friction to that of static friction. Are they different? Is one significantly different than the other, or are the two coefficients about equal?

d. Explain a possible reason the forces of static and sliding friction might not be equal.

5 | Friction between other surfaces

During the Investigation, you found the coefficients of static and sliding friction for felt on the tabletop. If time allows, determine the coefficients of friction for other combinations of surfaces. Some combinations you might try are the wood side of the block on a sheet of paper, felt on sandpaper, or wood on wood.

35

2 3 4 5 Example answers

2a. The friction force increased as the weight of the block increased.

2b. The friction force increased because the block pressed harder into the table when its weight increased.

2c. All of the values were approximately the same.

2d. Placing the block on a rougher surface would increase the coefficient of static friction.

Table 2: *Sliding Friction Data*

Mass (kg)	Weight (N)	Friction force (N)	Ratio
0.106	1.04	0.20	0.192
0.288	2.82	0.55	0.195
0.481	4.71	0.90	0.191
0.677	6.63	1.25	0.189

4a. The friction force increased as the weight increased.

4b. The relationship was similar, but the static friction force was slightly greater than the sliding friction force for any given weight of the block.

4c. The coefficient of sliding friction was slightly less than the coefficient of static friction.

4d. Static friction may be greater than sliding friction because it is hard to unstick the two surfaces. The surfaces must be separated to get the block moving. Once it is moving, it is not as hard to keep moving because the surfaces are not bonded together.

6.3 Equilibrium of Forces and Hooke's Law

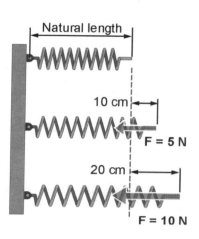

Natural length

10 cm

F = 5 N

20 cm

F = 10 N

Key Question: How do you predict the force on a spring?

Springs come in two basic types. An extension spring is designed to be stretched, or extended. A compression spring is designed to be squeezed or compressed. With both types of springs, the force created by the spring depends on the amount of extension or compression. In this Investigation, students will determine how much the spring extends per newton of applied force. They will measure the amount the spring extends as the applied force is changed. Hooke's law will be applied when working with both extension and compression springs. To determine the spring constant, students create a force versus extension graph and a force versus compression graph.

Reading Synopsis

Students read Section 6.3 Equilibrium of Forces and Hooke's Law after the Investigation.

Equilibrium exists when the net force is zero. Objects in equilibrium experience no change in motion (no acceleration). A free body diagram replaces all interactions between an object and its surroundings by forces. A common application of equilibrium and free body diagrams is to find an unknown force when equilibrium exists and some forces are known.

Hooke's law describes the forces created by springs, rubber bands, and other objects that stretch. According to Hooke's law the strength of the force exerted by a spring is the spring constant times the length the spring is extended or compressed ($F = -kx$). The negative sign indicates that the force created by the spring is in the opposite direction to the extension or compression. The spring-like behavior of all materials is what creates the forces between inanimate objects that "know" how to make the forces exactly equal and opposite.

The Investigation

Leading Questions
- Describe equilibrium and give examples.
- Does equilibrium mean all forces on an object must be zero?
- How can you tell how much force a spring will exert if it is stretched or compressed?
- How do inanimate objects "know" how much reaction force to exert to satisfy Newton's third law?

Learning Goals

By the end of the Investigation, students will be able to:
- Calculate the force exerted by extension and compression springs when given the spring constant and deformation.
- Calculate the deformation of a spring when given the spring constant and applied force.
- Build a force-measuring scale from a spring.
- Explain how Hooke's law solves the paradox of how inanimate objects "know" how much reaction force to exert to satisfy Newton's third law.

Key Vocabulary

equilibrium, free-body diagram, dimensions, spring, extended, compressed, deformation, constant (k), Hooke's law

Setup and Materials

Students work in groups of four or five at tables.

Each group should have:

- Ultimate pulleys set (in particular, the compression and extension springs and washers will be used)
- Physics stand
- Graph paper
- Meter stick

Details

Time One class period

Preparation 📝

📖 Section 6.3 Equilibrium of Forces and Hooke's Law in the **Student Edition** after the Investigation.

Skill Sheets 6.3 Equilibrium

Equipment Setup Ultimate Pulleys

Teaching the Investigation

1 Introduction
2 What is a spring?
3 Setting up the experiment
4 Analyzing the data
5 Testing the model
6 Compression springs
7 Analyzing the data
8 Testing the model
9 Hooke's law and Newton's third law

Introduction

Did you ever wonder why or how objects know to follow Newton's third law? How does a floor know exactly how much reaction force to exert on my foot to counteract my weight pushing down? Do you think the floor can calculate physics equations? Today's Investigation is going to solve this paradox. We will happily find that objects with no brains do not have to solve physics equations to know how to act. We are going to start by studying springs because springs are easy and will lead us quickly to the rule we need to know in order to understand more complicated systems, such as a floor.

Can anyone give me a definition of a spring?

A spring is an object which creates forces that resist stretching or compressing.

What is a spring?

A compression spring is designed to be squeezed.

An extension spring is designed to be stretched.

Today we are going to look at two different kinds of springs. A compression spring is designed to be squeezed, or compressed. An extension spring is designed to be stretched, or extended. There are other types of springs that are designed to resist twisting or bending. A property that all objects have is that they push back against any motion that tends to extend, compress, twist, or bend them. A spring is a device that is specially designed to push back with a controlled amount of force that is proportional to the amount of extension, compression, twist, or bending.

Demonstrating the relationship between force and deformation

The larger the force you apply, the greater the deformation of the spring.

The goal of the first part of the Investigation is to find a rule for how the extension of a spring depends on the applied force. We will first test these extension springs.

Hold up a spring and stretch it with a force scale attached to one end.

Try this with your spring. Watch the force measured on the scale as you stretch the spring. These springs are somewhat delicate, so do not stretch them too much. What do you notice about the connection between the force you apply and the length of the spring?

Students should see that the larger the force you apply, the longer the spring gets. This implies a proportional relationship between the force applied and the extension of the spring.

Setting up the experiment

1

We are going to do a careful experiment to determine the exact relationship between the amount the spring is extended and the force that is applied. Set the spindle to the 10th hole from the bottom of the stand. Attach one nut and one washer to the weight hanger and hook it on the spring. The spring will extend somewhat.

Students do this activity.

Measure the reference position distance, and measure the mass of the hanger with one washer on it.

Take a meter stick and measure the reference position, which is the distance between the bottom of the stand and the bottom of the washer. Record this distance in the first row of Table 1 and enter the number of washers. Remove the hanger and measure its mass; record the mass in Table 1 also.

Students record data and measure the mass of the hanger with a single washer.

Measure and record the mass and position of the spring for different numbers of washers.

Next, I want you to add washers to the hanger two or three at a time. For each different number of washers, measure the mass and position of the spring and record both in Table 1. Continue taking data until you have at least six different masses.

This is the primary part of the first half of the Investigation. Help students make the measurements and record the correct data.

Calculate the extension and force of the spring:

Extension = Stretched position - Reference position

Force = mass × 9.8 N/kg

When you are done, calculate the extension of the spring. The extension is the amount the spring stretches compared with its reference position when there was only one washer. Calculate the extension by subtracting the position in each row from the position recorded in the first row. Calculate the force by multiplying the mass by 9.8 N/kg.

Students complete Table 1 by doing the calculations.

UNIT 2: Motion and Force in One Dimension

6.3   Equilibrium of Forces and Hooke's Law

Question: How do you predict the force on a spring?

In this Investigation, you will:

1. Determine the strength of extension and compression springs.
2. Build a force-measuring scale from a spring.

Springs come in two basic types. An extension spring is designed to be stretched, or *extended*. A compression spring is designed to be squeezed, or *compressed*. With both types of springs, the force created by the spring depends on the amount of extension or compression.

1   Setting up the experiment

The goal of the first part of the experiment is to determine how much the spring extends per newton of applied force. You will measure the amount the spring extends as the applied force is changed. The data will allow you to determine the spring constant, which measures the strength of the spring.

1. Attach the spindle to the top hole in the stand using a knob.
2. Hang the extension spring from the spindle and use two spacers (one on either side) and the stop as shown in the diagram.
3. Attach one washer to the bottom of a hanger with two of the nuts. Tighten the nuts against each other so the washer does not move. This is your reference marker, DO NOT move it for the rest of the experiment.
4. Set a meter stick behind the spring and record the position of the bottom edge of the reference washer relative to the base of the stand. This is the reference position. Record it in the first row of Table 1.
5. Add a few washers to the hanger. When you attach it to the spring again, it should extend farther. Record the new position of the reference washer as the "Spring's position".
6. Measure the mass of the hanger and washers and record it in the same row of the table with the position of the spring.
7. Repeat steps 4 and 5 for different numbers of washers. Record all the data in Table 1.
8. Calculate the extension of the spring by taking the difference between each position and the reference position (first row). Calculate the force by multiplying the mass by 9.8 N/kg.

Table 1: Force and extension of a spring

Number of washers	Attached mass (kg)	Spring's position (cm)	Calculated extension (cm)	Calculated force (N)

Deformation

Scientists and engineers use the word "deformation" to describe the amount that an object's shape changes when a force is applied. If the force is small, the object returns to its original shape when the force is removed. This type of behavior is called elastic, like a rubber band. If the force is larger than a certain strength, the object does not return to its original shape but stays deformed permanently. A deformation that causes a permanent change in shape is called "inelastic."

Deformation is measured relative to the original shape before any force has been applied. For example, the deformation of a spring is typically measured from its natural, unstretched length. A spring which (unstretched) is 15 cm long and is stretched to 20 cm has a deformation of 5 cm. Extension is usually assigned a positive value, while compression is assigned a negative value.

1   Example answers

Table 1: *Force and extension of a spring*

Number of washers	Attached mass (kg)	Spring's position (cm)	Calculated extension (cm)	Calculated force (N)
0	.128	73.5	0	1.25
2	.155	71.5	2	1.52
5	.200	68.5	5	1.96

Analyzing the data

Make a graph of the force exerted by the spring versus deformation of the spring.

Hooke's law

$F = -kx = mg$

2 The rule we wish to find is usually given in a form that is the inverse of what we just measured. We measured deformation as we varied the force. Since springs are designed to create force that is proportional to deformation, the most useful form of model tells us how much force a spring will exert if it is deformed by a certain amount. Fortunately, according to Newton's third law, the force exerted BY the spring is equal and opposite to the force we exerted ON the spring by hanging a weight from it. Since we can determine the weight, we are also able to determine the force the spring exerts. Make a graph that shows the force exerted by the spring on the vertical axis and the deformation of the spring on the horizontal axis.

> Students should make the graph of force versus deformation.

The strength of a spring is described by its spring constant. The spring constant is a number that determines the ratio of force produced by the spring to deformation. For example, a spring with a spring constant of 10 newtons per meter will produce a force of 10 newtons if it is stretched by one meter. The force would be five newtons if the spring were stretched $1/2$ meter. The force produced by the spring is equal to the spring constant times the deformation. The negative sign indicates that the force is in the opposite direction to the deformation. If we stretch the spring it pulls with a force opposite to the direction we stretch. This formula is known as Hooke's law and it applies to many objects, not just springs.

> Write Hooke's law on the board and explain the variables.

10 N/m would be a very weak spring since a meter is a lot of stretching and 10 newtons is a pretty small force. Can anyone tell me how we might determine the spring constant from the graph of force versus deformation?

> Start a discussion. The slope of a line on a graph is the ratio of change in y to change in x. On this graph, the slope is the change in force divided by the change in length, which is exactly our definition of the spring constant.

The slope of the force versus deformation graph is the spring constant

k = slope = rise/run

The slope of the force versus deformation graph is the spring constant. The spring constant has units of force divided by length, or newtons per centimeter. Use your graph to determine the spring constant for the extension spring.

> Students should calculate the slope of their graph. Compare the spring constants measured by different groups. They should be similar if the springs are not damaged.

Testing the model

Use Hooke's law to predict the spring extension for 20 washers.

3 Use Hooke's law to predict how much the spring should extend for 20 washers. Set up the experiment and cast your prediction.

> To make the prediction students need to measure or calculate the weight of the hanger and 20 washers first. Students should then test the prediction by putting 20 washers onto the hanger and measuring the extension of the spring.

Compression springs

Collect data for mass and position of spring using a compression spring.

4 Some springs are designed to be compressed rather than extended. The next part of the Investigation looks at a compression spring. Remove the spindle and set it on the table or in the hole in the wooden pulley block. Follow the diagram in step 4 of the Investigation. This time, the reference position is the distance from the table to the bottom of the lowest washer. Take data on the position of the spring for different numbers of washers similar to what you did for the extension spring.

> Students follow the instructions in step 4 to set up the compression spring experiment. Circulate around the room to assist and check whether they are getting reasonable numbers.

2 3 Example answers

2a. Graph:

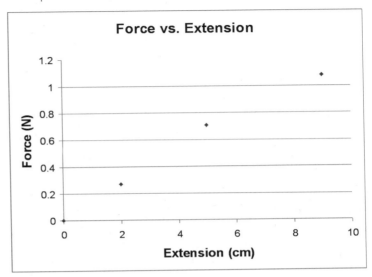

2 Analyzing the data

a. Make a graph of force versus extension for the spring.

b. The force from a spring can be described by a formula known as Hooke's law. The spring constant (k) is a measure of the strength of the spring. For example, a spring with $k = 1$ N/cm produces 1 newton of force for every centimeter of extension.

Hooke's law
(springs)

Force (N) $F = -kx$ ← Spring constant (N/cm)
Deformation (m)
(extension or compression)

Use your graph of force versus extension to determine the spring constant for the spring in the experiment. Express your result in N/cm.

3 Testing the model

a. Use your graph to predict how much the spring should extend for a hanger with 20 washers. You need to determine the weight of 20 washers (and the hanger) to make your prediction.

b. Set up the experiment and test whether the model (Hooke's law) gives the correct prediction.

c. How close did your prediction come to the actual extension of the spring? Calculate the difference between the measurement and the prediction as a percentage of the actual measurement.

4 Compression springs

The second part of the experiment looks at compression springs. Compression springs obey Hooke's law also but are designed to be compressed rather than extended. To measure the spring constant, you need to measure how much the spring compresses when different amounts of force are applied.

1. Set the spindle on the table and put one plastic washer on the shaft (diagram). Put the spring on the shaft, followed by the plastic spacer that has a flange on it. Set one washer on the flange.

2. Set a meter stick behind the spring and record the position of the washer (diagram). This is the initial reference position; record it in the first row of Table 2.

3. Collect a stack of three washers. Measure the mass of the stack and record it in Table 2.

4. Place the stack of washers on the spacer and the spring should compress. Record the new position of the lower edge of the washers in the same row you just used to record the mass of the stack of washers you added.

5. Repeat steps 4 and 5 for different size stacks of washers. Record all the data in Table 2.

6. Calculate the compression of the spring by taking the difference between the reference position and the new position for each different stack of washers. The compression comes from the weight of the added stack of washers (excluding the reference washer). Calculate the force by multiplying the mass of the added washers by 9.8 N/kg.

37

2b. I calculate a spring constant of 0.12 N/cm.

3a. The hanger plus 20 washers weighs 0.365 g for a force of 3.58 N. This means a force offset of 2.33 N. The extension offset should therefore be 19.4 cm.

3b. I measured an extension offset of 19.8 cm.

3c. The estimation was off by 2.0 percent.

Analyzing the data

force versus compression graph

Calculating the spring constant for the compression spring.

Testing the model

Use Hooke's law to predict the spring compression for 20 washers.

Hooke's law and Newton's third law

All objects act like springs to some degree, because they deform when forces are applied.

Even minimal force deflections can be calculated using Hooke's law.

Hooke's law explains how a reaction force is created and why it is equal and opposite to the applied force.

Use Table 2 to calculate the compression of the spring by subtracting the initial position from the final position. Calculate the force applied by multiplying the added mass by 9.8 N/kg. You do not need to include the mass of the first washer and spacer because the deformation is being determined relative to the length the spring has under this weight.

> Students complete calculations in Table 2.

5 Make a graph of force versus compression for the spring.

> Students make the force versus compression graph.

How does this graph compare with the graph you've made for the extension spring?

> Both graphs should be straight lines.

Use your graph to calculate the spring constant for the compression spring.

> Students calculate the slope of the graft to get the spring constant.

6 Using your model to predict the position of the spring if you were to add 20 washers. Set up the experiment and test your prediction.

> Students set up the test of Hooke's law for the compression spring using 20 washers and the spring constant they determined from the graph.

How much force would it take to cause a compression of 1 millimeter?

> Students use Hooke's law to calculate the force.

We now know how inanimate objects are able to obey Newton's third law. All objects act like springs to some degree. When I stand on the floor the floor bends slightly as predicted by Hooke's law. The floor bends an amount proportional to my weight. The bending of the floor creates a force upward against my feet according to Hooke's law. The floor keeps bending until the reaction force is equal and opposite to my weight. If the floor were weaker, it would bend more to produce the same reaction force. If the floor were stronger, it would bend less.

The rules for building floors state that the floor must deflect no more than 1/320 of its width when under a load of 50 pounds per square foot. If you jump on a floor you can easily feel the deflection. Suppose I made the floor stronger by adding more wood or concrete. What would happen to the deflection of the floor under my weight?

> Most students recognize that the deflection lessens if you make the floor stronger.

How does the spring constant of the stronger floor compare with the spring constant of the original floor?

> The stronger floor has a larger spring constant.

The spring constant for solid materials can be very large. A value of 100 million newtons per meter is not unusual for objects made of steel. With such a large spring constant, the deflection is very small and can only be measured with sensitive instruments. That is why a steel object does not appear to deflect under a force unless the force is very large. The subject of engineering includes the design of structures and objects to withstand forces with minimum deflection. Chapter 27 has more information on this subject for those of you interested in reading ahead.

6.3 Equilibrium of Forces and Hooke's Law

Table 2: Force and compression of a spring

Number of washers	Added mass (kg)	Spring's position (cm)	Calculated compression (cm)	Calculated force (N)
0	0			
5				
10				
15				

5 Analyzing the data

a. Make a graph of force versus compression for the spring.

b. The force from a compression spring can also be described by Hooke's law. As with extension springs, the spring constant (k) is a measure of the strength of the spring. For example, a spring with $k = 1$ N/cm produces 1 newton of force for every centimeter of compression.

Hooke's law
(springs)

Force (N) $F = -kx$ — Spring constant (N/cm)
— Deformation (m) (extension or compression)

Use your graph of force versus compression to determine the spring constant for the spring in the experiment. Express your result in N/cm.

6 Testing the model

a. Use your graph to predict how much the spring should compress when 20 washers are added. You need to determine the weight of 20 washers to make your prediction.

b. Set up the experiment and test whether the model (Hooke's law) gives the correct prediction.

c. How close did your prediction come to the actual compression of the spring? Calculate the difference between the measurement and the prediction as a percentage of the actual measurement.

d. Could this spring be used to measure the mass of one washer? If so, explain a procedure for how to make the measurement. If not, explain why not.

e. How much force would it take to cause a compression of 1 millimeter?

5 6 Example answers

Table 2: Force and compression of a spring

Number of washers	Added mass (kg)	Spring's position (cm)	Calculated compression (cm)	Calculated force (N)
0	0	13.5	0	0
5	0.060	10.8	2.7	.59
10	0.120	8	5.5	1.18
15	0.188	5	8.5	1.76

5a. Graph:

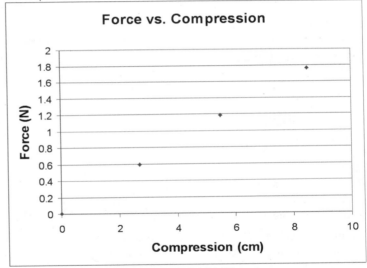

Force vs. Compression

5b. I calculate a spring constant of 0.21 N/cm.

6a. The weight of 17 washers is 0.204 g for a force of 2.00 N. The compression should be 9.5 cm.

6b. I measured a displacement of 9.1 cm.

6c. The difference between my prediction and the actual measurement was 0.1 cm, or 1.1 percent.

6d. If you knew the spring constant, you could measure the compression of the spring due to one washer and then calculate the force the spring exerted. You could then use Newton's second law to calculate the mass from the force (m = F/a).

6e. It would take 0.021 N to cause a compression of 1 millimeter.

7.1 Vectors and Direction

Key Question: How do we accurately communicate length and distance?

A vector is a quantity that includes information about both distance and direction. In this Investigation, students learn to read a compass and use the compass to make a map using vectors. They begin by adding vectors graphically using a protractor and ruler on graph paper. Students then calibrate their step length and walk the vectors. In the second part of the Investigation students convert vectors between polar and Cartesian components. They again walk the vectors, but this time using a map they have plotted from the Cartesian components of a three vector sequence.

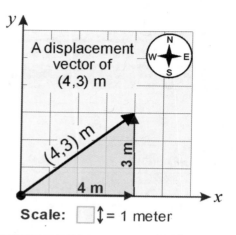

Scale: ☐ ↕ = 1 meter

Reading Synopsis

Students read Section 7.1 Vectors and Direction after the Investigation.

A scalar is a quantity that can be described by a single value, with units. A vector is a quantity that requires at least two values and includes information about magnitude and direction. The displacement vector has units of length and describes a movement relative to a coordinate system. The position vector describes the location of an object relative to a coordinate system.

Two dimensional vectors can be represented in (x, y) components (Cartesian) or in (r, θ) components (polar). Vectors are added or subtracted by adding or subtracting components. A triangle and trigonometry are used to find the components of a vector in one coordinate system from the components in another coordinate system. The Pythagorean theorem ($c^2 = a^2 + b^2$) is used to find the magnitude of a vector from the x and y components. The section reviews the use of calculators to determine the trigonometric functions and their inverses.

The Investigation

Leading Questions
- Why are vectors important?
- How do you show vectors on graph paper?
- How are vectors added or subtracted?
- How can a complex movement with many turns be represented?
- How does a compass aid in navigation?
- How do you use a compass?

Learning Goals

By the end of the Investigation, students will be able to:
- Write displacement vectors in Cartesian and polar coordinates.
- Convert vectors between Cartesian and polar coordinates.
- Represent a sequence of vectors to scale on a map.
- Use vectors to give very precise directions.
- Use a compass to tell direction in the field or from a map.
- Use vectors and a compass to construct a geometrically accurate map showing the position of an object.

Key Vocabulary

scalar, scale, displacement, position, resultant, component, Cartesian coordinates, x-component, y-component, polar coordinate, right triangle, sine, cosine, Pythagorean theorem

Setup and Materials

Students work in groups of four or five at tables.

Each group should have:

- Navigational compass
- Meter stick
- Protractor
- Graph paper

Teaching the Investigation

1   Introduction
2   What are scalars?
3   What are vectors?
4   Coordinate systems
5   The origin
6   How a compass works
7   Reading direction from a compass
8   Using a compass to point to a particular direction
9   Making a map
10   Calibrating your pace
11   Walking the vectors
12   Polar and Cartesian coordinates
13   Making a map in Cartesian coordinates
14   Adding vectors in Cartesian coordinates
15   Vector components
16   The resultant vector
17   Using the resultant vector
18   Converting to compass coordinates
19   Walking the vectors

Details

Time	⏱ One class period
Preparation	✎
Assignments	📖 Section 7.1 Vectors and Direction in the **Student Edition** after the Investigation.
Skill Sheets	7.1A Adding Displacement Vectors 7.1B Vector Components 7.1C Pythagorean Theorem
Equipment Setup	Compass

Introduction

Ways of representing direction.

What are scalars?

A scalar is a measurement that can be described by a single value and a unit: the magnitude

Examples of scalars: distance, temperature, mass

What are vectors?

A vector is a measurement that has at least two values with units: a magnitude and direction.

Examples of vectors: position, velocity, acceleration, force

Coordinate systems

1

A coordinate system is a reference system for defining a vector.

To understand motion in more detail, we need to be able to describe where objects go as well as how fast they go. In fact, the direction of many quantities is important. Force, velocity, acceleration, and position are all variables that can have a direction as well as a numerical value. Today's Investigation is about how direction is represented in physics. What we learn applies to much more than just physics. If you are ever lost in the woods, you will be able to use what we learn today to find your way out again, if you have a compass and a map.

To describe direction or location, we need to introduce a new kind of mathematical object. This object is called a vector. To understand a vector, let's take another look at the measurements we already know, such as distance. Can anyone tell me the approximate distance from here to the door?

> **Students should approximate the distance and give you a measurement, such as three meters or 12 feet. The units are not important as long as there ARE units. Keep pushing the discussion until students give you a numerical value and units. Write the measurement on the board.**

There are two bits of information in this measurement. One is a value, which is the number, and the second bit of information is the unit that tells what the value means. A measurement of distance is an example of a scalar. A scalar, in physics, is a measurement that can be completely described by a single value and a unit. Other examples of scalars include temperature and mass. Can anyone think of another measurement that is a scalar?

> **Discuss the concept of scalars with students. Other examples of scalars are pressure, density, speed, volume, and time. Some quantities can be either scalars or vectors, such as force. If force comes up in the discussion, save it for the next step.**

A vector is a quantity that cannot be described by a single value and unit. A vector has at least two values with units. Position is a good example of a vector. Earlier, you gave me the distance from here to the door. However, if I walked that distance in this direction, will I reach the door?

> **Turn and walk in a direction away from the door. Students should recognize that you need to walk the distance in the direction of the door.**

To communicate completely the position of an object, you need to provide information about both the distance and the direction. That means you must use a vector. If you had told me to walk three meters north, that would be a vector because there are two pieces of information given. Three meters is a distance and north is a direction. We could write the vector this way:

> **Write the vector $\vec{x}$ = (3m, north) on the board.**

We use a little arrow above the variable to indicate that the variable is a vector. The parentheses are used to group the information that makes up the vector.

There is one more important detail about vectors. To understand a vector, you need to know what coordinate system the vector is referenced to. A coordinate system is like a language. For example, the spoken word "one" means a single quantity in the English language, but that same sound means something different in other languages. To communicate the idea of a single object, you need to know which language is being spoken. With a vector, the language is called a coordinate system. For directions on a map, the coordinate system sets north as 0 degrees. Other directions are given as an angle measured clockwise from north. If you wanted to go east a distance of three meters, you would write the vector:

> **Write the vector $\vec{x}$ = (3m, 90°) on the board with a diagram showing the four compass directions.**

Left page (framed investigation sheet)

7.1 | **Vectors and Direction**

Question: How do you give directions in physics?

In this Investigation, you will:

1. Use a compass to navigate and tell direction.
2. Learn two different ways to write displacement vectors.
3. Learn how to create an accurate map using vectors.
4. Use vectors to give very precise directions.

A *position vector* is a quantity that includes information about both distance and direction. Vectors are the most descriptive way to give directions because they tell exactly how far and in exactly what direction you need to move.

1 | **Reading a compass**

A compass is a device that includes a tiny magnetic needle that points north. Around the needle is a rotating scale that has degrees marked clockwise from zero to 360. Zero degrees is straight north. 180 degrees is straight south. East is 90 degrees, and west is 270 degrees. A compass *bearing* means direction in degrees relative to north. For example, a *bearing* of 45 degrees is a direction northeast of where you are.

The base of the compass has an arrow you can use to find the compass bearing to a landmark. For example, suppose you wish to know the direction to a certain tree. Point the arrow on the base of the compass at the tree. Hold the compass firmly keeping the arrow on the base pointing at the tree and rotate the adjustable ring until the needle lines up with the North arrow in the dial of the compass. You can now read the compass bearing to the tree from the bottom of the arrow on the base. In the example, the tree is at a bearing of about 40 degrees.

The arrow on the base of the compass is also used to tell which direction to go when you know the compass bearing. For example, suppose you wish to walk on a compass bearing of 40 degrees. Rotate the adjustable ring until 40 degrees on the ring is aligned with the arrow on the base of the compass. Now take the compass, hold it level, and rotate the whole compass until the north tip of the needle is aligned with 0 degrees (the small arrow in the dial). The arrow on the base now points in the direction you need to walk. This technique works best when the compass is held near your body and you rotate the compass by rotating yourself so you always face the direction of the arrow on the base of the compass.

Reading a compass

Arrow on base — Adjustable ring

North arrow in dial — Compass needle

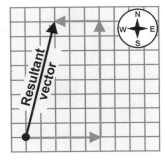

Rotate the whole compass until the needle aligns with the north arrow in the dial.

Read the compass bearing on the adjustable ring using the arrow on the base
(the example is 40 degrees)

39

Right page

Adding displacement vectors

You cannot usually add vectors like regular numbers. For example, if you simply added 5 m + 8 m + 3 m, the result is 16 m. This is the distance you walked, but it is not your final position. Suppose you walk 5 meters east, turn, go 8 meters north, then turn and go 3 meters west. Where are you relative to your starting point? You can represent each leg of the walk by a displacement vector. One vector starts at the end of the previous one, just like each leg of the walk starts at the end of the previous leg. The diagram below shows the trip as a sequence of three displacement vectors:

Adding displacement vectors

5 meters east

8 meters north

3 meters west

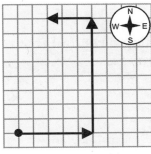

Scale: ⬜ ↕ = 1 meter

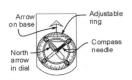

At the end of the trip, your position is 8 meters north and 2 meters east of where you started. In physics the position is where you are. The diagonal vector that connects the starting position with the final position is called the resultant.

The origin

Origin: the reference point for measuring zero. Usually assigned the value of zero.

How a compass works

A compass needle aligns with the magnetic field of Earth.

Reading direction from a compass

Directional signs: N, S, E, W

Compass base arrow for finding direction of travel

Rotating ring with bearings

Using a compass to point to a particular direction

Reading accurate compass bearings and finding direction.

The second important characteristic of a coordinate system is the origin. The origin is the reference point for measuring distance from. We usually assign a distance of 0 to the origin. You choose the origin at a convenient place. If you wished to tell me how to walk to the door from where I am, the most convenient origin would be my actual position. Telling me to walk three meters north is actually an instruction that tells me to walk three meters from WHERE I AM in the direction north. The instruction makes implicit reference to a coordinate system with its origin where I am, and for which the director of north is defined. Has anyone ever used a compass to navigate?

1

Show a compass and discuss any adventures that students may have had with a compass.

Earth has a magnetic field that causes magnets to align themselves in a particular way. A compass has a small magnetic needle that rotates around its middle. The needle rotates until it is aligned with the magnetic field of the Earth. The end of the needle that points north is called the north pole of a magnet. Notice how the compass needle stays pointing north even as I rotate the compass.

Demonstrate to the students by holding the compass level and slowly rotating it. The needle should stay aligned with north even though the compass is rotated underneath it. Have students repeat the demonstration with their own compasses.

The base of your compass has an arrow that is used to tell direction. On the dial of the compass is a rotating ring that can be turned to align the degree marks on the ring with the north-pointing needle of the compass. To find the direction to anything, like the door, start by pointing the arrow at the object.

Students should rotate their compasses until the arrow points to the door

Rotate the adjustable ring until the N mark at 0 degrees is aligned with the north pointing tip of the compass needle, which is painted red or black. You should hold the compass firmly to keep the arrow on the base pointing at the door while you rotate the adjustable ring.

Students should hold their compass so the arrow on the base remains pointing at the door while they adjust the ring to align north on the ring with the north tip of the compass needle.

You can now use the arrow on the base of the compass to read the compass bearing to the door. A direction in degrees referenced to North is called a compass bearing.

Have students read the compass bearings they measure. They all will be slightly different because the students are in different places relative to the door. Help groups who have gotten compass bearings that do not seem possible. Repeat the exercise choosing a distant object, such as a tree or building you can see through the window. It is important for groups to be comfortable using the compass accurately before they attempt the next part of the Investigation.

A compass can also be used to tell you which direction to go if you already know a compass bearing. Everyone take your compasses and rotate the adjustable ring until 90 degrees, or east, is aligned with the arrow on the base of the compass.

Allow students to do this. The position of the compass needle relative to the adjustable ring is not important as the compass bearing is being set.

Now hold the compass level and rotate the entire compass until the compass needle aligns with north on the adjustable ring. The arrow on the base points in the direction you want to go. In this case the arrow on the base points directly east.

Students should follow the procedure to identify the direction of east.

7.1 Vectors and Direction

2   Making a map

Your teacher will give you a sequence of two vectors. The vectors are in polar coordinates, making them easy to walk with a compass.

a. Take a sheet of graph paper and draw x- and y-axes pointing east-west (*x*) and north-south (*y*).

b. Draw the first vector on the graph, which should be to scale. For example, if you had graph paper with a 1 cm grid, an appropriate scale would be to choose 1 cm = 1 meter.

c. Draw the second vector starting from the end of the first vector. The graph paper now shows a map of two legs of a walking trip.

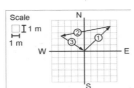

d. Take the graph paper and draw a third vector from the end of the second vector back to the start—this is the vector back home. Use a protractor and a ruler to measure the angle of the vector and determine its length in meters. Remember, you want compass bearings, so you should measure the angle clockwise from the positive *y*-axis, which is north on the compass.

3   Calibrating your pace

If you were exploring uncharted territory, you could keep track of how far you traveled by counting steps. For this technique to be accurate, you must know your own step length. Walk 10 steps at an average pace and use a meter stick to measure how much distance you covered. An average step for most people is between 1/2 and 3/4 meter. Record the step length for each group member in Table 1.

Table 1: Step lengths

Name	Distance of 10 paces (m)	Avg. length of 1 pace (m)

4   Walking the vectors

1. Take each of the three vectors and convert the distance in meters to the number of steps for each person in the group. Use Table 2 to record the calculations.

2. Take a compass and go out and walk the first vector.

3. Walk the second vector starting where the first vector ended.

4. Walk the third vector and see how close you come back to where you started.

Table 2: Vectors in units of steps

Vector	Distance in meters	Distance in steps

40

2 3 4   Example answers

2d. Adding the vectors $(10\text{ m}, 45^\circ)$ and $(20\text{ m}, 270^\circ)$ gives you a resultant vector of 14.74 m at 120 degrees from north.

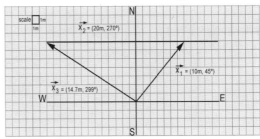

3. Sample table data:

Name	Distance of 10 paces (m)	Avg. length of 1 pace (m)
Michelle	6.51	0.651
Shawn	7.14	0.714

4. Sample table data for Michelle

Vector	Distance in meters	Distance in steps
1	10.0	15.5
2	20.0	30.5
3	14.75	22.5

Making a map

Scale drawings

Direction on a map

Drawing a vector on a map from polar coordinates (a distance and an angle).

Using a ruler to measure distance and a protractor to measure angles.

Calibrating your pace

Measuring a person's standard step.

Walking the vectors

Converting distance to steps.

Using the compass for direction.

2 Compass bearings are usually taken from a map. A map is a scale drawing, which means that a small distance on the map represents a larger distance in real life. Take out a sheet of graph paper. We are going to use a scale where the width of each box on the graph paper represents 1 meter. Draw a vertical line and a horizontal line so they intersect in the middle of the graph paper. Label the lines N, E, W, and S as shown in step 2 of the Investigation.

Students should create a blank map as shown in step 2 of the Investigation.

I would like everyone to draw a vector on the map representing a movement of 10 meters at a direction of 45 degrees. A vector is represented by an arrow. The arrowhead points in the direction of movement. This vector should start from the origin because it is the first vector in a trip that will include several vectors.

Write the vector $\vec{x}$ = (10m, 45°) on the board. Circulate around the room to see that students draw the vector correctly. They will need to use a ruler or paper to measure the correct length to use to represent two meters on an angle. A vector that has an endpoint that is 10 boxes over and 10 boxes up is not correct because its length will be more than 10 meters. See the instructions on the right for a convenient ruler.

Now draw the vector $\vec{x}$ = (20 m, 270°). In which direction does this vector point? Draw the vector so it starts at the end of the arrow for the first vector. This new second vector is the second leg of a trip.

Write the vector on the board. Students should recognize that this vector points directly west. Circulate around the room to see that students draw the second vector correctly.

Can anyone tell me the vector that can get back to the origin? Use your ruler and a protractor to find distance and the angle. Remember, the angle must be expressed relative to north. You may find it easier to measure angles relative to west or east and then add 90, 180, or 270 degrees.

Students should determine that the vector from the tip of the second vector back to the origin is approximately (14.7m, 299°). They will need to use a protractor to measure the angle and a ruler or scale to measure the length.

3 When walking in the woods, it is inconvenient to carry a long tape measure. For most trips it is accurate enough to count steps and to calibrate how long each step is. For the next part of the Investigation, we are going to measure a standard step for at least one person in each group. That person can then follow the vectors of our map by counting steps.

Have one person from each group walk 10 steps and measure the distance. Use Table 1 to record the distance of 10 steps and the average length of one step calculated by dividing that distance by 10.

4 Now that you know the length of one step, use Table 2 to convert the distances on the map into steps.

Students should take the distances from the three vectors (2m, 4m, 3m) and convert each distance to an equivalent number of steps.

Now let's go test the map. I want each person who is going to be walking to walk each of the three vectors in order, using the compass for direction and counting steps as prescribed by Table 2. Just as you drew on the map, you will walk each vector starting from the end of the previous vector.

Find an open area that is large enough to walk the vectors drawn on the map. Have at least one student from each group walk the three vectors using their compass to tell direction and the number of steps from Table 2 for distance. At the end of the third vector, students should come to within a meter of where they started.

5 Vectors in x-y coordinates

Your instructor will give you a second sequence of two vectors. This time the vectors are written in *x-y* coordinates.

a. Take a sheet of graph paper and draw *x*- and *y*-axes pointing east-west (x) and north-south (y).

b. Draw the first vector on the graph. The graph should be to scale; 1 cm equals 1 meter might be a reasonable scale. For example, to draw the vector $\vec{x} = (1,4)$m, you would go over 1 cm in the positive *x* direction (east) and go up 4 cm in the positive *y* direction (north).

c. Draw the second vector *starting from the end of the first vector*. The graph paper now shows a map of two legs of a walking trip.

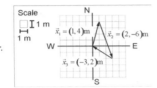

d. Calculate the resultant vector by adding up the *x* and *y* components of the two vectors you already have. For example, if $\vec{x}_1 = (1,4)$m and $\vec{x}_2 = (2,-6)$m, then $\vec{x}_1 + \vec{x}_2 = (3,-2)$m.

e. The *resultant vector* is the vector you could have walked straight from the origin (home) to the final destination. To get back home, you need to walk the resultant vector in the opposite direction. Mathematically, that means multiplying the components by -1. In the example, the vector back home would be $\vec{x}_3 = (-3,2)$m. You can see on the map that this is correct.

6 Converting to compass coordinates

A compass uses polar coordinates that specify a distance and an angle. Take each of the three vectors and convert them to polar coordinates by sketching the triangle shown in the diagram. You might have to add 90, 180, or 270 degrees to the angle θ of the triangle to get a compass bearing. Record the converted vectors in Table 3.

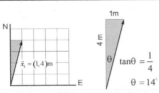

Table 3: Converting to polar coordinates

Vector in x-y coordinates	Angle from north (degrees)	Distance (m)	Distance (steps)

7 Walking the vectors

1. Take each of the three vectors and convert the distance in meters to the number of steps for each person in the group.
2. Take a compass and go out and walk the first vector.
3. Walk the second vector starting where the first vector ended.
4. Walk the third vector and see how close you come back to where you started.

41

5 6 Example answers

5. Adding the vectors (1,4)m and (2,-6)m gives you a resultant vector of (3,-2).

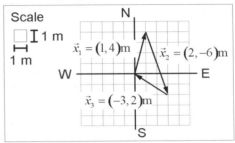

6. Sample table data:

Vector in x-y coordinates	Angle from north (degrees)	Distance (m)	Distance (steps)
1, 4	14	4.12	6.3
2, 6	161.5	6.32	9.7
-3, 2	304	3.6	5.5

Polar and Cartesian coordinates

Cartesian coordinates: x-y coordinates
vector example: (4,3) meters

Polar coordinates: compass bearings
using a distance and an angle
vector example: (5m, 37)

Making a map in Cartesian coordinates

Drawing vectors in Cartesian
coordinates.

Positive numbers are to the right in x
and up in y.

Negative numbers are to the left in x
and down in y.

Adding vectors in Cartesian coordinates

In Cartesian coordinates, vectors are
added by adding the x's and the y's
separately:
(1,4) + (2,-6) = (3,-2)

Vector components

The resultant vector

The sum of a series of vectors is called
the resultant.

The vectors we just used were expressed in polar coordinates. Polar coordinates use a distance and angle. Polar coordinates are very useful when navigating by map and compass. For other uses in physics, however, Cartesian coordinates are more useful. Cartesian coordinates are x-y coordinates like you would represent on a graph. For example, the first vector we had (10m, 45°) can be written in Cartesian coordinates as $(x,y) = (7.071, 7.071)$m. This means the end of the vector is 7.07 m east and 7.07 meters north of the origin. In Cartesian coordinates, the y-axis points north-south, and the x-axis points east-west. We will find that Cartesian coordinates make it much easier to do math with vectors, like adding them and subtracting them. Most of the formulas we have met, such as Newton's second law, are really vector formulas and are best written in Cartesian coordinates.

Take out another sheet of graph paper and mark it with x and y axes, as before. Place the origin at the center of the page. You can use the same scale as you did for the last map.

Students should create a blank map similar to the one they did for step 2.

We are going to do a similar exercise to what we just did, except this time we are going to use vectors in Cartesian coordinates. The first vector I want you to draw is (1, 4) meters. The first number in the parentheses is the distance along the x-axis, and the second number is distance along the y-axis.

Put the vector $\vec{X} = (1, 4)$m on the board and circulate around the groups as students draw the vector on the map.

The second vector to draw is (2, -6)m. The 2 means you go 2 more meters in positive x direction. The -6 means you go 6 meters in the negative y direction. In Cartesian coordinates, positive and negative numbers represent opposite directions. Positive numbers are to the right in x or up in y. Negative numbers are to the left in x or down in y. Again, draw your second vector starting from the end of the first vector.

Put the vector on the board and walk around to see if students draw it correctly.

What are the coordinates of the end of the second vector, which is your final position?

Students should be able to see that the second vector takes them to a point with coordinates (3,-2).

Can anyone tell me how to figure out where the second vector would end up without drawing a graph?

The final position in x is the sum of the two x coordinates from the individual vectors. For example, 1 + 2 = 3. The final y position is the sum of the y coordinates from the individual vectors, 4 - 6 = -2. Therefore (1, 4) + (2, -6) = (3, -2). Go through this process of addition on the board.

The result of moving several vectors one after another is calculated by adding the vectors. This is easy in Cartesian coordinates. You just add the x's and the y's separately to get the final vector. Be careful though! This simple technique for adding vectors DOES NOT work when the vectors are in polar coordinates, like we use with a compass. For example, (10m, 45°) + (20m, 270°) IS NOT (30m, 315°).

Work the example out on the board. Ask students what the sum of the two vectors in polar coordinates was. They should be able to look back and recall that it was (14.7m, 299°).

The parts of a vector are called components. The x number is called the x-component and the y number is called the y-component. The x-component of (1, 4) meters is +1m, or (1, 0)m. The y-component is +4m, or (0,4)m. The meters outside the parentheses indicates that both x and y components are measured in meters. Can anyone tell me one single vector that goes straight from the origin to the end of the trip?

Lead the students to recognize that (3, -2) is this vector.

The sum of a series of vectors is called the resultant vector, which represents the total movement.

Using the resultant vector

What is the vector that we need to get back to the origin? Well, the origin has coordinates (0,0)m. What vector must be added to (3, -2) to make it (0, 0)?

> Students should answer that the required vector is (-3, 2).

The vector (-3, 2) goes 3 meters to the left and two meters up and takes us back to the origin. We could have gotten the same result by multiplying the resultant vector by -1. Multiplying a vector by -1 reverses its direction.

> Draw the map and show how the vector (-3, 2) goes back to the origin. Work out -1 × (3, -2) = (-3, 2) on the board.

Converting to compass coordinates

6

Although math is easier in Cartesian coordinates, to use a compass you must convert back to polar coordinates. This is done vector-by-vector. For each vector you draw a triangle showing the vector by itself drawn from the origin. The triangle for (1, 4) looks like this.

Translating Cartesian coordinates to polar coordinates.

> Draw the triangle on the board with the length of the sides labeled.

To get a compass vector we need the length and the angle from north. The length we get from the Pythagorean theorem, which relates the three sides of a right triangle.

Pythagorean theorem
$a^2 + b^2 = c^2$

> Write down $a^2 + b^2 = c^2$ and work out that the length is the square root of 17 ($1^2 + 4^2$), or 4.12m.

The angle comes from trigonometry. The tangent of an angle is the opposite side divided by the adjacent side. In this case the tangent is 1 ÷ 4 = 0.25. Most scientific calculators have a way to find the angle that has a tangent of 0.25. On my calculator I press 0.25, then INV, then TAN. On another calculator I might press 0.25, then SHIFT then TAN-1. In either case, the result is 14 degrees. Everyone should try finding the inverse tangent on their calculator and show that INV TAN(0.25) = 14 degrees.

Using inverse tangent function on a calculator.

> Circulate and help students to do this calculation on a calculator. Many will have never used an inverse function and you may need to discuss the idea of an inverse function with the class.

With the vector (1, 4), the angle 14 degrees is already given relative to north. With other vectors you may have to add or subtract from 90, 180, 270, or 360 to get an angle relative to north. Take the three vectors we just calculated and convert them to compass coordinates.

For compass coordinates, the angle is relative to North.

> Students do the calculations. Many will require your assistance.

Walking the vectors

7

> If you have time, assign three new vectors in Cartesian coordinates. Have the students convert the new vectors to polar compass coordinates using a new Table 3. Make the new vectors at least five meters each so they can be walked. Since a person's step size tends to be greater than one-half meter, distances shorter than several meters are hard to measure accurately in steps.

7.2 Projectile Motion and the Velocity Vector

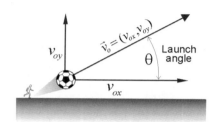

Key Question: Can you predict the landing spot of a projectile?

In this Investigation, students use physics to predict the landing spot of a ball launched horizontally off a table with a known velocity. Students should be familiar with the projectile motion equations before doing the Investigation. They must design their own procedure for the second part of the Investigation. Students learn whether their procedure was correct when they watch their flying ball either hit or miss the bull's eye of a target they place on the floor.

Reading Synopsis

Students read Section 7.2 Projectile Motion and the Velocity Vector before the Investigation.

Any object that moves through the air affected only by gravity is called a projectile. A projectile's velocity at any instant in time can be represented with a vector that shows its speed and direction. The velocity vector can be resolved into horizontal and vertical components. The equations of motion in one dimension apply separately to the x and y components in two-dimensional motion. The horizontal velocity of a projectile remains constant, while the vertical velocity changes because of gravity.

The horizontal distance a projectile travels is called its range. The range of a projectile depends on its speed, angle, and height when it is launched. The vertical component of a projectile's motion is the same as that of an object in free fall. The vertical component of motion is described by the equations for motion at a constant velocity.

The Investigation

Leading Questions
- How do we describe velocity, which includes information about speed and direction?
- How do we include the effect of gravity in two-dimensional motion?
- What is a projectile?
- What variables affect the distance a projectile travels?

Learning Goals

By the end of the Investigation, students will be able to:
- Determine the flight time of a horizontally launched projectile given its release height.
- Predict the range of a projectile given its launch speed and flight time.
- Calculate the velocity of a projectile after it is in the air for a specified time.

Key Vocabulary   projectile, speed, velocity, trajectory, range, parabola, vector, tangent

Setup and Materials

Students work in groups of three to four at tables.

Each group should have:

- Straight track
- 3/4-inch steel ball
- Timer and one photogate, AC adapter (or 9-volt battery), and a cord to connect the photogate to the timer
- Meter stick or metric measuring tape
- At least one calculator
- Sheet of carbon paper
- A blank sheet of paper for the target

Details

Time	⏲ One class period
Preparation	✎ Gather the materials and try out the experiment yourself before the Investigation.
Assignments	📖 Section 7.2 Projectile Motion and the Velocity Vector in the **Student Edition** before the Investigation.
Skill Sheets	7.2 Projectile Motion
Equipment Setup	Timer

Teaching the Investigation

1　Setting up the equipment
2　Measuring the initial speed
3　Predicting the landing spot
4　Testing the theory
5　Analyzing the results

Introduction

Projectile: a launched object moving under the influence of gravity.

Trajectory: the two dimensional motion of a projectile.

Sketch the velocity vector at various points to predict the motion of a projectile.

Setting up the equipment

1

Arrange tables as needed to accommodate the ball's range for the height of the table.

Measuring the initial speed

2

Launch speed is the ball diameter (0.19 cm) divided by the time to break the photogate.

Use the calculated launch speed to predict the range of the ball.

How many of you can shoot a basket with a basketball? How do you think about it when you set up the shot, just before you release the ball?

> Nearly all students have done this. Most recall tracing the trajectory in their mind before they release the ball. A good player has a mental model that intuitively relates the forces applied to the ball and the trajectory the ball follows. This model is learned through much practice and is a form of pretty sophisticated physics.

Today's Investigation is about the physics of launched objects that move under the influence of gravity. In physics, a flying object such as a basketball is called a projectile. We will find that all of what we already know about motion can be applied to this new problem, of figuring out the motion of a projectile. Because a projectile moves in a curved path, its motion is two-dimensional. For projectile motion, the two dimensions mean vertical and horizontal, which can be represented as x and y on a graph.

> Sketch a rough x-y coordinate system on the board and draw a rough parabola representing a trajectory, similar to Figure 7.8 on page 124 of the text.

A projectile can be described by a velocity vector. The velocity vector has a magnitude equal to the speed and a direction that always points in the direction of motion. Once we understand how the velocity vector works, we can predict the motion of a projectile.

> Sketch the velocity vector for a thrown ball at several places along the trajectory. Discuss that fact that both the speed and direction change as the ball moves.

Place the physics stand on the table and attach the straight track to it at the 10th hole from the bottom. Twist the end of the track so it turns upward to catch the ball at the bottom. Connect a photogate to input A on the timer. Set the timer to interval mode. The photogate should act as a support for the end of the track at the edge of the table.

> Make sure there is enough space between the tables in the room so each launched ball will have a clear path to the floor. Set up one set of equipment ahead of time and determine the ball's range for the height of your tables. Then arrange the tables as needed. If your tables can't be moved or there simply is not enough space in your room, you may want to change the release height. If students release the balls from a lower point on the track, the range will be shorter.

In this Investigation, you will apply what you know about projectile motion to predict the landing spot of a ball that rolls off a table. You are not allowed to let the ball roll off the table until you predict the landing location and mark it with a target. You will then test your prediction and hopefully hit the center of the target. First you must determine the launch speed of the ball. You will be releasing the ball from the peg at the top of the track. The photogate will measure the time it takes for the ball to break the photogate beam. The distance over which the ball breaks the beam is its diameter (0.019 m). How will this allow you to determine the launch speed?

> Speed is equal to distance divided by time. The launch speed is the diameter divided by the time measured by the timer.

Roll the ball five times. Record each time in Table 1 and calculate the speed for each trial.

> Make sure all groups have the ends of their tracks turned upward.

UNIT 3: Motion and Force in 2 and 3 Dimensions

7.2　Projectile Motion and the Velocity Vector

Question: Can you predict the landing spot of a projectile?

In this Investigation, you will:

1. Use a downhill track to launch a ball into the air at a known speed and angle.
2. Use the velocity vector to model the motion of the ball as it flies through the air.

During this Investigation, you will put your knowledge of projectile motion to use in a challenge. Your group will predict the trajectory of a ball launched horizontally from the end of the straight track. If your knowledge of physics is applied correctly, you will be able to accurately place a target on the floor so the flying ball lands at the center.

1　**Setting up the experiment**

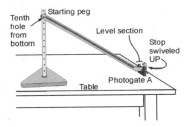

1. Attach the straight track to the physics stand at the 10th hole (measured from the bottom). Twist the end of the track so that it turns upward to catch the ball at the bottom.
2. Connect a photogate to input A on the Timer. Set the Timer to interval mode. Attach the photogate to the bottom of the track as shown. When the track is resting on the photogate, the end is level.

2　**Measuring the initial speed**

Your challenge for this Investigation is to predict the exact location where the ball will hit the floor after it is released on the track. You must do this without ever letting the ball move through the air. The first step in finding the landing spot is to find the initial speed of the ball.

Hold the ball so it is against the starting peg. Release it and allow it to roll down the track and through the photogate. Record the time in Table 1. The initial speed is 0.019 m ÷ the time it takes the ball to pass through the photogate. Repeat for a total of five trials.

Table 1: Ball's time and speed

Time (sec)	Launch speed (m/sec)

42

Teaching tip

Students enjoy this Investigation, especially if it is set up as a competition among groups. Challenge students to double-check their calculations and follow careful techniques to get as close to the center of the target as possible. They may be surprised at how close their predications come to the actual range.

2 3 4 **Example answers**

Table 1: *Ball's time and speed*

Time (sec)	Launch speed (m/sec)
0.0073	2.60
0.0074	2.57
0.0074	2.57
0.0073	2.60
0.0074	2.57

3a. The air time is calculated using

$$t = \sqrt{\frac{2y_0}{g}}$$

The range is then found using

$$x = v_0 t = v_0 \sqrt{\frac{2y_0}{g}}$$

3b. The average launch speed is 2.58 m/s. The launch height is 0.793 m. The range is then 1.04 m.

4. Use the ruler to carefully measure the height of the ball at the end of the track. Use the height to calculate the air time for the ball using the equation

$$t = \sqrt{\frac{2y_0}{g}}$$

Calculate the range of the ball using

$$x = v_0 t = v_0 \sqrt{\frac{2y_0}{g}}$$

Measure a distance equal to the range along the floor, starting directly under the edge of the track. Place the center of the target at this position on the floor. Look down the track to check whether the target should be moved to the right or left. Make any adjustments if necessary. Place the carbon paper on the track and let the marble roll onto the floor.

Predicting the landing spot

3

Horizontal speed: constant

Vertical speed: changes with gravity

Horizontal distance:
$x = v_{ox}t$

Horizontal speed:
$v_x = x/t$

Vertical distance:
$y = v_{oy}t - {}^1\!/_2(gt)$

Vertical speed:
$v_y = v_{oy} - gt$

Depending on the abilities of your students, you may or may not want to review the equations for projectile motion with the class. The Investigation is more challenging if students determine the mathematical relationships on their own. If you think this will be difficult for your students, lead a discussion of the equations for horizontal and vertical motion before students are left to make their predictions.

Your group will have to use the launch speed of the ball and motion equations to determine the place where the ball will hit the floor. The equations that describe the horizontal motion of a projectile are different from the equations for vertical motion. Why are the sets of equations different?

The horizontal speed is constant, and the vertical speed changes because of gravity.

What are the equations that you would use to calculate the horizontal distance and the horizontal speed?

Write the equations on the board.

Horizontal distance: $x = v_{0x}t$　　Horizontal speed: $v = x/t$

What are the equations you would use to calculate the vertical distance and vertical speed?

Write the equations on the board.

Vertical distance: $y = v_{0y}t - 1/2gt$　Vertical speed: $v_y = v_{0y} - gt$

If you want to find the location where the ball hits the floor, which of the variables must you know the value for?

The horizontal distance, x, indicates how far to place the target horizontally from the end of the track. To calculate the horizontal distance, you must know the horizontal speed and the time. Which of these quantities do you already have a value for?

The horizontal speed (launch speed) is known.

Now you and your group members must figure out how to determine the air time. You may not allow the ball to roll off the end of the ramp, so you can't measure the time. The only piece of equipment you may use is a meter stick.

Students can determine the air time by measuring the launch height of the ball. The vertical distance formula can then be solved for the air time.

Testing the theory

4

Place the target at the predicted landing spot.

Release the ball and see how close it lands to the target.

Once you think you have come up with a way to determine the landing spot, write a clear step-by-step procedure describing your method. Follow your procedure and locate your predicted landing spot on the floor. Place the target so its center is at the predicted landing spot. Place a piece of carbon paper, black side down, on top of the target. Twist the end of the track downward so the ball can roll off the end. Release the ball and see how close your prediction was to the actual landing spot. Be sure to watch where the ball rolls so you don't lose it.

You may want to have each group tell you before they are ready to test their prediction. Students enjoy watching other groups try to hit the target and will want to stop what they are doing for a minute to watch each group's trial.

Analyzing the results

5

Measure the horizontal distance traveled.

Measure the actual horizontal distance the ball traveled along the floor. If the ball went to the left or right, measure the distance from the center of the target to the landing spot.

7.2 Projectile Motion and the Velocity Vector

3 Predicting the landing spot

a. Work with your group members to come up with a theory that predicts the horizontal distance the ball moves before hitting the floor. The theory should take the form of a formula that involves only the initial height (y_0), initial speed (v_0), and the acceleration due to gravity (g). You should assume the ball leaves the track with a horizontal initial velocity.

b. Using the average of the initial speeds you measured in Part 2, use the theory to calculate how far from the table the ball should land.

4 Testing the theory

1. Write a clear step-by-step procedure that explains how you determine the landing spot relative to the track.
2. Follow your procedure and locate your predicted landing spot on the floor. Record any data you collect and show any calculations you perform.
3. Place the target so its center is at the predicted location. Tape the target to the floor. Place a sheet of carbon paper on top of the target with the dark side facing down.
4. Twist the end of the track so it curves downward, allowing the ball to fly off the track.
5. Release the ball and allow it to hit the ground. (Watch where the ball rolls so it does not get lost.)
6. Remove the carbon paper. There should be a mark on your target indicating where the ball landed.

5 Analyzing the results

a. How many centimeters is the landing spot from the center of the target? Did the ball travel too far, not far enough, to the left, or to the right?

b. Measure and record the distance along the floor between the landing spot and the place where the ball left the track. If your measurements and calculations were accurate, this distance should be the same as the distance you calculated.

c. Calculate the percent difference between the predicted distance and the actual distance the ball traveled.

d. Discuss some sources of error in the Investigation that may have resulted in your ball not landing in the center of the target.

e. When the ball was in the air, did its horizontal velocity change? Why or why not?

f. When the ball was in the air, did its vertical velocity change? Why or why not?

g. Calculate the velocity vector for the ball the moment before it hit the floor. Is the vector you calculate consistent with the motion of the ball after it hits the floor where the vertical component is abruptly reduced to zero?

h. Sketch each of the following graphs to describe the ball's motion as it was in the air: horizontal distance versus time, vertical distance versus time, horizontal speed versus time, and vertical speed versus time.

i. Imagine that you were to release the ball from a higher location on the track. Would you have to position the target closer to the table, farther from the table, or at the same distance? Why?

j. Now imagine that you were to release the ball with the track on a table that is twice as high off the ground. How far would you have to position the center of the target from the edge of the track? Show any calculations you perform to get your answer.

43

5 Example answers

5a. The ball was 1 cm short of hitting the target. It did not travel far enough.

5b. The distance was 1.03 m.

5c. The percent difference is 9.6%.

5d. The marble may have been pushed slightly when it was released. The table height may not have been measured as accurately as possible. The target may not have been perfectly aligned with the track in the left-right direction.

5e. The ball's horizontal velocity did not change because there were no horizontal forces acting on it once it left the track.

5f. The vertical velocity increased by 9.8 m/sec each second due to the force of gravity.

5g. The horizontal velocity was 2.58 m/s to the right, the same as the launch velocity. The vertical velocity was 3.94 m/s downward, found using the equation $v_y = v_{0y} - gt$. The resultant velocity is then 4.71 m/s at an angle of 57 degrees below the horizontal.

5h. Graphs:

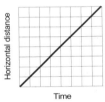
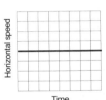
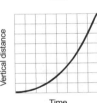
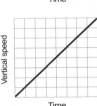

5i. If the ball were released from a higher location, the range would be farther because the ball would have a greater air time.

5j. If the ball were released from twice the height, the height would be 1.59 m. The launch speed would remain the same.

$$x = v_0 \sqrt{\frac{2y_0}{g}} = 2.58 \sqrt{\frac{2(1.59)}{9.8}} = 1.47 \text{ m}$$

The new range would be 1.47 m.

7.3 Forces in Two Dimensions

Key Question: How do forces balance in two dimensions?

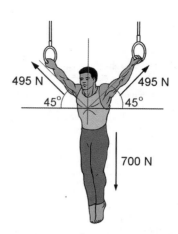

In general, force is a vector because it has both magnitude and direction. In this Investigation, students use spring scales to balance three forces acting at angles to each other. Using three force scales, students must apply three forces in directions that keep a small ring centered at the origin of a sheet of graph paper. Because of the angles, students must work with the forces as vectors in two dimensions. They show that when the ring is centered, all forces are balanced and the *x*- and *y*-components of the forces sum to zero. Students repeat the experiment with prescribed angles (forces vary) and also with prescribed forces (angles vary).

Reading Synopsis

Students read Section 7.3 Forces in Two Dimensions in the student text before the Investigation.

A force vector can be used to indicate the strength and direction in which a force is acting. A force vector can be specified with polar coordinates or *x-y* components. The magnitude of a vector stated as two components can be found with the Pythagorean theorem.

If an object is in equilibrium, all of the forces acting on it are balanced and the net force is zero. If forces act in two dimensions, the net force in the *x*-direction is zero, and the net force in the *y*-direction is zero.

Forces act in two dimensions on an object located on an inclined plane or ramp. The surface exerts a force on the object that is perpendicular to the slope. The force of gravity and friction also act on the object. Its acceleration can be found by resolving all of the forces into components, summing the components, finding the net force, and using Newton's second law.

The Investigation

Leading Questions
- What is meant by the term net force?
- What does it mean to say an object is in equilibrium?
- How can you find the components of a force?
- How do forces combine?

Learning Goals
By the end of the Investigation, students will be able to:
- Resolve a force vector into its components.
- Calculate the net force on an object.

Key Vocabulary force, vector, component, equilibrium

Setup and Materials

Students work in groups of four or five at tables.

Each group should have:

- Graph paper
- 5 N, 10 N, and 20 N spring scales
- Three 25-centimeter pieces of string
- Circular ring such as a metal key ring
- Scientific calculator with trigonometry functions

Details

Time   One class period

Preparation   Read section 7.3 Forces in Two Dimensions in the **Student Edition**

Assignments   Section 7.3 Forces in Two Dimensions in the **Student Edition** before the investigation.

Skill Sheets   7.3A Equilibrium in 2-D
7.3B Inclined Planes

Teaching the Investigation

1   Setting up the spring scales
2   Finding the force needed for equilibrium
3   The conditions of equilibrium
4   Determining the directions for equilibrium

Introduction

We have talked about the position vector and the velocity vector. The next important vector to consider is force. It should be clear that force is a vector because the direction of force matters. If I push something this way it moves this way, in the direction of about force I apply.

> Demonstrate by pushing something along the desktop.

Today's investigation is about the force vector. The force vector behaves just like the other vectors we have used, such as position and velocity. A force applied at an angle can be represented by components in x and y directions. That means the component forces have the exact same effect as the single force at an angle.

> Sketch a force at an angle on the board and its **x** and **y** components.

Can anyone defined equilibrium for me?

> Equilibrium is a condition where all forces cancel out, or balance. An object in equilibrium either stays at rest or continues moving at constant speed and direction.

In equilibrium, the net force is zero. What does this mean if the forces are in many directions?

> It means that the force in each direction must be zero separately.

Equilibrium means that the net force in any direction must be zero. When we are working in two dimensions, it means that the net force in the horizontal direction is zero and also that the net force in the vertical direction is zero. In terms of calculation, the requirement of equilibrium is a separate requirement for each component of the net force. The vector equation $\vec{F} = 0$ is really two separate equations: $F_x = 0$ and $F_y = 0$.

> Sketch the vector equation and separate component equations on the board.

Setting up the spring scales **1**

Check to see that all groups have calibrated their spring scales.

The objective of today's investigation is to demonstrate the equilibrium of forces in two dimensions. By applying forces with spring scales you are each going to try to keep this ring centered on the origin of your graph paper.

> Demonstrate the experiment in front of the class.

Check to see whether each spring scale is calibrated. Each should read 0 N when held vertically. Use the nut on top of the scale to adjust the calibration if necessary. Use the string to make a loop that connects the top of each spring scale to the ring. Position each knot so it is halfway between the ring and the loop at the top of the scale.

> Demonstrate the proper setup to the class. Check to see that all groups have calibrated their spring scales.

Finding the force needed for equilibrium **2**

Make sure students have positioned the knots on the strings so they are not rubbing on the ring.

Check to see that force 3 is held at the proper angle.

Three group members will be needed to hold the spring scales. Each person should hold one scale by the S-hook at the bottom. Hold the scales a small distance above the graph paper. Center the ring at the origin. The 5-N scale should be over the line marked force 1, the 10-N scale should be over the force 2 line, and the 20-N scale should be over the force 3 line.

> Make sure the students have positioned the knots on the strings so they are not rubbing on the ring.
> The knots could create friction and make the results inaccurate.

Pull the 5-N and 10-N scales with a force of 5 N each. Pull the 20-N scale with as much force as is needed to balance the other two scales. The ring should stay centered on the origin. Keep the scales parallel to the table and try to be as accurate as possible. It will take some practice to find the perfect balance. Record the magnitude of force 3 in Table 1.

> Circulate around the room and assist groups that have difficulty. Students may think they have found the correct balance of forces but may not have the forces 1 and 2 at exactly 5 N each. Also check to see that force 3 is held at the proper angle.

7.3 | Forces in Two Dimensions

Question: How do forces balance in two dimensions?

In this Investigation, you will:

1. Determine how to balance three forces so they are in equilibrium.
2. Calculate components of forces.
3. Combine components of forces.

In this Investigation, you will use spring scales to determine how to balance forces pulling in two dimensions. First, you will be given the specific direction in which to pull each scale and will have to measure the forces required to reach equilibrium. Then, you will be given the magnitude of three forces and must determine the directions the forces must have to reach equilibrium.

1 | Setting up the spring scales

1. Hold each spring scale vertically from its top loop and check to see that it is properly calibrated. If it needs to be adjusted, turn the nut at the top of the scale until it reads zero.
2. Attach the loop at the top of the 5-N scale to the ring by running a string through each 5-N scale and then tying a knot. Position the knot so that it is halfway between the scale and ring.
3. Repeat step 1, attaching the 10- and 20-newton scales to the ring as shown.

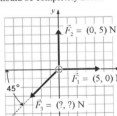
String loops — Ring

2 | Finding the force needed for equilibrium

1. Select three group members to each hold a spring scale by the S-hook at the bottom. The scales should be completely horizontal and held a few inches off the table.

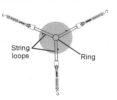
$\vec{F}_2 = (0, 5)\,\text{N}$
$\vec{F}_1 = (5, 0)\,\text{N}$
45°
$\vec{F}_3 = (?, ?)\,\text{N}$

2. Hold the scales on top of the graph paper in the configuration pictured on the right. Center the ring at the origin. Position the 5-N scale over the line marked force 1, the 10-N scale over the line marked force 2, and the 20-N scale over the force 3 line.

3. Pull the 5-N and 10-N scales each with a force of 5 N. The 20-N scale must be pulled with as much force as is needed to balance the other two scales. Hold the scales so they are parallel to the table and try to be as accurate as possible. It takes practice to get all of the scales balanced in the correct positions.

4. Enter the magnitude of force 3 in Table 1.

Table 1: Finding a force to balance two 5-N forces

	Magnitude (N)
Force 3	

44

Teaching tip

This Investigation requires students to coordinate their efforts and to have steady hands. It may be difficult for some groups to reach equilibrium with the spring scales all reading exact specified forces. Tell students in advance that this activity will not be as simple as it may seem at first. They should not expect to immediately find the correct orientation of the scales. You should also make sure students keep the ring centered on the origin. If equilibrium is achieved but the ring is not centered, moving the paper is easier than moving the scales.

2 | Example answers

Table 1: Finding a force to balance two 5-N forces

	Magnitude (N)
Force 3	7.4

The conditions of equilibrium

Determine the x and y components of forces 1,2, and 3. Use a negative sign to indicate a negative x or y direction.

Calculate the net force in the x and y directions. Use the Pythagorean theorem to calculate the magnitude of the net force on the ring.

The net force should be zero because the ring is in equilibrium

Determining the directions for equilibrium

Determine the direction for each force that will keep the ring centered on the origin. The three scales should read exactly 5, 10, and 12 N while the ring is centered.

Use a protractor to determine the angles of the forces. Calculate the x and y components, then find the net force on the ring.

3 Determine the x and y components of forces 1, 2, and 3. Use a negative sign to indicate a direction in the negative x or y direction. Record the values in Table 2.

Students should realize that they only have to do a calculation for the third force because the other two are directed along the axes.

Calculate the net force in the x-direction and the net fore in the y-direction. Then use the Pythagorean theorem to calculate the magnitude of the net force on the ring. Record the components and net forces in Table 2. What should the net force be? Why?

The net force should be zero because the ring is in equilibrium

How close is your net force to zero? Why might it be slightly different from zero?

The results may be slightly off due to the friction of the string against the ring, not reading the scales as accurately as possible, not holding the scales exactly in place, or not perfectly calibrating the scales.

4 This part of the Investigation is more challenging. You must pull the scales with specific forces but you must determine the directions for two of the forces. Place the 5-N scale along the x-axis and exert a force of 5 N. Pull the 10-N scale with a force of 10 N and the 20-N scale with a force of 12 N. The 10 N and 20 N forces can be directed at any angle. You must determine the direction for each force that will keep the ring centered on the origin. It will take some time to have the three scales read exactly 5 N, 10 N, and 12 N while the ring is centered. Once you have determined the proper positions, place a pencil inside each string loop and trace the direction of each force.

It is not easy to find the proper direction for each scale while pulling with a constant force. Encourage students to think about the force components that must be balanced to determine which direction to move each scale.

Use a protractor to determine the angles of the forces. Calculate the x and y components and record them in Table 3. Then find the net force on the ring. Is it what you expected?

It is likely that the results will be less accurate than in the first part of the Investigation because this procedure was more difficult.

3 The conditions of equilibrium

7.3 Forces in Two Dimensions

a. Calculate the x and y components of forces 1, 2, and 3 and enter the values in the table. Use a negative sign to indicate a direction in the negative x or y direction.

b. Calculate the x and y components of the net force on the ring. Then use the Pythagorean theorem to calculate the magnitude of the net force on the ring.

c. What should you have found the net force on the ring to be? Why?

d. Why might the net force be slightly different from the theoretical value? Discuss some sources of error that may be causing inaccuracy in your results.

Table 2: Finding a force to balance two 5-N forces

	Magnitude (N)	x-component (N)	y-component (N)
Force 1			
Force 2			
Force 3			
Net force			

4 Determining the directions for equilibrium

1. For this part of the Investigation, you will determine the proper directions to pull the spring scales to balance a specified force. Position the 5-N scale on the x-axis. You must choose the directions for the 10- and 20-N scales.

2. You and your group members must pull the 5-N scale (force 1) with a force of 5 N, the 10-N scale (force 2) with 10 N, and the 20-N scale (force 3) with 12 N. Keep the 5-N scale on the x-axis but adjust the positions of the other two until the ring is in equilibrium. It takes some time to do this accurately.

3. Draw the positions of the scales with forces of 10 and 12 N on the graph paper.

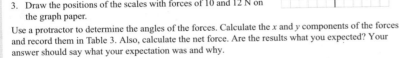

$\vec{F}_1 = 5$ N
$\vec{F}_2 = 10$ N
$\vec{F}_3 = 12$ N
$\vec{F}_1 = (5, 0)$ N

a. Use a protractor to determine the angles of the forces. Calculate the x and y components of the forces and record them in Table 3. Also, calculate the net force. Are the results what you expected? Your answer should say what your expectation was and why.

Table 3: Finding two forces to balance one 5-N force

	Magnitude (N)	x-component (N)	y-component (N)
Force 1	5	+5	0
Force 2	10		
Force 3	12		
Net force			

45

3 Example answers

3a. See Table 2.

3b. See Table 2.

3c. The net force should be zero because the ring is in equilibrium.

3d. There may be friction from the string against the ring. The spring scales may not have been pulled with exactly the correct amount of force. They also may not have been perfectly in position.

Table 2: Finding a force to balance two 5-N forces

	Magnitude (N)	x-component (N)	y-component (N)
Force 1	5	5	0
Force 2	5	0	5
Force 3	7.4	-5.2	-5.2
Net force	0.3	-0.2	-0.2

4a. Sample data:

Table 3: Finding two forces to balance one 5-N force

	Magnitude (N)	x-component (N)	y-component (N)
Force 1	5	5	0
Force 2	10	2.59	-9.66
Force 3	12	-7.39	9.46
Net force	0.28	-0.2	0.2

8.1 Motion in Circles

Key Question: How do you describe circular motion?

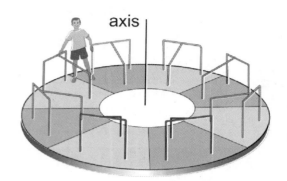

So far, students have worked with concepts developed in linear motion. In this Investigation, students will perform some simple activities that familiarize them with the description of circular motion. In circular motion the rate at which an object turns is described by angular speed. The students will explore the relationship between linear speed and angular speed. The first part of the Investigation uses a ball rolling on the floor to illustrate how the circumference of a rolling ball determines the relationship between the angular speed and the linear speed. In the second part of the Investigation, students will use a photogate to measure the angular speed of the pulley in an Atwood's machine and relate the angular speed to the linear speed of the falling and rising weights.

Reading Synopsis

Students read Section 8.1 Motion in Circles after the Investigation.

Objects in circular motion rotate or revolve around an imaginary line called the axis. The angular speed is the rate at which an object revolves or rotates. Angular speed is measured in revolutions per minute (rpm) or radians per second. Most physics problems use angular speed in radians per second. A radian is the angle defined by an arc equal in length to the radius of a circle, about 57.3 degrees.

The linear speed of a rolling object is related to its angular speed via the relationship $v = \omega r$. This relationship comes from the geometric fact that a rolling object moves a distance equal to one circumference in each rotation. Instruments such as speedometers and odometers derive the linear speed of a car or bicycle from the angular speed of the wheels.

The Investigation

Leading Questions
- How is circular motion different from linear motion?
- What is angular speed?
- How are linear speed and angular speed related?
- How is angular speed calculated?

Learning Goals

By the end of the Investigation, students will be able to:
- Create circular motion and relate it to linear motion.
- Measure angular speed in radians per second.
- Perform calculations with linear speed and angular speed including converting between the two when the radius is known.

Key Vocabulary   axis, rotates, revolves, angular speed, radian, circumference, angular displacement

Setup and Materials

Students work in groups of four or five at tables.

Each group should have:

- Ultimate pulleys set
- Physics stand
- Timer and one photogate, AC adapter (or 9-volt battery), and a cord to connect the photogate to the timer
- Ball (preferably a basketball)
- Masking tape
- Permanent markers

Details

Time One class period

Preparation

Assignment Section 8.1 Motion in Circles in the **Student Edition** after the Investigation.

Skill Sheets 8.1 Circular Motion

Equipment Setup Ultimate Pulleys

Teaching the Investigation

1 Introduction
2 Angular speed and radians
3 The relationship between angular speed and linear speed
4 Setting up an observation
5 Setting up an experiment
6 Measuring the average linear speed
7 Testing a hypothesis

Introduction

Circular motion is motion that repeats itself in circular patterns that return to where they started.

Angular speed and radians

Linear speed describes how far an object moves in a given amount of time.

Angular speed describes the angle through which an object rotates in a given amount of time.

Linear speed - meters per second.
Angular speed - radians or angles per second.

360 degrees = 6.28 radians
One radian = 57.3 degrees

The relationship between angular speed and linear speed

$v = \omega r$

v = linear speed (m/sec)
ω = angular speed (rad/sec)
r = radius (meters)

Setting up an observation

So far, we have applied the concepts of speed, position, and acceleration to what we call linear motion in physics. Linear motion is motion that goes from one place to another. Even if the motion path is curved, we still call it linear motion unless the curve comes back to where it starts. Circular motion is motion that repeats itself in circular paths that return over and over to where they start. It is said that fire and the wheel are humanity's greatest inventions. Today we are going to investigate the wheel and the relationship between circular motion and linear motion.

Linear speed describes how far an object moves in a given amount of time. Angular speed describes the angle through which an object rotates in a given amount of time. We used the variable v to represent linear speed. We will use a small Greek letter omega ω to represent angular speed. Can anyone guess what the units of omega are?

> Start a discussion. Linear speed has a units of distance over time, or meters per second. And your speed has units of angle over time such as radians per second or degrees per second.

In physics, we usually describe angles in radians instead of degrees. The radian is the natural measure of an angle. Think of an angle as a portion of a full circle. 360 degrees is a full circle and 90 degrees is a quarter circle. If I take the radius of a circle and wrap it around the circumference, it defines an angle. This angle is one radian. Since the circumference of a circle is 2π times the radius, there are 2π radians in a full circle. That means 360 degrees is approximately equal to 6.28 radians, making one radian about 57.3 degrees. Since one radian is really a ratio of two lengths, the units cancel out and a radian is a pure number. When we write an angle as 1.5 rad, we are really only using the "rad" to remind ourselves that we are measuring the angle in radians. This unit does not have to be "canceled out" like units of meters or seconds. This is the major reason that angles are given in radians for most physics problems.

> Go over the definition of a radian on the board, making a diagram similar to the one on the middle of page 145 of the text.

Suppose I roll this ball on the floor. How far does it move in one complete turn? What property of the ball determines how far it moves in each turn?

> Hold up a ball and then roll it on the floor. Pick up the ball again so the students can talk about what property determines how far it rolls in one turn. Everyone should recognize that the circumference of the ball is the property they seek.

A ball or wheel moves a distance of one circumference in each turn. The circumference of a wheel is $2\pi r$, where r is the radius of the wheel. If the wheel makes one turn in time (t) it moves forward with a speed of $2\pi r/t$. The quantity 2π is an angle in radians. The quantity $2\pi/t$ is the angular speed since it represents the angle turned divided by the time taken. We may therefore write the relationship between the linear speed and the angular speed of a wheel with the formula $v = \omega r$ as long as the angular speed (ω) is expressed in radians per second.

> Work out the derivation of this formula on the board.

1 We are going to test the relationship we propose between the linear speed and the angular speed. Each group has a large ball and I want you to take some tape and make a circle around the diameter of the ball, similar to the diagram in Part 1 of the Investigation. Make a mark on the tape that marks both sides where the tape overlaps. Remove the tape and measure the circumference of the ball with a meter stick

> Students follow the procedure to measure the circumference of their ball.

8.1

Motion in Circles

Question: How do you describe circular motion?

In this Investigation, you will:

1. Create circular motion and relate it to linear motion.
2. Measure angular speed in radians per second.

To describe circular motion, we need to develop concepts similar to the ones we used to describe linear motion. The *angular speed* (ω) is the rate at which an object's angle changes as it rotates. Units for angular speed could be degrees per second. For example, an object could rotate 90 degrees every second. If ω = 90 deg/sec, the object completes one full turn in four seconds.

In physics, it is more convenient to work with angles in units of radians. One radian is approximately 57.3 degrees. If the angular speed is expressed in radians per second, a simple relationship exists between the angular speed and the linear speed. This relationship comes from the fact that a point on the edge of a circle moves one circumference in one rotation.

Angular speed

Angular speed (rad/sec)

Angle turned (rad)

$$\omega = \frac{\theta}{t}$$

Time taken (sec)

Linear and angular speed

Radius (m)

Linear speed (m/sec) $v = \omega r$

Angular speed (rad/sec)

Setting up an observation

You will need a basketball or another ball of similar size.

1. Wrap masking tape around the ball so it makes a circle around the widest part. Make a mark where the tape overlaps as shown in the diagram.
2. Unwrap the masking tape and measure the distance between the marks. This is the circumference of the ball. Record the measurement.
3. Divide the circumference by 2π to calculate the radius of the ball.
4. Wrap another circle of masking tape around the ball the same way. This circle provides a reference as the ball is rolling.
5. Use the circumference to calculate the distance the ball moves in exactly five rotations. Mark out the distance on the floor with two strips of masking tape.
6. Set the ball on the floor so the masking tape stripe is straight up and down and aligned with the first mark. Slowly roll the ball with your hand so it makes five complete turns. How close does the ball come to the second mark?

Masking tape

Mark across tape

Circumference (C)

First tape   Second tape

Teaching tips

Relating angular speed to linear speed using the equation $v = \omega r$ requires students to measure angles in radians. Depending on the grade and level of math class, students may or may not have worked with radians before. Speak to math teachers in your school before introducing this topic in your class to determine whether you will be reviewing something the students have learned or teaching something entirely new.

When working with physics equations, the units on both sides of any equation must be the same. In the equation $v = \omega r$, it appears as if the units are not the same (m/sec on the left and rad-m/sec on the right). Explain to students that a radian is not a unit in the same way that a meter, second, or newton is. A radian is simply a fraction ($\frac{1}{2}\pi$ or 0.16) of a full circle. The radian unit can therefore be discarded when solving the equation for linear speed.

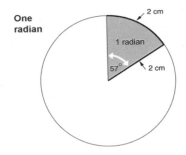

One radian

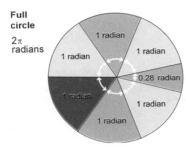

Full circle

2π radians

Setting up an observation (continued)

1 Multiply the circumference by five. Used two strips of tape to mark out a distance on the floor equal to five times the circumference.

Students should do this.

Put the masking tape back on the ball around its diameter. Set the ball on the floor so the masking tape stripe is straight up and down and aligned with one of the strips of tape on the floor. Make the ball rotate five rotations toward the second tape strip. Where does the ball end up?

The ball should end up on top of the second tape strip. This demonstrates that the ball moves five times its circumference in five complete turns.

Setting up an experiment

The motion out of the pulley is circular motion.

The motion of the moving weights is linear motion.

2 For the next part of the Investigation we are going to build an Atwood's machine just like we did a few weeks ago. Follow the instructions in step 2 to assemble the machine. Use the pulley that is marked "10 per radian." There are 10 stripes on this pulley for each radian of angle. Select the number of washers on each hanger so the heavier one has 2-3 more than the lighter one.

Students follow the instructions in step 2 and set up the pulleys, string and hangers.

Describe the motion of the pulley. Is this circular motion or linear motion? Describe the motion of the moving weights. Is this circular motion or linear motion?

The motion out of the pulley is circular motion. The motion of the moving weights is linear motion.

Attach a photogate just below the pulley so the stripes in the pulley break the light beam.

Measuring the average linear speed

Linear distance is the distance the weights move from top to bottom.

Average linear speed is the linear distance divided by the time it takes.

3 Measure the distance that the weights move from top to bottom. This is the linear distance. How would you calculate the average speed of the following or rising weights?

The average linear speed is this distance divided by the time it takes, measured with a stopwatch.

Use the stopwatch mode of the Timer to measure the average linear speed of the falling weights. Take at least three good trials to get an average time.

Students follow step 3 of the Investigation.

Testing a hypothesis

Measure the diameter of the pulley and calculate the radius.

Average angular speed of the pulley is:
$\omega = v/r$

Radians moved by the pulley are:
$\theta = \omega t$

Test the prediction using the count mode of the Timer

4 For about last part of the Investigation we are going to use to linear speed to predict how far the pulley turns. Wrap a piece of string around the pulley and measure the diameter if the circle made by the string. Calculate the radius by dividing by 2. How do you calculate the angular speed of the pulley?

Students should do the calculation using $\omega = v/r$.

How many radians should the pulley move during the time the weights are falling?

Students should do the calculation using $\theta = \omega t$.

If the pulley turns this many radians, what should the counter read at the moment the mass hits bottom?

The counter should read 10 times the total angle since there are 10 stripes per radian.

Repeat the experiment with the timer in count mode. Reset the count to zero, and then move the weights from top to bottom. How close is your measured angle to the angle you predicted? Remember, if you hit the reset button, one of two things will happen. If the timer is already counting, the reset button will freeze the display, allowing you to write down the number. If the display is already frozen, the Timer will reset to zero and start counting again. If nothing seems to be counting, the display may be frozen so hit reset ONCE to resume counting.

Students should check their prediction against the actual count. The difference should be < 5% and I often assign a grade equal to 100% minus the percent difference between prediction and measurement.

Setting up an experiment

2 **Setting up an experiment**

1. Attach the spindle to the top hole in the stand using a threaded knob. Find the pulley labeled "10 Hz = 1 rad/sec." Slide the pulley onto the spindle. Use plastic spacers and the stopper to keep the pulley from sliding off the spindle.

2. Attach unequal masses to the two hangers. The heavier hanger should have 2-3 more washers than the lighter one.

3. Attach a photogate just below the pulley as shown in the diagram. The striped pattern on the pulley should break the light beam of the photogate as the pulley rotates.

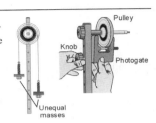

Pulley

Knob

Photogate

Unequal masses

3 **Measuring the average linear speed**

1. Measure the distance the hangers move from top to bottom. You need to hold the heavier hanger down on the base to make the measurement.

2. Use the stopwatch function to measure the time it takes the hangers to move the whole distance. Write the result in Table 1. Repeat three trials to be sure you get consistent results.

3. Calculate the average linear speed of the hangers by dividing the distance moved by the total time.

Table 1: Linear speed data

Distance (cm)	Time 1 (sec)	Time 2 (sec)	Time 3 (sec)	Avg. time (sec)	Avg. linear speed (cm/sec)

4 **Testing a hypothesis**

a. Remove the pulley and wrap a single turn of string around it. Use a meter stick to measure the diameter of the circle the string makes. Divide the diameter by two to get the radius of the pulley. This is the radius at which the string moves.

b. Use the relationship $v = \omega r$ to calculate the average angular speed (ω) of the pulley in rad/sec.

c. With linear speed, the distance (d) an object moves is calculated using the relationship $d = vt$ where v is the linear speed and t is the time. Write a similar relationship between the angle (θ) an object rotates, its angular speed (ω), and the time, t.

d. Use the relationship you just wrote in part (c) to calculate the total angle the pulley turns through while the falling mass moves from top to bottom. Express your answer in radians. There are 2π (about 6.28) radians in a full turn. An angle greater than 6.28 radians means the pulley rotated more than one turn.

e. There are 10 stripes on the pulley for every radian of angle. You can measure the angle (in radians) the pulley turns by counting the stripes and dividing by 10. The Timer has a count mode that works perfectly for this purpose. Set the Timer in count mode. Move the masses from top to bottom by hand and record the number of stripes that pass the light beam. Calculate the total angle the pulley turns (in radians) by dividing the count by 10. NOTE: Pressing reset once clears the display, twice freezes the display, three clears it again, etc. If nothing seems to be counting, press reset again ONCE.

How close did your predicted angle come to the angle you measured?

47

---

3 **Example answers**

Table 1: *Linear speed data*

Distance (cm)	Time 1 (sec)	Time 2 (sec)	Time 3 (sec)	Avg. time (sec)	Avg. linear speed (cm/sec)
87.0	1.54	1.50	1.52	1.52	57.2

4 **Example answers**

3a. We measured a diameter of 9.7 cm, and calculated a radius of 4.85 cm.

3b. $v = \omega r$ so $\omega = v \div r = 57.2 \div 4.85 = 11.8$ rad/sec

3c. $\theta = \omega t$

3d. The angle we calculate is (11.8 rad/sec) × (1.52 sec) = 17.9 radians.

3e. We did the experiment and measured 175 counts, which equals an angle of 17.5 radians. The difference is only 2% between the measurement and our prediction of 17.9 radians. We attribute the slight difference to errors in timing as the hanger bounced a bit when it hit the bottom.

8.2 Centripetal Force

Key Question: Why does a roller coaster stay on track upside down on a loop?

Centripetal forces are forces that cause a moving object to travel in a circular path. For the Investigation, students will roll a ball down a track that has a circular loop at the end. If the ball is moving is fast enough, it will stay on the track all the way around the loop and successfully land in the catcher. If the ball is too slow, it will fall off the track near the top of the loop. The challenge for students is to determine the minimum speed required for the ball to stay on the track all the way around the loop. Since the loop is a circle, the minimum speed is set by the relationship between the weight of the ball and the centripetal force supplied by the circular track.

Reading Synopsis

Students read Section 8.2 Centripetal Force after the Investigation.

Centripetal force is any force that causes an object to move in a circular path. Centripetal force always points toward the center of rotation. If the centripetal force causing an object to move in a circle is removed, the object travels in a straight line as predicted by Newton's first law.

The centripetal force required to cause an object of mass (m) to move in a circle of radius, r is given by about formula $F_c = mv^2/r$. If the centripetal force is increased, the radius of curvature decreases, and vice versa.

Centripetal acceleration is the radially inward acceleration experienced by an object moving in a circular path. Centripetal acceleration is caused by centripetal force. The centripetal acceleration depends only on the speed of the object and the radius of the circular path according to the equation $a_c = v^2/r$. Centrifugal force is not truly a force but an effect caused by an object's inertia.

The Investigation

Leading Questions
- What keeps a roller coaster on the track (even upside down) when it goes around a loop?
- How are velocity, radius, and centripetal force related?
- How does changing an object's mass affect centripetal force?

Learning Goals

By the end of the Investigation, students will be able to:
- Describe why there is a minimum height at which the ball must be started before it will make it around the circular loop on the track.
- Describe and sketch the balance of forces at the top of the loop using the concepts of centripetal force, normal force, and weight.
- Use the formula for centripetal force to solve problems when given any three of the four variables (speed, radius, mass, force)

Key Vocabulary   centripetal acceleration, centrifugal force

Setup and Materials

Students work in groups of four or five at tables.

Each group should have:

- Loop track
- Physics stand
- Steel ball
- Plastic ball
- Timer with photogates, AC adapter (or 9-volt battery), and cords to connect the photogates to the timer

Details

Time ⏲ One class period

Preparation ✎ Try out the experiment before class to anticipate student problems or questions.

Assignments 📖 Section 8.2 Centripetal Force in the **Student Edition** after the Investigation.

Skill Sheets 1.1 Solving Equations
5.2 Newton's Second Law (to review the formula)

Equipment Setup Loop Track

Teaching the Investigation

1. Introduction
2. Centripetal force
3. The loop track
4. Thinking about centripetal force
5. Forces acting on the ball at the top of the loop
6. Testing your theory
7. Analyzing the results

Introduction

Have students share their experiences with acceleration down a steep hill and on a loop roller coaster if any students have been on one.

Centripetal force

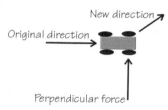

New direction

Original direction

Perpendicular force

Centripetal force - any force that rotates in a direction so it always points toward the center, resulting in circular motion.

The loop track

What determines whether the ball successfully makes it all the way around the loop, staying on the inside track?

1. Put one photogate at the bottom of the loop.
2. Measure the speed of the ball as it rolls through the photogate.
3. Release the ball from different heights and see if you can find a relationship between speed and staying on the track all the way around the loop.

How many of you have been on a roller coaster that has a loop? How many have seen such a roller coaster in an advertisement or on television? Can anyone tell me why the car does not fall off the track at the top of the loop?

Start a discussion. You will most likely get an explanation involving centrifugal force. A common statement is "the centrifugal force of the car moving around the loop balances of the weight that is trying to pull the car down." While this statement shows good physical reasoning, it is not quite correct.

Suppose I have a car going in a straight line like this. What sort of force would you apply to the car if you wished to bend its motion to the left?

Draw a car moving in a straight line up the blackboard. To bend the car's motion to the left students should recognize that you must exert a force on the car that points toward the left.

To bend the velocity vector to the left, you need to accelerate to the left which means applying a force to the left. Suppose I could change the direction of my force so it was always perpendicular to the motion of the car. What would the motion of the car look like then?

The car would continue to turn to the left and the motion would become a circle.

Any force that rotates in a direction so it always points toward a center is called a centripetal force. The word *centripetal* means "center pointing." Circular motion is the result of centripetal forces. If that centripetal force is strong, the motion is bent into a circle with a small radius. If the centripetal force is weak, the motion follows a circle with a large radius. Today's Investigation is about centripetal force and roller coasters.

If I roll this ball down this track, what do you think will happen when it comes to the loop?

Set up a loop track in front of the class to demonstrate. Roll the ball down a few times. Some of your rolls should start from high enough that the ball makes it around the loop. Demonstrate a few rolls that do not make it around the loop.

What do you think determines whether the ball successfully makes it all the way around the loop, staying on the track?

Discuss this with students. Most will recognize that the ball must be moving fast enough to stay on the track. A ball that is moving too slowly falls off before it reaches the top of the loop. A few students may anticipate the argument that the ball cannot reach a height higher than it started from. This is a good argument although conservation of energy is not covered until Chapter 10. Also, the ball needs to be released from a significantly higher point than the top of the loop, as we will see.

I want everyone to write a sentence stating a hypothesis about the relationship between the motion of the ball entering the loop and whether the ball successfully stays on the track around the loop.

Students should write down a one sentence hypothesis. It is best if the hypothesis is jointly agreed by the entire group so each student in the group shares the same hypothesis.

Let's do a little test. I want everyone to put one photogate at the bottom of the loop. When the ball rolls through the photogate, you can measure its speed. Release the ball from different heights, and see if you can find a relationship between its speed and whether it stays on the track all the way around the loop. If the ball stays on the track it will catch cleanly in the catcher without hitting the wood. If you listen carefully, you can hear the difference between a clean catch and a catch where the ball was a little off the track.

Students do this introductory activity and observe that there is a minimum speed above which the ball always stays on the track all the way around the loop.

UNIT 3: Motion and Force in 2 and 3 Dimensions

8.2 Centripetal Force

Question: Why does a roller coaster stay on track upside down on a loop?

In this Investigation, you will:

1. Determine the minimum release height required for a ball to make it around a loop on a track.
2. Compare the motion of balls of different masses on the track.
3. Observe a relationship between the forces acting on the ball that determines whether the ball stays on the track at the top of the loop.

Have you ever wondered how roller coasters stay on the track as they go around loops? Understanding centripetal force is essential to designing roller coasters that stay on the track as they move through loops. In this Investigation, you will use a rolling ball to simulate the motion of a roller coaster.

1 Introduction

The loop track has a downhill section where the ball picks up speed. If the ball stays on the track, it drops into the catcher without hitting the wooden lip at the opening of the slot. If the ball leaves the track, the catcher may not catch it at all, or the ball may catch but bounce against the wood at the opening of the slot. You can tell if the ball stayed on the track all the way around the loop by the sound it makes when it lands in the catcher.

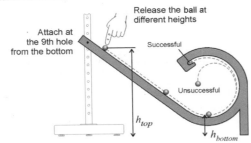

1. Attach the loop track to the stand using the 9th hole from the bottom. This sets the sloped part of the track to an angle of 45 degrees.
2. Drop the steel ball from different heights and observe whether it makes it around the track. Be careful to release the ball without pushing it.
3. Try dropping the plastic ball which has a much lower mass. Is the performance of the plastic ball different from the performance of the steel ball?

a. What do you observe as you dropped the ball from different heights? Think about the speed of the ball and whether it makes it around the loop successfully.

b. Write down a hypothesis about the conditions that are necessary for a ball to make it successfully around the loop.

48

---

1 Example answers

1a. The ball makes it around the loop successfully as long as it is dropped from the 20-centimeter mark or a point higher up the track. The ball doesn't seems to have enough speed to make it all the way around the loop if it is released from below the 20-centimeter mark.

1b. The ball will gain enough speed to successfully complete the loop when released from the 20-centimeter mark or higher on the track.

Thinking about centripetal force

Faster moving objects take more force to bend into a circle than slower moving objects.

Centripetal force depends on the speed of the object.

Formula:
$F_c = mv^2 \div r$

Forces acting on the ball at the top of the loop

Forces acting on the ball:
(1) the weight of the ball; and
(2) the normal (perpendicular) force acting on the ball exerted by the track.

2

Why should the ball have a minimum speed to stay on the track? The answer has to do with centripetal force. Suppose I have two objects of the same mass but moving at different speeds. I want both to travel in a circle, so I tie them to the end of a string. The string allows me to apply a centripetal force. I whirl the objects around my head to make them move in a circle and supply the centripetal force with my hand. Which object requires the greater centripetal force? The one that goes faster or the one goes slower? Or, do both require the same force since both move in the same size circle?

> Students will likely recognize that the faster moving object takes more force to bend into a circle than the slower moving object. The point is that centripetal force depends on the speed of the object.

The centripetal force required to cause an object to move in a circle of a given radius (r) is given by the formula $F_c = mv^2 \div r$. This formula tells us that an object moving twice as fast requires four times as much force to bend its motion into a circle of the same radius. The formula also says that more massive objects require more centripetal force to maintain circular motion. Finally, the centripetal force required is inversely proportional to the radius of the motion. It takes a more force to bend motion into a sharper curve.

Consider the forces acting on the ball at the top of the loop. What are in these forces?

> Prompt students to identify the forces acting on the ball. There are only two—the weight of about ball and the normal force acting on the ball from the track. Friction may also be present.

The ball's weight (mg) pulls straight down. The track exerts a normal force on the ball that keeps the ball from moving through the track. Other than friction, these are the only two forces that act.

Think about three different cases that apply to the motion of the ball. The centripetal force required to make the ball follow the circular track of radius (r) with speed (v) is $mv_2 \div r$.

Case #1: If the weight is greater than the required centripetal force, the ball moves in a tighter circle. The tighter circle takes the ball off the track and it does not catch cleanly.

Case #2: If the weight is exactly equal to the required centripetal force, the ball follows the track perfectly and catches cleanly in the catcher.

Case #3: If the weight is less than the required centripetal force, the ball moves in a larger circle than the track if it could. Instead, the track restrains the ball by exerting a normal force back on the ball forcing it to follow the circle of the track tightly and the ball catches cleanly in the catcher.

The condition for the ball to follow the track and catch cleanly is that the weight must be less than or equal to the centripetal force required to make the ball move in the circle of the track. As a formula, this means mv^2/r must be equal to or greater than mg. This relationship is why there is a minimum speed required for the ball to stay on the track. Use the relationship to derive a formula for the minimum speed the ball must have at the top of the loop to stay on the track.

> Students do the derivation. You may wish to circulate around the room and help groups do the math and check whether they have the correct result. The correct relationship is that the minimum speed (v) is the square root of the radius (r) *multiplied* by the strength of gravity (g = 9.8 N/kg).

2 Thinking about centripetal force

The force that causes an object to move in a circle is called a *centripetal force*. Any type of physical force can be a centripetal force if it results in circular motion. Some common examples of centripetal forces come from string tension, normal forces, friction, and weight. A centripetal force is always directed toward the center of the circle that the object's motion follows.

The centripetal force required to cause an object to move in a circle of a given radius *(r)* is given by the formula on the right. If the centripetal force is smaller, the object moves in a circle of larger radius. If the centripetal force is larger, the object moves in a circle of smaller radius. This is because a stronger centripetal force is able to bend the motion into a sharper curve.

Centripetal force

Mass (kg) — Linear speed (m/sec)

Centripetal force (N) $\quad F_c = \dfrac{mv^2}{r}$ Radius of path (m)

Consider the forces acting on the ball at the top of the loop. The ball's weight *(mg)* pulls straight down. Think about three different cases that apply to the motion of the ball. The centripetal force required to make the ball follow the circular track of radius *(r)* with speed *(v)* is $mv^2 \div r$.

1. Case number 1: If the weight is greater than the required centripetal force, the ball moves in a tighter circle. The tighter circle takes the ball off the track and it does not catch cleanly.

Case #1 $\quad mg > \dfrac{mv^2}{r}$

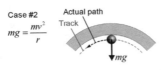

2. Case number 2: If the weight is exactly equal to the required centripetal force, the ball follows the track perfectly and catches cleanly in the catcher.

Case #2 $\quad mg = \dfrac{mv^2}{r}$

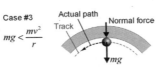

3. Case number 3: If the weight is less than the required centripetal force, the ball moves in a larger circle than the track *if it could.* Instead, the track restrains the ball by exerting a *normal force* back on the ball, forcing it to follow the circle of the track tightly and the ball catches cleanly in the catcher.

Case #3 $\quad mg < \dfrac{mv^2}{r}$

The condition for the ball to follow the track and catch cleanly is that *the weight must be less than or equal to the centripetal force required to make the ball move in the circle of the track.*

a. Using the formulas for weight and centripetal force, write a formula expressing the minimum speed *(v)* needed to keep the ball on the track.

b. Use the formula to calculate the minimum speed required for the ball to make it around the loop and stay on the track. The radius of the track is 10 centimeters.

c. Draw a free body diagram for the ball when it is at the top of the loop. Label the two forces acting on the ball and use vectors to show their directions.

d. Explain why it would *not be* correct to draw a third arrow on your free body diagram and label it "centripetal force."

49

2 Example answers

2a. min $v = \sqrt{gr}$

2b. min $v = \sqrt{9.8 \text{ m/sec}^2 \times .1 \text{ m}}$
min $v = 0.99$ m/sec

2c.

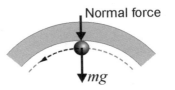

Normal force

mg

2d. Centripetal force is the net force on the object moving in a circular path. In this case, it is the net of weight and the normal force, not an altogether separate force.

Testing your theory

Have students measure the speed of the marble at the top of the loop at the slowest speed that will successfully make it around the loop.

1 Use the formula you derive to calculate the minimum speed the ball must have at the very top of the loop. The radius of the loop is 10 centimeters measured from the center of the loop to the center of the ball.

Students do the calculation and calculate the minimum speed of 0.99 m/sec.

Is the minimum speed different if you use the plastic ball instead of the steel ball? The mass of the steel ball is 28 grams and the mass of the plastic ball is 4 grams.

Students should reply that the minimum speed is the same since mass does not appear in the formula. Follow the steps in Part 3 of the Investigation to test the theory you just derived for whether the ball makes it around the loop on the track. Put a single photogate at the top of the loop so you can measure the speed of the ball. This technique will allow you to measure the speed of the ball as long as the ball stays on the track. If the ball gets off the track by more than a few millimeters, the photogate will give you the wrong data for calculating the speed. Can anyone tell me why the speed calculated from the photogate time gives the wrong answer if the ball leaves the track?

If the ball leaves the track, the light beam from the photogate does not cross the ball along its diameter. Therefore, calculating the speed as of the diameter of the ball divided by the time the light beam is broken gives the wrong result. The calculated speed will be higher than the actual speed.

Do the experiments for both the steel ball and the plastic ball.

Students do the experiments taking data for at least five or six different speeds for each ball. Circulate around the room helping groups to make measurements. Pay particular care to how they determine whether the ball made it into the catcher without hitting the lip or not. Also pay attention to the calculated speeds since they may be in error if the ball did not stay on the track.

There is a column in Table 1 for you to calculate the centripetal force. Calculate the centripetal force required to make the ball move in a circle of a 10 centimeter radius. Compare the calculation with the weight of the ball. Does your comparison agree with the hypothesis that the ball comes off the track when the weight exceeds the centripetal force?

Students should do the calculations and make the comparison. They should have found that the ball leaves the track at a speed that is within 5% of the predicted value. The usual source of error is not knowing precisely if the ball has left the track or not. The ball can move in a slightly smaller radius than the track and still catch in the catcher.

Analyzing the results

Have students compare their measured speed from their observations from the first part of the Investigation to what they calculated using the centripetal force formula.

Typically, the results will be well within 5% of each other.

What happens when the centripetal force is larger than the weight of the ball? The ball still moves in a 10-centimeter circle because the track forces it to. If the ball moves in a 10-centimeter circle, then the total centripetal force must be equal to mv^2/r. Where does the additional force come from?

The force comes from the track pushing against the ball. The track exerts a normal force against the ball. This force makes up the difference between the weight and the centripetal force needed to keep the ball moving in a circle with a 10 centimeter radius.

Real roller coaster loops are not circular but are shaped like teardrops. The name for this type of loop is a clothoid loop, and it has a smaller radius at the top than at the bottom. What advantage does this shape have over a circular loop?

The smaller the radius of curvature, the lower the minimum speed needed to stay on the track. Roller coasters with clothoid loops can run at lower speeds and therefore lower forces.

8.2 Centripetal Force

3 Testing your theory

1. Place a photogate at the top of the loop. The photogate allows you to measure the speed of the ball at the very top of the loop.
2. Release the steel ball from different heights and record the time it takes to pass through the photogate and whether the ball stayed on the track. Take data for a range of heights that give the ball speeds both greater and less than the minimum speed required to make it around the loop.
3. Calculate the speed of the ball at the top of the loop for each trial. Use the diameter of the ball (0.019 m) for the distance in the speed calculations. Also, calculate the weight of the ball and the centripetal force required to keep the ball moving in a circle with a radius of 10 centimeters. The mass of the steel ball is 28 grams. Record the measurements and calculations in Table 1.
4. Repeat steps 2 and 3 using the plastic ball. The mass of the plastic ball is 4 grams.

Table 1: Experimental loop-the-loop data

Mass (kg)	Weight (N)	Photogate time (sec)	Speed (m/sec)	Centripetal force at 10 cm radius (N)	Did the ball stay on the track (yes or no)

4 Analyzing the results

a. Compare the weight to the centripetal force for your experimental data on both balls. How should they be related? Do your experimental results confirm this?

b. If a group in your class found the centripetal force to be significantly larger than the ball's weight in trial 1 for one of the balls, what would you suspect they did wrong?

c. Describe how you would use the centripetal force and the weight to calculate the normal force on the ball.

d. Imagine that your job is to design a roller coaster layout containing a hill followed by a circular loop with a radius of 20 meters. Use what you learned in this Investigation to estimate the minimum speed required for the roller coaster to make it around the loop. Do you have to take the mass of the passengers riding the roller coaster into account in the previous question? Why or why not?

e. Real roller coasters are always designed to enter a loop after going down a hill that has more than the minimum height. Explain why.

f. You may have noticed that many roller coaster loops are not circular but teardrop-shaped. This is called a *clothoid* loop, and it has a smaller radius at the top than at the bottom. Use what you have learned in this Investigation to explain the advantages of a clothoid loop over a circular loop.

50

---

3 **4** Example answers

Table 1: *Experimental loop-the-loop data*

Mass (kg)	Weight (N)	Photo. time (sec)	Speed (m/sec)	Centripetal force at 10 cm radius (N)	Did the ball stay on the track (yes or no)
0.028	0.274	0.0191	0.99	0.274	yes
0.028	0.274	0.0199	0.95	0.253	no
0.004	0.039	0.0191	0.99	0.039	yes
0.004	0.0392	0.0199	0.95	0.036	no

4a. When the centripetal force was equal to or greater than the weight of the ball, the ball made it around the loop successfully. This agrees with the way they should be related and is confirmed by the results.

4b. They may not have recorded the time correctly or did not have the photogate positioned properly and measured the time interval through part of the marble that was less than the diameter, giving dramatically faster yet incorrect results for the speed calculation.

4c. Centripetal force is the net of the weight and the normal force. Subtracting the weight of the ball from the calculated centripetal force would equal the normal force.

4d. By comparing the speed of the steel and plastic balls, we found that the radius of the loop that determined the minimum speed required to make it around the loop, not the mass of the object.

Since min $v = \sqrt{gr}$ and the radius of the loop is 20 meters,

$$\text{min } v = \sqrt{9.8 \text{ m/sec}^2 \times 2}$$
$$\text{min } v = 14 \text{ m/sec}$$

4e. This is for safety reasons to ensure that the roller coaster has more than enough speed to make it all the way around in case something should happen to decrease the roller coaster's speed.

4f. The clothoid loop has a smaller radius at the top, meaning the car and riders would not require quite as much speed to make it around the loop. A smaller radius at the top would require a lower minimum velocity to make it around, and the roller coaster would not need to have as large of a hill leading into a clothoid loop as compared with a circular loop. With the lower speed going into the clothoid loop, riders would experience much less centripetal force going up the first part of the loop, making for a safer and more enjoyable riding experience.

8.3 Universal Gravitation and Orbital Motion

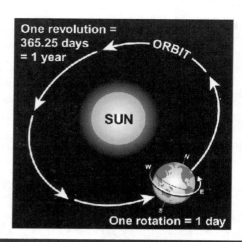

Key Question: How strong is gravity in other places in the universe?

In this Investigation, students use the law of universal gravitation to calculate the gravitational force between ordinary objects such as themselves, cars, and pencils. They quickly learn that gravity is a negligible force unless at least one of the objects such as a planet or star has a very large mass. They also calculate weight on planets with different masses. The last exercise in the Investigation is to derive the strength of gravity at the Earth's surface ($g = 9.8$ N/kg) from the law of universal gravitation.

Reading Synopsis

Students read Section 8.3 Universal Gravitation and Orbital Motion after the Investigation.

One of the most important sources of centripetal force is gravity. The force of gravity always acts toward the center of a spherical object such as a planet. Gravity keeps the planets moving in their orbits and you firmly attached to Earth's surface.

The law of universal gravitation describes the force of gravity between two objects of mass m_1 and m_2 separated by a distance r. The force between the objects is given by $F = G\ m_1 m_2 / r$, where G is the gravitational constant which is the same everywhere in the universe ($G = 6.67 \times 10^{-11}$ N·m²/kg²).

A satellite is an object bound by gravity to another object such as a planet or star. An orbit is the path followed by a satellite around another object under the influence of gravity. The orbits of most planets are nearly circular while the orbits of comets are highly elliptical.

The Investigation

Leading Questions
- How does gravity affect objects?
- How can we calculate the force of gravity between objects?
- How would gravity be different on different planets in our solar system?

Learning Goals

By the end of the Investigation, students will be able to:
- Use Newton's law of universal gravitation to calculate the gravitational force of attraction between various objects.
- Use Newton's law of universal gravitation to calculate the strength of gravity for different planets in the universe.

Key Vocabulary

law of universal gravitation, gravitational constant satellite, orbit, ellipse

Setup and Materials

Students work in groups of four or five at tables. This is mostly a calculation lab.

Each group should have:

- Calculator and paper
- Access to data on the planets from the Investigation book or a similar source.
- Access to a balance for measuring the mass of a few small items.

Details

Time	⏱ One class period
Preparation	✎
Assignments	Section 8.3 Universal Gravitation and Orbital Motion in the **Student Edition** after the Investigation.
Skill Sheets	8.3 Universal Gravitation
Equipment Setup	Loop Track

Teaching the Investigation

1. Introduction
2. The law of universal gravitation
3. The gravitational force between everyday objects
4. The gravitational force of attraction between people and planets
5. Calculate your weight on different planets
6. The value of g
7. Satellites and orbits

Introduction

Newton showed that the motion of the stars and planets is governed by the same rules that apply to objects on Earth.

The law of universal gravitation

Any two bodies that have mass attract each other with a force called gravity. The strength of the force is proportional to the product of the masses divided by the square of the distance between their centers.

$$F = G \cdot \frac{m_1 \cdot m_2}{r^2}$$

F = force, in Newtons
$G = 6.67 \times 10^{-11}$ Nm^2/kg^2
m_1 and m_2 = masses in kilograms
r = distance in meters

The gravitational force between everyday objects

Work out calculations in Part 1

The gravitational force of attraction between people and planets

Gravity forces are important only when one of the objects has a very large mass like the mass of a planet or moon.

Sir Isaac Newton is widely considered to be one of the most brilliant humans who ever lived. Prior to the time of Newton, scientists concerned themselves with understanding the workings of mechanical objects and things on Earth that they could touch and feel directly. It did not occur to people that the same laws which described phenomena on Earth also apply to the stars and planets far away. The law of universal gravitation, the subject of today's Investigation, changed all of that. Newton showed that the motion of the stars and planets was governed by exactly the same rules that apply to objects here on Earth. In many ways this was the true beginning of the scientific revolution.

The law of universal gravitation says that any two bodies that have mass attract each other with a force called gravity. The strength of the force is proportional to the product of the masses divided by the square of the distance between their centers. If one mass gets twice as large, the force gets twice as large. If both masses become twice as large, the force becomes four times as large. If the masses move so they are twice as far apart, the force decreases to one-fourth its previous strength.

Write about law of universal gravitation on the board and work out the force in imaginary unit; for example, if the mass is one kilogram, the second mass is one kilogram, and the distance between them is one meter, the force is one. If one mass is one kilogram, the second mass is two kilograms and the distance between them is one meter, the force is two. The idea is to illustrate the relationship between force, mass, and distance without getting confused by numbers that can only be expressed in scientific notation because they are so large.

If we want the force to come out in real units, we must multiply by the gravitational constant, G. G has the value 6.67×10^{-11} N·m^2/kg^2. If you put both masses (m_1, m_2) in kilogram and the distance (r) in meters, then the force will come out in newtons. The gravitational constant is very small. That means that the gravitational force between ordinary objects is also very small.

Write the formula for universal gravitation on the board along with the value of G.
How gravitationally attracted are you to another person or this pencil or a piece of cake? Does gravity play an important role in the forces between everyday objects? Use the law of universal gravitation to work out the force in newtons between the objects listed in Part 1 of the Investigation. You may approximate the masses of the objects. The exact value of the force is not important; all we want is to get a sense of how large the force is compared with forces we can feel.

Students work out the calculations in Part I a-d.

2 If the forces are very small, so gravity is not important? How can the force of gravity be made large?

At least one of the masses must be very large, the size of a planet or moon. Alternatively, the masses could be extremely close together; however, it is impossible to get two objects close enough for gravity to play a significant role and because the objects must themselves get smaller as they get closer together.

Gravity forces tend to be important only when one of the objects has a very large mass like the mass of a planet. For example, the Earth's mass is 5.97×10^{24} kg. Expressed without the help of scientific notation, this is 5,970,000,000,000,000,000,000,000 kilograms, or almost six trillion, trillion kilograms. That is a very massive object! Table 1 lists the mass and radius of the other planets in the solar system. Which planet has the greatest mass? Which plant has the smallest mass?

Jupiter has the greatest mass, and Pluto has the smallest mass of the nine planets.

8.3   Universal Gravitation and Orbital Motion

Question: How strong is gravity in other places in the universe?

In this Investigation, you will:

1. Use Newton's law of universal gravitation to calculate the gravitational force of attraction between various objects.
2. Use Newton's law of universal gravitation to calculate the strength of gravity for different planets in the universe.

All objects that have mass attract each other through gravity. The strength of the gravitational force that acts between two objects depends on the mass of those objects and the distance between their centers. This idea is known as *Newton's law of universal gravitation*. In this Investigation, you will use the law of universal gravitation to calculate the gravitational force of attraction between objects. You will also calculate the gravitational field strength (*g*) on the surface of different planets using the gravitational constant (*G*) which is the same everywhere in the universe.

Law of universal gravitation

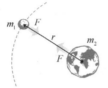

Mass 1, Mass 2 (kg)

$$\text{Force (N)} \quad F = G\frac{m_1 m_2}{r^2}$$

Gravitational Constant
$(6.67 \times 10^{11} \, N \cdot m^2/kg^2)$ ⌐ Distance between masses (m)

1 | The gravitational force between everyday objects

How gravitationally "attracted" are you to another person? Use Newton's law of universal gravitation to calculate the gravitational force of attraction between the following pairs of objects. For each situation, estimate the masses of the objects and the distances between them.

a. Your pencil and your calculator, having been placed next to each other on your desk.
b. Your left shoe and your right shoe as you stand comfortably.
c. You and another person of similar mass at a distance of two meters.
d. Two cars parked next to each other.

2 | The gravitational force of attraction between people and planets

Gravitational forces tend to be important only when one of the objects has a very large mass, like the mass of a planet. Note that the mass of any of the nine planets in our solar system is hugely greater than the mass of any ordinary object. For example, Earth's mass is 5.97×10^{24} kilograms. Expressed without the help of scientific notation, that is 5,970,000,000,000,000,000,000,000 kg., or almost six trillion, trillion kilograms. That is a massive object! Table 1 lists the mass and radius of the other planets in the solar system.

60 kg

586 N
(131 lbs)

Earth
10^{24} kg

51

1 Example answers

1a. pencil and calculator on desk ($m_{pencil} = 10$ g, $m_{calc} = 500$ g, $r = 10$ cm) $F = 3.3 \times 10^{-11}$ N

1b. left shoe and right shoe while standing ($m_{shoe} = 750$ g, $r = 10$ cm) $F = 3.8 \times 10^{-9}$ N

1c. you and another person while talking ($m_{person} = 60$ kg, $r = 2$ m) $F = 6.0 \times 10^{-8}$ N

1d. two parked cars ($m_{car} = 2,000$ kg, $r = 3$ m) $F = 2.96 \times 10^{-5}$ N

Answers to Part 3 are based on a person whose mass is 60 kilograms:

3a. 589 N at Earth's surface

3b. 440 N at a distance of 1,000 km above Earth's surface

3c. 1,556 N at Jupiter's surface

3d. 564 N at a distance of 5,000 km above Saturn's surface

3e. 532 N at Venus's surface

Calculate your weight on different planets

Use the law of universal gravitation to calculate your weight at the surface of each of the nine planets.

The value of g

At Earth's surface, g = 9.8 N/kg

Formula for finding g on other planets:

$$g = Gm^2/r^2$$

If distance increases by a factor of 2, then force decreases by a factor of one-fourth its value.

Satellites and orbits

Satellite - an object that is bound by gravity to another object in space such as a planet.

Orbit - the path of a satellite around the object it is bound to by gravity.

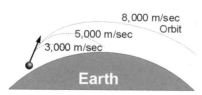

$$r = Gm_E/v^2$$

As you have already learned, the gravitational force between an object and a planet is called weight. Use of a law of universal gravitation and the information in Table 1 to calculate your own weight at the surface of each of the nine planets. Remember, the r in the equation stands for the distance between the centers of the two objects being considered. If you are standing on a planet, then r is the radius of the planet. The extra little bit of height your body adds is insignificant compared with the radius of a planet.

Have students work out the calculation for each of the nine planets. The Investigation also asks for the calculation at distances above the surface of Earth and Saturn. Check that they get their correct weight on Earth! One pound is 4.448 newtons. One sticky point is that the larger planets, being giant balls of gas, do not have a surface that we know of. The given radius is the approximate radius of the top of the atmosphere of the planet where the gas has become so thin it is close to empty space.

On Earth, we learned that you can calculate the weight of an object using the equation $F_w = mg$, where m represents the mass of the object and g represents the strength of gravity. At Earth's surface, $g = 9.8$ N/kg, meaning Earth exerts a gravitational force of 9.8 N per kilogram of mass. The law of universal gravitation can also be used to calculate g on other planets. Set the weight ($m_1 g$) equal to the gravitational force ($Gm_1 m_2/r^2$) and solve the equation to get a formula for g in the form $g = ...$ something.

Have the students work out the simple algebra to get $g = Gm_2/r^2$.

Use your equation to calculate the strength of gravity (g) in N/kg on each of the nine planets.

Give the students 10 minutes or so to do the calculations.

What happens to the strength of gravity as you get farther from the surface of a planet? How far away do you have to be before the force of gravity drops to one-fourth its value at the surface?

Because of the inverse square law, if the distance increases by 2, the force drops to one-fourth its value. Therefore, you need to be twice the planet's radius from the center of the planet, or one radius above its surface.

Earth has a radius of 6,370 kilometers. That is a little more than twice the distance from the tip of Maine to the tip of California. You would have to be this distance above the Earth's surface before the strength of gravity decreased to 2.4 N/kg, or one-fourth its value at the surface.

A satellite is an object in that is bound by gravity to another object such as a planet. The moon is a satellite of the Earth. The path a satellite takes is called an orbit. To understand why an object might orbit a planet, think about launching a cannon at an angle from Earth's surface. The higher the launch speed, the farther away the cannon ball gets before it hits the ground again. If the speed is high enough, the cannon ball keeps falling right around the planet and goes into orbit.

Sketch the drawing in Figure 8.8 on page 154 of the text.

The velocity at which an object goes into orbit around Earth is about eight kilometers per second, or 17,800 miles per hour. That is why you can't just throw a rock into orbit. It takes a powerful rocket to achieve this kind of speed. Right now there are hundreds of satellites above the Earth that affect you every day. Some satellites carry communications, some weather forecasting cameras, and some carry GPS equipment. The orbit of a satellite is a balance between gravity and centripetal force.

Write the orbit equation on the board. $m_s v^2/r = Gm_s m_E/r^2$ and solve it to get the radius of the orbit $r = Gm_E/v^2$, where v is the linear velocity of the satellite.

This equation tells us that fast moving satellites have closer orbits then slower moving satellites. It also tells us the velocity with which we must launch a satellite to achieve and orbit with a particular radius.

8.3 Universal Gravitation and Orbital Motion

Table 1: Mass and radius of the planets

Planet	Mass (kg)	Radius (m)
Mercury	3.18×10^{23}	2.43×10^6
Venus	4.88×10^{24}	6.06×10^6
Earth	5.97×10^{24}	6.37×10^6
Mars	6.42×10^{23}	3.37×10^6
Jupiter	1.90×10^{27}	6.99×10^7
Saturn	5.68×10^{26}	5.85×10^7
Uranus	8.68×10^{25}	2.33×10^7
Neptune	1.03×10^{26}	2.21×10^7
Pluto	1.40×10^{22}	1.50×10^6

3 Calculate your weight on different planets

When we talk about the gravitational force of attraction between an object and a planet, we call that force *weight*. Use the law of universal gravitation and the information in Table 1 to calculate your weight at several different locations in the universe. Remember, the *r* in the formula stands for the distance between the *centers* of the two objects being considered.

a. At the surface of Earth.
b. At a distance of 1,000 kilometers above the surface of Earth.
c. At the surface of Jupiter.
d. At a distance of 5,000 kilometers above the surface of Saturn.
e. At the surface of Venus.

4 The value of g

An object's weight can be calculated using the equation, $F_w = mg$ where *m* represents the mass of the object and *g* represents the strength of gravity. At the surface of Earth, $g = 9.8$ N/kg, meaning that Earth exerts a gravitational force of 9.8 newtons per kilogram of mass. The law of universal gravitation can be used to calculate *g* on other planets.

a. Set the weight $(m_1 g)$ equal to the gravitational force $(Gm_1 m_2 \div r^2)$ and solve the equation to get a formula for *g* in the form $g = \ldots$.
b. Calculate the value of *g* at the surface of each of the nine planets (including Earth) using the formula you found in Part a.
c. On the surface of which of the nine planets would you weigh the most? On the surface of which would you weigh the least? How do you know?
d. What happens to the strength of gravity as you get farther from the surface of a planet? Sketch a graph that illustrates this relationship.
e. **Advanced Problem:** A bowling ball has a mass of about 5 kilograms. Suppose you shrank the ball until it had a surface gravity equal to Earth's ($g = 9.8$ N/kg). What would the radius of the ball be? A single atom has a radius of about 10^{-10} meters. How does the size of the shrunken bowling ball compare with an atom? As strange as it seems, neutron stars exceed this incredible density!

3 Example answers

4a. $m_1 g = Gm_1 m_2 / r^2$
    Cancel m_1 from both sides.
    $g = Gm_2 / r^2$

4b.

Planet	g (N/kg)
Mercury	3.59
Venus	8.86
Earth	9.81
Mars	3.77
Jupiter	25.93
Saturn	11.07
Uranus	10.66
Neptune	14.07
Pluto	0.42

4c. You would weigh the most on the surface of Jupiter because it has the largest value of *g*. You would weigh the least on the surface of Pluto because it has the smallest value of *g*.

4d. As you get farther from a planet's surface, your weight decreases. A graph of weight as a function of distance from surface is an inverse-square relationship:

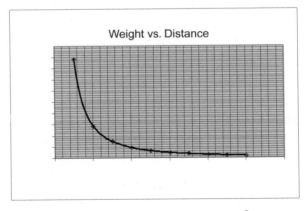

Weight vs. Distance

4e. The bowling ball would have a radius of 5.8×10^{-6} m. This radius is only about 10,000 times bigger than the radius of an atom ($10^{-6}/10^{-10}$). The bowling ball would be very dense.

Investigation 8.3 Universal Gravitation and Orbital Motion   147

9.1 Torque

Key Question: How does force create rotation?

In this Investigation, students wind up a string on a pulley and suspend a weighted hanger on one side. When the hanger is released, the pulley will spin because the hanging mass creates a torque equal to its own weight multiplied by the radius of the pulley. By studying this system, students discover that for rotational motion, you need to know more than the strength of the force. Students also need to know where the force is applied relative to the center of the rotation. In this Investigation, students calculate the torque created by the weight of the hanger and washers, explore equilibrium and torque, and investigate what happens when the force and distance producing a torque are not perpendicular.

Reading Synopsis

Students read Section 9.1 Torque after the Investigation

Force is the action that creates changes in linear motion. For rotational motion, the same force can cause very different results. For rotational motion, the torque is what is most directly related to the motion, not the force. This section is about torque and the relationship between torque and rotational motion.

A torque is required to rotate an object and is the rotational equivalent of force. Torque is created when the line of action of a force does not pass through the center of rotation. Torque is calculated by multiplying the length of the lever arm by the magnitude of the force. If more than one torque acts on an object, the torques are combined to determine the net torque. Rotational equilibrium exists when the net torque on an object is zero. Common units of torque are the newton-meter (metric) and the foot-pound (English).

The Investigation

Leading Questions
- What action changes rotational motion in a similar way as force affects linear motion?
- How is torque determined?
- How is torque related to the direction of a force?
- Can an object be at rest and still have torque acting on it?

Learning Goals

By the end of the Investigation, students will be able to:
- Calculate torque in units of newton-meters (N-m).
- Measure torque by measuring force and distance.
- Apply balanced and unbalanced torque to an object.
- Create rotational equilibrium by balancing torques.
- Draw a diagram showing the torques acting on a system.
- Explain how the concepts of line of action and lever arm are applied to understand how the same force can create different torques depending on its direction.

Key Vocabulary   torque, center of rotation, translation, rotation, lever arm, rotational equilibrium

Setup and Materials

Students work in groups of four or five at tables.

Each group should have:

- Ultimate pulleys set (using the 1-meter length of string)
- Physics stand
- Electronic scale or triple-beam balance (one per class)

Details

Time ⊕ One class period

Preparation ✎ Cut a meter's length of string for each group. Students may tie their own loops on the strings or you can do this ahead of time.

📖 Section 9.1 Torque in the **Student Edition** after the Investigation

Skill Sheets 9.1 Torque

Equipment Setup Ultimate Pulleys

Teaching the Investigation

1 Introduction
2 Units for torque, calculating torque
3 Setting up the experiment
4 Rotational equilibrium
5 Equilibrium and torque
6 Torque when the force and distance are not perpendicular

Introduction

Units for torque, calculating torque

Torque

$$\underset{\text{(N·m)}}{\overset{\text{Torque}}{\tau}} = \underset{\text{(m)}}{\overset{\text{Lever arm}}{r}} \times \underset{\text{(N)}}{\overset{\text{Force}}{F}}$$

Setting up the experiment

Make sure each pulley system is set up to spin with minimal friction for this investigation.

+τ   −τ

Showing torque in diagrams

Now that we have learned how to describe circular motion we need to think about how to cause or change circular motion. What action must be used to create a change in linear motion?

> Students should answer "force."

The equivalent to force for circular motion is called torque. We represent torque in formulas with a Greek letter tau, which looks like a small, curly "t." Today's Investigation will explore the basic idea of torque and how torque is related to circular motion.

Torque is related to force. Force creates torque. However, the same force may create different amounts of torque depending on where the force is applied. Suppose I push on the door here at the handle. Is it possible for my force to open the door? When the door opens, what sort of motion is the door making?

> Students should answer that it is indeed possible to open a door by pushing on its handle, and that a door rotates around its hinges as it opens. The motion of a door is circular motion.

Suppose I apply the same force here at the hinge side of the door. Is my force going to open the door?

> Students should recognize that a force applied to the hinge side of the door will not cause the door to rotate open, no matter how large a force is used.

A door opens when the torque applied to it is enough to cause the door to rotate around its hinges. The torque caused by a force is equal to the force multiplied by the distance between the point where the force is applied and the center of rotation. In this case, the torque is equal to the force I apply times the distance between the handle of the door and the hinge. The units of torque are units of force multiplied by units of distance. In the metric system what units does torque have? In the English system what units should torque to be expressed in?

> Drop the diagram of the door, but force, and the distance between the force and center of rotation.
> Students should recognize and discuss that torque has units of newtons times meters in the metric system and pounds times feet or pounds times inches in the English system.

1 To do the Investigation we are going to use the pulley and spindle. Attach the spindle in the top hole of the stand. Slide the pulley on the shaft, followed by the aluminum tube. Slide the spinner on after the aluminum tube. Align the teeth on the ends of the aluminum tube with the holes in the pulley and spinner. To hold everything together, add a plastic spacer and then the short length of tubing we use as a stop. Leave a little room on the shaft so everything can spin without much friction. The pulley and the spinner arm should spin together because they are connected by the teeth on the aluminum tube.

> Students set up the apparatus as shown in the diagram in step 1.

Attach some washers and a nut to one of the white plastic threaded rods. You will use the rod to hang weight from the pulley. Clip the weighted hanger onto a length of string that has a small loop at one end. The string should be shorter than the length of the pole. Measure and record the mass of the hanger and string.

> Students assemble the weight hanger and string and measure its mass.

The pulley has a small notch in the rim. If you catch the loop in the string over the notch, you can wind the string around the pulley, lifting the weighted hanger off the ground. Let the hanger fall and observe the motion of the pulley and spinner. What sort of motion do you observe and what is the cause of that motion?

> Students should observe that the pulley and spinner rotate when the hanger is released. The cause of the rotation is a torque. The torque is created by the weight of the hanger applied at a distance from the center equal to the radius of the pulley.

9.1   Torque

Question: How does force create rotation?

In this Investigation, you will:

1. Apply balanced and unbalanced torque to a rotating object.
2. Create rotational equilibrium by balancing torques.
3. Measure the acceleration caused by an unbalanced torque.

Force is needed to change an object's rotational motion just as it is needed to change an object's linear motion. For rotational motion, however, you need to know more than the strength of the force. You also need to know where the force is applied relative to the center of rotation.

A *torque* created by a force is equal to the force multiplied by the length of the *lever arm*. The lever arm is the perpendicular distance between the line of action of the force and the center of rotation. For example, a force (F) applied a distance (r) from the center of rotation (see diagram) exerts a torque of $\tau = r \times F$. You can see in the diagram that this torque tends to cause clockwise rotation.

The torque produced by a force

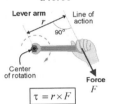

$$\tau = r \times F$$

1   Setting up the experiment

1. Attach the spindle to the top hole in the stand using a threaded knob.
2. Slide the pulley marked "10 Hz = 1 rad/sec" onto the spindle. Add the aluminum tube and the spinner arm (diagram). The aluminum tube has teeth on either end that engage with holes in the pulley and the spinner arm. Use a plastic spacer and the stop to keep everything on the spindle.
3. Attach five washers to one hanger. Make a 1-meter length of string with a small loop on one end. Attach the hanger to the other end and hook the loop over one of the notches in the pulley.
4. Wind the string up onto the pulley. When the hanger is released, the pulley spins because the hanging mass creates a torque equal to its own weight multiplied by the radius of the pulley.

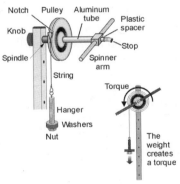

a. Measure and record the mass of the hanger and its calculated weight.
b. The radius of the pulley is 5 centimeters. Calculate the torque created by the weight of the hanger and washers. Give your answer in units of N-m.

53

1   Example answers

1a. I measured the mass to be 100 g; the calculated weight is 0.98 N.

1b. The torque created by the mass is 0.049 N·m.

Rotational equilibrium

Zero net torque does not always mean the object is not moving at all. The object may be rotating about an axis, but if its rate of rotation remains unchanged, there must be no net torque involved. Torque is an action that causes objects to rotate, or change an object's rate of rotation.

Equilibrium and torque

Torques created by each force

$$\tau_1 = r_1 F_1 \qquad \tau_2 = -r_2 F_2$$

Equilibrium

$$r_1 F_1 - r_2 F_2 = 0$$

Torque when the force and distance are not perpendicular

The line of action of a force

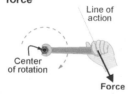

Line of action

Center of rotation

Force

The lever arm of a force

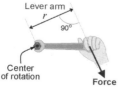

Lever arm
r
90°

Center of rotation

Force

With linear force, when the sum of all forces acting on an object was zero, we said that equilibrium existed. Can anyone define equilibrium for me?

> Students should define equilibrium as a situation where the net force on an object is zero and therefore the motion of the object continues unchanged.

Can a similar situation of equilibrium exist for an object in rotating motion? If so, what must the conditions be for equilibrium to exist?

> Students should recognize that an object can be in rotational equilibrium, and that the net torque exerted about the center of rotation must be zero for rotational equilibrium to exist. This may take some discussion to get through. You should emphasize that torque is always defined relative to a center of rotation. This restriction did not exist for linear force. It is special to circular motion and comes about because every circular motion has a center of rotation.

2 We are going to try to set up a system in rotational equilibrium. Thread a nut onto one end of the spinner rod followed by some washers and another nut. The diagram in step 2 shows this new weight attached to the spinner and also the force exerted by the weight of the hanger. See if you can adjust the position or number of washers on the spinner to achieve rotational equilibrium in which the spinner arm is horizontal when the weight is hanging from the pulley.

> Students should do the experiment. They will probably have to do both things, adjust the position of the washers, and add or subtract washers. The system is in equilibrium when it does not move when it is released. It usually takes 10 to 20 minutes to complete this part of the Investigation.

3 The previous definition we made for torque assumed that the force was applied perpendicular to a line from the center of rotation. Only a force applied perpendicular creates the greatest amount of torque. A force applied in any other direction results in less or possibly zero torque. In the extreme case, think about what happens if the force is applied parallel to the line from the center of rotation. In this case the torque created is zero! To make this clear we need to define two new concepts. The line of action of a force is an imaginary line in the direction of the force drawn through the point where the force is applied. The lever arm is the perpendicular distance from the center of rotation to the line of action of the force.

> Illustrate the concepts of line of action and lever arm on the board. Use the diagrams on page 161 of the text as a reference.

Move the washers to the end of the spinner arm as far as they will go. Wind the string up around the pulley so the spinner arm is horizontal. Is the system in equilibrium? If not, which direction should it rotate? How do you know?

> The system is not in equilibrium, as may be demonstrated if the hanger is released. The system should rotate so the weight on the spinner arm falls and the hanger rises. This happens because the weight on the spinner arm creates a larger torque than the weight on the hanger.

See if you can find an angle at which you can set the spinner arm so the system is in equilibrium.

> Students should rotate the spinner until they find an angle at which the system will stay motionless.

Explain why the system is in equilibrium now when all of the weights and distances are the same?

> Start a discussion. The system is in equilibrium because the weight force from the mass on the spinner arm is not perpendicular to the line from the center of rotation. The torque exerted by the spinner arm is therefore less than it was when the spinner arm was horizontal.

9.1 Torque

2 Equilibrium and torque

The net torque is the total of all torques acting on an object about a given center of rotation. For linear forces, a system is in equilibrium when the net force is equal to zero. For rotation, a similar equilibrium exists when the net torque is zero. To add torques, we usually assume a sign convention in which counterclockwise torque is considered positive and clockwise torque is considered negative.

1. Add some washers to one side of the spinner arm using nuts to hold them in place. Adjust the position of the washers (in or out) until the spinner arm is in equilibrium with the arm horizontal.

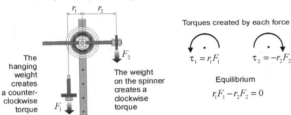

Torques created by each force

$$\tau_1 = r_1 F_1 \qquad \tau_2 = -r_2 F_2$$

Equilibrium

$$r_1 F_1 - r_2 F_2 = 0$$

The hanging weight creates a counter-clockwise torque

The weight on the spinner creates a clockwise torque

a. Calculate the torque created by the nuts and washers you added to the threaded rod. To do the calculation, use the distance measured from the spindle to the approximate center of the washers.

b. If you move the washers farther from the center, does the torque increase or decrease? For this question, consider only the magnitude of the torque and not the direction.

3 Torque when the force and distance are not perpendicular

1. Modify the configuration of the last step by moving the washers out from the center so the spinner rotates when you let go. This system is not in rotational equilibrium.

2. If you move the spinner so it makes an angle with the horizontal, you can find a position where the system is in rotational equilibrium. Find the position of the spinner that creates equilibrium.

Why can this be true?

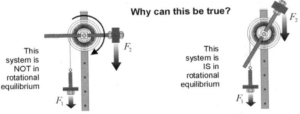

This system is NOT in rotational equilibrium

This system is IS in rotational equilibrium

a. Draw a diagram showing the torques acting on the system by the hanger on the string and the mass on the spinner arm. Make your drawing as accurate as you can, especially the angle of the spinner arm relative to horizontal.

b. Explain why the system is *not* in equilibrium when the spinner is horizontal but *is* in equilibrium when the spinner is at a certain angle. Your explanation should use the concept of lever arm and include a diagram showing the lever arm for both torques acting on the system.

54

2 3 Example answers

2a. The nuts and washers had a mass of 80 g for a weight of 0.78 N. The balancing point was at 6.5 cm from the center for a torque of 0.051 N·m.

2b. The torque increases as the washers are moved farther from the center.

3a. Sample sketch:

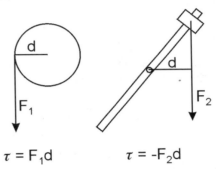

$$\tau = F_1 d \qquad \tau = -F_2 d$$

3b. When the spinner is in the horizontal orientation, the mass of the washers is creating a torque at a distance from the center equal to the radius. This torque is greater than the torque created by the hanger. However, when the spinner is at an angle, the washers create a torque equal to the force multiplied by the horizontal distance to the center (the lever arm), which is much smaller.

9.2 Center of Mass

Key Question: How do objects balance?

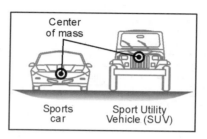

Center of mass

Sports car

Sport Utility Vehicle (SUV)

In this Investigation, students do three separate activities involving center of mass (closely related to the concept of center of gravity). First, students locate the center of mass of an irregularly shaped object by suspending it from several different places. The center of mass always falls in the line below the suspension point, so hanging it multiple times will result in the center of mass being located at the intersection of the lines. The second activity requires students to balance books at the edge of the table in such a way that the overhang is at a maximum, and asks them to explain the relationship between the number of books and maximum overhang distance. Finally, students do two short activities related to the body's center of mass.

Reading Synopsis

Students read Section 9.2 Center of Mass after the Investigation.

The center of mass of an object is the average position of all the particles that make up its mass. An object naturally tends to spin about its center of mass. An object's center of gravity is the average position of the object's weight. The center of gravity and center of mass of an object are located at the same place as long as the acceleration due to gravity is the same at all points on the object. This is the case for nearly all objects, so the terms center of mass and center of gravity are usually interchangeable.

If an object is suspended from one point at its edge, its center of gravity will always fall in the line below the suspension point. If an object is suspended from two or more points, the center of mass can be found by tracing the line below each point and finding the point where the lines intersect.

For an object to balance, its center of gravity must be above its area of support. The larger the area of support, the less likely an object is to topple over.

The Investigation

Leading Questions
- What is meant by the terms center of mass and center of gravity?
- How can we find an object's center of mass or center of gravity?
- How is center of gravity related to balance?

Learning Goals

By the end of the Investigation, students will be able to:
- Locate an object's center of mass.
- Explain how the position of an object's center of mass is related to its ability to balance.

Key Vocabulary   center of gravity, center of mass

Setup and Materials

Students work in groups of four or five at tables.

Each group should have:

- Piece of cardboard or thick paper
- Scissors
- Hole punch (hand-held)
- Piece of string at least as long as the largest dimension of the cardboard
- Washers or other mass to hang at the end of the string (you may use the washers from the ultimate pulleys set)
- Five identical books, dominos, or blocks for stacking
- Metric ruler
- Graph paper
- Chair

Details

Time		One class period
Preparation		
Assignment		Section 9.2 Center of Mass in the **Student Edition** after the Investigation.
Skill Sheets		3.2 Making Line Graphs

Teaching the Investigation

1 Locating the center of mass
2 Balancing books
3 Your body's center of mass

Introduction

What do you think I mean by the "center" of this eraser?

Hold up a chalkboard eraser. Have a discussion about what "center" means. It may mean the geometric center. It may also mean the center of mass, about which the eraser will rotate if it is thrown.

Suppose I stuck a heavy bolt in one end of the eraser. What does that do to its center?

It does not change the geometric center, but it greatly changes the center of mass.

Today's Investigation is about a specific definition of "center" that is important in physics. The "center" I mean is called the center of mass and all objects have a center of mass.

Locating the center of mass   **1**

What is meant by the term "center of mass"?

It is the average location of the mass of an object.

Is center of mass the same thing as center of gravity?

The two are usually at the same location. The only time there is a difference is when gravity is not uniform throughout the object, such as for a very tall building. The two terms are interchangeable in most cases, such as during this Investigation.

Sketch some shapes on the board (square, triangle, doughnut, irregular shape).

Finding the center of gravity

Where would the center of mass (or center of gravity) of each of these objects be located?

Mark the location for each. Ask students how they would determine the center of mass for the irregular object.

You are going to make an irregular object by cutting a piece of cardboard into any shape you choose. If you hang the object from a point along the edge, its center of mass will fall in a line below the suspension point. A string with mass at the end of it will always hang straight down toward the ground along the line on which the center of mass lies. If you trace this line with a pencil and then repeat by hanging it from other points on the object, you can find the center of mass. It will be at the intersection of the lines.

Demonstrate by cutting out a shape and poking a pencil point through it at an edge. The shape should be able to swing freely with little friction. Then hang a plumb line from the pencil. Allow students time to cut out their shapes and locate their center of mass.

Draw a dark circle at the intersection point. If you have accurately found the center of mass, your shape should balance on your fingertip at this point. Try it and see if it works.

If some groups aren't able to balance their shapes at exactly the points they located, have them think about what went wrong. Their three lines probably don't all intersect at one point. They may not have carefully traced the lines or there may have been too much friction for the shape to swing freely when suspended.

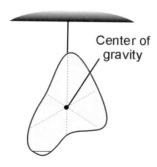

Center of gravity

Give your shape a light toss up into the air so it spins while it moves upward. Watch the circle you drew as the shape moves in the air. What do you notice?

The shape spins about the center of mass.

9.2 Center of Mass

Question: How do objects balance?

In this Investigation, you will:

1. Locate the center of mass of an object.
2. Explain why a stack of books can extend over the edge of a table.
3. Perform two balancing activities using your body.

The *center of mass* is the average location of the mass of an object. The center of mass is important because objects balance around it. If you hang an object from a string, the object will rotate so its center of mass is directly below the point of support. Closely related to the center of mass is the *center of gravity*. The center of gravity is the average location of the force of gravity exerted on an object (its weight). For objects that are small compared to planets, the center of gravity and center of mass describe the same point although they may differ in special cases. In this Investigation, you will locate the center of gravity of an irregularly-shaped object.

1 Locating the center of mass

1. Cut an irregular shape from a piece of cardboard.
2. Make a plumb line by tying a mass or some washers to the bottom of a piece of string. The string should be at least twice as long as the largest dimension of the shape you cut out.
3. Punch a small hole in your shape near the outside edge. Suspend the shape and the plumb line on the tip of a pencil as shown in the diagram at right. The shape should be able to swing freely on the pencil.
4. Carefully trace the path the string makes on the shape.
5. Repeat steps 3 and 4 using holes punched at different locations at the edge of the shape. Repeat again for a total of three lines.
6. The three lines should intersect at one point. Make a dark circle at this location. This point is the center of mass of the shape.

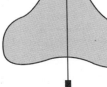

a. Remove the shape from the pencil and try to balance the shape on the tip of one finger at its center of mass. Try to balance the shape at other locations by supporting it with one fingertip. Explain why the shape balances at the center of mass but not at other points.

b. Gently toss the shape up into the air in such a way that it rotates while it moves up and then back down. Watch the circle at the shape's center of mass while it spins. What do you notice?

Teaching tip

If time does not allow you to do all of the activities together, you may opt to do only one or two. The third activity can easily be done by students at home, and the other two require only simple materials and could be done outside of class.

1 Example answers

1a. The shape balances at the center of mass because there is an equal amount of mass on all sides of the center of mass creating equal torques. The shape won't balance anywhere else because unequally distributed masses will create unequal torques and cause the shape to tip over.

1b. The shape spins around its center of mass.

Balancing books

This balancing act could theoretically go on forever. In practical terms things like wind and weather would interfere with balancing items. As long as the center of mass remains over its area of support the sky is the limit.

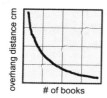

overhang distance cm

# of books

Your body's center of mass

You can do a fun demonstration if you have a pair of skis and ski boots. Stand on the floor with the skis parallel to each other. Keep your body straight and bend forward at the ankles. Students will be surprised at how far forward you can lean without falling.

2

In this activity you will be positioning books (or blocks or dominos) on top of each other so they extend over the edge of the table as far as possible without falling. You will have to work slowly and carefully. First start with one book. What fraction of the book can you have extend over the edge of the table?

Just about half of the book can extend over the edge.

Where is the book's center of mass in relation to the table?

The center of mass is right at the edge of the table.

Carefully measure the overhang distance and record the measurement in Table 1. Then place a second book on top of the first one. Adjust the positions of both books until you get the maximum total overhang. Measure the distance. How does it relate to the first overhang distance?

The overhang distance is $1\frac{1}{2}$ times as much, for a total of $\frac{3}{4}$ of a book length.

Now add another book and repeat. Keep going until you reach 5 books. Record each overhang distance. Be careful not to let the books fall to the floor.

Have students explain how they determined where to position the books each time. Some may have worked from the bottom up, while others worked from the top down. It is a bit easier to work from the top down, balancing the top book so half of it extends beyond the book below it. The top two books then balance on the third and so on. The center of mass of the whole stack must always be just at the edge of the table to get the maximum overhang.

Did you see any pattern in the overhang distances? Make a graph of overhang distance versus the number of books. Is it linear?

The graph is not linear. Each book adds a smaller overhang distance than the previous book.

3

Now you will be doing some activities involving your body's center of mass. Stand with your back and heels against a wall. Can you touch your toes? Explain what's happening.

It isn't possible for most students because when they bend over their center of mass is no longer over their feet. You may want to have students think of ways they could achieve this. Wearing skis instead of shoes would increase the support area and make it easy to bend over. Wearing heavy ankle weights would bring the center of mass closer to the feet and make it easier to avoid falling forward.

Now you will try another activity. Stand so you are facing a chair that is 2 feet away from your toes. Bend over with a flat back, touch the sides of the chair, and then stand up.

This should be easy for most students. Ask them why this was easier than the first activity. They should realize that this time they were not constrained by the wall and could adjust their bodies to position the center of mass over their feet.

Now bend over in the same way but this time grab onto the sides of the chair and try to stand up.

This should be much more difficult because holding the chair shifts the center of mass forward, away from the support area. Prompt a discussion of why some students are better at this than others. Students may think it is somehow related to strength, but it is related to body shape. Women naturally have a lower center of mass than men because they have wider hips and narrower shoulders.

9.2 Center of Mass

2   Balancing books

1. Place a book (or, alternatively, a domino or a block) on a table so that it extends over the edge as far as possible without falling. Measure the length of the book and its overhang distance. Record your measurements in Table 1.

2. What fraction of the length of the book is the overhang distance? Place a second identical book on top of the first. Adjust the positions of the two books to get the maximum overhang distance. Measure the distance and record. One group member should be ready at all times to catch the books in case they fall off the table's edge.

3. If the books are placed so that they have the greatest amount of overhang possible, where is the center of mass of the two-book combination in relation to the edge of the table? Explain.

4. Repeat step 3 with three, four, and five books. Try to achieve the greatest overhang distance for each number of books and measure each distance.

Table 1: Book overhang distances

Length of one book (cm)	Number of books	Overhang distance (cm)
	1	
	2	
	3	
	4	
	5	

a. Explain the method you used to determine how to position the books. Use the term *center of mass* in your explanation.

b. Make a graph of overhang distance versus number of books. Plot the distance on the *y*-axis and the number of books on the *x*-axis.

c. Explain the relationship between the number of books and the overhang distance. Is it linear?

d. How many books had to be stacked to reach an overhang distance of one book length?

e. How many books do you think it would take to reach an overhang distance of two book lengths?

3   Your body's center of mass

a. Stand with your back and heels against a wall. Slowly bend down and try to touch your toes. Explain what happens and why.

b. Position a chair so that it is facing you. Stand with your toes 2 feet away from the front edge of the chair. Bend over at the waist, touch the sides of the chair, and bend your body up to a standing position. Now bend over in the same way but grab the sides of the chair this time. Try to bend upward while holding the chair. Explain what happens and why.

c. Why might these activities be easier for some students than for others?

56

---

2 3   Example answers

Length of one book (cm)	Number of books	Overhang distance (cm)
30 cm	1	14.5
	2	20
	3	23.5
	4	27.5
	5	31

2a. Answers may vary, but should explain that students attempted to position the books as far as possible off the edge of the table while keeping the center of mass over the table.

2b. Graph:

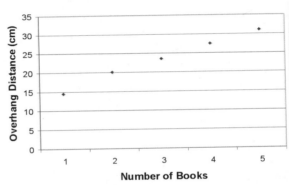

2c. The relationship between the number of books and the overhang distance is roughly linear.

2d. I had to stack 5 books before I reached an overhang distance of greater than one book length.

2e. I think about 10 books would reach a distance of two book lengths.

3a. When I tried to touch my toes, I started to fall over. My center of mass moved out past the tips of my toes and my body was no longer in equilibrium.

3b. The mass of the chair creates a large torque that makes balancing with my feet so far from the chair impossible.

3c. Some factors that can make these activities easier for some students: size of feet, body mass, strength of calf muscles, balance.

9.3 Rotational Inertia

Key Question: Does mass resist rotation the way it resists acceleration?

In this Investigation, students study the relationship between torque, angular acceleration, and moment of inertia. A hanging weight exerts a torque on a spinning rod for which the moment of inertia can be changed. Students measure the angular acceleration of the rod and determine how it is related to the moment of inertia. This is a relatively advanced Investigation and may be skipped if you do not plan to cover the concepts of moment of inertia and angular acceleration.

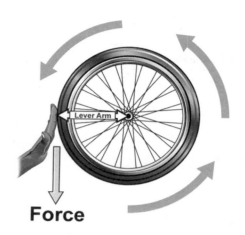

Force

Reading Synopsis

Students read Section 9.3 Rotational Inertia before the Investigation.

Rotational inertia is the term used to describe an object's resistance to a change in its rotational motion. An object's rotational inertia depends on its mass and the way the mass is distributed. When an object's mass is concentrated near its axis of rotation, the object is easy to spin. When the mass is far from the axis of rotation, the object is difficult to spin.

Newton's second law can be applied to rotational motion and relates torque, rotational inertia, and angular acceleration. Angular acceleration is the rate at which angular speed changes. It is directly proportional to torque and inversely proportional to rotational inertia.

The rotational inertia of a point mass is equal to mr^2, where m is the object's mass and r is the radius of the motion. When an object is not a point mass, the average value of mr^2 is calculated. The result of this calculation is called its moment of inertia.

The Investigation

Leading Questions
- What is rotational inertia?
- On which properties of an object does rotational inertia depend?
- What is required for an object to rotate?
- How does Newton's second law apply to rotating objects?

Learning Goals
By the end of the Investigation, students will be able to:
- Calculate the moment of inertia for point masses.
- Explain how moment of inertia, torque, and angular acceleration are related.
- Calculate angular acceleration if the change in angular speed and the time are known.

Key Vocabulary
rotational inertia, torque, angular acceleration, moment of inertia

Setup and Materials

Students work in groups of four or five at tables.

Each group should have:

- Ultimate pulleys set (use the 1 meter length of string)
- Physics stand
- Timer and one photogate, AC adapter (or 9-volt battery), and cords to connect the photogates to the timer
- Electronic scale or triple-beam balance

Details

Time ⏱ One class period

Preparation ✏ Students should be familiar with the timer and photogate. You should prepare two identical meter sticks by taping masses to them as shown in the diagram on the first page of the Investigation. The mass of a small paperback book is about right.

Assignments 📖 Section 9.3 Rotational Inertia in the **Student Edition** before the Investigation.

Skill Sheets 5.2 Newton's Second Law (to review the formula)

Equipment Setup Ultimate Pulleys

Teaching the Investigation

1 Setting up the experiment
2 Angular acceleration
3 Measuring angular acceleration

Introduction

Inertia: resists change in an object's linear motion and depends on the object's mass.

Rotational inertia: resists an object's change in rotational motion and depends on the object's mass and its mass distribution.

What property of an object causes it to resist a change in its linear motion? On what does this depend?

Inertia is the property. It depends on the object's mass.

What property of an object causes it to resist a change in its rotational motion? On what does it depend?

Begin a discussion. Rotational inertia is the property. It depends on the object's mass and also on the way the mass is distributed throughout the object. If the mass is concentrated toward the axis of rotation, the rotational inertia is less than if the mass is concentrated away from the axis. The calculated measurement of rotational inertia for an object is called its moment of inertia.

I have a meter stick here with two masses on it. I have a second meter stick with two identical masses. Which one is easier to spin? Why? The masses are the same!

Hold up the two meter sticks you prepared ahead of time to initiate the discussion. The one with the mass farther from the center is harder to spin. The reason is that when the meter stick is rotated, the mass must move faster if it is farther from the center compared with the mass close to the center. The students have a diagram on the first page of the Investigation.

Setting up the experiment

1

Moment of inertia: the calculated measurement of rotational inertia for an object.

In this Investigation you will be studying how an object's moment of inertia is related to the rate at which it spins. First you must set up the experiment. Use the spindle to attach the pulley to the top hole of the stand. Use the aluminum tube to connect the spinner arm to the pulley. Place a plastic spacer at the end to hold everything in place.

Point out the names of the pieces of equipment. It is helpful to have one piece of equipment set up ahead of time for students to refer to while they are assembling theirs.

Add 10 washers to each side of the spinner arm and adjust their positions until the arm balances in a horizontal position. Place 5 washers on the hanger. Connect a 1-meter piece of string to the hanger and tie a loop in the free end. Hook the loop on the notch in the pulley.

Assist any groups that have difficulty getting their equipment ready.

Turn the pulley so the string winds around it. Why does the pulley spin when the hanger is released?

The string exerts a force on the pulley which provides torque. If students simply state that there is a force that moves the pulley, ask whether it would spin if the string were connected right at the center of the pulley rather than at the edge.

When the mass is closer to the center of the spinner, the moment of inertia is smaller and the spinner turns more quickly.

Let the mass drop and observe how quickly the rod rotates. Then adjust the positions of the washers on the spinner, either moving them toward the center or away from the center. The washers should be placed in such a way that the spinner balances horizontally when the string is not exerting a torque on it. How is the rate at which the spinner turns related to the placement of the washers?

The spinner turns more quickly when the washers are close to the center. Ask students why they think this is the case. The spinner has a smaller moment of inertia when the masses are near the center. For each turn of the spinner, the masses have to move a smaller distance, so it is able to spin faster.

9.3   Rotational Inertia

Question: Does mass resist rotation the way it resists acceleration?

In this Investigation, you will:

1. Change an object's moment of inertia while keeping the object's mass constant.
2. Show how torque, angular acceleration, and moment of inertia are related.

An object with more mass is usually (but not always) harder to start rotating than an object with less mass. It is also possible for an object with less mass to be harder to start rotating than an object with more mass. If this seems very strange, it is because when objects are rotating, the arrangement of mass around the center of rotation is as important as the total mass itself.

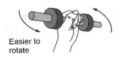

Easier to rotate

The *moment of inertia* is the property of an object that resists angular acceleration in a similar way as mass resists linear acceleration. The moment of inertia depends on both an object's mass and shape.

Harder to rotate

1   Setting up the experiment

1. Attach the spindle to the top hole in the stand using a threaded knob.
2. Slide the pulley marked "10 Hz = 1 rad/sec" onto the spindle. Add the aluminum tube and then add the spinner arm (diagram). The aluminum tube has teeth on either end that engage with holes in the pulley and the spinner arm. Use a plastic spacer and the stop to keep everything on the spindle.
3. Add 10 washers to each side of the spinner arm. Adjust their position until the spinner balances horizontally.
4. Attach five washers to one hanger. Make a 1-meter string with a loop on one end. Attach the hanger to the other end and hook the loop on a notch in the rim of the pulley.
5. When the hanger is released, the pulley spins because the hanging mass creates a torque equal to its weight multiplied by the radius of the pulley.
6. Observe how the rod spins if you move all the washers close to the center (Step 3-A) compared with when the washers are near the outside (Step 3-B). In both cases the mass of the spinner is the same and the torque applied is also the same. The *distribution* of mass on the spinner is different.

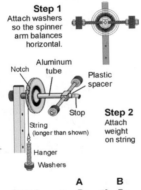

Step 1
Attach washers so the spinner arm balances horizontal.

Notch   Aluminum tube   Plastic spacer

Stop

String (longer than shown)

Hanger

Washers

Step 2
Attach weight on string

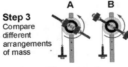

A   B

Step 3
Compare different arrangements of mass

a. Does the rod rotate faster when the washers are close to the center, near the outside, or does the position of the washers not affect the rotation speed? You may want to time how long it takes to spin 10 turns for both configurations.

57

Teaching tip

Use two meter sticks, some masses, and duct tape to give students a feel for rotational inertia. Tape the masses at the ends of one meter stick and near the center of the other meter stick. Let each student spin the two meter sticks about their centers to compare the difficulty. This works best if the masses are at least 500 grams each.

1   Example answers

1a. The spinner rotates much faster when the weights are moved closer to the center.

Angular acceleration

Newton's second law (linear motion)\

$$a = \frac{F}{m}$$

Newton's second law (rotational motion)

$$\alpha = \frac{\tau}{mr^2}$$

Moment of inertia

$$I = mr^2$$

Measuring angular acceleration

Angular speed:

$$\omega = \frac{1}{10T}$$

Angular acceleration:

$$\alpha = \frac{\Delta\omega}{\Delta t}$$

2 What is angular acceleration? What causes it?

Angular acceleration is the change in angular speed divided by the time. It is caused by a net torque acting on the object.

How can Newton's second law be used to relate torque and angular acceleration?

Angular acceleration is directly proportional to the net torque and inversely proportional to the moment of inertia.

Now you must calculate the moment of inertia for the spinner. You can ignore the mass of the white plastic rod because its mass is small compared with that of the washers. You can assume the washers act like a single mass located at the position of the center washer. What is the formula for calculating the moment of inertia for a single mass?

The formula is $I = mr^2$.

Take the appropriate measurements and determine the moment of inertia for your spinner. Express your answer in units of kg-m^2.

Students will have to determine the mass of the washers and the distance between the center of the spinner and the center of each set of masses. Have different groups compare their values so students can see that the placement of the washers is a big factor in the moment of inertia.

3 Now you will be measuring the angular acceleration of your pulley. Position the masses on your spinner so it balances. Set your timer to stopwatch mode. Wind the string around the pulley so the hanger is at the top of its path. Release the hanger and measure the time it takes to fall to the base of the stand. Record your value in Table 1. Repeat for three trials and calculate the average.

Students may notice that all of the masses do not fall at the same rate.

Attach a photogate to the third hole in the stand and connect it to input A on the timer. The infrared beam of the photogate should be in line with the stripes on the pulley. As the pulley spins, each stripe blocks the beam. Since there are 10 stripes per radian, the angular speed of the pulley is 1 ÷ 10T where T is the period between stripes passing the light beam, which you can measure with the Timer.

You may want to review the meaning of the radian unit with your students at this point.

Set the timer to period mode. Wind the string around the pulley and let the hanger fall. Watch the display on the timer. What do you notice? You want to record the maximum angular speed during the fall of the hanger. Where does this occur?

The period decreases, indicating that angular speed increases and there is angular acceleration. The maximum speed occurs at the bottom.

Pressing the reset button on the timer freezes the display so you can easily take a reading. Let the hanger fall and press reset just as the hanger gets to the bottom. Record the period. Repeat for three trials and calculate the average period. Calculate the average angular speed from the average period. Calculate the angular acceleration by dividing the angular speed by the time you measured earlier.

Write the relationships on the board and discuss the calculation of angular acceleration.

Move the masses on the spinner either in toward the center or out toward the edges. Repeat the experiment. How does the angular acceleration in this case compare with the angular acceleration earlier?

The angular acceleration should be greater when the masses are nearer the center. The smaller the moment of inertia, the greater the angular acceleration.

9.3 Rotational Inertia

2   Angular acceleration

The angular acceleration of an object is equal to the change in its angular speed divided by the change in time. For example, suppose an object starts at rest and five seconds later is rotating with an angular speed of 20 rad/sec. The angular acceleration is 4 rad/sec^2 (20 rad/sec ÷ 5 sec). Note that 4 rad/sec^2 means the angular speed increases by 4 rad/sec every second.

Angular acceleration is caused by net torque in the same way that linear acceleration is caused by net force. Newton's law for rotational motion is similar to the law you already know for linear motion. The linear motion variables of force, mass, and acceleration are replaced with their rotational motion counterparts: torque, moment of inertia, and angular acceleration.

Newton's second law
(linear motion variables)

$$a = \frac{F}{m}$$

Mass (kg)

Newton's second law
(rotational motion variables)

$$\alpha = \frac{\tau}{mr^2}$$

moment of inertia (kg·m^2)

The quantity that resists angular acceleration is the moment of inertia, mr^2. The m stands for mass and the r stands for the radius of the mass measured from the center of rotation.

a. Assume that the mass of the pulley itself and the white plastic rod is so small that it may be neglected compared with the mass of the steel washers. Assume the washers act like a single mass at a distance r from the axis. Calculate the moment of inertia. Your answer should come out in units of kg-m^2.

3   Measuring angular acceleration

1. Set masses inward or outward so the rod is balanced.
2. Set the Timer to stopwatch mode. Wind the string onto the pulley. Measure the time it takes the falling hanger to hit the base of the stand after it is released.
3. Attach a photogate to measure the rotational speed of the pulley. The pulley has 10 stripes per radian. Therefore the angular speed in rad/sec is 1 ÷ 10T where T is the period between stripes passing the light beam. Set the Timer to period mode. Rewind the string around the pulley and drop the hanger. Use the reset button to freeze the measurement on the Timer the moment the hanger hits the base at the point of maximum speed.
4. Repeat the experiment with the masses shifted to the opposite position. For example, if you started with the masses out, repeat the experiment with the masses in.

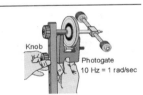

Knob

Photogate
10 Hz = 1 rad/sec

Table 1: Angular Acceleration Data

Masses in

Falling Time (sec)			
Period (sec)			

Masses out

Falling Time (sec)			
Period (sec)			

a. Calculate the average time and period for the three trials of each variation. Use the averages to calculate the angular speeds (from the period) then the angular accelerations (angular speed divided by falling time). The result should come out in units of rad/sec^2.

b. Compare the angular acceleration you measured in the two cases. Note that the mass is exactly the same in both cases. The torque applied is also exactly the same. Explain why the angular acceleration is different. Your explanation should use the concept of moment of inertia.

2 3 Example answers

2a. Each weight has a mass of 30 g and is positioned 0.055 m from the center, giving a moment of inertia of 0.182 kg·m^2.

Table 1: *Angular Acceleration Data*

Masses in	Three trials			Avg.
Falling time (sec)	0.73	0.69	0.68	0.70
Period (sec)	.0024	.0022	.0023	.0023
Masses out				
Falling time (sec)	0.93	0.99	0.95	0.96
Period (sec)	.0029	.0029	.0031	.0030

3a. The average acceleration with the masses close to the center was 62.0 rad / s^2. The average acceleration with the masses away from the center was 34.7 rad / s^2.

3b. Although the torque was the same in each case, the acceleration was different because the moment of inertia was different. The spinner with the masses farther from the center is harder to get rotating. This is analogous to Newton's second law with linear motion: Applying the same force to a heavier (more massive) object results in a smaller acceleration.

10.1 Machines and Mechanical Advantage

Key Question: How do simple machines work?

A machine is something created by human technology that makes a task easier. A simple machine accomplishes its task with no source of energy except for forces that are applied directly to the machine as the task is being done. This Investigation explores a simple machine that multiplies force. First, students use the Ultimate Ropes and Pulleys to measure the input and output forces of a machine that lifts a load with a single pulley and string. They discover that the forces are equal. The students the construct a sequence of block and tackle machines with mechanical advantages 2, 3, and 4. From their force measurements they deduce the rule for the mechanical advantage of a block and tackle.

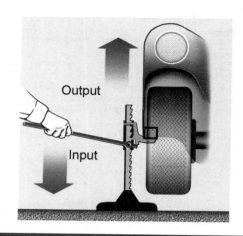

Reading Synopsis

Students read Section 10.1 Machines and Mechanical Advantage after the Investigation.

Machines can be described in terms of input and output, such as input force and output force. A simple machine has no energy source other than forces applied directly and immediately to the machine and functions with a single movement. Gears, levers, screws, ramps, wheel/axle, rope/pulley are simple machines.

Mechanical advantage is the ratio of output force to input force. The mechanical advantage of a lever is the ratio of lengths of the input and output arms. A lever works by balancing torques. The mechanical advantage of a rope and pulleys is the ratio of the number of strands supporting the load to the number of strands to which force is applied, usually 1. Gears and wheels manipulate torque instead of force. The mechanical advantage of a pair of gears is the ratio of their diameters. The mechanical advantage of a frictionless ramp is the ratio of length to height. A screw works like a rotating ramp.

The Investigation

Leading Questions
- What is a machine and why is it useful?
- How do we describe the action of a machine?
- What is mechanical advantage?
- How does a lever work?
- What is a block and tackle machine?

Learning Goals By the end of the Investigation, students will be able to:
- Build a simple block and tackle machine using ropes and pulleys.
- Measure the input and output forces of simple machines.
- Calculate the mechanical advantage of the block and tackle.
- Describe any machine conceptually in terms of input, output, and mechanical advantage.

Key Vocabulary machines, simple machines, input, output, input force, output force, mechanical advantage, mechanical system, lever, ropes and pulleys, gears, ramps, screw

Setup and Materials

Students work in groups of four or five at tables.

Each group should have:

- Ultimate pulleys set
- Physics stand
- Spring scales
- Electronic scale, or triple-beam balance
- Calculator
- Metric ruler

Time One class period

Preparation Become familiar with the ropes and pulleys set prior to the Investigation.

Assignments Section 10.1 Machines and Mechanical Advantage in the **Student Edition** after the Investigation

Skill Sheets 10.1 Mechanical Advantage

Equipment Setup Ultimate Pulleys

Teaching the Investigation

1 Introduction
2 Simple machines
3 Setting up the experiment
4 The block and tackle machine
5 Mechanical advantage
6 A mechanical advantage problem

Introduction

Machine - a device created by human technology that performs one or more tasks.

Complex machines - require a source of energy other than forces applied by humans.

Simple machines - perform simple tasks like moving or lifting objects, and require no source of energy except for forces applied directly to the machine.

Simple machines

Simple pulley - designed to lift an object when you pull down on a string or rope.

Output force = weight of the loaded pulley block.

Input force = force applied to the string to lift the pulley block.

Input and output forces on the simple pulley are equal.

Setting up the experiment

A machine is something created by human technology that makes tasks easier. We use many different types of machines every day. What machines have you encountered today?

> Students will probably respond by naming complex machines such as a hair dryer, dishwasher, automobile, elevator, or vending machine.

These complex machines require a source of energy other than forces applied by humans. Thousands of years ago, early humans had to figure out ways to manipulate forces to accomplish simple tasks like moving and lifting heavy objects. Simple machines such as levers, inclined planes, and ropes and pulleys were invented to accomplish a task with no source of energy except for forces applied directly to the machine. Look around the classroom. What simple machines do you see? Keep in mind that simple machines manipulate forces by reducing the effort force required or by simply changing the required direction of effort force.

> Examples of simple machines include a door, door knob, scissors, broom, stapler, pushpin, cart, window crank, stairs, and staple puller.

How does each of the simple machines you listed make a task easier? How advantageous is each of these simple machines? This Investigation explores a simple machine that multiplies force to make a task easier.

> In this Investigation students will set up different string and pulley systems to compare input and output forces and will develop an understanding of mechanical advantage.

Attach a spindle and pulley to the top hole in the physics stand as shown in the diagram, attach a string to the pulley block, and loop the string over the pulley. What exactly is the output task of this machine?

> Students should figure out by playing with the pulley setup that this is a simple machine designed to lift the pulley block and 15 washers when you pull down on the free end of the string. The objective of this part of the Investigation is to introduce a simple pulley setup.

How could we measure the output force of this machine?

> Students should use a balance or spring scale to measure the weight of the loaded pulley block, since lifting the pulley block is the output task.

How could we measure the input force required to hold up the pulley block when it is suspended from the top pulley?

> Students should attach a spring scale to the free end of the string and apply a downward force on the string. The scale will measure the input force. It is helpful to take a reading while slowly raising the pulley block and another reading while slowly lowering the pulley block, and then calculate an average input force.

How do the input and output forces compare?

> Students will find that they are equal.

1 What was the advantage of using this pulley system if the input force was no different from the output force?

> The simple pulley allows you to apply a downward force to lift the pulley block. This is helpful when raising a flag or window blinds.

10.1 — Machines and Mechanical Advantage

UNIT 4: Energy and Momentum

Question: How do simple machines work?

In this Investigation, you will:

1. Build a simple machine using ropes and pulleys.
2. Measure the input and output forces of simple machines.
3. Calculate the mechanical advantage of the ropes and pulleys.

A machine is something created by human technology that makes a task easier for humans to do. Of course, the word "easier" means different things for different tasks. A simple machine is a machine that accomplishes its task with no source of energy except for forces that are applied directly to the machine as the task is being done. This Investigation explores a simple machine that multiplies force.

1 Setting up the experiment

1. Attach the spindle to the top hole in the stand using a threaded knob.
2. Slide a pulley onto the spindle. Use plastic spacers and the stop to keep the pulley from sliding off the spindle.
3. Put 15 washers onto the wooden pulley block as shown in the diagram at right. Determine the weight of the loaded pulley block using a balance or spring scale (A). Record the weight in Table 1. This is the *output force* since lifting the pulley block is the output task of the machine.
4. Attach the string to the pulley block and loop it over the pulley.
5. Measure the force required to hold up the pulley block by applying a downward force on the string on the opposite side of the pulley (B). This is the *input force* since it is the force applied to the machine to accomplish the output task (lifting the block). Record the force in Table 1.

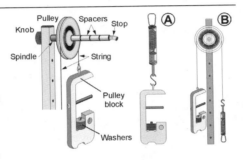

Table 1: Input and output forces

Number of pulleys	Input force (N)	Output force (N)
1		

a. Compare the input and output forces using a single pulley. Is one larger than the other, or are they the same strength?

Types of simple machines

There are a few basic types of simple machines that create mechanical advantage. The lever, wheel and axle, rope and pulleys, screw, ramp, and gears are the most common types. Complex machines such as a bicycle combine many simple machines into mechanical systems. A mechanical system is an assembly of simple machines that work together to accomplish a task.

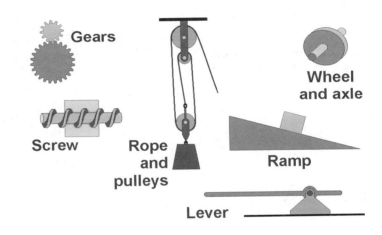

1 Example answer

Table 1: Input and output forces

No. of pulleys	Input force (N)	Output force (N)
1	3.80	3.82

1a. The input and output forces are about the same.

The block and tackle machine

Block and tackle machine - uses a single rope and multiple pulleys to multiply force.

2

Imagine you need to lift a heavy object like an automobile engine or raise a heavy sail on a ship. Also imagine it was 200 years ago and you had nothing but your own muscles to do the job. Probably, you would have used a machine called a block and tackle. A block and tackle is a machine that uses a single rope and multiple pulleys. By cleverly arranging the rope and pulleys it is possible to greatly multiply force with a block and tackle machine. A single human could easily lift an elephant with a suitable block and tackle.

For the next part of the Investigation, you will use the same pulley block loaded with 15 washers. Therefore, the output force will be the same as it was in the first part of the Investigation.

> Students will record the same output force in each row of Table 2, and this value is the same output force they recorded in Table 1.

Configure the block and tackle machines with 2, 3 and 4 supporting strings (not including the string you pull on).

Follow the procedure and diagrams to configure block and tackle machines with two, three, and four supporting strings. You will need to attach the string to either the spindle, or the block, depending on which configuration of pulleys you are building. For example, this block and tackle has two strings directly supporting the load. Note that the string is attached to the spindle. There are two supporting strings because these two strings directly support the lower block. This string that I pull on does not directly support the lower block so it is not counted.

> Demonstrate the two-string configuration by building it in front of the class. Also demonstrate how to count strings that support the load. There is only one long string for students to loop around multiple pulleys. The phrase "two string" refers to the fact that when the top pulley and bottom pulley are connected by a string, it actually forms two supporting strands. Do not count the section of string that is pulled on as one of the supporting strands.

The block should be raised and lowered slowly to correct for friction.

Record the input force as the average of the forces you need to raise and lower the block.

Record the input force required to lift the loaded pulley block in each set-up. To correct for the friction in the scale, you should slowly raise and lower the block at constant speed. The force you record should be the average of the forces you get raising and lowering.

> Students should practice their force-measuring technique. Spring scales have so much friction that it is easy to get results that are off by 20 percent or more by not being careful with technique. A small amount of mineral oil applied to the plastic plunger where it passes through the body of the scale can significantly reduce friction.

As the number of support strings on the block and tackle increases, less input force is needed to left the loaded block.

Compare the input and output forces for each different block and tackle set-up.

> The input force is less than the output force in all setups except the first. Some students might notice that when two supporting strands are used, the input force is 1/2 the output force, and when three supporting strands are used, the input force is 1/3 the output force, and so on.

Keep the strings nearly vertical

The actual force applied to the bottom block by each strand of string is always in the direction of the string. When the upper and lower pulleys get close together, one strand of the string makes a small angle with the vertical. Because of the angle, this strand only contributes part of its force to lifting the load. As a result the string tension must be slightly greater than it would be if all the strings were straight. To minimize this effect, students should measure the forces with the upper and lower pulleys as far apart as they can be.

2 Example answers

Table 2: *Input and output forces*

No. of pulleys	Input force (N)	Output force (N)
1	3.80	3.82
2	1.90	3.82
3	1.15	3.82
4	0.80	3.82

10.1 Machines and Mechanical Advantage

2 **The block and tackle machine**

A block and tackle is a machine built with multiple pulleys and a single rope. In this part of the Investigation you will create a block and tackle machine using a string and up to four pulleys. As in the previous part, the input force is applied to the string using a spring scale. The output force is the force required to lift the loaded pulley block. The output force will stay the same; however, you will measure considerable changes in the input force depending on how the pulleys and string are arranged.

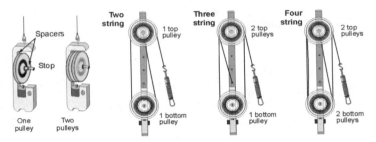

1. Record the output force you measured in Part 1 (the weight of the pulley block) in each row of Table 2. This value is the same for each trial of the experiment. Copy the data from Table 1 into the first row of Table 2, corresponding to one string supporting the lower block.

2. Remove the upper pulley from the spindle and slide the loop at the end of the string over the shaft. Replace the pulley and secure it with spacers and the stop.

3. Slide a single pulley onto the shaft of the pulley block. Use spacers to center the pulley under the string as shown in the diagram above. Put the stop on the end of the short shaft to keep the pulley from sliding off. Set the pulley block on the stand directly below the top pulley.

4. Loop the string around the lower pulley and then up over the upper pulley as shown in the diagram. Notice that when you lift the pulley block by pulling on the string that there are two strands of the string that directly support it.

5. Use a string clip to attach the spring scale to the string and measure the force required to lift the pulley block. Record the force in the second row (**Input force (N)**) of Table 2 because there are two strings supporting the hanger.

6. Configure the strings and pulleys to create three and four strings supporting the pulley block (see diagram). For each configuration, record the input force required to lift the hanger.

Table 2: Input and output forces

Number of strings	Input force (N)	Output force (N)
1		
2		
3		
4		

Mechanical advantage

3

Mechanical advantage:
M.A. = output force ÷ input force

The mechanical advantage of the block and tackle machine is greater than one: the output force is bigger than the input force. This means that you create more output force than you put into the machine.

Friction always reduces the mechanical advantage, and each additional pulley adds more friction.

The mechanical advantage of a machine is the amount by which the machine multiplies force. If the output force is bigger than the input force, the mechanical advantage is greater than one. Mechanical advantage can also be less than one. When the mechanical advantage is less than one, the output force is smaller than the input force.

Now we will determine the mechanical advantage of the block and tackle machine. The formula for mechanical advantage is the ratio of the output force divided by the input force.

> Put the formula on the board. Students should copy data from Table 2 into Table 3 and calculate the mechanical advantage by dividing output force by input force.

What does having a high mechanical advantage mean for the ropes and pulleys? Is there a rule you can deduce from your measurements that predicts the approximate mechanical advantage of a block and tackle?

> When the M.A. is greater than 1, the machine creates a larger output force than the input force applied to the machine. You can lift heavier objects using smaller forces. The rule is the mechanical advantage is approximately equal to the number of strands of string directly supporting the load. The rule is only approximate because of friction in both the pulleys and in the spring scales. Lead students through questions b - d to analyze data and draw conclusions.

You may have noticed that the mechanical advantage is not the same as its theoretical value. Why might this be true?

> Students may notice that there is friction and that the mechanical advantage may be greater or less than the theoretical value. For example, a block and tackle with four strands supporting the load should have a mechanical advantage of 4. In laboratory experiments with spring scales however, friction tends to increase the measured M.A. This is because the measurements are nearly static and friction binds the spring scales, causing them to read lower forces. The friction force is proportionally greater when measuring small input forces, raising the apparent M.A.

Do you think it would be realistic to build a block and tackle with a mechanical advantage of 100? Why?

> Friction always reduces the mechanical advantage of a moving system. A very accurate experiment would show that the actual output force is less than four times the input force. Each additional pulley adds more friction. A mechanical advantage of 100 is likely to have so much friction that a large input force is required just to overcome friction. Friction typically limits real block and tackle machines to mechanical advantages less than 20.

Where does the mechanical advantage come from? Why does a block and tackle work?

> Lead a discussion. The tension force in a string is the same all along the string. In a block and tackle with four strings supporting the load, the force on the load is four times the tension in the string. Therefore, in equilibrium, the load is just balanced when the string tension is one-fourth the weight of the load. This is why the mechanical advantage is equal to the number of strands directly supporting the load.

A mechanical advantage problem

4

Let's apply what we have learned about ropes and pulleys to a different situation.

> Encourage students to work in lab groups to discuss the tug-of-war scenario in Part 4. Have them give reasons for their answers using the concept of mechanical advantage.

3   **Mechanical advantage**

A system of ropes and pulleys can make work easier by reducing the amount of force you need to apply. In a block and tackle machine a small input force can create a large output force. *Mechanical advantage* is a term that describes the ratio of the output force divided by the input force. In a machine with a mechanical advantage greater than one, the output force is larger than the input force.

To find the mechanical advantage of a simple machine, divide the output force by the input force. Mechanical advantage does not have units. Because mechanical advantage is a ratio of force divided by force, the units cancel out, leaving a pure number.

a.   Use your data from Table 2 to calculate the mechanical advantage for each arrangement of the ropes and pulleys. Record your calculations in Table 3.

Table 3: Mechanical advantage

Number of pulleys	Output force (N)	Input force (N)	Mechanical advantage
1			
2			
3			
4			

b.   What is the relationship between the mechanical advantage and the configuration of the block and tackle machine?

c.   Explain in a few sentences why the mechanical advantage of a block and tackle machine should be what you proposed in (b). (This is a difficult question. HINT: The force in a string is the same anywhere in the string.)

d.   Describe how friction affects the mechanical advantage of a machine like the block and tackle. Would friction increase the mechanical advantage, decrease it, or have no effect?

4   **A mechanical advantage problem**

All the pulley systems you constructed served the same purpose: to lift something *up* by pulling *down* on a rope. In the picture on the right, two groups are playing tug-of-war. The pulleys are set up in a horizontal system. It may help to turn the picture sideways before answering the questions below.

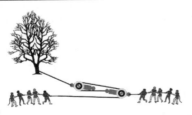

a.   Which pulley (the one on the left or the right) moves?

b.   Which group could use the smaller force to move the opposing team?

61

---

3 **4** **Example answers**

3a. Table 3 data:

Table 3: *Mechanical advantage*

No. of pulleys	Input force (N)	Output force (N)	Mechanical advantage
1	3.82	3.80	1.00
2	3.82	1.90	2.01
3	3.82	1.15	3.32
4	3.82	0.80	4.77

3b. The mechanical advantage is approximately equal to the number of pulleys used.

3c. When more pulleys are used, there are more strings running between the top and bottom blocks. With more strings, each string needs to support only a fraction of the hanging mass. Since the tension in the string is the same everywhere, the input force diminishes as the number of strings increases.

3d. Friction will add to the mechanical advantage slightly. Imagine a very light mass on the hanger. If there were just a little friction in the pulleys, it wouldn't take much force at all to keep the hanger lifted off the table. When the input force becomes smaller, the mechanical advantage goes up.

4a. The pulley on the right moves; it is like the hanger in our activity.

4b. The group on the left can use a smaller force on their string to move the team on the right. The group on the left is like the input force in our activity and the opposing team is like the output force.

10.2 Work

Key Question: What are the consequences of multiplying forces in a machine?

In the last Investigation, students learned how a simple machine can be arranged to create a mechanical advantage in force. In this Investigation, the students explore the nature of work and energy and come to a general conclusion that is true for all machines. The product of force and distance at the output of a simple machine can never exceed the product of force and distance at the input of the machine. The students use the rope and pulleys and a block and tackle machine to collect force and distance data and derive this result. In so doing, they learn what "work" means in physics and begin exploring the relationship between work and energy.

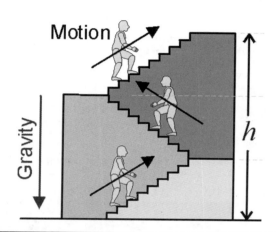

Reading Synopsis

Students read Section 10.2 Work after the Investigation.

All simple machines obey a rule that states that any advantage in force must be compensated by applying the force over proportionally longer distance. The law involves the physics meaning of work, which is the subject of this section.

Work is done by forces. The amount of work done is equal to the force times the distance over which the force acts, where distance is measured in the direction of the force. Work is the way mechanical systems change the amount of energy they have. When work is done on a system, its energy increases. When a system does work, its energy decreases. The unit of measurement for work is the joule. One joule of work is done by a force of one newton acting over a distance of one meter. Work done against gravity is equal to the weight of an object multiplied by its change in height, no matter what path is taken. Machines are described by input work and output work. The output work of a simple machine can never exceed the input work.

The Investigation

Leading Questions
- In physics, "work" has a special definition. What is "work"?
- What is the difference between force and work?
- Is more work involved in moving up three flights of stairs or riding an elevator those same flights?

Learning Goals
By the end of the Investigation, students will be able to:
- Discover what trade-off there must be for a machine to achieve a mechanical advantage greater than 1.
- Calculate the work done by a machine.
- State the relationship between work and energy.
- Calculate work in joules when given force and distance.
- Use arguments based on input and output work to explain the fundamental limitations of simple machines.

Key Vocabulary
work, joule, friction, input, output

Setup and Materials

Students work in groups of four or five at tables.

Each group should have:

- Ultimate pulleys set (use the 5 meter length of string)
- Physics stand
- Spring scales
- Metric ruler, meter stick, or metric measuring tape
- Calculator

Details

Time	One class period
Preparation	none required
Assignments	Section 10.2 Work in the **Student Edition** after completing the Investigation.
Skill Sheets	10.2 Work
Equipment Setup	Ultimate Pulleys

Teaching the Investigation

1 Introduction
2 Doing the experiment
3 Analyzing your data
4 Introducing the concept of work
5 Calculating work
6 The relationship between work and energy

Introduction

Mechanical Advantage

$$MA = \frac{F_o}{F_i} \quad \begin{array}{l} \text{Output force (N)} \\[1em] \text{Input force (N)} \end{array}$$

Doing the experiment

1

An experiment is a situation set up to measure what happens when one variable at a time is changed.

Input distance will change, and it should be measured and recorded.

Output force is kept constant by lifting the same weight (15 washers) for each trial.

How do input and output forces in a block and tackle machine compare when the mechanical advantage is greater than 1?

Students should remember from the previous Investigation that when the mechanical advantage is greater than 1, you end up with an output force that is greater than your input force.

How can a block and tackle machine be arranged to provide a mechanical advantage?

Students should remember from the previous Investigation that mechanical advantage increases as you add more pulleys and supporting strands to the machine.

You have probably heard the phrase "you can't get something for nothing." For a block and tackle machine to create large output forces from small input forces, there has to be a trade-off. In this Investigation, we will explore the block and tackle machine further to learn about trade-off, work, and energy.

The objective for this Investigation is to show that the multiplication of force comes at the cost of having to pull the string farther to lift the weight a given distance. The students will repeat the setup of the ropes and pulleys. However, this time they will measure the distance the weight is raised and the distance the string has to be pulled. Students will then explore and calculate work and the relationship between work and energy.

You will set up four different block and tackle machines just like you did in the previous Investigation. For each machine, you must choose a distance that you will lift the lower pulley block for each trial of the experiment. You should keep this distance the same for each machine, and it should be at least 20 centimeters. Why do you suppose the output distance will remain the same for each setup?

It is important to only change one variable at a time in a simple experiment. Students should realize that they are changing the mechanical advantage of each machine, so all other variables, including output force and output distance, should remain constant. To measure output distance, students will start with the pulley block on the base of the stand, lift the bottom pulley to the desired reference point on the stand, and measure the height difference.

You may have noticed that you have to use more of your string when rigging machines with higher mechanical advantage. We are going to look at this variable more closely. Input distance refers to how much string length you have to pull to lift the pulley block.

Measuring the input distance is slightly tricky but not complicated. The easiest method is to rig up the machine and start with the bottom pulley block on the base of the stand. Place the two cord stops together at the edge of the top pulley. Pull the free end of the string down by the cord stops until the bottom block is raised to the desired height (remember, the output distance remains the same for all machines). Once the bottom block is raised, simply slide the top cord stop back to the edge of the top pulley. You can measure the distance between the two cord stops and call this your input distance.

What other variables should we consider measuring when comparing different block and tackle machines? So far, we have discussed how to measure output distance and input distance.

Students should remember from the previous Investigation that output and input forces are also important when studying simple machines. Output force will be the same for all machines, as in the previous Investigation, and is measured by finding the weight of the pulley block (loaded with 15 washers). Input force is measured with a spring scale, just like we did in the previous Investigation.

UNIT 4: Energy and Momentum

10.2 | Work

Question: What are the consequences of multiplying forces in a machine?

In this Investigation, you will:

1. Discover what trade-off there must be for a machine to achieve a mechanical advantage greater than one.
2. Calculate the work done by a machine.
3. Learn about the relationship between work and energy.

In the previous Investigation, you learned how a simple machine can be arranged to provide a mechanical advantage. Ropes and pulleys (and other simple machines) create large output forces from small input forces. In this Investigation, you explore the nature of work and energy and come to an interesting conclusion that is true for all machines.

1 Doing the experiment

This Investigation compares the forces and distances traveled at the input and output of a machine.

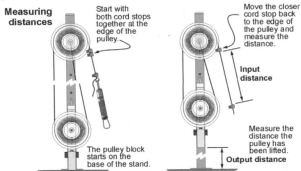

1. Set up the rope and pulley block and tackle machine as you did for the last Investigation (10.1).
2. There are two cord stops you will use to mark the distance you must pull the string to raise the loaded lower pulley block. Start with both cord stops close together, just touching the upper pulley where the string leaves it.
3. Choose a distance that you will lift the lower pulley block during each trial of the experiment. This is the *output distance*. Your output distance should be at least 20 centimeters. Use the same output distance for each trial of the experiment. Record that distance in Table 1.
4. Pull the string to lift the lower pulley block your chosen distance.
5. Measure how much string length you had to pull to lift the pulley block. This is the *input distance*. You can measure the input distance using the cord stops and a ruler as shown in the diagram. Record the input distance in Table 1.

62

Using a force scale

Getting accurate measurements when using a force scale can be quite challenging. It's very easy to make measurements with the force scale that are too low or too high. Basically, there's some friction in the force scale (specifically in the plastic plunger) that makes the plunger bind in the cap. Depending on the direction of the force, the reading on the scale can be smaller or larger than the actual force. For this reason, students may record data that seems to indicate the input work is smaller than the output work. To take accurate measurements, make sure the force scale is parallel to the string on the ropes and pulleys as shown below. If it is at an angle, the plunger can bind up and lower the reading.

Analyzing your data

With a rope and pulley system, increased mechanical advantage and the capacity to lift heavier objects with the same input force comes at the expense of having to pull more rope.

$$MA = \frac{\textit{distance input string pulled}}{\textit{distance output block lifted}}$$

Introducing the concept of work

Work (joules) ⟶ $\mathbf{W} = \mathbf{Fd}$ ⟵ Distance (meters)
Force (newtons) ⟶

2 Study the relationship between input distance and input force. How do these values compare from one trial to the next?

Lead students through the discussion questions in Part 2. Students should see that as the mechanical advantage increases, and less and less input force is required, the length of string that has to be pulled gets greater and greater. This is the trade-off!

Why do you have to pull the input end of the string a longer distance when there is a higher mechanical advantage?

Higher mechanical advantage comes from having more strands of string supporting the load. Each supporting strand must be shortened when the load moves up. The total motion of the input end of the string is equal to the sum of the amounts that each supporting strand must be shortened to raise the load. For example, if the mechanical advantage is 4, there are four strings supporting the load. To raise the load by one centimeter, each of the four strands must be shortened by one centimeter. The total length of string between the pulleys must be reduced by four centimeters to take up the slack when each of the four strands is shortened by one centimeter.

3 What were the two different quantities you measured as you investigated the block and tackle machine?

Students measured forces and distances.

Force and distance are important quantities to consider when studying any simple machine. Can you see how force and distance must both be considered when designing a lever to allow a human to lift a multi-ton block of limestone? Can you see how force and distance are related in the design of a hammer? (Try using a short-handled hammer to drive a large nail into a block of wood—it would be difficult!) How are force and distance related in a block and tackle machine?

In a block and tackle machine, as input force decreased, the distance over which you needed to supply the force (the length of the string pulled) increased. This was the trade-off. You sacrificed distance to gain the advantage of applying a smaller force. If you have ever seen a tall-masted sailing ship, you know that there is an abundance of line coiled up on the deck when the sails are raised.

In science, the word "work" describes the relationship between force and distance. The work done by a force is equal to the magnitude of the force multiplied by the distance moved in the direction of the force.

10.2 Work

6. Using the spring scale, measure the force needed to lift the hanger. This is the *input force*. Record the input force in Table 1.

7. Disconnect the lower pulley block and measure its weight with a spring scale. Record the weight as the output force in Table 1. The output force is the same for each trial of the experiment.

8. Rearrange the pulleys and strings so that you achieve mechanical advantages of one, two, three, and four. For each arrangement, record the input distance and input force in Table 1.

Table 1: Force and distance data

Mechanical advantage	Output force (N)	Output distance (m)	Input force (N)	Input distance (m)
	Both are the same for each trial			
1				
2				
3				
4				

2 Analyzing your data

a. As the mechanical advantage increases, what happens to the length of the string you have to pull to raise the hanger?

b. You may have heard the saying "Nothing is free." Explain why this is true of the ropes and pulleys. (HINT: What do you trade for using less input force to lift the lower pulley block?)

c. Write down a rule that describes the relationship between mechanical advantage and the input and output distances for the block and tackle machine.

3 What is work?

The word *work* is used in many different ways. For example, you *work* on science problems, you find that your toaster doesn't *work*, or you feel that taking out the trash is too much *work*. In science, however, *work* has one specific meaning: it describes a quantity that is calculated by multiplying force and distance. Your data shows that there is a relationship between the force needed to lift the block and the amount of string you had to pull to lift the block. As input force *decreased*, the distance over which you needed to apply the force *increased*.

In science, the word work describes this relationship. The work done by a force is equal to the magnitude of the force multiplied by the distance moved in the direction of the force.

work = force (N) × distance (m)

Just as you compared input and output force in the last Investigation, you can compare input and output work. Input work describes the amount of work done by you as you pulled the string. Output work describes the work done on the hanger to lift it.

Work is measured in units of newton-meters (N-m). Newton-meters are also called *joules* after British scientist Sir James Joule who discovered the importance of measuring work in a series of experiments performed between 1843 and 1847. One joule is equal to one newton-meter.

63

1 2 Example answers

Table 1: *Force and distance data*

Mechanical advantage	Output force (N)	Output distance (m)	Input force (N)	Input distance (m)
1	4.4	0.20	4.1	0.20
2	4.4	0.20	2.0	0.43
3	4.4	0.20	1.3	0.64
4	4.4	0.20	0.9	0.84

2a. As mechanical advantage increases, the length of string needed to raise the hanger the same distance also increases.

2b. In this case, nothing is free because reducing the input force (by increasing the mechanical advantage) means pulling over a longer distance (increased length of string).

2c. The input distance is approximately equal to the output distance times the mechanical advantage.

Calculating work

One joule of work is accomplished when 1 newton of force is used to move an object a distance of 1 meter.

The relationship between work and energy

Work is the way systems change the amount of energy they have. When work is done on a system, its energy increases.

Energy is the ability to do work.

Work is done by forces.

4 Just as you compared input and output forces and distances in this Investigation, you can also compare input and output work. What do you suppose input work and output work describe in reference to your block and tackle machine?

Input work describes the amount of work done by you when you pull on the string. Output work describes the work done on the bottom block to lift it.

How will you calculate input work and output work for each of your block and tackle machines?

Output work is calculated by finding the product of the output force and output distance. Input work is calculated by finding the product of the input force and input distance.

How do your values for output work and input work compare?

Lead students through the discussion questions. Don't forget that sample answers are provided on the facing page of this teacher guide.

5 You have explored the idea that work is done, in the scientific meaning of the word, when you operate a block and tackle system. Work is done when you raise the bottom block, but is work done when you hold the end of the string so the bottom block is suspended motionless above the table?

No work is done on the bottom block when it is suspended motionless above the table. Your hand might get tired from holding the string to keep the bottom block raised, but if the bottom block is not moved by the force you exert, you do not do any work on the bottom block.

What would happen if you suddenly let go of the string?

The bottom block would come crashing down on the table.

If you placed a thumbtack loosely on a piece of cardboard under the bottom block, what would happen to the thumbtack if you let the bottom block of the pulley fall on it from above?

The thumbtack would probably be driven into the cardboard by the force of the bottom block, and the bottom block of the pulley would do work on the thumbtack.

Work is done to lift the bottom block of the pulley, and the bottom block then has the ability to do work on the thumbtack when it falls on it. The ability to do work is called energy. Anything with energy can produce a force that is capable of acting over a distance. Work and energy are related, and both are measured in joules. Energy comes in many different forms, and all of them can do work. How does electricity perform work? How do we know that wind is a form of energy?

Electricity can turn a motor to exert forces. Wind has energy because it can exert forces on objects in its path. Lead students through the examples in Part 5 of the Investigation.

10.2 Work

4   Calculating work

1. Use your data to calculate the work done on the hanger (the **output work**). This work is equal to the *output force* (weight of the loaded pulley block) multiplied by the *output distance* (the height the block was lifted). Use Table 2 to record the output work for each different configuration of your machine.

2. Next, use your data to calculate the work you did as you pulled on the string to lift the block. This is the **input work**. In this case, multiply the *input force* by the *input distance* (the length of string that you pulled.)

Table 2: Output and input work

Mechanical advantage	Output work (joules)	Input work (joules)
1		
2		
3		
4		

a. For each mechanical advantage, how do output and input work compare?

b. Is output work ever greater than input work? Can you explain this?

c. Explain any differences between input and output work in your data.

5   The relationship between work and energy

You may already be familiar with the unit *joules* as a measurement of **energy**. Work and energy are related but not the same. Work is one form of energy but energy can also take other forms. Scientists sometimes define energy as *the ability to do work*. This means that anything with energy can produce a force that is capable of acting over a distance. The force can come from many different sources. Here are some examples:

Energy appears in different forms

- A moving ball has energy because it can exert forces on whatever tries to slow it down or stop it.
- Wind has energy because it can exert forces on any object in its path.
- Electricity has energy because it can turn a motor to exert forces.
- Gasoline has energy because it can be burned in an engine to exert force to move a car.

Energy and work are both measured in joules because energy is *stored work*. Any object with energy can use its energy to do work, meaning it exerts a force that acts over a distance.

The ropes and pulleys experiment illustrates a rule that is true for all simple machines. *You can never get more work out of a simple machine than you put into it.* In fact, in most machines, the output work is *less* than the input work. Other forces, like friction, use some of the input work before it reaches the output of the machine.

64

4   Example answers

Table 2: *Output and input work*

Mechanical advantage	Output force (N)	Output distance (m)
1	0.88	0.82
2	0.88	0.86
3	0.88	0.83
4	0.88	0.75

4a. For each mechanical advantage the input work and output work were roughly the same.

4b. The output work can appear to be greater than the input work. Friction can help hold up the hanger, reducing the force on the string and reducing the input work. It's important to note that when you consider the system as a whole (i.e. taking into account all sources of friction, etc.), input work should never be smaller than the output work.

4c. Differences between input and output work could be explained by:

friction in the pulleys

friction in the spring scale

any error in measurement (of distances or forces).

10.3 Energy and Conservation of Energy

Key Question: How is motion on a track related to energy?

To pedal a bike up hill, you have to work hard to keep it going. When you start down the other side of the hill, you hardly have to pedal at all. In this Investigation students make measurements of height and speed for a ball rolling along the loop track. From their measurements, students calculate the potential and kinetic energy of the ball as it moves. They show that the inverse relationship between speed and height can be understood in terms of conservation of energy. The observation that the plastic and steel balls have the same speed at similar places on the track can also be explained. The Investigation provides practice in applying the law of conservation of energy.

700 m³/sec

Reading Synopsis

Students read Section 10.3 Energy and Conservation of Energy before the Invest.

Our universe is made up of matter, energy and information. Matter is something that has mass and takes up space. Energy is the ability to make things change. Information describes where everything is and how it fits together. Energy appears in different forms, such as motion and heat. Energy can travel in different ways, such as light, or sound, or electricity.

A system that has energy has the ability to do work. This means that anything with energy can produce a force that is capable of acting over a distance. Energy is measured in joules, the same units as work because work is the transfer of energy. Work is the action of making things change. Energy moves though the action of work

There are different forms of energy such as mechanical, light, radiant, nuclear, electrical, chemical, thermal, and pressure.

Objects that have potential energy do not use the energy until they move. The energy of motion is called kinetic energy.

The Investigation

Leading Questions
- What is energy?
- Why is energy an important quantity n physics?
- How are speed and height on a roller coaster related?
- How are energy and motion related?
- What does it mean to state that energy is conserved in a system?

Learning Goals By the end of the Investigation, students will be able to:

- Explain the relationship between speed and height on the loop track using the conservation of energy.
- Calculate potential and kinetic energy.
- Describe how the law of energy conservation is used to analyze moving systems that include changes in height and speed, such as a ball rolling downhill.

Key Vocabulary energy, mechanical energy, light energy, radiant energy, nuclear energy, electrical energy, chemical energy, thermal energy, pressure energy, potential energy, kinetic energy, law of conservation of energy

Setup and Materials

Students work in groups of four or five at tables.

Each group should have:

- Loop track
- Physics stand
- Steel and plastic balls
- Timer and one photogate, AC adapter (or 9-volt battery), and a cord to connect the photogate to the timer
- Meter stick or metric measuring tape
- Graph paper
- Colored pencils

Details

Time	⏱ One class period
Preparation	✎
Assignments	📖 Section 10.3 Energy and Conservation of Energy in the **Student Edition** before the Investigation.
Skill Sheets	10.3 Potential and Kinetic Energy
Equipment Setup	Loop track

Teaching the Investigation		
	1	Introduction
	2	The energy of the ball
	3	Measuring the speed of the ball
	4	Graphing the data
	5	Analyzing the data
	6	Kinetic and potential energy

Introduction

What sensations have students experienced on a roller coaster?

Ask if anyone has been on a loop roller coaster and how did that feel?

What makes the ball stay on the track?

The energy of the ball

Discuss the potential and kinetic energy of the ball

Measuring the speed of the ball

Review with students how the photogate and timer can be used with the diameter of the ball to calculate speed.

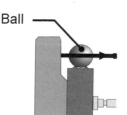

Ball

Have you ever been able to coast UP a hill on a bicycle? What has to be true for this to happen?
> You would have to start at the top of a higher hill and hope you had enough energy to make it over a second smaller hill.

How does a skateboarder ride UP the side of a half pipe?
> The skateboarder must first start at the top of the other side and ride down before coasting up the other side.

How did we define energy when working with the block and tackle machines?
> Energy is the ability to do work, and doing work requires energy.

How is the ball on the loop track able to roll up the hill of the loop and make it to the end of the track? This is a question we will explore in today's Investigation. We are going to study energy changes that accompany the motion of a ball on a loop track.

1 Attach the loop track to the 9th hole from the bottom of the stand. Release the ball from the starting peg at the top of the track and observe its motion. At which point do you think the ball moves fastest? At which point does it move slowest? You read about energy. What sorts of energy does the ball have?
> A wonderful aspect of this Investigation is that most students have definite ideas about the ball's motion in the beginning. They will be able to collect data that will clarify and confirm their initial suspicions with a satisfying explanation based on potential and kinetic energy.

The ball has potential energy equal to mgh and kinetic energy too. In the book the formula for kinetic energy was $E_k = 1/2\ mv^2$. This is true for sliding objects but the ball rolls. We have to add a bit more energy to account for the rolling motion. The total kinetic energy of a solid rolling ball is $7/10\ mv^2$, which is a little more than the kinetic energy of a moving object that is not rolling.
> Put these formulas on the board. I do not try to explain the reason why it is 7/10 instead of 1/2, but do try to explain that an object that is rotating and moving in linear motion must have more kinetic energy than an object that is only moving in linear motion. If your students are up to it, the formula for rotational kinetic energy is $E_{kr} = 1/2\ I\omega^2$. For a solid sphere $I = 2/5\ mr^2$ and $\omega = v/r$.

2 In an earlier Investigation with the loop track, you releasing the ball from different heights to find the minim speed needed to make it around the loop. This time you are going to make measurements all along the track to allow you to see how the energy of the ball changes as it moves. This will test the law of conservation of energy, which is one of the most powerful laws in all of physics.
> Students should read the procedure carefully and measure the vertical distance from the tabletop to the appropriate place on the photogate, and it is important to keep this technique consistent throughout the experiment.

Place the photogate at least 8-10 different places on the track. The first position you choose should be at the 5-centimeter position, and the others should include locations all the way up and over the loop. You should also choose two positions with equal heights, one as the ball moves downhill and the other as the ball moves uphill.
> Students will collect height and time data, calculate the speed of the ball at each position, and record all data and calculations in Table 1.

Once you get your data, calculate the potential and kinetic energy of the ball at each place you measured. Also calculate the total energy by adding the potential and kinetic energies.
> Have the students the calculations.

UNIT 4: Energy and Momentum

10.3 Energy and Conservation of Energy

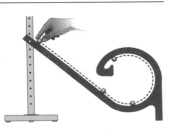

Question: How is motion on a track related to energy?

In this Investigation, you will:

1. Discover the relationship between speed and height on a track.
2. Describe how energy is conserved.

To pedal your bicycle up a hill, you have to work hard to keep it going. However, when you start down the other side of the hill, you hardly have to pedal at all. In this Investigation, you will find out what happens to the speed of a ball as it rolls along the loop track and how it relates to energy.

1 The energy of the ball

Attach the loop track to the 9th hole from the bottom of the stand. Place the plastic ball against the starting peg. Release the ball and observe its motion.

At which point do you think the ball moves fastest? At which point do you think it moves slowest? Why? Your predictions are the hypothesis for this Investigation.

a. Write down equations for the potential and kinetic energy of the ball. (note, the ball *rolls*)
b. Where is the kinetic energy largest? Where is it smallest?
c. Where is the potential energy largest and smallest?

2 Measuring the speed of the ball

To understand the ball's motion, measure its speed and height at different positions on the track.

1. Measure and record the masses of the steel and plastic balls.
2. Plug a photogate into input A and set the Timer to interval mode.
3. Attach the photogate to the track at the 5-centimeter position. Be sure that the photogate is flat against the bottom of the track. If the photogate is not attached properly, the light beam will not cross the center of the ball and the speed you calculate will not be accurate.

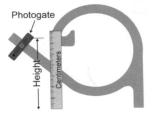
Photogate
Height
Centimeters

4. There are two small bumps on each photogate that mark the position of the light beam. The bumps are also in line with the center of the ball as it passes through the photogate. Measure the vertical distance from the tabletop to one of the bumps. Record that as the height in Table 1.
5. Place the ball so it is touching the peg at the top of the track. Release it and allow it to roll through the loop. Record the ball's time through photogate A in Table 1.

65

1a. $E_p = mgh$, $E_k = 7/10\ mv^2$
1b. The kinetic energy is largest when the ball has the greatest speed, at the bottom of the hill.
1c. The potential energy is largest when the ball has the greatest height, which is at the start.

2 3 Example answers

Table 1: Height, time, and speed data

Position (cm)	Height (cm)	Time t_A (sec)	Speed (cm/s)	Ep (J)	Ek (J)	E total (J)
5						
10	47.0	0.0195	97.0	0.129	0.018	0.147
20	39.7	0.0140	136	0.109	0.036	0.145
30	33.3	0.0115	165	0.091	0.053	0.145
50	18.9	0.0089	213	0.052	0.089	0.141
68	9.4	0.0080	238	0.026	0.111	0.137
83	18.9	0.0092	207	0.052	0.084	0.136
100	29.8	0.0113	168	0.082	0.055	0.137

Part 3 graph:

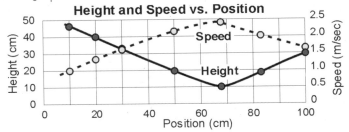

Height and Speed vs. Position

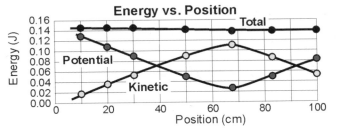

Energy vs. Position

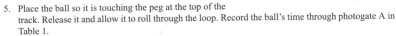

Investigation 10.3 Energy and Conservation of Energy **185**

Graphing the data

Students need to show both speed and height on the y-axis for their graph.

The energy graph shows large variation in Ep and Ek but the total stays nearly constant.

Analyzing the data

The relationship between kinetic and potential energy?

Kinetic and potential energy

Kinetic energy - the energy of motion.

Potential energy - energy that comes from the position of an object relative to Earth.

Conservation of energy - Energy cannot be created or destroyed, but can only be converted from one form to another.

3 What is the relationship between speed and height of the ball on the track? Make a graph that shows this relationship. What was the variable we manipulated in the experiment?

> Students should answer that we changed the position of the photogate, and this is the manipulated or independent variable, and it belongs on the x-axis of the graph.

Place both the speed and the height on the y-axis of the graph. Use two different colors or types of lines to distinguish between the two variables. It is helpful to plot these dependent variables on the same graph for the sake of comparison.

> Students should have two different lines on their graph, one that represents speed versus position, and one that represents height versus position. Use a smooth curve to connect the data points.

Make a second graph showing the three calculations of energy, potential, kinetic, and total. Plot all three on the same graph, again using position as the x-axis. How do the three graphs change as the ball moves along the track?

> The students make the energy graphs. The potential energy goes down then up again, just like the track itself. The kinetic energy starts low and is largest when the potential energy is lowest. The total energy is nearly constant, sloping down slightly due to friction.

4 Use your completed graph to answer the analysis questions in Part 4.

> Sample answers to these questions can be found on the next page of this teacher's guide.

5 The higher the ball's speed, the greater its kinetic energy. Potential energy is energy the ball has due to its position. The higher the ball is on the track, the greater its potential energy.

> Discuss the questions in Part 5. It may be helpful to have students label the parts of the graph they created with the places of high and low potential and kinetic energy.

You can see from this Investigation that as the ball moves from the top of the track to the end of the track, potential and kinetic energy conversions are taking place. How does the ball's motion illustrate the law of conservation of energy?

> Potential energy is converted to kinetic energy (and some is dissipated as heat and track deformation), and there is a constant trade-off between height and speed as the ball moves along the track. But total energy (potential energy plus kinetic energy at any position) is conserved and stays constant.

Think back to your experiments with the ropes and pulleys. How can you use the concepts of potential and kinetic energy to describe the motion of these simple machines?

> Students should respond that when they raise the bottom block, the energy used to do work on the block in order to lift it is now stored as potential energy as the block is suspended over the table.
>
> When you let go of the string, the bottom block's potential energy is converted to kinetic energy, and it has the ability to do work on an object below - hopefully not your fingers or hand!

If the total energy is constant, then the kinetic energy is completely determined by the difference between the initial height and the height the ball is at. Use the formulas for potential and kinetic energy to derive an equation that shows this. How does mass appear into this equation?

> Assist the students to derive the formula and point out that mass cancels out.

If mass does not appear, that means the speed of the ball is independent of its mass. Measure the speed of the steel and plastic balls at the same place on the track to test this hypothesis.

> Students do the test and see that the speed of the plastic and steel balls is the same.

10.3 Energy and Conservation of Energy

6. Calculate the speed of the ball through the photogate using the ball's diameter (0.019 m). Also calculate the ball's potential and kinetic energy. Add the potential and kinetic energy to get the total energy. Record your data and calculations in Table 1.

7. Move the photogate to a new position on the track. Repeat steps 2 through 5. Two of the positions you choose should include the locations in your hypothesis. You should also choose two positions with equal heights, one as the ball is moving downhill and the other as it is moving uphill.

Note: The photogate does not attach properly between 73 and 81 centimeters on the track, so do not use positions in this range.

Table 1: Height, time, speed and energy data

Position (cm)	Height (m)	Time through photogate (sec)	Speed (cm/s)	Potential Energy (J)	Kinetic Energy (J)	Total Energy (J)
5						

3 Graphing the data

a. Use your measurements to make a graph showing the relationship between speed and height. Plot the position of the photogate on the track on the *x*-axis. Plot both the speed and the height on the *y*-axis. You should have two separate lines on your graph. Use two different colors or types of lines (dotted and solid) to connect each set of points.

b. Plot a similar graph showing the potential energy, kinetic energy, and total energy on the y-axis and the position on the x-axis.

4 Analyzing the data

a. What can you tell from your first graph? Describe the relationship between the speed of the ball and the height. Where is the speed of the ball the greatest? Where is it the least? Does this agree with your hypothesis?

b. Does the uphill or downhill direction of the ball affect its speed, or is height the only important factor?

c. What can you say about the energy graph? Where is the potential energy largest and smallest? Where is the kinetic energy largest and smallest? How are the potential and kinetic energy related to the total energy?

5 Conservation of energy

On the loop track, potential energy is transformed into kinetic energy and vice versa. The total energy remains constant because of the *law of conservation of energy*.

a. Right before the ball is released at the top of the hill, which type of energy does it have? What is the total energy of the ball?

b. What happens to the ball's kinetic energy as it moves down the hill? What happens to its potential energy?

c. Use the law of conservation of energy to derive a formula that relates the speed of the ball to its height (h) and the initial height (h_0) from which it was released.

d. According to the equation you derived in part (c) above, what is the effect of mass on the speed of the ball? Measure the speed of the steel and plastic balls at the same position to test this hypothesis.

4 Example answers

4a. As its height above the ground decreases, the speed of the ball increases. The speed of the ball is the greatest when it is at the lowest point possible, at a position of about 68 cm and a height of 9.4 cm. The speed of the ball is the smallest when it is at the highest point measured, at a position of 10 cm and a height of 47.0 cm. This data agrees with the prediction.

4b. The uphill or downhill direction of the ball does not affect its speed; height is the only important factor.

4c. The potential energy and kinetic energy are inversely related. Where one is high the other is low. The graph shows that the total energy is conserved even though potential and kinetic energy vary considerably.

5 Example answers

5a. Right before the ball is released it has potential energy.

5b. The ball's kinetic energy increases as it moves down the hill. Its potential energy is converted to kinetic energy. As the ball moves uphill in the loop, its kinetic energy is converted back into potential energy. As the ball travels, it does not gain or lose energy; its energy is simply converted from one form to another.

5c.

$$v = \sqrt{\frac{10}{7}g(h_0 - h)}$$

5d. Mass has no effect because it cancels out of every term and does not appear in the formula for speed. We measured the speed of the steel and plastic balls at the bottom of the track and found them to be 238 cm/sec (steel) and 239 cm/sec (plastic). The difference is smaller than the variability in successive measurements therefore we conclude that the hypothesis (mass has no effect) is correct.

11.1 Efficiency

Key Question: How efficient is the straight track?

The conversion of potential energy to kinetic energy obeys the law of conservation of energy. This law states that energy cannot be created or destroyed but can be converted from one form to another. As the ball rolls down the track, its potential energy is converted into kinetic energy. The efficiency of a process is the ratio of the energy you get out of the process divided by the energy you start with. In this Investigation, students will explore whether the conversion efficiency from potential to kinetic energy for a ball rolling down the track is 100 percent. They collect potential and kinetic energy data by measuring the time and speed of a plastic ball and a steel ball rolling down the track.

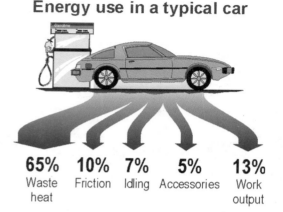

Energy use in a typical car

65%	10%	7%	5%	13%
Waste heat	Friction	Idling	Accessories	Work output

Reading Synopsis

Students read Section 11.1 Efficiency after the Investigation.

A process is any activity that changes things and can be described in terms of input and output. The energy efficiency of a process is the ratio of useful output energy to input energy. All processes can be described by an efficiency including human-built technology and natural systems. Scientists believe that efficiency less than 100% is a characteristic of all natural processes and is the reason time goes forward, not backward.

The efficiency of a mechanical system is always less than 100% because friction converts energy to heat or wear. In terms of natural systems efficiency is usually defined separately for each processes that use energy. For example, the Earth absorbs sunlight with an average efficiency of 78%. The other 22% is reflected back into space. The efficiency of biological systems tends to be very low, on the order of 1-10%.

The Investigation

Leading Questions
- What is efficiency?
- How are kinetic and potential energy related to efficiency?
- What are input and output energy and how are they related to efficiency?
- How does the concept of efficiency apply to mechanical technology, to natural systems, and to living things?

Learning Goals By the end of the Investigation, students will be able to:
- Calculate the efficiency of a process when given the input and output energy.
- Give at least one example of how efficiency is defined in a mechanical system, a natural system, and a living organism.

Key Vocabulary efficiency, process, calories, reversible, irreversible

Setup and Materials

Students work in groups of four or five at tables.

Each group should have:

- Straight track
- Plastic ball
- Steel ball
- Physics stand
- Timer and one photogate, AC adapter (or 9-volt battery), and cords to connect the photogates to the timer
- Mass balance for determining about mass of the steel and plastic balls (1 per class).

Details

Time ⏲ One class period

Preparation ✎

Assignments 📖 Section 11.1 Efficiency in the **Student Edition**. after the Investigation.

Skill Sheets 10.3 Potential and Kinetic Energy

Equipment Setup Straight Track

Teaching the Investigation

1   Introduction
2   Input and output energy
3   Setting up the straight track
4   Potential and kinetic energy
5   Efficiency
6   Perpetual motion machines
7   Efficiency in a living animal
8   Efficiency in a natural system

Introduction

Efficiency - how much of the energy you start with is transformed into the form you finish with.

Input and output energy

For the straight track:
Energy input = potential energy of the ball at the top of the track
Energy output = kinetic energy of the moving ball

Efficiency is the ratio of energy output divided by energy input.

100 percent efficiency means that all of the input energy becomes output energy.

What is the efficiency of the straight track?

Setting up the straight track   **1**

Set up the straight track on the tenth hole in the physics stand.
Connect the timer and put it in interval mode.
Collect data.

  2

The law of conservation of energy says that energy cannot be created or destroyed, only converted from one form to another. The law does not say that all of the energy in one form is converted to the form that you desire. For example, as a car drives along the road, the energy supplied by burning gasoline goes partly into kinetic energy of the moving car, but mostly into heat, overcoming air friction, and other forms of energy that are considered "waste." Today's Investigation is about efficiency. Efficiency is a very important concept that describes how much of the energy you start with is transformed into the form you finish with. Efficiency affects every process in the universe, in both living things and also in human technology.

    Set up a straight track near the front of the classroom that you can use for demonstration.
The experiment we are going to use to investigate efficiency is the straight track. What form of energy does the ball start with?

    Hold the ball at the top of the track. Students should answer that the ball starts with potential energy.
To talk about efficiency, we need to define what the energy input and energy output are. For the straight track, the energy input is the potential energy we give the ball at the start of the track.

    Release the ball and let it roll down.
Suppose we define the energy output as the energy in motion of the ball at the bottom of the hill. This would be appropriate if we were building a model of hydroelectric dam. In a dam, the energy of moving water flowing downhill is converted into electrical energy. Turbines are placed at the bottom of the hill where the kinetic energy of water is greatest and the potential energy of water is least. What is the energy output of the straight track?

    Students should answer that the energy output is the kinetic energy of the moving ball.
The efficiency of a process is the ratio of energy output divided by energy input. If a process is 100 percent efficient, then all of the input energy becomes output energy. For the ball that would mean that the kinetic energy at the bottom of the track is the same as the potential energy the ball started with at the top of the track. Do you think the straight track is 100 percent efficient? Can anyone give me a guess as to what the efficiency of the track is?

    Most students recognize that there is some friction, which lowers the efficiency of the process in which the output is a form of mechanical energy. Few students will have the experience to make a reasonable guess at the efficiency of the straight track and you may get numbers from 1 percent all the way to 99 percent. Record a few numbers to refer back to later in the lesson.
Set up the straight track at the 10th hole in the stand. Twist the catcher so it curves upward to catch the ball. Set a photogate on the level section of the track, as shown in the diagram. Connect the timer and put it in interval mode.

    Students set up the apparatus.
Use the starting peg to release the ball from that same position several times. Measure the time it takes the ball to pass through the photogate and record at least three trials. You will also need to measure the initial and final heights of the ball to calculate the potential energy. Measure the initial height from the table to the center of the ball while the ball is held against the starting point. Measure the final height from the table to the small dimple on the side of the photogate that indicates the center of the light beam. Repeat the experiment with the plastic ball and the steel ball.

    Students take data on the speed and height for both the plastic ball and the steel ball. Students record data in Table 1 and Table 2.

Example problem

To illustrate the concept of efficiency, work through the following problem with your students:

A 12-gram paper airplane is launched at a speed of 6.5 m/sec with a rubber band. The rubber band is stretched with a force of 10 N for a distance of 15 centimeters. Calculate the efficiency of the process of launching the plane.

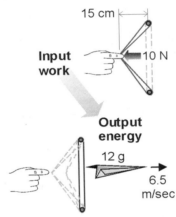

UNIT 4: Energy and Momentum

11.1 — Efficiency

Question: How efficient is the straight track?

In this Investigation, you will:

1. Calculate the kinetic and potential energy of a ball at the top and bottom of the straight track.
2. Determine the efficiency of the straight track.

The conversion of potential energy to kinetic energy obeys the *law of conservation of energy*. This law states that energy cannot be created or destroyed but can be converted from one form to another. As the ball rolls down the track, its potential energy is converted into kinetic energy.

The law of conservation of energy does *not* require that 100% of the potential energy become kinetic energy. Other forms of energy conversion are also allowed. For example, friction converts some potential energy to heat and wear. The *efficiency* of a process is the ratio of the energy you get out of the process divided by the energy you start with. In this Investigation, you will explore whether the conversion from potential to kinetic energy for a ball rolling down a track is 100%.

1 Setting up the straight track

Setting up the experiment

Tenth hole from bottom
Starting peg
Level section
Stop swiveled UP
Photogate

Measurements

Initial height (h_o)
Center of ball to table
Final height (h)
Speed (v)

1. Attach the straight track to the physics stand at the 10th hole (measured from the bottom). Twist the end of the track so it curves upward to catch the ball at the bottom of the track.
2. Connect a photogate to the Timer at input A and fix it to the level section at the end of the track. Position the track so it is set on the photogate as shown in the diagram above.

2 Collecting data

1. Place the plastic ball so it is against the starting peg at the top of the track. Release the ball and allow it to roll until it is caught at the bottom of the track.
2. Use Table 1 to record the time the ball takes to pass through the photogate.
3. Repeat step one for two more trials and record the times in Table 1. Calculate the average of the three times.
4. Hold the ball at the top of the track so it is pressed against the starting peg. Measure the vertical distance from the center of the ball to the tabletop. Record the height in meters in Table 1.

67

Solution:

1. You are asked for the efficiency.
2. You are given the input force and distance and the output mass and speed.
3. Efficiency is output energy divided by input energy.
   The input energy is *work* $= F \times d$.
   The output energy $E_k = {}^1/_2\, mv^2$.
4. Solve:
   $\varepsilon = (0.5)(0.012 \text{ kg})(6.5 \text{ m/sec})^2 / (10 \text{ N})(0.15 \text{ m}) = 0.26$ or 26%

Potential and kinetic energy

$E_k = 1/2\ mv^2$

$E_p = mgh$

Efficiency

The efficiency of any mechanical process will always be less than 100 percent because there is always some friction.

In the case of the track, the loss of energy output comes mainly from the kinetic energy of rotation, not from friction.

Perpetual motion machines

Perpetual motion machine - impossible because there is always friction present.

If the efficiency of a machine is less than 100 percent, eventually, all of the energy the machine starts with is dissipated in friction and motion stops.

3 To analyze the data we need to calculate the potential and kinetic energies of the ball. What are the formulas for potential and kinetic energies?

Students should respond with the formulas for potential and kinetic energy, which you should write on the board. $E_k = 1/2\ mv^2$ *and* $E_p = mgh.$

Use Table 3 to record the calculations of potential and kinetic energy for both the steel ball and plastic ball. You will need to measure the mass of the steel ball and plastic ball.

Students do calculations and complete Table 3. The measured masses should come out near 28 grams for the steel ball and 4 grams for the plastic ball.

Calculate the efficiency of energy transformation for the steel and plastic balls. The efficiency is the ratio of the output energy divided by the input energy.

Students should do the calculation of efficiency.

Do you think the efficiency is high or low? Can anyone give a reason why the efficiency is lower than 100 percent?

The efficiency is typically around 60-70 percent. Considering that the friction in the track is very small, this is actually much lower than it should be. The efficiency of any mechanical process will always be less than 100 percent because there is some friction; however, the true value of efficiency is closer to 90 percent. The culprit is not friction, but kinetic energy of rotation. The formula $E_k = 1/2mv^2$ *ignores the rolling motion of the ball. Rolling motion accounts for an additional* $1/5mv^2$, *which is 28 percent of the total kinetic energy. You may wish to explain this and go through the calculation of adding an additional* $1/5mv^2$, *making the total kinetic energy* $7/10mv^2$ *with students. This will raise the efficiency near 90 percent or higher depending on how clean your track is. The efficiency of the plastic ball is slightly different because friction is a larger force compared with the weight of the plastic ball than it is compared with the weight of the steel ball.*

4 The concept of efficiency is important in all areas of human technology. No mechanical process can be 100 percent efficient because all motion creates some friction. In a well-designed machine, friction may be very small, but it is always there. Many inventors have claimed to invent machines that run forever. These machines are called perpetual motion machines by scientists, and they are impossible. Any machine always has friction. Therefore the efficiency of any energy transformation in the machine must be less than 100 percent. If the efficiency is less than 100 percent, eventually all of the energy the machine starts with is dissipated in friction and motion stops. Dishonest inventors have hidden extra energy in many clever ways to try to fool investors or patent attorneys. Hidden electrical cords, hidden batteries, tanks that contain fuel, hidden reservoirs of pressurized air, and other tricks have been used. In one famous stunt, an inventor claimed to have invented a car that ran on water. He demonstrated pouring water into the tank, then starting and running the car. What the inventor did not reveal was that the inside of the gas tank was partly filled with a special chemical that reacted with water to produce flammable acetylene gas. The acetylene gas was burned to run the car. Eventually, the chemical was all used up and the car no longer worked! The dishonest inventor had hoped to trick investors into buying stock in his new company before they learned exactly how his machine worked. You should always be suspicious of a perpetual motion machine. Many gift shops sell devices that seem to run forever. Every one of these devices has a hidden battery or solar cell supplying energy to overcome friction.

11.1 Efficiency

5. When the ball passes through the bottom photogate, its center lines up with the bumps on the photogate's outer edges. Find the height of the ball at the bottom of the track by measuring the vertical distance from the tabletop to one of these bumps. Record the height in meters in Table 1.

6. Measure the mass of the ball in kilograms and record in Table 1. If your scale displays mass in grams, you need to convert to kilograms.

Table 1: Time, height, and mass data for plastic ball

Trial	Time through photogate (sec)	Initial height (m)	Final height (m)	Mass of ball (kg)
1				
2				
3				
Average				

7. Repeat steps 1 through 6 using the steel ball. Record your data in Table 2.

Table 2: Time, height, and mass data for steel ball

Trial	Time through photogate (sec)	Initial height (m)	Final height (m)	Mass of ball (kg)
1				
2				
3				
Average				

3　Potential and kinetic energy

The total energy of the ball on the track is a combination of potential and kinetic energies. Potential energy, also known as stored energy, depends on the *height* of the ball. Kinetic energy is related to motion and depends on the *speed* of the ball.

1. What is the speed of the ball at the instant you release it at the top of the track? What is its kinetic energy?

2. Use the average times from Tables 1 and 2 to calculate the speed of each ball through the photogate at the bottom of the track. Use the ball's diameter (0.019 meter) for the distance. Record in Table 3.

3. Calculate the potential and kinetic energy of the plastic ball at the top and bottom of the track. Record your results in Table 3.

4. The total energy at each position on the track is calculated by adding the potential and kinetic energies. Find the total energy at each position and record the results in Table 3.

2　3　Example answers

Table 1: *Time, height, and mass data for plastic ball*

Trial	Time through photogate (sec)	Initial height (m)	Final height (m)	Mass of ball (kg)
1	0.0075	.604	0.091	0.00043
2	0.0075			
3	0.0075			
Average	0.0075			

Table 2: *Time, height, and mass data for steel ball*

Trial	Time through photogate (sec)	Initial height (m)	Final height (m)	Mass of ball (kg)
1	0.0074	.604	0.091	0.00282
2	0.0074			
3	0.0074			
Average	0.0074			

3.1 The instant the ball is released it has zero speed. With zero speed it would have zero kinetic energy.

Efficiency in a living animal

1 food calorie = 4,187 joules of energy.

During strenuous exercise, the body burns about 660 food calories per hour.

660 × 4,187 = 2,763,420 joules of energy.

(70 kg)(9.8 N/kg)(1,000 m) = 686,000 joules

Efficiency of the human body in the example:

686,000 ÷ 8.3 million = 8%

Efficiency in a natural system

The total sum of the efficiencies for every single process using energy must equal 100 percent because according to the law of conservation of energy, energy cannot be destroyed and must go somewhere.

The concept of efficiency also applies to living systems and natural systems. Any process in which energy is transformed from one form to another has efficiency. For example, how much of the energy in the food you eat becomes physical work that you do with your body? To consider this question, how much energy is in the food you eat in one day?

> Students should discuss and come up with something in the range of 2,000-3,000 calories. This is a typical dietary energy consumption.

A single food calorie is equal to 4,187 joules of energy in physics units. During strenuous exercise, the body burns about 660 calories per hour. How much energy is that in joules?

> Do the calculation on the board: 660 × 4,187 = 2,763,420 joules. Almost 3 million joules! The human body transforms a great deal of energy every day.

So, the energy input is 2.7 million joules per hour. Let's make a simple estimate of the energy output. A strong climber can climb a 1,000-meter mountain in 3 hours. If the person has a mass of 70 kilograms, the total change in potential energy from the bottom to the top of the mountain is *mgh*, which works out to 686,000 joules. The energy consumed by the body in three hours is 8.3 million joules. Therefore, the efficiency is 686,000 divided by 8.3 million, which works out to 8 percent.

> Work the calculation on the board. The example is in the text on page 205.

Living creatures are not very efficient at transforming chemical energy in food to mechanical energy in work. In fact, if you did climb a mountain in three hours, it probably represents the bulk of all physical work you do in 24 hours. Over 24 hours, the average efficiency is even lower than 8 percent because a living body transforms energy even at rest. On the other side of the coin, the calculation of output energy was too simplistic. The climber had to do work against friction all the way up the mountain. This work should be counted as output work done by the climber in the calculation of efficiency. Even so, the calculation shows the correct order of magnitude.

The concept of efficiency also applies to systems in nature. For a natural system, efficiency is usually defined in terms of energy transformation between two processes. For example, how much energy does the Earth receive from the sun? Some of the sun's energy is absorbed by the Earth and some is reflected by the atmosphere back into space. We could define efficiency in terms of the fraction of the sun's energy that reaches the ground and is therefore available for direct use by plants and animals. Although it varies with the seasons and the weather, about 50 percent of the energy from the sun falling on the upper atmosphere makes its way down to the ground. However, this definition of efficiency does not describe all of the energy. It only describes the efficiency of transformation between one source of input energy and one source of output energy. We could also define efficiency of transfer between solar energy and the atmosphere, which is what causes weather to happen.

Suppose you calculated a separate efficiency for every single process that used energy in a natural system. What would the total be?

> Students should recognize that the total sum of the efficiencies for every single process using energy must equal 100 percent because according to the law of conservation of energy, energy cannot be destroyed and must go somewhere.

Table 3: Potential and kinetic energy

Type of ball	Location on track	Speed (m/sec)	Kinetic energy (J)	Potential energy (J)	Total energy (J)
plastic	top				
	bottom				
steel	top				
	bottom				

4   Efficiency

You might not have realized it but the straight track is a simple machine that converts energy from one form to another. The energy put into any machine is called *input energy*. You provide the input energy to a ball as potential energy when you lift it up to the top of the track. The useful energy supplied by a machine is called *output energy*. Imagine that you use the track as an egg-breaking machine. You place an egg at the bottom and roll a ball down the track. The output energy of the machine is the ball's kinetic energy at the bottom of the track. The greater the kinetic energy, the greater the ball's ability to do work on the egg and smash it.

The ratio of the output energy to the input energy for a machine is called its *efficiency*. An efficiency of 100 percent means that all of the input energy is converted to useful output energy. No machine is 100 percent efficient. Automobiles, for example, are typically only about 13 percent efficient.

Efficiency
(energy efficiency)

$$\text{Efficiency} \quad \varepsilon = \frac{E_o \quad \text{Energy output (J)}}{E_i \quad \text{Energy input (J)}}$$

a. Compare the total energy of each ball at the top of the track to its total energy at the bottom. Did each ball's total energy increase, decrease, or remain unchanged?

b. Calculate the efficiency for each ball.

c. Compare the two efficiencies. Why might they be slightly different?

d. The law of conservation of energy states that energy cannot be created or destroyed. If the efficiencies were less than 100 percent, does this mean the law of conservation of energy is not true? Was energy lost? Where did the energy go? Write a short paragraph explaining your answer. (HINT: The motion of the ball includes rotation as well as linear motion.)

e. CHALLENGE! If the efficiency for the steel ball were 100 percent, how fast would it be moving at the bottom of the track?

Table 3: *Potential and kinetic energy*

Type of ball	Location on track	Speed (m/sec)	Kinetic energy (J)	Potential energy (J)	Total energy (J)
plastic	top	0.0	0.0	0.0025	0.0025
	bottom	2.53	0.0014	0.0004	0.0018
steel	top	0.0	0.0	0.0167	0.0167
	bottom	2.57	0.0093	0.0025	0.0118

4a. Both the plastic and the steel balls had a decrease in total energy at the bottom of the track compared with the top.

4b. Efficiency for the plastic ball;

$E_P = 0.0018\ \text{j}/0.0025\ \text{j}$

$E_P = 0.72\ (72\%)$

Efficiency for the steel ball;

$E_S = 0.0118\ \text{j}/0.0167\ \text{j}$

$E_S = 0.707\ (70.7\%)$

4c. The efficiency was around 71 percent which means some of the energy did not go into the linear speed of the ball. Some of the energy was converted to heat by friction, but some of the energy also must have gone to the rotation of the ball as well. Some of the total energy gets used turning the ball around and around as it rolls down the ramp. We were not accounting for this in our calculations.

4d. 100 percent efficiency means $E_{top} = E_{bottom}$

$0.0167\ \text{j} = (1/2\ mv^2) + 0.0025\ \text{j}$

$0.0142\ \text{j} = 1/2\ (0.00282\ \text{kg})\ v^2$

$0.0142\ \text{j}\ /(1/2\ (0.00282\ \text{kg})) = v^2$

$10.07\ \text{m}^2/\text{sec}^2 = v^2$

$3.17\ \text{m/sec} = v$

11.2 Energy and Power

Key Question: How powerful are you?

This Investigation teaches students the physical meaning of a joule of work and a watt of power. Students first measure their own work and power while lifting an object a distance of 1.5 meters. They compare their power to that of a light bulb. They then measure their work and power while running up a flight of stairs. Students compare the work and power done in the first activity to those in the second activity. They also compare work and power among different students who climbed the stairs. Finally students calculate the number of Calories burned while climbing the stairs.

Reading Synopsis

Students read Section 11.2 Energy and Power after the Investigation.

Power is the rate at which energy flows or the rate at which work is done. Power can be calculated by dividing the quantity of work or energy by the time. An alternative way to calculate power is to multiply the force by the velocity. The unit in which power is measured is the watt. One watt is equal to one joule per second. The power of machines is sometimes stated in horsepower. One horsepower is equal to 746 watts.

Power is an important consideration in technology, and also applies to living things and systems in nature. An automobile has a power output of more than 100,000 watts. As an example of a natural system, the Earth gets power from the sun's radiant energy. Solar power drives weather patterns on Earth and supports the food chain that begins with green plants. The power developed by animals and plants ranges from 0.0001 watts for an insect to 375,000 watts for a blue whale. Humans typically produce a maximum power of 300 watts.

The Investigation

Leading Questions
- The work done in lifting an object is the same whether the object is lifted slowly or quickly. Yet lifting quickly feels harder than lifting slowly. What is the physical difference between work done slowly and work done quickly?
- How do we calculate power?
- What is power?
- How much power is used by common devices, like a light bulb?
- How much power do we produce with our bodies?
- What is the source of the output power in living things?

Learning Goals
By the end of the Investigation, students will be able to:
- Calculate the work done when lifting an object.
- Calculate the power output while lifting an object.
- Identify the factors that determine the work a person does and his or her power output.
- Calculate power in watts.
- Describe the difference between energy and power.

Key Vocabulary   energy, work, power, weight, force, watt, joule, Calorie

Setup and Materials

Students work in groups of three to five for the first part of the Investigation and as a whole class for the second part.

Each group should have:

- Timer or stopwatch
- Meter stick
- Object for lifting such as a small barbell, loaded backpack, brick, or heavy book
- Scale to determine the object's weight or mass
- Piece of masking tape

For the class activity, the class should have:

- Three timers or stopwatches
- Access to a set of stairs

Details

Time One class period

Preparation Students read sections 11.2 in the **Student Edition** before the Investigation

Assignments Section 11.2 Energy and Power in the **Student Edition** after the Investigation.

Skill Sheets 11.2 Power

Teaching the Investigation

1. Lifting power
2. Comparing the data
3. Stair-climbing work and power
4. What did you learn?

Introduction

How does a physicist define work?

How are power and work related?
Power is the rate at which work is done.

Lifting power

1

Work = Force x distance
W = F x d

Power = Work ÷ time
P = W ÷ t

Comparing the data

2

Each student does the same amount of work, because they lifted the same weight the same distance. To increase work, the weight or distance must increase.

Power output is different for each student; the person who lifted the object the fastest had the most power. To increase power, the work must increase or the time must decrease.

Suppose I ask you to push this desk across the room. How much work do you have to do in the physics sense of the word "work"?

> Students should answer that the work required is the force applied parallel to the floor times the distance they push the desk.

Suppose I ask the same task from two different people. One person moves the desk slowly and it takes them 20 minutes. The other person does it quickly and it takes them 1 minute. Both move the desk with the same amount of force. Who did more work?

> This is a trick question; both do the same amount of work.

Today's Investigation is about power. Power is the rate at which work is done. Both people may do the same amount of work but the person who did the work faster used more power.

In this Investigation, you will get a feel for the meaning of the units joule and watt. You will be measuring the work your body does and its power. If you lift an object, how can you determine the amount of work you did? Prompt a discussion.

> The work is the force you apply multiplied by the distance the object is lifted. The force against which you are working is the force of gravity, so the force is equal to the object's weight. This is the force needed to lift the object at a constant speed. A slightly greater force is needed at first just to get the object moving. The work done on the object can also be determined by measuring the change in its gravitational potential energy. Students may also comment on the fact that a person lifts his or her arm as well as the object and may want to include the weight of the arm. However, in this activity we are only concerned with the work done on the object.

How can you determine your power output while lifting something?

> Power is the work done divided by the time.

Now you will work in groups and determine each person's work and power when lifting an object. You will each lift it a distance of 1.5 meters, which you will measure and mark off with tape. You will also have to measure the object's weight. Record all of your results in Table 1. Each group member should take a turn.

> Each group should have an object with substantial weight, such as a small barbell, a loaded backpack, a brick, or a heavy book.

How did the work done by each person compare?

> Everyone did the same amount of work.

How did the power output of each person compare?

> The power was different for each person. The person who lifted the object the fastest had the greatest power.

We buy light bulbs according to their watts of power. A light bulb's power is electrical power, or the rate at which electrical energy is turned into heat and light energy. How does your power compare with the electrical power of a typical bulb (75 watts)?

> Answers will depend on the type of object lifted. Students may be as powerful as one or two light bulbs or may be less powerful than one.

How could you increase the amount of work done in this activity?

> Either lift the object a greater distance or use a heavier object.

How could you increase the power output?

> Either lift a heavier object or lift the object faster.

11.2 — Energy and Power

Question: How powerful are you?

In this Investigation, you will:

1 Determine the work done by your body and your power output.
2 Compare your power output with that of a common electric light bulb.

The power output of motors, cars, and other machines is often listed on the machine or in its owner's manual. What about the power output of the human body? In this Investigation, you will measure the work you do and the output power you produce while lifting an object and while climbing stairs.

1 Lifting power

1. During the first part of this Investigation, you will calculate the work you do and your power output while you lift an object. Listen to directions from your instructor about the type of object you will lift. Determine the weight of the object in newtons and record it in Table 1.
2. Find a location along a wall where your group will lift the object. Measure 1.5 meters up from the floor and mark this height on the wall with a piece of tape.
3. Now each person in your group will lift the object from the floor until the bottom of the object is at a height of 1.5 meters. Measure the time (in seconds) that it takes for each person to lift the object. You may choose to lift it quickly or slowly. Record each person's name and time in Table 1.
4. Calculate the work done in lifting the object. The force you should use is the weight of the object in newtons. Record the work done in Table 1.
5. Calculate each person's power in lifting the object. Record in Table 1.

Table 1: Lifting data

Name	Weight (N)	Distance (m)	Time (sec)	Work (J)	Power (W)
		1.5			

2 Comparing the data

a. Why is the object's weight used in the calculation of work done?
b. How did the amount of work done by each person compare? Why?
c. What determined the power of each person? Explain.
d. A typical light bulb has a power of 75 watts. How does this compare to your power output while lifting the object?
e. Discuss two ways you could increase the amount of work you do in this activity.
f. Discuss two ways you could increase your power output in this activity.

Teaching tip

Tell students about this Investigation the day before so they can wear sneakers if they wish to run up the stairs. Students love this activity and can tend to get loud, so choose a stairwell where the noise will not interfere with other classes. You could also use an outside set of stairs.

1 2 Example answers

Table 1: Lifting data

Name	Weight (N)	Distance (m)	Time (sec)	Work (J)	Power (W)
Erik			1.22	60	49.2
Marlon			0.94	60	63.8
Jake	40	1.5	1.63	60	36.8
Connie			0.81	60	74.1
Hannah			1.09	60	55.0

2a. The weight is used because to lift an object you must apply a force equal to its weight but in the opposite direction.

2b. Each person did the same amount of work because the same object was lifted for the same distance.

2c. The power depended on the time. The greater the time, the less the power.

2d. Answers will vary.

2e. The work could be increased by either lifting a heavier object or lifting it a greater distance.

2f. The power could be increased by either lifting a heavier object or lifting it more quickly.

Stair-climbing work and power

The work done by a person climbing stairs = the person's weight × height of stairs

The power used by a person climbing stairs = work done ÷ time to climb the stairs

What did you learn?

If force and distance are held constant, the work performed by two persons is equal. The amount of power depends on the time needed to accomplish the work.

3

Now we will be determining the work and power of students walking or running up a flight of stairs. I need several volunteers who want to have us time them climbing the stairs. Volunteers must give us their weight so we can determine the work. If you know your weight in pounds, convert to newtons by multiplying by 4.45.

> Write down each volunteer's name and weight in newtons on the board.

How will we figure out the work and power for each person?

> The work is the person's weight multiplied by the vertical distance he or she climbs. The power is the work divided by the time.

I need three volunteers to measure the time while each person climbs the stairs. I also need two volunteers to determine the height of the flight of stairs. What do you think is the easiest way to determine the height?

> The easiest way is to measure the height of one stair and then multiply by the total number of stairs that will be climbed.

We will now all go to the stairs and our volunteers will climb the stairs individually while the three timers measure the time it takes.

> Have the climbers line up at the bottom of the stairs. Tell them they may choose to walk or run. It is ideal to have them climb at different rates so there will be a range of powers. Give each student one turn to climb the stairs while three students simultaneously measure the time it takes.

Now you will use the data to determine the work and power for each person.

> Lead students back to the classroom and make sure everyone has the correct data.

4

How did the work done by different people compare? Why?

> Students with more weight did more work. They needed to exert more force to climb the stairs.

Who had the greatest power? What determined each person's power?

> The person's weight and his or her time determined the power. A heavy person who climbed the stairs quickly would have the greatest power.

How do the work and power running up the stairs compare with the work and power when lifting the object from the first part of the Investigation?

> Both are much less.

When we eat food, our body converts the food energy to energy we use to heat our bodies and to move. Food energy is often measured in Calories. One Calorie equals 4,186 joules. Choose one person who climbed the stairs and calculate the number of Calories of work the person did.

> Answers will depend on the height of the stairs and the person's weight, but the work is typically around 1 Calorie. Students may be surprised at how little this is.

Imagine two people have equal weights but climb the stairs at different rates. One walks and the other runs. Do they do the same number of Calories of work? Do they have the same power?

> The work is the same because each has the same force and distance. The person who runs has a greater power and does the work in less time.

3 Stair-climbing work and power

1. This part of the Investigation is done with your entire class. Select several people who want to walk or run up a flight of stairs while others record their times. Each person who volunteers must know his or her weight in newtons. (Weight in pounds can be converted to newtons using the conversion factor 1 pound = 4.45 newtons.) Record the names and weights of the volunteers in Table 2.

Table 2: Stair-climbing data

Name	Weight (N)	Vertical distance (m)	Time (sec)			Avg. time (sec)	Work (J)	Power (W)

2. Locate a suitable stairwell and measure the vertical distance from one flight to the next. An easy way to do this is to measure the height of one stair and count the number of stairs students are climbing. Record the measurement in Table 2.

3. Select three people to measure the time it takes for the three volunteers to climb the stairs. All three timers will measure the time at once; each stair climber will make only one trip up the stairs.

4. Each volunteer may climb the stairs slowly or quickly. Record the three times for each person.

5. Calculate the average time for each climber and record in the table.

6. Calculate the work done and power output for each climber. Record in the table.

4 What did you learn?

a. How did the work done by the different people compare? In the first part of the Investigation, every group member did the same amount of work. Why was this not the case with the stairs?

b. Which person had the greatest power? Which two factors determined each person's power?

c. Calculate the average work done and the average power for all of the stair climbers.

d. How do the average amounts of work and power for the stair climbing compare with your own work and power when lifting the object in the first part of the Investigation?

e. The human body is able to do work because energy is absorbed when we eat food. In physics, we usually measure work and energy in joules but food energy is usually measured in Calories. One Calorie is equal to 4,186 joules. Select one of the people who climbed the stairs and calculate the work done in Calories. These Calories come from food that is "burned" by the person's body. You may be surprised by how small the number is.

f. Imagine that two people having equal weights climb the same flight of stairs. One runs and the other walks. Do they do the same number of Calories of work (in the physics sense)? Do they have the same power output? Explain.

71

3 4 Example answers

i

Table 2: *Stair-climbing data*

Name	Wt. (N)	Vert. dist. (m)	Time (sec)			Avg. time (sec)	Work (J)	Power (W)
Ryan	668		6.80	6.71	6.92	6.81	4743	696
Jen	534		6.62	6.72	6.66	6.67	3791	568
Mike	801	7.1	9.24	9.10	9.03	9.12	5687	624
Chris	623		11.14	11.30	11.32	11.25	4423	393
Joan	450		7.44	7.31	7.49	7.41	3195	431

4a. Heavier people did more work when climbing the stairs because they had to exert more force.

4b. The power was determined by the person's weight and the time. The greater the weight and the shorter the time, the greater the power.

4c. Answers will vary.

4d. The work and power are much greater during the stair climbing because the object being lifted was much heavier.

4e. Answers will vary.

4f. They do the same amount of work, but the person who runs has the greater power.

11.3 Energy Flow in Systems

Key Question: Where did the energy go?

The flow of energy drives all processes, both in human technology and in natural systems, including living things. In this Investigation, students trace the flow of energy through its different forms in processes that are commonly experienced daily. They describe energy flow and transformations by drawing flow charts tracing how energy moves and what forms it takes.

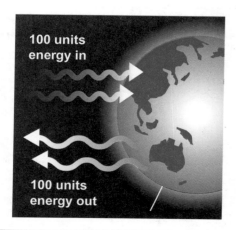

100 units
energy in

100 units
energy out

Reading Synopsis

Students read Section 11.3 Energy Flow in Systems before the Investigation.

Our universe consists of matter and energy organized in systems. In every system, energy flows, creating change. Energy flows almost always involve energy conversions. This chapter presents a few examples of how energy flows in a system.

One of the first steps to understanding an energy flow is to write down the forms that energy takes. The next step is to diagram the flow of energy from start to finish for all the important processes that take place. The last step is to try to estimate how much energy is involved and what are the efficiencies for each energy conversion.

Examples of these steps are given for energy flows in human technology, in natural systems, and in biological systems.

The Investigation

Leading Questions
- What happens to the energy in a process?
- How can we describe the flow of energy in a process?
- What are the similarities and differences between energy flow in human technology, and natural systems, and in living organisms?
- What form does energy take in technology, in natural systems, and in living organisms?

Learning Goals
By the end of the Investigation, students will be able to:
- Identify transformations where energy changes forms.
- Follow sequences in which energy changes forms in technical, natural, and biological systems.
- Sketch an energy flow diagram of technical, natural, and biological systems.

Key Vocabulary
energy conversions, energy flow, steady state, cycles, food chain, herbivores, carnivores, decomposers, food web, ecosystem

Setup and Materials

Students work in groups of four or five at tables.

Each group should have:

- Pencils and paper

Details

Time One class period

Preparation ✐ .

Assignments 📖 Section 11.3 Energy Flow in Systems in the **Student Edition** after the Investigation.

Skill Sheets 10.3 Potential and Kinetic Energy

Teaching the Investigation

1 An energy flow diagram

2 Where does the energy go?

An energy flow diagram

Conservation of energy: energy can be transformed from one form to another, but the total energy remains constant.

Where does the energy go?

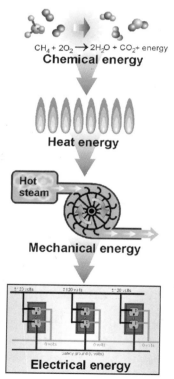

$CH_4 + 2O_2 \rightarrow 2H_2O + CO_2 +$ energy
Chemical energy

Heat energy

Mechanical energy

Electrical energy

Encourage students to be creative.

In previous Investigations, we studied block and tackle machines, motion on a loop track, and motion on a straight track. When we studied all of these different systems, we observed changes in position, height, speed, and forces. However, there was one quantity that didn't change. What was this quantity?

> Students should realize that total energy remained constant in each situation. The energy was transformed from one form to another, but the amount of energy available remained the same. This is called the law of conservation of energy.

What is the source of practically all our energy?

> The sun is the source of our energy.

What are some examples of different forms that energy can take when it is converted from one form to another?

> Potential and kinetic energy are forms of mechanical energy, as demonstrated nicely in the swinging of a pendulum. Other forms that energy can take include thermal, chemical, electrical, light, pressure, and nuclear.

1 An energy flow diagram is useful when you are trying to track how energy moves through a system and what forms the energy takes. Study the simple energy flow diagram example in Part 1 of the Investigation. What are the key components of the diagram?

> The energy flow diagram lists the forms of energy that are present at different times in the system's transformation (potential and kinetic). The diagram also explains what happens to the system as the energy is converted from one form to another (the ball is lifted, the ball is moving). The diagram also includes detail that shows where energy is dissipated as a result of friction.

Let's discuss an example scenario before you begin creating energy flow diagrams for the five scenarios in Part 2. Consider a hydroelectric power plant. What energy transformations take place?

> The potential height energy of the water behind the dam is converted to kinetic energy as the water is allowed to fall onto the blades of a giant turbine. The kinetic energy of the falling water is converted to mechanical energy as the blades of the turbine are turned. The turbine is connected to a generator that converts the mechanical energy to electrical energy.

Now that we have discussed the energy transformations that take place in a hydroelectric power plant, can you organize the information into an energy flow diagram? Don't forget to include places where usable energy is converted to unusable forms, such as in losses due to friction and heat.

> Students should practice drawing an energy flow diagram for this scenario. Take some time to have students look at one another's work. This will give everyone a good idea of how to tackle the more complicated scenarios in Part 2 of the Investigation.

Now let's draw an energy flow diagram for each of the scenarios in Part 2.

B

> You might want to assign a different scenario to each group and have the groups present their diagrams to the entire class. It is a good idea to use large pieces of newsprint and markers, or have students draw their diagrams on blank transparencies. This is a learning experience; some groups will inevitably leave out one or two transformations - which is why it is important to review all diagrams and allow the class to suggest additions/changes/deletions before the final diagram is drawn and displayed in the classroom.

11.3   Energy Flow in Systems

Question: Where did the energy go?

In this Investigation, you will:

1. Describe energy transformations in several scenarios.

The flow of energy drives all processes both in human technology and in natural systems, including living things. This Investigation challenges you to trace the flow of energy through its different forms in processes that you may experience.

| Potential energy | Kinetic energy | Thermal energy | Chemical energy | Electrical energy | Light energy | Pressure energy | Nuclear energy |

Energy can never be created or destroyed, only changed
from one form to another.

1   An energy flow diagram

An energy flow diagram is a type of flow chart that shows how energy moves and what forms it takes. For example, in a pendulum the energy flows back and forth between potential energy and kinetic energy. An energy flow diagram for a pendulum is shown below.

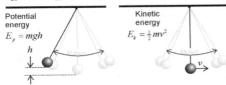

Potential energy
$E_p = mgh$

Kinetic energy
$E_k = \frac{1}{2}mv^2$

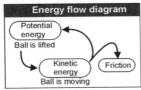

Energy flow diagram

Potential energy — Ball is lifted

Kinetic energy — Ball is moving

Friction

2   Drawing energy flow diagrams

Draw an energy flow diagram for each scenario described below. Your diagram must have enough detail to show at least three forms that energy takes. A short description (a few words) should accompany each different form of energy on your diagram. You may make your diagram as complex as you wish by including more forms of energy.

a. A car drives down a hill and then up and over the top of another hill.
b. A seagull in flight swoops down and snatches a fish to eat out of the water.
c. A calculator operates from a solar cell.
d. A camper uses a wood fire to heat up a pot of water for tea. The pot has a whistle that lets him know when the water boils.
e. A bicyclist rides at night, switching on her bike's generator so that the headlight comes on. The harder she pedals, the brighter the headlight glows.

2   Example answers

2a. Chemical energy (fuel is burned) → mechanical energy (transmission powers wheels) → kinetic energy (car accelerates) → potential energy (car moves uphill)

2b. Chemical energy (seagull burns food to power muscles) → kinetic energy (seagull flies up into air) → potential energy (height of seagull) → kinetic energy (seagull swoops down) → potential energy (seagull flies back up into the sky)

2c. Nuclear energy (hydrogen nuclei fuse together in sun's core) → light energy (light from sun) → electric energy (photovoltaic cell produces current)

2d. Nuclear energy (hydrogen nuclei fuse together in sun's core) → light energy (light from sun) → chemical energy (plant cells of tree produce tissue) → chemical energy (tree is burned) → radiant energy (tree is burned) → thermal energy (water in kettle is heated) → fluid energy (pressure from water conversion into steam) → sound energy (whistle on kettle blows)

2e. Chemical energy (rider burns food) → kinetic energy (muscles in legs turn cranks on bike) → mechanical energy (from front sprocket to rear sprocket via chain the rear wheel pushes bike and rider forward) → friction energy (tires grip road) → friction energy (generator's drive wheel comes in contact with wheel rim) → mechanical energy (gear in generator spins small turbine) → kinetic energy (turbine spins) → electrical energy (turbine spin produces current in wire) → heat energy (head lamp's bulb element heats up) → light energy (element glows)

12.1 Momentum

Key Question: What are some useful properties of momentum?

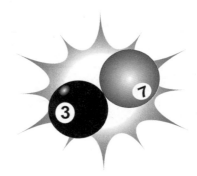

The law of conservation of momentum is the second of the great conservation laws in physics, after the conservation of energy. In this Investigation students will use the conservation of momentum to analyze one-dimensional collisions. The collisions are between hardened steel balls and are almost perfectly elastic. By measuring the velocity of a projectile ball before and after the collision, students must deduce the mass of the target ball without actually measuring it. They base their calculation of the unknown mass on the conservation of momentum and kinetic energy. The experiment is similar to how the atomic nucleus was discovered and proved to contain most of the mass in the atom.

Reading Synopsis

Students read Section 12.1 Momentum after the Investigation.

The momentum of a moving object is its mass multiplied by its velocity. The momentum of an object is a measure of the object's tendency to continue moving at the same speed in the same direction. Momentum is a vector. Kinetic energy also depends on mass and velocity but is not a vector.

In an isolated system, momentum is conserved. The total momentum before a collision equals the total momentum after the collision The conservation of momentum is a consequence of the third law. In an elastic collision, the colliding objects separate after the collision and conserve kinetic energy. In an inelastic collision, the objects stick together and do not conserve kinetic energy. Momentum is conserved in both elastic and inelastic collisions. Techniques and examples are presented for solving momentum problems.

In two and three dimensions, momentum is conserved separately in each dimension.

The Investigation

Leading Questions
- How can the momentum of an object be measured?
- What is the law of conservation of momentum?
- How can we use the law of conservation of momentum to predict what will happen when two objects collide?

Learning Goals
By the end of the Investigation, students will be able to:
- Show how collisions between moving objects obey the law of conservation of momentum.
- Use momentum conservation to estimate the mass of unknown objects.

Key Vocabulary
momentum, law of conservation of momentum, collision, elastic collision, inelastic collision

Setup and Materials

Students work in groups of four or five at tables.

Each group should have:

- Colliding pendulum
- CPO Timer and 2 photogates
- Mass balance for measuring the mass of the steel balls (one per class)

Details

Time	One class period
Preparation	✎
	📖 Section 12.1 Momentum in the **Student Edition** after the Investigation.
Skill Sheets	12.1 Momentum
Equipment Setup	Colliding pendulum

Teaching the Investigation

1. Introduction
2. Momentum is a vector
3. Conservation of momentum and energy
4. Making a collision
5. What happens in the collision
6. Analyzing the collision
7. Using photogates to measure the speed
8. Collecting the data
9. Analyzing the data

Introduction

Newton's first law:
Moving objects tend to continue moving with the same speed and direction unless acted on by an unbalanced force.

More mass = more inertia = greater reluctance to change in motion

The law of conservation of energy:
Energy can be absorbed, released, or change form, but is not loss or gained.

Momentum = mass × velocity

$$\vec{p} = m\vec{v}$$

Momentum is a vector

Equal momentum

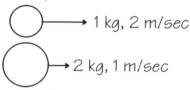

1 kg, 2 m/sec

2 kg, 1 m/sec

$$\vec{p} = m\vec{v}$$

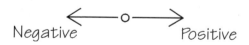

Negative   Positive

An object in motion tends to stay in motion. Can anyone tell me what property of the object is responsible for this tendency to continue moving?

The first law is a statement that objects tend to continue moving with the speed and direction that they have. Inertia (or mass) is the property of an object that describes its tendency to maintain its state of motion. However, mass is a scalar and therefore has no direction.

Objects with more mass have more inertia and therefore a greater reluctance to have their motion changed. But mass alone does not tell the whole story. Mass is a scalar quantity, so it contains no information about direction. Also, mass does not account for the fact that it takes more force to change the speed of a faster object compared with a slower object of equal mass. Can anyone think of a property of a moving object that depends on mass and speed?

Begin a discussion. Kinetic energy is a property that involves both mass and speed. However, kinetic energy is a scalar and therefore does nothing to maintain the direction of motion.

Energy does obey a conservation law and therefore it takes more energy to change the motion of an object with large kinetic energy than an object with smaller kinetic energy. However, kinetic energy is also a scalar quantity. That means there is no direction associated with the kinetic energy. According to the first law, in the absence of external forces, objects tend to continue both speed and direction. The faster an object is moving, the more force it takes to change direction. We need a vector quantity that involves both speed and mass. The quantity we are seeking is called momentum and momentum is the subject of today's Investigation.

The momentum of a moving object is its mass multiplied by its velocity. That means momentum increases with both mass and velocity. For example, if a one-kilogram ball and a two-kilogram ball are moving at the same velocity, the two-kilogram ball has twice as much momentum. The momentum is also equal if the one-kilogram ball is moving at twice the velocity of the two-kilogram ball. Momentum is measured in units of kilogram-meters per second, or kg-m/s. Can anyone tell me a combination of speed and mass that would result in a momentum out of 10 kg-m/sec?

Put the momentum formula on the board similar to step 1 of the Investigation. Students may specify any product of mass and speed that multiplies to 10 kg-m/sec, such as 5 kilograms moving at 2 m/sec, or 2.5 kg moving at 4 m/sec.

When working with momentum, it is necessary to include the direction of motion. Notice I wrote arrows on the variables for momentum (p) and velocity (v). The arrows remind us that momentum is always a vector and must always include information about direction. The experiment we are going to do today involves velocities that lie in a straight line, or a nearly straight line. In this case, we can use positive and negative numbers to provide directional information, instead of x and y components. Momentum to the right is considered positive, and momentum to the left is negative.

Put a diagram on the board illustrating the sign convention.

Aligning the colliding pendulum

Proper alignment of the colliding pendulum will ensure accurate results. Here is a complete alignment procedure to supplement the steps provided in Part 2 of the Investigation.

1. Find the side of the pole that is closest to parallel with one of the sides of the triangular physics base. Attach the arc to the lowest possible point on that side of the pole, securing it with a threaded knob. Attach the pendulum hanger higher up on the pole, leaving nine uncovered holes between the arc and the hanger.

2. Loosen the right post on the hanger and insert the string from one of the balls; this is the projectile ball. Gently tighten the post to secure the string so the ball hangs a little below the bottom of the arc.

3. Stand back and look at the string relative to the alignment mark on the arc. If necessary, adjust the leveling feet on the base of the stand until the string is lined up with the mark. Next, adjust the remaining leveling foot until the string is just touching the face of the arc.

4. If necessary, adjust the hanger slightly until the string lines up with the 0 (zero) degree line of the hanger.

5. Place the start block at the 10 degree position, ensuring the small hole is facing the pole. Fit the projectile ball in the start block hole, loosen the right post, pull the string taut, and re-tighten the post.

6. Place the start block at the 50 degree position, and loosen the knob on the arc. Adjust the arc until you can fit the projectile ball into the start block hole (make sure the start block is snug against the arc) and re-tighten the knob.

7. Loosen the left post on the hanger and insert the string from another ball; this is the target ball. Adjust the height of the ball until the center of the ball is at the same level as that of the projectile ball.

8. Slide the start block into one of the positions on the arc. To release the ball, grip it between two fingers and fit it in the hole in the start block. Release the ball by opening your fingers evenly, allowing the ball to drop straight from the start block.

12.1   Momentum

Question: What are some useful properties of momentum?

In this Investigation, you will:

1. Show how collisions between moving objects obey the law of conservation of momentum.
2. Use momentum conservation to estimate the mass of an unknown object.

This Investigation is about *momentum*, a property of moving matter. According to Newton's first law, moving objects tend to continue moving with the same speed and direction. Like mass, momentum measures the resistance of objects to changes in speed or direction. Unlike mass, momentum is a *vector*, meaning it has direction as well as magnitude. You can think of momentum as a property of moving mass that tends to maintain an object's direction and speed.

1   **Conservation of momentum and energy**

The momentum of a moving object is its mass multiplied by its velocity. That means momentum increases with both mass and velocity. For example, if a 25-gram ball and a 50-gram ball are moving at the same velocity, the 50-gram ball has twice as much momentum. However, the momentum would be equal if the 25-gram ball were moving at twice the velocity of the 50-gram ball. Momentum is measured in units of kilogram-meters per second, or kg-m/s.

Momentum

Momentum (kg·m/sec) $\vec{p} = m\vec{v}$ Mass (kg), Velocity (m/sec)

When working with momentum, it is important to include the direction of motion. Generally, momentum to the right is considered positive, and momentum to the left is negative. The symbol for momentum is a lower case "p" with an arrow over it ($\vec{p}$) to show that it is a vector.

Like energy, momentum obeys a conservation law. Consider the collision of two balls, one of which is initially at rest. The ball at rest is called the *target* ball. Because it is at rest, the target ball has zero momentum.

The projectile ball is initially moving with speed (*v*) and collides with the target ball. After the collision, both balls may be moving with different speeds and in different directions. The law of conservation of momentum says the total momentum after the collision must be equal to the total momentum before the collision.

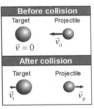

Kinetic energy may or may not be conserved in a collision. In an *elastic* collision, the objects bounce off each other with no loss in the total kinetic energy. In an *inelastic* collision, objects may change shape, stick together, and "lose" some kinetic energy to heat, sound, or friction.

Momentum is conserved in both elastic and inelastic collisions even when kinetic energy is not conserved. Conservation of momentum makes it possible to determine the speeds and directions of objects after a collision. If you observe objects after a collision, momentum conservation also allows you to determine how they were moving *before* the collision.

73

Conservation of momentum and energy

Before collision

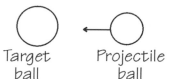

Target   Projectile
ball   ball

After collision

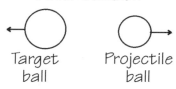

Target   Projectile
ball   ball

Making a collision

In elastic collisions, objects bounce off each other with no loss in the total kinetic energy.

1 Like energy, momentum obeys a conservation law. Consider the collision of two balls, one of which is initially at rest. The ball at rest is called the target ball. Because it is at rest, the target ball has zero momentum. The projectile ball is initially moving with speed (v) and collides with the target ball. After the collision, both balls may be moving with different speeds and in different directions. The law of conservation of momentum says the total momentum after the collision must be equal to the total momentum before the collision.

Draw the diagram with two balls on the board.

The total momentum we start with is mv, from the projectile ball. The momentum after the collision is equal to $m_t v_t + m_p v_p$ where the subscripts t and p refer to target and projectile. In general, after the collision, both balls will be moving with velocities that are different from before the collision. According to the law of conservation of momentum, $m_p v = m_t v_t + m_p v_p$.

Write the law of conservation of momentum for the collision on the board.

Energy is also conserved. However, kinetic energy might not to be conserved in a collision. In an elastic collision, the objects bounce off of each other with no loss in the total kinetic energy. In an inelastic collision, objects may change shape, stick together, or 'lose' some kinetic energy to heat, sound, or friction. Momentum is conserved in both elastic and inelastic collisions, even when kinetic energy is not conserved. Conservation of momentum makes it possible to determine the speeds and directions of objects after a collision. If you observe objects after a collision, momentum conservation also allows you to determine how they were moving before the collision.

2 The colliding pendulum allows us to make collisions between two balls that are made of hardened steel. Because the steel is so hard, it does not deform much and the collisions are almost perfectly elastic. Set up your colliding pendulum following the directions in step 2 of the Investigation. Choose both medium-sized balls. The arc and hanger must be attached to the pole so nine holes show uncovered between them. Hang both balls from the posts by threading the strings through the holes in the two posts. You can see the holes if you unscrew the post a few millimeters. The post will not unscrew completely, so do not try to remove it. Set the length of the string so both the balls hang slightly above the arc. You do not have to tighten the post very much to hold the string.

Circulate around the room and help students assemble the colliding pendulum apparatus. The trickiest part is getting the length of the string correct.

You can check your alignment by putting the starting block in one of the notches halfway up the arc. Bring the projectile ball up the arc until it fits against the hole on the front of the starting block. Adjust the string so the ball fits exactly against the hole. Let the ball hang at its lowest point and adjust the height of the target ball so its center is along the same horizontal line with the center of the projectile ball.

Check each group to see that they get the alignment correct.

To make a collision, pull the target ball up the arc and hold it against the starting block between your thumb and first finger. Release the ball carefully by opening your fingers. You want the ball to swing straight down the arc with no sideways motion. Any sideways motion will cause the target ball to move off at an angle after the collision. To make the math easier, we want to make head-on collisions where the target ball moves in the same direction as the projectile ball was originally traveling.

Circulate and help groups make collisions and observe what happens.

2 Making a collision

The colliding pendulum apparatus allows you to observe collisions between two balls of the same or different mass. The balls are made of hardened steel and the collisions are almost perfectly elastic.

1. Attach the arc at the lowest point it will go in the stand. Secure it with a threaded knob. Attach the pendulum hanger, leaving nine uncovered holes between the arc and the hanger.

2. Loosen the left post in the hanger and insert the string from one of the medium-sized balls. *Gently* tighten the post to secure the string so the ball hangs a little below the bottom of the arc.

3. Stand back and look at the string relative to the alignment mark on the arc. The string should be in line with the mark. Adjust the leveling feet on the base of the stand if necessary.

4. Loosen the post and readjust the length of the string until the bottom of the ball is 2 millimeters above the arc. Attach the other medium-sized ball to the right-hand post in the same way. The two balls should be at the same level relative to the arc.

5. Slide the starting block into one of the notches on the back of the arc. To release the ball, grip it between two fingers and hold it against the hole in the front side of the starting block. The hole ensures that the projectile ball drops from the right place to hit the center of the target ball. Release the ball by opening your fingers evenly, allowing the ball to drop straight out of the hole.

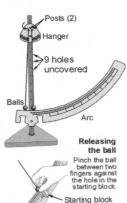

Posts (2)
Hanger
9 holes uncovered
Balls
Arc

Releasing the ball
Pinch the ball between two fingers against the hole in the starting block.
Starting block

3 Observing and analyzing the collision

The data from the experiment is easiest to analyze when the balls collide head-on. You can tell when this has occurred because the target ball moves straight along the same line that the projectile ball followed. It can be tricky to get the balls to collide head-on. Practice dropping the projectile ball until you can get a head-on collision most of the time.

a. Describe the motion of the projectile ball before and after the collision.
b. Describe the motion of the target ball before and after the collision.

Theoretically, the total momentum and kinetic energy must be the same before and after the collision.

Before collision	Conservation laws		After collision
Target $\quad$ Projectile $\vec{v}=0 \; \fbox{m} \leftarrow \fbox{m} \; \vec{v}_0$	**Momentum**	$mv_0 = mv_t + mv_p$	Target $\quad$ Projectile $\vec{v}_t \quad \vec{v}_p$
	Kinetic energy	$\frac{1}{2}mv_0^2 = \frac{1}{2}mv_t^2 + \frac{1}{2}mv_p^2$	

If the masses are equal, the momentum and energy equations reduce to the following:

$$\textbf{Momentum} \Rightarrow v_0 = v_t + v_p \qquad \textbf{Kinetic energy} \Rightarrow v_0^2 = v_t^2 + v_p^2$$

Combining these equations and eliminating v_0 produces the result that the product $v_t v_p = 0$. This means either $v_t = 0$ or $v_p = 0$. Looking at the collision, v_t cannot be zero because then $v_p = v_0$ and the projectile ball would have to go right through the target ball. Therefore, v_p must be zero, meaning the projectile ball stops at the collision and transfers *all* of its momentum and energy to the target ball.

Using the colliding pendulum to produce inelastic collisions

You can study elastic and inelastic collisions by making your own balls for the colliding pendulum. If you make balls out of soft modeling clay, they will be almost perfectly inelastic when they collide. Make a small loop in the end of the string to help the string stay embedded in the center of a clay ball. It also helps to work the clay in your hands to make it warm and soft before the collision.

To get elastic collisions with homemade balls, you can use rubber super balls that may be found in toy stores. A steel leather-sewing needle may be used to pull a heavy thread through the center of a rubber ball. I use a vise and pliers to get the needle through the ball. Try to make the string pass through the center of the ball along a major diameter. This will ensure that the ball hangs straight.

To use photogates you may have to color your rubber ball with a black indelible marker. The clear or translucent rubber in most super balls will not break the infrared light beam.

To study elastic and inelastic collisions, make clay balls and rubber balls of equal mass. Two rubber balls bouncing off each other are almost perfectly elastic.

Example answers

3a. The projectile ball is moving toward the bottom of the arc before the collision, and after the collision it's only swaying back and forth a few centimeters.

3b. The target ball is stationary before the collision. After the collision, it is moving away from the bottom of the arc quickly.

What happens in the collision

Analyzing the collision **3**

Law of conservation of momentum: total momentum after collision = total momentum before collision

Using photogates to measure the speed **5**

Conservation of momentum makes it possible to describe both the speeds and direction of objects after a collision.

Describe the motion of the projectile ball and the target ball after the collision.

The target ball should move straight forward and the projectile ball should virtually stop after the collision. Have each group work on their technique until they can reliably produce collisions that behave this way.

Let's apply the laws of conservation of momentum and kinetic energy to this collision. We know what happens. The target ball moves forward and the projectile ball stops.

Work out the analysis in step 3 of the Investigation on the board.

When you combine the equations and eliminate the initial velocity, you get a formula that says $v_t v_p = 0$. This means either $v_t = 0$ or $v_p = 0$, but both cannot be zero. Looking at the collision, v_t cannot be zero because then $v_p = v_0$ and the projectile ball would have to go right through the target ball! Therefore, v_p must be zero, meaning the projectile ball stops at the collision and transfers all of its momentum and energy to the target ball. Does this agree with what we observed?

Yes it does. This demonstrates to students how the law of momentum conservation is applied. The next application is more complex so it is important this simple application is understood first.

Suppose the target ball has a greater mass than the projectile ball. What do you think the velocities will be after the collision? Set up the colliding pendulum with the small ball and the large ball. Use the small ball as the projectile and the large ball as the target. Follow the same procedure to get both balls to hang the right height above the arc.

Students should set up the colliding pendulum with balls of unequal mass. Circulate and check that each group has set the length of the strings so the balls collide head-on.

Try the collision and see what happens. Again, you want to drop the projectile ball carefully so it swings straight down the arc and collides head-on with the target ball.

Each group of students should try until they can get reliable collisions where the projectile ball bounces backward after the collision and the target ball moves straight forward.

Describe the velocities of each ball after the collision.

The velocity of the target ball is slower than the velocity of the projectile ball. The target ball moves in the negative direction and the projectile ball moves in the positive direction after the collision.

We can use photogates to make careful measurements of the speed of both the target ball in the projectile ball before and after the collision. Attach the photogates by sliding them into the two notches in the base of the arc as shown in the diagram in step 5 of the Investigation. Connect the photogates to your timer and put the timer in interval mode.

Students attach photogates and connect their timers.

Using the timer is tricky because the projectile ball crosses the light beam twice, once before and once after the collision. Fortunately, the timer has a memory that remembers the last value for each of the three times, t_A, t_B, and t_{AB}. Remove photogate A and set it on the table. Turn the A light on by pressing the A button. Now move your finger slowly through the light beam once and then bring it back through the light beam again. The display shows the time your finger interrupted the beam on its second trip through. If you hold down the memory button, the display shows you the time from the first trial. As long as you do not hit reset, the timer saves the last time for each of the three internal clocks it keeps. You can see the last time by holding down the memory button while the appropriate lights on the timer are lit.

Students should go through this activity until they understand how the memory function works.

4 **The discovery of the nucleus of the atom**

In a famous experiment, British physicist Ernest Rutherford was able to show that almost all of an atom's mass was concentrated in a hard, tiny nucleus at the center. How did he do this?

In the experiment, Rutherford launched alpha particles at a very thin foil of gold atoms. He knew alpha particles had mass and traveled fast. At the time, people believed the atom was like a hard, round blueberry muffin. They believed the atom's positive charge was spread evenly through the "bread" part with the negative electrons embedded in the substance of the atom like the berries in the muffin. If this was how atoms were constructed, Rutherford predicted that fast alpha particles would mostly smash straight through and be deflected by a only small amount as they plowed through the "bread."

However, Rutherford found something completely different—nearly all the alpha particles went through with no deflection at all. Even more surprising, a few bounced off the heavy gold atoms, coming straight back at him. Rutherford was astounded and remarked that it was as if one fired an artillery shell at a piece of tissue paper and it bounced off and hit you!

According to the law of momentum conservation, the only way an alpha particle could have bounced straight back was if the mass of an atom were concentrated in a tiny nucleus. *Rutherford had discovered the nucleus of the atom.* Knowing only the mass and velocity vectors of the alpha particles before and after their collision with the nucleus, he was able to use the law of conservation of momentum to measure the mass and size of the nucleus.

5 **An experiment in momentum conservation**

In this part of the Investigation, you will cause a ball of known mass to collide with a ball of unknown mass. Using the laws of conservation of momentum and energy, you can determine the unknown mass of the target ball from the initial and final speeds of the projectile ball.

1. Replace the medium-sized target ball with the largest ball. Align the heights of the balls so the line joining their centers is parallel to the bottom of the arc.

2. Place two photogates in the notches at the bottom of the arc. When the balls pass through the light beams, you can use the photogates to measure their velocities.

3. Connect the photogates and set the Timer to interval mode. You will need the memory function of the Timer because the ball may pass through the same photogate before and after the collision. Pushing the memory button ("?") causes the Timer to display the last reading for the time indicated by the A and B lights. For example, pressing the memory button (?) when the A light is on displays the time the light beam was broken in the previous pass through photogate A.

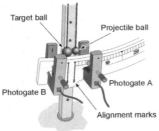

The centers of the balls should be on the same line

Target ball

Projectile ball

Photogate B

Photogate A

Alignment marks

Deriving the mass formula using momentum and energy conservation

In this derivation it is assumed all masses and all velocities are positive when in the direction shown in the diagram. The values will come out negative if the guess is incorrect. It is also possible to solve the problem without making this assumption.

Before collision

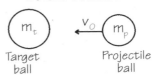

Target ball

Projectile ball

After collision

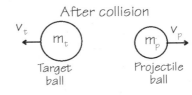

Target ball

Projectile ball

Momentum conservation

$$-m_p v_0 = -m_t v_t + m_p v_p$$

$$m_t v_t = m_p(v_0 + v_p)$$

$$v_t = \frac{m_p}{m_t}(v_0 + v_p)$$

Energy conservation

$$\tfrac{1}{2}m_p v_0^2 = \tfrac{1}{2}m_t v_t^2 + \tfrac{1}{2}m_p v_p^2$$

$$m_p v_0^2 - m_p v_p^2 = m_t\left(\frac{m_p}{m_t}(v_0 + v_p)\right)^2$$

$$m_p(v_0^2 - v_p^2) = \frac{m_p^2}{m_t}(v_0 + v_p)^2$$

$$m_t = \frac{(v_0 + v_p)^2}{(v_0^2 - v_p^2)}m_p$$

Collecting the data

6 The next trick to doing the experiment is to catch both balls after the collision before they pass through the photogates again. This takes coordination. One person from the group should release the projectile ball from the starting block. A second person should stand by to catch the two balls after the collision and after they move outside the photogates. The balls must be prevented from falling back through the photogates.

> Students should practice making the collisions and catching the balls until they can succeed on at least every other trial.

Because this experiment is so tricky to do, not all the data will be worth recording. Only record data for which you are certain you caught the balls in time, and the collision was head-on. If the target ball moves off at an angle, try again. Don't worry if you do ten trials to get one good one. In collision experiments using subatomic particles, physicists often look at thousands or millions of collisions before singling out the few that chanced to collide in just the right way.

> Circulate around the room and help students to conduct the experiment and record the proper data. This is the major portion of the Investigation, and it is a lot of fun as well as challenging. The key to making it fun is not to insist that students get it right every time, but allow them enough time to repeat the experiment until they are satisfied with the results they get.

Table 1 has places to record the time it takes either ball to pass through the photogates. There is also space to calculate and record the speeds before and after the collision. Remember, the speed of the target ball is zero before the collision. Record data for several different speeds of the projectile ball. To change the speed, place the starting block in a different slot along the arc. You may not be able to catch the target ball at very low speeds. Do not use data if you are not sure it is accurate.

Note: Speed of target ball before collision = zero

> Students complete the Investigation by taking data on collisions at different speeds between the small ball and the large ball. If students finish early, they may replace the large ball with a medium-sized ball or try any different combination of balls. The larger of the two balls may also be used as the projectile. In this case, both balls will move forward after the collision.

Analyzing the data

7 Now that you have data, you should be able to determine the mass of the large ball using only the mass of the smaller ball and the initial and final speeds of the smaller ball. To do this you will need to combine the momentum and energy equations to derive a formula of the form $m_t = ???$. The variables on the right side should only include the mass of the projectile ball and its speed before and after the collision. Make sure you properly account for the sign of momentum.

> Circulate and assist students to do the algebra to solve this problem. For students who are not comfortable with squares or solving simultaneous equations, you may wish to do the derivation on the board. The complete solution is given on the previous page.

Use the formula to calculate the mass of the target ball in kilograms. Do the calculation for each data point you were able to collect. Take the average of all your mass calculations as the estimated mass of the target ball. Use a balance to check the actual mass. How good was your prediction?

Momentum is conserved in both elastic and inelastic collisions even when kinetic energy is not conserved.

> Students should find the calculated mass is within about 5 percent of the measured mass.

Can anyone explain why the calculated mass might not exactly match the measured mass?

> The most significant error came from the assumption that the collision is perfectly elastic and kinetic energy is conserved. In fact, between two and five percent of the energy of the collision is dissipated in the collision itself. If you have time and motivated students, you can challenge them to determine the energy efficiency by measuring a collision between two balls of equal mass.

12.1 Momentum

Collecting the data

This is a tricky experiment to do because you must catch the target ball and projectile ball before they swing through the photogates again after the collision. The projectile ball swings in, bounces off, and then goes back through photogate A. You need to catch it before it passes through photogate A for a third time. The target ball moves through photogate B and you need to catch it before it swings back through photogate B again.

The second tricky part is that you need to keep only the data from head-on collisions. Repeat the trial and do not record the data if one or both of the balls move to the side after the collision. Practice causing collisions and catching the balls until you can make a good collision at least every other time.

1. Set the stop at the highest point along the arc. With the target ball at rest, drop the projectile ball and record the time it takes to pass through the light beam coming out of the collision. This is the time that displayed on the Timer with the A light on. Record the time under the column "Projectile after collision (t_p)."

2. Push the memory button and record the time under the heading "Projectile before collision (t_0)."

3. Turn off the A light and turn on the B light. Record the time it took the target ball to pass through photogate B under the column "Target after collision (t_t)."

4. Repeat the experiment for different velocities of the projectile ball. To change the velocity, move the stop to different slots along the arc. You will not be able to catch the large ball at the lowest positions along the arc, so do not use them for this experiment.

Table 1: Time and speed data

Projectile before collision		Projectile after collision		Target after collision	
Time (t_0)	Speed (v_0)	Time (t_p)	Speed (v_p)	Time (t_t)	Speed (v_t)

Analyzing the data

a. Calculate the speeds of the projectile and target balls before and after the collision. Enter the results in Table 1.

b. Write down the law of momentum conservation for the two balls using the variables shown in the diagram at right.

c. Solve the momentum conservation equation for the mass of the target ball. Your answer should be a formula of the form $m_t = ???$ where the right-hand side of the equation includes only the mass of the projectile ball and the speeds before and after the collision.

d. Calculate the mass of the target ball from the formula you derived in Part c. Measure the actual mass of the target ball. How close did your estimate come?

e. Give at least one reason the predicted mass and measured mass may be different and cause the deviation you observed.

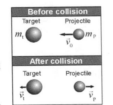

Before collision
Target — Projectile
m_t ⬤   ⬤ m_p
        ← $\vec{v}_0$

After collision
Target — Projectile
⬤   ⬤
$\vec{v}_t$ $\vec{v}_p$ →

Table 1: Time and speed data

Projectile before collision		Projectile after collision		Target after collision	
Time (t_0)	Speed (v_0)	Time (t_p)	Speed (v_p)	Time (t_t)	Speed (v_t)
0.0137	185 cm/sec	0.0464	-54.7 cm/sec	0.0256	124 cm/sec
0.0137	185 cm/sec	0.0448	-56.7 cm/sec	0.0255	124 cm/sec
0.0168	151 cm/sec	0.0574	-44.3 cm/sec	0.0316	101 cm/sec
0.0223	114 cm/sec	0.0797	-31.9 cm/sec	0.0419	75.9 cm/sec

7a. The speed is equal to the diameter of the ball (large = 1.25" = 3.18 cm, medium = 1" = 2.54 cm) divided by the time.

7b. The momentum conservation equation is:

$$m_p v_0 = m_p v_p + m_t v_t$$

Note: if the student has designated all the speeds as positive, they may come up with the following equation:

$$m_p v_0 = m_p v_p - m_t v_t$$

7c. The mass of the target ball is:

$$m_t = m_p (v_0 - v_p) / v_t$$

7d. I calculate the mass of the target ball to be 130.3 g. I measured it to be 131.1 g, 0.8 g off for a difference of less that 1%.

7e. The predicted mass may be different from the measured mass because:
   – the photogates weren't measuring the centers of the balls
   – the centers of the balls weren't at exactly the same height
   – there may have been some front-to-back motion of the balls after the collision that was not measured by the photogates

12.2 Force is the Rate of Change of Momentum

Key Question: How are force and momentum related?

According to Newton's second law, all changes in velocity require force. In some applications, it is useful to interpret the second law in terms of the change in momentum instead of the change in velocity (acceleration). In this interpretation, force is equal to the rate of change in momentum. In the Investigation, students collide rubber and clay balls with a standing block. They show that the force applied to the block depends on whether the collision is elastic or inelastic. The change in momentum is greater for an elastic collision and therefore the force is also greater. The students observe that an elastic collision will topple the block but an inelastic collision will not.

Reading Synopsis

Students read Section 12.2 Force is the Rate of Change of Momentum after the Investigation.

Momentum changes when a net force is applied. The converse is also true. If momentum changes, forces are created. The force is equal to the rate of change of momentum. Airbags and seat belts are two devices that slow down the change of momentum and therefore reduce the force acting on an occupant of a car during a collision.

Newtons second law can be written $\vec{F} = m(\Delta \vec{v}/\Delta t)$, or $\vec{F} = \Delta \vec{p}/\Delta t$. The momentum form is useful when analyzing forces that are exerted over a very short time. The impulse is the product of force and time. Impulse has units of newton-seconds. The total impulse exchanged during a collision is equal to the total change in momentum.

The Investigation

Leading Questions
- What causes momentum to change?
- What is the difference between elastic and inelastic collisions?
- How is momentum related to force?

Learning Goals

By the end of the Investigation, students will be able to:
- Observe elastic and inelastic collisions.
- Deduce the comparative strength of the forces that act during elastic and inelastic collisions.
- Show that the observations are explained if force is the rate of change of momentum.

Key Vocabulary   Newton's second law, momentum, elastic, inelastic, collision

Setup and Materials

Students work in groups of four or five at tables.

Each group should have:

- Physics stand
- A rubber ball about 5 centimeters in diameter
- Soft clay also about 5 centimeters in diameter
- A block of wood $5 \times 10 \times 25$ centimeters
- Paper clips (two)
- String (two meters)
- Meter stick

Details

Time	⏱ One class period
Preparation	✎
Assignments	📖 Section 12.2 Force is the Rate of Change of Momentum in the **Student Edition** after the Investigation.
Skill Sheets	12.2 Rate of Change of Momentum
Equipment Setup	Physics Stand

Teaching the Investigation

1 Introduction

2 Force, momentum, and Newton's second law

3 Calculating force from the change in momentum over time

4 Observing elastic and inelastic collisions

5 Reflecting on what you observed

Introduction

The relationship between force and the change in momentum.

Force, momentum, and Newton's second law

Newton's second law:
F = ma

$a = \Delta\vec{v}/\Delta t$

$m\Delta\vec{v} = \Delta\vec{p}$

If a force is applied to an object, its velocity may change. If the velocity changes, what happens to the momentum?

The momentum also changes. Review the connection between momentum and velocity.
We know that force is related to changes in velocity. Therefore, a relationship must exist between force and momentum also. Today's Investigation will look at the relationship between force and the change in momentum. It will give us a new perspective on Newton's second law.
The relationship between force and motion comes directly from the second law. Who can tell me the second law in a formula? What does acceleration mean in terms of velocity?

Students should respond with *F = ma* **or one of its variants. Acceleration is the change in velocity divided by the change in time, or the rate of change in velocity.**
Acceleration is the change in speed divided by the change in time. Remember, our mathematical shorthand way of writing "the change in." We use the Greek letter delta (Δ) which translates to "the change in." When you see the Δ symbol, replace it in your mind with the phrase "the change in." The acceleration can then be written as $\Delta\vec{v}/\Delta t$, which translates to "the change in speed divided by the change in time." Mass multiplied by the change in velocity ($m\Delta\vec{v}$) is the same as the change in momentum ($\Delta\vec{p}$). We can rewrite the second law in a form that shows force is equal to the rate of change in momentum.

Do the symbolic transformation on the board. Point out that the symbols really represent interpretations as well as values. Write the momentum form of the second law on the board similar to step 1 of the Investigation.
Large forces produce proportionally large and rapid changes in momentum. The reverse is also true. A large change in momentum that occurs rapidly will produce a large force. Consider two balls falling on the floor. One ball is made of rubber and bounces off the floor in an elastic collision. The other ball is made of clay and does not bounce when it hits the floor.

Hold up the rubber and clay ball. Drop each one and allow the students to see the results. You may also hand out rubber and clay balls to the students and have them make their own observations. The clay ball makes a better inelastic collision if you work the clay in your hands until it is relatively soft.
Which collision creates the greater change in momentum? Remember you need to consider the sign of the velocity before and after the collision when you calculate the change in momentum.

The change in momentum is the final momentum minus the initial momentum. The momentum of the rubber ball changes from positive to negative in the bounce. Its change in momentum is approximately twice its initial momentum. The change in momentum for the clay ball is its initial momentum.
The rubber ball has twice the change in momentum because the ball bounces. Its momentum goes from negative to positive. The total change in momentum is roughly twice the initial momentum if the ball bounces off the floor with the same speed it had going down. The clay ball starts with initial momentum and its final momentum is zero. Therefore the change in its momentum is just its initial momentum. Which ball do you think exerts a greater force on the floor?

It is usually necessary to work the change in momentum out on the board with numbers before students understand the concept. If the rubber ball has -2 kg-m/sec going down and +2 kg-m/sec going up after the bounce, its total change in momentum is +4 kg-m/sec (2 - (-2)). The rubber ball had a greater change in momentum and therefore exerts a greater force on the floor.

UNIT 4: Energy and Momentum

12.2   Force is the Rate of Change of Momentum

Question: How are force and momentum related?

In this Investigation, you will:

1. Observe elastic and inelastic collisions.
2. Deduce the comparative strength of the forces that act during elastic and inelastic collisions.
3. Show that the observations are explained if force is the rate of change of momentum.

Momentum changes when a net force is applied. The converse is also true: when momentum changes, forces must be present. If momentum changes quickly, large forces are involved. In fact, Newton's second law can be written in a form that directly relates force to momentum. The larger the change in momentum, the larger the force that is exerted or must be applied. In this Investigation, you will demonstrate how the strength of the force involved in a collision is related to how much the momentum changes.

1   Force, momentum, and the second law

The relationship between force and motion follows directly from the second law. Acceleration is the change in speed divided by the change in time. In this type of logic it is convenient to use the symbol Δ (the Greek letter delta), which translates to "the change in." When you see the Δ symbol, replace it in your mind with the phrase "the change in." Then acceleration can be written as $\Delta \vec{v}/\Delta t$, which translates to "the change in speed divided by the change in time."

Newton's
second law $F = m\dfrac{\Delta v}{\Delta t}$ $\xrightarrow{\text{translation}}$ mass $\times \dfrac{\text{change in velocity}}{\text{change in time}}$

Mass multiplied by the change in velocity ($m\Delta\vec{v}$) is the same as the change in momentum ($\Delta\vec{p}$). We can rewrite the second law in a form that shows force is equal to the rate of change in momentum. Large forces produce a proportionally large change in momentum.

Newton's second law (momentum form)   Force (N) $\vec{F} = \dfrac{\Delta \vec{p}}{\Delta t}$ ← Change in momentum (kg·m/sec)
← Change in time (sec)

Consider two balls falling on the floor. One ball is made of rubber and bounces off the floor in an *elastic* collision. The other ball is made of clay and does not bounce when it hits the floor.

a.   Which collision creates the greater change in momentum? Remember, you need to consider the sign of the velocity before and after the collision when you calculate the change in momentum.

Rubber   Clay

Initial momentum −2 kg·m/sec   Initial momentum −2 kg·m/sec

Final momentum +2 kg·m/sec   Final momentum 0 kg·m/sec

77

Extending the idea

As our understanding of physics has increased, the meaning of many concepts has changed. Momentum is one such concept which originally was defined in terms of mass and velocity. The momentum vector of a moving object is its mass multiplied by its velocity.

On the quantum level however, momentum exists even without mass! A photon of light carries momentum however it has zero mass. Momentum has turned out to be a fundamental property of matter and energy and may not always depend on the presence of mass. Whether an entity has mass or not, it's momentum vector behaves the same way. When a photon of light collides with an electron, the collision obeys the laws of conservation of momentum as if the photon were a particle with momentum, $\vec{p} = h \div \lambda$ where h is Planck's constant and λ is the wavelength of the photon.

In quantum mechanics the kinetic energy is also often defined in terms of mass and momentum rather than mass and velocity. A little algebra shows that the two formulas for kinetic energy given below are identical however one explicitly uses velocity and the other does not. In many ways it is more appropriate to interpret a particle as having a quantity of momentum rather than think of it as having a specific speed.

Mass and velocity $E_k = \dfrac{1}{2}mv^2$

Mass and momentum $E_k = \dfrac{p^2}{2m}$

1 Example answer

1a. The elastic collision (rubber ball) generates the larger change in momentum.

Calculating force from the change in momentum over time

Suppose you have a 0.5-kilogram ball moving at 20 meters per second. How much momentum does this object have? If you catch the ball, what is its final momentum?

> The initial momentum is 10 kg-m/sec and the final momentum is zero.

Now suppose two different people try to catch the ball. One person rigidly holds her arm out so the ball slaps into her hand, stopping quickly. A second person allows his arm to bend back when the ball first impacts. By allowing his hand to move, he spreads the change in momentum over a longer time. Which person feels a greater force from stopping the ball?

> Most students guess that the person that holds their arm out rigidly experiences a greater force although they probably do not know why.

Suppose the first person stops the ball in 0.1 seconds. The second person stops the ball in two seconds. Let's calculate the force. The total change in momentum is 10 kg-m/sec. For the first person, the rate of change in momentum is 10 kg-m/sec divided by 0.1 seconds, resulting in a force of 100 newtons. For the second person, the same calculation gives 10 kg-m/sec divided by two seconds for a force of five newtons. The second person feels only one-twentieth the force because the change in momentum occurs over a longer time.

> Work these calculations out on the board.

Many safety devices are specifically designed to slow down any changes in momentum. Cars are designed to crumple in the front to spread out the time over which the momentum changes. Ropes used by mountain climbers are designed to stretch when absorbing a fall. In both cases that total change in momentum is spread out over a large time interval, reducing the force exerted.

Observing elastic and inelastic collisions

2

Next we are going to demonstrate that force is proportional to the total change in momentum. Set the spindle in the top hole of the stand. Attach the arc of the colliding pendulum so there are 10 holes exposed between the spindle and the arc. Adjust the length of the string so both balls hang at the same height when the string is hung from the spindle. The arc allows you to measure the angle that the ball swings.

> Help students set up their apparatus. The students may make their own string and ball or you can prepare this ahead of time. It is important that the rubber ball and clay ball have the same mass. 2" rubber balls and clay balls about the same size have been used.

If we stand the wooden block on the base of the stand, the swinging ball can knock it over if it is moving fast enough. Both the rubber ball and the clay ball have the same mass. I want you to find an angle at which the rubber ball knocks the block over but the clay ball does not.

> This is about fun part of the Investigation. Students will swing both balls many times as they try to find an angle that satisfies your instructions. Remind them that both balls must swing through the same angle for the test to be fair.

Reflecting on what you observed

3

Who can explain why the rubber ball knocks the block over but the clay ball does not? Are both moving at the same speed?

> Both balls will be moving at the same speed when they hit the block if they are released from the same angle. The rubber ball exerts a greater force because it bounces off the block and its momentum changes twice as much as the momentum of the clay ball. The clay ball may also have a slower collision because the clay deforms as it hits the block.

Actually, what we can definitively say is that the product of force and time is twice as great for the rubber ball as it is for the clay ball. In physics, the product of force and time is called impulse.

12.2 Force is the Rate of Change of Momentum

2 Observing elastic and inelastic collisions

For this experiment, you need a rubber ball about 5 centimeters (2 inches) in diameter and an equal amount of soft clay. You also need a block of wood 5 × 10 × 25 centimeters (2 × 4 × 10 inches). The block does not need to be exactly that specified size but it should be within a few centimeters in any dimension.

1. Measure the mass of the rubber ball.
2. Make a clay ball that has the same mass as the rubber ball.
3. Attach 1 meter of string to each ball. Attach the string to the rubber ball by poking half a paperclip into the rubber to make a loop. Attach the string to the clay ball by burying it in the clay so that it passes through the center.
4. Tie a small loop in the free end of both strings. Make the distance from the loop to the ball about 70 centimeters. Use the same distance for both rubber and clay balls.
5. Attach the spindle to the top hole in the stand using a threaded knob. Either ball may now be swung from the spindle by looping the string over the steel shaft.
6. Set the block on the base of the stand directly in front of the pole. Hang the rubber ball from the spindle and swing it so that it collides with the block when you release it. Find the lowest height from which you can release the rubber ball and have it still knock over the wood block every time. Use a meter stick to record and measure the height. It will take many trials to locate the minimum height at which the block is always knocked over.
7. Replace the rubber ball with the clay ball. Release the clay ball from the same height you determined in step 6. The height must be sufficient enough to knock the block over every time. Observe what happens when the clay ball hits the block.

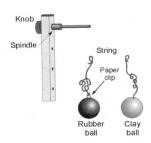

Knob

Spindle

String

Paper clip

Rubber ball   Clay ball

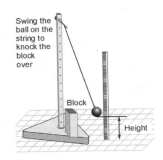

Swing the ball on the string to knock the block over

Block

Height

3 Reflecting on what you observed

a. Compare the velocities of the rubber ball and the clay ball just before they collided with the wood block. Are the velocities different or are they the same?

b. Compare the momentum of the rubber ball and the clay ball just before they collided with the block. Does the rubber ball have more, less, or about the same momentum as the clay ball?

c. Did the clay ball knock over the block? Explain the observations using the fact that force is equal to rate of change of momentum. Which ball experienced a greater change in momentum during the collision with the wood block?

3 Example answers

3a. The velocities of the two balls were approximately the same before they collided with the wooden block.

3b. The momentum of the rubber ball before the collision was about the same as the momentum of the clay ball (the two have approximately the same velocity and approximately the same mass, so the momenta must be about equal).

3c. The clay ball did not knock over the block. The force applied to the block is equal to the change in momentum of the clay ball. Because the ball stopped after the collision (unlike the rubber ball, which bounced back), the change in momentum did not result in a force great enough to knock over the wooden block.

12.3 Angular Momentum

Key Question: How does the first law apply to rotational motion?

Objects that are rotating tend to continue rotating at the same angular speed and with the same axis of rotation. The angular momentum of a rotating object plays a similar role in maintaining rotational motion as did linear momentum for linear motion. In this short Investigation, students use a rotating mass on a string to qualitatively experience the conservation of angular momentum. By pulling the string in through a straw and reducing the radius of the motion, students observe that the angular speed increases. The angular speed increases because the system tries to keep constant angular momentum.

Conservation of angular momentum

$\uparrow I \omega \downarrow \qquad \downarrow I \omega \uparrow$

Reading Synopsis

Students read Section 12.3 Angular Momentum after the Investigation.

Angular momentum is the rotational equivalent of linear momentum. The angular momentum of an object comes from the organized motion of each particle of mass around the center of rotation. Angular momentum obeys a conservation law similar to linear momentum. The angular momentum of an object can be changed by torques applied to the object.

The angular momentum of an object is its moment of inertia multiplied by its angular velocity. The units of angular momentum are kg-m²/sec. Angular momentum is a vector; however, the vector points along the axis of rotation and not in the direction of motion. If the angular momentum of a system is changed, the system exerts reaction torques acting in a direction to resist the change. A gyroscope is a device that uses angular momentum to maintain its orientation.

The Investigation

Leading Questions
- What is angular momentum?
- How is angular momentum related to moment of inertia?
- How do you calculate angular momentum?
- Is angular momentum a vector like linear momentum?
- How can the law of conservation of angular momentum be used to explain the motion of rotating objects?

Learning Goals

By the end of the Investigation, students will be able to:
- Observe how angular momentum tends to keep an object rotating at a constant angular speed.
- Show that angular momentum depends on both the angular speed and the moment of inertia.

Key Vocabulary

linear momentum, angular momentum

Setup and Materials

Students work in groups of four or five at tables.

Each group should have:

- One flexible straw
- String (about one meter long)
- Two washers

Details

Time One class period

Preparation

Assignments Section 12.3 Angular Momentum in the **Student Edition** after the Investigation.

Teaching the Investigation

1   Introduction
2   Thinking about angular momentum
3   A demonstration of angular momentum
4   The conservation of angular momentum
5   Observing the conservation of angular momentum

Introduction

What is angular momentum?

Thinking about angular momentum

Angular momentum results from the rotation (or spin) of an object.

$$\vec{L} = I\omega$$

L = angular momentum (kg-m²/sec)
I = moment of inertia (kg-m²)
ω = angular velocity (rad/sec)

A demonstration of angular momentum

Angular momentum has direction and behaves almost like any other vector.

Counterclockwise rotation has positive angular momentum.

Clockwise rotation has negative angular momentum.

1

Newton's first law also applies to rotating objects. An object that is rotating around a particular axis at a certain angular speed will tend to keep rotating at the same speed about the same axis unless torque is applied. Today's Investigation will be a very short introduction to angular momentum and the law of the conservation of angular momentum.
Consider a small mass rotating around at the end of a string.

Demonstrate whirling a small mass such as a washer around your head on a string with a radius of approximately one-half meter or so.

The mass rotating around this string is moving and therefore has linear momentum. However, the direction is constantly changing as the string moves around the circle. Because the motion is rotation, the mass has another kind of momentum called angular momentum. Angular momentum is a property of rotating objects with mass spread out over some volume. The angular momentum of this spinning washer is equal to its linear momentum multiplied by the radius of the motion. If the washer had a mass of one kilogram and was moving at one radian per second in a radius of one meter, its angular momentum would be one kg-m²/sec.

Draw this schematically on the board along with the units.

Now suppose we consider a solid disk that is rotating. The linear momentum of this object is difficult to define. Each particle of mass is moving with a different velocity. Particles far from the center are moving fastest. Particles close to the center are moving slower. The direction of all particles is constantly changing. This object does not have a well-defined linear momentum, but it does have a definite angular momentum. The angular momentum is the moment of inertia multiplied by the angular velocity.

At this point in the lesson you may wish to hold up a bicycle wheel. A heavy mountain bike wheel works very well. I spin the wheel and students observe that the wheel keeps spinning after I have stopped applying any force to it.

Why is angular momentum important? Because it obeys conservation laws like linear momentum. What happens if you suddenly change the direction of an object's linear momentum?

A force is produced with a strength proportional to the rate of change of momentum and in a direction that opposes the change in momentum. This point may take some discussion to reach and relies on concepts from Investigation 12.2.

Like linear momentum, angular momentum is also a vector. Also like linear momentum, any attempt to change the direction of the angular momentum vector results in a torque that opposes the change. The angular momentum vector points along the axis of rotation and obeys a right hand rule. If the fingers of your right hand curl in the direction of rotation, your thumb points in the direction of the angular momentum vector. I would like a volunteer to come up here and sit on this stool that can rotate. Hold the bicycle wheel vertically in your outstretched arms and then rotate it so it is horizontal. Is this difficult?

To do this demonstration, you will need a stool with a good bearing so the seat rotates and a bicycle wheel. The student should notice that it is easy to flip the bicycle wheel from vertical to horizontal as long as the bicycle wheel is not rotating.

The bicycle wheel has zero angular momentum if it is not spinning. Now I am going to spin the bicycle wheel. Hold it steady while I spin it. Now try to rotate the bicycle wheel from a vertical to horizontal. What do you feel now? Do you feel resistance?

Students will feel a reaction torque that opposes the change they are trying to make in the axis of rotation. The faster the bicycle wheel is rotating, the stronger the tendency to resist the current.

12.3   Angular Momentum

Question: How does the first law apply to rotational motion?

In this Investigation, you will:

1. Observe how angular momentum tends to keep an object rotating at a constant angular speed.
2. Show that angular momentum depends on both the angular speed and the moment of inertia.

Newton's first law states that an object tends to continue its state of motion unless acted upon by an unbalanced force. You can think of the first law in terms of momentum. The momentum of an object does not change unless force is applied. A similar situation applies to rotating motion except the quantity that tends to stay the same is the *angular momentum*. In this Investigation, you will observe some consequences of the law of conservation of angular momentum.

1   Thinking about angular momentum

Consider a small mass rotating at the end of a string. The mass follows a circle as it moves. Since the system of the mass and string is rotating, it has angular momentum. Like linear momentum, angular momentum obeys a conservation law. If a change is made to the system without producing any torque, the system reacts in such a way as to keep the total angular momentum constant.

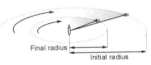

Final radius

Initial radius

a. List three variables that determine the angular momentum of the rotating mass on a string.

b. Discuss with your group what would happen if the radius of the circle were suddenly made smaller. Assume that the mass stays constant. How can the angular momentum stay the same when the radius decreases? Write a hypothesis describing what you believe will happen in an experiment where you are observing a mass revolving at the end of a string and the string is shortened during the motion.

2   Setting up the experiment

1. One person in each group should take the flexible straw and thread a string through the straw. Take one washer and put the straw and string through its center. The string should be about 1 meter long.
2. Securely tie a washer on either end of the string so the distance between washers is about 0.8 meter. The setup should look like the diagram at right.
3. Bend the straw so it makes it a 90-degree angle as shown in the diagram.
4. Hold one washer in one hand and use your other hand to hold the longer straight section of the straw. Arrange your hands so the bend in the straw is about the halfway point on the string and supported by the middle washer. Using a gentle movement of the hand holding the straw, you can whirl the washer around your head in a slow circular motion. The experiment requires slow, steady circular motion.

1/2 meter

washers

⚠ **Safety Notes: Do not whirl the washer fast! Spinning the washer around fast can be dangerous. Also, make sure no one is too near you when you are starting or spinning your washer**

When angular momentum changes

With linear momentum, we saw that the application of a force could cause of the momentum of an object to change. With angular momentum, the application of a torque can cause of the angular momentum of an object to change.

When you consider the entire system, momentum is absolutely conserved, separately for linear and angular forms. According to Newton's third law, every force generates an equal and opposite reaction force. Since the action and the reaction act on different objects, won the gains momentum in one loses momentum, on the whole, the total amount of momentum does not change. When you push off the ground with your foot to start your skateboard, you gained momentum. The Earth loses momentum exactly equal to the momentum you gain. The mass of the Earth is much larger than your mass, so the change in its velocity is completely negligible.

In a similar way, every torque generates an equal and opposite reaction torque. When you start the washer spinning you are changing its angular momentum. The washer exerts a reaction torque against your arm which changes the angular momentum of you and the Earth by an equal and opposite amount. The total angular momentum stays constant. Again, the Earth has such a large mass that the change in its angular momentum produces no noticeable change in its angular speed.

1   Example answers

1a. Answers are:

The mass of the object

The length of the string

The angular velocity of the object

The moment of inertia of the string and object system

1b. If the string is shortened, the angular velocity would increase.

The conservation of angular momentum

Law of conservation of angular momentum: A rotating body that has mass will tend to stay rotating at the same angular velocity and with the same axis of rotation.

Like linear momentum, angular momentum obeys a conservation law. If a change is made to a rotating system, the system will react in such a way as to keep the total angular momentum constant. That is why it is difficult to flip the bicycle wheel when it is spinning. To flip the bicycle wheel, you must change the direction of the angular momentum vector. You must supply a torque to do this and overcome the bicycle wheel's natural tendency to keep its axis of rotation pointing in the same direction. What else did you notice happened when you flipped the bicycle wheel over?

Students should notice that their whole body begins to rotate if the bicycle wheel is flipped from vertical to horizontal. The direction of rotation is opposite the direction of the bicycle wheel's rotation. You start spinning in a direction opposite to the rotation of the bicycle wheel. Can anyone offer a guess as to why this is true?

The system of student and bicycle wheel tries to maintain constant angular momentum. If the bicycle wheel is flipped on its side, the entire system compensates by rotating in the opposite direction.

This is a direct consequence of the law of conservation of angular momentum. A rotating body that has mass will tend to stay rotating at the same angular velocity and with the same axis of rotation. The tendency of an object to maintain speed and orientation is described by its angular momentum. The greater the angular momentum, the more torque must be exerted to change either the speed or the direction of the angular momentum vector.

Observing the conservation of angular momentum

2

3

For the last part of the Investigation we are going to make a rotating system and try to change its radius of motion. Follow step 2 of the Investigation and make your rotating mass with 8 m of string. A washer and a flexible straw as shown in the diagrams.

Students put their apparatus together. It is a wise idea to circulate around the room and checked people's knots to make sure the washers are firmly attached to the string.

What I want you to do is whirl the washer around your head with a radius of one-half meter. To set the radius, one person should use a meter stick while you make a mental note of the position of the lower washer relative to your body. The one-half meter distance does not have to be exact. Be very careful when you are whirling the washer above your head. Do not go fast, and make sure no one is in the way.

Demonstrate the technique to the students, similar to the diagram in step 3 of the Investigation. You want a steady swirling motion where the washer completes each circle in two or three seconds.

What would happen to the motion if the radius of the circle were suddenly made smaller? Assume that the mass stays constant. How can the angular momentum stay the same when the radius of the motion decreases?

Have the students discuss or write down a hypothesis describing what they believe will happen. Don't give the answer away by demonstrating just yet.

Now let's test what we think. Twirl the washer evenly above your head, and smoothly pull down on the string, drawing the washer in tighter as the string slides through the straw. You will have to do this several times because the effect happens quite quickly. Everyone in the group should try it. Pay attention to how fast the washer is rotating. Try to keep a steady twirling motion even as you are drawing the string in.

As the radius decreases, speed increases in order to maintain angular momentum.

Students should observe that the location, the washer speeds up considerably as it is drawn into the circle. This is a direct consequence of the law of conservation of angular momentum. If the radius is reduced, the speed must increase to keep the angular momentum constant. This is the same technique used by divers and figure skaters to change their speed of rotation.

12.3 Angular Momentum

3   Observing the conservation of angular momentum

By pulling the string through the straw, it is possible to change the radius of the motion while the mass is still moving. If the string is pulled carefully downward, the force applied is along a radius and therefore does not exert a torque about the center of rotation. If the torque is zero, angular momentum should be conserved. However, pulling the string down evenly while maintaining steady circular motion is tricky and requires practice.

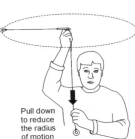

1. Once you have established a steady rhythm, others in the group should measure how long it takes to complete 10 full circles. The Timer in stopwatch mode may be used for this purpose. The data allows you to repeat the experiment under the same conditions if necessary.
2. With your lower hand, slowly pull down on the hanging string. This will pull in the rotating washer, thus decreasing its radius of motion. Try to keep the swirling motion of your upper hand steady while you pull the string.
3. Observe what happens to the motion of the rotating washer as the radius is decreased. You may wish to try the experiment several times to perfect your technique.

Pull down to reduce the radius of motion

4   Reflecting on what you observed

a. Explain how the conservation of angular momentum and the concept of moment of inertia apply to explain your observations from Part 3.

b. In many diving competitions, the diver jumps from the board or platform, turns one or two complete somersaults, and straightens out to land in the water with arms and head straight down and feet straight up in the air. While completing the somersault, the diver's body is tucked in tightly. Before entering the water, the diver's body extends to straighten out. Use the conservation of angular momentum to explain how a diver can spin rapidly in a somersault and then reduce rotational speed to enter the water vertically.

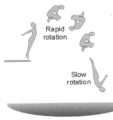

Rapid rotation

Slow rotation

c. Angular momentum behaves like a vector. Unlike the linear momentum vector however, the angular momentum vector does *not* point in the direction of an object's velocity. Instead, the angular momentum vector points along the axis of rotation. You can use your right hand to determine its direction. When the fingers of your right hand curl in the direction of rotation, your thumb points in the direction of the angular momentum vector. The law of conservation of angular momentum applies to the *direction* of the angular momentum vector as well as its magnitude.

It takes torque to change the direction of the angular momentum vector. The inverse is also true. If the direction of the angular momentum vector changes, reaction torques act back on the rotating object to resist the change. For example, it is harder to balance a bicycle that is standing still than a bicycle that is rolling. Use the conservation of angular momentum to explain why this is true.

3 4   Example answers

3.3 As the rotating string is shortened, the angular velocity of the object increases.

4a. If the radius were suddenly made smaller by shortening the string, the moment of inertia of the rotating object would be reduced. As a result, the angular velocity of the object would increase to compensate for a reduced moment of inertia to conserve angular momentum.

4b. As the diver contracts his body, the moment of inertia reduces. To conserve angular momentum, the diver's angular velocity increases. When the diver extends his body, the opposite happens and the angular velocity reduces, making it easier to control the spin and enter the water vertically.

4c. As the bicycle's tires spin, an angular momentum vector is created that points in the direction of the axis of rotation. Since it takes torque to change the direction of the vector, the faster the bicycle wheel spins, angular velocity increases, resulting in greater angular momentum and a greater amount of torque to change the direction of the vector. As a bicycle wheel spins, it will resist being moved from the direction in which it spins. If the bicycle wheel is not spinning, it will not have this resistance to changing its direction. This is why it is harder to tip a bike over with spinning bicycle wheels. The bicycle wheels themselves resist tipping over, thus making it easier to balance and stay upright.

13.1 Harmonic Motion

Key Question: How do we describe the back and forth motion of a pendulum?

Objects generally have two kinds of motion. Motion that goes from one place to another is called linear motion. We use words such as distance, time, speed, and acceleration to describe linear motion. The second kind of motion repeats itself over and over and is called harmonic motion. This Investigation introduces students to harmonic motion using a simple pendulum. The students determine which of three variables (length, mass, amplitude) have the greatest effect on the period of an oscillating pendulum. They apply their analysis to design a pendulum clock that measures 30 seconds. A double pendulum is then used to illustrate the concept of phase.

Pendulum

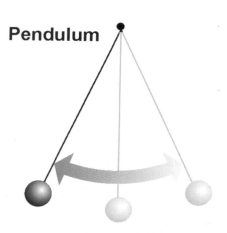

Reading Synopsis

Students read Section 13.1 Harmonic Motion after the Investigation.

There are two types of motion: linear and harmonic. Harmonic motion repeats itself over and over. A pendulum swinging back and forth is an example of harmonic motion. A cycle is a pattern of motion that repeats over and over. Harmonic motion is a sequence of repeating cycles.

A system that exhibits harmonic motion is called an oscillator. A pendulum moving back and forth and a spring bouncing up and down are examples of oscillators. The period of an oscillator is the time it takes to complete one cycle. The frequency of an oscillator is the number of cycles it makes per second. The amplitude of a cycle is the maximum amount the system moves away from equilibrium. Damping is the reduction of amplitude over time due to friction.

Harmonic motion graphs show cycles are usually drawn with time on the horizontal axis. Amplitude, period, and frequency can be determined easily from a graph of position versus time. The phase of an oscillator describes where the oscillator is in its cycle.

The Investigation

Leading Questions
- How do we describe repetitive motion in physics?
- What are some examples of harmonic motion and oscillators?
- Why does a pendulum clock need to be wound?

Learning Goals

By the end of the Investigation, students will be able to:
- Measure the amplitude and period of a pendulum.
- Describe any oscillator in terms of frequency, period, amplitude, and phase.
- Learn to read and represent frequency, period, amplitude, and phase on a graph.

Key Vocabulary

harmonic motion, oscillator, oscillation, period, frequency, hertz, amplitude, damping, periodic motion, hertz, phase, phase difference

Setup and Materials

Students work in groups of four or five at tables.

Each group should have:

- Pendulum (use at least 3 steel balls with string attached, two of which should be the same size)
- Physics stand
- Timer and one photogate, AC adapter (or 9-volt battery), and a cord to connect the photogate to the timer
- Calculator
- Graph paper

Details

Time One class period

Preparation Try out the experiment prior to the class to anticipate student problems and questions.

Assignments Section 13.1 Harmonic Motion in the **Student Edition** after the Investigation.

Skill Sheets 13.1 Harmonic Motion

Equipment Setup Pendulum

Teaching the Investigation

1 Introduction
2 The pendulum
3 Setting up the pendulum
4 Measuring the period
5 Variables that affect the period of a pendulum
6 Analyzing the data
7 Applying what you know
8 Phase

Introduction

Linear - one place to another, no repeats

Harmonic - back and forth, repeating

The pendulum

A pendulum is a good example of harmonic motion.

Setting up the pendulum

Cycle - The cycle is the repeating unit of motion.

Measuring the period

Period - The period is the time it takes to make one complete cycle.

Objects generally have two kinds of motion. One kind of motion goes from one place to another and is called linear motion. Give me some examples of linear motion from the Investigations we have done so far.

> A ball on a ramp (the translational aspect of the motion, that is), pulling down on a pulley string to raise a weight, and a projectile are some examples of motion that involves a movement from one place to another.

What characteristics of linear motion have we measured in our Investigations?

> Distance, time, speed, and acceleration.

The second type of motion repeats itself over and over like a child moving back and forth on a swing. This type of motion is called harmonic motion. Give some examples of harmonic motion that you encounter on a daily basis.

> The Earth's rotation, a pendulum, a swing, a heart beating, a clock ticking, a wheel spinning, and a ball rolling around and around as it moves down a ramp (the rotational aspect of the motion).

1 A pendulum is a good example of harmonic motion. Watch it move. How would you describe the motion? Imagine you are talking to someone on a cell phone a thousand miles away. You want to tell them exactly what the motion is doing. What do you say?

> Prompt the class for descriptive words. "Back and forth," "repeating," "cycles," and "swinging" are common responses. Lead them to be very specific, such as how long or how wide the swing is. Introduce the terms cycle, period, and amplitude.

2 Now you should work in your group to set up your pendulum. Attach the pendulum hanger to the top hole of the physics stand. Use the medium-sized ball on the string as your pendulum. Loosen the post and slip the string through the hole in the center of the post.

> As groups set up their pendulums, remind the students that the post does not unscrew all the way off. They should loosen the post just enough to expose the hole for the string to go through. The post should then be gently tightened enough to hold the string. Over-tightening the post will damage the string.

Because harmonic motion is so important, we have words to describe it so everyone can be clear about exactly what is happening. These words are different from the words we use to describe linear motion (distance, speed, acceleration). The **cycle** is one complete part of the motion. The whole motion is one cycle after another. That means the cycle has to include all of the motion. For the pendulum, if we start counting the cycle here, the cycle ends here, when the pendulum has come all the way back again. You can count cycles, one, two, three, etc.

> Use your finger to point to the start of a cycle as the pendulum swings all the way to one side. The cycle ends when the pendulum has returned to the same place again. Have the students swing their pendulums and practice counting cycles, just so they get used to the definition of a cycle.

The **period** of a pendulum is the time it takes to make one complete cycle. Faster pendulums have short periods. Slow pendulums have long periods. You can define a period for all harmonic motion. Can anyone tell me the period Earth's rotation? How about the period of a heartbeat?

> Prompt a discussion of period and cycles. The period of the rotation of Earth is one day and a heartbeat is about one second.

To measure the period, we can use the photogates. Use one of the threaded knobs to attach a photogate to the stand so that the pendulum ball breaks the light beam as it swings through.

13.1 Harmonic Motion

Question: How do we describe the back-and-forth motion of a pendulum?

In this Investigation, you will:

1. Measure the amplitude and period of a pendulum.
2. Determine how to change the properties of a pendulum.
3. Learn to read and represent frequency, period, amplitude, and phase on a graph.

Objects generally have two kinds of motion. One kind of motion goes from one place to another like a person walking from home to school. This is *linear motion*. We use words such as distance, time, speed, and acceleration to describe linear motion. The second kind of motion repeats itself over and over like a child going back and forth on a swing. This kind of motion is called *harmonic motion*. The word *harmonic* comes from the word *harmony* meaning "multiples of." Any system that exhibits harmonic motion is called an *oscillator*.

1 The pendulum

A pendulum is an oscillator made from a mass on a string. The mass is free to swing back and forth.

- A *cycle* is one complete back-and-forth motion.
- The *period* is the time it takes to complete one full cycle. The period of a pendulum is the time it takes for the pendulum to swing from left to right and back again.
- The *amplitude* describes the size of the cycle. The amplitude of a pendulum is the amount the pendulum swings away from equilibrium.

Period
The *period* is the time to complete one cycle.

Amplitude
Equilibrium (center)
The *amplitude* is the maximum amount the system moves away from equilibrium

2 Setting up the pendulum

1. Attach the pendulum hanger to the top hole in the physics stand.
2. You will use the medium-sized ball on the string as your pendulum. Loosen the post and slip the string through the hole in the center of the post. Note: The post does NOT unscrew all the way off. Loosen it just enough to expose the hole for the string to go through. Gently tighten the post to hold the string. DO NOT tighten the post too tight or you will damage the string. It takes very little pressure to hold it.
3. Use one of the threaded knobs to attach a photogate to the stand so that the pendulum ball breaks the light beam as it swings through. You may need to adjust the leveling feet on the stand to make the ball swing through the center of the photogate. It does not matter if the pole is not exactly vertical.

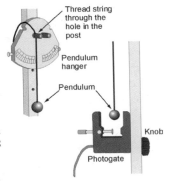

Thread string through the hole in the post

Pendulum hanger

Pendulum

Knob

Photogate

81

4 Graphs from question 4b:

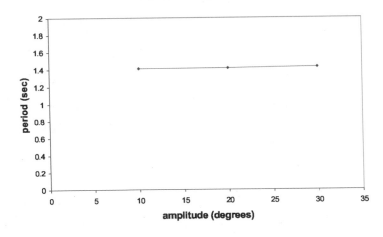

Period vs. Amplitude

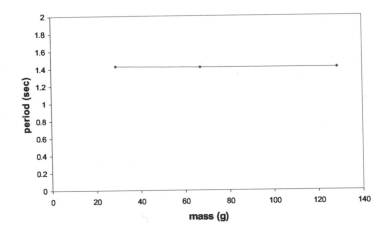

Period vs. Mass

Variables that affect the period of a pendulum

Set the timer on "period."

The pendulum breaks the light beam on the photogate twice in each cycle.

In period mode, the time measures the time interval between one break of light and the next.

Analyzing the data

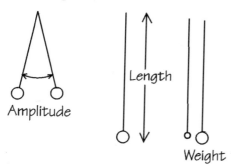

Amplitude

Length

Weight

String length is the most important variable.

A larger amplitude raises the pendulum higher above the lowest point so there is more potential energy at the start so the speed is higher.

Weight had little affect because more force is compensated by additional inertia due to greater mass.

3 It is somewhat tricky to get the pendulum to swing through the photogate without hitting it. You have to release the ball with no twisting. The best way to release the ball is to stand to one side and carefully release it with two fingers.

> Demonstrate how to get the pendulum swinging without hitting the photogate. Circulate to each group and help them develop a good technique.

Set the timer on "period." When the pendulum swings through the light beam, the timer measures the period. It takes a few swings to make the measurement. If you hit the reset button once, it freezes the display so you can write down the number. If you hit reset a second time, the timer starts back at zero.

> Circulate around the class and help students use the timer to measure the period.

Watch the pendulum. How many times does it pass the light beam in one cycle?

> Prompt the class to observe and notice that the pendulum breaks the beam twice in each cycle, once moving to the left and once moving to the right.

The timer measures the period of whatever is breaking the light beam. It does not know that you have a pendulum. How do we get the true period of the pendulum from the measurement on the timer?

Help the students see that the period of the pendulum is twice the time indicated on the timer. The timer in period mode measures the time interval between one break of the light beam and the next. This time interval is only half the period of a pendulum because a pendulum swings through the photogate twice on each cycle

4 What did you discover about the three variables? Which one had the greatest effect?

> Discuss results with the class. Everyone should have discovered that the string length was the most important variable. Mass and amplitude made some difference but not much compared with changing the length of the string.

Why do you think the mass of the ball did not have much of an effect?

> Students should recall that under the acceleration of gravity, the effect of more weight (force) is compensated by the additional inertia due to the increase in mass. The pendulum is another example of heavier and lighter objects accelerating at the same rate under the influence of gravity.

Why do you think making the amplitude larger did not make more of a difference? You increased the distance the pendulum had to swing by three times, or 300 percent! Usually traveling a longer distance takes more time, so the period should have gotten much longer. Think about energy and the roller coaster.

> A larger amplitude raises the pendulum higher above the lowest point. That means there is more potential energy at the start. This gets converted to more kinetic energy, giving a higher speed. The higher speed almost exactly compensates for the larger distance, leaving the period almost unchanged.

> There is a slight change of period with amplitude, however, and it is not an experimental error.

Take your data and make a graph for each of the three variables. You want to show the effect on the period. How should you set up the graphs? The scale of your graph is important. You can be fooled by graphs that seem to show big changes because the scales are different. For example, suppose the period changed from 1 second to 1.05 seconds as I decreased the mass from 129 g washers to 28 g. When the vertical scale goes from 1.0 to 1.1 the change it looks like a lot. If the scale goes from zero to 1.5, the change looks very small. When comparing graphs, they all should have the same scale.

> Have students make their graphs. If time allows, have them share their graphs with the class.

13.1 Harmonic Motion

3 The three pendulum variables

In this experiment, the period of the pendulum is the dependent variable. There are three independent variables: the mass, the amplitude of the swing, and the length of the string.

1. Put the Timer in period mode and attach the photogate to input A. When the A light is on, the display shows the period defined by successive breaks in the light beam as the pendulum swings through. The red (O) button resets the Timer to zero. It takes a few swings for the Timer to make the measurement.

2. The Timer in period mode measures the time interval between one break of the light beam and the next. This time interval is only half the period of a pendulum because a pendulum swings through the photogate *twice* on each cycle. To determine the period of the pendulum, multiply the Timer reading by two. Record your information in Table 1.

3. The length of the string can be changed by sliding it through the hole in the post. Measure the length from the underside of the post to the center of the steel ball. Put your data in column 3.

4. Change the mass by using one of the other sizes of steel balls.

5. The amplitude can be changed by varying the angle that the pendulum swings.

Design an experiment to determine which of the three variables has the greatest effect on the period of the pendulum. Your experiment should provide enough data to show that one of the three variables has much greater an effect than the other two. Be sure to use a technique that gives you consistent results.

Table 1: Period, amplitude, mass, and length data

Mass (g)	Amplitude (degrees)	String length (cm)	Time from Timer (seconds)	Period of pendulum (seconds)

4 Analyzing the data

a. Of the three things you can change (length, mass, and angle), which one has the biggest effect on the pendulum, and why? In your answer, you should consider how gravity accelerates objects of different mass.

b. Split up your data so that you can look at the effect of each variable by making a separate graph showing how each one affects the period. To make comparison easier, make sure all the graphs have the same scale on the *y*-axis (period). The graphs should be labeled as shown in the example below:

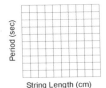

3 4 Example answers

Table 1: Period, amplitude, mass, and length data

Mass (g)	Amplitude (degrees)	String length (cm)	Time from timer (seconds)	Period of pendulum (seconds)
29.0	10	50	0.7144	1.428
67.2	10	50	0.7085	1.417
128.8	10	50	0.7067	1.413
29.0	20	50	0.7079	1.415
29.0	30	50	0.7142	1.428
29.0	10	20	0.4420	.8840
29.0	10	40	0.6295	1.259
29.0	10	60	0.7734	1.547

4a. insert answer

4b. Additional graph:

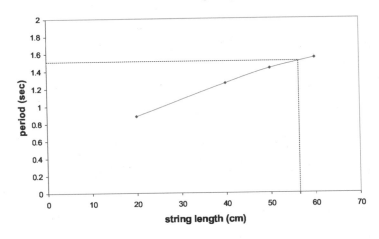

Investigation 13.1 Harmonic Motion **233**

Applying what you know

Design problem: create a clock that measures a time interval of 30 seconds.

5 I have a design problem for you. You are to create a clock and your clock must measure a time interval of 30 seconds. That means you need to say "start" and then "stop" as close as possible to 30 seconds later. Your clock needs to work by counting cycles of a pendulum. This is how grandfather clocks work. The minute and hour hands are really just counters for the pendulum.

To start, figure a basic design. How many cycles do you want to be equal to 30 seconds? Will your pendulum swing that long? Is there a way to make it swing longer without slowing down as much?

> Circulate and help the students pick designs. More mass means more energy storage for a given amplitude, so the pendulum swings longer. A longer period helps too since you don't have to count as many cycles. A successful design might be 20 cycles of a pendulum with a 1.5 second period, or 30 cycles of a pendulum with a 1 second period. When each group is ready, visit their table and use the timer as a stopwatch to test their clock. They have to tell you "1, 2, 3, start" and then "stop" when they have counted the requisite number of periods. Most groups will get between 29 and 31 seconds, and it is not uncommon to have times between 29.7 and 30.3 seconds, which is less than 1 percent error! You may choose to grade the experiment on the percent error.

Phase

Set up a dual pendulum.

See if you can make the dual pendulums swing in phase, the out of phase by 180 degrees.

6 Phase is another important concept to understand when comparing one oscillator to another. Set up a dual pendulum as shown in the diagram in Part 6 of the Investigation. The strings wrap over and around the side pegs. The two pendulums will swing alongside the pole as shown.

> Demonstrate how to set up a dual pendulum.

Start with equal string lengths. See if you can make the dual pendulums swing in phase, and then out of phase by 180 degrees (one-half cycle). Next, set the pendulum strings to different lengths. Start them in phase and see what happens to the phase as they keep swinging. See if you can construct a pair of pendulums where one has twice the period of the other.

> This is a great opportunity for students to explore examples of in-phase and out-of-phase oscillators. This will support students' understanding of sound and light wave constructive and destructive interference in future Investigations.

5 Applying what you know

Pendulum clocks were once among the most common ways to keep time. You can still buy beautifully made contemporary pendulum clocks. To make a pendulum clock accurate, the period must be set so that a certain number of periods equals a convenient measure of time. For example, you could design a clock with a pendulum that has a period of 1 second. The gears in the clock mechanism would then have to turn the second hand 1/60th of a turn per swing of the pendulum.

a. Using your data, design and construct a pendulum that you can use to accurately measure a time interval of 30 seconds. Test your pendulum clock against the Timer set to stopwatch mode.

b. Mark on your graph the period you chose for your pendulum.

c. How many cycles did your pendulum complete in 30 seconds?

d. If mass does not affect the period, why is it important that the pendulum in a clock be heavy?

e. Calculate the percent error in your prediction of time from your pendulum clock.

6 Phase

The concept of *phase* is important when comparing one oscillator with another. Suppose you observe two identical pendulums, with exactly the same period. If you start them together, their graphs would look like the picture on the left (below). You would describe the two pendulums as being *in phase* because their cycles are aligned and each one is always at the same place at the same time. If one pendulum is started later than the other, their cycles would be *out of phase*. The graphs on the right (below) show two pendulums that are out of phase by 1/4 of a cycle.

Two oscillators **in-phase**

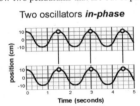

Two oscillators **out-of-phase** by 90 degrees (1/4 cycle)

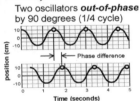

1. Set up a dual pendulum as shown in the diagram. The strings wrap over and around the pegs on either side of the pendulum hanger. The two pendulums swing alongside the pole as shown.

2. Make the string lengths equal for both pendulums. See if you can make them swing in phase, and then out of phase by one-half cycle (180 degrees).

3. Set the pendulums to different lengths. Start them in phase and see what happens to the phase as they keep swinging.

4. Can you construct a pair of pendulums where one has twice the period of the other? Try it.

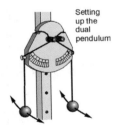

Setting up the dual pendulum

a. What is the relationship between the lengths of the strings if one pendulum has twice the period of the other?

b. Describe how the phase of the pendulums in step 3 changes over time.

5 6 Example answers

5a. No student response required.

5b. We chose a period of 1.5 seconds.

5c. Our pendulum completed 20 cycles in 30 seconds.

5d. A heavy pendulum in a clock helps make the pendulum swing more steadily and longer.

5e. Our measured time was 29.7 seconds. The difference between the measured and predicted time is 0.3 seconds. 0.3/30 = 0.01 = 1% error.

6a. The pendulum with twice the period has half the string length.

6b. The pendulums begin swinging in phase, then they go out of phase by 90 degrees, then 180 degrees, then they go back to being in phase, and then the pattern begins again.

13.2 Why Things Oscillate

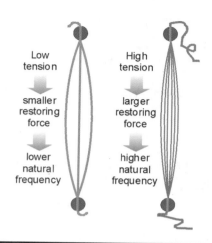

Low tension → smaller restoring force → lower natural frequency

High tension → larger restoring force → higher natural frequency

Key Question: What kinds of systems oscillate?

Motion occurs when we disturb a system in equilibrium. Sometimes the motion is harmonic motion, and sometimes it is not. In this Investigation students explore the conditions which create harmonic motion, including stability (or instability) and the presence of restoring forces. The role of inertia in harmonic motion is demonstrated. With a mechanical system like a pendulum, harmonic motion comes from the interaction of the restoring force form gravity and inertia. In the Investigation, the students build a mechanical oscillator and measure its natural frequency. They must use the concepts of inertia and restoring force to come up with a procedure for changing the natural frequency and predicting beforehand whether the natural frequency should increase or decrease.

Reading Synopsis

Students read Section 13.2 Why Things Oscillate after the Investigation.

Harmonic motion occurs throughout nature. Harmonic motion occurs when a system is stable, has restoring forces, and has some property that provides inertia.

Systems that exhibit harmonic motion move back and forth around a central or equilibrium position. A system is stable when equilibrium is maintained by restoring forces. A restoring force is any force that always acts to pull the system back toward equilibrium. When disturbed from equilibrium, inertia causes a stable system to overshoot equilibrium. Harmonic motion is the result.

Stable systems have a natural frequency at which they tend to oscillate when disturbed. The natural frequency depends on the ratio of the strength of the restoring force compared with the inertia of the system. Strengthening the restoring force increases the natural frequency of a system. Increasing the inertia decreases the natural frequency.

The Investigation

Leading Questions
- Why do some systems have harmonic motion while others do not?
- Is it possible to predict when harmonic motion will occur?
- Why do systems in harmonic motion tend to have a specific frequency at which they always oscillate?
- Is it possible to change the natural frequency of a system?
- restoring force relate to equilibrium?
- What is inertia?
- What is natural frequency?

Learning Goals

By the end of the Investigation, students will be able to:
- Create an oscillator and measure its period.
- Apply the concepts of restoring force and inertia to change the period of an oscillator.

Key Vocabulary

equilibrium, restoring force, unstable equilibrium, stable equilibrium, natural frequency

Setup and Materials

Students work in groups of four or five at tables.

The following are some suggested materials to make a mechanical oscillator:

- Rubber bands
- String
- Elastic bands
- Curved tracks
- Steel marbles
- Wood block
- Steel bolt

The group also needs the following:

- Rulers
- Photogate
- Stopwatch
- Calculator

Details

Time One class period

Preparation You will need a wok with a rounded bottom and a tennis ball to do the first demonstration. You need a completely rounded surface; a wok that has a flat section on the bottom will not work.

Assignments Section 13.2 Why Things Oscillate in the **Student Edition** after the Investigation.

Skill Sheets 13.1 Harmonic Motion

Teaching the Investigation

1 Introduction
2 Stable and unstable
3 Restoring forces
4 Building an oscillator
5 The natural frequency
6 Changing the natural frequency

Introduction

Oscillation is the action of moving backward and forward between two points.

Stable and unstable

Unstable systems: forces act to pull the system away from equilibrium when disturbed.

Stable systems: forces act to restore the system to equilibrium when it is disturbed.

Stable equilibrium leads to harmonic motion; unstable equilibrium does not.

Restoring forces

A restoring force always tries to pull a system back toward equilibrium.

Today we are going to investigate why things oscillate. When you push a push a cart off the top of a hill, it rolls away and does not come back. If you push a child on a swing, the child swings away then comes back. The cart that rolls away down the hill is not in harmonic motion. The child on the swing is in harmonic motion. What kinds of conditions lead to oscillation and harmonic motion?

I can balance this tennis ball on the top of this wok. However, the slightest tap disturbs the equilibrium. What happens? How do you describe the motion?

1
> Turn the wok upside down and show that you can get a tennis ball to balance on the highest point. Students should recognize that the ball does not show any harmonic motion. It accelerates down the side of the wok and does not return to the top.

Now suppose I start the ball here, and give it a push. Describe the motion you see.

> Flip the wok over and start the ball in the bottom. Push it halfway up one side. It should oscillate back and forth in the valley as it slows down and finally stops. Students should recognize harmonic motion and damping.

Can anybody tell me why we saw harmonic motion the second time, but not the first time?

> Prompt the class to discuss reasons. Encourage responses that lead the class to the idea of a force that always pulls back toward the starting point.

When the ball is on top of a hill, if I push it, there are forces that make it roll farther away from the start. This is called **unstable** equilibrium, and we don't get harmonic motion. At the bottom of the valley things are different. If I push the ball to the right, the hill makes a force that returns it back to the left. Pushing to the left makes a force that returns the ball to the right. There is always a force that tends to make the ball return to its equilibrium position. We call this **stable** equilibrium. How does this relate to harmonic motion?

> Prompt the class until they recognize that stable equilibrium leads to harmonic motion and unstable equilibrium does not.

2
We call any force that tends to return a system to equilibrium a **restoring force**. With the wok and tennis ball, the shape of the valley creates the restoring force. What creates the restoring force on the pendulum?

> Set up a pendulum in front of the class. Discuss that gravity combined with the constraint of the string creates the restoring force.

What is the restoring force on the pendulum at its lowest point?

> Let the pendulum hang motionless. It is in equilibrium, and there are no forces acting to pull it one way or the other.

OK, then when I push the pendulum a little to one side, I see there is a force that pulls it toward the center.

Why does it keep going when it gets to the center where there is no force acting on it anymore?

> Prompt the class until they come up with the explanation that inertia is what keeps the pendulum going through the center.

Why does a pendulum oscillate?

> Lead a discussion that the restoring force pulls it back to center, but the inertia makes it overshoot and keep going. Restoring force pulls back to the center again, inertia makes it overshoot again, and the pendulum oscillates.

Oscillation is caused by the combination of restoring force and inertia. Any system which has restoring forces and inertia will oscillate and show harmonic motion.

UNIT 5: Waves and Sound

13.2 Why Things Oscillate

Question: What kinds of systems oscillate?

In this Investigation, you will:

1. Create an oscillator and measure its period.
2. Apply the concepts of restoring force and inertia to change the period of your oscillator.

Motion results when we disturb a system in equilibrium. We *sometimes* get harmonic motion. For example, consider a cart balanced on top of a hill. If you push the cart even a little, it quickly rolls downhill and does not return. This is motion but not harmonic motion. A cart in a *valley* is a good example of a system that *does* show harmonic motion. If you move the cart partly up the hill and release it, harmonic motion results as the cart rolls back and forth in the bottom of the valley.

Unstable equilibrium

Stable equilibrium

1 Stable and unstable systems

The top of a hill is an example of *unstable* equilibrium. In unstable systems, forces act to pull the system *away* from equilibrium when disturbed. The bottom of a valley is an example of *stable* equilibrium. In a stable system, forces always act to restore the system to equilibrium when it is disturbed. We find harmonic motion in stable systems.

a. Describe your example of a stable system in one or two sentences. What happens when you push it a little away from equilibrium? Write one sentence that describes the motion.

b. Describe your example of an unstable system in one or two sentences. What happens when you push the unstable system a little away from equilibrium? Write one sentence that describes the motion.

2 Restoring forces

With mechanical systems like a pendulum, harmonic motion comes from the action of forces and inertia. A *restoring force* is any force that always tries to pull a system back toward equilibrium. For example, gravity always pulls the pendulum toward the center no matter which side it is on. Because it has inertia, the pendulum passes right through the middle and keeps going. The restoring force then slows it and accelerates the pendulum back toward equilibrium. However, the pendulum overshoots again and goes too far. The cycle (see below) repeats over and over to create harmonic motion.

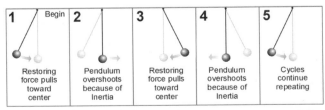

1 Begin	2	3	4	5
Restoring force pulls toward center	Pendulum overshoots because of Inertia	Restoring force pulls toward center	Pendulum overshoots because of Inertia	Cycles continue repeating

84

Teaching tip

You may want to give students an added challenge and run this Investigation as a competition. Tell students that they will be using their oscillators as timing devices. Do not tell them the exact amount of time they will be required to measure, but give them an approximate range (5-15 seconds for example). Once all of the groups have finished the Investigation, have students determine the time it takes for you to walk a lap around the room, a ball to roll across the floor, or another action to take place. You should use a stopwatch to measure the time. Each group should submit their best estimate of the time measured with their oscillator, and the accuracy of the different oscillators can be compared.

1 Example answers

1a. An example of a stable system is a marble sitting at the bottom of a hill on a hilly track. If you push the marble a little bit up one side of the hill, it will move back to equilibrium, overshoot it a bit, come back to equilibrium again, and continue in this fashion until it is sitting once again at the bottom of the hill. Thus, when displaced, the marble moves to equilibrium.

1b. An example of an unstable system is a marble placed on the very top of a hill. The marble is unstable, and will immediately roll away from equilibrium when displaced, and will not return.

Building an oscillator

Building an oscillator requires a restoring force connected to a mass that provides inertia.

The natural frequency

The frequency at which objects tend to move in harmonic motion is the natural frequency.

Natural frequency (f_n) relates restoring force (F) and inertia (m).

$$f_n \propto \frac{F}{m}$$

Changing the natural frequency

The length of the period is affected by the amount of inertia and force.

3 Now that we understand what makes things oscillate, I want you to make an oscillator out of things you can find in the room. Springs, rubber bands, cardboard, marbles, or whatever. Once you make your oscillator, identify where the restoring force and inertia come from

This is the core activity. Have each group construct something that oscillates. Some examples are illustrated to the right. The activity usually takes more than one class period.

4 Once you have a working oscillator, estimate its period. This is easiest to do using the stopwatch and counting cycles. If five cycles take 10 seconds, what is the period?

Prompt the class to answer 2 seconds.

Use the timer as a stopwatch. You can also use the photogates if you can figure out how to make the oscillator break the light beam. If you use photogates, be sure to determine whether the oscillator breaks the beam once or twice (or more) in each cycle.

Circulate and help groups build an oscillator. It does not have to be complicated. A tennis ball in a wok makes a great oscillator. So does a flexible clear plastic ruler with a wad of clay on the end. The tricky part is measuring the period. If the oscillator is fast, like a rubber band vibrating, the photogates are necessary because the cycles are too fast to count.

Do you notice that the oscillator always has the same period? If you start and stop your oscillator three times in a row, you will see that it oscillates with the same period every time. Why do you think that is?

This is a long discussion that is important but subtle. Let the students talk out some ideas.

In physics, we say the oscillator has a natural frequency. The natural frequency is the frequency at which an oscillator tends to oscillate. Because period and frequency are related, if you know one, you know the other. Remember, period is one over frequency. For a pendulum, the frequency is so low, we tend to measure the natural period instead. For a vibrating rubber band it is more convenient to measure the natural frequency. In either case, the concept is the same. Systems in harmonic motion tend to have a preferred frequency (or period) called the natural frequency.

Discuss the cause of natural frequency. The frequency of an oscillator depends on two factors: the strength of the restoring force and the amount of inertia. Any specific oscillator has a frequency that is fixed by the ratio of restoring force to inertia. If the inertia and restoring force stay the same, the oscillator will always oscillate with the same frequency.

How do you make the period shorter? If the period is shorter, the oscillator cycle is faster.

Prompt a discussion. In general, there are two strategies to make the period shorter, or increase the natural frequency. Decrease the inertia (less mass), or increase the force.

How do you make the period longer?

Continue the discussion. To lengthen the period (decrease the natural frequency), you increase the inertia (more mass), or decrease the force.

5 Design and test a technique to make the period longer and shorter for your oscillator. You will need to write down what you did. In your writing, you should mention inertia and restoring force and how each concept relates to changing the period of your oscillator.

This will take some time. Students need a minimum of 15-20 minutes to implement and test a strategy for changing the period of their oscillator. Writing and sketching diagrams could take more time. Be sure to allow enough time for several iterations of the design cycle (concept-build-test-analyze-revise design). Students will become frustrated if they are not allowed to succeed.

3 4 5 Example answers

3a, b, and c:

> We chose to use a 1 meter piece of foam pipe insulation (sliced in half lengthwise) as a marble track. We made a valley out of the track and let the marble roll back and forth in the valley.

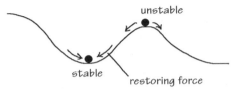

1. We measured the period of a marble rolling back and forth in a valley of the track with a stopwatch. We measured the time it took the ball to roll back and forth in the valley (we released the marble, let it go through one cycle, and then found how long it took to go from release point, down the hill, up the other side, and back down the hill and then up again to its highest point on the release side). This is one complete cycle, and the time it takes to complete that oscillation would be the period. The period turned out to be 1.15 seconds.

2. The natural frequency of our system is 1/1.15 or .869 cycles/sec.

Teacher note: If any of the student groups set up an oscillator that depends on gravity for the restoring force, as we did in our example, changing the mass of the oscillator will have no effect on the natural frequency. If groups set up a spring or rubber band to provide a restoring force, mass will be important.

5a. For our system, we increased the natural frequency by making the sides of the valley steeper (flexible foam pipe insulation works great for this purpose)

5b. To decrease the natural frequency, we made the sides of the valley very shallow. This is essentially the same thing as changing the string length of a pendulum to increase or decrease the natural frequency.

---

3 ### Building an oscillator

To make a mechanical oscillator, you need to provide some kind of restoring force connected to a mass that provides inertia. Rubber bands, strings, elastic bands, and curved tracks can all provide restoring forces. Steel marbles, wood blocks, or even a rubber band have mass to supply inertia. The oscillation can go back and forth, up and down, twist, circle, or create any other motion that can be repetitive. A rubber band with a steel bolt tied to the middle makes both a back-and-forth oscillator and a twisting oscillator. A large bowl and a tennis ball can make a back-and-forth oscillator or a circular oscillator. See if you can find a creative way to make your own oscillator.

a. Create a system that oscillates. You may use anything you can find including springs, rubber bands, rulers, balloons, blocks of wood, or anything else that can be safely assembled.
b. Draw a sketch of your system and identify what makes the restoring force.
c. On your sketch, also identify where the mass that provides the inertia is located.

4 ### The natural frequency

When you pluck a stretched string, it vibrates. If you pluck the same string 10 times in a row, it vibrates at the same frequency every time. The frequency at which objects tend to move in harmonic motion is called the *natural frequency*. Everything that can oscillate has a natural frequency and most oscillators have more than one.

1. Estimate or measure the period of your oscillator in seconds. You may use photogates or stopwatches to make your measurements. Describe how you made your measurement and write down some representative periods for your oscillator.
2. Calculate the natural frequency by dividing 1 by the period. Any oscillator you construct in the lab for which you can actually see the cycles probably has a natural frequency between 0.1 and 10 Hz.

> **Period and frequency relationship**
>
> Frequency (Hz) $f = \dfrac{1}{T}$ Period (sec)

5 ### Changing the natural frequency

The natural frequency is a balance between the strength of the restoring force and the mass providing the inertia. To change the natural frequency, change the balance between force and inertia.

Natural frequency is proportional to the ratio $\dfrac{\text{Restoring force}}{\text{Mass (inertia)}}$

To increase the natural frequency	to decrease the natural frequency
decrease the mass	increase the mass
increase the restoring force	decrease the restoring force

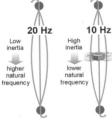

a. Describe and test a way to increase the natural frequency of your oscillator. Increasing the natural frequency makes the oscillator go faster.
b. Describe and test a way to decrease the natural frequency of your oscillator. Decreasing the natural frequency makes the oscillator go slower.

85

13.3 Resonance and Energy

Key Question: What is resonance and why is it important?

In this Investigation, students observe what happens when they drive a pendulum with a small force at its natural frequency, and then at higher and lower frequencies. After reflecting on their observations of the pendulum system, students explore the relationship between energy and the harmonic motion of the pendulum, and how resonance can be understood in terms of the flow of energy in the system. As a result of this Investigation, students will be able to grasp the concept of resonance and the fact that harmonic motion depends not only on the strength of a periodic applied force, but also on the *frequency* of the periodic force.

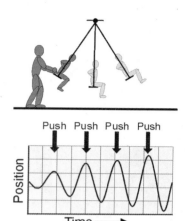

Reading Synopsis

Students read Section 13.3 Resonance and Energy after the Investigation

A force that oscillates in strength or direction is called a periodic force. Periodic forces create harmonic motion. The frequency of a periodic force affects the motion as well as the magnitude and direction. Even a small force applied at the natural frequency can produce large amplitude motion (resonance).

Resonance occurs when the frequency of a periodic force matches the natural freqency of a system. The amplitude of harmonic motion increases dramatically at resonance. Resonance is common because every system that can oscillate has a natural frequency and most systems have more than one.

In resonance, an applied force efficiently transfers energy to the oscillating system. The energy builds up over time. The amplitude of the motion typically increases until a balance is reached between friction (damping) and the applied force.

The Investigation

Leading Questions
- Is the relationship between force and motion the same for harmonic motion as it is for linear motion?
- Why is the natural frequency important?
- What is resonance and why is it important to understand?
- How does friction effect systems in harmonic motion?

Learning Goals
By the end of the Investigation, students will be able to:
- Describe the relationship between resonance, energy and natural frequency.
- Describe how to create resonance in a system in harmonic motion.
- Represent and recognize resonance on a graph of amplitude versus period or amplitude vs. frequency.

Key Vocabulary
periodic force, resonance, steady state, piezoelectric effect

Setup and Materials

Students work in groups of four or five at tables.

Each group should have:

- Physics stand and base
- Pendulum hanger
- Wiggler
- Timer, AC adapter, 2 telephone wires and 1 photogate
- Wave generator and wires
- Steel ball on a string (medium-sized ball)
- graph paper
- meter stick

Details

Time   One class period

Preparation

Assignments   Section 13.3 Resonance and Energy in the **Student Edition** after the Investigation.

Skill Sheets   13.1 Harmonic Motion
10.3 Potential and Kinetic Energy

Equipment Setup   Pendulum, wiggler, steel ball on string

Teaching the Investigation

1. Introduction
2. What is resonance?
3. A general "system view" of resonance
4. Creating resonance in a system
5. Measuring the natural frequency (or period)
6. Applying a periodic force
7. Creating resonance
8. Energy and harmonic motion
9. Frequency, amplitude, and energy
10. Resonance and energy

Introduction

What is resonance?

1

Resonance is a large oscillation created when the frequency of a driving force matches the system's natural frequency.

When a force matched to the natural frequency of a system is applied, you can get a very strong response.

A general "system view" of resonance

NOTE: Draw the diagram relating the force being applied to the system and response on the board.

Today we are going to see one of the more interesting twists in harmonic motion. Remember, according to Newton's second the law the acceleration of a system is proportional to the force applied and inversely proportional to the mass being accelerated. With harmonic motion, a new variable becomes important, the frequency at which a force is applied. Today we will see that systems respond very differently to forces applied at different frequencies, even if the forces are the same strength.

The subject of the Investigation is resonance. Resonance is something that happens when you apply a force to a system that is capable of harmonic motion. If you push at the right frequency, the system builds up its amplitude and can become quite energetic, even when the force applied is small. If you push at the wrong frequency, even a strong push may not produce a strong response.

The most familiar example of resonance you may have experienced is a swing. Does anyone remember how to get started on a swing all by yourself?

This is the start of a discussion. Almost everyone remembers doing this however describing exactly what to do is not easy.

Okay, imagine I am on a swing with a cell phone 1,000 miles away from you. Tell me what to do to get myself swinging.

Encourage the students to talk. They often start with words like kick, pull on the rope, pump, etc. The key idea you are looking for is that the kicking or pumping motion must be synchronized to the movement of the swing. For example, one technique is to kick your legs every time the swing is at its highest point. The first step is always to push off the ground in start the swaying moving so you can do whatever you do in synchronization with the movement of the swing. I often try to act out the suggestions in front of the class. It is amusing and gets students talking.

There are many techniques that will work, and they all share a single important detail. The important detail is WHEN to do what you do. What ever you do to apply force to the swing, you must do it at the same time in each cycle. If your action matches the natural cycle of the swing, then each small force adds to all the forces previously exerted. The amplitude of the swing motion builds gradually and can get very large, even though each individual push is very small. This is what we call resonance. Resonance is an interaction between a periodic force and a system in harmonic motion.

Think about the interaction between pushing and the resulting motion in a three-step process. The swing is a system. Remember, and science, we often choose a system to focus on what care about, and exclude irrelevant details. If you are concerned about the motion of the swing, you don't need to worry about the color of the grass or the temperature of the air.

We can separate the interaction into three parts. The first part is the system itself, which may or may not already be in harmonic motion. The second part is in the force applied which on a graph looks like this. This is called a periodic force because it is a force applied once per each period of time. The last thing to consider is the response of the system. If you push at the right frequency, once per cycle, then the response can be very large, as when the swing starts swinging with a very large amplitude. A large response is what we call resonance. If you do not push at the right frequency, the swing will dangle around near its lowest point but will not build up a large swinging motion.

Draw the diagram near the bottom of the Investigation showing the three part approach to understanding resonance.

Developing a general principle

The general approach to looking at interactions in three parts applies to much more than just harmonic motion. Nearly every process in technology can be thought of in terms of stimulus, system, and response. For example, consider how a computer network knows that another computer is connected. One computer continually sends out packets of data that say "i am here and this is my name". Any other computers on the network receive the packets and send out packets of their own in response that say "I recognize you and here is my name". The network maintains connection between the computers on the basis of this call and response activity. You can think of the packet sent from the server as the stimulus, the whole network as a system, and each remote computer as generating a response.

The analogy also applies to natural systems and living organisms. For example, a change in air temperature is a stimulus. Consider the system to be the atmosphere which contains a certain amount of moisture. The responses is to rain if the temperature change (stimulus) is large enough to cool the air below the dew point. the pattern of stimulus and response is a fundamental part of animal behavior in the behavior of all living organisms, even plants.

Much research in science is aimed at understanding the exact relationship between stimulus and response. In fact, that is the purpose of experiments. An experiment tests the response of a system to a well described and controlled stimulus. And understanding of what goes on in a system is built up by looking at the response to a wide range of stimuli. If a system is well understood, then you can predict its response to any given stimulus. Of course, we are quite far from understanding all the detail in the response of complex systems such as the human body.

UNIT 5: Waves and Sound

13.3   Resonance and Energy

Question: What is resonance and why is it important?

In this Investigation, you will:

1. Learn about resonance and its relationship to energy and natural frequency.
2. Learn to create resonance.

In ordinary linear motion, Newton's second law allows you to calculate the acceleration if you know the net force and mass. With harmonic motion, a new twist occurs. Newton's laws still apply; however, the frequency at which a force is applied often makes a tremendous difference in the resulting motion. This Investigation is about resonance, which can allow very small forces to create very large motions.

1   What is resonance?

 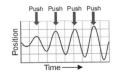

Think about the last time you pushed a child on a swing. If you do it right, each additional push causes the swing to increase its amplitude. Over time, a very large motion builds although each single push by itself is only a small force. No single push is enough to get the swing to its maximum height. The large motion builds from a succession of pushes applied at the same point in each cycle.

The diagram below shows a useful way to think about the interactions that take place when a person pushes a swing. The person supplies a *driving force* to the swing. The swing is a system that can respond to the force in different ways. If the frequency is just right, the swing's amplitude builds. A large amplitude of motion is a strong response to the force applied. At other frequencies, the swing may not build a large motion. When no large motion occurs, we say the response of the system is weak.

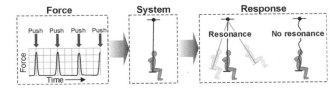

The response of a swing to a periodic push is an example of *resonance*. Resonance happens when the force you apply to a system matches its natural frequency (or a multiple of that natural frequency). When you apply a force matched to the natural frequency of a system, you can get a very strong response. Resonance is what we call the especially strong response we find when an oscillating force is applied to a system at its natural frequency.

Creating resonance in a system

Periodic force is a force that oscillates in strength or direction.

Periodic forces create harmonic motion.

Measuring the natural frequency (or period)

Frequency (f) = 1/T; where T = period

Applying a periodic force

2

In the next part of the Investigation, we are going to create resonance by driving a pendulum with a periodic force. The experiment is a little tricky to set up so pay attention carefully and follow the diagram on Part 2 of the Investigation. The green box is a wavy generator and it puts out pulses of electricity at regular intervals that are controlled by the frequency knob here on the right.

Hold up the wave generator and show students the frequency control.
Connect a photogate to input A of the timer with a telephone cord. Attach the pendulum hanger to the top of the stand with a threaded knob. This device is called the wiggler.

Hold up the wiggler and show it to that students.
Attach the wiggler to the physics stand so the pointed arm face is down as shown in the diagram. The wiggler should be three or four holes up from the bottom of the stand. Take one of the steel balls with the string attached, and thread the end of the string through one of the posts on the pendulum hangar. Bring about string down across the face of about wiggler and slip the string into the tiny notch at the end of about wiggler arm, as shown in the diagram. When about wiggler swings back and forth, it will apply a small periodic force to the string. Since a pendulum is a system that has harmonic motion, we can use of the wiggler to explore how the frequency of a driving force creates resonance. I just thought length of about straining so that distance from the tip of about wiggler arm to the center of the steel ball is between 10 and 15 cm.

Walk around the room and assist students in setting up this experiment. There are many parts and wires to keep track of.
Attach the photogate to that stand about the same level as the pendulum ball, as shown on the right hand diagram in step two of your Investigation. Set the timer in period mode. Swing the ball so that it breaks the light beam at the farthest point in its swing, but not so far that it passes completely through the beam. The ball breaks the light beam only once per cycle if it does not pass all the way through the beam. The period on the timer is therefore the period of the pendulum. Measure the period of the pendulum and write it down in your notebook.

Students measure the period of the pendulum.
What is the relationship between frequency and period? Calculate the natural frequency of the pendulum from the period you've measured. The natural frequency is the frequency at which the pendulum swings all by itself. Almost all systems that show harmonic motion have a natural frequency.

Students should answer that frequency is one over period (f = 1/T) and should calculate the natural frequency of the pendulum. A 15-cm pendulum has a period of 0.78 seconds and a natural frequency of 1.29 Hz.
Disconnect the photogate and connect the wave generator to input A of the timer with the telephone cord. Use of the black wire to connect the wiggler with the weighted generator. Switch the wave generator to waves (with the yellow button) in the wiggler should start oscillating back and forth. The display on the timer should give you the period of the back and forth motion of about wiggler. When the timer is connected to the wave generator it reads the period of the driving force which you are now applying to the pendulum.

You should walk around the room and observe different groups to see that they have connected their equipment correctly. The timer should still be in period mode and the display should show a period of 0.1 seconds if they have just turned the equipment on, without adjusting the frequency knob (yet).

2 **Creating resonance in a system**

13.3 Resonance and Energy

A pendulum is a simple oscillator that has a natural frequency. You may have already learned that the natural frequency of a pendulum depends on the length of the string. In this part of the Investigation, you will observe what happens when you drive a pendulum with a small force at its natural frequency. Because the frequency is very low, we will actually measure the period instead. Remember, the frequency is one over the period.

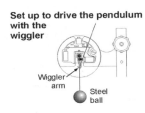

Set up to drive the pendulum with the wiggler

Wiggler arm

Steel ball

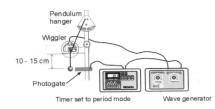

Pendulum hanger

Wiggler

10 - 15 cm

Photogate

Timer set to period mode   Wave generator

1. Attach the pendulum hanger to the stand near the top of the pole. Attach the medium size steel ball to one of the posts in the pendulum hanger.

2. Attach the wiggler to the pole with the wiggler arm pointing upside down as shown in the diagram. Hook the string of the pendulum through the small slot at the end of the wiggler arm. The string should hang down behind the wiggler arm. Adjust the length of the string so the distance between the tip of the wiggler arm and the center of the ball is about 15 cm.

3. Place a photogate on the physics stand as shown. Use the photogate and Timer to measure the period of the pendulum. This works best if you swing the pendulum so it breaks the light beam only once per swing. Record the period of the pendulum and calculate the natural frequency.

4. Disconnect the photogate and connect the wave generator to the Timer with the same cord used for the photogate. Set the Timer so it measures period.

5. Connect the wave generator and the wiggler with the black wire that has headphone plugs on both ends. After connecting the wiggler, set the wave generator to *waves* and the wiggler arm should start moving back and forth. The Timer should measure a period of about 0.1 seconds, giving a frequency of 10 Hz. The wiggler arm applies a periodic force to the pendulum as it moves back and forth.

6. Vary the frequency control and observe what happens to the motion of the pendulum as the frequency of the driving force from the wiggler gets close to the natural frequency of the pendulum. At low frequencies, it is more accurate to measure period and calculate frequency.

7. See what happens when you drive the wiggler at twice the natural period, which is one half the natural frequency.

3 **Reflecting on what you observed**

a. Explain how the force applied by the wiggler causes the response of the pendulum. Your answer should make direct reference to your observations and explain why the natural frequency is important.

b. Make a rough sketch of a graph showing amplitude versus period. Your x-axis (period) should range from zero to at least twice the natural period. The graph is NOT a straight line or simple curve.

87

2 **Example answers**

Part 2 step 3.
 l = length of the pendulum
 l = 15cm
 T = .796s
 F = 1.26Hz

Teacher note: When students first turn on the wave generator, the timer will read 10 hertz for frequency or 0.1 seconds for period. Students will adjust the frequency from that point.

Part 2, Step 6:

We recorded the value for the period in seconds from the timer display, and measured the amplitude in centimeters. It works great to clamp a metric ruler between the photogate screw and the physics stand, so that the ruler extends out behind the swinging pendulum. This makes it very easy to measure the amplitude. Our values were as follows for a 15cm pendulum:

Period (sec)	Amplitude (cm)
.6500	.100
.7037	.150
.7585	.400
.7953	2.00
.8030	1.20
.8470	.400
.9084	.300
.9494	.100
1.0154	.050
1.5809	1.00

Part 2, Step 7:

At twice the natural period, the amplitude was roughly 1/2 what it was at the maximum amplitude recorded at the natural period. At periods between the natural period and twice the natural period, the amplitude decreased until twice the period was approached, when the amplitude began to maximize again.

Creating resonance

Resonance occurs at the natural frequency.

3 At what frequency would you expect resonance? What should the period displayed on the timer be?

> Students should answer "at the natural frequency". The period should be one divided by the natural frequency, or somewhere around 0.78 seconds if the pendulum has a length of 15 cm.

Adjust the frequency until the periodic force applied by the wiggler has the same period as the natural period (1/ nat frequency) of the pendulum. Observe what happens to the amplitude of the motion as the period of the driving force becomes very close to the natural period of the pendulum.

> Students should see that the amplitude of the pendulum remains very small until the period of the (wiggler) driving force is very close to the natural period of the pendulum. When the driving force is at the natural period, the amplitude of the pendulum builds up to a swing of several centimeters.

Try doubling the period of the driving force so the pendulum gets a kick every other swing instead of every swing.

> Students should find that they can create resonance (large amplitude) at twice the natural period or even three times the natural period, although the amplitude gets smaller because the force is spread over more swings while frictional resistance damps every swing.

Energy and harmonic motion

Harmonic motion involves both potential and kinetic energy.

4 We have now seen how resonance works and I want to talk about resonance and energy. The energy in the pendulum alternates between two forms as the ball swings back and forth. What are they?

> Students should answer "potential energy and kinetic energy".

The energy of the pendulum is kinetic energy at the middle of the swing when the ball is at its lowest point and is moving fastest. The energy is potential energy at the extreme ends of each swing when the ball is at its highest point. The energy in the pendulum oscillates back and forth between kinetic and potential.

> It is useful to draw the graph shown in the upper right corner of the page in step 4 of the Investigation. Explain that when potential energy goes down kinetic energy goes up and vice versa. This occurs because of the law of conservation of energy.

All forms of harmonic motion involve the exchange of energy between different forms. With a pendulum the exchange is between potential energy and kinetic energy. With a vibrating rubber band the exchange is between kinetic energy and elastic potential energy. When we discuss waves we will see that sound waves are oscillations of air in which the energy is transformed between kinetic energy and pressure.

Frequency, amplitude, and energy

As the frequency of an oscillator increases, its energy increases as the amplitude increases.

Suppose the frequency of an oscillator is increased. What do you think happens to the total amount of energy if the amplitude stays the same but the frequency gets higher? Explain why you think so.

> Start a discussion. If the frequency gets higher things are moving faster therefore the energy must increase. The energy also increases if the amplitude gets larger. The energy in an oscillator depends on both the frequency and the amplitude.

Resonance and energy

Damping is the decrease in energy caused by friction in an oscillator.

5 It is useful to think about resonance in terms of energy. Energy comes into the system from the wiggler pushing back and forth on the string. Sometimes this energy is just dissipated against friction. At resonance the efficiency of energy transfer between the driving force and the pendulum is very high. Small amounts of input energy are stored as the amplitude of the motion builds. Each additional kick of the wiggler adds to the total energy of the oscillation. What forces act reduce the amplitude of the oscillation?

> Students should answer that friction works against the amplitude growing. The amplitude of the oscillation is a balance between the input energy from the wiggler in the loss of energy to friction.

4 **Energy and harmonic motion**

Kinetic energy

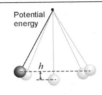
Potential energy

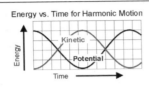

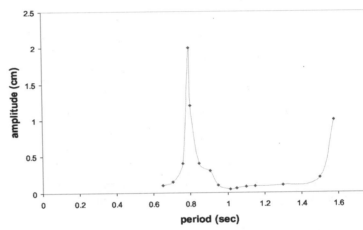
Energy vs. Time for Harmonic Motion

Harmonic motion involves both potential energy and kinetic energy. At the highest point of the cycle, the pendulum is momentarily stopped. It has no kinetic energy because the speed is zero. The pendulum *does* have potential energy though because it is raised above its equilibrium position. At the low point of the cycle, all the potential energy has been converted to kinetic energy. The pendulum has its highest speed at the bottom of the cycle. As the pendulum swings through the low point, it climbs up again, converting its kinetic energy back into potential energy.

Oscillators such as a pendulum or a mass on a spring continually exchange energy back and forth between potential and kinetic. The total energy is a combination of potential and kinetic energy. A graph of energy versus time shows the exchange. The potential energy is low when the kinetic energy is high and vice versa.

a. If the *frequency* of an oscillator is increased, what happens to the total energy? Your answer should state whether you think the total energy goes up, goes down, or stays the same. Explain the physical reasoning behind your answer.

b. If the *amplitude* of an oscillator is increased, what happens to the total energy? Your answer should state whether you think the total energy goes up, goes down, or stays the same. Explain the physical reasoning behind your answer.

5 **Resonance and energy**

Think about resonance in terms of the flow of energy. When the force is matched to the natural frequency, energy is efficiently transferred from the wiggler to the pendulum. As a result, the total energy (potential plus kinetic) increases.

If the force is at a frequency different from the natural frequency, the energy transfer is not very efficient. As a result, the amplitude of the motion stays small.

Why doesn't the amplitude of the driven pendulum keep increasing? There are two explanations. The first one is friction: friction increases as the amplitude and frequency of the motion increase. When the energy lost to friction equals the energy supplied by the wiggler, the amplitude of the motion stops growing. If the wiggler is turned off, you can see the effect of friction quite quickly. The swinging of the pendulum slows down and comes to a stop. The decrease in energy caused by friction in an oscillator is called *damping*.

The second reason the amplitude reaches a limit is that the natural frequency of a pendulum has a small variation with amplitude. As the amplitude increases, the natural frequency shifts so that it no longer matches the frequency of the force from the wiggler.

3 **4** **Example answers**

3a. The force applied by the wiggler made the pendulum vibrate, but when it was at a frequency equal to the natural frequency, the amplitude was at a maximum.

3b. Graph:

Amplitude vs. Period

4a. If the frequency of an oscillator is increased, its energy is also increased. This is due to the increase in the kinetic energy of the oscillator, which has the same mass traveling at a higher speed.

4b. If the amplitude of an oscillator is increased, its energy is also increased. This is due to the increase in the potential energy of the oscillator, which has the same mass displaced a greater distance from equilibrium.

14.1 Waves and Wave Pulses

Key Question: What is the speed of a wave?

One common confusion in the study of waves is identifying exactly what the speed of a wave means. When a wave moves through a medium, the medium itself, on average, stays in the same place. What moves is the disturbance. A disturbance in one area can propagate and eventually disturb another area far away. In this investigation students launch wave pulses on a length of elastic string. The pulses break the light beams in a pair of photogates. By measuring the time interval between breaking the light beams, the students measure the speed of the pulses. They then vary the tension in the string and show that the speed of a wave increases as the tension in the string increases.

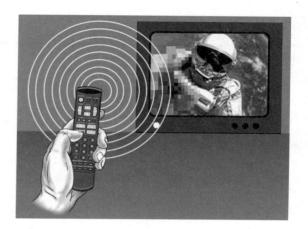

Reading Synopsis

Students read Section 14.1 Waves and Wave Pulses after the Investigation.

Waves are traveling oscillations that move energy from one place to another. The energy might be in the form of actual motion, or it might be in sound, light, or another form of energy that can support oscillations. When a wave moves across the surface of water, the water itself does not move with the wave. What is moving is the energy of the wave, and a wave can be described as a traveling form of energy.

Waves have cycles, frequency, and amplitude, just like oscillations. They have properties of wavelength and speed. The amplitude of a wave is the largest amount that it moves above or below the equilibrium level. Wavelength is the length of one complete cycle of a wave. For a water wave this would be the distance from one point on one wave to the same point on the next wave, such as from crest to crest or trough to trough.

Waves can be transverse or longitudinal, and these categories of waves are explored and studied in this section.

The Investigation

Leading Questions
- What is a wave and what are some examples of waves?
- What do we mean by the speed of a wave?
- How the speed of a wave be measured or calculated?
- How is the speed of a wave influenced by the physical parameters of a system, such as mass or restoring force?

Learning Goals
By the end of the Investigation, students will be able to:
- Create wave pulses on an elastic cord.
- Measure the speed at which wave pulses travel.
- Observe how changing conditions can speed up or slow down a wave.
- Describe the difference between the speed of a wave and the speed of a moving object.

Key Vocabulary   hertz, pulse, wave pulse, continuous, transverse wave, longitudinal wave

Setup and Materials

Students work in groups of four or five at tables.

Each group should have:

- Timer with photogates, AC adapter (or 9-volt battery), and cords to connect the photogates to the timer
- Elastic string (three meters long; use the string that comes with the sound and waves equipment module)
- Tape strong enough to attach the string to a desk or table
- Chair
- A 5-newton spring scale
- Meter stick or tape measure

Details

Time One class period

Preparation 🖊

Assignments 📖 Section 14.1 Waves and Wave Pulses in the **Student Edition** after the Investigation.

Skill Sheets 14.1 Waves

Teaching the Investigation

1 Introduction
2 Demonstrating a traveling pulse
3 Measuring the speed of a wave pulse
4 Changing the string tension

Introduction

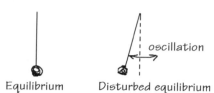

Equilibrium   Disturbed equilibrium

With a pendulum, disturbing the
equilibrium created an oscillation.

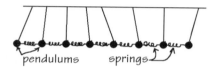

pendulums   springs

In an extended, connected system, the
oscillation travels as a wave.

Demonstrating a traveling pulse

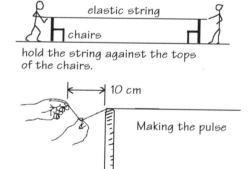

elastic string

chairs

hold the string against the tops
of the chairs.

10 cm

Making the pulse

1

How many people can think of an example of a wave? Why do you think it is an example of a wave?

> Prompt the class to discuss where they think waves are. Water waves, sound waves, and light waves are all good answers. Why they are waves is much harder to answer. The truth is they behave like waves, so they must be waves. However, we don't yet know how waves behave!

A good definition is that a wave is an oscillation that moves. The pendulum kept its oscillations in one place. If you drop a stone in a puddle, the wave can carry the oscillation far from where it started. Why are waves important to us?

> Waves carry information and energy, such as cell phone conversations, heat, light, and sound.

To start harmonic motion, we took a system that was in equilibrium and disturbed it a little, like pulling the pendulum to one side and letting go. Imagine you have lots of pendulums all connected with rubber bands. When you start one moving, the oscillation spreads to the next one, and the next. You get a wave. Waves happen when we make a disturbance in something that is extended and connected to itself. To make a wave, we also make a disturbance, except this time the disturbance is spread out over some distance. I am going to take this elastic string and pluck it. What do you see?

> Gently stretch a string between two chair backs that are at least 10-15 feet apart. The string should have only a little tension. Have a student volunteer hold one end of the string. Take the other end, and pluck it as shown in the picture at left. When you release the string, a pulse will run up the string that everyone should be able to see.

2

What happened when I plucked the string?

> Prompt the students to describe a pulse, or disturbance that moved along the string.

A wave pulse is a short burst of a wave. Radar uses wave pulses to detect aircraft in flight. This elastic string is a good tool for making wave pulses and studying how they move. Each group will need 3 meters of elastic string. Stretch the string between two people so that a spring scale attached to one end reads about one newton. The end opposite the spring scale should rest on the back of a chair. The person holding this end of the string should pull the string down about 10 centimeters and release it. Observe what happens, and try changing the tension of the string to see what happens.

> Students should experiment with the setup. You will have to circulate among the groups to help them with their technique. Students will see the pulse move along the string. The string itself oscillates up and down, and the oscillation moves pretty fast. The tighter the string, the faster the waves move.

Describe what happens when you snap a wave pulse on one end of the string. What happens to without pulse? What happens when it reaches about far end of the string?

> Students should describe that the wave pulse moves along the strength. It reflects from the far side and tries to go back.

In thinking about waves, think about the undisturbed system in equilibrium, like the string lying flat on the table. We create a disturbance by snapping the pulse. The disturbance is what moves. The pulse moves along the string carrying the disturbance from one place to another. If you place a penny on top of the string at the far end of the table, the passing wave pulse will knock the penny off the string. This shows that a wave can carry energy from one place to another. Is the string itself moving from one place to another?

> Discuss this with students. The string is not moving from one end of the table to the other. A wave moves through a material carrying energy however the material, on average, stays in the same place.

14.1 Waves and Wave Pulses

Question: What is the speed of a wave?

In this Investigation, you will:

1. Create wave pulses on an elastic cord.
2. Measure the speed at which wave pulses travel.
3. Observe how changing conditions can speed up or slow down a wave.

1   The speed of a wave pulse

A wave pulse is a short burst of a wave. The wave pulse is launched and can move and reflect from objects it encounters. Radar uses wave pulses to detect aircraft in flight or speeding cars. An elastic string is a good tool for making wave pulses and learning how they move.

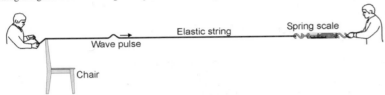

Wave pulse   Elastic string   Spring scale

Chair

1. You need about 3 meters of space to make your wave pulses. You also need about 3 meters of elastic string.
2. One person should take one end of the string and make a knot for attaching a spring scale that can measure 5 newtons of force. The string should be stretched so that the scale reads 1 newton.
3. The second person holds the string with his or her left hand about 10 centimeters away from the back of a chair (diagram above). The string should rest against the top of the chair. With the right hand, this person should pull the string down about 10 centimeters and release it (diagram at right).
4. A wave pulse should move down the string toward the spring scale.
5. Observe the wave pulse as it moves.
6. Try changing the tension in the string. Observe whether changing the string tension has any effect on the speed of the wave pulse.

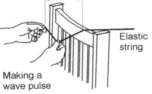

10 cm

Elastic string

Making a
wave pulse

2   Reflecting on what you observed

a.   Describe how the speed of a wave differs from the speed of a moving object such as a car. HINT: What is it that moves in the case of a wave?

b.   How did the tension affect the speed of the wave pulse?

Teaching tip

A relatively low amount of tension (absolutely no more than 3 newtons) should be maintained on the string. While the string is being stretched both ends need to be securely held in place. Letting the string go while under tension should be avoided at all times. Any knots tied in the string should be checked to be sure they will not come undone when the string is stretched.

2   Example answers

2a. The speed of the wave is constant; as soon as it starts moving down the string, it is going a certain speed and it stays at that speed the whole time. A car needs to accelerate up to a certain speed. Once it gets there, it can remain at that speed, but unlike a wave, it doesn't start out with a constant speed.

2b. The wave gets slower as the tension decreases and faster as the tension increases.

Measuring the speed of a wave pulse

3 The pulse moved along the string. The string itself oscillated up and down, but the oscillation moved pretty fast. In this Investigation, we are going to measure the speed of the pulse on the string. Can anyone think of a way to do this?

> Lead the discussion toward using photogates as shown in the Investigation guide. Set up one demonstration in front of the room. This is a fairly tricky experiment to do because the string can break the light beams multiple times. You want data where a single pulse breaks gate A then gate B and gives a time from A to B. The tricky part is knowing when the time is from a single pulse or from other movement of the string. A good technique will give you a usable time about every other try. It may take 10 tries or more to get a good reading the first few times. Be patient with the students, and let them keep at it. Once they get the technique, the experiment goes quickly.

Measure the distance between the photogates. How do you calculate the speed of the wave?

> Students should respond that the speed is the distance between the gates divided by the time from gate A to gate B. Have the students make at least three good runs and calculate the speeds in the data table.

Not every pulse gives you an accurate reading. In fact, most pulses will not give you an accurate reading because the string bounces and each bounce can break the light beam in the photogate. You only want to record data when you are sure the movement of the pulse (and not bounces) triggered BOTH photogates A and B. For tensions greater than one-half newton, the times should fall between 0.01 and 0.02 seconds. Measurements longer than 0.04 seconds are probably a result of extra bounces of the string, so they should not be recorded. Another way to tell when you have good data is consistency. Random bounces will generate times that vary a great deal. Since the speed of the pulse stays constant, good data will be repeatable. For example, if you get a string of numbers: 0.0121, 0,654, 0.0122, 0.0045, 0.0009, 0.124 , you can see that there is a consistent value around 0.0122 that recurs. All the other numbers are scattered and you may assume they are caused by random bouncing of the string. The time it takes the pulse to pass from photogate A to photogate B in this experiment would be about 0.0122 seconds.

> Circulate an assist students to do this experiment. It is a simple thing to do but difficult to get good data. Students must practice to develop a good technique for snapping the pulse.

Changing the string tension

4 What do you think will happen if we stretch the string tighter?

> Discuss what might happen. The pulse gets faster because the force gets larger and the inertia stays the same. The pulse also gets smaller, so it can be more difficult to measure the time. In the discussion you can point out that Newton's second law applies. Acceleration is forced divided by mass. If the string gets tighter, the force pulling it back toward its resting position (restoring force) gets larger. If the force gets larger the acceleration also gets larger and the pulse moves faster.

Use the spring scales to try different tensions. Values between 1 and 3 newtons work well. Take enough data to evaluate our hypothesis about how the tension should affect the speed of the wave.

14.1 Waves and Wave Pulses

3   Measuring the speed of a wave

Because the pulse moves so fast, you need photogates to measure its speed.

1. Set up two photogates about one-fifth meter apart on the table nearest to where you launch the pulse. The photogates should be upside down and centered on the elastic string (diagram at right).
2. Connect the electronic Timer in interval mode with both A and B lights on to measure the time interval between photogates A and B.
3. When you snap the pulse, it will break the beam first in A and then in B. You can calculate the speed of the pulse by dividing the distance from A to B by the time it takes to get from A to B.
4. Not every pulse gives you an accurate reading. The string bounces and each bounce can break the light beam in the photogate. You only want to record data when you are sure the movement of the pulse (and not bounces) triggered both photogates A and B. For tensions greater than one-half newton, the times should fall between 0.01 and 0.02 seconds. Measurements longer than 0.04 seconds are probably a result of extra bounces of the string, so they should not be recorded.

Make a few trials and calculate the speed of the wave pulse. If you are careful to make each pulse start with the same size, your timing data should be repeatable to about 0.001 seconds or better.

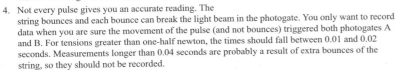

Elastic — Photogates — B — A — Wave pulse — Measuring the speed of the wave pulse

Table 1: Initial data on the speed of the wave pulse

Trial #	Distance between photogates (m)	Time from A to B (seconds)	Speed of pulse (m/sec)

4   Changing the string tension

Try measuring the speed of the wave pulse with the string stretched tighter. Tensions between 1 newton and about 3 newtons will give you good results.

a. What effect does changing the tension have on the speed of the wave pulses?

b. From what you know about forces, explain why you think the higher tension makes the waves move faster.

Table 2: String tension data

String tension (N)	Distance between photogates (m)	Time from A to B (seconds)	Speed of pulse (m/sec)

90

3 4   Example answers

Table 1: *Initial data on the speed of the wave pulse*

Trial #	Distance between photogates (m)	Time from A to B (seconds)	Speed of pulse (m/sec)
1	0.23	0.0071	32
2	0.23	0.0069	33
3	0.23	0.0072	32

4a. Making the string tighter makes the waves go faster.

4b. If the restoring force gets stronger, there is more force pulling the string back straight again. More force means higher acceleration, which leads to higher speeds.

Table 2: *String tension data*

String tension (N)	Distance between photogates (m)	Time from A to B (seconds)	Speed of pulse (m/sec)
1	0.23	0.0075	31
2	0.23	0.0060	38
3	0.23	0.0040	57

14.2 Motion and Interaction of Waves

Key Question: How do waves move and interact with things?

Waves are oscillations that spread out from where they start. Waves can reflect from boundaries and pass through openings. In this Investigation, students will use a shallow pan of water to create plane waves and circular waves. These are the easiest wave shapes to create and study, and may be combined to understand the motion of arbitrary wave shapes. Students will observe the interaction of water waves with hard boundaries creating reflection and with narrow gaps, creating diffraction.

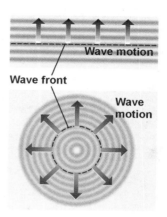

Reading Synopsis

Students read Section 14.2 Motion and Interaction of Waves after the Investigation.

A wave can be described by a series of high points (crests) and low points (troughs). The shape of a wave crest is called the wave front. Circular waves have circular wave fronts that move outward from the center. Plane waves have straight wave fronts that move in a line perpendicular to the wave front. Waves propagate through continuous media, such as the surface of a pond.

A wave approaching a boundary is an incident wave. Reflection describes how waves bounce off a boundary. Refraction describes how waves bend crossing a boundary. Diffraction describes how waves spread out passing through openings and around edges. Absorption describes the loss of energy as a wave is absorbed by passing through a material.

More than one wave may exist in a space at one time (superposition principle). When two or more waves are present they may combine to make a larger wave (constructive interference) or a smaller wave (destructive interference).

The Investigation

Leading Questions
- How is a two dimensional wave described?
- How do waves move through water?
- What are the basic types of two dimensional waves?
- How does the shape of a wave affect how the wave moves?
- What happens when a wave hits a boundary, such as a wall?
- What happens when a wave passes through an opening?

Learning Goals

By the end of the Investigation, students will be able to:
- Create plane and circular waves in water.
- Describe how the shape of a wave affects its propagation.
- Use the concept of diffraction to describe what happens when a wave passes through a slit that is narrow compared to its wavelength.
- Use of the concept of reflection to describe what happens when a wave strikes a hard boundary.

Key Vocabulary

trough, crest, wave fronts, plane waves, circular waves, propagation, boundary, boundary conditions, fixed boundary, open boundary, reflection, incident wave, reflected wave, refracted wave, refracted wave, absorption, diffraction, superposition principle, constructive interference, destructive interference

Setup and Materials

Students work in groups of four or five at tables.

Each group should have:

- Flat tray that can be used for making water waves. A cookie tray or baking pan that is 12 x 18 inches works well. You may also want to adhere laminated grids on the bottom of the trays.
- Container for transferring water. A plastic gallon milk jug works well.
- Ruler or other straight edge that can be used to make waves inside the tray.
- Two blocks of wood or plastic that can be used to block the width of the tray except for a small opening.
- Metric ruler
- Aprons or lab coats.

The teacher should have:

- One gallon of water mixed with one 1-oz. bottle of blue or green food coloring (red and yellow do not work as well). This amount will fill 5-6 wave trays with enough left to replace spills in a few. You can get food coloring in the baking section of most grocery stores. It is nontoxic and washes off.
- Slinky[TM] spring toy to demonstrate transverse and longitudinal waves. Slinkies[TM] can be plastic or metal. Both types will work.

Details

Time	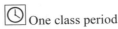 One class period
Preparation	
Assignments	Section 14.2 Motion and Interaction of Waves in the **Student Edition** after the Investigation.

Teaching the Investigation

1. Making plane waves
2. Making circular waves
3. Diffraction
4. Reflection
5. How waves interact with boundaries

Introduction

Making plane waves

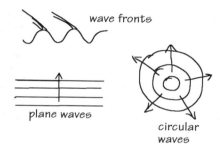

wave fronts

plane waves

circular waves

You can think of wave fronts as the crests of the waves.

a TRANSVERSE wave

oscillation | direction of travel

Water is a transverse wave.

Making circular waves

What happens when two waves hit each other, or hit a wall?

> Discuss with the class the basic wave interactions such as reflection, refraction, diffraction, and absorption.

Today's investigation is going to explore how waves interact with each other and with objects they encounter. We are going to use water waves because they are big and slow, so you can see the details of what happens. Light and sound waves are harder to study directly because light waves are small and fast, and sound waves are invisible. Almost every process we observe with water waves also occurs with sound and light waves.

1 The wave pulses you created on the elastic string were waves in one dimension. The waves moved along the string. The next waves we are going to explore are waves in two dimensions, like waves that occur on the surface of water. These waves have different shapes. First, take your pan, and put about one-half centimeter of water in it.

> Have the students fill their wave pans with one-half centimeter of colored water. You will need to make up the colored water before class. It can make a mess, so you will definitely want students to wear lab aprons.

Take your ruler and place it in the wave pan. Make a single back and forth motion with the ruler and describe what you see. How is it like the wave we saw on the string? How is it different?

> The students are making an approximation of a plane wave. The wave is like a straight ripple that moves away from the ruler toward the edge of the pan. It is like the pulse on the string in shape except it has width. Waves in water also move much slower than the wave on the string.

A wave front is an imaginary shape of the highest point along the wave, called the crest. What shape are the wave fronts in your waves?

> They are approximately straight lines.

These are called plane waves because the water moves up and down in a plane. The up-and-down motion is perpendicular to the direction the wave travels. That makes water waves transverse waves. A transverse wave has its oscillations at right angles to the motion of the wave. The other kind of wave is called a longitudinal wave. A longitudinal wave has its oscillations in the same direction as the wave travels.

> Take a Slinky (TM), and ask for a volunteer from the class. Stretch the Slinky (TM) and make a transverse wave and a longitudinal wave to show the difference.

2 Next, try poking one finger into the water. Your finger makes a wave. What shape is this wave? How does it move? How would you describe the wave fronts?

> This is a circular wave, and it moves radially outward from the disturbance. The wave fronts are circles.

Circular waves spread out from where they are made. Dropping a stone in a puddle makes circular waves. Sketch how the wave fronts look with some arrows to show how they move.

> Circulate among the groups, assisting with sketches and observations. Encourage every student to describe what they see. Encourage them to use terms like "wave front" in their conversation. If they use the words, they will have a better retention of their meanings.

14.2 Motion and Interaction of Waves

Question: How do waves move and interact with things?

In this Investigation, you will:

1. Create waves in water.
2. Observe how waves can pass through holes and bend around corners.
3. Observe how waves reflect from boundaries.

Waves are oscillations that spread out from where they start. A ball floating on water is a good example of the difference between a wave and ordinary harmonic motion. If you poke the ball, it moves up and down (A). The oscillating ball creates a wave on the surface of the water that spreads outward, carrying the oscillation to other places (B). A second ball floating farther away also starts oscillating as soon as the wave reaches it (C). The wave started by an earthquake can travel all around the world and reach places far away from where it began.

1　Making plane waves in a ripple tank

Fill your flat pan with about one-half centimeter of colored water. The color helps you see the waves.

Find a ruler or other straight object that fits in the tray. If you make a single, gentle back-and-forth motion with the ruler, you can launch a wave that goes across the tray. The ruler makes nearly straight plane waves.

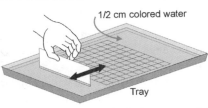

1/2 cm colored water

Tray

a. Draw a sketch that shows the wave front of your plane wave. Also on your sketch, draw an arrow that shows the direction the wave moves.

b. Is the wave front parallel or perpendicular to the direction the wave moves?

c. Would you consider your water wave a transverse wave or a longitudinal wave?

2　Circular waves

Next, poke the surface of the water with your fingertip. Disturbing a single point on the surface of the water makes a circular wave that moves outward from where you touched the water.

a. Draw another sketch that shows the circular wave fronts and include at least four arrows that show the direction in which each part of the wave moves.

b. At every point along the wave, are the wave fronts more parallel or perpendicular to the direction in which the wave moves?

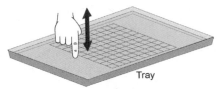

Tray

91

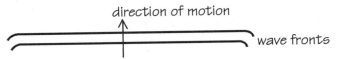
1a. Plane waves:

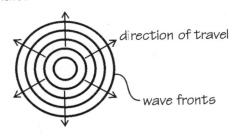

direction of motion

wave fronts

1b. The wave fronts are perpendicular to the direction the wave moves.

1c. The waves are transverse because the up-and-down oscillation is perpendicular to the direction the wave moves.

2a. Circular waves:

direction of travel

wave fronts

2b. The wave fronts are more perpendicular to the direction the wave moves.

Diffraction

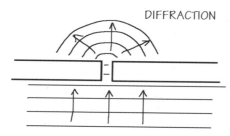

DIFFRACTION

Waves spread out after going through cracks

Reflection

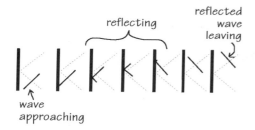

reflecting

reflected wave leaving

wave approaching

How waves interact with boundaries

DIFFRACTION
spreading out through cracks and openings and around corners
REFLECTION
bouncing off walls
REFRACTION
bending
ABSORPTION
disappearing into a material

3 Take two blocks of wood, and put them in your tray so they make a very small opening about a centimeter wide. Make a plane wave with the ruler, and watch what happens as it passes through the opening. What do you see? Did the shape of the wave change?

> The plane wave should become almost circular as it passes through the opening. The circular shape spreads the wave out.

Diffraction is the process by which a wave changes its shape when it goes through or around obstacles. Changing shape is how waves change their direction. Diffraction turns a plane wave into a circular wave. If you look carefully, diffraction also makes the edges of your plane wave rounded. You have read that sound is a wave. All waves are affected by diffraction when they pass through narrow openings or past corners. Does this have anything to do with why you can hear someone around the corner even though you can't see them?

> Yes. Diffraction is the reason. When a wave passes a corner, the edges bend into circular waves that carry the sound even though there is no more line of sight

4 Diffraction is only one of the ways waves interact with boundaries. Take the blocks back out of your wave trays. Using the ruler again, launch a wave at the edge of the tray at an angle of about 45 degrees. What do you see?

> The wave should hit the side of the pan and bounce off. Circulate around the room, and help students make sense of what they are seeing. The reflected wave is not always clear.

What do we call it when a light wave bounces off a mirror?

> Reflection

Actually, all kinds of waves show reflection. The water wave just showed reflection. When we get to light waves, we will see that the angle of the reflected wave depends on the angle at which the original wave approaches the boundary.

5 There are four basic ways that waves interact with boundaries and materials. They are diffraction, reflection, refraction, and absorption.

Diffraction is how waves change shape and direction when passing through openings or around obstacles.
Reflection is how waves bounce off things.
Refraction is how waves can be bent when they pass through a boundary. We will see how glass lenses bend light waves in a later Investigation.
Absorption is when waves are diminished by passing through a substance. Theaters use heavy curtains to absorb sound waves from backstage.

> Write the four ways on the board with some lines and arrows drawing wave fronts and obstacles.

We often use lines and circles to represent wave fronts and arrows to represent the direction the wave is moving. Draw a little sketch showing how the original and reflected waves look with wave fronts and arrows.

> Circulate around the class helping students to sketch the waves they see.

Is it possible to have more than one of the four wave processes happen at the same time? Explain.

> In fact, almost all four are present to some extent in all wave interactions. A light wave is partly absorbed and partly reflected by sunglasses. A water wave at the beach is refracted (bent) as it moves up the slope but is partly absorbed as well.

14.2 Motion and Interaction of Waves

3 Diffraction

1. Take some blocks of wood or other objects and put them in your tray so they block the whole width except for a small opening near the center. The opening should be about 1 centimeter wide.

2. Make a plane wave that moves toward the center and observe what happens to the part of the wave that goes through the opening.

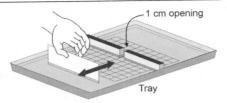
1 cm opening
Tray

Diffraction is a process that reshapes waves as they move through and around openings or corners. Because of diffraction, waves spread out after passing through openings or around corners.

a. Sketch the shape of the wave fronts before and after the opening.

b. Does the wave change shape when it passes through the opening? If you see any change, your answer should say what kind of shape the wave changes into.

4 Reflection

1. Take the straight wave maker and make a plane wave that moves at an angle toward the edge of the tray.

2. Observe what happens to the wave as it hits the edge.

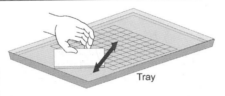
Tray

Reflection is the process of waves bouncing off obstacles like the side of the tray. When a wave reflects, it changes its direction. The wave may also change its shape.

a. Draw a sketch that shows what happens to the wave front when it hits the side of the tray.

b. Draw an arrow showing the direction of the wave approaching the side.

c. Draw another arrow showing the direction of the wave after it reflects from the side.

d. Do you see any relationship between the incoming and outgoing arrows?

5 Applying your knowledge

a. You can easily hear a person talking through a crack in the door although you cannot see them. Do any of your observations provide a clue to how sound can get through tiny cracks?

b. Ocean waves can get many meters high. Big waves on the ocean tend to occur on very windy days. Explain how wind might contribute to making big waves. Use a sketch in your explanation.

3 4 5 Example answers

3a. Sketch of wave fronts

3b. The wave changes shape as it passes through the opening. It changes from a plane wave to a circular wave.

 before

 after

4a,b,c The wave bends when it hits the side of the tray. The sketch shows the approaching and reflected direction.

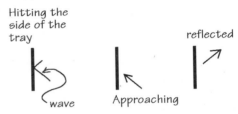

Hitting the side of the tray

wave

Approaching

reflected

4d. It is hard to see, but the direction of a reflected wave changes if we make the approaching wave come at different angles.

5a. Diffraction causes the sound wave to spread out after passing through the crack.

5b. The wind pushes on the sides of the waves. The pushing gives some energy to the waves and makes them bigger.

wind
water

14.3 Natural Frequency and Resonance

Key Question: How do we make and control waves?

In this Investigation, students apply a periodic force to a vibrating string to create and study standing waves. The Wave Generator and Timer allow the students to accurately measure and control the frequency of the applied force. Students will discover that the standing wave patterns appear only at certain frequencies, the natural frequency and its harmonics. Students discover the relationship between wavelength and frequency and that the speed of a wave is the product of its frequency times its wavelength. They also explore the connection between frequency and energy, and between amplitude and frequency. Finally, students investigate how the speed of a wave pulse varies with the tension applied to the elastic string.

268 Hz

980 Hz

873 Hz

1010 Hz

Reading Synopsis

Students read Section 14.3 Natural Frequency and Resonance after the Investigation

The natural frequency of a wave depends on the wave and also on the boundaries of the system that contains the wave. A standing wave is a wave trapped between boundaries. Resonance in standing waves comes from the interaction of a wave with reflections from the boundaries. The concepts of resonance and natural frequency apply to a huge range of natural and human-made systems that include waves.

Most real, three dimensional systems have many natural frequencies, usually one or more fundamentals each with a series of harmonics. The energy in a wave is proportional to frequency and amplitude.

Waves can be described by wavelength. The wavelength is the distance between three successive nodes or antinodes. In a one dimensional system like a string, the nodes are points where the string does not move. In two or three dimensional systems the standing wave patterns are more complex and the nodes and antinodes may be curves or surfaces.

The Investigation

Leading Questions
- How do we make and control waves?
- What is resonance?
- Is there a relationship between the wave properties of frequency, wavelength, and speed?
- What is the relationship between waves and energy?

Learning Goals
By the end of the Investigation, students will be able to:
- Describe how frequency, wavelength, and speed are related.
- Recognize and apply the concept of resonance to any system that can vibrate.
- Measure the wavelength and frequency for a vibrating string.
- Recognize and apply the concept of harmonics in resonant systems.
- Define and apply the concept of natural frequency.
- Describe and apply methods for changing the natural frequency of a system.
- Describe how natural frequency and resonance are involved in musical instruments.

Key Vocabulary natural frequency, standing wave, resonance, wavelength, harmonics, fundamental, amplitude

Setup and Materials

Students work in groups of three to five at tables.

Each group should have:

- Sound and waves equipment module
- Timer with the AC adapter and a cord to connect the sound and waves console to the timer
- Physics stand
- Meter stick or metric tape measure
- Spring scale
- Graph paper
- At least one calculator

Teaching tip

It will be helpful to have a discussion about waves prior to this Investigation. Where have students seen waves? Where do waves come from? It is important not to introduce any terminology during this discussion. The important terminology is introduced as students complete the Investigation and after they have had some hands-on experience with generating waves on a vibrating string.

Details

Time Two to three class periods

Preparation Prepare the wigglers by making sure the elastic string is in the wiggler arm. You will also need to tie a small loop at the free end of the string to attach a spring scale.

Assignments Section 14.3 Natural Frequency and Resonance in the **Student Edition** after the Investigation.

Skill Sheets 14.1 Waves

Equipment Setup Timer and Photogates
Sound and Waves Generator

Teaching the Investigation

1 Introduction
2 Harmonics of the string
3 Waves on the vibrating string
4 Analyzing the data
5 Natural frequency and resonance
6 Energy and waves

Introduction

Set timer on "frequency"
Set sound & waves to "waves"
Connect wiggler with black cord

Harmonics of the string

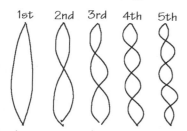

1st 2nd 3rd 4th 5th

fundamental

The beautiful patterns of the string look like this.

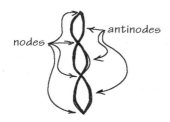

nodes ← → antinodes

Nodes and antinodes

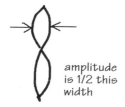

amplitude is 1/2 this width

Amplitude is one-half the width of the widest point.

1 Take out the green sound and waves control boxes, and hook them up to the timer like this. Attach the wiggler to the bottom of the stand and the fiddlehead to the top. Loosen the knob at the top of the fiddlehead, and fit the elastic string between the washers. Give it a little stretch, but not too much. About 2 cm of stretch is right. Gently tighten the knob so it grips the elastic, but don't make it tight.

> Have the students set up the sound and waves experiment as shown in the Investigation. Show them how by demonstrating the assembly procedure with one group.

Turn on the timer. Push the button until the timer reads frequency; the light under the word frequency should be on. Set the sound and waves to waves using the button on the green box. The wiggler should start wiggling!

> Circulate and help the students correct their setups until each one gets the wiggler wiggling. The timer should read a frequency close to 10 Hz.

When you turn the controls for frequency, you can see the speed of the wiggles changes. The timer reads the frequency. When you first turned things on, the string was wiggling 10 times each second. What is the frequency if the wiggler goes back and forth 10 times each second?

> Prompt a discussion of frequency. The answer is 10 Hz. Use this to refresh the definition of Hz and the meaning of frequency.

Frequency means "how often." A frequency of 10 Hz means things happen 10 times per second. Now change the frequency and watch the string. At some special frequencies you get pretty patterns like this. I want everyone to try to get some of the wave patterns by adjusting your frequencies.

> Go to one group, and adjust their wiggler frequency until you get a wave pattern with two or three bumps (second or third harmonic). This should happen between 15 and 40 Hz. If the string is too tight, the waves will be small and have a higher frequency. Circulate to each group, answering questions and checking setups. If necessary, loosen (or tighten) the string until the second harmonic is between 17 and 25 Hz for everyone. This allows everyone to get up to the tenth or higher harmonic later in the experiment. This 5-10 minute period is relatively unstructured "play" time where students should be encouraged to get familiar with the equipment and what to look for.

The beautiful patterns look like this (draw on board) How do you describe the patterns you see?

> Prompt a discussion. Words like "bumps," "waves," and "wiggles" are common.

This pattern has three bumps. We call it the third harmonic. What do you think we call this pattern?

> Point to the second harmonic sketch on the board. Students should answer "the second harmonic" and so on for each one you have drawn.

You can figure out which harmonic it is by counting the bumps on the string. The second harmonic has two bumps, the third has three, and so on. The places between the bumps are called nodes. At a node, the string is not moving. You can touch the string there, and the wave keeps going.

> Have students touch the wave at a node. This is usually approached with trepidation, although there is no danger.

The places where the wave is widest are called antinodes. You measure the amplitude of the wave at the antinodes. How would you measure the amplitude of the wave?

> Prompt the class to remember that amplitude is one-half the width of the widest point. It can be measured easily with a ruler to an accuracy of +/- 2 millimeters or so.

14.3　Natural Frequency and Resonance

Question: *How do we make and control waves?*

In this Investigation, you will:

1. Make standing waves on a vibrating string.
2. Measure the frequency and wavelength of standing waves.
3. Learn how the frequency and wavelength relate to the speed of a wave.
4. Learn how the energy of a wave depends on frequency and amplitude.
5. Learn how the boundary conditions affect a standing wave.

In this Investigation, you will explore the connection between the frequency of a wave and its wavelength. The vibrating string is perfect for investigating waves because the waves are large enough to see easily. What you learn applies to guitars, pianos, drums—to almost all musical instruments.

1　Setting up the experiment

Connect the Timer to the sound and waves generator as shown in the diagram. The telephone cord connects the Timer and wave generator. The black wire goes between the wave generator and the wiggler.

1. Attach the fiddle head to the top of the stand as high as it will go.
2. Attach the wiggler to the bottom of the stand as low as it will go.
3. Stretch the elastic string a little (5 to 10 centimeters) and attach the free end to the fiddle head. Loosen the knob until you can slide the string between any two of the washers. GENTLY tighten the knob just enough to hold the string.
4. Turn on the Timer using the AC adapter.
5. Use the button on the lower left of the front panel to set the wave generator to *waves*. The wiggler should start to wiggle back and forth, shaking the string.
6. Set the Timer to measure frequency. You should get a reading of about 10 Hz, meaning the wiggler is oscillating 10 times per second.
7. Try adjusting the frequency of the wiggler with the frequency control on the wave generator. If you watch the string, you will find that interesting patterns form at certain frequencies.

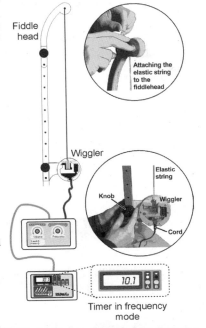

Fiddle head

Attaching the elastic string to the fiddlehead

Wiggler

Elastic string

Knob　Wiggler

Cord

10.1

Timer in frequency mode

93

How to draw wave patterns

Here is a good way to sketch wave patterns on the board quickly. Start at the top and move your hand (and chalk) slowly down while also going back and forth. When you get to the end of the wave pattern you want to draw, start at the top again and do the back and forth motion in the opposite direction as you go down the board. To make different patterns go back and forth more quickly. Try to make all the patterns the same length, like they are on the string. With a little practice it is easy to sketch the first through the fourth harmonics. Getting the fifth and higher is more difficult, especially if you want them the same length!

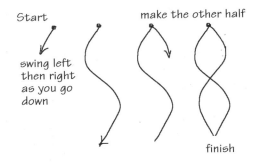

Start

swing left then right as you go down

make the other half

finish

Waves on the vibrating string

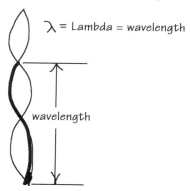

λ = Lambda = wavelength

wavelength

One wavelength

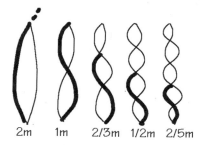

2m 1m 2/3m 1/2m 2/5m

The wavelength of the second harmonic is 1 meter. The third has a wavelength of 2/3 meter; the fourth, 1/2 meter; the fifth, 2/5 meter, etc.

wavelength

Measuring the wavelength when there is not a node at the bottom (wiggler end) of the string.

2 What changes between one pattern and the next?

> Discuss the variables. Frequency, harmonic number, amplitude, and the size of the bumps, or the wavelength, which is the next important concept. When you narrow the discussion to how to tell one pattern apart from the next, your aim is to help students define the word "wavelength" by having the students try to describe what they see without this word.

The **wavelength** is the length of one wave. A wave is one complete oscillation, just like a cycle. This means the string makes a complete "S" shape. The string moves so fast your eye blurs it into the wave pattern, but at any one moment, the string really is in only one place.

> Draw four patterns (or five) starting with the first harmonic.

The string is exactly 1 meter long from the bottom of the fiddle head to the tip of the wiggler. So, what is the wavelength of this pattern?

> Point to the picture of the second harmonic. The wavelength is 1 meter since one complete wave fits exactly on the 1 meter string.

How about this one?

> Point to the third harmonic. The wavelength is 2/3 meter.

The wavelength is 2/3 meter. One whole wave is two bumps. The number of bumps make a meter, so two out of three is 2/3 meter. How about this next one? What about the fundamental?

> Point to the fourth harmonic (0.5 meters) and then the fundamental, which has a wavelength of 2 meters.

The wavelength of the fundamental is 2 meters because only 1/2 the complete wave is on the string. We now know that frequency and wavelength change for the different patterns, which we called harmonics. I want you to find at least the first 8 harmonics. Write the frequency and wavelength for each one in the data table. You don't have to fill in the last column (freq × wavelength) yet. You may have noticed that a particular pattern occurs in a narrow range of frequencies. You might see the third harmonic pattern from 32 Hz to 34 Hz. Try to adjust the frequency so the wave has the biggest possible amplitude before recording the number. Turning the control knob slowly makes the frequency change in small amounts. Turning it fast makes the frequency change in larger amounts.

> This is the bulk of the Investigation. Circulate and point out things to each group.

Where did you find the different wave patterns? Is there a relationship between the different harmonics?

> Lead a discussion of the results. Students should recognize that the frequencies are multiples of the first, which is why the first is called the fundamental. Some students might also recognize that frequency and wavelength are inversely related. Compared with the fundamental, when frequency doubles, wavelength is reduced to half. If the frequency triples, wavelength is decreased to one-third, and so on.

Fill in the third column by multiplying frequency and wavelength for each harmonic. What do you see?

Students should multiply the data and notice that the numbers are nearly the same for every harmonic. It is helpful for you to take one example set of data and put it on the board for harmonics one to six.

2 Waves on the vibrating string

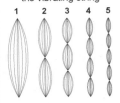

The first five harmonics of the vibrating string

1 2 3 4 5

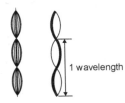

1 wavelength

The *frequency, f,* is the rate at which the string shakes back and forth, or oscillates. A frequency of 10 Hz means the string oscillates 10 times each second.

At certain frequencies, the vibrating string forms wave patterns called *harmonics*. The first harmonic has one bump, the second harmonic has two bumps, and so on.

The *wavelength,* λ, is the length of one complete wave. One complete wave is two "bumps." Therefore, wavelength is the length of two bumps. The string is 1 meter long. If you have a pattern of three bumps, the wavelength is two-thirds of a meter since three bumps equal 1 meter and a wave is two bumps.

The *amplitude,* A, of the wave is the maximum amount the string moves away from its resting (center) position. A *node* is a point where the string does not move. An *antinode* is a point where the amplitude is greatest. You can measure the wavelength as the distance separating three consecutive nodes.

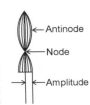

← Antinode

← Node

← Amplitude

Adjust the frequency to obtain the first 8 to 10 harmonics of the string and record the frequency and wavelength for each one in Table 1. You should fine-tune the frequency to obtain the largest amplitude before recording the data for each harmonic. Look for harmonics 2 to 6 before looking for the first one. The first harmonic, also called the *fundamental,* is hard to find with exactness. Once you have the frequencies for the others, they provide a clue for finding the frequency of the first harmonic.

Table 1: Frequency, harmonic, and wavelength data

Harmonic #	Frequency (Hz)	Wavelength (m)	Frequency times wavelength
1			
2			
3			

3 Analyzing the data

a. In one or two sentences, describe how the frequencies of the different harmonic patterns are related to each other.

b. Why is the word *fundamental* chosen as another name for the first harmonic?

c. Give an equation relating frequency (f) and wavelength (λ) that best describes your observations.

d. If the frequency increases by a factor of two, what happens to the wavelength?

e. Propose a meaning for the number you get by multiplying frequency and wavelength.

2 3 Example answers

Table 1: *Frequency, harmonic, and wavelength data*

Harmonic	Frequency (Hz)	Wavelength (m)	Frequency times wavelength
1	10.0	2	20.0
2	20.1	1	20.1
3	30.5	2/3	20.3
4	40.3	1/2	20.1
5	52.2	2/5	20.9
6	64.4	1/3	21.4
7	70.6	2/7	20.2
8	81.4	1/4	20.3
9	90.1	2/9	20.2
10	102.7	1/5	20.5

3a. The frequencies of harmonics 2 through 10 are all multiples of the frequency for the first harmonic.

3b. The first harmonic is called fundamental because all of the frequencies of all of the other harmonics are multiples of the first harmonic's frequency.

3c. The product of frequency times wavelength does not change.

3d. As frequency increases, wavelength gets smaller by the same amount. There is an inverse relationship between frequency and wavelength.

3e. Frequency times wavelength is in units of meters per second, so it is equal to the speed of the wave.

Analyzing the data

harmonic	frequency	wavelength	f x λ
1	10.0	2m	20 m/sec
2	20.1	1m	20.1
3	30.5	2/3m	20.4
4	40.3	1/2m	20.2
5	52.2	2/5m	20.9
6	64.4	1/3m	21.4

Multiply frequency and wavelength together.

$$\left(\frac{1}{sec}\right)\left(meters\right) = \frac{meters}{sec} = speed$$

frequency × wavelength

FREQUENCY × WAVELENGTH = SPEED

Natural frequency and resonance

Energy and waves

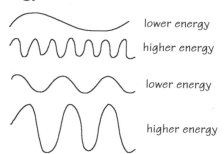

lower energy

higher energy

lower energy

higher energy

Higher frequency means more energy.
Bigger amplitude means more energy

3 The product of frequency and wavelength is always the same! If frequency goes up, wavelength goes down the amount needed to keep the product of frequency and wavelength constant. If wavelength is in meters, and frequency is "per second," what do I get when I multiply wavelength and frequency together?

> You get units of meters per second, which is a speed.

What speed is it? It is the speed of the wave. Frequency times wavelength is the speed of the wave. It is true for light waves, sound waves, water waves, and the waves on this string. I next want to talk about why we only got waves at certain frequencies and not others. If I pluck the string with my finger, what pattern is this? What is its frequency?

> Go to a table with the wiggler turned off and pluck the string. It vibrates in a pattern that looks like the fundamental. It IS the fundamental and its frequency is the fundamental frequency.

This is the fundamental and it vibrates at the **natural frequency** of the string. All objects that can vibrate have a natural frequency that comes from the balance between inertia and restoring force, just as we saw earlier. The natural frequency is important because if we know it, we can predict how an object will vibrate. If we know how an object vibrates, we can use it to make waves of specific frequencies, like a guitar string. We use the natural frequency to create and control waves. When you vibrate an object at its natural frequency, you can get pretty big motions. This is called **resonance**.

> Lead a discussion. Students generally have done this with swings themselves and will give advice like "kick your legs" or "lean back." Steer the discussion to the key concept of rhythm. Whatever you do, it must be in rhythm with the natural motion of the swing.

When you shake something at its natural frequency, you get resonance. Each little push adds to the next one in phase and the repetitive little pushes build up a large motion. You are applying forces to the swing at its natural frequency. That is resonance. Resonance is how we make things vibrate at the frequencies we want. If I want a guitar string to vibrate a exactly 440 Hz, I make it the right length, thickness, and tension so its natural frequency is 440 Hz.

4 It takes energy to feed the resonance and grow a wave. How much energy? Do some waves take more energy than others? I want you to find some of your harmonics again, and this time use the ruler to measure the amplitude of the wave. Pick a spread of harmonics including at least the second and eighth as well as two more in between. Fine-tune the frequency to make the waves as big as possible before measuring the amplitude.

5
> Circulate with each group and help them find and measure the amplitude of the waves. They should find that the higher the frequency, the smaller the amplitude. High harmonics (like the tenth) can be little wider than the string itself.

If a wave has a bigger amplitude, it takes more force to stretch the string longer. What can we say about the relationship between energy and amplitude?

> Higher amplitude requires more energy. Waves with larger amplitudes store more energy than waves with smaller amplitudes. Most students find this a reasonable and intuitive relationship.

If the wiggler puts out about the same amount of energy for every frequency, what does the experiment tell us about how the amount of energy in a wave is related to frequency?

> The higher the frequency, the more the energy. That is why the high frequency waves have smaller amplitudes. The wiggler cannot supply enough power to drive large amplitudes at high frequencies.

Table 2: *Frequency vs. amplitude data*

Harmonic	Frequency (Hz)	Amplitude (cm)
2	20.1	3.5
4	40.3	1.7
6	64.4	1.0
8	81.4	0.5
10	102.7	0.4

5a. Graph of data:

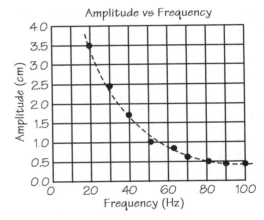

5b. As frequency increases, the amplitude of the wave decreases.

5c. Higher frequency waves have more energy.

5d. The higher frequency wave has more energy.

14.3 Natural Frequency and Resonance

4 Frequency and energy

Waves are useful because they carry energy from one place to another. The energy of a wave can also carry information such as a voice signal from a cell phone or a TV picture. The next part of the Investigation looks at how the energy of a wave is related to frequency and amplitude.

Set up several wave patterns and measure the amplitude for each harmonic. The amplitude is one-half the width of the wave at its widest point. Use Table 2 to record your measurements. Measure at least 5 different harmonics, including the 6th or higher.

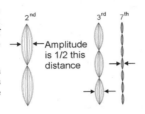

2nd　3rd　7th

Amplitude is 1/2 this distance

Table 2: Frequency vs. amplitude data

Harmonic #	Frequency (Hz)	Amplitude (cm)

If the amplitude of the wave is larger, the wave has more energy because it takes more force to stretch the string a greater distance.

No wave
Unstretched string (zero energy)

Small amplitude wave
Stretched 25% (some energy)

Larger amplitude wave
Stretched 50% (more energy)

5 Interpreting the data

The wiggler applies energy to vibrate the string. Assume that the wiggler supplies about the same amount of energy at all frequencies.

a. Make a graph showing how the amplitude changes with frequency.

b. What happens to the amplitude of the waves as their frequency increases?

c. How does the energy of a wave depend on its frequency? For a given frequency, the amplitude of a wave depends on energy. More energy means larger amplitude. Assume the wiggler supplies the same amount of energy to each wave, independent of frequency. Use your observations of amplitude and frequency to propose a relationship between frequency and energy.

Equal amplitude but different frequency

Which has the most energy?

d. Suppose you had two waves of different frequencies but the same amplitude (see diagram at right). Which has more energy, the lower-frequency wave or the higher-frequency one?

95

15.1 Properties of Sound

Key Question: What is sound and how do we hear it?

In this Investigation, students explore the perception of sound. Humans hear frequencies between 20 and 20,000 hertz. The actual range that one hears varies with each individual. Students discover this by measuring their own sensitivity to sound as well as the sensitivity of their classmates. In the process of the Investigation, students learn about the qualities of a good experiment. In particular, students learn how to perform a double-blind experiment, and learn about the usefulness of this technique in scientific studies. At the end of the Investigation, a short introduction to probability is presented and used to explain how tests and surveys use more than one question to reduce the chance of getting misleading results from random guessing.

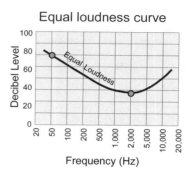

Reading Synopsis

Students read Section 15.1 Properties of Sound after the Investigation.

Sound is a traveling oscillation of pressure carried by solid, liquid, or gas. Like other waves, sound has properties of frequency, wavelength, amplitude, and speed. Humans hear frequencies between 20 Hz and 20,000 Hz as sounds of different pitch. Most sound contains many frequencies (superposition principle). The loudness of sound is measured in decibels and depends mostly on the amplitude of the wave. The decibel scale is logarithmic; each increase of 20 dB represents a sound wave with 10 times greater amplitude.

Sound is created by anything that vibrates with a frequency between 20 Hz and 20,000 Hz. Speakers create sound by using a oscillating electrical signal to drive a vibrating element. A microphone is a device that transforms a sound wave into an electrical signal with the same pattern of oscillation. Each second of a digital sound recording, such as on a CD, stores the oscillating electrical signal as a sequence of 44,100 numbers. Stereo sound includes two separate recordings for the left and right speakers.

The Investigation

Leading Questions
- What is the range of human perception of sound?
- How are experiments on human perception designed and carried out?
- How is the reliability of an experimental conclusion assessed?
- How can a scientist be confident people are not just guessing the right answers?

Learning Goals

By the end of the Investigation, students will be able to:
- Identify the range of frequencies humans can hear.
- Identify the qualities of a good experiment.
- Design double-blind experiments and explain their importance in discovering scientific information free from bias.
- Apply a simple binary decision tree to evaluate the chances of guessing through a multiple-question test.

Key Vocabulary   frequency, hertz, histogram, double-blind experiment, trial, outcome, chance

Setup and Materials

Students work in groups of four or five at tables.

Each group should have:

- Sound and wave equipment module (speakers and sound and waves console)
- Timer with the AC adapter and a cord to connect the sound and waves console to the timer
- Graph paper

Details

Time ⊙ One class period

Preparation ✎ .

Assignments 📖 Section 15.1 Properties of Sound in the **Student Edition** after the Investigation.

Skill Sheets 15.1 Decibel Scale Problems

Equipment Setup Sound and Waves Generator

Teaching the Investigation

1 Introduction
2 The range of hearing
3 How high a frequency can you hear?
4 Experimental bias
5 Probability, chance, and experiments
6 Perceiving differences in frequency

Introduction

The range of hearing

Warm-up activities to help students build association between numerical frequency and perceived sound

People have widely varying opinions of what is low, medium and high. Good introduction to the difficulty of doing reliable experiments on human perception.

How high a frequency can you hear?

Quick test of upper hearing limit

Review histograms

Identify possible bias in the experiment and also the presence of confounding factors such as extraneous noise.

Sound is one of the fundamental ways in which we experience our environment. I am sure many of you have spent money collecting sounds that you like to hear such as by buying CDs by your favorite musician. Today we are going to experiment with how sound is created and what kinds of sounds we can hear. Take out the green sound and waves control boxes, and hook them up to the timer again. This time, instead of attaching the wiggler, attach the speakers instead. Set the control box to "sound" with the button. You should hear sound from the speaker. If the timer is on frequency, it will display the frequency of the sound from the speakers. You can change the frequency with the control. You can also change the volume with the volume control.

> Circulate and help students in connecting their experiments. Encourage them to play with the frequency controls and listen to the sounds. This is a noisy experiment; you may need aspirin when the class is over! Have people keep the volumes low to mitigate the noise.

We hear different frequencies of sound as high and low. I want each group to come up with a frequency of sound that you think is a representative low frequency. Do the same for medium, high, and very high frequencies. Write the results in the table.

> The purpose of this activity is not to get that same answers from each group, but to have that students build familiarity with the association between the pitch of a sound they hear and the numerical frequency they measure. Circulate and help students to decide on what to call low, medium, high, and very high. This is a subjective experiment, and everyone's selections will be different.

Let's compare what each group decided. I want someone from each group to put your choices for low, medium, high, and very high on the board.

> Have a student from each group fill in their data on the board. Lead a discussion on why the numbers are not always the same. People's ears are different, and people of different cultures and experiences may hear sounds differently in terms of what they consider low, medium, and high.

Our ears do not hear all frequencies of sound equally well. Some people can hear higher frequencies than can others. Many animals hear different frequencies of sound than humans do. Dogs and cats hear much higher frequencies. I am going to play sounds of different frequencies. Raise your hand if you think you hear the frequency. Can someone help me count hands?

> Get a volunteer from the class to count hands. Take one sound machine up front, and play a succession of different frequencies. Put the machine out of sight where the students cannot see it. Choose about a dozen frequencies randomly between about 10,000 Hz and 20,000 Hz. To make the graphing easier, make the frequencies close to even multiples of 2,000. Keep the volume off while you set the frequency, and then raise the volume to see if students hear the sound.

How many people have ever made a histogram? This is a kind of graph that is good for showing data that comes in groups, like how many people heard each frequency.

> Put the data on the board, and have make a histogram of the data from the range of hearing experiment. You may have to review histograms and circulate to help students make the graph.

What does the graph show us about the range of sounds that people can hear?

> Very few will be able to hear 20,000 Hz. Most people cannot hear beyond 15,000 Hz or so.

Can anyone think of any problems with the test we just did?

> Discuss the fact that students could see each other's hands and might influence each other's decisions. There are also other's sounds in the room.

UNIT 5: Waves and Sound

15.1 Properties of Sound

Question: What is sound and how do we hear it?

In this Investigation, you will:

1. Learn about the range of human perception of sound.
2. Learn how to design double-blind experiments.
3. Learn how to use probability to evaluate the reliability of experiments.

The ear is a remarkable sensor: sound waves that we can hear change the air pressure by one part in a million. In this Investigation, you will learn about the range of frequencies the ear can detect and how small a difference in frequency we can perceive. Because sound is about perception and people are different, you will learn useful techniques for making experiments on human perception reliable.

1 How high can you hear?

The accepted range of frequencies the human ear can hear ranges from a low of 20 Hz to a high of 20,000 Hz. There is tremendous variation within this range as people's hearing changes greatly with age and exposure to loud noises.

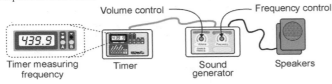

Connect your sound generator to a Timer set to measure frequency. Connect a speaker to the sound generator. When you turn the Timer on, you should hear a sound and the Timer should measure a frequency near 440 Hz.

There are knobs for frequency and volume control. Try adjusting the frequency and see how high and low it goes.

See if you and your group can agree on frequencies where you hear the sound as low, medium, high, or very high frequency. Use Table 1 to record the frequencies of sound that you perceive as low, medium, high, or very high frequency. Don't try to be too exact because the words "low," "medium," and "high" are not well defined. It is difficult to agree exactly on anything that is based completely on individual human perception.

Table 1: How we hear frequencies of sound

Description	Frequency (Hz)
Low	
Medium	
High	
Very high	

Teaching tip

People have long been fascinated with the question of whether animals can exhibit intelligent behavior. One of the most striking claims came from Germany at the beginning of the twentieth century. The horse "Clever Hans" of Berlin, some claimed, could do math: adding, subtracting, multiplying and dividing integers and fractions. Hans communicated with his questioners by tapping numbers with his front hoof.

Hans's fame attracted the attention of Oskar Pfungst, a young graduate student in the new science of psychology. Pfungst was careful to follow the scientific method: each possibly significant factor was observed, changed, and then observed again. Hans's success depended on the questioner knowing the correct answer to his question and on the horse being able to see the questioner.

Pfungst proved that Clever Hans was picking up subtle, visual cues from the human questioners. Hans knew nothing of math, but had learned to respond to body language. The slight forward inclination of the questioner's head, to better see Hans's hoof tapping, was the signal for him to begin tapping an answer. Pfungst demonstrated that even when no question was asked, this slight movement caused Hans to begin tapping. He also observed that questioners tended to lean further forward when the answer was a large number as though they were settling down for a long wait, and Hans responded to this by tapping faster.

The Clever Hans experiment stands as a milestone in psychology, a warning that experimenters can unintentionally but subtly communicate their expectations in their experiments. Only by careful experimental design can this effect be eliminated.

1 Example answers

Table 1: How we hear frequencies of sound

Description	Frequency (Hz)
Low	150
Medium	350
High	2,000
Very high	5,000

Experimental bias

	Frequency	Play? Yes	Play? No
1	12,000	✗	
2	14,000		✗
3	10,000		✗
4	16,000	✗	
5	16,000		✗
6	18,000	✗	
7	12,000	✗	
8	20,000		✗
9	10,000		✗
10	20,000	✗	
11	14,000		✗
12	16,000	✗	
13	12,000		✗
14	20,000		✗
15	10,000	✗	
16	18,000		✗
17	18,000	✗	
18	20,000	✗	
19	14,000	✗	
20	10,000		✗
21	18,000	✗	
22	16,000		✗
23	12,000	✗	
24	16,000		✗
25	20,000		✗
26	18,000	✗	
27	14,000	✗	
28	10,000		✗
29	14,000	✗	
30	12,000	✗	

3

I'm going to tell a true story about a horse who could count. Think about the story and our experiment.

Tell the story of clever Hans, the counting horse. The point is to illustrate the subjectivity of experiments with living things that can take in information from their surroundings.

Experiments involving people and perception are complicated by many variables outside the control of the experiment. In many medical studies, it has been shown that giving someone a sugar pill instead of an aspirin was just as effective at reducing a headache. This is called the placebo effect, and the fake aspirin is called a placebo, which means a nonworking substitute. That doesn't mean you shouldn't take aspirin, but it makes it difficult to test the effectiveness of aspirin in a way that is not affected by people's perceptions. Can anyone think of a way to test the limit of hearing that is less sensitive to perceptions?

Lead a discussion of bias in experiments. Bias can occur when the researcher wants to see a particular result and (often subconsciously) makes choices in the experiment that favor getting the result that is desired. Many people feel all experiments show some bias. Certainly many news articles, history books, and television reports show bias. The next experiment is designed to minimize bias in the sound experiment yet still be practical in a classroom where everyone can see everyone else.

When researchers do experiments that involve perception, they often employ a technique called double-blind. This means neither the observer nor the subject knows if they are getting a placebo or the real thing. I have some cards to hand out that have numbered spots. For each number, I will play a frequency, and you check "yes" if you heard it or "no" if you did not hear it. I may not actually play the sound.

Hand out the photocopied response forms. Find a volunteer to help you know when everyone has recorded his or her result. You should be hidden from view of the class so they cannot see you and take cues from your body language or expression. It takes about 30 seconds to play each frequency, ask for a response, and move to the next frequency. Call out the number for each one as you go. There are six frequencies and each one is repeated five times. They are all shuffled, and the checks tell you whether to play the sound or not play it.

Let's take a look at the data. I'm going to collect all the sheets, shuffle them, and hand them out again. You should have a paper that is not yours. For 10,000 Hz, number 3 should be no, number 9 should be no, number 15 should be yes, number 20 should be no, and number 28 should be no. Raise your hand if you have a paper that has these exact responses.

Quickly go through the trials in six groups of five in the order that they appear in the answer key. If you followed the order on the next page for playing the sounds, the answer key represents the correct responses. Record the number of papers with all five correct responses on the board for each of the six frequencies.

How does this data compare with the survey we took by raising our hands? Suppose you were designing a stereo system that could perfectly reproduce all the sounds the human ear can hear. Which is a more accurate way to measure the high frequency limit of human hearing?

Lead a discussion of the double-blind method and the difficulty of getting accurate survey data. Good examples of this kind of investigation are TV viewing polls, election polls, people who design clothes, test marketing for a new breakfast cereal, and the list goes on. Whenever it is important to know how a large group of people will respond, some type of survey is required. All surveys are subject to bias, and it is difficult to get results that are objective.

2 — Testing the upper frequency limit of the ear

To start with a simple experiment, your teacher has a sound generator that can make frequencies up to 20,000 Hz. When the teacher asks, raise your hand if you can hear the sound. Do not raise your hand if you cannot hear it. Someone will be appointed to count hands and survey the class to see what fraction of students can still hear the sound.

a. The objective of the test is to determine how high a frequency people can hear.

b. Make a histogram showing your class response to frequencies between 10,000 and 20,000 Hz. You should have 10 bars, one per 1,000 Hz. Each student who raises a hand is counted as a positive response on the graph.

c. Do you think the method of counting raised hands is likely to give an accurate result? Give at least one reason you believe the method is either good or bad.

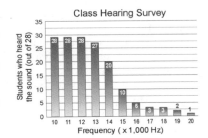

Class Hearing Survey

3 — Doing a more careful experiment

Another way to do the experiment is with a hidden ballot. The researcher running the experiment will ask if anyone can hear a certain frequency of sound and you check yes or no on a piece of paper. The researcher may or may not play the sound. Each frequency will be played five times and the five repetitions will be mixed up so there is less chance for error. Everyone in the class does one response survey.

Compile the data from the survey sheets and record it in Table 2.

Table 2: Frequency survey data

# Right	10,000 Hz	12,000 Hz	14,000 Hz	16,000 Hz	18,000 Hz	20,000 Hz
5						
4						
3						
2						
1						

Plot another histogram showing only people whose choices matched the key all five times at each frequency. It is hard to fake a response (or guess) because you have to choose correctly five times for each frequency. This kind of experiment is called a double-blind test since neither you nor the researcher can see anyone else's response. The results from a double-blind experiment are much more reliable than other forms of surveys. Researchers use the double-blind method to test new medicines.

2 3 Example answers

2b. Graph:

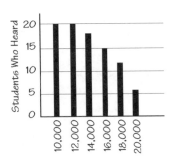

2c. Raising our hands may not be reliable because we can see each other and might be affected by how others in the class respond.

3.

Table 2: *Frequency survey data*

# Right	10K Hz	12K Hz	14K Hz	16K Hz	18K Hz	20K Hz
5	20 (of 20)	18	18	10	3	2
4	0	1	1	2	5	4
3	0	1	0	2	4	6
2	0	0	1	4	5	4
1	0	0	0	2	3	4

Graph:

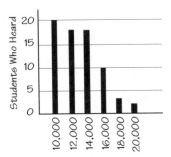

Probability, chance, and experiments

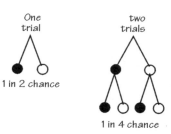

One trial

1 in 2 chance

two trials

1 in 4 chance

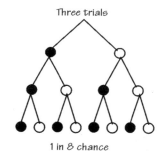

Three trials

1 in 8 chance

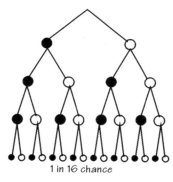

1 in 16 chance

Why do you think I chose to repeat each frequency five times instead of just playing each one once?

> People should recognize that more trials make the data more reliable since it is harder to keep guessing correctly. We want to make the intuition more quantitative.

Fortunately there is a very accurate way to eliminate or at least reduce the chance that your results are due to random guessing. The technique is part of a branch of mathematics called statistics. Statistics can tell you exactly how much confidence you may have in the results of an experiment. Suppose a question can be either right or wrong. I can draw a diagram with two branches, one for right and one for wrong. If 100 people guess at the answer, how many are likely to be right?

> Fifty people, or 50 percent. Most students intuitively know this.

The chance of guessing correctly is equal to the number of correct answers divided by the total number of answers. If there is one correct answer out of two possible answers then the chance of a guess being correct is one out of two or 50 percent. Now suppose I have two questions, and you have to get both right. Each branch of my tree has two choices. There are four possible combinations of guesses and only one is right. If 100 people guess at my two-question test, how many will get both right purely by luck?

> Go through the calculation. There is one path with two correct answers out of four possible paths.
> The chance of guessing correctly twice in a row is therefore one out of four, or 25 percent. Of course this argument assumes equal probability for each of the four outcomes.

Each of the four outcomes is equally probable, so one out of four people, on average, will guess correctly twice. If a sample of 100 people took the test, then I would expect about 25 people to guess correctly twice in a row. Suppose I have three questions. How many possible outcomes are there? Each one of my branches now has two more branches.

> Students should see that the chance of three correct guesses is one in eight, or 12.5 percent. Keep the illustration going to four questions when there are 16 possible outcomes. The chance of getting four right answers is 1 in 16, or about 6 percent. Leave the five-question example for homework.

Can anyone recognize a formula that describes the chance of guessing N true-false questions correctly?

> The total number of possible outcomes is equal to 2^N. The chance of guessing correctly N times in a row is $(1/2)^N$. Work through a few examples so students see how it describes the cases already discussed.

This explains why a good experiment repeats each test multiple times. If there are four trials, the chance of guessing correctly four times in a row is only 6 percent. A scientist would say that the results obtained from the experiment have a 94 percent confidence factor. The confidence factor tells you exactly how reliable the conclusions of the experiment are. Suppose we wish to determine whether a magician is able to read your mind and tell which card you are holding. There are 52 cards in a deck. What is the chance the magician can guess your card?

> The chance is one in 52 or about two times out of 100, or 2 percent.

What is the chance that magician can guess correctly three times in a row?

> $(1/52) \times (1/52) \times (1/52)$ which works out to 7 out of one million.

The chance is only seven out of one million. If the magician correctly gets the answer three times in a row you could argue scientifically that this is proof of mind-reading ability because the chance of guessing is only seven out of one million. Or, the cards are marked!

15.1 Properties of Sound

4 Probability, chance, and experiments

A very good way to ensure accurate results in a survey test is to make it improbable that anyone could get the correct response purely by chance. A single true-false test is not enough to rule out getting a result by guessing. Consider that on each test you have a 50 percent chance to guess right. That means one out of every two times you could get the right response just by guessing—which is not very reliable to someone aiming to accurately record an experiment.

The advantage of doing multiple trials

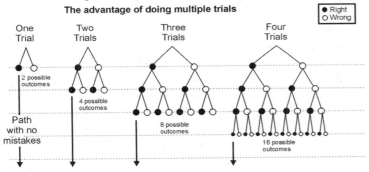

● Right ○ Wrong

One Trial — 2 possible outcomes

Two Trials — 4 possible outcomes

Three Trials — 8 possible outcomes

Four Trials — 16 possible outcomes

Path with no mistakes

The diagram above shows a decision tree for an experiment with one to four trials. With each additional trial, the total number of possible outcomes increases by two. There is only one path with no mistakes. With two trials, you have one right path out of four choices. That means there is only a 1-in-4 chance someone could guess twice correctly. With three trials, there is only a 1-in-8 chance of guessing correctly three times in a row. With four trials, those chances diminish to 1 in 16.

a. What is the chance of guessing correctly every time with five trials?

b. If 100 people did a true-false test with five trials and everybody guessed, how many people would be likely to make five correct choices in a row?

c. Suppose there were three choices for each question. What is the chance of randomly guessing the right answer for a single question with three choices?

d. You design an experiment to compare three sets of stereo speakers (A, B, and C). The same song plays sequentially on each set of speakers and people pick whether the first, second, or third sounded best. You set up a screen so your listeners cannot see the speakers. To rule out chance, you scramble the order in which you play each speaker and repeat the test three times. You figure if a person picks the same speaker all three times, it really must sound better than the other two. What is the chance that someone could randomly select the same set of speakers three times in a row?

Speakers

 A   B   C   Screen   Listener

4a. $1/32 \times 100\% = 3.125\%$

4b. Three people would be likely to guess all five answers correctly.

4c. $1/3$

4d. Since the listener has three choices each speaker has a 1 in 3 chance of selection. So for three trials the chances of randomly selecting the same set of speakers would be:
$1/3 \times 1/3 \times 1/3 = 1/27$ or 3.7%

Table 3: *Comparative frequency data*

Frequency A (Hz)	Frequency B (Hz)	Frequency diff. (Hz)	Percent diff.	# of correct responses
438	437	1	0.26%	
378	379	1	0.26%	
320	313	7	2.2%	
283	267	16	5.7%	

5b. The data supports the proportional difference model.

Answer key for sound survey

10,000	12,000	14,000	16,000	18,000	20,000
3-No	1-Yes	2-No	4-Yes	6-Yes	8-No
9-No	7-Yes	11-No	5-No	16-No	10-Yes
15 Yes	13-No	19-Yes	12-Yes	17-Yes	14-No
20-No	23-Yes	27-Yes	22-Yes	21-Yes	18-Yes
28-No	30-Yes	29-Yes	24-Yes	26-Yes	25-No

Perceiving differences in frequency

Point out how powerful the brain is at recognizing meaning in sound.

The sense of pitch is relative not absolute.

How close do two sounds have to be in frequency before we can tell the difference? This is a very important problem for people who are trying to teach computers to recognize speech. I am going to write a sentence on the board. Read it aloud.

Write "It's hard to wreck a nice beach" on the board. Have the class read this sentence which is extremely close to sounding like "It's hard to recognize speech."

I am going to play two frequencies, A and then B. You check off which one sounds higher. Part 2 of the experiment sheet has places for checking whether A or B sounds higher.

Go through the list on the next page and play the frequencies A and B. Have the students record their responses on a piece of paper. The selections are made to demonstrate that we hear percentage differences, not absolute differences. For example, you can hear a 2 Hz difference at 200 Hz, but not at 2,000 Hz. That is because at 200 Hz, 2 Hz is a 1% change, but at 2,000 Hz, 2 Hz is only a 0.1% change, which is 10 times smaller. Stop after each group, and discuss the significance of the responses.

The correct responses are A, A, B, B, and A. How many people have all five correct?

Have the class respond. Write the number of correct responses on the board, and go to the next group of frequencies. After the 400 Hz group is done, stop and talk about the data.

At 400 Hz, could we hear a difference of 1 Hz? How about a difference of 4 Hz? How about 40 Hz? How big is 1 compared with 400? How big is 4 compared with 400? How about 40?

Have the students work out the percentages. Then move to the 1,000 Hz group, and the 5,000 Hz group and repeat the same process.

What can we tell about the ability of the human ear to tell two frequencies apart?

Discuss the results. Research shows that we have a percentage threshold above which we can perceive the differences between two frequencies. The threshold varies from person to person, but is around 1%.

Human perception is sensitive to percent change rather than absolute change. In science, percent change means the amount of change relative to the entire amount. Absolute change means just the change without any reference to the original amount. As an example consider a jar of candy. If the jar has five identical pieces of candy and I remove one when you are not looking, could you tell him with a quick look that one piece has been removed?

Students respond yes.

Suppose the jar had 1,000 identical pieces of candy and I removed one. Could you tell with a quick look that one piece was missing?

No you could not tell.

In both cases the absolute change is the same, one piece out candy is removed. In the first case the percent change is 20 percent or one out of five. A 20 percent change is easy to see. In the second case the percent change is 1/10 of 1 percent, or one out of one thousand. A change of 1/10 of 1 percent is much more difficult to see. Our Investigation shows that the human ability to discriminate between frequencies of sound is based on percent difference instead of absolute difference.

Frequency difference survey

Set up two sound and wave experiments, one at each frequency to make the survey quicker

	Freq. A	Freq. B
1	4,000	4,001
2	4,001	4,000
3	4,001	4,000
4	4,000	4,001
5	4,001	4,000

correct response: B, A, A, B, A

	Freq. A	Freq. B
1	400	401
2	400	401
3	401	400
4	400	401
5	400	401

correct response: B, B, A, B, B

	Freq. A	Freq. B
1	4,004	4,000
2	4,004	4,000
3	4,000	4,004
4	4,000	4,004
5	4,004	4,000

correct response: A, A, B, B, A

	Freq. A	Freq. B
1	400	404
2	404	400
3	404	400
4	400	404
5	404	400

correct response: B, A, A, B, A

	Freq. A	Freq. B
1	4,040	4,000
2	4,040	4,000
3	4,040	4,000
4	4,040	4,000
5	4,000	4,040

correct response: A, A, A, A, B

	Freq. A	Freq. B
1	440	400
2	440	400
3	440	400
4	400	440
5	400	440

correct response: A, A, A, B, B

	Freq. A	Freq. B
1	4,400	4,000
2	4,000	4,400
3	4,400	4,000
4	4,400	4,000
5	4,000	4,400

correct response: A, B, A, A, B

15.1 Properties of Sound

5 Perceiving differences in frequency

Can you tell the difference between a sound with a frequency of 400 Hz and a sound at 401 Hz? The next experiment is to test the ability to distinguish if one sound has higher frequency than another.

In this experiment, the researcher will play two frequencies and you mark which one is higher.

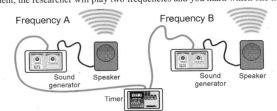

Survey
Which frequency was higher?

#	A	B
1	✓	
2		✓
3		✓
4	✓	
5	✓	
6	✓	✓
7	✓	
8		✓
9	✓	
10		

Key

#	Frequency A	Frequency B
1	400	401
2	404	400
3	390	400
4	1000	1001
5	1050	1000
6	995	1000
7	5005	5000
8	5050	5000
9	4500	5000
10		

To analyze the results, you want to know how many people got the right answer for each frequency range. Make a data table like Table 3 that is large enough to hold all your results.

Table 3: Comparative frequency data

Frequency A (Hz)	Frequency B (Hz)	Frequency diff. (Hz)	Percent diff.	# of correct responses
1,000	995	5	0.5%	7
1,000	1,050	50	1%	15
1,000	1,001	1	.1%	8

a. Calculate the percent difference in frequency for each test.

b. There are two ways to look at sensitivity. In one way, the ear responds to *absolute* differences in frequency. If the ear was sensitive to absolute differences, you would hear a 5 Hz difference no matter if the two frequencies were 500 and 505 Hz, or 5,000 and 5,005 Hz. The second possibility is that the ear only hears proportional differences. For example, suppose you could hear a proportional difference of 1%. That means you could tell the difference between 500 Hz and 505 Hz because the difference of 5 Hz is 1%. However, you could *not* hear the difference between 5,000 and 5,005 Hz because 5 Hz out of 5,000 Hz is a proportional difference of only 0.1 percent. To hear a 1% difference from 5,000 Hz, the second frequency would have to be 50 Hz higher or lower. Which model does the data support?

15.2 Sound Waves

Key Question: Does sound behave like other waves?

A science book will tell you that sound is a wave. Why is sound a wave? Ask students this question and they tell you they cannot see the wave going up and down. What experimental evidence exists that demonstrates sound is a wave? In this Investigation, students create resonance and interference of sound waves using the Sound Generator, a tuning fork, a wine glass, and a bottle. Through their exploration of the properties of sound, students prove to themselves that sound is a wave because the phenomena they observe can be explained using the properties of waves. Students learn how to use resonance to control the frequency of sound waves for useful purposes.

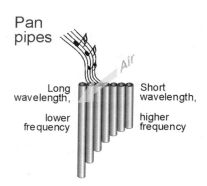

Pan pipes

Long wavelength, lower frequency

Short wavelength, higher frequency

Air

Reading Synopsis

Students read Section 15.2 Sound Waves before the Investigation.

The pressure oscillations in a sound wave are very small, typically a few millionths of an atmosphere. Sound travels through matter but cannot travel through the vacuum of space. Like other waves, the speed of sound is equal to frequency multiplied by wavelength. The speed of sound is 343 m/sec at room temperature and pressure. If a sound source is moving relative to an observer, the frequency of the sound heard by the observer may change. This phenomenon is called the Doppler effect. An object is supersonic if it is moving faster than the speed of sound.

Enclosed spaces or vibrating objects can support resonance and standing sound waves. Resonance is applied to the construction of musical instruments. Multiple reflection of sound from the walls of a room is called reverberation and is an important criteria for concert halls and auditoriums.

Fourier's theorem states that any complex wave can be represented as a sum of single frequency waves.

The Investigation

Leading Questions
- What happens when more than one frequency of sound is present at the same time?
- Are interference and resonance related?
- How does the size of an object influence the sound it makes?

Learning Goals   By the end of the Investigation, students will be able to:
- Use interference to measure the wavelength of a sound wave.
- Demonstrate resonance of sound in different systems.

Key Vocabulary   longitudinal waves, wavelength, Doppler effect, subsonic, supersonic, shock wave, resonance, reverberation, Fourier's theorem, frequency spectrum

Setup and Materials

Students work in groups of four or five at tables.

Each group should have:

- Sound and waves equipment module (speakers and sound and waves console)
- Timer with the AC adapter and a cord to connect the sound and waves console to the timer
- Tuning fork
- 3 wine glasses (for each group or for demonstration)
- A pitcher or large cup of water for filling the wine glasses

Details

Time	🕐	One class period
Preparation	✏️	
Assignments	📖	Section 15.2 Sound Waves in the **Student Edition** after the Investigation.
Skill Sheets		13.1 Harmonic Motion
Equipment Setup		Sound and Wave Generator

Teaching the Investigation

1 Introduction

2 Reviewing the concept of phase

3 Beats

4 Explaining what you hear

5 Interference

6 Reflecting on what you have observed

7 Resonance

8 Thinking about what you observed

9 Resonance in other systems

Introduction

Reviewing the concept of phase

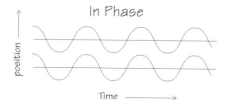

In Phase

position →

Time →

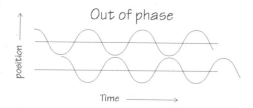

Out of phase

position →

Time →

Beats

Students listen to beats and hear that the beat frequency is the difference between the two frequencies being played.

How do we know sound is a wave? I told you, and someone else taught me, but how did the first person figure it out? What are some of the properties of waves that we have learned about?

> Discuss general properties of wavelength, frequency, amplitude, and speed.

Does sound have these properties? How do we know sound has frequency? How do we know sound has speed? What about amplitude?

> Discuss evidence for these properties. We hear different frequencies. Sound has speed because we can hear echoes several seconds after we make a sound. Sound has amplitude that we hear as different loudness. Reflection, refraction, diffraction, and absorption are other properties.

Remember phase describes where an oscillation is in its cycle. Waves also have phase, and the next two experiments are going to demonstrate some wave-like effects with sound. Since sound is invisible, we are first going to watch these two pendulums. How do you describe the phase of one with respect to the other?

> Set up the dual pendulum as shown in step 6 of Investigation 13.1. Set the string length on each pendulum to be different by about 10 percent. The two pendulums will drift in and out of phase as they oscillate. You can also give each student group the apparatus to investigate for themselves. The two pendulums are sometimes in phase and sometimes out of phase.

Let me draw a graph of the motion of each pendulum. The two graphs are identical when the two pendulums are in phase. The graph of one pendulum is shifted one-half wave with respect to the other when they are out of phase by 180 degrees, or one-half cycle.

> Draw the graphs shown on the left.

When your ear hears two simultaneous sound waves, it responds to the sum of both waves. If each wave is represented by a pendulum, what is their sum when they are in phase? What is the sum when they are out of phase by $1/2$ wavelength? In terms of sound, what do you hear when the waves are in phase compared with when they are out of phase?

> When both pendulums are in phase, the sum of both graphs has an amplitude twice as great as either individual graph. When the two pendulums are out of phase by $1/2$ wavelength, the sum has an amplitude that is less than either individual graph, or even zero. Waves that are in phase are louder, and waves that are out of phase are softer.

1

I am going to hook up two sound generators at the same frequency. I am then going to change the frequency of one while the frequency of the other stays the same. I want everyone to get up and stand over there and listen to the combination of the two sounds I am playing.

> Assemble two sound and waves setups with timers and speakers at one end of the room. Have the students go to the other end so that they are equally distant from both sets of speakers.

The first sound is at 440 Hz, the second one is at 441 Hz. What do you hear?

> Students should hear a slow alternation of loudness in the sound.

Do your hear the "woo-woo-woo" alternation of loud and soft? I am going to make this one 442 Hz now while the other sound is still at 440 Hz. What happened to the sound?

> The alternation should get faster.

I'll raise the higher sound to 443, then 444 and then 445. What do you hear?

> The alternation gets faster as the difference between the two frequencies gets larger.

If I have the 445 Hz by itself, do you hear the beats? How about the 440 Hz by itself?

> Play the sounds alone. The beats are not heard unless both sounds are present.

Extension activity

In the Investigation, students adjust the positions of two speakers so the waves generated are out of phase and cancel out. The same effect can be demonstrated in a more dramatic manner using a stereo and large speakers. Normally speakers are connected so they produce sound waves that are in phase with each other. You can easily reverse the phase of one of the speakers by switching where the red and black wires plug into the stereo. Simply plug the black wire into the red input and vice versa. Be sure that the other speaker is connected in the normal way. Position the two speakers so they are facing each other an inch or so apart. Place a piece of cardboard or other material between the two speakers and play the stereo loudly. The cardboard prevents the two waves from interacting and canceling out. If you then remove the cardboard, the sound gets noticeably quieter! The sound can also be made louder by unplugging one speaker. This demonstration works best with music that is not recorded in stereo and that contains sounds of lower freqencies. Experiment for yourself before demonstrating to the class to find a song that provides the most dramatic effect.

15.2 Sound Waves

Question: Does sound behave like other waves?

In this Investigation, you will:

1. Use interference to measure the wavelength of a sound wave.
2. Demonstrate resonance of sound in different systems.

Nearly any science book will tell you that sound is a wave. How do we know sound is a wave? What experimental evidence is there that sound as the properties of waves? In this investigation you will use interference to measure the wavelength of sound. The fact that sound can produce interference with a characteristic wavelength is strong evidence that sound is a wave.

1   Beats

Suppose two sounds reach your ear at the same time. What you hear is the addition of the two waves.

1. Set up two sound generators close together on the same table.
2. Tune one to 440 Hz and the other to 441 Hz.
3. Stand back and listen to the sound when both are at equal volume.
4. Turn down the 440 Hz sound and listen only to the 441 Hz sound.
5. Turn down the 441 Hz and listen to the 440 Hz sound only.
6. Turn both back up equal again and listen to the combination.
7. Keep one sound generator at 440 Hz and adjust the frequency of the other one between 430 and 450 Hz. Listen to the combinations of sound.

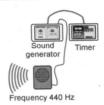

Sound generator   Timer

Frequency 440 Hz

Sound generator   Timer

Frequency 441 Hz

When two waves are close, but not exactly matched in frequency, you hear beats. Beats are an example of the interference of sound waves. Beats are caused by small differences in frequency. The sound gets alternately loud and soft as the waves drift in and out of phase with each other. Sometimes they are in phase and the result is twice as loud. A moment later they are out of phase and they cancel out, leaving periods of quiet. The alternation of loud and soft is what we hear as beats.

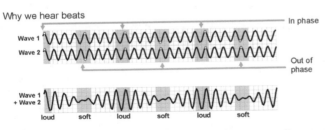

Why we hear beats

Wave 1

Wave 2

In phase

Out of phase

Wave 1 + Wave 2

loud   soft   loud   soft   loud   soft

100

Explaining what you hear

Explain that beats are caused by the interference of two sound waves that have a very small difference in frequency.

We hear alternating loud and soft because the waves drift in and out of constructive and destructive interference.

Interference

waves in-phase

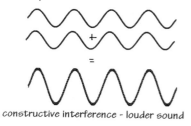

constructive interference - louder sound

waves 180 degrees (1/2 wavelength) out of phase

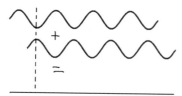

destructive interference, softer sound (or no sound)

You can sit back down now. The alternation of loud and soft you heard is called beats, and beats are caused by two sounds that are close in frequency, but not the same. The beats are caused by both sounds together. Beats are a form of interference. Remember from the last chapter, interference describes what happens when more than one wave is present. The diagram in step 1 of the Investigation shows you why beats occur. Heat can be explained using the property of waves. If the two frequencies are slightly different, then the relative phase of the two waves changes in time. Suppose about two waves start with the same phase. If the second wave has a higher frequency, its phase slowly gets ahead of the first wave. We hear the sound get softer as the difference in phase gets to be one-half cycle. For example, the first wave might complete 10 cycles while the second wave completes $10^1/_2$ cycles. At the end of 10 cycles, the first wave is up. At the end of $10^1/_2$ cycles, the second wave is down. The two waves are out of phase. If we wait a little longer, the second wave completes 21 full cycles in the same time as the first wave completes 20 cycles. Because both waves complete a whole number of cycles, they are in phase again and the sound gets louder. The two waves drift in and out of phase and we hear beats. Note that the beats get slower and slower as the two frequencies get closer together. There are no beats when the two frequencies are the same.

Demonstrate this to the class by having them temporarily get up and listen again.

2 There is another way to demonstrate the interference of sound waves. We can make two identical waves and change the distance between the speaker and our ears. Hook your sound generators to your timers. Attach the speakers. Set the control box to "sound" and the timer to frequency mode.

Circulate and help students connect their experiments. Encourage them to play with the frequency controls and listen to the sounds. Have people keep the volumes low to mitigate the noise.

Everyone except one group should unplug their speakers. This experiment needs to be done one group at a time to hear the subtle difference in sound you are looking for. Take your two speakers, and set one behind the other about one-half meter apart. Stand in front of the two like this. Slowly move the back speaker farther away. Do you hear the sound change?

Demonstrate the technique to the class. The sound should change as the two waves change from in phase to out of phase. This works best when the wavelength is between 50 centimeters and 2 meters. That means frequencies between a few hundred Hz and 1,000 Hz.

If the sound is at its softest point, the waves are out of phase with each other. At the loudest point the waves are in phase. How far apart are the speakers in terms of the wavelength of the sound?

The speakers are separated by a half wavelength (or $1^1/_2$) when the sound is soft and a full wavelength (or 2) when the sound is loudest.

If the sound goes from loud to soft too loud again the distance between the speakers must have changed one whole wavelength. Follow along with the Investigation, and see if you can determine the wavelength of the sound by slowly moving one speaker relative to the other and listening for the transition from loud, to soft, and back to loud again. The difference is subtle and hard to hear. Each group should try it in turn while the other groups are quiet.

Circulate and help students try to find the wavelength by moving the speakers from loud, to soft, to loud again. If one whole cycle of loud-soft-loud is heard, the distance between the speakers must have changed by one wavelength.

15.2   Sound Waves

2 Interference

Suppose you have two identical sound waves and you are standing where you can hear them both. For certain positions, one sound wave reaches your ear in the opposite phase with the other wave and the sound gets softer. Move over a little and the two sound waves add up to get louder. These effects are another example of interference and are easy to demonstrate.

1. Set up one sound generator with two speakers. Place one speaker about 1/2 meter behind the other.

2. Set the frequency between 400 and 800 Hz.

3. Stand 3 or 4 meters in front of one speaker and have your lab partner slowly move one of the two speakers away. You will hear the sound get loud and soft and loud again when the distance between speakers has changed by one wavelength.

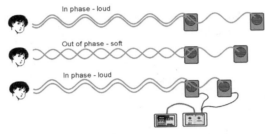

In phase - loud

Out of phase - soft

In phase - loud

When two speakers are connected to the same sound generator they both make the exact same sound wave. If you move around a room you will hear places of loud and soft whenever your distance from each speaker differs by one wavelength.

a. Try to make an approximate measure of the wavelength of sound by changing the separation of the two speakers. The speakers have been moved one wavelength when the sound heard by the observer has gone from loudest, to softest, and back to loudest again. For this to work you need to keep the observer and both speakers in the same line.

b. Interference can be bad news for concert halls. People do not want their sound to be canceled out after they have bought tickets to a concert! Why do we usually not hear interference from stereos even though they have two speakers?

3 Resonance

Many objects that can create sound also have natural frequencies and resonance. When struck, played, or rubbed, these objects produce a characteristic sound at their natural frequency. A tuning fork is a good example.

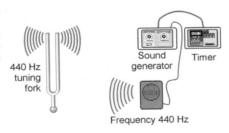

440 Hz tuning fork

Sound generator

Timer

Frequency 440 Hz

1. Select a tuning fork and tap it on your knee or another firm (but not hard) surface.

2. Listen to the sound. Does it change in frequency or do you hear a single frequency that does not change?

101

2 Example answers

2a. We measured the wavelength of sound to be about 30 centimeters at 1,100 Hz.

2b. We don't get interference because there are many frequencies of sound bouncing off many surfaces. Even if one frequency cancels,

3 Example answers

Table 1: *Resonant frequencies for tuning forks*

Tuning-fork description	Measured resonant frequency (Hz)	Labeled resonant frequency (if any)
C	522.9 - 523.8	523.3
A	438.9 - 441.7	440
E	329.1 - 331.1	329.6
C	522.9 - 523.8	523.3

4 Example answers

4a. The larger the tuning fork, the slower the frequency. For example, the 11.1 cm tuning fork vibrated at a frequency of about 523 Hz (the note C). The 13.1 cm tuning fork vibrated at a frequency of about 330 Hz (the note E).

4b. The note C: 522.9-523.8 Hz (range of 0.9 Hz)
The note A: 438.9-441.7 Hz (range of 2.8 Hz)
The note E: 329.1-331.1 Hz (range of 2.0 Hz)

4c. When I placed the base of the tuning fork on the window, the sound got much louder. The tuning fork caused the window to vibrate at the same frequency, increasing the amplitude of vibration, or the volume.

Reflecting on what you have observed

Speed is frequency times wavelength.

Resonance

Resonance occurs when the frequency of a periodic force matches a natural frequency of the system.

Resonance in tuning forks.

Students use beats and the sound generator to measure the frequency of each tuning fork.

Thinking about what you observed

Sound is amplified when the vibrating surface is made larger.

Resonance in other systems

The resonant frequency of a wine glass is affected by the depth of water in the glass.

Does anyone remember the relation between frequency and wavelength? Is there a way to predict the wavelength of the sound?

Frequency multiplied by wavelength is the speed of sound, which is about 343 m/sec under ordinary temperature and atmospheric pressure.

How does your estimate of the wavelength compare with a theoretical calculation from the frequency? Try a few different frequencies.

3 Next, we are going to explore another characteristic of sound: resonance. You learned about resonance earlier in this unit. What is an example of resonance?

Resonance happens when the cycle of force applied to a system exactly matches the frequency of the system. Pushing a child on a swing is a good example. If each push occurs when the swing is in its furthest back position, then the little pushes will combine to form create a large motion. Resonance also happens when something is vibrated at its natural frequency.

A tuning fork is a device that is designed to have a very precise resonant frequency. Next, we are going to use what we know about the interference of sound to measure the resonant frequency of a tuning fork. We can measure that frequency of the sound from the speakers with the timer. We can determine the frequency of the tuning fork by matching its sound with sound from the speakers. When the sounds are close to the same frequency, you will hear beats. The closer the sounds get into frequency, the slower the beats will become. The two sounds are exactly matched in frequency when you can no longer hear beats. Follow the directions in step 6.

Circulate around the room, helping students to coordinate an exchange of tuning forks so that each group can try three or four different sizes.

When you are finished, answer the questions in Part 4.

4 What did you discover about the relationship between tuning fork size and frequency?

They should have noticed that the pitch of the tuning forks is related to size. The larger tuning forks produce lower notes. As the tuning forks get smaller, the notes get higher.

What happened when you placed the base of the tuning fork against the window?

When the base of the tuning fork is held against a window pane, there is a remarkable increase in the volume of the sound. This occurs because the window is forced to vibrate at the same frequency as the tuning fork. The increase in surface area of the vibrating body amplifies the sound. The paper cone inside a speaker serves the same purpose.

5 Next, we are going to observe the property of resonance in a wine glass. One person in each group will rub a moistened finger around the rim of the wine glass. Try applying different amounts of pressure as you run your finger over the rim until you hear a ringing sound. Another member of the group will then try to match the sound using the sound generator. When you no longer hear beats, you have found the frequency of the ringing sound.

Allow students some time to figure out how to create the resonant sound. Remind students to treat the glass with care so that it doesn't break.

Now add some water to the glass and try again. Measure and record the frequency of the sound and the height of the water in the glass. Add more water to the glass and repeat the procedure one more time. Record your results in Table 2.

Students will find that the resonant frequency goes down as more water is added to the glass.

15.2   Sound Waves

3. Use the sound generator to measure the frequency of the resonance by matching the frequency of the sound generator with the sound you hear from the tuning fork. When you get to within about 15 Hz of the frequency you will hear a rapid oscillation called beats. Beats are created by two frequencies which are very close together but not exactly the same. As the frequency from the sound generator and from the tuning fork get closer together the beats become slower. The frequency of sound from the speakers is the same as the sound from the tuning fork when you no longer hear any beats.

4. Try several different tuning forks and use the chart below to record the resonant frequencies.

Table 1: Resonant frequencies for tuning forks

Tuning fork description	Measured resonant frequency (Hz)	Labeled resonant frequency (if any)

4   Thinking about what you observed

a. Did you observe any relationship between the size (or shape) of the tuning fork and the frequency at which it was resonant?

b. What range of frequencies did you hear that seemed to match the frequency of the tuning fork? Give your answer in the form of a range written, for example, like 429 Hz - 451 Hz.

c. Strike the tuning fork and hold the bottom end against a hard, thin surface such as a window. Does the sound get louder, softer, or remain unchanged? Explain what you hear by describing what might be happening between the tuning fork and the surface it touched.

5   Resonance in other systems

Almost all objects show some kind of resonance. A good example is a wine glass. If you take a wine glass and rub a moistened finger around the rim, you can hear a resonant sound. Adding water to the glass changes the sound. Try the following experiment.

1. Obtain a good quality wine glass, like the ones shown in the diagram.
2. Take a moistened finger and rub the rim to hear the resonance.
3. Use the sound generator to match the frequency as closely as you can to the sound of the glass.
4. Fill the glass to different heights with water and use the same technique to find the resonant frequency for each different height.
5. Use the table below to record the height of the water in the glass and the resonant frequency you found for each different height.

Use different heights of liquid.

Table 2: Resonant frequencies of glasses of water

Trial #	Water height	Frequency (Hz)

5   Example answers

Table 2: *Resonant frequencies of glasses of water*

Trial #	Water height	Frequency (Hz)
1	0 cm	380.7 Hz
2	6 cm	363.5 Hz
3	9 cm	314.8 Hz

5. In the case of the wine glasses, as the height of the water increased, the frequency decreased. In the wine glass experiment, the glass and the water were both vibrating. As the mass of the vibrating material increased, the resonant frequency decreased. These results are similar to what we observed with the vibrating string experiments. There we saw that as the wavelength of the string increased, the resonant frequency decreased.

15.3 Sound, Perception, and Music

Key Question: How is musical sound different than other types of sound?

The musical scale was known to humans 20,000 years before the invention of writing, even before the wheel and axle. Musical sound is made from complex patterns of multiple frequencies and rhythms. The frequencies of musical notes are derived from an elegant mathematical foundation of simple fractions and ratios. In this Investigation, students are introduced to the basic mathematics that define a musical scale. They play multiple frequencies of sound and construct consonant and dissonant intervals and chords. In the final part of the Investigation the students are shown how resonance and wavelength are used in the construction of musical instruments.

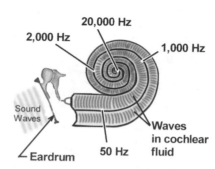

Reading Synopsis

Students read Section 15.3 Sound, Perception, and Music after the Investigation

The meaning in sound is encoded in how thousands of individual frequencies perceived by the brain change over time. A sonogram is a graphical representation showing how the frequency spectrum changes with time. The sense of hearing comes from the cochlea, a part of the inner ear.

Musical sound is a pattern of pitch and rhythm. Pitch describes the frequency of sound and rhythm describes the regular time-pattern in a sound. A musical scale is a collection of frequencies called notes. The 8 notes in the Western musical scale have a simple mathematical relationship based on ratios of frequency. The frequencies of the notes are chosen to minimize dissonance. Dissonance is caused by beats which occur when two frequencies are close together but not exactly the same.

Musical sounds contain harmonics as well as the fundamental note. The relative balance between the loudness, attack, and decay of the different harmonics gives each instrument its characteristic sound.

The Investigation

Leading Questions
- What do frequency and wavelength have to do with pitch and the musical scale?
- What is an octave?
- What creates consonance and dissonance in sound?
- How are the frequencies of musical notes chosen?

Learning Goals
By the end of the Investigation, students will be able to:
- Describe how beats create dissonance.
- Calculate the frequencies of the 8 notes of the musical scale when given the first note.
- Describe the frequency relationship between two notes that are an octave apart.
- Describe how resonance, frequency, and wavelength are used to create musical instruments that play the correct frequencies of notes.

Key Vocabulary   cochlea, rhythm, musical scale, beat, consonance, dissonance, note, harmonics,

Setup and Materials

Students work in groups of four or five at tables.

Each group should have:

- Sound and Wave generator
- Timer
- Speakers

Details

Time One class period

Preparation

Assignments Section 15.3 Sound, Perception, and Music in the **Student Edition** after the Investigation.

Skill Sheets 13.1 Harmonic Motion

Equipment Setup Sound and Wave Generator

Teaching the Investigation

1 Introduction
2 Chords
3 Consonance and dissonance
4 The musical scale
5 Octaves
6 The interpretation of sound

Introduction

How is musical sound different from non-musical sound?

Chords

A chord is a group of two or more musical notes played together.

Today's Investigation will explore the perception of sound. So far, we have discussed the physics of sound and sound waves. We learned about frequency, wavelength, and amplitude. Today we are going to talk about musical sound and why some sounds are pleasant to hear and others are not. Can anyone describe the difference between musical sound and non musical sound?

Music is highly subjective and different people consider different types of sound musical. This is usually an interesting discussion and may include history, culture, and many "non-scientific" perspectives.

I know there will be differences however most people could agree with a definition of music as a combination of sound and rhythm that people create specifically for the purpose of listening to it.

1 Put your sound generators together with the timer and speakers.

Give out the timers, sound and waves sets, and speakers. You will need at least three groups, and five groups work best.

I want you to tune the sounds to some specific frequencies. Use the timer, and keep the volume off. When you get the frequency I ask, raise your hand. You only have to get within 1 Hz. One group go to 264 Hz, another to 330 Hz, another to 396 Hz, one group to 315 Hz, and one to 528 Hz.

Assign frequencies to tune to. If you only have three groups, use 264 Hz, 330 Hz, and 396 Hz.

Now when I tell you, raise your volume to match the other sounds, but don't change the frequencies any more. Bring up the 264 Hz. Bring up the 330 Hz. Bring up the 396 Hz. Bring up the 528 Hz. What do these sounds sound like together?

Most people like this sound. It is a C-major chord and is very consonant and smooth. Discuss the sound combination, especially if there are any musically inclined students in your class.

Everybody turn back down again. Now bring up the 264, 315, 396, and 528. What does this sound like?

This should sound darker, or spooky, or moody.

We only changed one note. Which one was it?

The 330 Hz was replaced with the 315 Hz. Try playing both combinations again. Ask the class their impressions of the sounds.

The first sound was C-major, which has the first, third, and fifth notes of the musical scale in it. This is a very popular sound. The second group was C-minor. Minor scales are often used to create drama, or tension, like in horror movies.

Consonance and dissonance

Consonance and dissonance are related to beats.

Consonance: when we hear more than one frequency of sound and it sounds good

Dissonance: when the combination of sounds is unsettling or bad.

2 I am going to repeat something we did earlier by making two sounds that are close but not exactly matched in frequency. Do you remember what we heard?

Have the students temporarily move to the back of the room and set up the demonstration of beats as described in step one of Investigation 15.2. Most people cannot stand the sound of beats when the frequency difference is more than 3 Hz and less than 15 Hz.

Most people find a combination of 440 Hz and 450 Hz very unpleasant to listen to. Does anyone know the meaning of the words consonance and dissonance?

Prompt a discussion of consonance and dissonance and their relation to beats. Beats causing dissidents, and the absence of beats is necessary for consonance.

Use your sound generators to give me three examples of frequency pairs that are dissonant, and three more that are consonant. This is not a "scientific" test in the sense that there is no single correct answer.

Students should experiment with sound to test dissonance and consonance. Groups will have to work together to share equipment to make two sounds of different frequencies.

15.3   Sound, Perception, and Music

Question: How is musical sound different from other sound?

In this Investigation, you will:

1. Investigate how beats arise from the interference of two sound waves.
2. Demonstrate resonance of sound in different systems.

We rarely hear only one sound wave at a time. Our brains and ears are constantly processing sound from many sources, at many frequencies and intensity levels. In fact, the meaning in sound comes from patterns in frequency and loudness. Speech is actually a pattern of frequencies and amplitudes of sound that you have learned to interpret as words with meaning. Musical sounds have special relationships between the frequencies they contain and the patterns of repetition, or rhythm.

1   Chords

Musical notes are different frequencies of sound. Over thousands of years people have found combinations of frequencies that sound good together.

264 Hz (C)
330 Hz (E)
396 Hz (G)

Combination of 264 Hz, 330 Hz, and 396 Hz
(C major chord)

1. Set up your sound generator and timer.
2. Turn down the volume so that you cannot hear the sound but you can still read the frequency.
3. Each group in the class will be given a different frequency to tune to. Tune your frequency using the timer until you are within +/- 1 Hz.

Your instructor will tell each group to turn up and down different frequencies so they can be heard together. Don't change the frequency, just adjust the volume up and down when you are asked.

a. Describe the sound of the three frequencies 264 Hz, 330 Hz, 396 Hz, and 528 Hz when you hear them together.

b. Describe the sound of the three frequencies 264 Hz, 311 Hz, 396 Hz, and 528 Hz when you hear them together.

c. Contrast the two sounds. Does one sound more happy or sad compared with the other? Does one sound spookier than the other? Which combination reminds you more of spring, which of fall?

2   Consonance and dissonance

When two frequencies sound bad together, we call it dissonance. Beats are the biggest cause of dissonance. When two different frequencies of sound are within 10 - 15 Hz of each other, the beats are perceptible and create dissonance. The opposite of dissonance is consonance. When different frequencies sound good together we call it consonance. Sounds that don't make beats combine more smoothly and are usually consonant. Work with another group to explore how far apart two frequencies have to be to sound consonant together.

a. Give three examples of frequency pairs that are dissonant.

b. Give three examples of frequency pairs that are consonant.

1   Example answers

1a. The C major chord sounds good

1b. Not a chord, dissonance can be heard.

1c. Sound combination (a) sounds happier

Sound combination (b) sound spookier

Sound combination (a) reminds me of Spring

Sound combination (b) reminds me of Fall.

2   Example answers

1a. Three examples of frequency pairs that are dissonant are: (f1 = 439.8 & f2 = 443.8), (f1 = 445.6 & f2 = 437.8), and (f1 = 511.4 & f2 = 524.7).

1b. Three examples of frequency pairs that are consonant are: (f1 = 200.3 & f2 = 400.7), (f1 = 225.1 & f2 = 450.7), and (f1 = 250 & f2 = 503.8).

The musical scale

The notes on a musical scale are related to the first note by ratios of frequency.

3 The musical scale is a special set of frequencies that are related to each other by ratios.

> Write the scale and ratios on the board similar to the diagram in step three of the Investigation. Give the notes and ratios their names do, re, mi, fa, so, la, ti, do.

People invented the musical scale so musicians would be able to play together. You can pick many different combinations of notes from the scale that sound consonant together. There are also combinations that create dissonance. Let's pick a few to try. A chord has at least three notes in it. Can anyone pick three notes we can tune to?

> Have some fun tuning the sound machines to several different chords. Adding the seventh note is a jazz favorite.

The notes in a musical scale are related to the first note by ratios of frequency. For example, the fifth note has a frequency 3/2 times the frequency of the first note. If the first note is C-264 Hz then the fifth note has a frequency of 1.5 times 264, or G-396 Hz. Suppose of the first note had a frequency of 100 Hz. What would the frequency of the third note of the scale be?

> The frequency of the third note is 5/4 (1.25) times the frequency of the first note, or 125 Hz.

How do we control the frequency of a wave?

> Prompt the discussion until you get to the point where you are talking about resonance. Use examples from the vibrating string Investigation.

When a system is in resonance, the frequency and wavelength are related. If we want to control the frequency, we just have to find a way to control the wavelength. How could we do that?

> The easiest way is to the change the length of whatever is vibrating.

Remember the vibrating string. If the frequency goes up, what happens to the wavelength? If the frequency doubles, how much does the wavelength change by?

> When the frequency goes up, the wavelength goes down. The relationship is an inverse. If the frequency doubles, the wavelength must be reduced by half.

So, if I want to make the second note in the scale, I need to raise the frequency by 5/4ths. What do I need to make the wavelength? Suppose I want to make a chime. The length of the wave is the length of the chime. If my first chime is 100 centimeters, what is my third one which must have a frequency 5/4 higher than the first?

> Start drawing the chimes and ratios on the board. If the frequency goes up by 5/4, then the wavelength must go down by the inverse, or 4/5ths.

If the first chime is 100 cm, the third one is 4/5ths times 100, or 80 cm.

> Go on though the eight notes, prompting someone to calculate the lengths.

Have you ever see a set of ratios of lengths like this on a musical instrument? Which one?

> Spark a discussion of musical instruments. Harps, xylophones, pianos, and chimes are the more obvious example because you can see the lengths of the vibrating elements. Guitars, violins, and other stringed instruments change the lengths to the same ratios using the fingers of the musician. Brass and wind instruments use valves to force nodes and antinodes in a tube of air. The effect is to create the same ratios in the wavelengths of the air in the tube.

3 The musical scale

15.3 Sound, Perception, and Music

Almost every culture comes up with a musical scale. The notes of a scale are a special set of frequencies that are related to each other by ratios. Musicians can play together in a band because all their instruments are tuned to the same musical scale. The table below is an example of the C-major scale that is common to many songs.

Musical instruments hired devices designed to play specific frequencies of sound, usually from the musical scale. Instruments work on the principle of resonance. for example, the natural frequency of a chime is proportional to its length, just like a vibrating string. Longer chimes have lower natural frequencies because they are resonant at longer wavelengths. Because frequency and wavelength are inversely related, a chimes that must vibrate a a frequency $5/4^{ths}$ higher than another chime must be $4/5^{ths}$ as long. This proportionality rule is the basis for constructing almost all musical instruments. .

C major scale	C	D	E	F	G	A	B	C
Frequency (Hz)	264	297	330	352	396	440	495	528
Ratio to C-264	$\frac{1}{1}$ $\frac{264}{264}$	$\frac{9}{8}$ $\frac{297}{264}$	$\frac{5}{4}$ $\frac{330}{264}$	$\frac{4}{3}$ $\frac{352}{264}$	$\frac{3}{2}$ $\frac{396}{264}$	$\frac{5}{3}$ $\frac{440}{264}$	$\frac{15}{8}$ $\frac{495}{264}$	$\frac{2}{1}$ $\frac{528}{264}$
Length Ratio	1	$\frac{8}{9}$	$\frac{4}{5}$	$\frac{3}{4}$	$\frac{2}{3}$	$\frac{3}{5}$	$\frac{8}{15}$	$\frac{1}{2}$

a. Find two notes that sound dissonant when played together.

b. Find two notes that sound consonant when played together.

c. Suppose you wish to design a musical chime to play the notes C, E, and G. If the chime that plays the note C is 1 meter long, how long should you make the chimes that play the notes E and G?

4 Octaves

When the frequency doubles, the new note has the same name. The note with a frequency of 440 Hz is named A. The note with a frequency of 880 Hz (double 440) is also named A. Notes that are an **octave** apart are double in frequency. The note with a frequency of 220 Hz is also an A because two times 220 is 440 Hz (A). Two notes where one is half the frequency of the other are also an octave apart. Calculate the missing frequencies for each of the notes below using the rules for the octave.

The Octave Below Middle C **Middle C**

Note	C	D	E	F	G	A	B	C	D	E	F	G	A	B
Frequency								264	297	330	352	396	440	495

104

3 Example answers

3a. Dissonant note combination: C & D, C & E

3b. Consonant note combinations: C & F

3c. Using the table,

C chime is 1 m long

E chime is (4/5) m long = 80 cm

G chime is (2/3) m long = 66.7 cm

4 Example answers

Note	C	D	E	F	G	A	B
Frequency	132.0	148.5	165.0	176.0	198.0	220.0	247.5

Octaves

What is an octave?

Two notes are an octave apart when the frequency of one note is double the frequency of another.

4

Two notes that are an octave apart when the frequency of one note is double or half the frequency of the other. Notes that are an octave apart are given the same name since they sound similar. For example, the note C has a frequency of 264 Hz. Frequencies of 132 Hz and 528 Hz are also named "C" because they are an octave apart from C-264 Hz. I would like three or four groups to tune there sounded generators to the following frequencies: 264, 528, 1056, 2112 Hz. Like before, keep your volumes off and just use the timer to measure the frequency.

> Students should tune to the given frequencies, which are octaves apart. Have the students play the frequencies one at a time and together. Although the pitch is different, each note also sounds similar to the others. You will have to adjust the volume controls to make the sound equal in perceived loudness.

Notes whose frequencies are multiples of 2 always share the same name. 528 Hz is 2 times 264 Hz so it is named C. 1,056 Hz is 2 times 528 Hz and it is also named C. Why is 2,112 Hz named C?

> Students should answer that it is 2 times 1,056 Hz.

Notice that the volumes were adjusted to different levels to make the four frequencies sound equally loud. The volume adjustment is necessary for two reasons. One, the speakers do not respond equally to all frequencies. Smaller speakers cannot move back and forth with enough amplitude to create low frequencies which have large wavelengths. That is why woofer speakers are large compared to tweeter speakers. The second reason is that your ear does not respond equally to all frequencies. The ear is most sensitive to frequencies near 2,000 Hz. The bottom of page 288 in the text shows a graph of equal perceived loudness at different frequencies. The graph shows that a 2,000 Hz sound at 40 decibels is perceived to be the same loudness as a 50 Hz sound at 80 decibels.

The interpretation of sound

How do we hear sound?

Draw a diagram of the inner ear structure on the board. Label the eardrum, bones, and cochlea. Discuss how each part works to help us hear sound.

5

Sound carries a tremendous amount of information. But how? How is information such as words and music encoded in sound?

> This can be an interesting discussion. The information in sound is encoded in the way the amplitude of thousands of frequencies changes over time.

Think about reading one single word from a story. You recognize the word, but it does not tell you much about the story. When you read the whole story you put all the words together to get the meaning. The brain does a similar thing with different frequencies of sound. A single frequency is like one word. By itself there is not much meaning. The meaning comes from patterns in many frequencies together. The brain continuously listens to thousands of frequencies. Each frequency has a loudness that rises and falls with time. Your brain has learned to attach meaning to the patterns in the way certain groups of frequencies rise and fall, just as you have learned to attach meaning to combinations of letters that make words. Speech contains thousands of simultaneous frequencies of sound and so does music. When a musical instrument plays the note C there are many more frequencies and just the fundamental 264 Hz. suppose you listen to the note C-264 Hz played on a guitar and the same C-264 Hz played on a piano. A musician would recognize both notes as being C because they have the same frequency and pitch. But the guitar sounds like a guitar and the piano sounds like a piano. Why?

> Lead a discussion that brings students back to their experiments on the vibrating strain where they observed many harmonics. Almost all vibrating objects vibrate in many different harmonics at the same time and therefore the sounded they create contains a mixture of harmonics as well as the fundamental frequency. The mixture of harmonics is what gives each instrument its individual sound.

5 The interpretation of sound

Think about reading one single word from a story. You recognize the word, but it does not tell you much about the story. When you read the whole story you put all the words together to get the meaning. The brain does a similar thing with different frequencies of sound. A single frequency by itself does not have much meaning. The meaning comes from patterns in many frequencies together. You probably noticed that a single frequency such as 440 Hz sounds "thin" while a combination of frequencies sounds much richer. Speech contains thousands of simultaneous frequencies of sound.

The same note sounds different when played on different instruments. As an example, suppose you listen to the note C-264 Hz played on a guitar and the same C-264 Hz played on a piano. A musician would recognize both notes as being C because they have the same frequency and pitch. But the guitar sounds like a guitar and the piano sounds like a piano.

Instruments have unique sounds because the notes they play are not single pure frequencies. The most important frequency is still the fundamental note (for example, C-264 Hz). The variation comes from the harmonics. Remember, harmonics are frequencies that are multiples of the fundamental note. We have already learned that a string can vibrate at many harmonics. The same is true for all instruments. A single C from a grand piano might include 20 or more different harmonics. A good analogy is that each instrument has its own recipe for the frequency content of its sound.

The rate at which loudness builds and falls off also influences how we hear a sound. The rise time is the time it takes to reach maximum loudness. The fall time is the time over which the sound dies away. Rise time and fall time are related to resonance and damping in an instrument, and are different for each instrument. Rise and fall times are also different for each harmonic, even from the same instrument! Higher harmonics have faster rise times and shorter fall times.

a. Describe the construction of the human ear. What are the three major components? What part converts the vibration of a sound wave into signals that are carried by the auditory nerve?

b. Research how many different frequencies of sound the human brain and ear can respond to. As a comparison, the eye contains about 120 million photoreceptors that each see a dot of brightness. The brain assembles the individual signals (dots) into a picture. The ear works in a similar way. The brain assembles a sonic "picture" from the signals received on the auditory nerve.

c. Describe how an electronic keyboard or synthesizer is able to sound like many different instruments at the touch of a button.

d. Suppose a 1.2 meter long string vibrates at a frequency of 440 Hz. What length of string would vibrate one octave higher? What length would vibrate one octave lower? Assume the tension in the string is the constant.

e. (Challenge question) The western musical scale has 8 notes: do-re-mi-fa-so-la-ti-do, where the 8th note is an octave above the first. A piano keyboard has 12 keys spanning an octave. Describe why there are five extra keys (the black keys) between one note and the same note one octave higher. Your answer should be a short paragraph.

f. (Challenge question) What sounds "good" to your ear is largely due to the sounds you heard during your childhood years. Different cultures use different musical scales. Some scales emphasize dissonance, others emphasize consonance. Research the musical scale of a different culture and describe the relationships between the notes.

105

5 Example answers

5a. The three major parts are the eardrum, a set of small bones, and the cochlea. The cochlea is what converts the vibration of a sound wave into nerve signals.

5b. The ear and brain together can distinguish up to 15,000 different frequency bands simultaneously however this number varies widely among people and over time as the ear ages.

5c. An electronic keyboard or synthesizer builds a complex sound by adding component frequencies with different amplitudes to the fundamental. Each component frequency is given its own attack and decay time. Some professional keyboards use 64 component frequencies to make up each note.

5d. If a 1.2 meter long string vibrates at 440 Hz, then a string half as long (0.6 m) would vibrate at double the frequency, or one octave higher.

5e. The musical scale defines the eight notes based on frequency ratios relative to the first note of the scale. For example, if C-264 Hz is the first note then the next 8 notes are D-297 Hz, E-330 Hz, F-352 Hz, etc. Suppose you start a new 8-note scale on the second note, D-297 Hz. For this scale the second note is also a 9/8 higher than the first and therefore has a frequency of 334 Hz. This note is close enough to E-330 that it is also labeled E. However, the next note is 5/4 x 297 or 371 Hz. This note is between F-352 Hz and G-396 Hz and perceptibly different from either. It is called F-sharp and is one of the black keys on the piano. If you begin the eight note sequence from a different note each time, you find that you need five extra in-between notes and this is why there are the five black keys between the white keys on each octave of the piano keyboard.

5f. (Challenge question) What sounds "good" to your ear is largely due to the sounds you heard during your childhood years. Different cultures use different musical scales. Some scales emphasize dissonance, others emphasize consonance. Research the musical scale of a different culture and describe the relationships between the notes.

16.1 Properties and Sources of Light

Key Question: What are some useful properties of light?

It is hard to imagine living in a world without light. Light has many properties that make it important, both in nature and to humans. In this Investigation, the students explore two optical tricks with reflection and refraction from a mirror and prism. They are challenged to explain what they see using diagrams and drawing light rays. Students do a few simple calculations involving the speed of light to get a sense of how fast light really moves. The last part of the Investigation looks at the inverse square law. Students are introduced to the concept of intensity and do some calculations that show how the intensity falls off like the inverse square of the distance.

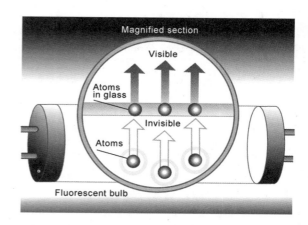

Reading Synopsis

Students read Section 16.1 Properties and Sources of Light after the Investigation.

Every time we look at something, light is involved. Light has properties of color, intensity, and power. Electric light is produced by hot material in a incandescent bulb and by atomic processes in a fluorescent bulb. The intensity of light is the amount of energy per second per unit of surface area. The intensity of a point light source diminishes as the inverse square of the distance.

Light carries information. Light is used to transmit pictures, sound, or computer data, and other information. Light is a form of energy that travels at 3×10^8 m/sec.

Light ordinarily travels in straight lines but can be bent by mirrors or lenses. Reflection describes the bouncing of light from a surface. Refraction describes the bending of light crossing through a surface.

The Investigation

Leading Questions
- What is light?
- How can we describe the behavior of light?
- What are reflection and refraction?
- Why does it seem as if we see things instantaneously as soon as the light switch is turned on?
- How fast does light move?
- Why do far away objects appear dimmer than identical objects that are nearby?

Learning Goals

By the end of the Investigation, students will be able to:
- Use simple ray diagrams to show how mirrors, lenses, and prisms cause objects to appear to be where they are not.
- Calculate the time it takes light to move ordinary distances.
- Use the inverse square law to explain why stars appear dimmer or brighter.
- Calculate the intensity of light from the inverse square law when given the power and distance.

Key Vocabulary

incandescence, fluorescence, intensity, spherical pattern, inverse square law, speed of light, reflect, refract, light rays

Setup and Materials

Students work in groups of four or five at tables.

Each group should have:

- Light and Optics kit, specifically the mirror and prism
- Graph paper
- White paper or index cards
- Calculator
- Ruler

Details

Time ⊕ One class period

Preparation ✎ none

Assignments 📖 Chapter 16.1 Properties and Sources of Light in the **Student Edition** after the Investigation.

Skill Sheets 16.1 Light Intensity Problems

Equipment Setup Light and Optics

Teaching the Investigation

1 Introduction
2 The example of a mirror
3 A simple experiment in reflection
4 An optical trick using reflection and refraction
5 Perception and the properties of light
6 The speed of light
7 The inverse square law

Introduction

Can you imagine a world without light?

The example of a mirror

Where does the light come from to create the image you see when you look at yourself in a mirror?

A simple experiment in reflection

Mirrors reflect light so that you can see images.

An optical trick using reflection and refraction

Light can be reflected or refracted. Refraction is the bending of light as it passes through a transparent surface.

Perception and the properties of light

Light has many properties that make it useful to nature and to humans.

It would be extremely difficult to imagine a world without light. Light carries energy from the sun and light is also what we use to see the world around us. In fact, all of the fancy special effects you see in movies really come from clever ways of manipulating light. This Investigation will begin our exploration of the properties of light.

How many of you looked in a mirror today at least once? When you look in the mirror you see an image of your self. You see light. Where did the light come from to create the image of your self in the mirror?

Most students will have looked into a mirror many times in a given day. The image in a mirror is formed from light that came from the sun or from an electric light and was is reflected from the person in front of the mirror. Almost everything we see is reflected light. It is worth pushing the discussion by asking some questions designed to drag out some common misconceptions. For example, ask if the light comes from within the mirror itself. If students answer that the light comes from their clothes, ask them if they can still see their clothes in a completely dark room. The answer is no, demonstrating that the light they see comes from other sources and is just reflected from their clothes. You cannot see clothes in a darkroom because clothes do not get off their own light. You can see a television in a darkroom because a television does give off its own light.

1 A mirror works because it reflects light. Draw an arrow on a sheet of graph paper as shown in the Investigation in Part 1. Use a folded card to block your view of the arrow. There is a small mirror in the optics kit mounted on a block of wood. Take the mirror and see if you can arrange it so you can see around the card and see the arrow.

Students follow the directions in step one end arranged the mirror so they can see the arrow on the graph paper in the mirror but cannot see the arrow directly.

Describe how light gets from the arrow to your eye when you see the image of the arrow in the mirror

The light leaves the arrow, bounces off the mirror and then reaches your eye

2 Light can also bend when it passes through transparent objects, like this prism made of glass. Without bending of light as it passes through a transparent surface is called refraction. Eyeglasses, telescopes, microscopes, and camera lenses work because of refraction. A shiny transparent surface like the glass face of a prism, can show both refraction and reflection. Make an X and an O on a sheet of a graph paper as shown in step two of the Investigation. Fold the graph paper around the corner of the prism as shown. Look into the face of the prism as you rotate the prism up and down. You should be able to see the X change into an O and vice versa as you rotate the prism.

Students should follow the Investigation and take turns looking into the prism rotating it up and down to see the X and O. This optical trick works because of the critical angle of reflection.

When your eye detects an image, the brain assumes the object you see is where the image appears to come from if the light had traveled in straight lines directly to your eyes. Because they bend light, mirrors and prisms can trick the brain into seeing an image in a different place from the actual object. This Investigation and the next few chapters will show you how optical devices manipulate light in useful ways, such as to magnify an object or project an image on a distant screen. But, before we move on to optics, we should spend some time discussing light itself. Can anyone list some characteristics of light?

Light travels in straight lines, light has color, light can be reflected and refracted, light carries heat and energy, light can travel through space, light can be blocked by opaque objects, light is produced by hot objects such as a light bulb filament, light can be bright or dim, etc.

Teaching tip

Example answers

1a. Drawing should show light ray leaving folded paper from location of arrow, moving in a straight line to location on mirror where image of arrow appears, reflecting off mirror, and moving in straight line from mirror to location of student's eye.

2a. & 2b.

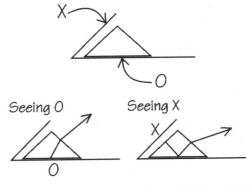

2c. The image in the prism is always refracted. When the image of the X is seen, the image is both refracted and reflected.

UNIT 6: Light and Color

16.1   Properties and Sources of Light

Question: What are some useful properties of light?

In this Investigation, you will:

1. Show how mirrors, lenses, and prisms cause objects to appear to be where they are not.
2. Calculate the time it takes light to move ordinary distances.
3. Explain why stars appear dimmer or brighter and seem to twinkle.

It is hard to imagine living in a world without light. Light has many properties that make it important, both in nature and to humans. In this Investigation, you will explore a few useful properties of light.

1   **Fooling the brain with light**

Prisms, mirrors, and lenses are devices that can affect the way light travels from an object to your eyes. Your brain perceives an object to be where the light from that object appears to come from. The object may not be where the light appears to come from—but that is where your brain tells you the object is.

1. Set a sheet of graph paper on the optics table. Draw an arrow on the paper as shown in the diagram at right.
2. Fold a piece of paper and set it on the optics table so that it blocks your view of the arrow.
3. A mirror is a shiny surface that reflects light very well. Arrange the mirror so that you can see the arrow around the folded paper.

a. Draw a sketch that uses lines to show how the light from the arrow on the paper reaches your eyes by reflecting from the mirror.

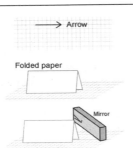

→ Arrow

Folded paper

Mirror

2   **Seeing reflection and refraction at the same time**

1. Take a piece of graph paper and draw a line 5 centimeters from one edge. Draw an X and an O on opposite sides of the line.
2. Fold the paper on the line and wrap it around one of the corners of the prism that is not a right angle.
3. Look into the prism. Move your head up and down to change the angle at which you look.

Both refraction and reflection often occur when light hits a boundary between materials such as the boundary between glass and air. The amount of light reflected or refracted depends on the angle at which you are looking relative to the surface.

a. Draw a diagram showing the path of the light when you see the X.
b. Draw a diagram showing the path of the light when you see the O.
c. Is the image in the prism always reflected or refracted or can there be both reflection and refraction at the same time?

Draw the X and O

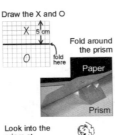

X 5 cm
O fold here

Fold around the prism

Paper

Prism

Look into the prism at different angles

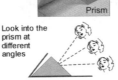

The speed of light

Speed of light $= 3 \times 10^8$ m/sec

The inverse square law

The inverse square law of intensity:

Intensity has units of watts per meters squared. (W/m²)

$$I = \frac{P}{4\pi r^2}$$

3 In everyday language the word "light" means white, red, green, blue, and all the other colors we see. To a physicist, light has a much broader definition. The physics definition of light includes infrared, ultraviolet, and other forms of radiant energy that we cannot see, such as radio waves and x-rays. You will see why these other forms of radiation are called light when we cover the wave properties of light. For now, remember that visible light, which is the colors of the rainbow, is only a small portion of an entire group of waves that all travel at the same speed and which physicists also call "light".

When we describe light it is useful to draw arrows that represent the direction the light is moving. Think about a window shade with a small hole in it. The hole lets in a ray of light. We draw an arrow to represent the ray of light in a diagram. For example, can you describe the path of a light ray that I see when I look at your shirt?

> Students discuss this with you. The light ray probably starts in the light fixture in the room, travels to the shirt, bounces off the shirt, and then travels to your eye.

You don't see light rays moving because light travels very fast. The speed of light is 300,000,000 m/sec. That is three hundred million meters per second. In everyday units the speed of light is 186,000 miles per second. Fast enough to go around the Earth more than seven times in the time it takes you to blink an eye. When you turn the light on, light spreads our from the bulb at 186,000 miles per second. The light reflects from everything in the room. You eyes see the reflected light nearly instantaneously. It takes sensitive instruments to measure the actual movement of light.

As an example of speed, calculate the time it takes a ray of light to get from your paper to your eye.

> Student do the calculation. They will need to use scientific notation. The typical result is $1 \text{ m} \div 3 \times 10^8$ m/sec $= 3.3 \times 10^{-9}$ seconds. Three billionths of a second is an incredibly short time. The fastest that humans can respond to stimuli is about 0.01 seconds, ten million times slower!

4 As light travels, it spreads out. Think about the light from a single bulb. The light spreads out almost equally in all directions. As the light spreads out, its energy is dispersed over a larger and larger area. That is why you cannot see a light bulb from a mile away. The intensity is a property that describes how much light falls on a square meter of surface area. Bright light has high intensity and dim light has low intensity. An intensity of one watt per square meter means one watt of light power crosses one square meter. Power, you recall, is energy per second. So an intensity of 1 W/m² represents 1 joule of light energy shining on a surface every second.

If light spreads out equally in all directions, then the intensity at any given distance (r) is the power of light divided by the surface area of a sphere of radius, r. The area of a sphere is $4\pi r^2$, therefore we can write the intensity of light at a distance r as $I = P/4\pi r^2$. This formula is known as the inverse square law, and we will meet it again when we talk about radiation.

> Draw a circle of radius r on the board with the area formula $A = 4\pi r^2$.

The inverse square law explains why distant objects' are harder to see. The light power that is received by your eye is really the intensity on you eye times the area of the pupil in your eye. When it is dark, your pupil expands to admit more light so you can see. In bright light your pupil contracts to block some of the light.

3 The speed of light

Light travels so fast that it is hard to comprehend the interval of time it takes to get from one place to another. Sound also travels fast but not as fast as light. You can perceive effects due to the limited speed of sound. For example, you can hear an echo off a distant wall. The time delay between making a sound and hearing the echo is due to the time it takes sound to travel to the wall and back to your ears. The speed of light is so fast (3×10^8 m/sec) that there is no apparent delay between shining a light on a mirror and receiving the light back into your eyes.

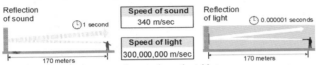

Reflection of sound — 1 second — 170 meters

Speed of sound 340 m/sec

Speed of light 300,000,000 m/sec

Reflection of light — 0.000001 seconds — 170 meters

a. Measure the distance from the arrow you drew on the optics table to your eyes.
b. Calculate the time it takes light to travel this distance.
c. Calculate how far light would travel in one second.

4 The inverse square law and light from distant stars and galaxies

Depending on where you live, the intensity of visible sunlight reaching your eyes is 300-600 watts per square meter at noon on a clear day in summer. The stars you see in the night sky are actually as bright as the sun (or brighter) but they are extremely far away.

The light from a point source spreads out in a sphere centered on the source. The intensity of light falling on the inner surface of the sphere is equal to the total power of light divided by the surface area of the sphere. Suppose a source of light has a power *(P)* in watts. The surface area of a sphere is given by the formula $A = 4\pi r^2$. Therefore, the intensity of light a distance *(r)* away from a point source is given by the intensity formula on the right. When power is in watts and area is in square meters, the intensity *(I)* has units of watts per square meter (W/m²).

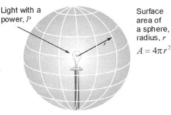

Light with a power, *P*

Surface area of a sphere, radius, *r*
$A = 4\pi r^2$

The inverse square law of intensity

$$\text{Intensity (W/m}^2) \quad I = \frac{P}{4\pi r^2}$$

a. Suppose a star like the sun were a distance of 4×10^{16} meters away. What is the intensity of the light from that star that reaches Earth?
b. How much time did the light take to get from the star to Earth? As we look out into the universe, we are also seeing backward in time because the light from distant stars and galaxies has traveled many years before reaching human telescopes. Using this technique, we are able to see more than one billion years back in time.
c. A typical 100-watt light bulb makes about 20 watts of light and 80 watts of heat. Calculate the intensity of light from the bulb by using the light power (20 W) and the intensity formula. Repeat the calculation for a distance of 1 meter, 100 meters, and 500 meters away. A human eye is a very sensitive light detector; you can still see a 100-watt bulb at a distance of 500 meters.

107

3a. Sample; distance = 50 cm = 0.5 m

3b. Speed of light = 300,000,000 m/sec
t = d/r
t = 0.5 m/(300,000,000 m/sec)
t = 1.67×10^{-9} sec

3c. d = r × t
d = (300,000,000 m/sec) × 1 sec
d = 300,000,000 m

4a. Assuming our sun's intensity at 600 W/m² and distance of 1.49×10^{11} m to the sun;
I = P/4πr²
P = I × 4πr²
P = (600 W/m²) × (4π(1.49×10^{11} m)²)
P = 1.67×10^{26} W = power of our sun
for the sun-like star;
I = P/4πr²
I = (1.67×10^{26} W)/(4π(4×10^{16} m)²)
I = 8.31×0^{-9} W

4b. t = d/r
t = (4×10^{16} m)/(300,000,000 m/sec)
t = 1.33×10^8 sec = 4.2 years

4c. 1 m = 15.7 W/m²100 m = 1.59×10^{-4} W/m²500 m = 6.37×10^{-6} W/m²

16.2 Color and Vision

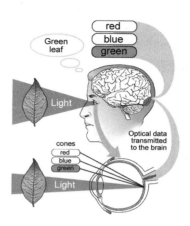

Key Question: How do we see color?

All the colors of visible light can be created using a combination of three primary colors: red, blue, and green. In this Investigation, the students use red, green, and blue colored lamps to mix different colors of light. They observe that white light is made from equal amounts of red, green, and blue. The students use a diffraction grating to observe the spectrum of the colored lamps. They see that ordinary light, even colored light, contains a range of colors. They also observe that a red laser has only one pure red color in its spectrum. By removing the color filter from one of the lamps and looking at the spectrum of the white bulb inside, the students learn how color filters work.

Reading Synopsis

Students read Section 16.2 Color and Vision after the Investigation.

Our eyes can see colors from deep red, through yellows, greens, and blues, to deep purple like violet. The order of colors is always the same when white light is separated with a prism: red, orange, yellow, green, blue, indigo and violet. We call the combination of all colors white light. All the colors in the rainbow are actually light of different energies. Moving through the rainbow from red to yellow to blue to violet, the energy of the light increases.

Special rod and cone cells in the retina of the eye are sensitive to color and intensity. There are different receptor cells for red, green, and blue light. The brain perceives a variety of color using the RGB additive process.

We see mostly reflected light. The CMYK process creates color in reflected light by selective absorption of colors from white light. Green plants reflect green light and absorb red and blue. Color TV's and computer monitors create colored images using thousands of red, green, and blue pixels.

The Investigation

Leading Questions
- How do we perceive color?
- How is color created by objects that give off light, such as a TV?
- How is color created by objects that reflect light, such as printed pictures or clothes?
- How is white light created?
- How do we know what colors are in any given light?

Learning Goals

By the end of the Investigation, students will be able to:
- Show that the white light can be made from red, green and blue.
- Interpret the rainbow that appears when a light source is viewed through a diffraction grating.
- Explain how a color filter makes colored light from white light.

Key Vocabulary

white light, color, cones, rods , additive process, primary colors-red, green and blue, subtractive process, pigments, magenta, black, ultra violent, infrared

Setup and Materials

Students work in groups of four or five at tables.

Each group should have:

- Light and Optics kit with red, green, and blue lamps, mounted lens, screen, table, and laser
- Diffraction grating glasses
- colored pencils
- Paper

Details

Time	⏱	One class period
Preparation	✎	none
Assignments	📖	Section 16.2 Color and Vision in the **Student Edition** after the Investigation.
Equipment Setup		Light and Optics

Teaching the Investigation

1   Introduction
2   Mixing primary colors of light
3   Explain what you see
4   More about rod and cone cells
5   Breaking apart white light

16.2 Color and Vision

Introduction

ROY-G-BIV is the acronym for the colors of the spectrum.

Mixing primary colors of light

1

All the colors of visible light can be created artificially using a combination of three primary colors: red, blue, and green.

Explain what you see

2

Three color receptors in the eye allow us to see millions of different colors. These color receptors are called cone cells.

Today's Investigation is about color and the perception of light. If you look at the rainbow you see colors in the order red orange yellow green blue indigo violet. The spreading of colors in light is called a spectrum. You can remember the order of colors in the spectrum of visible light by the acronym ROY-G-BIV.

Take out your optics set and connect the red green and blue lamps to the power supply. The lamps have magnetic bases that stick to the surface of the optical table. For the first part of the Investigation, we are going to mix light.

Students take components out and plug the three different color lamps into the power supply. Each group will need access to a wall socket to get power.

Take a one of about lenses that is mounted in a metal holder. The base up about metal holder also is magnetized and sticks to the optical table. Take the red and green lamps and place them about eight inches in front of about lens. Place the wooden screen on the other side of the lens from the lights. Move the lights and lens around until you get circles of red and green light on the screen. Make the circles overlap to see what color you get when red and green light are mixed.

Students should follow the instructions in the Investigation by setting up the colored LED lamps to project circles of different colors on the screen.

Try combining the three combinations of lamps you have: red and green, read and blue, and blue and green. Also try combining all three colors red green and blue. Write the observations you make in table 1.

Students write their observations in table 1 as they rearrange the three lamps to mix the different colors. Discuss with the students the colors you get when you mix red green and blue light. Many will be surprised that yellow is a combination of red and green. Many students have heard that white light is a mixture of colors, but they may not have tried this for themselves.

What does this experiment tell us about white light?

White light is a mixture of many colors. If the students can get three circles of equal intensity to overlap the screen shows a pretty clear white in the area where red green and blue circles overlap.

This experiment is as much about human perception as it is about physics. For example, when you mixed green light and red light you saw yellow. You probably did not expect to see yellow because yellow is a light color and red and green seem like darker colors. You see yellow because of how the human eye and brain detect and perceive light. The retina of the eye has three types of color sensors called cone cells. Each type of cone cell is receptive to a particular energy of light. Red light has the lowest energy compared with the other colors in visible light. One type of cone cell is responsive to red light, and does not respond to green or blue. Another type of cone cell responds to medium energy light, which you see as green. The third type of cone cell responds to higher energy light, which is blue. When high energy light is received by the eye, only the blue cone cells send signals to the brain. We have learned to associate these signals with the name "BLUE". Suppose the cone cells for medium energy are active. What color do you see?

Students should answer "green". We see green when the brain gets signals from cone cells which respond to medium energy light.

What happens if the energy of light is between low and medium? The low-energy cone cells and the medium-energy cone cells both send signals to the brain. What color do you see?

The experiment just proved that we see a color that we call yellow when there is an equally strong signal from both the red cone cells and the green cone cells.

16.2 Color and Vision

Question: How do we see color?

In this Investigation, you will:

1. Show that white light can be made from red, green, and blue.
2. Explain the colors we see in terms of subtracting colors from white light.

All the colors of visible light can be created artificially using a combination of three primary colors: red, blue, and green. In this Investigation, you will use a white light source and color filters to discover what happens when you mix different colors of light. You will also learn how those filters work.

1 Mixing primary colors of light

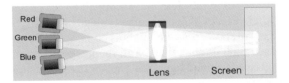

1. For this Investigation, you will use red, blue, and green LEDs (light emitting diodes). Attach each LED to the power supply and plug in the whole assembly.
2. Place the three LEDs side by side on one edge of the optics table. Set one of the lenses in the middle. Set the screen (on the back of the mirror) at the opposite edge from the LEDs. You should see three spots of color in the screen corresponding to the red, green, and blue LEDs.
3. Move the lens and screen to make the three spots overlap and observe the colors on the screen.

2 Explaining what you see

Use Table 1 to record the answers to the following questions about your observations.

a. What color do you see when you mix red and green light?
b. What color do you see when you mix red and blue light?
c. What color do you see when you mix blue and green light?
d. What color is produced when all three colors of light are equally mixed?

Table 1: Mixing primary colors of light

LED color combination	Color you see
Red + Green	
Green + Blue	
Blue + Red	
Red + Green + Blue	

How does a color TV work?

Television screens use the three primary colors of light to create the images we see. If you examine a TV with a magnifying glass, you will see that the screen is made of tiny red, green, and blue dots of light. By turning on the tiny lights at different intensities, TV screens can mix the three colors to make millions of different colors. From far away, your eyes can't see the tiny dots but blend them together to see a nice clear picture.

2 Example answers

2a. Red and green light make yellow.

2b. Red and blue make a pinkish color (magenta).

2c. Blue and green make a turquoise / sky blue color (cyan).

2d. All three colors make white.

Table 1: *Mixing the primary colors of light*

LED color combination	Color you see
Red + Green	yellow
Green + Blue	pink (magenta)
Blue + Red	sky blue (cyan)
Red + Green + Blue	white

More about rod and cone cells

Rod cells, a fourth type of light sensing cell, sense the overall intensity of light.

Rod cells allow us to see black and white.

Rod cells are more sensitive than cone cells.

Breaking apart white light

When we see an object, the light that reaches our eyes can come from two different processes:

1. The light can be emitted directly from the object.
2. The light can come from somewhere else, like the sun, and we see objects reflected by light.

White light is a combination of all the colors of light.

The human eye actually contains a fourth type of light sensing cell, called a rod cell. Rod cells sense the overall intensity of light and therefore see in black and white, they do not see color. Because they can respond to all colors, rod cells are much more sensitive and can detect lower levels of light then cone cells. That is why colors seem washed out in the dark. The lower the overall level of light, the more the eye just sees black and white images. There are about 130 million rod cells and only 7 million cone cells. That means the sharpness in our vision is mostly seen in black and white. The color associated with each triplet of 3 cone cells is associated with the brightness seen by 60 - 100 rod cells. Essentially, the image that you see is assembled in your brain from 130 million black and white dots and 7 million colored dots. This is similar to how the image is created on a computer monitor or TV set. If you look closely at a computer monitor with a magnifying glass you can see the individual dots that make up the image.

3 Who around the room has a blue shirt? Why does the blue shirt look blue?

Start a discussion on why things looked the color that they do. That shirt looks blue because it reflects blue light. That means there must be blue light in what ever light falls on that shirt to be reflected. Turn out the lights and shine a red light on a blue shirt, the blue shirt looks black.

Blue cloth looks blue because there are dyes in the cloth that absorb all colors of light except blue. When white light falls on the fabric, everything except blue is absorbed. Since blue light is what is reflected to your eye, the shirt looks blue. It is easy to show that white light is composed of many colors. Pick up the diffraction grating glasses and look at a light through them. You should see a central bright spot and rainbows up down and to the side. The glasses separate light into a spectrum which shows the component colors in the rainbows on the sides of the central bright spot.

Students should look through the diffraction grating glasses at a light source. One of the LED lamps works very well as a light source.

Even when a light looks green, it probably contains other colors. A light looks green if green is the dominant color, even if the light includes other colors as well. Take the diffraction grating glasses and look at each of the colored lamps. What do you see? Compare the spectrum you see from the red, green, and blue lights with each other.

Students should notice that all of the colored lamps have a broad spectrum. The red lamp has mostly red but it also has some green and a tiny bit of blue. The blue lamp has mostly blue but it has a small amount of green and even some red.

4 Take the colored plastic lens off one of the colored lamps and look at the white light underneath through the diffraction grating glasses. How does the spectrum of the white light compare with the spectrum of the colored light when the cover is on? Based on your observation, how does a color filter work?

Students remove one cover and look at the lamp underneath. A color filter works by subtracting or blocking colors. For example, the red plastic lens of the red lamp contains chemical dyes that absorb colors of light other than red. The lamp looks red because red light is allowed through the filter.

Plug in the laser and shine the laser onto the white surface of the screen. Look at the laser dot on the screen through the diffraction grating glasses. What kind of a spectrum do you see from this red light? Do not look directly into the laser beam. You should never allow a laser beam to fall directly into your eye.

Students should see that spectrum from the laser beam contains only one color, pure red. Explain the difference between monochromatic light like a laser and ordinary red light like the light from the red lamp. Monochromatic light has only one color and is made by lasers.

Left column

3   Breaking apart light

Most of the light we see is made of a mixture of different colors. The diffraction grating glasses can separate out those different colors. If you look at a bright light through the diffraction grating glasses, you see rainbows on all sides. The rainbows spread out all the colors that are present in the light coming through the bright spot in the center. Technically, the rainbows are called a *spectrum*. A spectrum shows what different colors of light make up a particular sample of light.

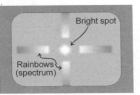

Bright spot

Rainbows (spectrum)

You have three different sources of colored light. The green light looks green but just how "pure" is the green? In this part of the Investigation, you will examine the light produced by each colored LED and learn how a *color filter* works. You will use the diffraction glasses to make your observations. The diffraction glasses allow you to see the different colors of the spectrum that a light source produces.

For each observation, look at the spectrum you see through the diffraction grating glasses. Observe the mixture of colors and record your observations in Table 2. You may wish to use colored pencils if they are available.

1. Look at the red LED through the diffraction glasses.
2. Look at the blue LED through the diffraction glasses.
3. Look at the green LED through the diffraction glasses.
4. Unscrew the color filter from one of the color LEDs. Look through the diffraction glasses at the light produced by the white LED and record your observations in the table.
5. Shine the red laser onto the screen. Look at the spot on the screen through the diffraction glasses.

➤**Safety Note: DO NOT LOOK DIRECTLY AT THE LASER BEAM.**

Table 2: Examining light sources

Red LED	Green LED	Blue LED
White LED		Red laser spot

4   Explaining what you see

a. Describe the similarities and differences you observed in the spectra from the red, blue, and green LEDs. You may want to use colored pencils to sketch the colors in the spectrum.

b. Describe what you saw looking at the white LED. Compare the spectrum from the white LED with the spectra from red, green, and blue. You may want to use colored pencils to sketch the colors in the spectrum.

c. Describe the spectrum you saw looking through the diffraction grating glasses at the spot made by the red laser on the screen. How is the spectrum of the red laser different from the spectrum of the red LED?

d. Based on your observations, explain how the colored filters transform the white light of the LEDs inside the lamps into red, green, and blue.

Right column

3 4   Example answers

Table 2: *Examining the light sources*

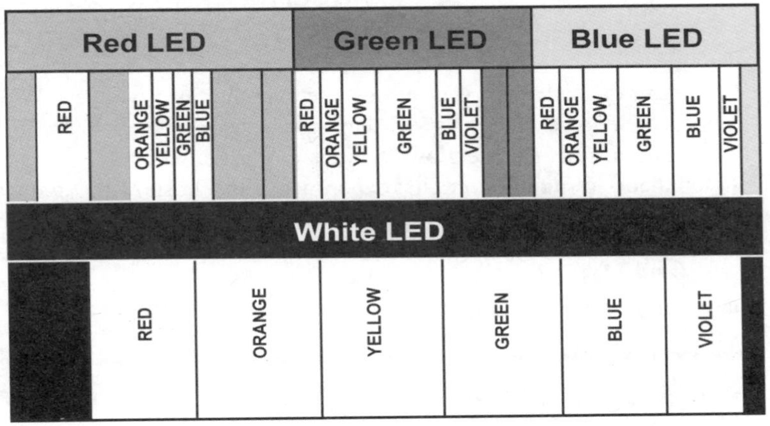

Red LED				Green LED						Blue LED					
RED	ORANGE / YELLOW / GREEN / BLUE			RED	ORANGE	YELLOW	GREEN	BLUE	VIOLET	RED	ORANGE	YELLOW	GREEN	BLUE	VIOLET

White LED					
RED	ORANGE	YELLOW	GREEN	BLUE	VIOLET

4a. The red LED - Had a lot of red, more than any other color of the spectrum. There was a small gap between the red part and the other colors. There wasn't a lot of blue, green yellow or orange. Didn't see any violet.

The blue LED - Had large amounts of green and blue, and smaller amounts of all other colors more or less in equal amounts.

The green LED - Lots of green, more than any other color. All other colors were all in about equal amounts.

4b. The white LED had all colors represented in equal amounts.

4c. The red laser had bright spots emanating out from the central brightest spot. The dots were spaced evenly apart and in a cross shaped pattern. The spots were progressively dimmer as they were further from the center. The dots were always the red color of the laser, instead of repeating spectrums of colors like the LEDs.

4d. The filters absorb some light from all colors of the entire spectrum. The color or colors that are least absorbed most influence the actual color that we end up seeing. The color we end up seeing is shifted toward the color that pass through the filter in the greatest amount, but all colors contribute a little since small amounts of all colors make it through the filter.

16.3 Photons and Atoms

Key Question: How does light fit into the atomic theory of matter?

When atoms absorb energy, electrons rise to higher energy levels. When the electrons fall back to their lower energy state, they may release energy in the form of light. In this Investigation, students use glow-in-the-dark plastic to observe some consequences of the photon theory of light. In the first experiment, student show that glow in the dark material does not glow if it is not first "charged up" by exposure to white light. The students then use the red, green, and blue LED lamps will determine which colors are most effective at causing the plastic to glow. They observe that blue light has enough energy to make the plastic glow but red light does not, no matter how bright.

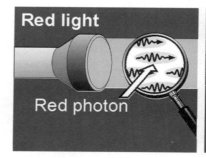 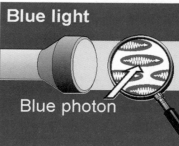

Reading Synopsis

Students read Section 16.3 Photons and Atoms after the investigation.

Light energy comes in tiny, discrete bundles called photons. The energy of a photon is proportional to its frequency. Blue photons have a higher energy than red photons Because blue light has a higher frequency than red light. The intensity of light is determined by the number of photons and by the energy of each photon. Equal intensities of red and blue light represent different numbers of photons because blue photons individually carry more energy than red photons.

In the atomic theory, each atom interacts with only one photons at a time. The phosphorus atoms in glow-in-the-dark plastic require a minimum energy to absorb light that can be released later as a photo luminescent glow. A white page looks white because the atoms absorb and re-emit photons of all energies equally. Black ink looks black because the atoms absorb all colors of visible photons and emit none

The Investigation

Leading Questions
- How is light produced?
- How do photo luminescent (as in glow-in-the-dark) materials work?
- How is light described in the atomic theory of matter?
- What color light has the highest energy?

Learning Goals

By the end of the Investigation, students will be able to:
- Described the basic idea behind the photon theory of light
- Explain why blue light causes a photo luminescent plastic to blow while red light does not, even when the red light is made brighter than the blue light.

Key Vocabulary   photons, photoluminescence

Setup and Materials

Students work in groups of four or five at tables.

Each group should have:

- Optics board
- LEDs: red, green and blue

Details

Time ⊙ One class period

Preparation

Assignments 📖 Section 16.3 Photons and Atoms from the **Student Edition** after the investigation.

Equipment Setup Light and Optics

Teaching the Investigation

1 Introduction
2 How light is produced
3 How colors are produced by inks and dyes
4 Glow-in-the-dark plastic
5 Thinking about what you observed
6 The effect of different colors of light
7 The quantum (photon) theory of light

Introduction

Now that we know a little about how light behaves, let's talk about how light is created. Almost all the light you see is created inside atoms. Although atoms are so small we cannot see them directly, in this Investigation we will demonstrate an observable consequence of the relationship between energy, atoms, and light. In many ways the technology of using atoms to make light is still being developed. The ordinary incandescent and fluorescent light bulbs that you can buy in the store today will one day be replaced by LED lamps that use less electricity and last 100 times longer. LED's rely on certain special types of atoms to make light in a similar way to how light is produced in lasers.

How light is produced

1

Almost all light is produced by atoms.

We know that light carries energy. If you stand outside on a sunny day, your skin gets warm. The warmth comes from the energy carried by sunlight. You also know that energy obeys the law of conservation of energy. When light falls on a surface, what happens to the energy?

> This is the starting point for a discussion. The energy of light is partly absorbed and partly reflected. On the atomic level, both absorption and reflection involve atoms. Reinforce the point that the energy must go somewhere and eventually must come back out again for energy to be conserved.

Light is one way that individual atoms exchange energy with the environment so they can obey the law of conservation of energy. When light falls on an atom, one of two things can happen—the energy is absorbed by the electrons in the atom, or the energy can be reflected by the electrons in the atom.

When atoms absorb energy, electrons rise to higher energy levels. When electrons fall back to their lower energy state, they many release energy in the form of light.

You can think of energy absorption as making the electrons move a little farther away from the nucleus. Since the electrons are attracted to the nucleus, moving farther away takes energy.

> Draw a diagram on the board showing an electron moving from nearer to the nucleus a little bit farther from the nucleus, like the diagram in step 1 of the Investigation.

When light is reflected, the electron falls immediately down closer to the nucleus, giving off light of the exact same energy as the light that was absorbed. Since the color of light is related to the energy, the color of reflected light from the atom is the same as the color of the light that was absorbed. The process of reflection is really a process of absorption of light by an atom and the immediate re-emission of identical light.

Not all atoms emit light immediately after absorbing it or emit light of the same energy that it absorbed. Some atoms convert some or all of the absorbed light to heat energy. In fact, some atoms convert certain colors of light to heat and reflect other colors. This occurs because the electrons in atoms are very sensitive to light of certain specific energies. Different types of atoms and molecules are most sensitive to different energies of light. We will come back to this idea later in the Investigation, but it explains how inks and dyes are able to absorb certain colors of light while reflecting other colors.

How colors are produced by inks and dyes

Different types of atoms and molecules are most sensitive to different energies of light.

Glow-in-the-dark plastic

2

On the back side of the optics table board is a pale green square of plastic. Leave the board upside down for a moment and don't look at the plastic yet. Wait for me to turn off the light. This plastic is special because it glows in the dark. When I turn off the light, flip the board over so the glow-in-the-dark plastic is exposed. Place your hand over the glow-in-the-dark plastic and hold it there while I turn the light on and back off again.

> After you turn out the light, students flip the board over and put their hand on the glow-in-the-dark plastic. They should hold their hand there while you flip the light back on for 30 seconds and then turn it off again.

UNIT 6: Light and Color

16.3　Photons and Atoms

Question: How does light fit into the atomic theory of matter?

In this Investigation, you will:

1. See how light fits into the atomic theory that describes matter.
2. Examine a photoluminescent material and explain its behavior using the photon theory of light.
3. Observe that different colors of light carry different amounts of energy.

1　How is light produced?

Almost all the light you see is produced by atoms. When atoms absorb energy, electrons rise to higher energy levels. When the electrons fall back to their lower energy state, they may release energy in the form of light.

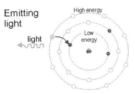

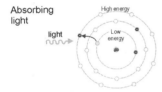

In some elements, it takes time for the energized electrons to fall back and give up their energy. These elements store energy and give off light slowly over a period of time. This is how glow-in-the-dark material works. Embedded in the material are atoms of the element phosphorus. When light energy hits the phosphorus atoms, some of the electrons absorb energy. When the electrons fall back, they release the stored energy and the material glows. The glow stops when all the electrons have returned to the lowest energy level. The process is called *photoluminescence*. The word *photo* means light and *luminescence* means glowing.

2　Examine the effects of light on glow-in-the-dark material

1. Uncover the glow-in-the-dark material (on the underside of the optics board) in a darkened room.
2. Cover part of the material and turn the lights back on or shine a flashlight onto the material.
3. Turn off the light source, remove the covering, and record your observations.
4. Expose the material to light completely uncovered.
5. Turn off the light and wait a minute and place your hand over part of the material.
6. Remove your hand and record your observations.

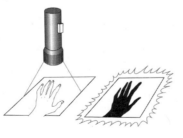

Teaching tip

Many students are quite fascinated by the glow in the dark material on the back side of the optics board. You may want to get a discussion started before students look at the Investigation sheets. Ask students how they think the material works. Why does the material glow? Where does the light energy come from? Can any type of light be used to "charge up" the material? Why does the material continue to glow for some time? What might affect the time for which the material glows?

The Investigation only has students compare the effects of different colors of visible light on the material. You can extend the activity to include ultraviolet light and infrared light if you have access to UV and infrared light sources. Another extension is the study the effects of temperature. Cooling the material, such as with an ice cube, will temporarily stop it from glowing.

You might also want to have students analyze the light emitted by the material by viewing it with a spectroscope or through diffraction grating glasses.

Thinking about what you observed

What is photoluminescence?

Photoluminescence is the process of releasing stored energy as light.

The effect of different colors of light

NOTE: Students need to make a table to record their observations for this section of the Investigation.

The quantum (photon) theory of light

A photon is a small quantity of light like a particle.

The intensity of light describes how many photons are produced or absorbed in one second.

3 What do you see when you remove your hand?

> Students should see that the glow-in-the-dark plastic is glowing everywhere except the area that was covered by their hand.

The plastic glows in the dark because it contains atoms of the element phosphorus. Phosphorus atoms absorb light but do not re-emit the light immediately. The electrons in phosphorus atoms fall back toward the nucleus and re-emit light over a period of time. That is why the material glows for several minutes after it has been exposed to light. Can anyone explain why some areas of the plastic are glowing and some are not?

> Students should recognize that the area that was covered by their hand does not glow because it wasn't able to absorb any light when the room lights were on. Atoms in this area therefore have no energy so they cannot emit light. Areas that were exposed to the room light were able to absorb energy, and therefore these areas have atoms with enough energy to give off light and glow.

4 In terms of energy, green light is between red light and blue light. Red light has lower energy, and blue light has higher energy. We can do an experiment that shows that different colors of lights have different amounts of energy. I am going to turn off the room lights for the next part of the experiment. Take each of the colored lamps and see if you can make the plastic glow using light of different colors. Use a piece of paper to record whether each color was able to make the plastic glow. Try changing the brightness by moving the lamp toward the plastic or away from it to see if brightness has any effect.

> The students follow Part 4 of the Investigation and shine light of different colors on the glow-in-the-dark plastic. They may also use the laser. The students should discover that blue light makes the plastic glow quite well. Blue light makes the plastic glow even when the lamp is held a few centimeters away. Red light does not make the plastic glow at all even if the light is made very bright by holding the lamp right against the plastic.

Can anyone come up with an explanation for why blue light makes the plastic glow but red light does not?

> This is the start of a discussion of the idea that different colors of light have different amounts of energy. Blue light has more energy than green light; therefore, if an atom absorbs blue light, it has enough energy to emit green light. Red light has less energy than green light. If an atom absorbs red light, it does not have enough energy to emit green light.

5 The energy of light is divided into small bundles called photons. This is one of the discoveries of quantum mechanics. You can think of a photon as a tiny particle of light, except the "particle" is really pure energy and has no mass. Because they are pure energy, photons travel at the speed of light. Blue photons have more energy than red photons. Green photons have energy between red photons and blue photons.

Atoms can absorb and emit whole photons but never parts of a photon. A phosphorus atom that absorbs a blue photon gains enough energy to emit a green photon. An atom that absorbs a red photon does not gain enough energy to emit a green photon because green photons have more energy than red photons.

> You may wish to have an extended discussion of the photon theory of light, including the information that atoms typically only interact with one photon at a time. Another way to think of a photon is a short burst of a wave as shown in the diagram in Part 5 of the Investigation. Photons have classical wave properties such as frequency and wavelength and behave like discrete particles.

3 4 6 **Example answers**

3a. The material did not glow at all because no energy was added to the material.

3b. The material glowed because light energy of a particular wavelength energized the material. Since my hand blocked any light getting to the material, there was no glow produced. This resulted in a dark area on the material in the shape of my hand.

4. The red and green lights produce a faint glow while the blue produces a bright glow. Blue is the only color that has any real effect from a distance. Red and green glow only when they are very close to the material's surface.

6a. Blue has the highest energy and red has the lowest. Blue had the largest effect on making the glow-in-the-dark material glow. Red had very little effect, and any glow it did produce was probably due to small amounts of blue light that passed through the red filter.

6b. All three LEDs seemed to be about the same brightness, yet it was the blue LED that produced the only significant glow observed.

6c. If the electrons had been able to absorb any amount of energy, the red would have made it glow as well, perhaps not as brightly as the blue. Same with the green. But that did not happen. It was only the blue light that produced real glow, meaning red and green did not have enough energy to be absorbed. Since blue produced the glow and the other two did not, the quantum theory accurately predicts what was observed.

16.3 Photons and Atoms

3 Recording and analyzing your results

In answering these questions, think in terms of light and energy. Explain what happens to the energy in each of these situations:

a. What happened when the light was not allowed to strike the glow-in-the-dark material? Explain.

b. What happened when your hand was allowed to rest on the glow-in-the-dark material? Explain.

4 Examining the effect of different colors of light

In Part 2, you used a source of white light to add energy to the phosphorus atoms in the glow-in-the-dark material. White light is a mixture of all colors of the rainbow. In this section, you will determine what happens when more restricted colors of light are used to add energy to the phosphorus atoms. You need to make a table to record your observations.

1. Allow the glow-in-the-dark material to stop glowing by leaving it in the dark for a few minutes.

2. Switch on the red LED and shine it on the glow-in-the-dark material from a distance of about 10 centimeters. Wait 15 seconds and take the LED away and record your observations.

3. Try the same experiment again with the red LED 5 centimeters away and then again with the LED held right up against the surface. Decreasing the distance increases the intensity of the light without changing its color.

4. Repeat the procedure with the green LED. Record your observations.

5. Repeat the procedure with the blue LED. Record your observations.

5 The quantum theory of light

A *photon* is a small quantity of light like a particle. You can think of a photon like a short burst of a wave. The *intensity* of light describes how many photons per second are produced (or absorbed). The *color* of each photon depends on its energy. Different colors of light are produced by photons with different energies. High-energy blue photons have shorter wavelengths than low-energy red photons.

What is a photon?	**The difference between intensity and energy**
Wave $\wedge\wedge\wedge\wedge\wedge\wedge\wedge\wedge$	High energy (blue) photon Low intensity = few photons per second
Photon $\sim\!\!\wedge\!\!\sim\!\!\rightarrow$	
A photon is like a short burst of a wave	Low energy (red) photon High intensity = lots of photons per second

To glow, an electron in a phosphorus atom must first absorb energy from a photon of light. That means a photon must have enough energy to boost the electron up one whole level to be absorbed. If the photon does not have enough energy, the phosphorus atom cannot absorb it.

6 Thinking about what you learned

a. Based on the observations you made in Part 4, what color light has the highest energy? What color light has the lowest energy? Your answer should state how your observations support your conclusion.

b. Intuitively you might think the more intense the light is that you shine, the more brightly the phosphorus should glow. Explain how your observations support or refute this hypothesis.

c. How does what you observed support the quantum theory of light and atoms? HINT: What would have happened if electrons were free to absorb any energy rather than just certain energies?

17.1 Reflection and Refraction

Key Question: How do we describe the reflection and refraction of light?

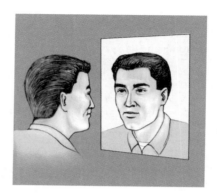

The reflection and refraction of light is observed by nearly everyone, everyday. In this Investigation, students determine the quantitative rules governing how light interacts with surfaces. They use a mirror and a laser to trace incident and reflected rays to determine the law of reflection. By tracing the beam from the laser through a prism, students demonstrate the law of refraction (Snell's law). Students determine the index of refraction of glass from a prism and also observe the critical angle of refraction in the prism.

Reading Synopsis

Students read Section 17.1 Reflection and Refraction after the Investigation.

The study of how light behaves is called optics. Optical devices include lenses, mirrors, cameras, telescopes, and microscopes. A ray diagram uses imaginary lines called light rays to describes how light travels. A normal line is perpendicular to a surface.

The law of reflection states that the angle of reflection is equal to the angle of incidence. The index of refraction for a material determines the ability of that material to bend light rays. Snell's law of refraction states that $n_i \sin\theta_i = n_r \sin\theta_r$ where the subscripts i and r refer to the incident and reflected rays. All angles are measured relative to the normal line.

Depending on the angle of incidence, light crossing a surface for which $n_i > n_r$ may be reflected instead of refracted. If the angle of incidence is greater than the critical angle, the light is reflected in a process called total internal reflection. The index of refraction typically varies with the color of the light creating a phenomenon called dispersion. Dispersion causes blue light to be bent more than red light in a prism or lens.

The Investigation

Leading Questions
- How does reflection change the path of light rays?
- How does refraction change the path of light rays?
- What does the index of refraction tell you about a material?
- How is the critical angle affected by the index of refraction?

Learning Goals

By the end of the Investigation, students will be able to:
- Trace light rays from a laser using a prism and a mirror to find the angles of incidence.
- Measure the index of refraction and observe the critical angle for glass.

Key Vocabulary

optics, geometric optics, lens, mirror, prism, incident ray, specular reflection, diffuse reflection law of reflection, normal line, ray diagram, refraction, index of refraction, angle of refraction, Snell's law internal reflection, critical angle, fiber optics dispersion

Setup and Materials

Students work in groups of four or five at tables.

Each group should have:

- Light and Optics Kit
- Mirror
- Graph paper
- Pencils

Details

Time	⊕	One class period
Preparation	✐	
Assignments	📖	Section 17.1 Reflection and Refraction in the **Student Edition** after the Investigation.
Skill Sheets		17.1A The Law of Reflection 17.1B Refraction
Equipment Setup		Light and Optics

Teaching the Investigation

1   Introduction
2   The law of reflection
3   Measuring the angles
4   Refraction
5   Snell's law
6   Tracing rays through a prism
7   Finding the index of refraction
8   The critical angle of refraction

Introduction

Optics is the study of how light behaves.

The law of reflection

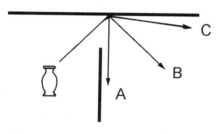

The law of reflection states that light rays reflect from a mirror with the same angle at which they arrive.

Today's Investigation begins with the study of how light behaves. How does light act when it meets objects such as mirrors, prisms, and lenses? This part of physics is called optics. You use optical devices every day, including glasses, windows, mirrors, television screens, and LED's. The study of optics begins with reflection and refraction. Can anyone define these processes for me?

Review with students that reflection describes how light bounces off a surface. Refraction describes how light passes through a transparent surface.

1 Imagine trying to see the object in the mirror as I have drawn here. Which place do you stand to see the object?

Most students recognize that they would stand in position B to see the object in the mirror.

What is it about position B that allows you to see the object in the mirror? What is different about position B compared to positions A or C?

Students respond that the angle of position B is correct for seeing the object while the angle for positions A or C is not correct. They probably will not know how to define "angle" relative to the mirror but most people recognize that the angle is important.

When you see an object in the mirror, the light comes from the object, bounces off the mirror, and reaches your eye. We can represent the path of the light using a ray diagram. The incident ray is the ray that travels from the object to the mirror. The reflected ray is the ray that travels from the mirror to your eye.

Draw a ray diagram on the board similar to the diagram in step 1 of the Investigation. Show the incident ray and the reflected ray.

In the first part of the Investigation, we are going to figure out where you must be to see an object in a mirror. We know that angles must be involved. In optics we define angles relative to an imaginary line drawn perpendicular to the surface and passing through the point where the light ray hits the surface. This line is called a normal line. The angle of incidence is the angle between the incident ray and the normal line. The angle of reflection is the angle between the normal line and the reflected ray. The rule we are searching for is a relationship between the angle of incidence and the angle of reflection.

Add the normal line, and the angles of incidence and reflection to your diagram on the board.

Take out your optics board and find the laser and the mirror. Set a sheet of graph paper on the board and attach it with the magnetic strips. Draw a horizontal line on the paper and set the mirror so its front surface is on your line. Connect the laser and place it on the board so the beam bounces off the mirror. Use a pencil to locate and mark several points along the laser beam before and after it hits the mirror. Remove the mirror and use a ruler to connect the dots and draw the incident and reflected rays.

Students follow the directions in Part 1 of the Investigation through step 6. You should demonstrate how to use a square edged business card to find and mark the location of the laser beam.

The incident and reflected rays you drew should meet at a point on the surface of the mirror, which you represented with your horizontal line. If the rays do not meet on the line, get a fresh sheet of graph paper and try the experiment again.

UNIT 6: Light and Color

Reflection and Refraction

Question: How do we describe the reflection and refraction of light?

In this Investigation, you will:

1. Trace light rays from a laser using a prism and a mirror to find the angles of incidence, reflection, and refraction.
2. Measure the index of refraction and observe the critical angle for glass.

We observe the law of reflection every day. Looking in a mirror we see ourselves reversed left-to-right. Our sense of sight depends on light reflected from objects around us. Light rays can also bend when they cross an interface between two different materials. The bending of light rays by a boundary between materials is called *refraction*. Prisms and lenses use refraction to manipulate light in telescopes, binoculars, cameras and even your eyes. In this Investigation, you will take a closer look at reflection, apply geometry to predict exactly where reflected light goes, and determine the rules for how and to what degree light is refracted by glass.

1 The law of reflection

1. Set a sheet of graph paper on the optics table and fix it with the magnetic strips.
2. Draw a line on the paper (see below) and set the mirror so the shiny surface is right on the line.
3. Connect the laser to the power supply and place it on the optics table so that the beam bounces off the mirror at an angle.
4. Use your pencil and an index card to trace the incident and reflected light rays from the laser.
5. Change the graph paper and repeat steps 1-4 with the laser beam set at a different angle. Do the experiment for at least four different angles.
6. Take each ray diagram you just made with the laser and use a ruler to extend the incident and reflected rays so they meet at the mirror surface. The *normal* is a line perpendicular to the surface of the mirror. Draw the normal from the mirror surface at the point where the laser beams hit.
7. Use a protractor to measure the angle between the incident ray and the normal for each diagram. Also, measure the angle between the normal and the reflected ray. Enter the angles in Table 1.

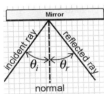

Table 1: Angles of incidence and reflection

	Diagram #1	Diagram #2	Diagram #3	Diagram #4
Angle of incidence				
Angle of reflection				

a. Write down your own statement of the law of reflection, describing the relationship between the angle of incidence and the angle of reflection.

---

1 Example answers

Table 1: *Angles of incidence and reflection*

	Diagram #1	Diagram #2	Diagram #3	Diagram #4
Angle of incidence	48°	23°	33°	66°
Angle of reflection	48°	23°	33°	66°

1a. The angle of reflection is equal in size and opposite in direction to the angle of incidence for a light ray reflected off a mirror.

Measuring the angles

The angle of incidence and the angle of reflection are always measured between the light rays and the normal line.

2

Carefully draw the normal from the point where the two rays meet the mirror line. Use a protractor and carefully measure the angles between the normal and the incident ray and the normal and the reflected ray.

Students measure the angles of incidence and reflection.

What is the relationship between the angle of incidence and the angle of reflection?

They should be equal, so if they differ at all it should only be by a few degrees.

When light hits a mirror, the light reflects so the angle of reflection is equal to the angle of incidence. This is known as the law of reflection. For the law of reflection, we always measure the angles relative to the normal line and not to the surface of the mirror.

To justify measuring the angle from the normal, you might show the students what happens if the laser beam hits a makeup or shaving mirror, which is curved. Using the normal makes measuring the incident and reflected rays easier and less dependent on the surface of the reflective material.

Now that you have learned about the law of reflection, what are some situations in which the law of reflection might apply (even if light is not involved)?

At this point, discuss and perform the demonstration described on the facing page.

Refraction

Refraction is the bending of light waves as they cross a surface between two different materials.

Incident ray: the light ray falling on a surface.

Refracted ray: the light ray passing through a surface.

1

In the next part of the Investigation we are going to look at refraction, or how light bends crossing a surface between two different materials. A light ray falling on a surface is called the incident ray. The light ray passing through the surface is called the refracted ray. You may assume the light rays move in straight lines except at the point where they cross the surface. Again, we use a normal line as the reference for measuring the angles. Consider a light ray falling on a block of glass. The angle of incidence is the angle between the incident ray and the normal line. The angle of refraction is the angle between the refracted ray and the normal line. The angle of refraction is measured inside the glass.

Draw a diagram similar to diagram in step 2 of the Investigation showing a light ray passing from air into glass.

For refraction, the law relating the angle of incidence and the angle of refraction is not as simple as for reflection. Different materials have different abilities to bend, or refract, light. This is because light traveling through matter propagates slower than light traveling through vacuum. The index of refraction is the ratio of the speed of light in a vacuum to the speed of light in a material. The index of refraction of air is 1.0 because air contains very little matter light travels at equal speeds through air and vacuum (nearly). The index of refraction for glass is around 1.5 because light travels 1.5 times faster in vacuum than it does in glass. The amount light bends depends on the difference in index of refraction between the material containing the incident ray and the material containing the refracted ray. We use the symbol n_i for the index of refraction on the incident side of a surface and n_r for the refracted side. For a light ray moving from air into glass $n_i < n_r$ and the ray bends toward the normal. The angle of refraction is less than the angle of incidence. For a light ray moving from glass back into air, the opposite is true. In this direction glass is on the incident side of the surface and air on the refracted side. Therefore, $n_i > n_r$ and the ray bends away from the normal. The angle of refraction is greater than the angle of incidence.

Draw diagrams showing both cases—air into glass, and glass into air—similar to the diagrams in step 2 of the Investigation.

When thinking about refraction you must be careful to draw careful diagrams for each surface the light crosses. The diagrams should label the material on both sides of the surface so you can tell which material is on the incident side and which is on the refracted side of the surface.

Teaching tip

Stress to students that angles of incidence, reflection, and refraction are always measured from the normal line. Inevitably, some students measure from the surface of the mirror or prism and wonder why their results do not match those of other groups. Measuring from the surface rather than the normal does not lead to problems when studying reflection but will yield incorrect results when using Snell's law. If you stress the proper method of measuring angles when students study reflection, they will be more likely to measure correctly when they get to refraction.

17.1 Reflection and Refraction

2 Refraction

The normal line is also used to describe how refraction works. Remember, the normal is a line perpendicular to the surface. A light ray falling on a surface is called the *incident ray*. The light ray passing through the surface is called the *refracted ray*. You may assume these light rays move in straight lines except at the point where they cross the surface.

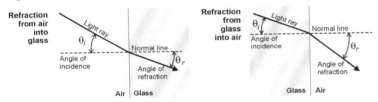

The *angle of incidence* is the angle between the incident ray and the normal line. The *angle of refraction* is the angle between the refracted ray and the normal line. Snell's law of refraction states the relationship between the angle of incidence and the angle of refraction.

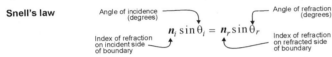

Snell's law

$$n_i \sin \theta_i = n_r \sin \theta_r$$

Angle of incidence (degrees)

Angle of refraction (degrees)

Index of refraction on incident side of boundary

Index of refraction on refracted side of boundary

The incident and refracted rays are defined in terms of the direction the light is going as it crosses the surface between two materials. Going from air into glass, the incident ray is in air and the refracted ray is in glass. Going from glass into air, the incident ray is in glass, and the refracted ray in is air.

3 Tracing rays through the prism

1. Place a prism on the center of the piece of paper on the optics table. Put the long flat side facing the left of the paper. Use your pencil to trace the outline of the prism.

2. Put the laser on the left side of the prism. Shine the laser at the prism and make sure that the beam comes out the opposite short side. A good way to do this is to place the laser below the level of the prism and shine it at the upper part of the prism.

3. The beam is entering the prism from the air and passing through the prism into the air again. Using your pencil, trace the path of the laser beam from the prism into the air. See the diagram at right.

4. Remove the laser and prism from the paper.

5. Draw the lines connecting the beam through the glass, labeling the diagram as shown.

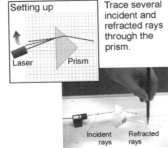

Trace several incident and refracted rays through the prism.

113

Snell's law

$$n_i \sin \theta_i = n_r \sin \theta_r$$

Snell's law of refraction is the rule that tells us the relationship between the angle of incidence and the angle of refraction.

Write Snell's law on the board.

The incident and refracted rays are defined in terms of the direction the light is going as it crosses the surface between two materials. Going from air into glass, the incident ray is in air and the refracted ray is in glass. Going from glass into air, the incident ray is in glass, and the refracted ray is in air.

You may wish to review the sine of an angle and how to calculate the sine of an angle and the angle from a sine (inverse sine) using a calculator.

Tracing rays through a prism

To observe refraction we are going to trace the path of a laser beam as it goes through a glass prism. The prism has three sides; the laser beam will pass through two of them. Follow the instructions in step 3 of the Investigation to trace the laser beam through the prism.

Students trace a ray diagram using the laser and prism.

Carefully extend the lines you drew until they intersect the outline of the prism. The light ray traveling through the glass must connect the two points where the entering and exiting laser beams cross the surface of the prism.

Students should draw the connecting light ray through the prism itself.

Finding the index of refraction

The index of refraction describes the ability of a material to bend light rays.

Draw the normal lines to both surfaces of the prism. Measure the angles of incidence and refraction for the light rays going from air to glass and from glass to air. Record your measurements in Table 2.

Students measure and record the angles. Make a tracing from a student's ray diagrams on a transparency and show the transparency on an overhead projector. This enlarges the image making it easier to show students how to measure the angles.

If you know the angle of incidence and the angle of refraction, you can calculate the sine with your calculator. If the index of refraction of air is 1.0, what is the index of refraction of glass? Calculate the index of refraction of glass using your measurements going both ways—from air into glass and from glass into air.

Students should do the calculation. For air into glass, $n_i = 1$ and $n_r = (\sin\theta_i/\sin\theta_r)$. For light traveling from glass into air, $n_r = 1$, and $n_i = (\sin\theta_r/\sin\theta_i)$. The two values should be between 1.4 and 1.6.

The critical angle of refraction

The critical angle is the angle of incidence that makes the angle of refraction exactly 90 degrees.

When light is going from a glass into air, the ratio n_i/n_r is greater than one. That means the angle of refraction (θ_r) must be greater than the angle of incidence (θ_i). If you think about it, when the angle of refraction becomes greater than 90 degrees, it becomes reflection. The critical angle is the angle of incidence that makes the angle of refraction exactly 90 degrees. When the angle of incidence exceeds the critical angle, light is reflected because the angle of refraction becomes greater than 90 degrees. Scientists and engineers use the term total internal reflection to describe light reflecting back into a high index material from a boundary with a low index material.

Shine the laser into the long side of the prism. Observe what happens as you change the angle of incidence by rotating the prism. For some angles the laser is refracted and exits the prism to the left. For other angles the laser comes out on the right!

Students should follow the procedure and step 5 of the Investigation.

Try to identify the angle at which the laser beam makes the transition between refracting and reflecting when it reaches the boundary between glass and air.

Example answers

4a. Light bends toward the normal when passing from a low index material (air) to a higher-index material (glass).

4b. Light bends away from the normal when passing from a high index material (glass) to a low-index material (air).

4c. Sample data:

Table 2: *Angles of incidence and refraction*

	Angle/incidence	Angle/refraction
Going from air to glass	21°	16°
Going from glass to air	30°	53°

4d. Going from air to glass:

$$n_{air} = 1$$

$$n_a \sin\theta_i = n_g \sin\theta_r$$

$$\sin\theta_i = n_g \sin\theta_r$$

$$n_g = \frac{\sin\theta_i}{\sin\theta_r}$$

$$n_g = \frac{\sin 21°}{\sin 13°} = \frac{0.358}{0.225} = 1.6$$

4e. Predicted angle of refraction going from glass to air:

$$n_g \sin\theta_i = n_a \sin\theta_r$$

$$\sin\theta_r = n_g \sin\theta_i = 1.6 \times \sin 30° = 0.8$$

$$\theta_r = 53°$$

4f. My measured angle of refraction going from glass to air was 53°, which was exactly as I predicted in question 4e. This observation supports Snell's law of refraction.

5. The critical angle for the glass prism seems to be approximately 42° as measured from the glass/air boundary.

17.1 Reflection and Refraction

4 Finding the index of refraction

The *index of refraction* is a property of a material that describes its ability to bend light rays. Air has an index of refraction of 1.0. The index of refraction for different types of glass ranges from 1.4 to 1.6. The higher the index of refraction, the more the material bends light.

Table 2: Angles of incidence and refraction

	Angle/incidence	Angle/refraction
Going from air to glass		
Going from glass to air		

a. Draw the normals to the two faces of the prism the beam passed through. When light goes from a low-index (air) to a higher-index (glass) material, does it bend toward the normal or away from the normal?

b. When light goes from a high-index (glass) to a low-index (air) material, does it bend toward the normal or away from the normal?

c. Use the two normals and a protractor to determine the angles of incidence and refraction for both surfaces crossed by the light beam. Use Table 2 to record the angles.

d. Apply Snell's law to the light ray entering the prism. The incident material is air ($n = 1$); the refracting material is glass ($n = n_g$). Calculate the sines of the angles of incidence and refraction. Use your calculation to determine the index of refraction of glass (n_g).

e. Apply Snell's law to the light ray leaving the prism. Using the index of refraction for glass, predict what the angle of refraction should be when the laser beam goes from glass to air.

f. Compare your predicted angle of refraction to the angle you measured. Comment on any differences between your prediction and your measurement. Do your observations support Snell's law? Your answer should be supported by your observations of the laser beam.

5 The critical angle of refraction

When light is going from a high-index material into a lower-index material, the ratio n_i/n_r is greater than one. That means the angle of refraction (θ_r) must be greater than the angle of incidence (θ_i). When the angle of refraction becomes greater than 90 degrees, it becomes—reflection! The *critical angle* is the angle of incidence that makes the angle of refraction exactly 90 degrees. When the angle of incidence exceeds the critical angle, light is reflected because the angle of refraction becomes greater than 90 degrees. Scientists and engineers use the term *total internal reflection* to describe light reflecting back into a high-index material from a boundary with a low-index material.

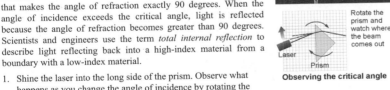

Observing the critical angle

1. Shine the laser into the long side of the prism. Observe what happens as you change the angle of incidence by rotating the prism. For some angles, the laser is reflected and exits the prism to the left. For other angles, the laser comes out on the right.

2. Try to identify the angle at which the laser beam makes the transition between refracting and reflecting when it reaches the boundary between glass and air.

17.2 Mirrors, Lenses, and Images

Key Question: How does a lens or mirror form an image?

An image is formed where many rays from the same point on an object meet, or appear to meet, in a point. In this Investigation, students start by tracing rays with the laser to show how and where the virtual image forms in a mirror. They then repeat the process for a cylindrical lens and learn about focal point and focal length. Students describe the characteristics of images as right-side-up, or inverted, real or virtual, and magnified, reduced, or life-sized. In the final parts of the Investigation students look at the image formed by a single convex lens when used to project an image (real) and as a magnifying glass (virtual). They also discover that magnification changes with distance and that there is a limit to how much magnification you can have with a given lens.

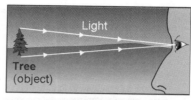

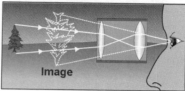

Reading Synopsis

Students read Section 17.2 Mirrors, Lenses, and Images after the Investigation.

Objects are real physical entities that give off or reflect light. Images are patterns of light formed where many rays from the same point on an object meet, or appear to meet, in a point. A virtual image is formed when light rays appear to come from a point, like the image in a mirror. A real image is formed when light rays actually come to a point, like the image formed by an overhead projector. The magnification of an image is the ratio of the image's size divided by the object's size. Images may be right side up or inverted.

Ray diagrams may be used to determine the location and characteristics of an image. The image formed by a convex lens can be analyzed by tracing three principal rays. A convex (converging) lens forms a real image when the object is beyond the focal length and a virtual image when the object is within the focal length. A diverging lens always forms a virtual image.

The Investigation

Leading Questions
- How does a mirror form an image?
- What does the focal length of a convex lens indicate about how light rays passing through it will be affected?
- How does a convex lens form an image?
- What is magnification and how is it calculated?

Learning Goals

By the end of the Investigation, students will be able to:
- Use the laser beam to trace light rays from a lens to determine its focal length.
- Show how ray diagrams are used to predict where images form with lenses and mirrors.

Key Vocabulary

objects, images, virtual image, optical axis, focal point, converging lenses, diverging lenses, convex lenses, focus, focal plane, magnifying glass, real image, magnification, optical axis, diverging lenses

Setup and Materials

Students work in groups of four or five at tables.

Each group should have:

- Light and Optics Kit
- Graph paper
- Ruler
- Prism
- Mirror
- Lasers

Details

Time ⏱ One class period

Preparation ✏

Assignments 📖 Section 17.2 Mirrors, Lenses, and Images in the **Student Edition** after the Investigation.

Skill Sheets 17.2 Ray Diagrams

Equipment Setup Light and Optics

Teaching the Investigation

1 Introduction
2 The law of reflection
3 Measuring the angles
4 Refraction
5 The image formed by a lens
6 Characteristics of the image
7 The image from a single lens
8 Lenses changed our understanding of biology
9 Finding the magnification of a lens

Introduction

Mirrors and lenses are used to create and alter the size or position of images.

The law of reflection

1

Images are pictures of objects that are formed in space where light rays meet.

Mirrors follow the law of reflection.

A virtual image is formed when many light rays from one point on an object appear to come from another point.

One of the most important reasons we care about optics is because we see images. To understand how optical systems work, we start with the idea of objects and images. Objects are the real things that exist. We see objects because light bounces off them. Images are what we see. Technically, we DON'T ever see objects directly. We see images of the light that bounces off objects and is collected by our eyes. If we make the light go through mirrors or lenses, the images may be changed. The images could be bigger, smaller, or appear to come from a different place. Today's Investigation is going to look at how images are formed by lenses and mirrors.

For the first part of the Investigation, we are going to use a mirror to see how an image is formed. Take some clean graph paper and draw a line and arrow like this (draw on board). Set the paper on your optics table and stand up the mirror with its silver edge right on your line. Can you see an image of the arrow in the mirror?

> It is fine if the students play around with the mirror while doing this activity. Circulate and make sure each group has the sketch correct and that everyone has seen the image in the mirror. Students will have to move their heads to get the right angle to see the image.

Where is the object? Where is the image? Where does the image appear to come from?

> The object is the arrow they drew on the paper. The image is "in" the mirror. It appears to come from behind the mirror.

To figure out why the image appears where it does, we need to use the laser to trace one ray of light at a time. Move your laser so the beam passes right over the tip of the arrow and bounces off the mirror. Use the edge of a card to locate the center of the laser beam so you are sure it goes where you want it to. Mark at least two points on the incident ray and the reflected ray. When you are through, your incident ray should end up going from the tip of the arrow to the mirror.

> The students will need to stand for this activity so that they can look at the beam from above rather than from the side.

Now adjust the laser so the beam again passes over the tip of the arrow, but from a different angle. The second position of the laser beam simulates another ray of light that comes from the tip of the arrow. In reality there are an infinite number of such rays, but if we trace two of them we can find out where all the rays meet to form the image. Use the card to mark spots on the incident and reflected rays. Trace the second ray on the same sheet as the first.

> The diagram shows what students should have drawn after completing Part 2 of the Investigation. Make sure they understand the difference between the incident ray and the reflected ray.

Take the mirror off and extend the two *reflected* rays by drawing lines. They should meet at a point behind the mirror! This is the same point where you "saw" the tip of the arrow reflected in the mirror. The place where the reflected rays meet tells you where the image is. An image forms where many rays that leave an object from the same point meet up again.

> Students should draw the extended reflected rays and see that they meet at a point behind the mirror that is directly opposite from the real arrow and an equal distance behind the mirror as the real arrow is in front of the mirror.

A virtual image is formed when many light rays from one point on an object appear to come from another point. The image in the mirror is a virtual image because the reflected light rays appear to come from a point behind the mirror, which is where you see the image.

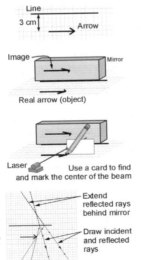

UNIT 6: Light and Color

17.2 Mirrors, Lenses and Images

Question: How does a lens or mirror form an image?

In this Investigation, you will:

1. Use the laser beam to trace light rays from a lens to determine its focal length.
2. Show how ray diagrams are used to predict where images form with lenses and mirrors.

A lens uses the refraction of light to bend light rays to form images. A mirror also forms an image but with reflected light instead of refracted light. In this Investigation, you will trace light rays to learn how images are formed by mirrors and lenses.

1 The image in a mirror

When you see the tip of an arrow, your eye collects all the light rays coming from the tip of the arrow. Since light travels in straight lines, your brain perceives the tip of the arrow to be at the point where all the light rays *appear* to come from. If the light rays appear to come from somewhere other than the actual arrow, the place from which they appear to come is called an *image* of the arrow.

Now suppose you observe the tip of an arrow in a mirror. The light rays are reflected. The reflected rays *appear* to come from somewhere behind the mirror. You see an image of the arrow reflected in the mirror because your brain perceives the arrow where the light rays *appear* to come from instead of where they actually *do* come from.

1. Secure a sheet of graph paper to the optics table with the magnetic strips. Draw a line on the paper to mark where you will place a mirror. Draw a 1-centimeter-long arrow on the graph paper about 3 centimeters away from your line. The arrow should be parallel to the line.
2. Place the reflecting surface of the mirror along this line. Move your head until you can see the reflection of the arrow in the mirror. The image of the arrow appears to be behind the mirror.
3. Set the laser on the optics table so the beam passes directly over the tip of your arrow. Use the edge of a card to locate the beam. Use a pencil to mark the paper directly under the beam.
4. Use the edge of the card to locate and mark another point on the incident laser beam and two points on the reflected laser beam.
5. Move the laser so the beam passes over the arrow tip from a different angle but still hits the mirror. Mark the position of the second beam with a card and your pencil as in steps 3 and 4.
6. Remove the mirror. Use a ruler to connect the points and draw the incident and reflected rays for both positions of the laser.
7. Use the ruler to extend the two reflected rays beyond where the mirror was. They should meet in a point on the side of the line where the mirror was. This point is where you saw the image of the tip of the arrow.

Demonstrating the law of reflection

Like light, particles such as bounced objects obey the law of reflection. To demonstrate the law, have one student bounce a tennis ball off the chalkboard to another student. Measure the angle of the path the ball takes relative to the normal. To do this, stretch a string between the incident ray student and the board and the reflective ray student and the board (the two strings will make a "v" with the point of the "v" on the board). Using another string, make a normal to the board. Measure the angles with a large protractor made for chalkboard use.

Measuring the angles

The images formed by a lens are created in the same way as the images formed by a mirror.

2

Images can also be formed with a lens. Remember how light rays were bent by traveling through a prism? Because the shape of a lens is curved, rays striking different places along the lens bend different amounts. The laser allows us to follow the path of the incident and refracted rays.

Prompt a discussion of how the shape is different. The surface of a lens is curved. With a lens, every ray can be bent a different amount if it hits the lens at a different place.

We are going to use the laser to trace a few rays of light through a convex lens. A convex lens has a shape that is thicker in the center than at the edges. Follow the instructions in step 2 of the Investigation and draw the horizontal and vertical lines on a large sheet of graph paper. Follow the direction to center your lens on the intersection of these two lines. The long horizontal line that passes through the center of the lens is called the optical axis. Use the laser to send three light beams through the lens parallel to the optical axis—one beam along the axis, one above the axis and one an equal distance below the axis.

Circulate and help students trace the parallel rays before and after the lens. They should use the same square edge of a card to locate and mark the center of the beam on the graph paper. It is important that the incident rays are parallel to the axis of the lens to show the focusing effect. Once they are finished, you or a student should draw an example on the board.

Describe what happens to the light rays after they pass through the lens.

Have the students discuss how the rays all seem to come together again. They may not meet at a single point because of imperfections in the lens. When the rays do not meet at a point, the image is blurred like a camera or microscope that is out of focus. The students will learn more from talking about why things are sometimes blurry than they would if all the rays came to a perfect focus.

Refraction

Lenses follow Snell's law of refraction.

The focus is where the rays from a point on the object come back together to form the equivalent point on the image.

3

A property of a convex lens is to bend rays traveling parallel to the optical axis so they intersect at the focal point. The distance between the surface of the lens and the focus is called the focal length. Measure the focal length of the flat lens. If you traced many rays, they will not all come together in the same point because this lens does not have a perfect shape.

To determine the focal length, draw a circle around the points where the refracted rays cross the axis, and use the center of this circle as the focus. The distance from the focus to the midpoint of the lens is the focal length. The lenses supplied in the optics kit have a focal length in the range of 8 to 10 centimeters.

You could get a better (less blurry) focus by changing the shape of the lens. The lens's surfaces are shaped like part of a circle. For a circular shape, the rays farther from the principle axis bend too much compared with rays closer to the principal axis. A lens with a parabolic shape would make a better focus but would be more expensive to manufacture. The lens in your eye is flexible. Small muscles in the eye contract to change its shape so that we can see both faraway and close-up objects clearly.

The image formed by a lens

4

A lens forms an image in a similar way as does a mirror. The lens collects light rays coming from an object and causes them to come together again. With a lens the image can be real because the light rays actually come together. You can see a real image on a screen like a projected picture. To determine where the image forms, we can use the laser to trace several light rays from the tip of an arrow as they pass through the lens. Follow the directions in Part 4 to prepare an 11×34 inch sheet of graph paper. Next, draw your vertical and horizontal axes. Place the lens at the intersection of your axes. Draw the arrow described in step 4.

Students prepare their graph paper to set up the experiment.

17.2 Mirrors, Lenses and Images

2 Refracting light through a lens

Like a prism, a converging lens bends light. Because the shape of a lens is curved, rays striking different places along the lens bend different amounts. The laser allows us to follow the path of the incident and refracted rays. Rays that approach a lens *parallel to the axis* meet at a point called the *focal point*. The distance between the center of the lens and the focal point is called the *focal length*.

Focal Point

Focal length

1. Take a large (11 × 17-inch) sheet of graph paper and draw a horizontal line through the center. We will refer to this line as the *axis*. Draw a second line in the middle of the paper perpendicular to the axis.

2. Place your "flat" lens on the intersection of the two lines as shown at right.

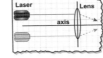
Laser   Lens
axis

3. Place the laser to the left of the lens so the notch in the base is centered on the axis. Turn on the laser and shine the beam through the lens.

4. If the beam goes through the exact center of the lens, it will not appear to be refracted at all. Adjust the lens so that the beam goes through the exact center. Trace around the border of the lens with your pencil.

5. Now move the laser to a point 15 centimeters to the left of the vertical line and 2 centimeters **above** the axis. Shine the laser beam through the lens along a line parallel to the axis. Plot the incident and refracted rays on the graph paper using a card and pencil as you did for the mirror.

6. Repeat step 5 with the laser 2 centimeters *below* the axis. Plot the incident and refracted rays.

3 Analyzing what you observed

a. Describe the path of the laser beam as it travels along the axis and through the lens. Compare the paths of the incident and the refracted rays.

b. Describe the path of the laser beam as it travels parallel to the axis and above or below the axis. Compare the paths of the incident and refracted rays.

c. The two refracted rays that you traced in Part 1 crossed the axis. Mark the axis where these rays crossed. This is the focal point for your lens. Due to imperfections in the lens, these two rays may not meet in exactly one point. In this case, choose the mid-point between the two points as your focal point.

d. Measure the distance between the focal point and the center of your lens. This distance is the focal length of your lens.

e. Label the focal point and focal length on your ray diagram.

3 Example answers

3a. As the laser beam travels along the axis, it goes through the lens and straight out in the same path. It does not appear to be refracted at all.

3b. When the laser beam travels to the lens parallel to the axis and above or below the axis, it is bent toward the principal axis.

3c,d. The two refracted rays both cross the axis at a point 9 centimeters away from the lens. The focal length of the lens is 9 centimeters.

Characteristics of the image

How does the image of the arrow relate to the original arrow?

The image from a single lens

Focal point: the point at which light rays either meet or diverge after passing through a lens parallel to the principle axis

Focal length: the distance from the center of a lens to the focal point

Lenses changed our understanding of biology

The magnifying glass is an example of a lens that helped biologists to see microorganisms.

5 Use the laser to trace a ray from the tip of the arrow that travels parallel to the horizontal axis. Next, find your focal length from Part 3. On the left side of the lens, make a dot on the axis that marks off a length equal to the focal length. Shine your laser so that the beam passes through both the tip of the arrow and the dot you just made. Trace this ray.

> The ray that goes through the focal length dot on the left side of the lens will be refracted so that it emerges from the lens in a path parallel to the horizontal axis.

The two rays from the tip of the arrow will meet. The point where they meet is where the image of the tip of the arrow forms. Remember, an image forms where many rays that leave from the same point on an object come together again. Draw an arrowhead where the rays meet. Then, draw a vertical line from the arrowhead to the axis. This is the image of your arrow. How does this relate to the actual arrow, the object?

> The image is inverted and smaller than the object. The image is also farther away from the lens than the object.

6 The flat cylindrical lens is good for tracing rays from the laser to understand how lenses form images. However, this lens cannot form actual images because it only bends light in one plane. Your optics set also includes several spherical convex lenses mounted in metal holders. Take one of these lenses out and look at it. They are called spherical because the surface of the glass in these lenses is shaped like part of a sphere, as shown in Figure 17.19 on page 340 of your text.

> Students should take out one of the convex lenses to examine it.

These lenses also have a focal point and they are much more accurately made than the plastic cylindrical lens we just used with the laser. To find the focal point we can use the property that a convex lens focuses light rays traveling parallel to the axis. The rays meet at the focal point of the lens. Take your lens and hold it 15 centimeters or so in front of a wall so it is between the wall and a bright object like a window or lamp. Slowly move the lens closer and farther from the wall. At a certain distance you will see a tiny image of the window or lamp on the wall. When the image is in sharp focus, the distance between the lens and the wall is the focal length of the lens.

> Students should use this technique to determine the focal length of one or both of the small lenses. Describe the image formed by the lens. Is it smaller or larger than the real object? Is it inverted or right side up?

> The image formed by a single convex lens used in this way is smaller than the object and inverted.

This is exactly how your eye forms an image. The image in your eye must be smaller than the object because you can see a wide field of vision and the back of your eyeball is very small. The human eye has a single convex lens right behind the pupil. The image formed by your eye is actually upside down. Your brain has learned to interpret the signals from the eye to make the image appear right side up.

> How many of you believe there are things such as cells or bacteria?

> Almost all students accept that these things exist and a few may have seen them directly.

How do you know? Can you see a bacteria with your eye? The invention of optics revolutionized our understanding of biology because it allowed us to see the structures inside living things and to see that the world is filled with creatures too small to see with the naked eye. People once believed that disease was caused by evil spirits. Now we understand that many diseases are caused by microorganisms much smaller than the head of a pin. The proof that such tiny beasts actually existed came with the invention of the magnifying glass and its use by Anton Leeuwenhoek to observe bacteria in 1683.

17.2 Mirrors, Lenses and Images

4 Finding the image formed by a lens

When all the rays from a point on an object meet again, they form an *image*. You can use the laser to locate images formed by a lens.

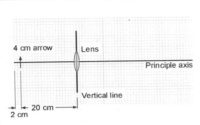

1. Tape two large (11 × 17) sheets of graph paper together so that you have a new (11-by-34-inch) working surface. Draw a horizontal axis all the way across the graph paper.

2. Draw a vertical arrow 4 cm tall and 2 centimeters from the left edge of the graph paper. The middle of the arrow should be on the axis. This arrow will serve as your "object."

3. Next, draw a vertical line 20 centimeters to the left of the arrow. Place the lens at the intersection of the lines.

4. Use the laser to center the lens, just as you did in steps 3 and 4 of Part 2. Trace around the lens with your pencil.

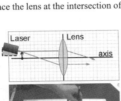

5. Place the laser at the tip of the arrow. Shine the beam through the lens in a line parallel to the axis. Trace the incident and refracted rays.

6. Check to see that the lens is still centered on the axis. On the left side of the lens, make a dot on the axis that marks off a length equal to the focal length.

7. Place the laser at the tip of the arrow. Turn the laser so that the beam passes through the dot you made in step 6. Verify that this is happening by placing the edge of your index card at the location of the dot.

8. Trace the incident and refracted rays.

9. The two refracted rays that you have drawn should intersect somewhere on the right side of the lens. Mark the intersection with an upside-down arrowhead. You have just located the image of the tip of your arrow!

10. Draw a vertical line from your "image" arrowhead to the axis. You have now sketched the image of your arrow.

5 Characteristics of the image

Compare the image of the arrow to the original arrow.

a. Is the image larger or smaller? Calculate the magnification by dividing the length of the image by the length of the original arrow.

b. Is the image right side up or is it inverted?

c. Is the image closer to the lens than the original arrow or is it farther away?

5 Example answers

5a. The image is smaller than the object. 1.5 cm/2 cm = 0.75 magnification.

5b. The image is inverted.

5c. The image is closer to the lens than the object. The image is 16 centimeters away from the lens; the object is 20 centimeters away from the lens.

117

Finding the magnification of a lens

Demonstrating a single lens used as a magnifying glass

Measuring the magnification of a single convex lens

The magnification depends both on the focal length of about lens and also on the distance between the lens and the object

A magnifying glass, the subject of our next experiment, is a single lens. Take one of the small glass lenses and hold it 5 or 10 centimeters above a printed page. You should see the letters appear magnified.

Students should take a few minutes to do this activity.

Magnification is the ratio of the size of an image to the actual size of the real object. A magnification greater than one means the image appears to be bigger than the object really is. Look through the lens at some graph paper. Move the lens closer and farther from the paper. Do you see an image of the graph paper in the lens? Does the image appear larger or the same size as the actual graph paper?

Students need to look directly down at the lens when they hold it above the graph paper. They should see the squares of the graph paper appear larger in the lens.

Count the number of magnified squares that cross the diameter of the lens. For example, the picture in your Investigation shows $4\,^{1}/_{2}$ squares across the lens. This is the magnified image. If you set the lens down on the graph paper you see that it covers 10 squares from edge to edge. That means in the magnified image in the lens, $4\,^{1}/_{2}$ squares appeared as large as 10 squares. The magnification is therefore 10 divided by $4\,^{1}/_{2}$, or 2.22. This magnifying glass has a magnification of 2.22. Do the experiment with your own lens. Count the number of magnified squares and then put the lens against the graph paper to count how many squares are covered by the lens itself.

Students should try this to determine one value for that magnification of the lens. Students need to look directly down at the lens when they hold it above the graph paper. If they look through the lens at an angle, they will see more of the graph paper and obtain an inaccurate reading. The magnification depends on the distance between the paper and the lens so students will get different results.

Try the experiment again using a ruler to measure the distance between the lens and the paper. Notice that the magnification changes with different distances. Record the results in Table 1.

Some students may have lenses of different sizes and magnification.

What is the object? What is the image?

The object is the graph paper squares. The image is the magnified squares seen through the lens.

Note: Traditionally, magnification is found by dividing image size by object size. It can be tricky to find the size of the image—you would have to hold the lens perfectly still and try to measure the image with a ruler held above the lens. A simpler, more accurate "shortcut method' is provided here.

Instead of measuring size, we count the number of squares that can be seen in the lens. This works because as the magnification increases, the field of vision decreases. For example, if you double the width of each square, you will only be able to see half as many squares across the lens. By counting the number of unmagnified and magnified squares, we can figure out the magnification power of the lens. Simply divide the number of unmagnified squares by the number of magnified squares. If you would like to use the traditional image size ÷ object size calculation, the ratio on the next page can help your students find the image size accurately.

17.2 Mirrors, Lenses and Images

6   The image from a single lens

The image from a distant light source forms at a place that is one focal length away from a single lens. This provides a convenient way to measure the focal length.

1. Find a wall at least 3 or 4 meters away from a lamp or sunlit window. Tape a piece of white paper to the wall to create a screen for seeing the image.
2. Get one of the round convex glass lenses in the metal holders. Hold the lens at different distances from your screen. Try distances between 10 and 20 centimeters.
3. You will see a sharp image of the lamp or window on the screen when your lens is exactly one focal length away from the wall. Use this technique to determine the focal lengths for both lenses in the optics kit.

Images can be smaller or larger than the object that created them. Images can also be right side up or inverted.

a. Was the image created by a single lens smaller or larger than the object?
b. Was the image right side up or was it inverted?

7   Finding the magnification of a lens

1. Get one of the round convex glass lenses in the metal holders. Set your lens directly on a piece of graph paper and count the number of *unmagnified* squares that cross the diameter of the lens. In the example, the lens is 10 squares wide.
2. Next, examine a section of graph paper with your lens held above the paper. Move the lens closer to and farther away from the paper until you have the biggest squares you can still see clearly in the lens.
3. Count the number of *magnified* squares that cross the diameter of the lens. For example, the picture shows 4 1/2 squares across the lens.
4. The magnification can be calculated by dividing the number of *unmagnified* squares by the number of *magnified* squares. In the example, you see 10 *unmagnified* squares and 4.5 *magnified* squares. The magnification is 10 ÷ 4.5, or 2.22.
5. Try the experiment again using a ruler to measure the distance between the lens and the paper. Notice that the magnification changes with different distances. Record the results in Table 1.

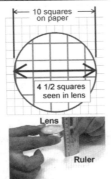

10 squares on paper

4 1/2 squares seen in lens

Lens

Ruler

Measuring the distance from the lens to the paper

Table 1: Magnification data for a single lens

Distance to paper (cm)	# of squares on the graph paper (unmagnified squares)	# of squares in the lens (magnified squares)	Magnification

118

6 7   Example answers

6a. The image was smaller than the object.
6b. The image was inverted.

7. Sample data:

Table 1: Magnification data for a single lens

Distance to paper (cm)	# of squares on the graph paper (magnified squares)	# of squares in the lens (magnified squares)	Magnification
10	7.5	6.5	1.15
5	7.5	6	1.25

17.3 Optical Systems

Key Question: How are the properties of images determine?

An image forms where many rays from the same point on an object meet again in a point. In this Investigation, students start by experimentally finding the image from a convex lens at different object distances. They then construct a model of the lens using geometrical optics by drawing the three principal rays. The predictions of the model for the location and characteristics of the image are compared with the experimental evidence. By using red and blue objects, students demonstrate chromatic aberration. In the last part of the Investigation of the students use the thin lens formula to predict the image distance when given the object distance and focal length.

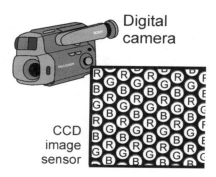

Digital camera

CCD image sensor

Reading Synopsis

Students read Section 17.3 Optical Systems after the Investigation.

An optical system is a collection of mirrors, lenses, prisms, or other optical elements that performs a useful function with light. Characteristics of optical systems include location type and magnification of images; amount of light collected; accuracy in sharpness, color, and distortion; ability to change image characteristics; and the ability to record an image. The quality of an image is limited by chromatic aberration, spherical aberration, and diffraction.

The thin lens formula is used to determine image and object distances. This formula is an algebraic representation of the geometrical optics approach of tracing rays. Multiple lenses such as in a telescope or telephoto lens allow an optical system to change the size of an image. Multiple lenses can be analyzed in sequence by considering the image formed by one lens as the object for the next lens.

The Investigation

Leading Questions
- What is an optical system?
- What will a ray tracing diagram tell you about an image?
- How are different colors affected by a convex lens?
- How can the location of an image formed by a convex lens be predicted?

Learning Goals

By the end of the Investigation, students will be able to:
- Use the principles of geometric optics to predict where images form with lenses.
- Use the thin lens formula to predict how and where images are formed by a single convex lens.
- Explain chromatic aberration and show how single lenses suffer from this defect.

Key Vocabulary aberrations, chromatic aberration, spherical aberration, diffraction, thin lens formula, image relay, resolution, pixels

17.3

Optical Systems

Setup and Materials

Students work in groups of four or five at tables.

Each group should have:

- Light and Optics Kit
- Lens
- Graph paper

Details

Time One class period

Preparation [pencil icon]

[book icon] Section 17.3 Optical Systems in the **Student Edition** after the Investigation.

Skill Sheets 17.3 Thin Lens Formula

Equipment Setup Light and Optics

Teaching the Investigation

1   Introduction
2   Projecting an image with a lens
3   Measuring the angles
4   Analyzing what you observed
5   Dispersion
6   Chromatic aberration
7   The thin lens formula
8   The image from a single lens

Introduction

An optical system is a collection of optical elements working together to accomplish a specific function with light.

Projecting an image with a lens

1

HINT: The separation between the LED and the screen MUST be more than four times the focal length of the lens in order to get a clear image.

Measuring the angles

2

With the exception of a magnifying glass or your eyeglasses, most of the optical devices you use contain several lenses, mirrors, prisms, or other optical elements. In fact, even a magnifying glass or eyeglasses are multiple lens systems because they work in conjunction with the lens in your eye. A microscope and a telescope have at least two lenses. Better telescopes and microscopes may have five or more mirrors and lenses. Today we are going to talk about optical systems. An optical system is a collection of optical elements working together to accomplish a specific function with light. Although we are going to use a single lens, the things we learn also apply to more complex optical systems.

One of the simplest optical systems you have all seen is a projector. A projector takes the light from an illuminated image and projects the image on a screen. We are going to build a model of a projector using a single lens. Take out the red and blue LED lamps from your light and optics kit. Look at the colored lenses on the front of the lamps. What to do you see there?

The red and blue LED lamps have a letter *F* etched on the front of their colored lens caps.

The letter *F* etched into the colored caps is an illuminated object that can be used to make images with lenses. Set up a the optics table with one lens, the red light, and the screen as shown in the diagram. The screen should be at least four times the focal length away from the LED lamp. You will probably have to put the screen off the optics table to get enough distance. Put the lens in the middle between the light and the screen. Move the lens back and forth between the light and screen until you see a sharp image of the letter *F* on the screen.

Help students until each group has made a sharp image of the letter *F* on the screen.

The object distance is that distance between the object and the front surface of the lens. The image and distance is that distance between the back surface of the lens and the image. When you have the image in sharp focus measure the object distance and image.

Help students measure the object and image distances.

Try a few different distances between the lamp and screen that are larger than four times the focal length. You can even use distances many meters away. HINT: You will not be able to get a clear image if the separation between the lamp and screen is less than four times the focal length of the lens. Observe the image and record your observations in Table 1. For image orientation record whether the image is inverted or not. For image height, measure the height of the image with a ruler to the nearest millimeter. The magnification is the image height divided by the object height. Use a ruler to measure the height of the *F* on the red light.

Students follow the directions in Part 1 of the Investigation.

What general comments can you make about the images you saw?

All the images are inverted and smaller than the object.

For the next part of the Investigation we are going to develop a theory that can predict the location, size, and orientation of the image from a single lens. Take a sheet of graph paper and choose a scale so the entire distance between the object and image fits on the paper. Draw a line through the center of the page. This line is the optical axis. Draw an arrow for the object on the left side of the paper going up from the optical axis. Measure a distance equal to the object distance and draw a line perpendicular to the optical axis to represent the lens.

Check that students set up their drawing correctly. In particular, check that they have chosen a reasonable scale and have placed the object and lens the correct scaled distance apart.

17.3   Optical Systems

Question: How are the properties of images determined?

In this Investigation, you will:

1. Use the principles of geometric optics to predict where images form with lenses.
2. Use the thin-lens formula to predict how and where images are formed by a single convex lens.
3. Explain chromatic aberration and show how single lenses suffer from this defect.

Geometric optics describes a way to use scale drawings and geometry to analyze optical systems. Rays of light are represented by lines. Virtual rays are represented by dotted lines. Images form where the rays leaving a point on the object come together again. The images are *real* when actual light rays meet and *virtual* when virtual rays meet. In this Investigation, you will use geometric optics and the thin lens formula to determine the characteristics of an image formed by a single lens.

1   Projecting an image with a lens

The red and blue lights have the letter "F" etched into the colored caps. The F is an object that can be used to make images with the lenses.

1. Set up the optics table with one lens, the red light, and the screen as shown in the diagram at right. The screen should be at least four times the focal length away from the light. You will probably have to put the screen off the table to get enough distance.

2. Put the lens between the light and the screen. Move the lens back and forth between the light and screen until you see a sharp image of the letter F on the screen.

3. When you have the image in sharp focus, measure the object distance and image distance as shown in the diagram. The object distance is measured from the front of the light to the surface of the lens. The image distance is measured from the surface of the lens to the front of the screen.

4. Try a few different distances larger than four times the focal length. You can even use distances many meters away. HINT: You will only be able to get a clear image if the separation between the LED and the screen is more than four times the focal length of the lens.

5. Observe the image and record your observations in Table 1. For image orientation, record whether the image is inverted. For image height, measure the height of the image with a ruler to the nearest millimeter. The magnification is the image height divided by the object height. Use a ruler to measure the height of the F on the red light.

Table 1: Image data for a single lens

Object dist. (cm)	Image dist. (cm)	Image orientation	Image height (mm)	Magnification

---

1   Example answers

Table 1: *Image data for a single lens*

Object dist. (cm)	Image dist (cm)	Image orientation	Image height (mm)	Magnification
22.5	29	inverted	4	1.3
26	26	inverted	3	1.0
30	22	inverted	2	1.5

Analyzing what you observed

Rules for drawing rays:

1. A ray parallel to the axis is bent to pass through the far focal point.

2. A ray passing through the near focal point emerges parallel to the axis.

3. A ray passing through the center of the lens is not deflected at all.

magnification = image size ÷ object size

2 Next draw the near and far focal point on either side of the lens. The near focal point is on the object side of the lens and the far focal point is on the image side of the lens. You will need to know or measure the focal length of the lens you were using.

Students draw and label the focal points at the correct scale distances from the lens.

To draw the ray diagram and find the image, we only have to draw three rays from the object through the lens. These three rays are called the principal rays, and they are drawn according to these rules:

1) A ray entering the lens parallel to the axis emerges to pass through the far focal point.
2) A ray passing through the near focal point emerges from the lens parallel to the axis.
3) A ray passing through the center of the lens is not deflected at all.

Use these rules to draw three principal rays from your object through your lens.

Help students draw their ray diagrams. If the diagrams have been set up properly to scale, drawing the principal rays is easy and accurate.

All three rays should meet in a point on the far side of the lens. Draw an arrow from the principal axis down to the point where the three rays intersect as shown in step 2 of your Investigation. Use the scale you've chosen for your diagram to determine the image distance. If you chose a scale of 5 centimeters per square on the graph paper, then 20 squares on the graph paper represents one meter of actual distance.

Compared the image distance predicted by your ray diagram with the image distance you've measured.

Students draw the arrow representing the image on their ray diagram. You will typically see image distances within 5 percent of the measured image distances. The key to success is having the object, lens, and focal points drawn to the correct scale.

Complete ray diagrams for each combination of object and image distance you measured in Table 1.

Students complete three or more ray diagrams.

Look at the ray diagrams and see if you can determine the magnification. The magnification is equal to the image size divided by the object size. In this case, the magnification will be less than one since the images are smaller than the objects. Measure the size of the image and object arrows and calculate the ratio. Compare your predicted magnification with the magnification you measured.

Students should measure the size of the arrows they drew in their rate diagrams and calculate the theoretical magnification. the agreement with measurement is usually within 10 percent and would be better except it is difficult to measure the size of the image in the experiments. If you have a set of vernier calipers, this makes the experiment much more precise.

Dispersion

Dispersion is the variation in the amount of refraction that occurs when different wavelengths of light cross a boundary from one transparent medium to another, resulting in the breakdown of constituent wavelengths seen as spectrum.

3 How many people have seen a rainbow that is created by a prism?

This is illustrated in one of the color teaching tools if students have not seen it.

A prism splits light into its component colors because the index of refraction of glass depends on the frequency of the light. Light of higher frequency and shorter wavelength sees a higher index of refraction than light of lower frequency and long wavelength. That means blue light bends more than red light. What do you think this means for a lens? Should a lens focus red light and blue light at the same place?

Discuss with the students that the bending of light by a lens is done by refraction. Therefore, blue light will be bent by a lens slightly more than red light. The effect is small but measurable with the equipment you have. An image of the blue LED lamp will form at a slightly shorter image distance than the red LED lamp.

This effect is called dispersion and is a property of all lenses.

17.3 Optical Systems

2 **Analyzing what you observed**

Drawing the three principle rays

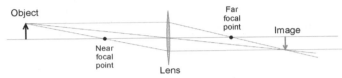

You can usually find what you need to know by drawing three light rays as shown in the diagram above. The rules for drawing the three rays are:

1. A ray parallel to the axis is bent to pass through the far focal point.
2. A ray passing through the near focal point emerges parallel to the axis.
3. A ray passing through the center of the lens is not deflected at all.

a. Make a scale drawing showing the positions of the object, lens, and screen. Measure and mark the near and far focal point of the lens. Draw an arrow for an object at the correct object distance from the lens corresponding to one of your experiments. Draw the three principle rays from the tip of the arrow using the rules above. The place where the rays meet is where the image forms.

b. Measure the image distance from your drawing and the height of the image. The height of the image is the length of the image arrow from the optical axis to the tip. Make a similar scale drawing for each of your experimental trials.

c. Record the theoretical image distance for each drawing in Table 2. Calculate and record the magnification, too. The magnification is the height of the image arrow divided by the height of the object arrow.

Table 2: Ray tracing analysis for a single lens

Object dist. (cm)	Image dist. (cm)	Image orientation	Image height (mm)	Magnification

d. How do your ray-tracing predictions compare with your actual measured images? Write one or two sentences comparing measured and calculated data.

3 **Chromatic aberration**

Repeat the experiment you did in Part 1 using red and blue images. Measure the image distance for the red light and the blue light while keeping each light at the exact same distance from the lens (that is, the same object distance). Make a table similar to Table 2 to record your results.

a. With a prism, you may have observed that red light and blue light are bent by different amounts. This is why prisms spread light into a rainbow. In a lens, the effect is called *chromatic aberration* and it affects the color in images formed by lenses. How does chromatic aberration explain the difference you saw in the image distances formed with red and blue light?

120

2 **3** Example answers

Table 2: *Ray tracing analysis for a single lens*

Object dist. (cm)	Image dist. (cm)	Image orientation	Image height (mm)	Magnification
26	26	inverted	3	1.0
30	23	inverted	2	1.5

2d. The theoretical image distances and heights were close to the measured distances and heights. For an object distance of 26 centimeters, which is twice the focal distance, both the measured and theoretical distance and height were accurate. At twice the focal distance, the magnification is zero and the image distance equals the object distance. For an object distance of 30 centimeters, the theoretical distance was within one centimeter and the theoretical image height and magnification were accurate.

3a. The image formed by the red light was several millimeters further away from the lens than the image formed by the blue light. The lens refracts or bends the red and blue light differently, resulting in a change of image distances for the red light and the blue light. The images differences for the colors of light illustrate the chromatic aberration of the lens. The lens focuses different colors of light slightly differently.

Chromatic aberration

What is chromatic aberration?

Chromatic aberration is the distortion of an image by a lens caused by variations in the angle of refraction of different wavelengths of light resulting in color fringes.

3 In the next part of the Investigation we are going to see if red and blue light focus in the same place. Set up the red LED lamp, lens, and screen as you did in step 1 with a fairly long image distance (a meter or more). Adjust the position of the lens until the red image is in sharp focus. Carefully mark the location of the red lamp. Without changing anything else, substitute the blue lamp for the red lamp. Is the image of the *F* in focus for the blue lamp?

The blue F should be noticeably out of focus.

Take a sheet of paper and place it on the screen so the image is on the paper. Move the paper toward the lens. Does the blue *F* come into sharp focus?

The students should see that the blue F comes into sharp focus at a slightly shorter image distance than the red F.

This effect is called chromatic aberration and it affects the lenses in cameras, telescopes, microscopes and other optical instruments. Chromatic aberration causes a small blurring of color in the image formed by a lens. The blurring occurs because an image sensor, such as film is in one place relative to the lens. If the red light from an image focuses to a sharp point, then the blue light from the image is slightly blurry. Very good camera lenses and telescopes correct chromatic aberration by using both converging and diverging lenses made of different types of glass.

The thin lens formula

$$\frac{1}{d_o} + \frac{1}{d_i} = \frac{1}{f}$$

d_o = object distance in cm
d_i = image distance in cm
f = focal length in cm

4 It is tedious to draw ray diagrams every time you wish to analyze a lens. The geometric relationships in a ray diagram can be represented by a formula that relates the object to distance (d_o), the image distance, (d_i), and the focal length (f) of the lens.

Write the thin lens formula on the board.

The thin lens equation provides a way to calculate where images form given the positions and focal lengths of all objects and/or lenses in the system. The thin lens equation is a good approximation as long as the object and image distances are much greater than the thickness of the lens. When using the thin lens equation, you have to keep track of some sign conventions. These are written assuming that light goes from left to right. When the object and image appear like the diagram above, all quantities are positive.

Draw the diagram shown in step 4 of the Investigation on the board

1 Object distances are positive to the left of the lens and negative to the right of the lens.

2 Image distances are positive to the right of the lens and negative to the left of the lens.

3 Negative image distances (or object distances) mean virtual images (or objects)

In systems with more than one lens, the image from one lens becomes the object for the next lens. In this manner the thin lens equation can also be used to analyze multiple lens systems.

The image from a single lens

5 Set the red LED lamp 2.5 times the focal length away from a single lens. Use the thin lens formula to calculate the image distance (d_i) using the focal length of the lens and the object distance you measure. Place the screen at the predicted image distance and locate the image. Try at least two other object distances and record the predictions and measured data in Table 3.

Students should use the thin lens formula to predict the image distance for several different object distances. This prediction is usually accurate to within a few millimeters.

Example answers

Table 3: *Predicted and measured image distances*

Object dist. (cm)	Focal length (cm)	Predicted image (cm)	Measured image (cm)
32.5	13	21.6	21.5
19	13	46.8	42.2
25	13	27	27
36	13	20	20

5a. The predictions of the image distance were within 1% of the actual measured image distance except for one trial for which the difference between prediction and measurement was almost 10%.

5b. Sample data:

Object dist. (cm)	Focal length (cm)	Predicted image (cm)	Measured image (cm)
22.5	13	31	29
26	13	26	26
30	13	23	22

The calculations are close to the measurements:

$$\frac{1}{d_o} + \frac{1}{d_i} = \frac{1}{f} \qquad \frac{1}{d_i} + \frac{1}{f} = \frac{1}{d_o} \qquad d_i = \frac{1}{\frac{1}{f} - \frac{1}{d_o}}$$

For f = 13 and d_o = 22.5:
$$d_i = \frac{1}{\frac{1}{13} - \frac{1}{22.5}} = 31 \text{ cm}$$

For f = 13 and d_o = 26:
$$d_i = \frac{1}{\frac{1}{13} - \frac{1}{26}} = 26 \text{ cm}$$

For f = 13 and d_o = 30:
$$d_i = \frac{1}{\frac{1}{13} - \frac{1}{30}} = 23 \text{ cm}$$

17.3 Optical Systems

4 The thin-lens formula

Geometric optics are useful for understanding how lenses work but there are much faster mathematical ways to predict the locations of objects and images. The thin-lens equation provides a way to calculate where images form given the positions and focal lengths of all objects and/or lenses in the system. The thin-lens equation is a good approximation as long as the object and image distances are much greater than the thickness of the lens.

The thin lens equation

$$\frac{1}{d_o} + \frac{1}{d_i} = \frac{1}{f}$$

Object distance (cm) Image distance (cm) Focal length (cm)

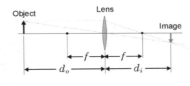

When using the thin-lens equation, distances are either positive or negative depending on a *sign convention*. The equation is written assuming that light goes from left to right. When the object and image appear like the diagram above, all distances are positive.

1. Object distances are positive to the left of the lens and negative to the right of the lens.
2. Image distances are positive to the right of the lens and negative to the left of the lens.
3. Negative image distances (or object distances) mean virtual images (or objects).

The image from one lens becomes the object for the next lens. In this manner, the thin-lens equation can also be used to analyze multiple-lens systems.

5 The image from a single lens

1. Set up the optics table with the red light about 2.5 times the focal length away from a single lens. The F engraved on the light is the object. Use Table 3 to record your data.
2. Calculate the image distance (d_i) using the focal length of the lens and the object distance you measure from step 1.
3. Place the screen at the predicted image distance and locate the image.
4. Try at least two other object distances and record the predictions and measured data in Table 3.

Table 3: Predicted and measured image distances

Object distance (cm)	Focal length (cm)	Predicted image distance (cm)	Measured image distance (cm)

a. How close did your prediction of the image come to the actual image? Answer with a percentage.
b. Use the thin-lens formula to calculate the image distances for the previous experiments you did in Part 1 of this Investigation (Table 1). Do the calculations agree with the measurements?

121

18.1 The Electromagnetic Spectrum

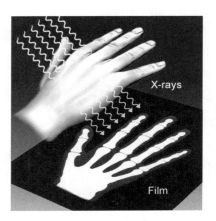

X-rays

Film

Key Question: What is the electromagnetic specutrum?

The electromagnetic spectrum is the entire range of electromagnetic waves of which visible light is a small part. This Investigation is really a research project to introduce students to the different waves of the electromagnetic spectrum. Each group of students will be assigned one type of electromagnetic wave such as microwaves or infrared light. The group is responsible for researching and reporting their findings to the rest of the class.

Reading Synopsis

Students read Section 18.1 The Electromagnetic Spectrum before the Investigation.

The electromagnetic spectrum includes visible light and all other forms of electromagnetic radiation. Electromagnetic waves are traveling oscillations in the electromagnetic field. The waves can travel through vacuum. Like other waves, the speed of electromagnetic waves is equal to frequency multiplied by wavelength. In vacuum, electromagnetic waves travel at the speed of light, or 3×10^8 m/sec. Electromagnetic waves travel slower when passing through matter such as light through glass.

Radio waves have the lowest energy and longest wavelength of the spectrum. The wavelength of radio waves ranges from a few centimeters to kilometers or longer. Microwaves have higher energy than radio waves. Moving up the spectrum in energy are infrared light, visible light, ultraviolet light, x-rays, and gamma rays.

This section presents applications for each category of waves.

The Investigation

Leading Questions
• What uses do different types of waves have?
• How do you use electromagnetic waves in your everyday life?

Learning Goals
By the end of the Investigation, students will be able to:
• Research one type of wave that is part of the electomagnetic spectrum.
• Prepare a poster containing the information they discover.
• Make an oral presentation to share the information with the class.

Key Vocabulary
electromagnetic spectrum, radio, infrared, microwave, x-ray, visible light, gamma ray, ultraviolet light

Setup and Materials

Students work in groups of four or five at tables.

Each group should have:

- This is a research Investigation, so no equipment is necessary to complete it.
- Poster board

Details

Time One class period

Preparation

Assignments Section 18.1 The Electromagnetic Spectrum in the **Student Edition** after the Investigation.

Skill Sheets 18.1 The Speed of Light

Teaching the Investigation

1   Introduction
2   Conducting research

Introduction

The electromagnetic spectrum is a group of waves, all traveling at the same speed but having different wavelengths and frequencies.

What are some properties of waves?

What is oscillation?

Oscillation is a motion that varies periodically back and forth between two values.

Speed = frequency × wavelength

Conducting research

Today's Investigation is really a discussion followed by a research project. The discussion is about electromagnetic waves, of which visible light is one form. We use electromagnetic waves for a tremendous variety of human technology including microwave ovens, cell phones, radio and TV broadcasting, and medical diagnosis and therapy. Did you know that most cell phones use the exact same kind of microwave that microwave ovens use to heat food? Why doesn't your cell phone cook your brain?

The power used in a cell phone is typically one to three watts and the power used by a microwave oven is 1,000 watts.

Why don't we start by listing some of the properties of waves.

Students should list off properties of waves that can be written on the blackboard. Some expected responses are frequency, wavelength, speed, amplitude, energy, interference, and resonance.

Another good question is what is waving in an electromagnetic wave? How do we start such a wave? The answer is that the wave is an oscillation in the electric and magnetic field. If you shake a string up and down, you can see a wave traveling on the string. If you shake a magnet up and down, it creates an oscillation of magnetic energy that may affect another magnet far away. The oscillation of magnetic energy that spreads out from your shaking magnet is an electromagnetic wave. Can anyone guess how I would show the presence of this wave?

Any conducting rod such as an antenna is a detector for electromagnetic waves. The moving magnet sends out waves that cause electricity in the antenna to oscillate back and forth. This is how a radio works. The back and forth oscillation of electricity carries the music.

If you make electricity go back and forth in a wire, the back and forth motion of the electricity would also create an electromagnetic wave. The transmitting tower of a radio broadcasting station creates radio waves in exactly this way. Electricity is forced to move up and down the metal in the tower creating an electromagnetic wave that travels away from the tower carrying the radio signal. In fact, any oscillation or acceleration of an electrical or magnetic particle creates electromagnetic waves.

The wavelength of visible light is between 400 and 700 nanometers. A nanometer is one-billionth of a meter. The frequency of visible light is related to the wavelets by the same relationship we find for all waves. Speed is frequency times wavelength. Electromagnetic waves all travel at the speed of light, which is 3×10^8 m/sec. Therefore, the frequency of violet light (400 nm) is 3×10^8 m/sec divided by 400×10^{-9} meters, or 4.6×10^{14} Hz. 460 trillion Hz is very fast. That is why shaking a magnet up and down does not produce light you can see. You would have to shake the magnet up and down 460 trillion times per second to make violet light.

In terms of wavelength, electromagnetic waves have wavelength that ranges from bigger than Earth to much smaller than the nucleus of an atom. The longest range of wavelengths, longer than a few centimeters, are radio waves. Microwaves have a wavelength of a few centimeters to a few millimeters. Gamma rays have the shortest wavelength; they are smaller than the size of the nucleus of an atom.

1
2

For the Investigation there are seven questions I would like you to research and answer. You may use any reference that you think is reputable. You may find some of the information in your textbook. Each group should organize the information on its assigned wave in the form of a poster including any drawings if appropriate. Make a bibliography of your sources and put it on the back of your poster.

UNIT 6: Light and Color

18.1 The Electromagnetic Spectrum

Question: What is the electromagnetic spectrum?

In this Investigation, you will:

1. Research one type of wave that is part of the electromagnetic spectrum.
2. Prepare a poster containing the information you discover.
3. Make an oral presentation to share the information with your class.

The *electromagnetic spectrum* is a group of waves that all travel at the same speed (3×10^8 m/s) but have different wavelengths and frequencies. The waves in this spectrum are called *electromagnetic waves* and include visible light, microwaves, radio waves, and X-rays. In this Investigation, you will research the history, properties, and uses of one of these types of waves.

1 Researching your electromagnetic wave

Your teacher will assign your group one type of electromagnetic wave that you will research using the Internet or reading. You will construct a poster displaying the information you gather about your type of wave. You will also present what you have learned to your classmates. All of the posters made by the class will be displayed in the order of the waves that make up the electromagnetic spectrum.

Your research should include the answers to the following questions. Do not limit yourself to these questions; include other interesting information as well. Record the sources you use for a bibliography.

1. What is the range of wavelengths for your type of wave?
2. What is the range of frequencies?
3. What is the source of the wave?
4. Who discovered this type of wave and when?
5. Are these waves easily blocked or can they pass through objects?
6. Do the waves have an effect on people? Are they harmful?
7. Discuss the uses for the waves. These may include inventions that we use in our everyday lives, medical uses, or ways scientists use the waves for research. You should spend the greatest amount of time on this part of your research.

Gamma rays
X-rays
Ultraviolet light
Visible light
Infrared light
Microwaves
Radio waves

2 Sharing your information

Organize your information on a poster. You should include drawings where they are appropriate. Make a bibliography of your sources and put it on the back of your poster.

Present what you learned to the other groups in your class. You should be able to discuss the uses for your type of wave.

Listen to the presentations made by other groups. Which type of wave do you think is the most useful to us? Why?

122

1 Example answers

Example answers for ultraviolet light:

1. Range of wavelength: 10-400 nm (1×10^{-8} to 4×10^{-7} m)
2. Range of frequencies: 7.51×10^{14} Hz to 3×10^{16} Hz
3. The sun is our largest natural source of ultraviolet light. Man-made equipment, such as UV lamps and arc welders, also are sources of ultraviolet light.
4. Ultraviolet light was discovered by Johann Wilhelm Ritter in 1801 while he was studying the effects of radiation from the sun on silver chloride.
5. Ultraviolet light is easily blocked by sunblock, sunglasses, and clothes. In the atmosphere, ozone blocks the ultraviolet rays.
6. Ultraviolet light can cause darkening of the skin, burns to the skin, and increase the risk of skin cancer. It can also cause sensitivity of the eyes and different eye disorders, including cataracts. Some exposure to ultraviolet light is necessary to help the body produce Vitamin D.
7. Ultraviolet light is used in suntanning, in sterilizing things by killing bacteria, in industrial processes of curing inks and resins, and in welding. Ultraviolet light is also used in medical treatments for psoriasis and newborn jaundice.

Bibliographical References:

Licker, Mark D. (Publisher). McGraw-Hill Dictionary of Scientific and Technical Terms, Sixth Edition. New York: McGraw-Hill Companies, Inc., 2003.

Imagine the Universe website [Online].
Available: http://www.imagine.gsfc.nasa.gov/ [14 January 2004]

Canadian National Occupational Health & Safety Resources [Online]. Available: http://www.ccohs.ca/oshanswer/phys_agents/ultravioletradiation.html [14 January 2004]

18.2 Interference, Diffraction, and Polarization

Key question: What are some ways light behaves like a wave?

Students first observe how a diffraction grating separates white light into a spectrum. Next, they use a grating spectrometer to measure the wavelength of the yellow mercury doublet line from a fluorescent bulb. Students first model polarization with mechanical waves on a spring, showing they can be vertically or horizontally polarized depending on how the spring is shaken. The students then explore how two polarizers act as an adjustable filter for light.

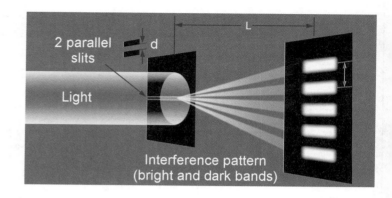

Reading Synopsis

Students read Section 18.1 Interference, Diffraction, and Polarization after the Investigation.

We say light is a wave because the results of many experiments with light demonstrate properties of waves. Young's double slit experiment is a good example of interference. A diffraction grating creates an interference pattern similar to the double slit. The first order bright spot in a diffraction pattern results from constructed interference that occurs when the grating equation ($\lambda = d \sin\theta$) is satisfied. A spectrometer is a device that measures the wavelength of light.

Polarization is a property of transverse waves. The direction of polarization is a vector perpendicular to the direction the wave propagates. The polarization vector of light points in the direction of the electric field of the wave. A polarizer is a material that is sensitive to the polarization of light. One polarization is absorbed. The perpendicular polarization is transmitted, or emitted. Applications of polarizers include sunglasses and LCD computer screens.

The Investigation

Leading Questions
- What does a diffraction grating do to light passing through it?
- How does an interference pattern produced by a diffraction grating support the wave theory of light?
- What uses does a spectrometer have?
- What does a polarizing filter do to light passing through it?

Learning Goals

By the end of the Investigation, students will be able to:
- Observe and explain how a diffraction grating creates a rainbow.
- Observe and explain what happens when a laser shines through a diffraction grating.
- Explain the interaction of light and polarizers using the wave theory of light.

Key Vocabulary

constructive interference, destructive interference, diffraction grating, spectrometer, polarization, polarizer, transmission axis, polarized

Setup and Materials

Students work in groups of four or five at tables.

Each group should have:

- Light and optics kit (laser)
- Diffraction grating glasses
- Metric ruler
- Spectrometer
- Two polarizing filters
- A large spring or Slinky$^{(TM)}$ spring toy to demonstrate waves. Slinkies$^{(TM)}$ can be plastic or metal. Both types will work.

Details

Time 🕐 One class period

Preparation

Assignments 📖 Section 18.1 Interference, Diffraction, and Polarization in the **Student Edition** after the Investigation.

Equipment Setup Diffraction grating glasses and a laser

Teaching the Investigation

1 Introduction
2 The diffraction grating
3 How a diffraction grating works
4 A diffraction pattern comes from the interference of light
5 Interpreting the diffraction pattern
6 Measuring the wavelength of laser light
7 The spectrometer
8 Polarization of a transverse spring wave
9 Describing and applying what you see
10 The polarization vector
11 The polarization of light
12 How to explain what you see

Introduction

In this Investigation we are going to look at some experiments that provide evidence that light is a wave. Since the wavelength of light is very small and the frequency is very high, we will not be able to see individual waves of light. The evidence from experiments takes some analysis and careful thinking to interpret. Don't worry if you don't get it right away. These experiments have been thought about for a very long time by many smart people. The explanations we are going to discuss were not obvious to the people who did the experiments first either.

The diffraction grating

What is a diffraction grating?

A diffraction grating is a precise array of tiny engraved lines, each of which allows light through.

A diffraction pattern is the light scattered off the engraved lines.

The first thing we are going to investigate the diffraction grating. Remember when we used the diffraction grating to separate light into a spectrum when we were doing experiments with color? Today we are going to explain how a diffraction grating works. A diffraction grating works because light is a wave and uses the interference of light waves to produce a spectrum. Take out your diffraction grating and look at a bright blue light such as one of the LED lamps. Where does the spectrum appear?

Have students describe what they see. The spectrum appears as rainbows on the sides of the image of the lamp seen through the transparent diffraction grating.

The rainbows that we call a spectrum are an example of a diffraction pattern. If you could look at the diffraction grating through a powerful microscope you would see that the surface is covered with a crisscross pattern of very fine scratches. You see the image of the lamp as if the grating were a window because most light passes right through. However, some of light is scattered from the scratches. The light scattering from the scratches is what creates the spectrum.

Draw a crisscross pattern on the board.

The scratches are evenly spaced and the distance between adjacent scratches is comparable to the wavelength of light. We see interference patterns because the pattern of scratches on the grating is regular and of a size that is comparable to a wavelength.

How a diffraction grating works

1

The diffraction grating works by creating an interference pattern of light.

To understand why a grating works, we start by assuming there are only two scratches. The scratches are separated by a distance (d). Light falls on the scratches, passes through and falls on a distant screen. The screen is a distance (L) away from the grating.

Draw the diagram in step 1 on the board.

Most of the light goes straight through making a central bright spot directly in front of our two scratches. Some of the light is scattered from the scratches. Consider light reaching a point on the screen a distance W away from the central bright spot. The light from the left hand scratch travels a slightly shorter path than the light from the right hand scratch. This difference in path length is what creates the interference pattern.

Draw the two waves from the scratches to the screen on your diagram.

Suppose the difference in path length is exactly one wavelength. That means the waves reaching the spot arrive in phase with each other and we see brightness. Next, consider what happens if the difference in path length is one-half of a wave. The waves arrive at the screen out of phase with each other by one-half wavelength. One is up while the other is down. As a result we see darkness there because the two waves interfere destructively.

As we move away from the central bright spot, the path difference between the two waves increases. The intensity of light on the screen is lowest when the path difference is one-half wavelength. The intensity increases and reaches a maximum when the path difference is a full wavelength. Going farther, the intensity drops off again and becomes darkest when the path difference is $1^1/_2$ wavelengths. Keep going and another maximum appears when the path difference is exactly two wavelengths.

18.2   Interference, Diffraction, and Polarization

Question: What are some ways light behaves like a wave?

In this Investigation, you will:

1. Observe and explain how a diffraction grating creates a rainbow.
2. Observe and explain what happens when a laser shines through a diffraction grating.
3. Explain the interaction of light and polarizers using the wave theory of light.

The diffraction grating is a precise array of tiny engraved lines, each of which allows light through. When you look at a small bright light through a diffraction grating, you see two things:

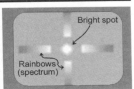

1. You see the light straight ahead as if the grating were clear glass.
2. You see rainbows on all sides of the light that come from the light scattering off the engraved lines of the diffraction grating.

The light scattered off the lines is called a spectrum and it is an example of a *diffraction pattern*. The precise array of lines separates the light according to its wavelength and produces the spectrum. Most of the light we see is a mixture of many different wavelengths. A spectrum shows how much there is of each wavelength in a sample of light. Because we see different wavelengths as different colors, your eye sees the spectrum as a rainbow.

1   **How a diffraction grating works**

The light that forms the spectrum is the fraction of incident light that is scattered from the parallel grooves of the diffraction grating. The light reaching a point on the screen is a combination of waves from many different grooves. The diffraction pattern (spectrum) is created by the interference of light reaching the screen from adjacent scratches. If the waves are in phase when they reach the screen, you see brightness, or constructive interference. If the waves are out of phase, you see darkness, or destructive interference.

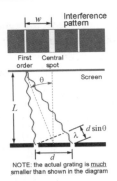

When a laser beam passes through a diffraction grating, most of the light goes straight through, making a central bright spot. The interference pattern is the additional bright spots that appear to the sides of the central bright spot. The closest set of additional spots is called the *first order* and they form where the strongest constructive interference occurs. A second, dimmer set of spots appears farther out from the central spot (the second order), and then an even dimmer third set, and so on.

NOTE: the actual grating is <u>much</u> smaller than shown in the diagram

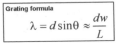

Grating formula

$$\lambda = d\sin\theta \approx \frac{dw}{L}$$

The condition of constructive interference allows you to calculate the wavelength of the light if you know the spacing of the grooves on the diffraction grating. The grating formula (at right) comes from the condition for constructive interference between light from adjacent grooves. Two waves interfere constructively when the difference in the path between them is exactly one wavelength.

123

Interference pattern with two scratches

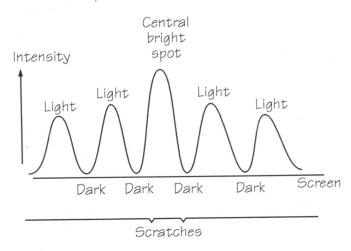

Interference pattern with many scratches

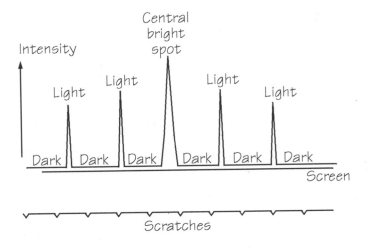

A diffraction pattern comes from the interference of light

Grating formula

$$\lambda = d\sin\theta \approx \frac{dw}{L}$$

Interpreting the diffraction pattern

The first-order bright spots appear to the side of the central spot and come from waves that are one whole wavelength different in phase.

The second-order bright spots are dimmer and farther out from the central spot. They correspond to a difference of two wavelengths.

2 What we see is a pattern of light and dark bands around the central bright spot. The bright bands correspond to constructive interference. The dark bands correspond to destructive interference.

Draw the intensity pattern on the board labeled as shown in the diagram on the right side of the preceding page.

By applying geometry to the situation, we can calculate the difference in distance traveled by the two light beams from the scratches. This distance is equal to the spacing between the scratches multiplied by the sign of the angle shown here. The angle is formed by a line going straight to the central bright spot and another line going to the first bright spot in the interference pattern.

Complete the diagram as shown in step 1 of the Investigation.

We see a the first bright spot when this distance is equal to one wavelength. The result is an equation called the grating formula. The grating formula allows us to calculate the wavelength of light if we know the spacing (d) between the scratches on the grating and we measure the distance (L) between the screen and the grating and the distance (w) to the first bright spot.

Put the grating formula on the board and explain how it comes from the geometry of the experiment. So far our analysis has assumed there were only two scratches in the grating. Actually, there are many scratches, all separated by precisely the same spacing. The effect of having multiple scratches is to shrink the width of the bright areas so they are narrow compared to the dark areas in between. This makes it much easier to read the diffraction pattern and measure the distance between the central bright spot and the bright spots of the diffraction pattern on either side.

Draw the intensity pattern in the lower diagram on the right side of the preceding page. This shows that the bright spots are the same spacing relative to the central bright spot, except the peaks in the interference pattern are narrower.

3 The bright spots on either side of the central bright spot are grouped into orders. The first order includes the closest spots to the left and right of the central bright spot. The first order spots correspond to a path difference of one wavelength. The second order is the second closest pair of spots that correspond to a path difference of two wavelengths. It is possible with our diffraction greetings to see up to the third and fourth orders in the diffraction pattern. Take the laser from your optics kit and shine it through the diffraction grating so the laser beam falls on a distant wall. Observe the central spot and the diffraction pattern. Notice there are spots to the right, left, above, and below the central bright spot. This is because the grating we are using has scratches in two perpendicular directions, vertical and horizontal. If there were only vertical scratches, you would only see interference patterns to either side. Horizontal scratches would give you spots that are above and below. Since the grating has scratches in both directions, you see spots to the side as well as up and down. Can you identify the spots in the first order? Which spots are in the second order?

Have students shine the laser through the diffraction grating as shown in step 2 of the Investigation. The first order spots are the four spots closest to the central bright spot. The second order includes the four spots in line with the first order but farther out. The faint spots on the corners are also caused by interference by light scattered by the intersections of the scratches. These are not used for measurement purposes.

18.2 Interference, Diffraction, and Polarization

2 Measuring the wavelength of laser light

1. Set up a place where you can project the laser onto a screen or blank wall. You can reduce any errors you might make with your measurements by placing the laser as far away from the screen as possible.

2. Place the diffraction grating glasses in front of the laser and adjust the placement of the glasses so that you can see bright spots. The center spot is the brightest. The closest bright spots to the right, left, above, and below are the *first order bright spots.*

3. Measure the distance between the screen and the diffraction grating glasses. This is distance *L*.

4. Measure the distance between two first-order bright spots (ones that are in line and on either side of the central bright spot). Divide this number by two to calculate the distance from the central bright spot to a first-order bright spot (*w*).

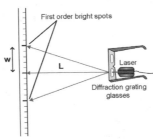

a. Use the value for the spacing of the grooves on the diffraction grating from your instructor for *d*. Use the grating formula ($\lambda = dw \div L$) to calculate the wavelength of the laser light (λ).

b. Does the value of wavelength of the laser fall within with the range of wavelengths that appear red to the human eye?

3 The spectrometer

A *spectrometer* is an instrument that is designed around a diffraction grating. The spectrometer allows you to measure the wavelength of light of different colors. When light of a single wavelength falls on a diffraction grating, the first-order bright spot forms at a specific place that depends on the wavelength. When multicolored light falls on a grating, each color (wavelength) creates constructive interference at a different distance corresponding to its wavelength. Multicolored light is spread out into its component wavelengths which we see as different colors.

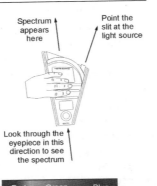

1. Use the spectrometer to look at red, green, and blue lights. Use Table 1 to record the range of wavelengths you see.

2. Shine the red laser on a white piece of paper. Look at the spot it makes with the spectrometer. Record the range of wavelengths you see.

3. Look at a fluorescent light bulb. What range of wavelengths do you see? You will probably see two bright yellow lines in the spectrum from the fluorescent bulb. The yellow lines are the signature of the element mercury and come from the mercury vapor in the bulbs.

2 Example answers

2a. Calculation:

$$w = 15 \ cm$$

$$L = 100 \ cm$$

$$d = 4.33 \times 10^{-4} \ cm$$

$$\lambda = \frac{dw}{L} = \frac{(4.33 \times 10^{-4} \ cm)(15 \ cm)}{100 \ cm}$$

$$\lambda = 6.5 \times 10^{-4} \ cm = 650 \ nm$$

2b. Yes, the wavelengths that appear red to the human eye are between approximately 620-740 nanometers and the laser wavelength of 650 nanometers is within that range.

Teaching Tip

It can be difficult to see the red, green, and blue filtered lights through the spectrometer because the light source is so small. If the students place the filtered light right up to the spectrometer slit, fitting it inside the opening on the spectrometer, the spectrum will be much easier to see and there will be less interference from any fluorescent room lighting.

Do not use this method with the laser source. The students should examine the laser light by reflecting it off a piece of white paper, and they should not shine the laser directly into the spectrometer.

Measuring the wavelength of laser light

Now, we are going to use the diffraction grating to measure the wavelength of the red light from your laser. Set up the experiment as shown in Part 2. Measure the distance between the diffraction grating and the screen and the distance from the central spot to the first order bright spots on either side. Use the grating formula to calculate the wavelength of laser light. Obtain the spacing between the scratches from your instructor. The diffraction grating glasses have 13,500 lines per inch, which equals a spacing of 1.88×10^{-4} cm between scratches.

> Students follow Part 2 of the Investigation and determine the wavelength of laser light. This may vary with the specific laser but should be around 650 nanometers, or 6.5×10^{-7} m.

The diagrams are drawn, and our analysis assumes that the light has a single wavelength. The spacing of the spots in the interference pattern depends on the wavelength of the light. Light of longer wavelength creates spots that are farther away from the central bright spot. Light of shorter wavelength creates spots that are closer to the central right spot.

> If you have a green laser it is very instructive to shine this through so the central bright spots from red and green line up. Green light has a shorter wavelength than red light. That means the path difference to get constructive interference is smaller, and therefore the first order green spots are closer to the central bright spot. Green laser pointers are available from science supply companies.

The spectrometer

What is a spectrometer?

A spectrometer allows you to measure the wavelength of light of different colors?

If light containing many different wavelengths passes through a diffraction grating, each different wavelength creates a constructive interference at a different distance from the central bright spot. That is why you see a rainbow when you look at white light through a diffraction grating. Each different color in the rainbow corresponds to a different wavelength of light. A spectrometer is an instrument specifically designed to measure the wavelength of light. The spectrometer you have contains a diffraction grating in the eyepiece. There is a small slit on the opposite end of the spectrometer to allow light in. To see the spectrum point the slit at a light source and look to the left of the slit through the eyepiece. The spectrometer is constructed so you can read the wavelength directly on a scale below the spectrum.

> Have students use the spectrometer to look at any bright light source (EXCEPT the sun!). This is a little tricky because they need to point the slit at the light and look to the left.

Look at a fluorescent light through the spectrometer. You will see two bright yellow lines that correspond to the element mercury. Use the spectrometer to measure the wavelength of the two yellow lines in the mercury spectrum.

> Students should do this and record the wavelength of the two yellow lines.

4

Next, we are going to talk about the polarization of light. One property that we learned about in the previous unit is that waves can be either transverse or longitudinal. Can someone define these terms for me?

> Transverse waves oscillate perpendicular to the direction of wave travel, while longitudinal waves oscillate in the same direction as the wave travels.

Polarization of a transverse spring wave

Polarization of a wave describes the direction of oscillation relative to the direction the wave moves.

Polarization is a property of transverse waves. Sound is a longitudinal wave. Light is a transverse wave. To get a sense of polarization we are going to look at waves on a spring first. Take a spring and shake it up and down until you make a wave. When the spring is moving up and down, this is an example of vertical polarization. Now shake the spring side to side until you make another wave. When the spring is shaking side to side, this is an example of horizontal polarization.

> Students complete the activity in step 4 of the Investigation. If you do not have long springs, a length of bungee cord or flexible rubber tubing also works.

Investigation page (left)

18.2 Interference, Diffraction, and Polarization

Table 1: Spectrometer observations

Apparent color	Observed range of wavelengths	Appearance of lines

4 Polarization of a transverse spring wave

A transverse wave on a spring can oscillate in two perpendicular directions: sideways (horizontal) or up and down (vertical). The two directions of oscillation are examples of *polarization*. The polarization of a wave describes the direction of oscillation relative to the direction the wave moves.

1. Find a partner. Each of you should take one end of the spring and stretch it. Do not let go or the spring will snap back suddenly.
2. One person should hold the spring firmly without moving.
3. The other person should shake the spring up and down at a frequency to get the second harmonic wave. It has a shape like the diagram on the right. This wave is vertically polarized since it oscillates up and down in the vertical direction.
4. Stop shaking the spring and let it settle down.
5. Shake the spring side to side at the same frequency and you can also get the second harmonic wave. This time the wave is horizontally polarized since the oscillations are in the horizontal direction.

Up - down shaking produces vertical polarization

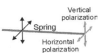
Sideways shaking produces horizontal polarization

Vertical polarization
Spring
Horizontal polarization

5 Describing and applying what you see

a. Describe the motion of the spring using the terms *horizontal polarization* and *vertical polarization*. Your description can be in words, diagrams, or both.

b. Suppose you try to sandwich your spring wave between two boards. What happens to the waves if you make them pass through the narrow space between the boards? If the boards were oriented like the picture below, discuss how the two different polarizations of waves would behave. Which would get through the slot and which would be blocked?

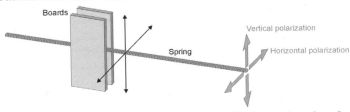
Boards
Spring
Vertical polarization
Horizontal polarization

c. Describe the polarization of water waves. Are there two polarizations (like the spring) or only one? What is it about a water surface that makes it different from a spring?

125

Example answers (right)

3 5 Example answers

Table 1: *Spectrometer observations*

Apparent color	Observed range of wavelength	Appearance of lines
green	410-700	a spectrum
blue	410-690	a spectrum
red	410-710	a spectrum, but missing the green
red laser	645	a red line
fluorescent light	540, 570	two yellow lines

5a. First I shook the spring up and down. The wave moved above and below the horizontal plane as it traveled down the spring. Because the wave went up and down we say it had vertical polarization. Next I shook the spring from side to side. This time the wave moved left and right as it traveled down the spring. As a result, we say that this wave had horizontal polarization.

5b. If I tried to get my two waves to pass through the narrow space between the vertical boards, the first wave would go through unchanged because it oscillated up and down. My second wave would be blocked by the boards because it was oscillating side to side. Only vertically polarized waves could get through.

5c. Water waves are vertically polarized. The surface of water is like a continuous horizontal plane so the water doesn't have the freedom to move side to side like the spring.

Describing and applying what you see

The polarization vector

Polarization is a vector that has two basic states: horizontal and vertical.

The polarization of light

A polarizer is a material that allows one polarization of light to pass but blocks the other polarization.

How to explain what you see

5

To understand the behavior of polarizers, consider trying to make the spring wave pass between two boards as shown in step 5 of the Investigation. Which polarization can pass through the boards? Which polarization is blocked by the boards?

> Students should easily recognize that vertical polarization passes and horizontal polarization is blocked.

With the spring you saw that a transverse wave can have more than one orientation. In other words, it can oscillate up-and-down, or side-to-side. Do you think it could oscillate in directions other than these?

> Yes. It could oscillate at a 45° angle, for example. In fact, there are an infinite number of angles, or polarizations, in which the wave could oscillate.

Remember the properties of vectors? A vector can be represented by components in two perpendicular directions, such as x and y. Polarization is a vector and therefore any polarization can be represented by two components that are perpendicular to each other. Therefore there are only two basic states of polarization, which we will call vertical and horizontal. Light waves from sources such as candles, incandescent or fluorescent lights, sunshine, and even fireflies contain a mixture of all polarizations. When light waves from a source contain all polarizations equally, we say that the light is not polarized, or unpolarized. Polarized light, on the other hand, contains only waves of a single polarization.

As for what exact feature of light waves oscillates to create polarization, remember our earlier demonstration of shaking a magnet up and down to create a wave. If electricity oscillates up and down in a vertical wire it creates a wave with an electric field oscillating up and down in a vertical direction. We called this wave vertically polarized. If we oscillate the electricity in a horizontal wire it makes a wave whose electric field oscillates side to side. This wave has horizontal polarization. Light is just a very high frequency version of this same wave. The polarization of a light wave describes the direction in which the electric field of the wave oscillates. We will talk more about electric and magnetic fields in the next unit.

Now you are ready to experiment with the polarizing filters. These sheets of plastic contain long, thin molecules that are lined up in neat rows. The spacing of the molecules is comparable to the wavelength of light. As result, the molecules affect the polarization of light waves similar to the way the boards constrained the polarization of spring waves. The rows of molecules absorb and block light waves that are polarized in one direction and pass light waves polarized in the perpendicular direction. Follow the instructions in Part 6 using the two polarizers you have.

> Allow students about 15 minutes to complete the activity and questions.

7

How does the diffraction grating support the hypothesis that light is a wave? How does the behavior of the polarizers support the hypothesis that light is a transverse wave?

> The pattern of spots observed with the diffraction grating can be explained by the constructive and destructive interference of two waves. Interference is a wave property and observing interference of light is therefore evidence that light is a wave. Experiments with polarizers demonstrate that light waves have exist in two characteristic types which are identical in all respects but their response to a polarizer. This is evidence that light is a transverse wave and cannot easily be explained if light were a longitudinal wave.

18.2 Interference, Diffraction, and Polarization

6 The polarization of light

If you were to observe polarization, it would be strong evidence that light is a transverse wave. A *polarizer* is a material that allows one polarization of light to pass but blocks the other polarization. A polarizer works like the two boards except the "boards" are long, thin molecules. The molecules let light waves oscillate one way but absorb light that oscillates the other way.

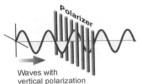

Waves with vertical polarization get through

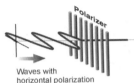

Waves with horizontal polarization get stopped by the polarizer

1. Take one sheet of polarizer and look through it. Observe the effect of looking through the polarizer. Try rotating the polarizer and see if it makes a difference.
2. Take a second sheet of polarizer and look through it. Observe the effects, just as with the first sheet.
3. Look through both sheets of polarizer together. Leave one fixed and rotate the other one as shown in the diagram below. Observe how much light you see through both polarizers as you rotate the second one.

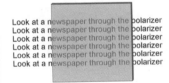

Look at something through one polarizer.

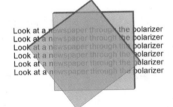

Look at something through two polarizers as you rotate one of them.

7 How do you explain what you see?

a. The light from the sun (or a lamp) is not polarized, meaning it is a mixture of light that is polarized equally in all directions. Explain why the light is reduced passing through one polarizer.

b. When the light passes through the first polarizer, it becomes polarized. We say light is polarized when it consists of only one polarization. Explain why rotating the second polarizer changes the amount of light you see coming through.

c. The glare from low-angle sunlight reflecting from water and roads is polarized in the horizontal direction. Ordinary sunlight is not polarized. Explain how polarizing sunglasses can stop most of the glare but still allow half the regular (unpolarized) light to come through.

7 Example answers

7a. The light is reduced when it passes through one polarizer because all of the light rays that are not oscillating in line with the rows of molecules in the filter get blocked out.

7b. As the second polarizer is rotated, more and more of the light rays get blocked until finally the two polarizers are at right angles to each other and then no light can get through.

7c. Polarizing sunglasses have polarizers that are oriented vertically. This allows them to block out the horizontal light waves caused by glare while still allowing vertically polarized light waves to pass through unchanged.

18.3 Special Relativity

Key Question: What are some of the implications of special relativity?

This investigation provides students with a taste of special relativity. Since it is difficult to do hands on investigations of relativistic motion in the classroom, we are constrained to paper and pencil calculations. Students use a table of pre-calculated time dilation factors to estimate the effect of relativistic motion on time. Students solve a non-relativistic problem using frames of reference. Finally, students do a few calculations using Einstein's mass energy formula $E = mc^2$.

In the ship the light goes straight up and down

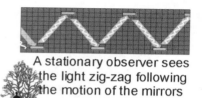

A stationary observer sees the light zig-zag following the motion of the mirrors

Reading Synopsis

Students read Section 18.3 Special Relativity

The theory of special relativity describes what happens to matter, energy, time, and space when the speed of a moving object becomes close to the speed of light. The speed of light is the same for all observers regardless of their relative motion. This implies that time passes more slowly for a moving observer compared to a stationary observer. Light emitted from a moving source is perceived by a stationary observer at a different frequency from the frequency measured by an observer moving with the light source.

Einstein's formula $E = mc^2$ describes the equivalent of mass and energy. Matter cannot exceed or even reach the speed of light. The reason is because energy can be converted to mass instead of speed.

The concept of simultaneity is affected by special relativity. Events that are simultaneous to one observer may not be simultaneous to a second observer moving relative to the first observer.

The Investigation

Leading Questions
- Does time move at the same speed for everyone everywhere?
- What is the relationship between frames of reference and time dilation?
- How are energy, mass, and the speed of light related?
- What does Einstein's mass - energy formula tell us about the potential for possible sources of energy?

Learning Goals

By the end of the Investigation, students will be able to:
- Explore some consequences of time dilation.
- Calculate the equivalence of mass and energy using Einstein's formula $E = mc^2$.

Key Vocabulary

time dilation, speed of light, rest energy

Setup and Materials

Students work in groups of four or five at tables.

Each group should have:

- Calculators
- No other equipment is necessary because most of the Investigation centers around students completing calculations.

Details

Time   ⏱ One class period

Preparation   ✏

Assignments   📖 Section 18.3 Special Relativity in the **Student Edition** after the Investigation.

Skill Sheets   18.3 Albert Einstein

Equipment Setup   No equipment is necessary

Teaching the Investigation

1   Introduction
2   Four implications of special relativity
3   Time dilation
4   When does special relativity become important?
5   Relativity and frames of reference
6   The equivalence of mass and energy

Introduction

Science fiction writers love to make up interesting effects such as time travel. It may surprise you, but time travel into the future is actually possible! It just takes a lot of energy, much more energy than we know how to get or control. Time travel backwards we believe to be impossible. Einstein's theory of special relativity makes a connection between time and space that depends on how fast you are moving. When it was first proposed, the theory of special relativity was considered shocking because it upset the very foundation of how science believed the universe works. Nonetheless, experiment after experiment proves that special relativity is correct and the universe envisioned by Newton is actually more complicated than he saw. Today we are going to go on a brief tour of the theory of special relativity and touched on top few of the major points. Unfortunately, we cannot do experiments because we do not have the facilities to make objects go at speeds approaching that speed of light.

Four fundamental implications of the theory of special relativity are

1   Time moves more slowly for an object in motion than it does for objects that are not in motion. In practical terms, clocks run slower on moving spaceships compared to clocks on the ground. This effect is known as time dilation.

2   As objects move faster, their mass increases. The closer the speed of an object gets to the speed of light, the more of its kinetic energy becomes mass instead of motion. For this reason, matter can never equal or exceed the speed of light because adding energy creates more mass instead of increasing an object's speed.

3   The definition of the word "simultaneous" changes. Two events that are simultaneous to one observer may not be simultaneous to another who is moving.

4   The length of an object measured by a person at rest will not be the same as the length measured by another person who is moving close to the speed of light. The object does not get smaller or larger, space itself gets smaller for an observer moving near the speed of light.

Table 1 gives you an example of how a clock would behave on a moving spaceship compared to an identical clock that was not moving. The time intervals are given to a ten thousandth of a second, the same precision as we are able to measure with our photogate timer. At what speed does the difference between the two clocks become measurable with our photogate timer?

Students should look at table 1 and notice the first difference occurs at a speed of 1×10^7 m/sec. What is this speed in miles per hour? Have you ever gone this fast?

224 million miles per hour. No human has ever gone this fast. The maximum speed reached during the apollo missions was 25,000 mph, about 10,000 times slower.

The fact that time slows down for an observer in motion is called time dilation. The time dilation factor is six hundredths of one percent at a speed of 1×10^7 m/sec, which is a bit over 3 percent of the speed of light. If you look at table 1 you see that the effect of time dilation increases as the speed gets closer and closer to about speed of light. The time dilation factor is 34 percent for a space ship moving at 67 percent that speed of light, or 200 million meters per second. Suppose you were on a spaceship ship traveling at 97 percent of the speed of light. Suppose you travel for one year at this speed. How much time has passed back here on Earth?

The time dilation factor is 3.94 therefore 3.94 years have passed on Earth while you experience only one year on your space ship.

Four implications of special relativity

Einstein's mass-energy formula:

$E = mc^2$

E = energy (J)
m = mass (kg)
c = speed of light
   $= 3 \times 10^8$ m/sec

Time dilation

Time dilation: according to Einstein's theory, a clock appears to run slower to an observer moving relative to the clock than to an observer who is at rest with respect to the clock.

UNIT 6: Light and Color

Special Relativity

Question: What are some of the implications of special relativity?

In this Investigation, you will:

1. Explore some consequences of time dilation.
2. Calculate the equivalence of mass and energy using Einstein's formula $E = mc^2$.

Time moves more slowly for an object in motion than that it does for an object that is not in motion. In practical terms, clocks run slower on moving spaceships compared to clocks on the ground. By moving very fast, it is possible for one year to pass on a spaceship while 100 years passes on the ground. This effect is known as *time dilation*. Table 1 gives some examples of how time dilation affects the perception of 1 second of time for observers moving relative to each other at different speeds.

Moving observer

Observer at rest

Table 1: Speed and Time Dilation

Speed			Time for the observer at rest	Time for the moving observer
m/sec	mph	% of c	(sec)	(sec)
100	224	3.3×10^{-5}	1.0000	1.0000
1,000	2,240	3.3×10^{-4}	1.0000	1.0000
10,000	22,400	0.0033	1.0000	1.0000
1,000,000	2.24×10^6	0.33	1.0000	1.0000
1.00×10^7	2.24×10^8	3.3	1.0000	1.0006
1.00×10^8	2.24×10^8	33	1.0000	1.0607
2.00×10^8	2.24×10^8	67	1.0000	1.3424
2.80×10^8	6.26×10^8	93	1.0000	2.7981
2.90×10^8	6.49×10^8	97	1.0000	3.9434
2.99×10^8	6.69×10^8	99.7	1.0000	13.6976

1 **When does special relativity become important?**

a. A high-performance aircraft flies at a speed of 1,340 m/sec, or 4 times faster than the speed of sound (340 m/sec). At this high speed, will the effects of time dilation be perceived by a person with an ordinary watch?

b. A rocket traveling to Mars must have a speed greater than the minimum speed required to break Earth's gravitational attraction. This minimum speed is called the escape velocity. Use research to find Earth's escape velocity. Is the escape velocity fast enough that relativity must be considered for normal purposes such as synchronizing two clocks?

c. The numbers in Table 1 were calculated using a formula proposed by Einstein. Research the formula to identify what the variables mean.

127

---

1 **Example answers**

1a. At a speed of 1,340 m/sec the effects of time dilation cannot be perceived by a person with an ordinary watch. The aircraft would have to be traveling much faster, closer to 10,000,000 m/sec to see the effects of time dilation.

1b. Earth's escape velocity is 11,300 m/sec, which is not fast enough to have to consider relativity.

1c.

$$t_{rest} = \frac{t_{motion}}{\sqrt{1 - \left(\frac{v}{c}\right)^2}}$$

Where, t_{motion} is the time seen by the object in motion, t_{rest} is the time seen by the object at rest, c is the speed of light, and v is the speed of the object in motion.

When does special relativity become important?

Relativity and frames of reference

Relativity in Einstein's theory means that velocity can only be determined relative to a reference frame.

1

2

Use table 1 to answer the questions in part one of the investigation.

The time dilation factor is given by the equation $\gamma = (1 - v^2 / c^2)^{-1/2}$. This parameter is often called the gamma factor because it is written as the Greek letter γ.

The word relative in the special theory of relativity has an important meaning. It means that velocities can only be determined relative to a reference frame. To a physicist, It makes no sense to say an object is moving at 1 m/sec without providing a reference. For example, you might measure the 1 m/sec relative to your lab or classroom. However, the Earth itself is rotating and also circling the sun. A velocity of 1 m/sec relative to the lab (on Earth) is not the same as a velocity of 1 m/sec relative to the sun. Consider the situation shown in the diagram in part 2 of the investigation. A person on a train throws a dart at a dart board. Relative to the train, the dart travels a distance of 5 meters to the dart board in 0.5 seconds. The training is moving forward at a speed of 30 m/sec. What is the speed of the dart relative to the train? What is the speed of the dart relative to the ground?

The dart moves 5 meters in 0.5 seconds therefore its speed is 10 meters per second relative to the train. The train moves forward 15 meters in the same 0.5 seconds. Relative to the ground, the dart has moved 20 meters in 0.5 seconds therefore its speed is 40 meters per second. You can also calculate the speed of the dart relative to the ground by adding its speed relative to the train to the speed of the train relative to the ground.

The same person leans out the window of the train and throws a dart forward at the same speed toward a dartboard on a pole beside the track. How fast does the second dart approach the dart board on the pole?

The second dart approaches the pole at 40 m/sec, the speed of the dart relative to the ground.

There are to reference frames important to understand the motion of the darts. What are they and what are their relative velocities?

The first reference frame is the train. The second reference frame is the ground. The first reference frame is moving at 30 m/sec relative to the second reference frame. 30 m/sec must be added to any velocity specified in the first reference frame to find the velocity in the second reference frame.

All of the effects of special relativity relates to the differences seen by observers in reference frames that are moving relative to each other. If two space ships are moving at 97 percent of the speed of light in the same direction, their relative velocity is zero. The clocks on both ships tick at the same rate. This is similar to what you experience when driving beside someone on the highway at the same speed. You look out your window and the person in the other car appears to be motionless relative to you.

The equivalence of mass and energy

3

The formula $E = mc^2$ is probably the most famous equation in all of physics. At, least to people other than physicists. What do the symbols in the equation stand for?

E stands for energy, m stands for mass, and c is the speed of light, 3×10^8 m/sec.

According to this formula, how much energy would I get from one kilogram of mass if I could convert the mass completely to energy?

You get c^2 joules, which works out to 9×10^{16} joules.

This is an almost unimaginably large amount of energy. According to Einstein's theory of special relativity mass and energy are two forms of the same thing. One way to think about mass is as extremely concentrated energy. Work out the problems in part three of the investigation. They will give you a sense of the relationship between mass and energy

Students who work out 3 a - f. Circulate and assist them as needed.

2 3 Example answers

2a The two reference frames for the motion of the darts are:

1) the motion of the darts relative to the train, and
2) the motion of the darts relative to the ground.

2b. Relative to the train, the first dart travels 5 meters in 0.5 seconds, or 10 m/sec.

2c. Relative to the ground, the first dart travels 10 m/sec within its frame of reference, plus its frame of reference is moving at 30 m/sec. Seen from the ground, the speed of the dart equals 40 m/sec.

2d. The second dart travels 10 m/sec within its frame of reference, plus the train is moving at 30 m/sec, so the speed of the second dart as seen from the ground is 40 m/sec.

3a/ Left on continuously for a year, a 100 W light bulb would use $(100 \text{ J/sec}) \times (3.15 \times 10^7 \text{ sec/year}) = 3.15 \times 10^9 \text{ J/year}$

3b According to the mass-energy formula, 1 kg of mass is equivalent to 9×10^{16} joules of energy. This amount of energy could keep the bulb lit for $(9 \times 10^{16} \text{ J}) \div (3.15 \times 10^9 \text{ J/year}) = 2.86 \times 10^7$ years.

3c. $(9 \times 10^{16} \text{ J}) \times (0.0007 \text{ efficiency}) = 6.3 \times 10^{13} \text{ J}$

3d. 1,000,000 people × 10 light bulbs/person × 100 W/bulb × $(3.15 \times 10^7 \text{ sec/yr.}) = 3.15 \times 10^{16} \text{ J/yr.}$

3e. Uranium in a nuclear reactor produces 6.3×10^{13} joules/kg

It takes $(3.15 \times 10^{16} \text{ J}) \div (6.3 \times 10^{13} \text{ J/kg}) = 500$ kg of uranium to produce 3.15×10^{16} joules of energy

3f. $(3.15 \times 10^{16} \text{ J}) \div (5 \times 10^9 \text{ J/barrel}) = 6.3 \times 10^6$ barrels, or 6,300,000 barrels of gasoline.

18.3 Special Relativity

2 Relativity and frames of reference

The word *relative* in the special theory of relativity means that velocities can only be determined relative to a *reference frame*. It makes no sense in physics to say an object is moving at 1 m/sec without providing a reference. For example, you might measure a speed of 1 m/sec relative to your lab or classroom. However, Earth rotates and also circles the sun. A velocity of 1 m/sec relative to the lab (on Earth) is *not* the same as a velocity of 1 m/sec relative to the sun.

Consider the following experiment. A person on a train throws a dart at a dart board. Relative to the train, the dart travels a distance of 5 meters to the dart board in 0.5 seconds. The training is moving forward at a speed of 30 m/sec. The same person leans out the window of the train and throws a dart forward at the same speed toward a dartboard on a pole beside the track.

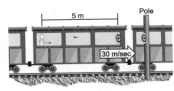

a. There are two reference frames important to understand the motion of the darts. What are they and what are their relative velocities?
b. What is the speed of the first dart relative to the train?
c. What is the speed of the first dart relative to the ground?
d. How fast does the second dart approach the dart board on the pole?

3 The equivalence of mass and energy

Einstein's mass - energy formula

Energy (J) $E = mc^2$ — Mass (kg), Speed of light $(3 \times 10^8 \text{ m/sec})$

According to Einstein's theory of special relativity mass and energy are two forms of the same thing. One way to think about mass is as extremely concentrated energy. In fact, according to the mass-energy formula (above), 1 kilogram of mass is equivalent to 9×10^{16} joules of energy.

a. Calculate the amount of energy used by a 100 W light bulb that is left on continuously for one year.
b. Suppose you could extract all of the energy in 1 kg of mass with 100 percent efficiency. How long could this amount of energy keep the 100 W light bulb lit. Give your answer in years.
c. Nuclear reactors convert a tiny fraction of the mass of uranium atoms into energy. Assume that 0.07% of the mass of uranium is converted to energy. How much energy do you get from 1 kg of uranium in a nuclear reactor?
d. To appreciate the energy obtained from a kg of uranium, estimate the electric power used by a city of one million people. Assume that each person in the city uses an amount of electricity equal to 10 light bulbs that use 100 watts each. Calculate the total energy used by multiplying the total power in watts by the number of seconds in one year (you will get a very large number).
e. How many kilograms of uranium must be used in a nuclear reactor to produce this amount of energy?
f. One barrel of ordinary gasoline yields about 5×10^9 joules of energy. Calculate how many barrels of gasoline are required to produce the energy you estimated in Part d.

19.1 Electric Circuits

Key Question: What is an electric circuit?

Electricity is an integral part of our lives. Our homes, stores, and workplaces use many electrical devices such as electric ovens. TVs, stereos, toasters, motors, and light bulbs. In this Investigation, students will do the first basic experiments in understanding electricity, i.e., light a bulb with a battery and wires. They will also be introduced to circuit diagrams and circuit concepts, such as open and closed circuits.

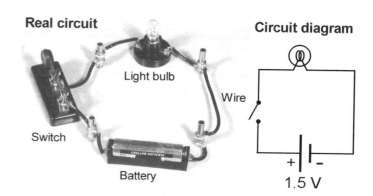

Real circuit — Light bulb, Switch, Battery, Wire

Circuit diagram — + − 1.5 V

Reading Synopsis

Students read Section 19.1 Electric Circuits after the Investigation.

Electricity refers to the presence of electric current in wires, motors, light bulbs, and other devices. Like water, electric current flows. However, electric current is not normally visible because it flows through solid metal.

Electric current flows in circuits and can transmit energy and power. Electric circuits are represented by circuit diagrams. A circuit diagram contains symbols that represent electrical components such as resistor, batteries, and switches.

An open circuit has a break that prevents current from flowing. A closed circuit makes a complete path allowing current to flow. A short circuit is a potentially dangerous, low resistance path that may allow too much current to flow.

The Investigation

Leading Questions
- What is electricity?
- How does a circuit work?
- What are open, closed, and short circuits?
- Why doesn't electricity leak from an open circuit?

Learning Goals

By the end of the Investigation, students will be able to:
- Construct simple electric circuits using a battery, bulb, switch and wires.
- Draw circuit diagrams using electrical symbols.
- Explain the concepts of open, closed, and short circuits.

Key Vocabulary

electricity, electric current, electric circuit, wires, circuit diagram, electrical symbols, resistor, closed circuit, switches, short circuit

Setup and Materials

Students work in groups of four or five at tables.

- Electric circuits kit components: bulb and socket, wires, switch
- One C-cell battery

Details

Time ⊙ One class period

Preparation ✎ No preparation is required except to check that the bulbs are working and the batteries are not dead.

Assignments 📖 Section 19.1 Electric Circuits in the **Student Edition** after the Investigation.

Skill Sheets Skill Builder: Safety Skills (review)

Equipment Setup Electric Circuits

Teaching the Investigation

1 Introduction
2 How do you make a bulb light?
3 Using the electric circuits set
4 Drawing circuit diagrams
5 How does a switch work?
6 What did you learn?

Introduction

What we know about electricity:
-Travels through wires as current
-Causes light bulbs to light
-Can be turned on and off with a switch
-Travels in a circuit
-Is a form of energy
-Measured in volts

How do you make a bulb light?

1

Circuit path - the flow of electricity
through a circuit.

Electricity needs a complete path, or
closed loop, in order to light a bulb.

The bulb always has one connection on
the thread and one connection on the
point at the bottom.
Successful circuits:

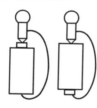

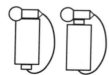

Today, we are beginning a new topic in physics: electricity. We use electricity all the time in our lives and the variety of electrical devices is truly astounding. We know that these devices have lots of wires and mysterious electrical components inside. We also know that harnessing and using electrical force and electrical energy is central to the way we live. However, the use of electricity has become so routine that many of us don't stop to think about what happens when we switch on a light or turn on a motor. Even if we do think about it, it's not obvious to our senses what's going on inside those wires and devices. Because electricity is not often directly sensed, it's important to remember that our intuition regarding electricity will not always be reliable.

Before we begin our Investigations into electricity, let's write out a list of everything we already know about it. You can say things you learned in a previous class, heard on TV or in conversation, read in a newspaper or magazine, or have observed. I'll go around the room and give everyone a turn.

Write down students' ideas on a piece of chart paper or on the chalkboard and keep the list up throughout the unit. Make sure students have copies of Investigation 6.1 and hand out one battery, bulb, and wire to each group.

In our first Investigation into electricity, each group will use only one wire, one battery, and one bulb. You will use them to build a simple electric circuit.

Demonstrate the items.

Each group has to try to discover *four different ways* you can light the bulb. Each working circuit will have different connections between the battery, bulb, and wire. As you work, keep track of which configurations work, and which configurations *don't* work. Use the symbols shown in the Investigation.

Observe groups as they work. Remind students to describe in words or pictures which configurations work and which don't. If a group is struggling, give several hints to help them finish the assignment.

Good — everyone is finding the four different ways they can light the bulb. Can someone show me one way that works?

Have volunteers from four different groups provide the four solutions. Record the solutions.

On each circuit I will trace the flow of electricity. This is called the circuit path. I'll start at this end of the battery, which is called the positive terminal, and end at this end of the battery, which is called the negative terminal.

On each drawing, show the circuit path. Start each time at the positive battery terminal.

Are there any breaks in the circuit path from the positive terminal to the negative terminal?

One important idea should emerge at this point: that electricity needs a complete path, or a closed loop, in order to light the bulb.

In each of our working circuits, there is a complete path from one battery terminal to the other. There is something else that we notice about our circuits. The bulb always has one connection on the thread and one connection on the point at the bottom. Look at your bulbs closely. Where is the circuit path through the bulb?

Have students examine the bulbs and try to identify the circuit path through the filament.

Draw several more circuits on the board, some that will work and some that won't.

Which circuits will work? Which circuits won't work?

Try to call on students that haven't contributed yet. Ask students to give reasons a certain configuration will or won't work.

UNIT 7: Electricity and Magnetism

Electric Circuits

Question: What is an electric circuit?

In this Investigation, you will:

1. Construct simple electric circuits using a battery, bulb, switch, and wires.
2. Draw circuit diagrams using electrical symbols.

Electricity is an integral part of our lives. Our homes, stores, and workplaces use many electrical devices such as electric ovens, TVs, stereos, toasters, motors that turn fans, air conditioners, heaters, and light bulbs. In fact, the use of electricity has become so routine that many of us never stop to think about what happens when we switch on a light or turn on a motor. If we stop to look, we find that most of what is "happening" is not visible. What exactly is electricity? How does it work?

> **⬦ Safety Precautions:**
> Do not use batteries that are damaged. If a battery or wire gets hot, disconnect the circuit immediately and ask for assistance. Do not allow any wire to connect directly from one terminal of the battery to the other terminal. This would be a short circuit and could start a fire.

In this Investigation, you will make a light bulb light. As you build circuits, you will discover that electricity travels through a specific path, much like water travels through pipes or streams.

---

1   Building circuits with a battery, a bulb, and a wire

a. Using *only* one battery, one bulb, and one wire, find four different ways you can arrange these three parts to make the bulb light. As you work, determine the kinds of connections that are needed to make the circuit work.

b. Record all your circuit attempts. Draw both successful and unsuccessful attempts. The drawing at right shows a simple way to draw the bulb, battery, and wire.

c. Make sure your drawings show the difference between the two ends of the battery. Also show exactly where the bulb is touching the wire and the battery.

d. Explain why you think some configurations work and others do not. Record your first thoughts and impressions—and don't worry if they are right or wrong.

Using simple geometric shapes (circle, rectangle, triangle) and a line, you can draw representations of the light bulb, battery and wire.

---

2   Using the electric circuits set

In this part of the Investigation, you will build the same circuit you made in Part 1 except that you will now use the electric circuits set. The set includes a small board with metal posts, battery holders, and light bulb holders. Your completed circuit should include one battery and battery holder, one bulb and bulb holder, and two wire connectors. The bulb should light in the completed circuit.

129

---

1   Example answers

1b. Circuit sketches:

1d. To work, all the parts must be touching each other. The battery must be connected at each end, on the silver part. The bulb must have one connection on the side and one connection on the bottom.

Using the electric circuits set

Drawing circuit diagrams

Circuit diagrams are used to draw circuits schematically.

There are electrical symbols for wires, switches, batteries, and bulbs. These are shown in Part 1.

How does a switch work?

A switch breaks the circuit path and turns the circuit on or off.

Closed circuit - the switch is in the "on" position.

Open circuit - the switch is in the "off" position.

What did you learn?

2

It was awkward trying to hold the battery, bulb, and wire together in the first part of the Investigation. An easier way to wire our components together is to use a system that will hold all the parts. The system that we're using is called the electric circuits set.

> Demonstrate the parts of the set and hand out additional materials as necessary.

The table has holders for the batteries and bulbs, and we can attach them together by sliding the ends onto the posts. Let's use the electric circuits set to build our circuit with one battery and one bulb.

> Circulate among the groups to make sure everyone understands how the circuits set works.

Does everyone have a working circuit?

> Assist any groups that don't have a working circuit.

3

If we keep trying to record our circuits using drawings of what we see, it gets very messy drawing circuits with wires twisting every which way. Each of us might draw a battery or a bulb in a different way. To solve this problem, a graphical language of circuit diagrams was developed. A circuit diagram is a shorthand way to draw a circuit. A circuit diagram uses standard electrical symbols, which are simple symbols that represent the wires and electrical component of a circuit. By using electrical symbols, you don't have to draw a battery and bulb realistically every time you record a circuit. The electrical symbols are easy to draw and can be read by anyone familiar with electricity. Let's review some of the symbols used.

> Draw and identify the symbols for a battery, bulb, switch, and wire. Point out to students the + and − terminals of the battery and show them the corresponding parts on the battery symbol.

Now, each of you should practice drawing a circuit diagram and using the symbols by drawing the circuit on your circuit table. Look at the circuit table as you draw; don't look at someone else's drawing, because then you won't learn how to translate the physical circuit into a circuit diagram. You may want to trace the circuit path with your pencil or pen as you draw the diagram.

> Check on students' work as they draw the circuit diagrams.

4

What do we use to turn a light on or off?

> Students should know that a switch is used to turn lights on and off.

Look at your set. What part is the switch?

> Have students identify a switch.

Wire one of the switches into your circuit. It doesn't matter where the switch is in relation to the battery and bulb. You may need to use one more connecting wire when you add the switch.

> Circulate among groups and make sure everyone understands how to add the switch to the circuit.

This switch is part of the circuit path. I want you to determine how it is part of the circuit path and how it works to turn the circuit on and off.

> Students should see that the switch works by breaking the circuit path, and then reconnecting that path.

Since electricity needs a complete path, the switch works by breaking the path. With the switch on, we have a **closed** circuit. With the switch off, we have an open circuit. Some people use the terms closed and open rather than the terms on and off. Remember: Closed is connected, or on, and open is disconnected, or off.

5

> Give students several minutes to answer the questions in Part 5 and then go over the answers with the class.

3 Drawing circuit diagrams

It can be time-consuming to draw pictures of batteries and bulbs every time you make a circuit diagram. People who work with electricity have short-cut methods for drawing electric circuits. All the electrical parts in a circuit are represented by standard pictures called *electrical symbols*. Some electrical parts and their corresponding symbols are shown in the picture at right. Study the symbols and practice drawing them.

Using these symbols, draw a picture of the circuit you built using the electric circuits set. This type of drawing is called a *circuit diagram*. There are examples of circuit diagrams in Chapters 19 and 20 of your *Foundations of Physics* textbook.

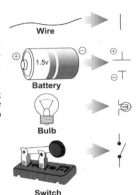

4 Observing how a switch works

1. Add a switch to your circuit. You may need another wire connector.
2. Check that the switch turns the light bulb on and off.

a. Examine the switch as it turns the bulb on and off. Explain how the switch works. You may use both words and drawings.

5 What did you learn?

a. Water can travel through air but cannot travel through a solid. Using what you learned in this Investigation, describe some materials that electricity can and cannot travel through.

b. The word *circuit* comes from the same root as the word "circle." Describe the similarities between a circle and the circuits that you built.

c. A circuit that is on and working is sometimes called a *closed circuit*. Based on your observations of the switch, explain what *closed* means in a circuit.

d. A circuit that is off or that is not working is sometimes called an *open circuit*. Based on your observations of the switch, explain what *open* means in a circuit.

130

3 4 5 Example answers

3. Circuit diagram:

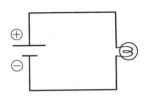

4a. The switch works when the lever is down and touching. When the lever is up, the bulb doesn't light because the circuit path is broken. The circuit path through the switch is shown below.

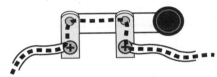

5a. Electricity travels through metal but does not travel through air.

5b. A circuit and a circle are both continuous.

5c. Closed means there is a connection between all parts of the circuit and current can flow.

5d. Open circuit means that part of the circuit is not connected and there is an opening therefore current does not flow.

19.2 Current and Voltage

Key Question: How does current move through a circuit?

When you put a battery in a circuit, electric current flows through the wires and provides energy to the bulb. The energy comes from the battery and is carried by the electric current. A battery transforms chemical energy into electrical energy. The voltage of a battery is a measure of the amount of power the electric current from the battery can carry. The higher the voltage, the more power that can be carried by the same amount of current. In this Investigation, students will build two test circuits for which they will measure current and voltage. Students will learn how to use a digital multimeter to make basic voltage and current measurements.

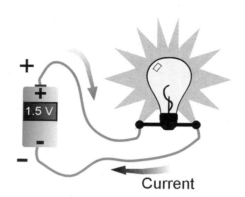

Current

Reading Synopsis

Students read Section 19.2 Current and Voltage after the Investigation.

Current and voltage are the two most important concepts to understanding electricity. Current is what actually flows through wires, carries energy and does work. Voltage measures the difference in energy between two places in a circuit. Current flows in response to differences in voltage just like water flows in response to differences in height.

Current is measured in amperes, or amps. Voltage is measured in volts. One volt means each amp of current carries one watt of power. Both voltage and current can be measured with a multimeter. To measure voltage the leads of the meter are touched to two points in a circuit. The meter measures the voltage difference between the two points. To measure current, the meter must be inserted in the circuit so that the current is forced to flow through it.

The Investigation

Leading Questions
- How is electrical current measured?
- What is voltage and how is it measured?
- What is the function of a battery in a circuit?

Learning Goals
By the end of the Investigation, students will be able to:
- Measure electrical current with a multimeter.
- Compare current in circuits with one or two bulbs.
- Measure voltage with a multimeter.
- Combine two batteries to increase the voltage in a circuit.

Key Vocabulary
amperes, amps, voltage, volts, multimeter, battery, ammeters, watts, power

Setup and Materials

Students work in groups of four or five at tables.

Each group should have:

- Multimeter with red and black leads
- Electric circuits kit components: circuit board, two bulbs and sockets, wires, switch, battery holder
- Two C-cell batteries

Details

Time One class period

Preparation Check the equipment: The batteries must not be dead, the light bulb should light itself, and the meter must not have a broken fuse. It is also useful to build a circuit yourself before class that you can use for demonstration, such as inserting the multimeter to measure current.

Assignments Section 19.2 Current and Voltage in the **Student Edition** after the Investigation.

Skill Sheets 19.2 Using an Electric Meter

Equipment Setup Electric Circuits

Teaching the Investigation

1 Introduction
2 Measuring the current in a circuit
3 Building circuit no. 2
4 What did you learn?
5 Measuring voltage from a battery
6 Measuring voltage in a circuit
7 What did you learn about voltage?
8 How does a battery work?
9 How do you connect batteries?

Introduction

Electric current is like the flow of water. It is measured in amperes, or amps.

Voltage is to electricity, like height is to the flow of water. Current flows from high voltage to low voltage just as water flows from higher to lower areas.

Building circuit no. 1

1

Most of the power from the battery in the circuit becomes heat and very little becomes light.

Measuring the current in a circuit

2

You can think of electric current much as you would think of the flow of water. In fact, the flow of water is also called current. If a faucet is on, you can measure the rate of water flow by seeing how many gallons come out of the faucet per minute. Electric current is measured in amperes, or amps. One amp is like a gallon per minute except that what is flowing is electricity and not water. Electric current flows because there is a difference in voltage. Voltage is to electricity as height is to the flow of water. Water flows downhill from higher height to lower height. Electric current flows from higher voltage to lower voltage. Today's Investigation is going to explore the concepts of current and voltage in a simple electric circuit.

Draw the diagram from Figure 19.9 in the text (page 384) on the board. This illustrates the analogy of water flowing from high to low. Draw a battery with one end labeled +1.5 volts and the other labeled 0 volts. Current flows out of the battery from the 1.5 volt end, through a circuit and returns to the 0 volt end. Electric current flows from higher voltage to lower voltage just as water flows from higher to lower levels.

Our first step is to build the same circuit we have been working with, which has one battery and one bulb.

Draw the circuit diagram from step 1 of the Investigation on the board and wait for students to build and test their circuits.

When you close the switch, electrical current flows around the circuit, carrying power from the battery to the light bulb. Some of that power becomes light. What happens to the rest of the power?

Students should touch the bulb gently and notice that it gets hot. Some of the power from the battery becomes heat. In fact, most of the power becomes heat and only a little becomes light.

With water, you can see the current flow; you can measure it in buckets. With electricity, you cannot see the current flowing because it is actually very tiny particles flowing around and in between the atoms in the solid metal wire. To measure electrical current we use a device called a multimeter. To measure current you must break the circuit and force the current to flow through the multimeter.

Using the circuit you prepared before the class, demonstrate how to use the meter in a circuit. Show students how to attach the probes to the meter, the correct setting, and how to place the meter in the circuit in series.

When measuring current, always place the red probe closest to the positive battery terminal. The meter will measure current this way as positive. If the probes are reversed, the meter will measure current as negative. This is because of the convention that current flows from the positive terminal to the negative terminal.

You will notice that the circuit diagram indicates two points — one on each side of the bulb. We're going to compare the current in the circuit at these two points. First, measure the current at point A. When you are done, record your value in Table 1 and also write it on the board.

Circulate among groups and help students learn how to use the meter to measure current. To measure the current at point A, they must first break the connection at point A. They should then use the meter leads to remake the connection, forcing the current to flow through the meter. As groups finish, remind them to have one team member write on the board the value of current at point A. Each group should have similar values.

19.2   Current and Voltage

Question: How does current move through a circuit?

In this Investigation, you will:

1. Measure and compare current at different points in a circuit.
2. Compare current in circuits with one and two bulbs.
3. Measure the voltage of a battery in and out of a circuit.
4. Learn how batteries must be connected together to increase voltage in a circuit.

Why does a bulb light? When you put a battery in a circuit, electric current flows through the wires and provides energy to the bulb. The energy comes from the battery in the circuit. A battery transforms chemical energy into electrical energy. The *voltage* of a battery is a measure of the amount of energy the current in the circuit will carry to the devices in the circuit. The higher the voltage, the more energy that can be carried by the same amount of current.

> **Safety Precautions:**
> Do not use batteries that are damaged. If a battery or wire gets hot, disconnect the circuit immediately and ask for assistance. Do not allow any wire to connect directly from one terminal of the battery to the other terminal. This would be a short circuit and could start a fire.

1   Building test circuit #1

Build test circuit 1 that includes a battery, battery holder, bulb, bulb holder, and two connecting wires as shown in the diagram at right. There are two points marked on the diagram, A and B, which are where the connectors are attached to the bulb holder. Make sure that you can easily identify these points in your circuit.

Circuit 1

2   Measuring current through test circuit #1

To measure current, the meter must be placed *in* the circuit so that the current has to flow through it. Follow the instructions below carefully.

1. Set the multimeter to measure DC amps (current).
2. Remove the connector between the positive terminal of the battery and the bulb holder.
3. Place the red positive lead of the multimeter on the post attached to the positive terminal of the battery.
4. Place the black negative lead on the free post attached to the bulb holder. You should now have a complete circuit. The bulb should light and you should get a reading on the multimeter.
5. Record the current at point A.
6. Remove the meter and reconnect the circuit.

Circuit breakers and fuses

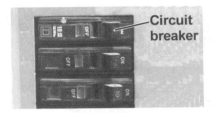

Circuit breaker

Electrical circuits in your house have a *circuit breaker* that opens if the current is too high. Many wires in your house can carry 15 or 20 amps of current. If they carry more current, the wires can get dangerously hot.

One of the things that can overload a circuit is using too many electrical appliances at once, such as an air conditioner and an iron on the same circuit. If the appliances draw too much current, the circuit breaker trips and breaks the circuit before the wires get hot enough to cause a fire.

A circuit breaker uses temperature-sensitive metal that expands with heat. The expanded metal bends and breaks the circuit. If this happens in your home, you will have to unplug some appliances and reset the circuit breaker.

Another type of protection against high current is a *fuse*. A fuse contains a material that melts at high temperature. When the fuse melts, the circuit is broken. Unlike circuit breakers, fuses have to be replaced when a circuit has overloaded.

A fuse can be demonstrated by using a single strand of steel wool. Place the steel wool in a circuit. Increase the current gradually until the steel wool melts.

How do you measure current in circuits (continued)

The bulb only lights when there is current. Current must be flowing to transfer power from the battery to the bulb.

Power flows from the battery only when there is current.

Building circuit no. 2

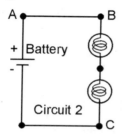

A•────────────•B

+ | Battery

Circuit 2

•────────────•C

What did you learn?

Current is the same everywhere on the circuit path. Current does lose power as it travels around the circuit.

Bulbs were dimmer in the second circuit because:
-Two bulbs must split power from the battery.
-There was less current flowing.

Now you will measure current at point B in the circuit.
> Indicate point B on the circuit diagram on the board.

Predict what you think the value of current will be before measuring it. What are your predictions?
> Write several predictions on the board. Ask students to explain their predictions. Some students might think that current is "used up" in the bulb.
> Wait for students to complete their measurements.

Did your results match your predictions? What do the values of the current you measured tell you?
> Students should conclude that value of current is the same at any point in the circuit.

Measure current once more at any point in the circuit. Disconnect the circuit and watch the meter as you do it. What happens to the value of current? What happens to the light bulb?
> Students see that current falls to 0 and the bulb goes out.

Why do you think the light bulb went out?
> Student should conclude that the bulb only lights when there is current. Current must be flowing to transfer power from the battery to the bulb.

One of the most important things to remember about current is what you just observed with the light bulb. Power flows from the battery only when there is current.

3 In Part 3 of the Investigation, we are going to look at current in a circuit with two bulbs and a battery.

Leave test circuit 1 on and build test circuit 2 next to it. Observe the bulbs in the two circuits.
> Draw the circuit diagram on the board and wait for students to build test circuit 2.

What's the difference between the two circuits?
> The second circuit will have very dim bulbs.

Now, measure current at the three points indicated on circuit 2.
> Wait for students to measure current in test circuit 2.

What are your results? What's the difference in current between the two circuits?
> Students will find that current in test circuit 2 is the same at all three points. The current in this circuit is lower than the current in test circuit 1.

4 In your groups, complete the questions in Part 4 of the Investigation.
> Give students several minutes to answer the questions and then go over the answers with the class.

Why is the current lower when another bulb is added to the circuit?
> Record student answers on the board. Use these answers in the next Investigation.

You found out in today's Investigation that current is the same everywhere on a circuit path. All the current that goes into the circuit at one end must come out at the other end. What the current does lose as it travels around the circuit, however, is its power. Because we used a single 1.5 volt battery in both circuits, each amp of current carried 1.5 watts of power. In the second circuit the bulbs were dimmer for two reasons. First, two bulbs must split the power from the battery so each receives less power and is therefore less bright. Second, there was less current flowing in test circuit 2 compared with test circuit 1. Less current means less power was carried from the battery. Less current also means the battery will last longer before using up all its energy.

19.2 Current and Voltage

7. Break the circuit between the battery and point B.
8. Predict what the current at point B will be. Record your prediction.
9. Following the same procedure you did for point A, use your meter to measure current at point B. The positive lead of the multimeter should be closest to the positive battery terminal and the negative lead should be closest to the negative battery terminal.
10. Record the current at point B.
11. Remove the meter and reconnect the circuit so the bulb lights.

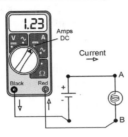

3 ### Test circuit #2

1. Gather the following additional materials: one battery and battery holder, two bulbs and bulb holders, and three connectors.
2. Build the circuit shown in the diagram at right. Make sure that you can easily identify points A, B, and C where the connectors are attached.
3. Using the same procedure you followed in Part 2, measure and record the current at point A.
4. Predict what the current will be at points B and C.
5. Using the same procedure you followed in Part 2, measure and record the current at points B and C.

4 ### What did you learn about current?

a. Review the two current readings for circuit 1. What conclusions can you draw from these results?
b. Review the three current readings for circuit 2. What conclusions can you draw from these results?
c. Transfer all your results for circuit 1 and circuit 2 into the table below. Compare the current readings in the two circuits. What happened to current when you added a bulb to the circuit?

	Current in circuit 1 (amps)		Current in circuit 2 (amps)
Point A	.092	**Point A**	.070
Point B	.091	**Point B**	.070
		Point C	.068

d. In which circuit were the light bulbs brighter? Offer a possible explanation for this.

5 ### Measuring voltage across a battery

1. Remove the battery from your circuit.
2. Set the multimeter to measure DC voltage. Place the red positive lead of the meter on the positive terminal of the battery. Place the black negative lead on the negative terminal of the battery.
3. Look at the voltage reading. If the number is not close to 1.5 volts, the battery may be dead and you need to get a fresh one.
4. Record the exact voltage of the battery.

132

Common misconceptions

Because a light turns on almost instantly, we often imagine that electric current moves very quickly through a wire. In fact, the electric current is not really that fast. The reason the light turns on quickly is the same reason that water instantly comes out of your faucet when you turn it on. The pipes are full of water but the water cannot move until you open the faucet. You don't have to wait for water to get to the house and come all the way up to the faucet.

Similar to the water in a pipe, the particles that move to make electric current are already in the wire everywhere. They are just not moving all the time. When a voltage is applied and a circuit is made, the particles start moving and current flows everywhere, even though the battery may be distant from the bulb. You can think of the battery as pushing the current out its positive end, which forces current to flow all through the circuit since current is not allowed to "pile up" anywhere (except in a capacitor!).

4 **5** ## Example answers

4a. The current is the same at both points in the circuit.

4b. Again, the current is the same in the three places we measured.

4c. The current went down when a second bulb was added to the circuit.

4d. The bulb in circuit #1 was brighter. Having two bulbs in the circuit slows down the charges moving through the wire. The lower current affects the brightness of the bulb. We don't know exactly why the charges are slowed down when there is a second bulb.

5. (step 4)　　1.48 V

Measuring voltage from a battery **5**

Voltage is the amount of power (energy per second) carried by each amp of electric current.

Voltage is measure in volts.

Measuring voltage in a circuit **6**

Predict what will happen to the voltage of the battery while it is lighting the bulb.

What did you learn about voltage? **7**

How does a battery work?

The battery drops some of its voltage pushing current out. The more current that flows, the greater the voltage drop across the battery.

How do you connect batteries? **8**

Voltage is the way we measure the amount of power, or energy per second, carried by each amp of electric current. Voltage is always measured between two points, just like height is measured between two points. I'm going to show you how to use the meter to measure the battery voltage, so watch carefully.

Demonstrate to students how to use the meter to measure the voltage across the battery. Show students how to connect the probes to the meter, and the correct meter setting (DC volts).

Voltage is measured in units of volts. The voltage is equal to the power in watts carried by each amp of current. A 1.5-volt battery can deliver 1.5 watts of power for each amp that flows. If the current moves through a device like a light bulb that uses energy, the power is transferred to the device.

Summarize these points on the board.

Next, use this battery and build a circuit with one bulb. What happens to the voltage of the battery while it is lighting the bulb? In your groups, predict what you think it will be, then measure the voltage of the connected battery.

Circulate among the groups and make sure students make their predictions before measuring the battery voltage. When students have made their predictions, they may need help in measuring voltage with the connected battery. The probes can be placed on the battery terminals or on the posts that the battery is connected to.

What were your predictions of the battery voltage in the circuit? Did your predictions match your measurements? What does this tell you about the battery?

Students may think that the voltage will be a lot lower when the battery is placed in the circuit, since it is being "used up" as it lights the bulbs. This is only partly true. The battery itself drops some of its voltage pushing the current out. The more current that flows, the greater the voltage drop at the battery.

These results tell us that the battery maintains its voltage pretty well. In fact, if we leave the circuit on and test the voltage again in a little while, the voltage will probably be the same. Why is it important that the battery maintain its voltage? What would happen to a toy or radio if the voltage started dropping as soon as the battery was put in it?

Students should realize that a device would keep slowing down if the voltage dropped.

Batteries are designed to stay at a constant voltage because otherwise they wouldn't be very useful. The voltage is maintained because chemical reactions occurring inside the battery are continually converting chemical energy to electrical energy when the battery is working. Therefore, until the chemicals in the battery run out, the voltage will stay about the same.

If you use a device that requires more energy, such as a large flashlight or a large portable radio, you often use more than one battery. How do you connect batteries? In Part 8 of the Investigation, you will determine how to do this by building four configurations of two batteries. Since the reference point is no longer as obvious, for each picture shown in the Investigation, place the black probe on the terminal farthest to the left, and the red probe on the terminal farthest to the right.

Circulate among groups and check that students make predictions before measuring battery voltage. You will then need to demonstrate how to measure voltage across two batteries and across a lighted bulb. Students will get some negative values of voltage.

When you are finished, answer the questions in Part 8.

6 **Measuring voltage across a battery and bulb in a circuit**

1. Build a circuit with the battery you just tested, a battery holder, one bulb, a bulb holder, and two connectors.
2. Predict what the voltage of the battery will be while it lights the bulb. Also, explain the reasoning behind your prediction.
3. Measure the voltage across the battery as shown at right. DO NOT DISCONNECT THE CIRCUIT.
4. Record the voltage of the battery while it lights the bulb.
5. Predict what the voltage across the bulb will be while it is lit by the battery.
6. Connect the positive lead to the side of the bulb that is connected to the battery's positive terminal. Connect the negative lead to the side of the bulb that is connected to the battery's negative terminal. Record the voltage across the bulb.

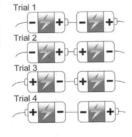

7 **What did you learn about voltage?**

a. Were your predictions correct?
b. Was there much difference in the battery voltage when it was not lighting the bulb and when it was?
c. How did the battery's voltage compare with the bulb's voltage? Why do you think this is?

8 **Building circuits with two batteries**

How many batteries does a small flashlight use? How about a large radio? What happens when you wire batteries together?

Build a circuit with two batteries and two holders, one bulb and holder, and three wires. Connect the two batteries in four different configurations as shown. For each configuration, do the following:

1. Measure voltage across both batteries before adding the bulb.
2. Predict whether the bulb will light and then connect the bulb and check.
3. Measure voltage across the bulb. Do this by placing one meter lead on one side of the bulb holder and the other meter lead on the other side of the bulb holder.

Examine your data carefully. Then discuss the following questions with your group and record your answers:

a. Describe how you should wire batteries together to light the bulb.
b. Each battery is 1.5 volts. Explain how to calculate voltage when two batteries are connected.
c. Compare the brightness of a bulb in a one-battery circuit to that of a bulb in a two-battery circuit. How is the bulb's brightness related to energy transfer in each circuit?
d. Explain the meaning of the voltage reading across the bulb.

Real-world connections

What is the difference between AA, A, C, and D batteries? If you measure the voltage of each, you will see that it is the same. The main difference between them is that the AA battery is small, and does not store as much energy. AA batteries will not last as long as D batteries. Think of two identical cars, one with an extra big gas tank and one with a regular gas tank. Both cars go the same speed, but the one with the big gas tank will keep going longer.

9 V   D   C   AA AAA

If you need charge that has more energy, you must increase the voltage. Radio batteries have 9 volts and car batteries have 12 volts. In a 12-volt battery, each charge that flows carries 12 joules of energy. Some kinds of batteries can be recharged. Batteries made with nickel and cadmium (NiCad) are used in cellphones and power tools because they can be recharged many times.

6 **7** **8** **Example answers**

6. (step 4)   1.46 V
6. (step 6)   1.46 V
7a. No. We thought the voltage would go down a lot.
7b. The voltage is a little lower when the battery is in the circuit.
7c. The voltage of the battery and the voltage of the bulb were the same. This seems to indicate that all the voltage provided by the battery is used by the bulb.
8a. One kind of end of one battery must be connected to the other end of the second battery. Pos. to Neg. or Neg. to Pos.
8b. The voltages of the batteries add together if connected as above. If the same kinds of ends are connected, the voltages subtract and total voltage is zero.
8c. The bulb is brighter with two batteries. There is more transfer of energy to the bulb when voltage is higher.
8d. The meaning of the voltage reading is that most of the energy of the two batteries is transferred to the bulb, since the voltage across the bulb is almost the same as the battery reading.

19.3 Electrical Resistance and Ohm's Law

Key Question: How are voltage, current, and resistance related?

Electrical devices like light bulbs are designed to use the right amount of current when connected to the proper voltage. To design electrical devices it is important to understand the relationship between current, voltage, and resistance. This relationship is called Ohm's law. In this Investigation, students will deduce Ohm's law by observing and measuring voltage, current, and resistance. They will vary the current through a resistor using a potentiometer, and measure the voltage dropped across the resistor. The voltage versus current curve will be determined for a fixed resistor and for a light bulb, which has a resistance that changes with current.

Parallel Hybrid

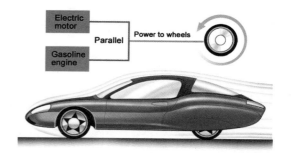

Reading Synopsis

Students read Section 19.3 Electrical Resistance and Ohm's Law after the Investigation.

You can apply the same voltage to different circuits and different amounts of current will flow. The amount of current that flows in a circuit is determined by the resistance of the circuit. The resistance in ohms is the voltage (volts) divided by the current (amps) according to Ohm's law. Every device that uses electrical energy adds resistance to a circuit. The current that flows in a circuit is directly proportional to the voltage and inversely proportional to resistance.

Conductors have low resistance and insulators have high resistance. A resistor is an electrical device with a controlled resistance. A variable resistor is called a potentiometer. Potentiometers are used to control or adjust the current and voltage in a circuit.

The Investigation

Leading Questions
- How does a circuit know how much current to use?
- How do we control the amount of current that flows in a circuit?
- What is the relationship between voltage, current, and resistance?
- How do you compare and contrast conductors and insulators?
- Why won't a 1.5-volt battery light up a 100-watt light bulb?

Learning Goals

By the end of the Investigation, students will be able to:
- Build circuits using variable and fixed resistors.
- Measure the current when the resistance is changed.
- Use the current versus voltage graph to find a relationship between voltage, current, and resistance.
- Use Ohm's law to predict voltage, current, or resistance when two of the three variables are known.

Key Vocabulary

resistance, ohms, Ohm's law, conductor, electrical insulators, semiconductors, electrical conductivity, resistor, potentiometer

Setup and Materials

Students work in groups of four or five at tables.

Each group should have:

- Multimeter with red and black leads
- Electric circuits kit components: circuit board, potentiometer, switch, battery holder, bulb and socket, 20Ω resistor, wires
- One D-cell battery
- Graph paper

Details

Time	⊙ One class period

Preparation 🖊 Check that batteries are live, meter does not have a broken fuse, and bulbs are not burned out.

Assignments 📖 Section 19.3 Electrical Resistance and Ohm's Law in the **Student Edition** after the Investigation.

Skill Sheets 19.3A Ohm's Law
19.3B Ben Franklin

Equipment Setup Electric Circuits

Teaching the Investigation

1. Introduction
2. Building the first circuit and doing informal observation
3. Resistance and current
4. Units of resistance
5. Voltage versus current for a fixed resistor
6. Building the circuit
7. Discussing the data
8. Voltage and current for a light bulb

Introduction

If you connect a light bulb to a battery, electric current flows and energy is carried from the battery to the light bulb. It seems reasonable to ask how much current flows? Does more current flow if two light bulbs are connected? What happens if you use two batteries instead of one? Does that cause more current to flow? These questions are the motivation for our next Investigation, which will show us the relationship between voltage current and the electrical resistance of an electrical device, such as a light bulb.

Building the first circuit and doing informal observation

1

Build the circuit shown in step 1 of the Investigation. Connect the meter in series so it can measure the current flowing in the circuit. The apparatus with the knob on it is called a potentiometer. Once you have the circuit connected, turn the potentiometer and observe what happens to the current and also to the brightness of the bulb.

> Students construct the circuit can spend five or 10 minutes observing. They shouldn't notice that turning the potentiometer in the clockwise direction decreases the brightness of the bulb and also lowers the current in the circuit. In fact, below a minimum current the bulb will give off no light at all even though current is still flowing.

Resistance and current

> Resistance is a measure of how difficult it is to make current flow through a device.

> Voltage in a circuit provides the driving force that moves electric current through the circuit.

All electrical devices have a property called resistance. Resistance is a measure of how difficult it is to make current flow through the device. If a device has low resistance, then even a low voltage can cause a large current to flow. If a device has a high resistance, then proportionally higher voltage is needed to cause the same current to flow. A good analogy is a bucket full of water with a hole in it. If the hole is small, there is high resistance to the flow of water and the current is small. If the hole is large, there is low resistance to the flow of water and a large current flows.

> It is useful to draw on the board a bucket with large and small holes, like Figure 19.10 on page 386 of the text. Note to the students that the height of water in the bucket is analogous to the voltage in the circuit. The rate at which water comes out is analogous to the current in the circuit.

Can I get a large flow of water to come out of a small hole? How could I do this?

> Students should answer that if the water in the bucket was very deep, creating a lot of pressure, then even a small hole would allow a large flow of water to come through.

What electrical quantity drives the flow of electric current in a similar way that the depth of water in the bucket drives the flow of water through the hole?

> Students should answer that voltage in a circuit provides the driving force that moves electric current, just like water pressure in the bucket provides the driving force that pushes water through the hole.

Units of resistance

> Electrical resistance is measured in units of ohms (Ω).

> Increasing the resistance in a circuit causes the amount of current flowing to decrease.

Electrical resistance is measured in units of ohms indicated with a capital Greek omega (Ω). A resistance of 100 Ω is read as 100 ohms. If a device has a resistance of one ohm then one amp of electric current flows if one volt is maintained across the terminals of the device. Can anyone tell me what would happen to the amount of electric current flowing if the resistance in a circuit was increased?

> Students should answer that increasing the resistance of a circuit causes the amount of current flowing to decrease.

Can someone explain the operation of the potentiometer and the relationship between the position of the dial, the current, and the brightness of the light bulb?

> Students should explain that turning the dial of the potentiometer increases its resistance. If the resistance is increased, then the current in the circuit decreases. This is consistent with what the students have observed.

19.3 Electrical Resistance and Ohm's Law

Question: How are voltage, current, and resistance related?

In this Investigation, you will:

1. Build circuits using variable and fixed resistors.
2. Measure the current when the resistance is changed.
3. Use the current vs. voltage graph to find a relationship between voltage, current, and resistance.

Electrical devices such as light bulbs are designed to use a certain amount of energy each second. For example, a 10-watt bulb uses 10 joules each second. Too much energy and the bulb burns out; too little and the bulb gives off no light. Energy is carried by electrical current and devices like light bulbs are designed to use the right amount of current when connected to the proper voltage. To design electrical devices (and use them properly), it is important to understand the relationship between current, voltage, and resistance. German physicist Georg S. Ohm (1787-1854) experimented with circuits to find out how voltage, current, and resistance are related. The relationship he discovered is called *Ohm's law* and is the basis for understanding how electrical devices regulate how much energy they use.

1 **Resistance and current**

A *resistor* is used in a circuit to provide resistance. A *variable resistor* allows you to change its resistance by turning a dial. A variable resistor is also called a *potentiometer*. In this part of the Investigation, you will use a potentiometer to control the current in a circuit. The higher the resistance, the lower the current.

Inside the potentiometer is a circular resistor. The dial selects how much of the resistor is connected between the terminals A and B. When the dial is turned so the wiper is near terminal A, the resistance is very low since the current only passes through a small part of the resistor. When the dial is turned so the wiper is near terminal C, the resistance between A and B is high because the current must go through nearly the whole resistor. Many dials you use every day, like dimmer switches, are actually potentiometers.

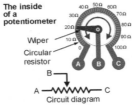

The inside of a potentiometer

Wiper
Circular resistor

Circuit diagram

1. Build a circuit with a battery, one bulb, the potentiometer, and the meter as shown in the diagram at right. The meter is set to measure current in the circuit and should be set to DC amps.
2. Turn the dial of the potentiometer up and down and observe what happens to the current and the amount of light produced by the bulb. Note: The wires in your potentiometer are connected to terminals A and B shown in the potentiometer circuit diagram to the right.

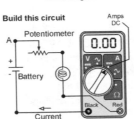

Build this circuit

a. Explain why the current changes when the dial of the potentiometer is turned. The dial controls the resistance of the potentiometer, which varies from 0Ω (ohms) to 105Ω.
b. Explain why the bulb is dim or bright depending on the position of the potentiometer. Your answer should use the concepts of resistance, energy and current.

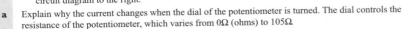

Making electrical measurements

When you make a measurement of voltage or current what you really want is to know what these values are in the circuit *without the meter*. Unfortunately, inserting a meter into a circuit always changes the voltage and current you are trying to measure because the meter itself is an electrical device. The two most troublesome complications are described below.

When measuring voltage, the meter itself acts like a very large resistor. That means some current flows through the meter, which may change the other currents flowing in the circuit. Most meters have a resistance in voltage-mode of more than 1 million ohms. If you need to measure voltages across circuit components that have comparably high resistance, you must correct for the internal resistance of the meter.

When measuring current the problem is more serious. In current-mode the resistance would ideally be zero, so no voltage was dropped as the current passed through the meter itself. Unfortunately, most meters measure current by measuring the voltage drop across a small resistor in the meter. If the resistance of the meter is 5Ω, then 5V will be dropped across the meter for every amp of current that flows through! This means the circuit with the meter contains an extra 5Ω resistor compared with the circuit without the meter.

1 **Example answers**

1a. The amount of current changes because turning the dial changes the resistance in the circuit. The resistance in the circuit determines how much current will flow in the circuit. Changing the resistance will change the amount of current. Increasing the resistance with the potentiometer will reduce the current, and decreasing the resistance will increase the current.

1b. The potentiometer's adjustable resistance is controlled by turning the dial. The more resistance a circuit has, the less current that flows. The bulb's brightness is directly related to the current; increasing the current makes the bulb brighter and decreasing the current makes the bulb dimmer. Current carries energy in a circuit, so increasing current increases the energy getting to the bulb.

Voltage versus current for a fixed resistor

The experiment will determine how the voltage drop across a resistor changes as the current changes: What is the rule that relates voltage, current, and resistance?

Building the circuit

Build a circuit with two batteries, the potentiometer, the green resistor, and a switch.

Measure the voltage drop across the resistor.

To measure current, the meter must be inserted into the circuit.

Discussing the data

The voltage decreases by one-half if the current decreases by one-half.

Change in voltage is proportional to change in current.

A graph of voltage vs. current is a straight line that passes through zero.

V = m × I where m is the slope of the line.

Resistance is the slope of the line of the voltage vs. current graph.

2

For the next part of the Investigation we are going to measure the relationship between current and voltage for a device that has a fixed resistance. This device is called a resistor and resistors are found in almost all electric circuits. In fact, for analyzing the current flowing in circuits, almost any device is treated as if it were a resistor, including light bulbs, motors, and other electrical appliances.

When current passes through a resistor, some of the energy carried by the current is dissipated in the resistor. If the resistor is a motor, that energy goes to turning the motor. If the resistor is a light bulb, some of the energy goes to light and some to heat. Because the energy carried by the current decreases, the voltage drops as the current flows through the resistor and the output terminal. Our experiment will determine how the voltage drop across a resistor changes as the current changes. The result of the experiments will be a rule relating voltage, current, and resistance that applies to all circuits.

Build the circuit shown in Part 2 with two batteries, the potentiometer, the green resistor, and a switch.

Students build the circuit, which is similar to the last circuit except the switch has been added and the bulb has been removed.

The tricky part of this experiment is that you need to measure voltage and current, but you have only one meter. So, this is what you do. When the switch is closed, set the meter to voltage and use it to measure the voltage drop across the resistor by touching the leads to the terminals of the resistor. To measure current, the meter must be inserted into the circuit so all the current flows through the meter. This can be done by opening the switch and touching the leads of the meter to the terminals of the switch. With the switch open all the current is forced to flow through the meter where it can be measured. Use the potentiometer to control the current in the circuit. Settings between 50 and 100 on the potentiometer work the best. Record the voltage drop across the resistor for various currents in Table 1. Take at least five different values.

Students take voltage and current values and record data in Table 1.

3

Can anyone describe the pattern in the data? When the current goes down what happens to the voltage drop across the resistor?

Students should report that the voltage drop decreases as the current decreases.

If the current decreases by one-half, how much does the voltage change by?

Students should note that the voltage decreases by one-half if the current decreases by one-half. This indicates that the change in voltage is proportional to the change in current.

Draw a graph that shows the voltage drop on the y-axis and the current on the x-axis.

Students should draw this graph which should be fairly linear (see note on the right).

This graph is a straight line that passes through zero. Straight lines can be represented by a formula that looks like $y = mx$, where m is the slope of the line. In our case the variables are not x and y, but voltage and current (V, I). How can we rewrite the equation of the line using the variables of voltage and current?

$V = mI$ where m is the slope of the line.

Notice that the slope has units of volts/amps. The interpretation is that the slope represents how many volts it takes per amp to force the electric current to flow through the resistor. In fact, the slope is precisely the definition of resistance. The resistance is the slope of the voltage versus current graph. If the resistance is 5 Ω, then the voltage drop increases by 5 V for every amp of current. If the resistance is 10 Ω, then the voltage drop increases by 10 V for every amp of current. This relationship is known as Ohm's law and is written $V = IR$ where V is the voltage in volts, I is the current in amps, and R is the resistance in ohms.

2 The current and voltage relationship for a fixed resistor

In this part of the Investigation, you will use two types of resistors. A *fixed resistor* has a constant resistance. You will use the potentiometer (variable resistor) to control the current in the fixed resistor. This experiment requires both current and voltage measurement. The meter must be connected in different ways for each type of measurement. To avoid connecting and disconnecting wires for each measurement, use the switch to break the circuit.

1. Build a circuit with two batteries, a green resistor, a switch, and the potentiometer as shown in the diagram at right.

2. Start with the dial of the potentiometer turned half way. For each trial, turn the dial further clockwise.

3. To measure voltage across the resistor, set the meter to DC volts. Close the switch and connect the meter voltage across the fixed resistor.
   Record the voltage in Table 1.

4. To measure current through the resistor, set the meter to DC amps. Open the switch and touch the meter leads to the *terminals of the switch*. With the switch open, all the current flows through the meter where it can be measured.
   Record the current in Table 1.

5. Change the setting of the potentiometer and measure current and voltage again. Repeat for at least six settings covering the whole range of the potentiometer.

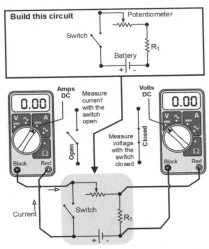

Build this circuit

Table 1: Voltage vs. current

Potentiometer setting	Current (A)	Voltage (V)

3 Finding the relationship between voltage, current, and resistance

a. Examine the data in Table 1. Describe in words what happens to the voltage across the fixed resistor as the current decreases.

b. Graph the data from Table 1. Put voltage on the *y*-axis and current on the *x*-axis. Label your *x*- and *y*-axes and title your graph.

c. Draw a best-fit line that matches the trend of the points on your graph. Calculate the slope of the line.

d. The resistance of the green fixed resistor is 5 ohms. How does this value compare with the slope of your graph?

e. The equation that relates current, voltage, and resistance is called Ohm's law. Write the mathematical equation for Ohm's law using *V* for voltage, *I* for current, and *R* for resistance.

2 3 Example answers

Table 1: *Voltage vs. current*

Potentiometer setting	Current (A)	Voltage (V)
1	0.048	0.253
2	0.043	0.226

3a. As the current decreases, the voltage across the fixed resistor decreases.

3b. Graph:

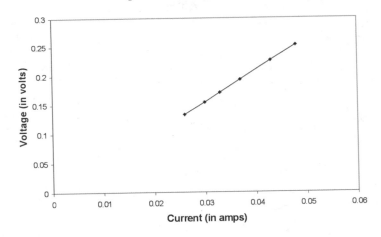

Voltage vs. Current (fixed resistor)

3c. Slope of line = 0.253 - 0.133/0.48 - 0.26 = 5.45 Ω.

3d. The slope of the graph is pretty close to the given value of 5 Ω.

3e. V = IR or I = V/R

More about Ohm's law

For a given voltage, the resistance of a device determines how much current flows.

What is the resistance of a saw that draws 12 amps of current at 120 volts?

R = V ÷ I = (120 V) ÷ (12 A) = 10 Ω

I = V ÷ R tells you how much current flows if you know the voltage and resistance.

V = IR tells you how much voltage is dropped across a resistor when a given current flows.

R = V ÷ I tells you what the resistance needs to be when you are given voltage and current.

Voltage and current for a light bulb

Resistance often changes with temperature.

Resistance decreases as temperature increases.

Resistance of a light bulb increases as current increases.

Ohm's law is one of the most useful relations you will ever learn regarding electricity. Although we just discovered it using the voltage drop across a resistor, the formula is true for any circuit (or part of a circuit) containing resistance. For example, do you think an electric saw or a light bulb uses more power?

Students should answer that the saw uses more power.

How is it that you can plug them both into the same electrical outlet yet the saw gets more power than the bulb? The voltage is the same.

After some discussion students should realize that the two devices draw different amounts of current.

A saw draws 10-15 amps of current whereas a light bulb draws less than 1 amp.

How does an inanimate object like a saw tell the outlet how much current to send?

After some discussion, steer the conversation onto the idea of resistance and Ohm's law.

For a given voltage, the resistance of a device determines how much current flows. Ohm's law is the key. For example, the voltage in a wall socket is 120 volts. Suppose you wished to make a light bulb that used 1 amp of current. According to Ohm's law, $I = V/R$. That means you need a resistance of 120 Ω. Light bulbs are designed to have about this resistance. How about the saw? What should the resistance of the saw be so that it draws 12 amps of current at 120 volts?

Work this out on the board. According to Ohm's law $R = V/I = (120\ V) \div (12\ A) = 10\ Ω$ The saw is designed to have a resistance of 10 ohms, so it draws the correct current of 12 amps when plugged into a 120 V outlet.

In the form $I = V/R$, Ohm's law tells us how much current flows if we know the voltage and resistance. In the form $V = IR$, Ohm's law tells us how much voltage is dropped across a resistor when a given current flows. In the form $R = V/I$, Ohm's law tells us what the resistance needs to be in order to have a current, I, flow when the voltage is V.

Write out the three arrangements of Ohm's law on the board as you explain how each is used.

4

The resistance of an electrical device may not always stay the same. Resistance often changes with temperature, and may also change with current. When metals heat up the resistance increases. Large electric motors always have cooling fans to keep the electrical wires inside from overheating. When electronic devices like computer chips heat up, their resistance decreases. Computers have fans inside to cool off the circuits for this reason. The next part of the Investigation will look at how the resistance of a light bulb changes. Connect the circuit of Part 5 substituting the light bulb for the resistor.

Students build the circuit

Repeat the voltage drop versus current measurements you did for the resistor, only this time use the light bulb. Again, use five or six settings for the potentiometer to control the current.

Students take the data for voltage versus current for a light bulb.

How is the light bulb different from the resistor?

Students should notice that the slope of the voltage versus current graph changes (the graph is a curve), whereas the slope for the resistor was constant. The increasing slope shows that the resistance of the light bulb increases as the current is increased.

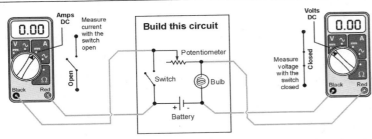

19.3 Electrical Resistance and Ohm's Law

4 Voltage and current for a light bulb

Measure current with the switch open

Build this circuit

Potentiometer

Switch   Bulb

Battery

Measure voltage with the switch closed

1. Replace the fixed resistor in your circuit with a light bulb. The circuit should contain two batteries, a light bulb, a switch, and a potentiometer.
2. Start with the dial of the potentiometer turned all the way counterclockwise. For each trial, turn the dial further clockwise.
3. To measure voltage across the bulb, set the meter to DC volts. Close the switch and connect the meter across the terminals of the bulb resistor. Record the voltage in Table 2.
4. To measure current through the bulb, set the meter to DC amps. Open the switch and touch the meter leads to the *terminals of the switch*. With the switch open, all the current flows through the meter where it can be measured. Record the current in Table 2.
5. Change the setting of the potentiometer and measure current and voltage again. Repeat for at least six settings covering the whole range of the potentiometer.

Table 2: Voltage vs. current for a bulb

Potentiometer setting	Current (amps)	Voltage (volts)

5 Analyzing the bulb's current, voltage, and resistance

a. What happened to the brightness of the bulb as you deacreased the current?
b. Graph the data from Table 2. Put voltage on the *y*-axis and current on the *x*-axis. Label your *x*- and *y*-axes and title your graph.
c. Compare the shape of the graph for the light bulb to the shape of the graph for the fixed resistor.
d. Use Ohm's law to calculate the resistance of the light bulb for each pair of voltage and current values.
e. How is the resistance of the light bulb related to the amount of current through it?
f. Discuss a possible reason for the bulb's resistance changing.

136

---

4 5 Example answers

Table 2: *Voltage vs. current for a bulb*

Potentiometer setting	Current (A)	Voltage (V)
1	0.111	2.88
2	0.077	1.31
3	0.058	0.546
4	0.046	0.219

5a. The bulb got dimmer and then was no longer lighted as the current was decreased.

5b. Graph:

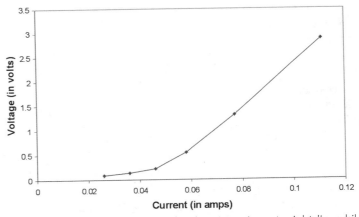

Voltage vs. Current (bulb)

5c. The shape of the graph of the fixed resistor is a straight line while the shape of the graph of the bulb is a curved line.

5d. Between 1 & 2 - 46.2 Ω
Between 2 & 3 - 40.2 Ω
Between 3 & 4 - 27.3 Ω
Between 4 & 5 - 8.2 Ω
Between 5 & 6 - 4.8 Ω

5e. A bulb's resistance decreases as the current through the bulb decreases. There is a direct relationship between a bulb's resistance and the current through the bulb.

5f. The temperature of the bulb decreases as the current decreases, and as a result the resistance decreases as well.

20.1 Series and Parallel Circuits

Key Question: How do series and parallel circuits work?

There are two fundamental ways to connect electrical components in circuits. In a series circuit the current flows in a single loop and goes through all components. In a parallel circuit the current may branch and flow through the circuit taking more than one path. As a result, the current flowing through each component of the circuit may be different. In this investigation, students build both series and parallel circuits. They observe that the voltage drops across each component in a series of circuit. However, the current flowing through each component of a series of circuit is the same. They then observe that the voltage is the same across each component in a parallel circuit, but the current through each branch may not be the same.

Parallel circuit

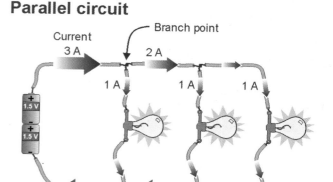

Reading Synopsis

Students read Section 20.1 Series and Parallel Circuits after the Investigation

Series circuits have only one path for current to flow. The total resistance in a series circuit is the sum of the individual resistances ($R_T = R_1 + R_2 + ...$). The voltage drop across each resistance in a series circuit is calculated using Ohm's law ($V = I \div R$).

Parallel circuits have branches and multiple paths for current to flow. Each electrical component in a parallel circuit sees the same voltage. However, because the circuit contains the branches, the current through each component made not to be that same. Adding additional resistances in parallel lowers the total resistance of a parallel circuit. This is because each new resistance adds another independent path for current to flow. For a parallel circuit the total resistance is calculated by $1/R_T = 1/R_1 + 1/R_2 + ...$.

The Investigation

Leading Questions
- In what ways can electrical components be connected together to make circuits?
- What are the rules for how current and voltage behave in a circuit with many components?

Learning Goals

By the end of the Investigation, students will be able to:
- Explain the difference between a series and parallel circuit.
- Calculate the total resistance in series and parallel circuits.
- Describe what happens to the voltage across to each component in a series circuit.
- Give two important advantages parallel circuits have over series circuits.

Key Vocabulary

series circuit, voltage drop, Kirchhoff's voltage law, parallel circuits, Kirchhoff's current law, short circuit

Setup and Materials

Students work in groups of four or five at tables.

Each group should have:

- Multimeter with red and black leads
- Two D-cell batteries
- Electric circuits kit components: circuit board, potentiometer, switch, two battery holders, three bulbs and sockets, wires

Details

Time	One class period
Preparation	.
Assignments	Section 20.1 Series and Parallel Circuits in the **Student Edition** after the Investigation.
Skill Sheets	20.1 Parallel and Series Circuits
Equipment Setup	Electric Circuits

Teaching the Investigation

1   Introduction
2   Build the circuit
3   Measure the initial circuit and 2-bulb and 3-bulb variations
4   Thinking about what was observed
5   More about series circuits
6   Analyzing a series circuits to predict the current
7   Verifying the prediction
8   Introducing parallel circuits
9   In a parallel circuit each bulb sees the full voltage of the battery
10   The current in a parallel circuit is higher
11   Electrical devices operate independently in a parallel circuit
12   Comparing series and parallel circuits

Introduction

Today we will explore more complex circuits.

Build the circuit

❶

Measure the initial circuit and 2-bulb and 3-bulb variations

Measuring voltage - when the switch is closed, set the meter to DC volts and measure the voltage drop across each bulb.

Measuring current - set the meter to DC amps and open the switch. Touch the meter leads to the terminals of the switch.

Add a second bulb and repeat. Add a third bulb and repeat.

Thinking about what was observed

One volt is a watt per amp so three volts means the current carries three watts per amp.

❷

The simplest circuit has one electrical device, a battery, and a switch. This is the circuit you find in a flashlight. For more complicated jobs, the circuits get more complex. Fortunately all circuits obey Ohm's law. But, figuring out current, voltage, and resistance in a complex circuit takes some new techniques. Today we are going to build some different circuits that demonstrate the two fundamental ways to connect multiple electrical devices. We call the two ways series and parallel, and the reason we call them that will become clear later.

Build the circuit with one bulb shown in step one of the Investigation. The diagram shows three bulbs, and we will add the other two later. For now, just use one bulb. Use two batteries. Make sure the circuit works by testing that the bulb lights up when you close the switch.

Students construct the circuit. Allow five or ten minutes to build and test the circuit.

Next, you need to measure voltage and current. When the switch is closed, set the meter to DC volts and measure the voltage drop across the bulb. To measure current, set the meter to DC amps then open the switch. Touch the leads of the meter to the terminals of the switch. With the switch open all the current is forced to flow through the meter where it can be measured. Record the voltage drop across the bulb and the current in the circuit in the first column of Table 1 where it says "1-bulb circuit".

Students take voltage and current values and record data in table 1.

Next, add a second bulb. Arrange the wires so the current goes through the first bulb, comes out, and then goes through the second bulb before going back to the battery. Repeat the voltage and current measurements, except this time measure the voltage separately across each bulb. Record the data in Table 1 under the heading "2-bulb circuit".

Walk around and make sure students connect the second bulb correctly. It is helpful to have them trace the flow of current with a finger out of the battery, around the circuit and back to the battery again.

Add a third bulb to the circuit. All three bulbs should be connected in a chain so the current goes out of one and into the next. Measure the total current in the circuit and the voltage across each bulb. Use the third column of Table 1 to record your measurements.

Students connect the third bulb in series with the other two and make measurements.

With two batteries, how much power does each amp of current carry?

This may require discussion, the answer is three watts. One volt is a watt per amp so three volts means the current carries three watts per amp.

Based on your observations, how does the power divide among the three bulbs? Is this consistent with the voltage drops you measured?

Students should see that all three bulbs are equally bright, implying that each is getting the same amount of power. Each bulb should have the same voltage drop, confirming this conclusion. For example, if the voltage dropped 1 V and the current was 1 amp, then each bulb used 1 watt of power.

20.1 Series and Parallel Circuits

Question: How do series and parallel circuits work?

In this Investigation, you will:

1. Determine how to calculate the total resistance in series and parallel circuits.
2. Learn how voltage and current divide among multiple resistances in series and parallel circuits.
3. Apply your understanding of parallel circuits by building a test voltage circuit.

In this Investigation, you will build parallel circuits and measure their electrical quantities. Parallel circuits are complex and not intuitive, so you will need to examine your data carefully to understand how these circuits work.

Safety Precautions:

Do not use batteries that are damaged. If a battery or wire gets hot, disconnect the circuit immediately and ask for assistance. Do not allow any wire to connect directly from one terminal of the battery to the other terminal. This would be a short circuit and could start a fire.

1 Voltage and current in series circuits

1. Using two batteries, build the simple circuit with one light bulb and a switch as shown at right.
2. Set the meter to DC volts. Close the switch and measure the voltage across the bulb by touching the meter's leads to the bulb's terminals. The bulb should be lighted. Record the value in Table 1.
3. Set the meter to DC amps. Measure the current by opening the switch and inserting the leads of the meter between the terminals of the switch. Opening the switch forces the current to flow through the meter where it can be measured.
4. Add a second bulb to the circuit as shown at right. Repeat the voltage and current measurements and record the results in Table 1.
5. Add a third bulb to the circuit. Repeat the voltage and current measurements and record the results in Table 1.

Build this circuit

Measure voltage across the terminals of each bulb with the switch closed

Measure current across the switch terminals with the switch open

Table 1: Comparing series circuits

	1-bulb circuit	2-bulb circuit	3-bulb circuit
Battery voltage (V)			
Current (A)			
Bulb 1 voltage (V)			
Bulb 2 voltage (V)			
Bulb 3 voltage (V)			

137

House wiring is parallel

The electric circuits in homes and buildings are parallel circuits. Two properties of parallel circuits make them a better choice than series circuits.

1 Each outlet has its own current path. This means one outlet can have something connected and turned on (with current flowing), while another outlet has nothing connected or something turned off (no current flowing).

2 Every outlet has the same voltage because the hot side of every outlet is connected to the same wire that goes to the main circuit breaker panel.

If outlets and lights were wired in series, turning off anything electrical in the circuits would break the whole circuit. This is not practical; you would have to keep everything on all the time just to keep the refrigerator running. Also, in a series circuit, everything you plugged in would use some energy and would lower the voltage available to the next outlet.

Each room in a house typically has its own parallel circuit, protected by the appropriate sized circuit breaker. For example, all the outlets in one bedroom might be on one circuit and the outlets in the living room might be on a separate circuit. By dividing the circuits up, many electrical devices can be connected without drawing too much current through any one wire (see sidebar).

1 Example data

Table 1: Comparing series circuits

	1-bulb circuit	2-bulb circuit	3-bulb circuit
Battery voltage (V)	2.94	2.96	2.97
Current (A)	0.125	0.092	0.076
Bulb 1 voltage (V)	2.93	1.51	0.97
Bulb 2 voltage (V)		1.44	0.93
Bulb 3 voltage (V)			1.06

Thinking about what was observed

A series circuit has only one path for the current to flow. Because there is only one path, the current passes through each device in series.

More about series circuits

In a series circuit, all the current must pass through all of the devices in the circuit. If any device breaks the circuit, the current cannot flow.

Analyzing a series circuits to predict the current

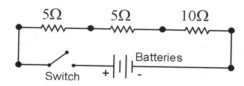

Verifying the prediction

If each bulb is drawing the same amount of power out from the current, what should happen to the voltage as the current flows through each bulb?

Students should answer that the voltage drops across each bulb as the power in the current is dissipated. This is also predicted by Ohm's law since each bulb is a resistance.

Wain should happen to the current as it passes through each bulb? Does the current diminish or stay the same?

Students should answer that the current must be the same through each bulb because there is nowhere else for the current to flow.

We call this kind of circuit a series circuit since there is only one path for current to flow. Because there is only one path, the current passes through each electrical device in series. The current delivers some of its power to each bulb, leaving less power for the next bulb in the series.

Suppose we added a fourth bulb in series with the other three. What would happen to the current flowing in the circuit? Would it increase, decrease, or remain the same?

Students should answer that the current would decrease because each time they added a bulb the current decreased in the circuits they already built and measured.

What do you think would happen to the other two bulbs if one bulb is removed from the circuit? Try and see what happens.

Students should remove one bulb and see that all the bulbs go out.

In a series circuit all the current must pass through all the electrical devices in the circuit, if any device is removed it breaks the circuit and current cannot flow. Therefore all the other devices in the circuit stop working.

3

Let's use what we just learned about series circuits to predict what will happen before we build the circuit. Suppose we make this circuit with three resistors whose resistance we already know.

Draw the circuit in Part 3 on the board with the values of resistance.

Imagine you are at the battery and you are deciding how much current needs to flow in the circuit. How much total resistance do you see?

After some discussion students should come to the conclusion that the total resistance is 20 Ω which is the sum of the resistances of each resistor. This is true because all of the current must flow through each resistor in a series circuit and so that total resistance is the sum of resistances from each individual resistor.

How much current should flow in this circuit given that the battery maintains 3 V?

Use Ohm's law, $I = V/R$ = 3 V/20 Ω = .15 amps

4

Build the circuit and test it to see if your prediction is correct?

Students build and test the circuit. The prediction is usually pretty accurate if the internal resistance of the meter is not too large. If the meter has a large internal resistance then the current will be a little bit less than the prediction because some of the battery voltage is dropped across the internal resistance of the meter.

20.1 Series and Parallel Circuits

2 Thinking about what you observed

a. Use the data in Table 1 to explain the relationship between the battery voltage in a circuit and the voltage across the bulb or bulbs connected in series.

b. What did you notice about the brightness of the bulbs as you increased number of bulbs in the circuit? Why do you think this is? How do the measurements you made support your hypothesis about why the bulbs changed in brightness?

c. What happens to the other two bulbs when one bulb is removed from the three-bulb circuit? Explain why the circuit behaves as it does.

3 Determining the total resistance of resistors in series

a You will use two 5-ohm and one 10-ohm resistor during this Investigation. Predict what the total resistance of the circuit will be when all three resistors are connected in series.

Build this circuit

b. Predict the circuit's total current when 3 volts are applied using two batteries.

4 Measuring the current and resistance in series circuits

1. Build the circuit in the diagram in Part 3. Use two 5-ohm and one 10-ohm resistor.
2. Measure the battery voltage applied to the circuit. Record the value in Table 2.
3. Measure the current through the circuit. Record the value in Table 2.

Table 2: Three-resistor series circuit measurements

Current (amps)	Voltage (V)	Resistance (ohms)

a Use Ohm's law (in the form $R = V/I$) to calculate the total resistance in each circuit from the combined battery voltage (Table 1) and the current for each circuit (Table 2). Record your results in the bottom row of Table 2.

b. Compare your measurements with the predictions of Part 3. Explain the effect that adding resistors has on the current flowing in a series circuit.

5 Parallel circuits

A parallel circuit has more than one branch so current may divide and flow "in parallel" among the branches of the circuit.

1. Build a circuit with two batteries, a switch, and three bulbs as shown in the diagram below:

Build this circuit

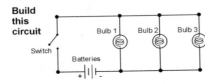

2a. The voltage provided by the battery in a series circuit is divided up between the bulbs in the circuit. The sum total of the voltage across all bulbs in a circuit is equal to the voltage provided by the battery.

2b. The brightness decreased as bulbs were added to the circuit. Since the voltage from the battery gets divided up by the bulbs in the circuit, adding more bulbs means each bulb gets less voltage. We observed less voltage across the bulbs as we added more, and as this happened the bulbs also got dimmer.

2c. When one bulb is removed the other two go out. This happens because removing a bulb interrupt the circuit, and current stops flowing. Without a complete path from one end of the battery to the other there will be no current and the bulb will not be lit.

3a. The total resistance of a series circuit will be the sum of all resistors in the circuit.

$5\,\Omega + 5\,\Omega + 10\,\Omega = 20\,\Omega$

3b. The voltage from two batteries was about 3 v in Part 1.

$V = IR$; $V/R = I$; $3\,v/\,20\,\Omega = 0.15$ amps

Table 2: *Three-resistor series circuit measurements*

Current (amps)	Voltage (V)	Resistance (Ω)
0.139	3.04	21.9

4a. $R = V/I$

$R = 3.04\ v/\ .139\ a$

$R = 21.9\ \Omega$

4b. $21.9 - 20 = 1.9$

$1.9/\,20 = 0.95 = 10\%$ error

Adding resistors to a circuit decreases the current in a circuit.

Table 3: *Comparing series circuits*

	Totalircuit	Bulb 1	Bulb 2	Bulb 3
Voltage (V)	2.77	2.73	2.73	2.72
Current (A)	0.388			
Resistance (Ω)	8.2			

Introducing parallel circuits

Parallel circuit - current may divide and flow in parallel along multiple branches of the circuit.

In a parallel circuit each bulb sees the full voltage of the battery

Voltage drop in the parallel circuit is three times larger across each bulb than it was in the series circuit.

The current in a parallel circuit is higher

Current is much larger in the parallel circuit compared with the series circuit.

Electrical devices operate independently in a parallel circuit

Comparing series and parallel circuits

Parallel circuits use more current than series circuits and will drain the battery faster.

5 Series of circuits have several disadvantages. The most serious one is that any break in the circuit interrupts current to every device connected to the circuit. Imagine all of the outlets in your house were connected in a series circuit. That means turning off a light would also turn off the refrigerator the clock and everything else in the house! Fortunately, there is another way to connect circuits that does not suffer from this problem. Connect the circuit shown in step 5 of the Investigation. this circuit is called a parallel circuit because current may divide and flow in parallel along multiple branches of the circuit. Test the circuit to see that it works. When you close the switch, all three light bulbs should light up.

Students connect the three bulb parallel circuit as shown in the diagram for step 5. Walk around the room to help them connect this circuit, which is more complex than that series circuit.

How it does the brightness of each bulb compared with the series circuit when you also had three bulbs?

Students should notice that the three bulbs connected in parallel are much brighter than three bulbs connected in series.

Measure the voltage across each bulb and record the results in the first row of table 3. Also measure the voltage across the battery and record this as the total circuit voltage in the first column. Compare the voltage across the each bulb in the parallel circuit with the voltage drop across each bulb in the series circuit. What do you notice?

Students should notice that the voltage drop in the parallel circuit is three times larger across each bulb that it was in the series circuit. Explain this means each bulb in the parallel circuit is dissipating three times as much power per amp of current that it was in the series circuit. This is one reason the bulbs in the parallel circuit are so much brighter. The other reason is that the current is higher also!

Set the meter to DC amps to measure the total current flowing in the circuit. As before, open the switch and touch the leads of the meter to the switch terminals, forcing the current to flow through the meter. Write the result in Table 3. How does the current you measured in the parallel circuit compare with the current in the series circuit which also had three bulbs?

Students should notice that the current is much larger in the parallel circuit compared with the series circuit. In fact, the current in the parallel circuit is about three times the current that they measured in the single bulb series circuit.

6 What happens when you remove one bulb from the parallel circuit? Try it and see what happens.

Students should notice that the other two bulbs remain lit when one bulb is removed.

In a parallel circuit each electrical device has a separate connection back to the battery that does not pass through other electrical devices. That means that each device sees the full voltage of the battery and operates independently of other devices on the circuit. This is how the outlets in your house are connected. Each appliance you plug-in has a parallel connection to the power in the house.

You never get something for nothing. The three bulbs in the parallel circuit were brighter than the three bulbs in the series circuit however the parallel circuit uses much more current than the series circuit and will drain the energy of the batteries faster. Use the data you collected from the single bulb circuit and the three bulb series and parallel circuits to fill in table 4 and answer the questions.

You may wish to walk the students through using Ohm's law to calculate the overall resistance of the parallel circuit from the overall measured current and voltage. You will need to demonstrate how resistances are combined in parallel for students to solve the last question in step 6.

20.1 Series and Parallel Circuits

2. Set the meter to DC volts. Close the switch and measure the voltage across the battery by touching the leads of the meter to the terminals of the battery. All three bulbs should be lighted. Record the value in Table 3.

3. Observe the brightness of the bulbs compared with their brightness when all three were connected in series.

4. Measure the voltage across each bulb by touching the leads of the meter to the terminals of each bulb separately. Record the values in Table 3.

5. Set the meter to DC amps. Measure the total current in the circuit by opening the switch and inserting the leads of the meter between the terminals of the switch. This forces the current to flow through the meter where it can be measured.

Table 3: Comparing series circuits

	Total circuit	Bulb 1	Bulb 2	Bulb 3
Voltage (V)				
Current (A)				
Resistance (Ω)				

6   **Comparing series and parallel circuits**

a. Use Ohm's law and the total circuit voltage and total circuit current from Table 3 to calculate the total resistance of the circuit with three bulbs in parallel. Record the result in the last row of Table 3.

b. Use Table 4 to summarize the total circuit current and voltage measurements from the single-bulb circuit and the two different three-bulb circuits (series and parallel).

Table 4: Comparing series and parallel circuits

	Single-bulb circuit	3-bulb series circuit	3-bulb parallel circuit
Current (A)			
Voltage (V)			
Resistance (Ω)			

c. Compare the total resistance of the single-bulb circuit with the total resistance of the three-bulb series circuit. Which circuit resistance is greater? Why do you think this is?

d. Compare the total resistance of the single-bulb circuit to the total resistance of the three-bulb parallel circuit. Which circuit resistance is greater? Why do you think this is?

e. How are the branch currents in the parallel circuit related to the total current supplied by the batteries? Explain how you arrived at your answer.

f. Compare the total current in the single-bulb circuit, the three-bulb series circuit, and the three-bulb parallel circuit. Is there an approximate relationship between the currents that also agrees with the observed brightness of the bulbs in each circuit?

g. If you wish to brightly light three bulbs with one battery, should you connect them in series or parallel?

h. Calculate the total current that should flow when three resistors (of 5, 5, and 10 ohms) are connected in parallel as shown. Build and test the circuit to evaluate your prediction. How close was your prediction to the actual measurements?

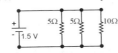

6a. R = V/ I; R = 2.77 v/ .338 a; R = 8.2 Ω

6b. Data table:

Table 4: *Comparing simple and parallel circuits*

	Single-bulb circuit	3-bulb series circuit	3-bulb parallel circuit
Current (A)	0.125	0.076	0.139
Voltage (V)	2.94	2.97	3.04
Resistance (Ω)	23.5	39.1	21.9

6c. The three-bulb series circuit resistance is greater. It is greater because the total resistance is the sum of all three bulbs in the circuit, while the single-bulb circuit has only one bulb's resistance as its total resistance.

6d. The single-bulb circuit has greater circuit resistance than the three-bulb parallel circuit. The current has more paths to travel which lowers total resistance.

6f. The three-bulb series circuit had the least total current, followed by the single-bulb circuit, while the three-bulb parallel circuit had the most total current. The greater the current in a circuit, the observed brightness of the bulbs in the circuit.

6g. For the brightest bulbs, the three-bulb parallel circuit should be used. This would however drain the battery fastest as well.

6h. I = V/R

To calculate total R, or Rt

1/Rt = 1/5 Ω + 1/5 Ω + 1/10 Ω

1/Rt = 2/10 Ω+ 2/10 Ω + 1/10 Ω

1/Rt = 5/10 Ω

1/Rt = 1/2 Ω

Rt = 2 Ω

I = 1.5/ 2 Ω

I = 0.75 amps predicted

Measurements:

total current - .381 amps

0.75 - 0.381 = 0.369

0.369/0.381 = 0.97 = 97% error

20.2 Analysis of Circuits

Key Question: How do we analyze network circuits?

The electrical components in most real circuits are not all connected in serial nor are they all connected in parallel. When devices are combined using both series and parallel connections a network circuit is created. In this Investigation, students build and analyze some simple network circuits. They learn the technique of reducing a network to find the equivalent total resistance for the circuit. Near the end of the Investigation, students analyze a puzzling network circuit with three light bulbs. Removing one of the three bulbs causes one of the remaining bulbs to get brighter and the other to get dimmer! Students explain the behavior of this circuit using what they know about both series and parallel circuits.

Network circuit of three 3 Ω bulbs

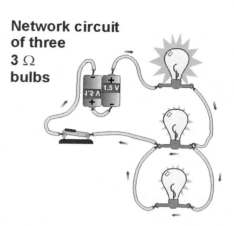

Reading Synopsis

Students read Section 20.2 Analysis of Circuits after the Investigation

All circuits work by manipulating currents and voltage. The process of circuit analysis means figuring out what the currents and voltages in a circuit are. there are three basic laws that are the foundation of circuit analysis. Ohm's law relates voltage and current and resistance. Kirchoff's current laws states that the sum of currents leaving a branch point must be equal to the currents entering the branch point. Kirchoff's voltage law says the sum of the voltage changes around any loop in a circuit must be zero. Together with the formulas for combining resistors, Ohm's law and Kirchoff's current and voltage laws are the foundation of circuit analysis.

A voltage divider is a commonly used resistor circuit that produces an output voltage that is a fraction of the input voltage. The voltage divider and other examples of network circuits are discussed.

The Investigation

Leading Questions
- Can circuits only be connected in either series or parallel?
- Is there a process for analyzing complicated circuits?
- How is a complex circuit designed?
- How can the behavior of a complex circuit be understood?
- Why is circuit analysis useful?

Learning Goals
By the end of the Investigation, students will be able to:
- Build a network circuit.
- Determine the total resistance of a 3 element resistor network circuit.

Key Vocabulary
circuit analysis, network circuit

Setup and Materials

Students work in groups of four or five at tables.

Each group should have:

- Multimeter with red and black leads
- Two D-cell batteries
- Electric circuits kit components: two 5-ohm resistors, one 10-ohm resistor, one 20-ohm resistor, two battery holders, wires, 3 bulbs and sockets

Details

Time ⏱ One class period

Preparation 🖉

Assignments 📖 Section 20.2 Analysis of Circuits in the **Student Edition** after the Investigation.

Skill Sheets 20.2 Network Circuits

Equipment setup Electric Circuits

Teaching the Investigation

1 Introduction
2 Measuring resistance
3 Building the first circuit
4 Measuring or calculating current and voltage
5 How current divides between resistors
6 Kirchoff's current law
7 Calculating equivalent resistance to analyze a circuit
8 What happens if a resistor is changed?
9 Solving a circuit puzzle
10 Solving a new network circuit problem

Introduction

Measuring resistance **1**

Building the first circuit **2**

R₂ and R₃ are in parallel with each other.

R1 is in series with both R₂ and R₃.

Measuring or calculating current and voltage **3**

How current divides between resistors

R2 has the greater current because it had lower resistance.

Current that flows through R₁ splits up and divides to flow through R₂ and R₃.

Kirchoff's current law

Kirchoff's current law - the total current flowing out of any node must equal the total current flowing in.

The two basic types of circuits are series and parallel, but that does not mean all circuits are one or the other. Most circuits have some components connected in series and other components connected in parallel. Today's Investigation will examine some examples of network circuits. A network circuit is one that combines serial and parallel connections.

For the first part of the Investigation we need the precise resistance of each of the resistors we are going to use. Set you meter to measure resistance and record the value of resistance for each resistor in Table 1

Students measure resistances and complete Table 1.

Construct the circuit shown in the diagram in step 2 of the Investigation.

Students construct the circuit.

Which resistors are in parallel? Which are in series?

Students should answer that R₂ and R₃ are in parallel with each other while R1 is in series with both R₂ and R₃.

Close the switch and measure the battery voltage. Record the voltage in Table 2. Open the switch and measure the total circuit current. Set the meter to DC amps and touch the leads to the terminals of the switch while the switch is open. Record the result in Table 2.

Students make the current measurement.

For the next part of the Investigation you need to determine the current flowing through each resistor and the voltage across each resistor. Measure the voltage by touching the leads of the meter to the terminals of each resistor separately. You can break the circuit to measure the current or you can use Ohm's law to calculate it from the voltage and resistance. To use Ohm's law the current through each resistor is equal to the measured voltage across the resistor divided by the previously measured value of resistance. Which is easier?

Students complete Table 2 using measured voltages and calculated currents.

Which resistor of R_2 and R_3 had the greater current? How do you explain this?

Students should answer that R2 had the greater current because it had the lower resistance. Both resistors saw the same voltage. According to Ohm's law, $I = V/R$ so the resistor with the higher resistance always has the lower current.

What can you say about the currents flowing through all three resistors? Think about traffic coming into an intersection. No matter how fast the cars are going all the cars that enter the intersection must leave it by one path or another. How does the current in a circuit act in a similar way?

Students should recognize that the current that flows through R₁ splits up and divides to flow through R₂ and R₃.

This is an example of a powerful rule that applies to all circuits. The rule is called Kirchoff's current law. Kirchoff's current law applies to a node in a circuit. A node is a point where a circuit branches. Kirchoff's current law says that the total current flowing out of any node must equal the total current flowing in. For example suppose we have a circuit with a node that has four wires leading to it. Suppose we measure 10 amps of current flowing into the node along one wire. If two amps flow out on the second wire and three amps flow out on the third wire, then how much current must flow out along the fourth wire?

Students should answer that five amps flow out on the fourth wire because 5 = 10 -2 -3. According to Kirchoff's current law, all the current flowing out of a node must equal the current flowing in.

20.2 Analysis of Circuits

Question: How do you analyze network circuits?

In this Investigation, you will:

1. Build network circuits.
2. Determine the current at different points in a network circuit.
3. Determine the total resistance of a network circuit.

In the previous Investigation, you worked with series and parallel circuits. When devices are combined in both series and parallel in a single circuit, a network circuit is created. You will build and analyze network circuits in this Investigation.

> ⬧ **Safety Precautions:**
> Do not use batteries that are damaged. If a battery or wire gets hot, disconnect the circuit immediately and ask for assistance. Do not allow any wire to connect directly from one terminal of the battery to the other terminal. This would be a short circuit and could start a fire.

1 **Determining the resistance of each resistor**

You will use two 5-ohm, one 10-ohm, and one 20-ohm resistor during this Investigation. Label the 5-ohm resistors R1 and R2, the 10-ohm resistor R3, and the 20-ohm resistor R4.

Use the multimeter to measure the resistance of each resistor and enter the results in Table 1.

Measuring resistance

Table 1: Measured resistance values

	R1	R2	R3	R4
Resistance (Ω)				

2 **Building a network circuit**

1. Use a battery, resistors 1, 2, and 3, and as many wires as necessary to construct the network circuit shown in the diagram at right.
2. Measure the voltage across the battery. This is the total circuit voltage. Then measure the voltage across each of the resistors. Record your measurements in Table 2.
3. Measure the current through each resistor. Record your measurements in Table 2. You have to break the circuit temporarily to insert the meter and make each current measurement. Be sure the meter is set to DC amps.

Build this circuit

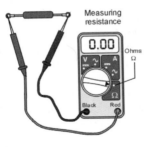

Applying the current law

Kirchoff's current law and Ohm's law can be used together to solve for the currents and voltages in the network circuit of Part 2. Although the algebra has a few steps to it, there is nothing more complicated than multiplying and dividing. The trick to solving circuits like this is to be very careful naming the currents and voltages and keep track of the subscripts you use to name them. A neat and accurately labeled diagram is essential.

Let the voltage from the positive terminal of the battery be V_B. The voltage at the node is V_1. The current through R_1 is then (by Ohm's law) $I_1 = (V_B - V_1) \div R_1$. The current through R_2 is $V_1 \div R_2$ and the current through R_3 is $V_1 \div R_3$.

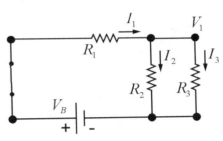

$$I_1 = I_2 + I_3$$

According to Kirchoff's current law the total current into the node equals the total current out of the node. Mathematically: $I_1 = I_2 + I_3$.

$$\frac{V_B - V_1}{R_1} = \frac{V_1}{R_2} + \frac{V_1}{R_3}$$

$$(V_B - V_1)R_2R_3 = (R_1R_2 + R_1R_3)V_1$$

$$V_1 = \left(\frac{R_2R_3}{R_1R_2 + R_1R_3 + R_2R_3} \right) V_B$$

1 Example data

Table 1: *Measured resistance values*

	R1	R2	R3	R4
Resistance (Ω)	5.0	4.9	9.8	19.9

Calculating equivalent resistance to analyze a circuit

3

$$R_T = (R_2R_3) \div (R_2 + R_3)$$

$$R_T = (5\Omega \times 10\Omega) \div (5\Omega + 10\Omega) = 3.33\Omega$$

The total resistance of the circuit is equal to R_1 (5Ω) + 3.33Ω = 8.33Ω

The first step to analyzing a network circuit is often to reduce series and parallel combinations of resistors by replacing them with a single equivalent resistance. For example resistors R_2 and R_3 are a simple parallel connection. We can use the formula for combining parallel resistances to calculate an equivalent resistance that includes both R_2 and R_3.

> Work out the parallel combination of R_2 and R_3 on the board with the result that the parallel combination of a 5Ω and 10Ω resistor gives an equivalent resistance of 3.33Ω $R_T = (R_2R_3) \div (R_2 + R_3)$

The equivalent resistance is lower than either the five or ten ohm original resistors. That is because the original resistors present two paths for current to flow. For the same current to flow through a single path, but resistance of the single path must be lower than any resistance in the parallel connection.

What type of connection is there between the remaining resistor R_1 and the 3.33Ω equivalent resistance we just calculated?

> Students should answer that this is a series connection.

What is the total resistance of the circuit?

> Students should answer that the total resistance is 8.33 Ω which is the sum of R_1 and 3.33 Ω

Calculated the actual resistance of the circuit from your measured values for current and battery voltage. How does the theoretical resistance compared with the actual resistance?

> If you use a meter with a low internal resistance then the calculated theoretical resistance should be very close to the actual resistance. By actual resistance I mean the resistance calculated by dividing the measured voltage by the measured current. The actual resistance will be higher than the theoretical resistance by an amount equal to the internal resistance of the meter in current measuring mode. For example, if the meter has an internal resistance of 5Ω then the theoretical resistance will be 5Ω lower than the actual resistance.

What happens if a resistor is changed?

4

The parallel combination has an equivalent resistance of 4Ω which is only a little greater than the previous parallel combination (3.33Ω).

The total circuit resistance with the 20Ω resistor is then 9Ω compared with 8.3 Ω with the old $(10 \ \Omega)$ value for R_3

Suppose resistor R_3 is replaced with a higher value, such as 20Ω. What do you think will happen to the total current flowing through the circuit? should not current increase, decrease, or stay about the same?

> Students should answer that the total current should decrease because the resistance increases. It is instructive to expand on this intuition since it is correct but the actual change in total circuit resistance is not very large. The change is not large because the 20Ω resistor is combined in parallel with a 5Ω resistor. The parallel combination has an equivalent resistance of 4Ω which is only a little greater than the previous parallel combination (3.33Ω). The total circuit resistance with the 20Ω resistor is then 9Ω compared with 8.3 Ω with the old $(10 \ \Omega)$ value for R_3.

Build the circuit and measure the voltage and current.

> Students build circuits and measure voltage and current.

3   Analyzing the circuit

Table 2: Voltage and current measurements

	Battery (total circuit)	R1	R2	R3
Voltage (volts)				
Current (amps)				

a. Which of the two resistors is connected in parallel?

b. Which resistor is in series with the other two?

c. How does the voltage across the parallel resistors (R_2 and R_3) compare?

d. How does the voltage across the parallel resistors relate to what you learned about voltages in a parallel circuit in the previous Investigation?

e. Voltage is the measure of the amount of energy carried by the current in a circuit. Trace the path of the current from the positive end of the battery, through the circuit, to the negative end of the battery. There are two possible paths because of the parallel part of the circuit but each path will only pass through two of the resistors. Does the amount of energy lost through the resistors equal the amount of energy supplied by the battery? Is this the case for each possible path? Explain.

f. How does the current flowing through R_1 compare with the current through R_2?

g. How does the current coming out of the battery compare with the sum of the currents flowing through R_2 and R_3? Explain this relationship.

h. Use what you know about series and parallel circuits to calculate the theoretical total resistance of the circuit. The formulas for finding the total resistance are:

Series circuit	Parallel circuit
$R_{tot} = R_1 + R_2$	$\dfrac{1}{R_{tot}} = \dfrac{1}{R_1} + \dfrac{1}{R_2}$

i. Now calculate the total resistance of the circuit using Ohm's law, the battery voltage, and the total circuit current you measured.

j. How does the total resistance calculated using Ohm's law compare with the theoretical total resistance found above?

4   Predicting the effect of changing a resistor

a. Replace the 10-ohm resistor (R_3) with the 20-ohm resistor (R_4). Use what you have learned about network circuits to predict the total circuit resistance and total circuit current. Show the process you used to make your predictions.

b. Measure the voltage across the battery and each resistor and the total current in the circuit. Use Ohm's law to find the total circuit resistance. You will need to make a data table similar to Table 2.

c. How did the predicted values compare with the measured ones?

3 4 Example answers

Table 2: Voltage and current measurements

	Battery	R1	R2	R3
Voltage (volts)	1.45	0.868	0.568	0.565
Current (amps)	.148	0.148	0.098	0.051

3a. R2 and R3 are connected in parallel.

3b. R1 is in series with the other two resistors.

3c. The voltage across these two resistors is the same.

3d. The voltage in each branch of a parallel circuit will be equal, and they are.

3e. The total voltage drop of the two possible paths will be the same. The sum of each path will be equal to the voltage provided by the battery. The amount of energy lost to the resistors is measured by the voltage drop. Since the voltage drops equal the voltage provided by the battery, the energy lost to the resistors is equal to the energy supplied by the battery.

3f. The current through R1 is greater than the current through R2.

3g. The sum of the currents through R2 and R3 are equal to the current coming out of the battery. The total current coming out of the battery splits when encountering two paths, the amount in each path depends on the resistance in each path. When the wire comes back together, the currents come back together and if measured at that point would equal the sum of both branches.

3h. $R_{tot} = R_1 + R_{par}$
$1/R_{par} = 1/R_2 + 1/R_3$; $1/R_{par} = 1/4.9\,\Omega + 1/9.8\,\Omega$
$1/R_{par} = 2/9.8\,\Omega + 1/9.8\,\Omega$; $1/R_{par} = 3/9.8\,\Omega$
$R_{par} = 9.8\,\Omega/3$; $R_{par} = 3.3\,\Omega$; $R_{tot} = 5.0\,\Omega + 3.3\,\Omega$; $R_{tot} = 8.3\,\Omega$

3i. $R = V/I$; $R = 1.45\,V/0.148\,A$; $R = 9.8\,\Omega$

3j. $9.8 - 8.3 = 1.5$
$1.5/8.3 = 0.18 \times 100 = 18\%$

4a. $R_{tot} = R_1 + R_{par}$
$1/R_{par} = 1/R_2 + 1/R_4$; $1/R_{par} = 1/4.9\,\Omega + 1/19.9\,\Omega$
$1/R_{par} = 0.204\,\Omega + 0.5\,\Omega$; $1/R_{par} = 0.209\,\Omega$
$R_{par} = 4.78\,\Omega$; $R_{tot} = 5.0\,\Omega + 4.78\,\Omega$
$R_{tot} = 9.78\,\Omega$ (predicted)
measured 1.27 V for total circuit voltage in this configuration
$1.27\,V/9.78\,\Omega = 0.130\,A$ (predicted)

Solving a circuit puzzle

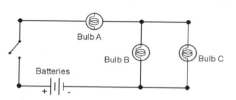

5 Build the network circuit shown in Part 5 of the Investigation using three bulbs instead of three resistors.
> Students build the circuit.

Compare the brightness of bulbs A, B., and C
> Students should note that bulb A is the brightest while bulbs B and C are dimmer and equal in brightness to each other.

Disconnect (or remove) bulb B with the circuit switched on. What happens to the brightness of the remaining bulbs?
> Students should notice that bulb A gets dimmer then it was but bulb C gets brighter than it was previously! Bulbs A and C are also now about equal in brightness. Students should be encouraged to put bulb B back in the circuit and see that the brightness relationship returns to what it was.

Explain why this happens.
> Bulb A sees the total circuit current which is determined by the total circuit resistance. When bulb B is removed, the total circuit resistance increases because the parallel combination of two bulbs has a lower at resistance than either bulb by itself. The brightness of bulb A decreases because the current in the circuit decreases in response to the increase in total resistance.
>
> Bulb C originally got 1/2 the current in the circuit because the current was divided equally between the two parallel branches. With bulb B gone, bulb C gets all of current in the circuit. As a result, bulb C is brighter than it was because the total current, while less than it was before, is still greater than half of what it was before.

Solving a new network circuit problem

Equivalent resistance for the entire circuit is calculated with this equation:

$$R_T = (R_1 + R_2)(R_3 + R_4) \div (R_1 + R_2 + R_3 + R_4)$$

6 We have one more challenge to do. Build the circuit shown in Part 6 of the Investigation. This circuit has four resistors.
> Students build the circuit of Part 6.

Describe the connections between the four resistors in the circuit. Which are connected in parallel, and which are connected in series?
> Students should answer that R_1 and R_2 are in series with each other and R_3 and R_4 are also in series with each other. The combination of R_1 and R_2 is in parallel with the combination of R_3 and R_4.

Combine resistances using what you know about how to add series and parallel resistors. What should the equivalent resistance of the entire circuit to be?
> Students do the calculation to find the equivalent resistance of the total circuit. The series resistances are combined first, then the parallel resistances. The total resistance should come out to be given by
> $$R_T = (R_1 + R_2)(R_3 + R_4) \div (R_1 + R_2 + R_3 + R_4)$$

Measure the current and voltage in the actual circuit and see if the circuit behaves as you think it should.
> Students make measurements and compare with their predictions based on the equivalent total resistance they just calculated. If the predicted current comes out smaller it is due to any internal resistance of the meter as discussed previously

20.2 Analysis of Circuits

5 **A circuit puzzle**

Build this circuit

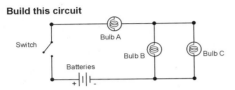

Switch · Bulb A · Bulb B · Bulb C · Batteries

1. Build the circuit shown in the diagram above with 2 batteries, a switch, and three bulbs.
2. Turn the switch on and observe the brightness of each bulb.
3. Temporarily interrupt the current to bulb B by disconnecting one wire from the terminal post.
4. Observe how the brightness of the other two bulbs changes.

  a. When bulb B is disconnected, does bulb A get dimmer, brighter, or stay the same?
  b. When bulb B is disconnected, does bulb C get dimmer, brighter, or stay the same?
  c. Use what you know about series and parallel circuits to propose an explanation for what you observed.

6 **Challenge: Analyze a four-resistor network circuit**

  a. Build the circuit shown in the diagram at right.
  b. Use what you have learned about network circuits to predict the total circuit resistance and current. Show the process you used to make your predictions.
  c. Use the meter to measure the voltage across the battery and each resistor and the total circuit current. Use Ohm's law to find the total circuit resistance.
  d. How did the predicted values compare with the measured ones?

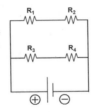

R_1 R_2
R_3 R_4
$\oplus$ $\ominus$

4 5 6 **Example answers**

4b. Total current measured = 0.137 A
    Total voltage measured 1.27 V
    $R_{tot} = V_{tot}/I_{tot}$; $R_{tot} = 1.27$ V/0.137 A; Rtot = 9.27 Ω

4c. 9.78 Ω - 9.27 W = 0.51 Ω
    0.51/9.27 = 0.055 × 100 = 5.5 % error

5-2. B & C are not really lit, just barely glowing. A is pretty bright.

5- 4. A gets dimmer, but C finally lights up and is the same brightness as A.

5a. A gets dimmer.

5b. C gets brighter, it finally lights up.

5c. The amount of current in the circuit gets split between the two branches, and the amount of current each branch winds up with is not really enough to produce light in the bulbs. Even though the bulbs are not lit, there is still current going through them. That same amount of current that gets split between the two branches goes through bulb A by itself, which is more than enough to light it.

6b. 1st branch (R_F): $R_F = R_3 + R_4$; $R_F = 9.8\Omega + 19.9\Omega$; $R_F = 29.7\Omega$
    2nd branch (R_S): $R_S = R_1 + R_2$; $R_S = 5.0\Omega + 4.9\Omega$; $R_S = 9.9\Omega$
    Total resistance (R_C): $1/R_C = 1/R_F + 1/R_S$; $1/R_C = 1/29.7\Omega + 1/9.9$ Ω; $1/R_C = 0.034\Omega + 0.101\Omega$; $1/R_C = 0.135\Omega$; $R_C = 1/0.135\Omega = 7.4\Omega$
    $I = V/R_C$; $I = 1.5$ V/7.4Ω = .203 A (predicted)
    with added resistance of multimeter: $I = 1.5$ V/(7.4Ω + 1.4Ω)
    $I = 1.5$ V/8.8 W; $I = .171$ A

6c. Measurements: Circuit current - 0.156 A
    $R_C = 1.41$ V/0.156 A; $R_C = 9.0\Omega$

6d. Resistance:
    9.0 W - 8.8Ω = 0.2Ω difference between measured and predicted
    0.2Ω/9.0Ω = 0.022 × 100 = 2.2% error
    Current:
    0.171 A - 0.156 A = 0.015 A diff. between measured and predicted
    0.015 A/0.156 A = 0.096 × 100 = 9.6 % error
    We used 1.5 volts for our prediction, based on the D cell voltage.
    If we had used 1.41:
    1.41 V/8.8 W = 0.160 A (predicted)
    0.160 A - 0.156 A = 0.004 A
    0.004 A/0.156 A = 0.026 A × 100 = 2.6% error

20.3 Electric Power, AC, and DC Electricity

Key Question: How much does electricity cost and what do you pay for?

The electricity we use every day comes in the form of 120 VAC (120 Volt Alternating Current) from the power company. In this Investigation, students learn how to read power ratings on electrical appliances and use this information to estimate electrical costs in their homes. They use of the concepts of volts, amps, and watts to calculate how much power a typical appliance uses and then how much energy in kilowatt-hours the appliance uses in an average month. Students must do some research to find the cost of power in their area, which is usually between $0.05 and $0.15 per kilowatt-hour.

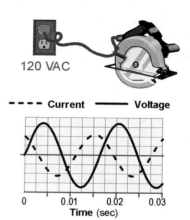

120 VAC

- - - - Current ——— Voltage

Time (sec)

Reading Synopsis

Students read Section 20.3 Electric Power, AC, and DC Electricity after the Investigation

The watt (W) is a unit of power. Power measures the rate of energy transfer. One joule per second is equal to one watt. A 100-watt light bulb uses 100 joules of energy *every second*. Electrical power in a circuit id the product of voltage and current (P = VI).

Utility companies charge for a unit of energy called the kilowatt-hour. One kilowatt-hour is 3.6 million joules, which is the equivalent of one kilowatt of power for one hour.

A battery supplies and DC power, which means of a positive and stays positive always. Most electricity supplied to homes and businesses is AC rather than DC. In household AC electricity, the voltage on one terminal alternates between +170V and -170V sixty times per second. The average absolute value is 120 volts therefore this type of electricity is known as 120 VAC (120 Volt Alternating Current). Because the voltage and current may be out of phase with each other, power in an AC circuit is usually less than the average voltage times the average current.

The Investigation

Leading Questions
- How is the energy and power in electricity measured?
- What do we mean when we say that household appliances use electricity?
- What do the terms on an electric bill mean?
- Which household appliances are costliest to operate?

Learning Goals
By the end of the Investigation, students will be able to:
- Explain power in terms of energy and time.
- Calculate power in a DC circuit when given the current and voltage.
- Rank the amount of power used by various household appliances.
- Estimate the cost per month of using a common household appliance.
- Use dimensional analysis to show that a kilowatt hour is a unit of energy not a unit of power.

Key Vocabulary   watt, power, kilowatt, power rating, kilowatt-hour

Setup and Materials

Students work in groups of three to five at tables.

The class should have:

- Two or three small appliances labeled with power ratings, such as an iron, toaster oven, electric drill, desk lamp, or hair dryer
- Calculators

Sample Power Rating Data

For students who are not able to complete the home data collection between the first and second class periods, provide the sample power rating data shown below.

Appliance	Power (watts)
Electric stove	5,000
Electric heater	1,500
Hair dryer	1,200
Iron	800
Washing machine	750
Light	100
Small fan	50
Clock radio	10

Teaching the Investigation

1   Introduction
2   Power in watts and kilowatts
3   The power formula for DC electricity
4   AC electricity
5   How much power do electrical appliances and devices use?
6   Power for AC appliances
7   How much power do electrical appliances and devices use?

Details

Time Two class periods; there is a home assignment between the two periods

Preparation Collect several small appliances that have power ratings listed on them. Students will learn how to find the power rating stamped on each appliance.

Obtain the price per kilowatt-hour charged by the utility company or companies in your area. This can usually be accomplished through a simple phone call to the utility company's public relations department.

Assignments Section 20.3 Electric Power, AC, and DC Electricity in the **Student Edition** before the Investigation.

Students must complete parts 1 and 2 of the Investigation at home between the first and second class periods. If students are unable to complete this assignment, provide them with the sample power rating data at left.

Skill Sheets 20.3 Electric Power

Introduction

1

Today, we are going to begin using what we've learned about electricity in practical situations. Let's look at some common household appliances. List some electrical appliances you used in the last week.

Students list household appliances, which may include an iron, toaster oven, electric drill, desk lamp, or hair dryer that you brought from home. Ask a few students to report on the electrical information they recorded for each appliance, usually stamped onto the back or the bottom of the device. Students should respond that watts, amps, AC volts (VAC), and 60 Hz are listed on most appliances.

A watt is a measure of power. It's a very helpful measurement to understand as we look at electricity in the home. Let's review what we learned about power. Power, you may remember, is a measure of the rate at which work is being performed. We can state this in another way: Power is the amount of energy (in this case, electrical energy) that is converted to another form of energy per unit of time. Your electrical appliances transform electrical energy into some other form in order to accomplish their job. What sorts of energy transformations occur in the appliances you researched?

Allow students an opportunity to discuss their appliances. Have them share their ideas with the class. They should recognize, for example, that a toaster oven converts electrical energy to heat and light, that a hair dryer converts electrical energy to heat and kinetic energy (to turn the fan), and so on.

Okay, we know that power is the measure of the rate that electrical energy is being changed into some other form. Can anyone remember the fundamental unit of energy?

The students should recall that energy is measured in joules.

Power is the number of joules of energy that your appliance transforms each second. We can write this as a fraction: Power equals joules over seconds. We call "joules per second" by the name watt. A 1,500-watt toaster, for example, transforms 1,500 joules of energy each second into heat and light. When a larger unit is convenient we use kilowatts. One kilowatt is equal to 1,000 watts. So the 1,500-watt toaster could be renamed a 1.5 kilowatt toaster, if you prefer.

We can actually derive an equation for power from the electrical quantities we already know. Who remembers how to write voltage and current in fundamental units?

Students should remember that voltage is equal to joules per coulomb, and that amperes is equal to coulombs per second. Write these on the board.

Let's look at what happens when you multiply the voltage of a circuit by its amperage:

joules per coulombs times coulombs per second. You have coulombs in the numerator and coulombs in the denominator, so they are going to cancel out. What units remain?

Write the mathematical expression on the board. Then show the students that coulombs cancel. It should be made obvious that you are left with joules per second.

So we can see that volts times amps will give us power in watts. More formally, we say that power equals voltage times current.

Actually the formula $P = VI$ does not tell the whole story because it is only accurate for DC electricity, such as comes from a battery. The electricity in your home is not the same as of electricity from a battery. With DC electricity, like a battery, the positive terminal is always positive. With a wall outlet, that is not true. The electricity in your house is AC, which stands for alternating current. That means one terminal in the outlet switches back and forth between +170 V and -170 V 60 times per second.

Draw the AC power cycle on the board (text, page 411). Draw a wave that goes from -170 volts to positive 170 volts every 0.0167 seconds (60 cycles/sec or 60 Hz).

Power in watts and kilowatts

Watt is a measure of power.

Power is a measure of the rate at which work is performed.

Power is the amount of energy that is converted to another form of energy per unit time.

Joule = fundamental unit of energy.

Power is in units of watts (joules per second).

The power formula for DC electricity

Voltage = joules per coulomb of charge.
Amperes = coulombs per second.

Power = voltage × amps

$$Power = \frac{joules}{coulomb} \times \frac{coulomb}{second} = joules/second$$

AC electricity

Electric Power, AC, and DC Electricity

20.3

Question: How much does electricity cost?

In this Investigation, you will:

1. Read appliance labels to determine their power ratings.
2. Calculate the approximate number of kilowatt-hours each appliance uses in a month.
3. Calculate the approximate cost of running each appliance using electric company rates.

You have learned how to measure three electrical quantities: voltage, current, and resistance. In this Investigation, you will learn about a fourth quantity, power, which you have already studied in the context of mechanical systems (Chapter 11). You will find the power ratings of electrical appliances and use this information to estimate electricity costs.

1 **Find the power rating of home appliances**

You will need to complete the first part of this Investigation at home. Your assignment is to find five electrical appliances that have a label with the device's power rating in watts (W) or kilowatts (kW). Some appliances you might look at are a blender, coffee maker, toaster oven, microwave, television, hair dryer, space heater, room air conditioner, or a computer. The rating is often stamped on the back or the bottom of the appliance. In the example below, the power rating is 1.05 kW.

Coffeemaker
AC 120 V   8.75 A
1050 W Heating Element

a. Fill out the first two columns of Table 1 as you find the power rating of each appliance. The second column should be in kilowatts.

b. Convert any power ratings listed in watts to kilowatts. To convert to kilowatts, divide the number of watts by 1,000. For example, 1,500 watts is equal to 1,500 ÷ 1,000, or 1.5 kilowatts.

c. Estimate the number of hours the device is used each month. Assume that one month equals 30 days. If your coffee maker is used for a half hour each morning, you would calculate a monthly usage of 15 hours (0.5 hr/day × 30 days).

Table 1: Power rating, usage, and cost of household appliances

Appliance	Power rating in kW	Est. usage hrs. per mo.	No. kWh per mo.	Price per kWh	Total cost per mo.

What is a watt?

One watt is an energy flow of one joule per second.

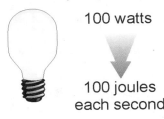

100 watts

100 joules each second

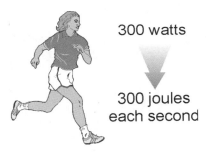

300 watts

300 joules each second

1 **Example answers**

Table 1: Power rating, usage, and cost of household appliances

Appliance	Power rating in KW	Est. usage hrs. per mo.	No. KWh per mo.	Price per KWh	Total cost per mo.
coffee maker	0.900	3.0	2.70	0.12868	0.347
bulb	0.100	150	15.0	0.12868	1.930
microwave	1.000	10.0	10.0	0.12868	1.287
hair dryer	1.625	5.0	8.125	0.12868	1.0455
VCR	0.020	20.0	0.40	0.12868	0.051

How much power do electrical appliances and devices use?

Students complete an at-home project of gathering power information about five appliances and estimating the total time the appliance is used in a month.

How much does it cost to use the electrical appliances in your home?

1

If time permits, you may wish to work through a sample problem using this formula. Here's one possible scenario: If we know that a refrigerator is plugged into a 110V outlet, and with a meter we measure that it draws 9.09 amps of current, then we can find the power rating. 110 volts × 9.09 amps = 999.9, or approximately 1000 watts.

Now that we are equipped with a working knowledge of the meaning of "power" and "watts," let's take a look at Part 1 of your Investigation sheet. Before our next class, you will need to fill out the first three columns of Table 1 at home.

2

In order to complete the columns, you will need to choose five appliances you have at home. Find the **power rating** on each appliance, just like our volunteers did in class today. Record the power ratings in column two. If the rating is given in watts, divide by 1000 to record the power rating in kilowatts.

Next, think about how often the appliance is used in your household each month. Let's say for example that you and your sister listen to a radio while you get ready each morning. You use it for about half an hour every morning, Monday through Friday. That's 2.5 hours per week, or 10 hours per month. You ask your sister how often she uses it and she estimates 20 minutes on weekdays, but she also uses it on Saturday mornings when she's getting ready for work. That's 20 minutes times 6, or 120 minutes each week. One hundred-twenty minutes divided by 60 minutes per hour gives us 2 hours per week. Multiply that by 4 weeks per month, and you get 8 hours per month. So the radio is used for 10+8, or 18 hours per month.

This is a real-life assignment. That means in order to collect the most reliable data possible, you may need to interview other household members. Making an accurate estimate of the time used is an important factor in obtaining meaningful results in our Investigation.

Before the class is dismissed, remind students that the three columns must be completed before the next class meeting.

Additional activity: If time permits, you may wish to ask students to guess which appliance in their home has the highest power rating. Use this question to reinforce the concept that "power" means energy transformed per unit of time. Then ask the students to guess which appliance costs the most per month to use. These questions may help your students begin to see that cost per month depends on both the power rating and the frequency of use. You may wish to compile a class list of students' guesses, or have them write their guesses on paper or in a journal.

3

This is the beginning of the second class period. Students should have completed the first three columns of their data sheet. Although they don't need any circuit equipment for this activity, students will need to sit with their lab groups so that they can compare and discuss their data.

During our last class, you learned about a fourth electrical quantity, the watt. What does a watt measure?

Students should respond that a watt is a measure of power. It tells us how many joules of electrical energy have been converted to another form of energy each second.

After that class, you went home and found the power ratings of five household appliances. You should have already completed the first three columns of your data sheet. Does anyone have questions about the conversion of watts to kilowatts?

Quickly check to see that students divided watts by 1000 to get kilowatts. Some may have multiplied by 1000, which would give an absurdly large number.

It looks like we are ready to move to the next section.

20.3 Electric Power, AC, and DC Electricity

2 Estimate the number of kilowatt-hours each appliance uses in a month

a. Multiply the power rating in kilowatts (from the second column) by the number of hours the appliance is used each month. For example, if you use a 1-kilowatt toaster for five hours a month, multiply 1 times 5. Write your answers in column 4 of Table 1 as shown in the sample below:

Appliance	Power rating in kW	Est. usage hrs. per mo.	No. kWh per mo.	Price per kWh	Total cost per mo.
Microwave	1.4 kW	22 hours	30.8		

3 Determine the monthly cost of using your appliances

Utility companies charge consumers for the number of kilowatt-hours of electricity they use each month. Many houses and apartments have a meter attached to the outside of the building. The meter uses a system of spinning disks to record how much electricity you use. Someone from the electric company reads the meter each month.

a. Find out how much you pay per kilowatt-hour. In some areas, one utility company provides all the electricity to an entire region while in other places several companies compete for customers.

b. Write the price per kilowatt-hour in column 5 of Table 1.

c. Calculate the amount of money your household spends to operate each appliance during one month. Multiply the kilowatt-hours per month by the price per kilowatt-hour to determine your cost.

4 Analyze your data

a. Compare your results with those of the other members of your group. List the three appliances from your group that had the highest power ratings in Table 2.

b. Think about the function of each appliance listed in Table 2. What kind of work is being done? In other words, electrical energy is converted into what other type(s) of energy?

c. Do you see any similarities in the kinds of work being done by the three appliances in Table 2? If so, what are these similarities?

d. Suggest one practical way you or another group member could reduce your electricity bills.

e. Discuss the effect of climate on electricity use. What climate factors might influence which month has the peak electricity use in your area?

f. Name one other factor (not related to climate) that may influence which month has the highest electricity use in your area.

Table 2: Appliances with the highest power ratings

Appliance	Power rating in kilowatts

144

2 3 4 Example answers

2a. See Table 1, column 4.

3b. See Table 1, column 5.

3c. See Table 1, column 6.

4a.

Appliance	Power rating in KW
hair dryer	1.625
1.500	1.500
microwave	1.000

4b. The hair dryer and the space heater convert electrical energy to heat, and the microwave creates microwaves.

4c. High-power appliances create heat or heat things.

4d. Do less heating. Also, keep lights off when not in use.

4e. In a hot climate, people will use a lot of electricity in the summer to keep cool. In a cold climate, people will use a lot of electricity in the winter to keep warm.

4f. People might use a lot more electricity during a holiday season, because they are staying up later, having people over, and doing special things that use more electricity.

Power for AC appliances

Sample calculation:
IF V = 120 VAC and I = 2.5 Z,
then VI = 300 V-A

For an appliance with a power rating of
220 watts, the power factor is:
220 ÷ 300 = 73%

How much power do electrical appliances and devices use?

4

You often hear AC electricity called 120 VAC, where the letters VAC stand for Volts AC. 120 volts is an average, approximately the average of the absolute value of the voltage. The true average of an AC voltage is zero. Technically, 120 VAC is the root-mean-square voltage, for those of you who wish to look up what root-mean-square means. Did anyone research an appliance with an electric motor inside? What current, voltage, and power did you find?

Ask a student for the power, current, and voltage from an appliance with a motor. If you multiply current times voltage you will get a result that is larger than the rated power for the appliance.

With AC electricity, the power is usually less than the product of the average voltage times the average current. Many devices, like electric motors, cannot switch the direction of current instantaneously. When the voltage reverses from positive to negative, there is a short time delay while the current reverses. Page 412 of the book has a diagram that shows what I mean. For AC electricity the electrical power is equal to the average voltage (120 VAC) multiplied by the average current multiplied by a power factor. The power factor is typically between 60% and 80% for motors and transformers. This is why the power rating for your appliance is not the same number as you get by multiplying volts times amps. In fact, we can calculate the power factor by dividing the product of volts times amps by the actual power consumed.

Do an example calculation. IF V = 120 VAC and I = 2.5 Z, then VI = 300 V-A. A typical small appliance with this size motor will have a power rating of 220 watts. The power factor is 220 ÷ 300 = 73%.

Use the data you took at home to fill out the first three columns of Table 1. Record the power ratings in column two. If the rating is given in watts, divide by 1000 to record the power rating in kilowatts.

Next, think about how often the appliance is used in your household each month. Let's say for example that you and your sister listen to a radio while you get ready each morning. You use it for about half an hour every morning, Monday through Friday. That's 2.5 hours per week, or 10 hours per month.

Students should have completed the first three columns of their data sheet. Although they don't need any circuit equipment for this activity, students will need to sit with their lab groups so that they can compare and discuss their data. Quickly check to see that students divided watts by 1000 to get kilowatts. Some may have multiplied by 1000, which would give an absurdly large number.

To measure the power consumption of a house, utility companies use a unit called the kilowatt-hour. One kilowatt-hour is the amount of electrical energy used when one kilowatt of power is used for one hour. Multiply kilowatts by the number of hours per month that each appliance is in use and put the result in the fourth column of Table 1.

Give the students time to calculate kilowatt-hours. Provide an example on the board if needed.

Many houses and apartments have a meter attached to the outside of the building. It uses a system of spinning disks to record the number of kilowatt-hours used. Often, a utility company employee is sent out to read the meters once each month. Sometimes an estimate of household usage is made instead. Here is the price (or prices) per kilowatt-hour charged by the utility company (or companies) in our region. Use the price per kWh to calculate the cost of running your appliance for a month (column 6).

If there are several competing utility companies in your area, you may have some students who don't know which one company serves their household. You can help them find an average value. Although they may not be able to determine the exact cost, they will still gain valuable insight into the cost of operating various types of appliances.

20.3 Electric Power, AC, and DC Electricity

5 What do you buy from the electric utility company?

People often use the phrase "power plant" to refer to their local electric (or public utility) company. You may have heard people say that electric companies "sell power" to their customers or that there was a "power shortage" in a particular area. Let's take a look at these phrases from a scientific perspective. What exactly do electric companies sell?

1. Electricity bills are calculated based on the number of kilowatt-hours used per month.

2. Change kilowatt-hours into units of watts and seconds:

$$1 \text{ kilowatt·hour} \times \frac{1000 \text{ watts}}{\text{kilowatt}} = 1000 \text{ watt·hours}$$

$$1000 \text{ watt·hour} \times \frac{3600 \text{ seconds}}{\text{hour}} = 3{,}600{,}000 \text{ watt·seconds}$$

3. Power is the amount of energy that flows per unit of time. One watt is equal to one joule per second. Substitute the fundamental units of joules per second for watts.

$$3{,}600{,}000 \left(\frac{\text{joules}}{\text{second}} \right) \cdot \text{seconds} = ?$$

a. Which units in the last equation cancel?

b. After canceling the units that appear in both the numerator and denominator, what fundamental unit remains?

c. Is the remaining unit a measure of energy, work, or power?

d. Do electric companies sell energy, work, or power?

Common household electricity

The 120 VAC electricity comes into a typical home or building through a circuit breaker panel. The circuit breakers protect against wires overheating and causing fires. The wires in a house are different sizes to carry different amounts of current safely (Figure 20.16). For example, a circuit made with 12-gauge wire can carry 20 amps. This circuit is protected with a circuit breaker rated for 20 amps that opens the circuit automatically if more than 20 amps of current flows.

Each wall socket has three wires feeding it. The hot wire carries 120 volts AC. The neutral wire stays at zero volts. When you plug something in, current flows in and out of the hot wire, through your appliance (doing work) and back through the neutral wire. The ground wire is for safety and is connected to the ground (0 V) near your house. If there is a short circuit in your appliance, the current flows through the ground wire rather than through you.

21.1 Electric Charge

Key Question: How do electric charges interact?

Fundamentally, electricity comes from the movement of tiny particles carrying electric charge. Although electric charge cannot usually be seen directly, its properties may be inferred by observing what happens in controlled experiments. In this Investigation, students create a simple electroscope using clay, straws, and plastic tape. They observe evidence for two kinds of static electricity. By the end of the Investigation, students should understand how people discovered that there are only two kinds of charge. By describing the attraction and propulsion of charged objects, the students also gain a qualitative understanding of the forces created by electric charge.

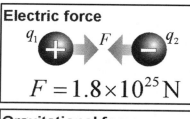

Electric force

$$F = 1.8 \times 10^{25} \, \text{N}$$

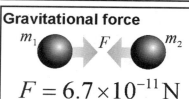

Gravitational force

$$F = 6.7 \times 10^{-11} \, \text{N}$$

Reading Synopsis

Students read Section 21.1 Electric Charge after the Investigation.

Electric charge is a fundamental property of matter. There are two types of charge we call positive and negative. Like charges repel each other and unlike charges attract. Forces between charges hold the atom together and cause electric current to flow.

Electrons to carry negative charge and protons carry positive charge. Electric current is moving charge. It is normally the negative electrons that move. In a conductor, many electrons are free to move independently of the atoms they belong to. These electrons carry current. In an insulator, electrons are bound tightly to atoms and are not free to move. Insulators block the flow of electric current. A semiconductor has a few mobile electrons and can carry small amounts of current.

We do not ordinarily see charged matter because positive and negative are perfectly balanced leaving zero net charge. We called a material electrically polarized if there is an uneven distribution of positive or negative charge.

The Investigation

Leading Questions
- What causes electricity?
- What causes electrical current to move in a circuit?
- How did people study electricity in the past?
- What is moving through the wires of a circuit?

Learning Goals

By the end of the lesson, students will be able to:
- Charge pieces of tape and observe their interactions with an electroscope.
- Identify electric charge as the property of matter responsible for electricity.
- List the two forms of electric charge.
- Describe the forces electric charges exert on each other.

Key Vocabulary

electric charge, positive charge, negative charge, electroscope, static electricity, electrical forces, versorium

Setup and Materials

Students work in groups of two to three at tables.

Each group should have:

- Two rectangles of clay, about 2-by-2-by-4 centimeters
- Four flexible straws
- Metric ruler
- Scotch^{TM} brand magic tape
- Small light objects such as pieces of thread and small pieces of paper (optional)
- Pairs of materials that can be charged, such as plastic combs rubbed with wool, glass rubbed with wool, and dry wood rubbed with glass (optional)

Details

Time	One class period
Preparation	Following the instructions in Investigation 6.2, practice making and using the electroscope. Keep the electroscope for demonstration.
Assignments	Section 21.1 Electric Charge in the **Student Edition** after the Investigation.
Skill Sheets	19.3B Ben Franklin

Teaching the Investigation

1. Introduction to the Investigation
2. Building and using an electroscope
3. The forms of charge and the forces they exert
4. Extension: historical connections

21.1

Electric Charge

Introduction to the Investigation

Definitions and concepts:

Electric charge is a fundamental property of matter. It is the cause of all electrical and magnetic events.

Electric charge has two forms, positive charge and negative charge.

We've been discussing what we know about electricity and we've built some circuits and observed the effects of electricity.

How did people understand electricity well enough to build circuits? Electricity is hard to see and hard to understand, so it has taken thousands of years of study in order for people to know enough.

Today, we're going to re-create one of the important experiments that helped scientists to begin to understand electricity. We are going to learn about and indirectly observe electric charge.

Electric charge is a fundamental property of matter. It is the cause of all electrical phenomena, and as you will find out later in Chapter 10, the cause of all magnetic phenomena as well. Charge flows through all circuits, including our own bodies.

   Summarize these points on the board.

Some of the most important early discoveries relating to charge were experiments that demonstrated that there are two forms of charge, positive charge and negative charge. These experiments were done with an instrument called an electroscope. In this Investigation you will build your own electroscope, using clay, straws, and Scotch™ brand transparent tape. You'll observe the presence of the two kinds of electric charge in an ordinary material—tape.

   Make sure students have copies of Investigation 6.2 and hand out the clay, straws, ruler, and tape to each group.

Building and using an electroscope

1 To build your electroscope, follow the instructions on the Investigation guide. Place two straws in each rectangle of clay and bend the arms down.

   Show students the demonstration electroscope you have made.

2 What we are doing in Part 2 of the Investigation is to create extra electric charge on pieces of tape. We sometimes call a buildup of charge static electricity.

The first step is to place a long piece of tape on the table. This is your base tape. Now tear off a piece of tape and create a little handle at the end by turning the tape down. Place this piece of tape, sticky side down, on the base tape. Smooth the tape down.

   Quickly tear the handled tape away and wrap the top part of it around one of the electroscope arms. Take another piece of tape and repeat what you just did. Now place the second piece of tape on an arm on the second piece of clay.

   Demonstrate the procedure. Monitor groups as they prepare the tapes.

3 Now that the tapes are prepared, move the two containers so that the tapes' non-sticky sides are facing each other about 6 inches apart. Slowly move the arms closer together and observe what happens.

   When students move the two arms together, the two pieces of tape should repel each other.

What happened to the two pieces of tape when you moved the arms of the electroscope together?

   Make sure that students agree that the two pieces of tape moved away from each other.

21.1 Electric Charge

Question: How do electric charges interact?

In this Investigation, you will:

1. Build a simple electroscope and show there are two types of electric charge.
2. Observe the electrostatic forces exerted by charged pieces of tape on each other.

To understand electricity, people studied events such as lightning and the sparks that occur when certain materials are rubbed together. We now know that the movement of electric charge causes these events. Charge is a concept somewhat difficult to grasp; we see its effects around us but we cannot "see" charge. In this way, charge is like the wind—we cannot see the moving air but we know it exists because it blows against our faces and moves objects around.

Charge comes in two forms called positive charge and negative charge. In this Investigation, you will observe how these two forms of charge interact with each other.

1   **Building a simple electroscope**

1. Obtain the following materials: two blocks of clay about $2 \times 2 \times 4$ centimeters, four flexible straws, a ruler, and ordinary clear plastic tape like the kind you find in a desktop tape dispenser.
2. Anchor a flexible straw in each end of each piece of clay. You will thus have two clay bases and four straws.
3. Bend the flexible straws away from each other in each piece of clay. The bent part is called the arm. The arms should be at the same height.
4. Line up the two pieces of clay so that the arms are parallel to each other and about 16 centimeters apart.

2   **Creating static charges: Part I**

1. Place a piece of tape about 20 centimeters long sticky side down on your table. This is your "base tape." It will always stay on the table.
2. Get a second piece of tape that is about 15 centimeters long. Turn over about half a centimeter at the end to make a handle.
3. Place this piece of tape sticky side down on top of the base tape. Smooth the tape down.
4. Quickly tear away the tape with the handle and wrap the top part of it around one of the electroscope arms. Most of the tape should be dangling.
5. Repeat steps 2 through 4 except this time place the second piece of tape on an arm in the second piece of clay. (You should still have two free arms on your electroscope.)

3   **Observing the interaction between the tapes: Part I**

1. Line up the two electroscope halves so that the two pieces of tape are parallel to each other. Slowly move the two pieces of clay toward each other.
2. Observe and record what happens to the two pieces of tape.

Lightning and Benjamin Franklin

Lightning is caused by a giant buildup of static charge. Before a lightning strike, particles in a cloud collide and charges are transferred from one particle to another. Positive charges tend to build up on smaller particles and negative charges on bigger ones.

The forces of gravity and wind cause the particles to separate. Positively charged particles accumulate near the top of the cloud and negatively charged particles fall toward the bottom. Scientists from the National Aeronautics and Space Administration (NASA) have measured enormous buildups of negative charge in storm clouds. These negatively charged cloud particles repulse negative charges in the ground, causing the ground to become positively charged. This positive charge is why people who have been struck by lightning sometimes say they first felt their hair stand on end.

The negative charges in the cloud are attracted to the positively charged ground. When enough charges have been separated by the storm, the air breaks down under the electrical forces. All the accumulated negative charges flow from the cloud to the ground, heating the air along the path (to as high as 20,000 °C!) so that it glows like a bright streak of light.

Benjamin Franklin (1706-90) studied lightning to learn more about electricity. The terms *positive* and *negative* to describe the opposite kinds of charge were first used by Franklin. He and other scientists were seeking ways to describe their new observations about electricity.

Building and using an electroscope (cont.)

4

In Part 4 of the Investigation, we're going to again charge two pieces of tape, but we'll do it differently. Place one piece of tape on your base tape, make a handle, and label the tape A. Place a second piece of tape on top of the A tape, make a handle, and label this piece of tape B. Remove A and B together from the base tape. Quickly separate A and B and place one tape on one electroscope arm and the other tape on the other arm.

Demonstrate the procedure. Monitor groups as they prepare the tapes. Make sure students label the pieces of tape as instructed.

5

Move the two pieces of tape toward each other. What happens?

Make sure that students agree that the two pieces of tape moved toward each other.

6

How many types of interaction did you observe between the pieces of tape?

Help students to summarize that there were two types of interaction.

With the electroscope, we saw the tapes move in two different ways. How would you describe these two kinds of movement?

Help students to summarize that the unlike pieces of tape attract each other and the like pieces of tape repel each other.

The tapes begin to move without any apparent push. What is causing the force on the tapes?

You want students to realize that the charge on the tapes must be the cause of the force.

The charged tapes are exerting force on each other. This is called electrical force, or electrostatic force.

Summarize these points on the board.

Answer 6(c) in your groups and then we'll discuss your ideas.

Have groups provide their explanation for how the tapes became charged.

The forms of charge and the forces they exert

Unlike charges attract each other. Like pieces of tape repel each other.

These attractions and repulsions are caused by electrical force.

Extension: historical connections

7

In the sixteenth century, William Gilbert built the first electroscope, which he called the versorium. If you have access to the Internet, there are many sites which have information about Gilbert.

In sixteenth-century England, Queen Elizabeth I had a physician named William Gilbert who was very interested in magnetism because he thought that it might help his patients. Gilbert discovered that rubbing semiprecious stones would cause them to attract light objects. Like others of his time, Gilbert thought that static attraction was caused by magnetism. In his experiments, he found that some stones attracted better than others. To measure just how well these objects worked, he invented the first electrical instrument, the versorium. The versorium was the earliest version of today's electroscope.

Objects like paper and straw that were attracted to the versorium Gilbert called "electrics." Those that were not attracted, he called "nonelectrics." From these two words, Gilbert gets credit for making up the word electricity.

Let's use the electroscope to re-create Gilbert's experiment from so long ago. Prepare an A and a B tape and place them on different parts of your electroscope. You will use these tapes to test the objects I will give you.

If you are doing this part of the Investigation, hand out the light objects or pairs of materials that can be charged. Demonstrate how to use the electroscope and how to create charge on the pairs of materials. Circulate among the groups and comment on interactions students observe. Students can also test other objects besides those given out. Students may need to prepare more sets of tapes as the first tapes lose their charge.

4 Creating static charges: Part II

1. Separate the two pieces of clay so that they are once again about 16 cm apart. Position them so that the two free arms are parallel to each other.
2. Tear off a 15-cm long piece of tape and turn over about 1/2 cm at the end to make a handle.
3. Place this piece of tape sticky side down on the base tape.
4. Label the handle A.
5. Tear off another 15-cm long piece of tape and again make a handle.
6. Place this piece of tape sticky side down on the A tape, which is still stuck to the base tape.
7. Label the handle of this second piece of tape B.
8. Remove the A and B tapes, keeping them stuck together.
9. While holding them in the air, quickly tear apart the A and B tapes.
10. Place the A tape on one free arm of the electroscope.
11. Place the B tape on the last free arm of the electroscope.

5 Observing the interaction between the tapes: Part II

1. Line up the two electroscope halves so that the A and B pieces of tape are parallel to each other. Slowly move the two pieces of clay toward each other.
2. Observe and record what happens to the two pieces of tape.
3. Now see how the A and B tapes interact with the first two pieces of tape you prepared. Record what you observe.

6 What did you learn?

a. How many types of interactions did you observe between the pieces of tape?
b. The first tapes you prepared pushed each other away, or *repelled,* each other. This makes sense since you prepared the tapes in the same way. On the other hand, the A tape has one kind of charge and the B tape has a different kind of charge. Are the first tapes you prepared both A tapes or both B tapes? Explain how you figured this out.
c. Give your hypothesis for how the A and B tapes might have acquired different kinds of charge.

7 Extension: Using the electroscope to detect other charged objects

In sixteenth-century England, William Gilbert, the queen's physician, built the first electroscope. He noticed that the electroscope attracted lightweight objects. See if you can reproduce his results.

1. Remove the tape from your electroscope.
2. Prepare and label a fresh set of A and B tapes and place them on two arms anchored in one piece of clay.
3. Take light objects such as thread, small pieces of paper, and hair and slowly bring them close to both the A and B tapes.
4. Record your observations.

Learning connections

Use the attraction and repulsion of charged pieces of tape to strengthen students' understanding of the concept of force. As the concept of charge is presented, refer back to students' ideas about electricity from Investigation 6.1, if that is appropriate.

Challenge question

A coulomb of charge is equivalent to 6.25×10^{18} electrons. Calculate the charge on one electron in coulombs.

(Answer: 1.6×10^{-19} coulombs)

⧗ History of using scientific evidence

William Gilbert helped create the Scientific Revolution because he was among the first thinkers to test theories with experiments. His attempts to prove his ideas also led him to invent the versorium.

6 Example answers

6a. There are two types of interaction between the tapes.

6b. We tested the tapes with the electroscope. The tapes from Part 2 are the same as the B tape. The A tape is different.

6c. One kind of charge left one of the tapes and moved onto the other tape. This is why they are charged differently.

✋ More hands-on practice

Have students use the electroscope to test pairs of materials that can be charged, such as plastic combs rubbed with wool, glass rubbed with wool, and dry wood rubbed with glass. Have students use the electroscope to identify each item as an "A" material or a "B" material.

21.2 Coulomb's Law

Key Question: How strong are electrical forces?

In this Investigation students gain an understanding of the strength of electrical forces. They first use Coulomb's law to determine the theoretical force between two charged pennies. Then students charge balloons by rubbing them on their hair. The repulsive force between the balloons is found by hanging one on a string and using the other to lift it. Coulomb's law can then be used to determine the charge on the balloons.

$$F = K \frac{q_1 q_2}{r^2}$$

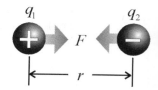

Reading Synopsis

Students read Section 21.2 Coulomb's Law before the Investigation.

The electrical force between two charged objects increases if they move closer together or if the amount of either charge increases. Coulomb's law relates the force between charges, their separation distance, and the magnitude of the charges. Electrical forces attract if the charges are opposite and repel if the charges are the same. Electrical forces are very strong, even when only small amounts of charge are present. We do not usually notice the strength of electrical forces because positive and negative charges in matter are not usually separated from each other.

The interaction between two charges is transmitted by the electric field. A charge creates an electric field around it. Another charge placed in the field experiences a force ($\vec{F} = q\vec{E}$). Electric field lines can be drawn to show the direction of the electric field. The field lines point from positive to negative, showing the force on a positive test charge.

The Investigation

Leading Questions
- What are the types of electrical charges?
- How do different types of electrical charges interact?
- What determines the strength of the electrical force between charged objects?
- What is Coulomb's law?

Learning Goals

By the end of the Investigation, students will be able to:
- Calculate the electrical force between charged objects.
- Compare electrical and gravitational forces.
- Calculate the charge on objects if the electrical force between them is known.

Key Vocabulary   force, charge, electron, proton, positive, negative, Coulomb's law, coulomb

Setup and Materials

Students work in groups of four or five at tables.

Each group should have:

- Two small balloons, such as those meant to be water balloons
- Meter stick
- Small ruler or stick
- Balance or digital scale
- Piece of light string or thread, approximately 50 cm long
- Piece of tape

Details

Time 🕐 One class period

Preparation ✏️

Assignments 📖 Section 21.2 Coulomb's Law in the **Student Edition** after the Investigation.

Skill Sheets 21.2 Coulomb's Law

Teaching the Investigation

1   Electrical forces in a penny
2   Charged balloons
3   Analyzing the data

Introduction

What does it mean that the electrical force between charges is very strong?

Electrical forces in a penny

Coulomb's law

$$F = K \frac{q_1 q_2}{R^2}$$

F is the force in newtons
q_1 and q_2 are the charges in coulombs
R is the distance in meters
K is a constant equal to 9×10^9 N-m^2/C^2

1 electron = 1.602×10^{-19} coulombs

1

The force between electrical charges is incredibly strong. Compared to gravity this force is roughly 1040 times as strong. It is difficult to imagine a number this large, a ne with 40 zeros after it. Why doesn't the electrical force pull everything together into a tiny ball if it is so strong?

> This is a good discussion point. The electrical force WOULD pull everything together with incredible forces if positive and negative charge ever got separated by very far, as the students will soon calculate in this investigation.

The reason things don't all clump together is that positive and negative forces are never allowed to separate by very far. The electrical force is so strong that it maintains nearly perfect balance between the positive and negative charge. Each atom has the exact same number of positive and negative charges. Electricity does not leak out of an open wire for the same reason. If electrons did leak out of a wire a charge separation would develop. The electrical force is so strong that large-scale charge separation is just not allowed to occur and therefore electrons do not leak out of an open wire.

What determines the strength and direction of the force between charged objects?

> The direction depends on the type of charges. Two positive charges repel each other. Two negative charges repel each other. A positive and a negative charge attract each other. The strength depends on the amount of charge and the distance between the charges (measured center to center).

Which law explains this relationship?

> Coulomb's law explains the relationship. Write the equation on the board, including the value of K.

In this Investigation you will be using Coulomb's law to determine the force between charged objects. First you will do some calculations to practice using Coulomb's law. Most objects contain equal amounts of positive and negative charge. What is the net charge of such an object?

> The net charge is zero.

Imagine that you have two pennies. You remove all of the electrons from penny number one and place them on penny number two. Which type of net charge does each penny have now?

> Penny one is positive, and penny two is negative.

A penny contains approximately 7×10^{23} electrons and an equal number of protons. A single proton or electron has a charge of 1.602×10^{-19} coulombs. How many coulombs of electrons and protons are in a penny?

> Write the conversion between coulombs and electrons or protons on the board. A penny has approximately 1.12×10^5 C of protons and electrons.

Calculate the force of attraction between the penny with the extra electrons and the penny that is missing its electrons. Imagine that the pennies are held 1 meter apart.

> The force is 1.13×10^{20} N.

A diesel locomotive weighs approximately 1,000,000 N. How many locomotives would it take to have a weight equal to the strength of the force between the pennies?

> It would take 1.13×10^{14} locomotives!

Objects become charged in everyday life, such as when you rub your socks on the carpet or when clothes brush against each other in the dryer. How much charge do you think is transferred from one object to another during these activities?

> The amount of charge that is transferred is very small, only a tiny fraction of the charge present in the objects.

UNIT 7: Electricity and Magnetism

21.2   Coulomb's Law

Question: How strong are electrical forces?

In this Investigation, you will:

1. Calculate the force between two charged objects.
2. Compare gravitational and electrical forces.
3. Use Coulomb's law to determine the charge on two objects.

All objects contain charges that exert forces on each other. The forces between like charges are attractive. The forces between opposite charges are repulsive. Objects normally contain equal numbers of positive charges (protons) and negative charges (electrons). However, it is possible to transfer electrons from one object to another. You may have seen the effect of this when you were removing clothes from a dryer and got a shock from static electricity. Static electricity is the movement of electrons with negative charge from one object (the clothes) to another (your hand).

In this Investigation, you will use Coulomb's law to calculate the force between two charged objects. You will then investigate the relationship between charge, distance, and force using charged balloons.

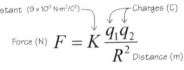

Coulomb's law

Constant $(9 \times 10^9 \, \text{N·m}^2/\text{C}^2)$ Charges (C)

Force (N) $F = K \dfrac{q_1 q_2}{R^2}$ Distance (m)

1   Electrical forces in a penny

Pennies are made of copper and zinc. A single penny is made of approximately 2×10^{22} atoms that contain 7×10^{23} electrons and an equal number of protons.

a. A single proton or electron has a charge of 1.602×10^{-19} coulombs. How many coulombs of protons and electrons are in each penny?

b. Imagine you have two pennies, A and B. You remove all of the electrons from penny A and place them on penny B. Is penny A positively or negatively charged? Is penny B positively or negatively charged?

c. Calculate the force of attraction between the two pennies if they are held 1 meter apart.

d. A diesel locomotive weighs approximately 1,000,000 newtons. Determine the number of locomotives necessary to have a weight equal to the strength of the force between the pennies.

e. You were probably surprised when you calculated the force between the pennies. What does your answer tell you about the amounts of charge normally transferred in activities such as brushing your socks on carpet or rubbing a balloon on your hair?

Teaching tip

The balloon activity works much better on a dry day when the humidity is low. If it is raining you may want to wait until another day. If it is warm and humid, you can do the activity in an air-conditioned room.

1   Example answers

1a. $(7 \times 10^{23}) \times (1.602 \times 10^{-19} \, \text{C}) = 112{,}140 \, \text{C}$
There are 112,140 coulombs of protons and 112,140 coulombs of electrons in each penny.

1b. Penny A would be positively charged and Penny B would be negatively charged.

1c. $d\left(F = K \dfrac{q_1 q_2}{R^2} \right)$

$F = \left(9 \times 10^9 \dfrac{\text{N·m}^2}{\text{C}^2} \right) \dfrac{112{,}140 \, \text{C} \times 112{,}140 \, \text{C}}{1 \text{m}^2}$

$F = 1.132 \times 10^{20} \, \text{N}$

1d. $(1 \text{ locomotive}/1{,}000{,}000 \, \text{N}) \times (1.132 \times 10^{20} \, \text{N}) = 1.132 \times 10^{14}$ locomotives

1e. The charges normally transferred in daily activities are very small compared to the force between the pennies.

Charged balloons

2 Now you will be using Coulomb's law to determine the net charge on two balloons. Each group should inflate two balloons. Label one A and the other B. Measure the mass of each balloon and record it in Table 1.

> If the balloons are small, they will be hard to inflate. Students should first stretch the balloons for several seconds.

Tie a piece of string around the knot of balloon A. Attach the other end of the string to the end of a ruler. Charge each balloon by brushing the end opposite the knot against your hair three times. Do not touch the charged part of the balloon after you rub it on your hair. Hold the ruler at arm's length so balloon A hangs straight down. Hold balloon B near the knot. Position it below balloon A and slowly move it upward. What happens?

> Demonstrate this procedure. Balloon A should move upward when balloon B is brought near it. The balloons are both negatively charged, so they repel each other.

Position balloon B so it forces balloon A to be horizontal and so the string is slackened. Measure the distance between the two locations where the balloons were charged.

> Demonstrate the procedure. It will take some practice for students to be able to quickly measure the distance without the balloons jumping around. They will not get a very accurate measure of the distance, but assure them that a rough value is fine.

Now repeat this procedure but rub each balloon on your hair 10 times.

Analyzing the data

3 How did the distance in trials 1 and 2 compare? Why?

> The distance was greater in trial 2 because the balloons had a greater amount of charge on them.

When the string becomes slack, its tension is zero. Which two forces on balloon A must be equal when this happens?

> The balloon's weight and the electrical force balance each other.

Calculate the weight of balloon A. Then use Coulomb's law to determine the net charge on each balloon for each trial. You can assume the balloons had an equal amount of charge. Then determine the number of excess electrons on the balloons in each trial.

> Depending on the math skills of your students, they may need help solving for the charge in Coulomb's law. If they have difficulty, work through an example on the board.

$$F = K\frac{1q_1q_2}{R^2} = K\frac{q^2}{R^2}$$

$$q^2 = \frac{F \times R^2}{K}$$

$$q = \sqrt{\frac{F \times R^2}{K}}$$

2 | Charged balloons

21.2 Coulomb's Law

1. Inflate two small balloons. Carefully label one balloon A and the other balloon B.
2. Use a balance or digital scale to find the mass of balloon A. Record the mass in kilograms in Table 1.
3. Cut a piece of string approximately 50 centimeters long. Tie one end of the string to the knot of balloon A. Tape the other end of the string to the end of a ruler.
4. Charge each balloon by brushing the end of the balloon opposite the knot against your hair (or the hair of a group member) three times. This causes the balloons to be negatively charged. Use the same method for charging both balloons.
5. Hold the ruler at arm's length with balloon A hanging as shown in the diagram at right. There should be no other objects near the balloon.
6. Hold balloon B near the knot. Position it below balloon A and slowly move it upward. What happens to balloon A? Why?
7. Move balloon B until it pushes balloon A into a completely horizontal position and the string slackens. This may take a few tries. Measure the distance between the two locations on the balloons where they were charged as shown in the diagram at right. Record the distance for trial 1 in Table 1.
8. Charge each balloon again by brushing it 10 times on your hair or a piece of fur.
9. Repeat steps 5 through 7 and record the distance for trial 2 in Table 1.

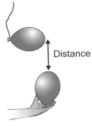

Distance

Table 1: Balloon charging data

Mass of balloon A (kg)	Trial	Distance (m)
	1	
	2	

3 | Analyzing the data

a. How did the distance in trials 1 and 2 compare? Why do you think this is?
b. When the interaction between the balloons causes the string to become slack (tension is zero), what two forces on balloon A must be equal?
c. Calculate the weight of balloon A.
d. Use Coulomb's law to calculate the charge on each balloon (in coulombs) for each trial. You can assume each balloon is charged the same amount.
e. Calculate the number of excess electrons on the balloons in each trial.

2 3 Example answers

Table 1: *Balloon charging data*

Mass of balloon A (kg)	Trial	Distance (m)
	1	0.05
0.0005	2	0.18

3a. The distance in trial two is a little more than three times the distance of trial one.

3b. The force of repulsion between the balloons must equal the force of gravity on balloon A.

3c. F_{weight} = mass × gravity
F_{weight} = 0.0005 kg × 9.8 N/kg
F_{weight} = 0.0049 N

3d. Trial 1
$$F = Kq^2/R^2$$
$$0.004\ n = (9 \times 10^9\ nm^2/C^2)q^2/(0.05\ m)^2$$
$$(0.004\ n)(0.05\ m)^2/(9 \times 10^9\ nm^2/C^2) = q^2$$
$$1.11 \times 10^{-15}\ C^2 = q^2$$
$$3.33 \times 10^{-8}\ C = q$$

Trial 2
$$F = Kq^2/R^2$$
$$0.004\ n = (9 \times 10^9\ nm^2/C^2)q^2/(.18\ m)^2$$
$$(0.004\ n)(.18\ m)^2/(9 \times 10^9\ nm^2/C^2) = q^2$$
$$1.44 \times 10^{-14}\ C^2 = q^2$$
$$1.2 \times 10^{-7}\ C = q$$

3e. Trial 1
1 electron = 1.602×10^{-19} C
$$\frac{1\ e}{(1.602 \times 10^{-19}\ C)} \times (3.33 \times 10^{-8}\ C) = \text{number of electrons}$$
2.08×10^{11} electrons

Trial 2
$$\frac{1\ e}{(1.602 \times 10^{-19}\ C)} \times (1.27 \times 10^{-7}\ C) = \text{number of electrons}$$
7.49×10^{11} electrons

Investigation 21.2 Coulomb's Law   **417**

21.3 Capacitors

Key Question: How does a capacitor work?

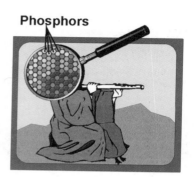

Phosphors

In this Investigation, students study the charging and discharging rates of a capacitor. They take readings at regular time intervals as a capacitor charges and discharges, and use the data to construct graphs. They discover that the relationship between voltage and time is not linear. Students then compare the charging rates when different resistors are used in the charging circuit. They see that the greater the resistance (lower current), the longer the time it takes for the capacitor to charge or discharge. The investigation reinforces the concept that electric charge is what carries electric current. The behavior of the capacitor can be understood in terms of filling up and emptying out the stored charge.

Reading Synopsis

Students read Section 21.3 Capacitors before the Investigation.

A capacitor is a device that stores charge. A capacitor can be charged with a battery or other source of current. The voltage across the terminals of a capacitor is proportional to the amount of charge stored and to the capacitance. The capacitance is the ratio of charge stored per volt and depends on the structure of the capacitor and the materials of which it is made. Capacitance is measured in farads.

The rate of charging and discharging of a capacitor depends on the current allowed to flow. The greater the current (low resistance) the faster the capacitor charges and discharges. The current and capacitor voltage vary with time. As a capacitor charges, the current decreases and the capacitor voltage increases. As a capacitor discharges, the current and capacitor voltage decrease.

The simplest type of capacitor is called a parallel plate capacitor. It is made of two metal plates that are close together. One plate becomes negative and the other positive.

The Investigation

Leading Questions
- What is a capacitor?
- What does it mean to say a capacitor is charged?
- How can a capacitor become charged?

Learning Goals
By the end of the Investigation, students will be able to:
- Explain how the voltage across a capacitor varies with time as it charges.
- Explain how the voltage across a capacitor varies with time as it discharges.
- Explain how the current in a circuit with a capacitor changes with time as it charges and discharges.
- Explain the relationship between the circuit resistance and the charging rate of a capacitor.

Key Vocabulary capacitor, charge, capacitance, farad, current, voltage

Setup and Materials

Students work in groups of four or five at tables.

Each group should have:

- Multimeter with red and black leads
- Two D-cell batteries
- Electric circuits kit components: two battery holders, two switches, wires
- Circuits RC pack: one 470 μF capacitor, one each of 22kΩ, 47kΩ, and 100 kΩ resistors
- Timer with AC adapter (or 9-volt battery)
- Graph paper

Details

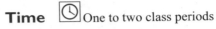

Time	One to two class periods
Preparation	Read Section 21.3 Capacitors in the **Student Edition** before the Investigation.
Assignments	Section 21.3 Capacitors in the **Student Edition** after the Investigation.
Skill Sheets	19.3A Ohm's Law 3.2 Making Line Graphs

Teaching the Investigation

1. Current and voltage for a capacitor
2. Setting up the experiment
3. Charging and discharging the capacitor
4. The effect of changing the charging or discharging current

Introduction

Capacitance and the units of capacitance

Capacitance is measured in Coulombs per volt. One Coulomb per volt is called one farad.

Current and voltage for a capacitor

Capacitor - a device that stores charge.

Capacitors   Symbol

   ———| |———

Setting up the experiment

The circuits we have constructed in the last few weeks contained only resistances. In resistor circuits the current stops flowing immediately when the voltage is removed. The subject of today's investigation is a device called a capacitor which holds charge, like a bucket holds water. If the voltage is removed from a circuit containing a capacitor, the current keeps going for a while, until the capacitor is empty of charge. Almost all electric appliances, including televisions, cameras, and computers, use capacitors in their circuits. Capacitors are also a useful tool for investigating the relationship between electric charge, voltage, and current.

Hold up a few capacitors or passing them around so students can take a look at them.

Capacitors come in all sizes and shapes. Some are tiny and some are large at least large for electronic components.A capacitor of one farad stores 1 Coulomb of charge when there is one volt applied to its two terminals. One farad is a very large amount of capacitance. Most of the capacitors you will find in circuits have values measured in microfarads or picofarads. A microfarad is a millionth of a farad ($1~\mu F = 10^{-6}F$) and a picofarad is a million-millionth of a farad ($1~pF = 10^{-12}F$).

Put these values up on the board as a quick review of scientific notation.

1 A capacitor is a device that stores charge. If you have ever used a camera with a flash, you have used a capacitor. You might have noticed that it takes time for the flash to be ready again after you use it. This is the time it takes for capacitor to become fully charged. In this Investigation you will be working with capacitors. It is very important that you follow the directions and connect the circuit components in the way you are instructed in order to avoid injury. Capacitors can be connected in circuits just as resistors can. Circuit diagrams are useful tools to show you the proper way to build a circuit.

Draw the symbols for a capacitor, resistor, battery, and switch on the board.

The current and voltage in a circuit with a capacitor is not as simple to determine as it is in a circuit containing only resistors. The current in or out of a capacitor depends on three things. They are the amount of charge already on the capacitor, the voltage applied to the capacitor by the circuit, and the resistance in the circuit. Do you think the current in a circuit with a capacitor is constant over time, or do you think it varies?

The current is not constant. Students will be determining how current varies with time in this Investigation.

2 Open your two switches. Build a circuit with the two open switches, two batteries, a 470 μF capacitor, and a 47 kΩ resistor. Set your meter to measure DC voltage and connect it across the terminals of the capacitor.

Sketch the circuit diagram on the board.

Which path will the current take if switch 1 is closed and switch 2 is open?

Current flows out of the positive terminal of the battery, through switch 1, through the resistor, and to the capacitor. The capacitor charges.

Which path will the current take if switch 1 is open and switch 2 is closed?

Current flows from the positive side of the capacitor, through the resistor, and to the negative side of the capacitor. The capacitor discharges.

21.3

UNIT 7: Electricity and Magnetism

Capacitors

Question: How does a capacitor work?

In this Investigation, you will:

1. Measure the voltage across a capacitor as it charges and discharges.
2. Construct a graph of voltage versus time for the capacitor.
3. Determine the effect of circuit resistance on a capacitor's charging rate.

A capacitor is a device that stores charge. Electric current flowing into a capacitor charges it. Once it is charged, current can flow out until the capacitor is discharged. If you have used a camera with a flash, you have used a capacitor. You might have noticed that after you use the flash once, you have to wait a few seconds to use it again. This is because it takes time for charge to build up in the capacitor. In this Investigation, you will charge and discharge capacitors in different circuits and measure the current and voltage produced.

1 Current and voltage for a capacitor

The symbol for a capacitor in a circuit and sketches of actual capacitors are shown in the diagram. Capacitors can be connected in series or parallel in circuits, just like resistors. Unlike resistors, the current and voltage for a capacitor have a more complex relationship. The current into or out of a capacitor depends on three things:

- The amount of charge already in the capacitor, measured by its voltage.
- The voltage applied to the capacitor by the circuit.
- Any resistance that limits the current flowing in the circuit.

2 Setting up the experiment

1. Open your switches if they are not already open. Build a circuit with the two open switches, two batteries, a 470 μF capacitor, and a 47 kΩ resistor (diagram at right).
2. Set your multimeter to measure DC voltage. Use it to measure the voltage across the terminals of the two batteries.
3. Connect the multimeter across the terminals of the capacitor as shown in the diagram.

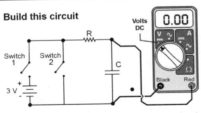

a. Describe the flow of current when switch 1 is closed and switch 2 is open. This is the *charging* circuit for the capacitor.

b. Describe the flow of current when switch 2 is closed and switch 1 is open. This is the *discharging* circuit for the capacitor.

⚠️ **Safety Note: DO NOT CLOSE SWITCH 1 AND 2 AT THE SAME TIME!** This would create a short circuit.

150

Teaching tip

If time is limited, you may want to have each group use only one resistor. Students can then share data between groups and compare the charging rates when the different resistors were used.

2 3 Example answers

2a. Current flows from the positive terminal of the battery, through switch 1, through the resistor, through the capacitor, and finally to the negative side of the battery. Current slows as the capacitor collects charge and finally stops when the capacitor voltage and battery voltage are equal.

2b. Current flows from the positive side of the capacitor around the circuit to the negative side of the capacitor. The capacitor quickly loses its charge when switch 2 is closed. When there is no voltage difference in the capacitor, current stops flowing.

Table 1 and 2: *Charging and discharging data*

Charging		Discharging	
Time (sec)	Voltage (V)	Time (sec)	Voltage (V)
0	0	0	2.77
5	.651	5	2.25
10	.993	10	1.86
15	1.34	15	1.53
20	1.64	20	1.29
25	1.88	25	1.07
30	2.09	30	.882
35	2.27	35	.739
40	2.42	40	.618
45	2.52	45	.511
50	2.62	50	.428
55	2.70	55	.349
60	2.77	60	.303
65	2.77		
70	2.77		

Charging and discharging the capacitor

Charging the Capacitor

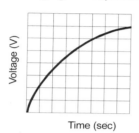

Discharging the Capacitor

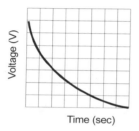

The effect of changing the charging or discharging current

The greater the resistance, the greater the time to charge the capacitor.

3 This Investigation will require you to work carefully with your group members to collect data. You will be measuring the voltage across the capacitor as it charges. Set your timer to stopwatch mode. You will be closing switch 1 and starting the timer at the same instant. As the capacitor charges, you will record the voltage across it every 5 seconds for the first 60 seconds. At 60 seconds, you will open switch 1 and then record the voltage 5 and 10 seconds after the switch is open (65 and 70 seconds on the timer). Make sure you know exactly what you will be doing before you start the timer and close the switch.

You may want to suggest students assign specific jobs to group members. One can operate the switch, one can read out the time every 5 seconds, and one can write down the voltages.

Now you will discharge the capacitor. Reset the timer. Close switch 2 and record the voltage across the capacitor every 5 seconds for 60 seconds. Keep the switch closed until the capacitor's voltage reaches zero.

Make sure all of the capacitors are fully discharged.

Use your data to make a graph of the capacitor's voltage versus time for charging and discharging the capacitor. Are the graphs linear?

The graphs should be exponential rather than linear. Prompt a discussion of why the graphs are not linear. When charging, charge quickly flows to the capacitor at first. As more charge builds up, the charges already on the capacitor repel the new charges entering the capacitor. When discharging, charges exit the capacitor at a high rate at first because the charges all repel each other. When the capacitor becomes discharged, there are fewer remaining charges to repel each other.

If you were to keep charging the capacitor for a long time, would the voltage level off or keep climbing?

The voltage would level off and reach a maximum equal to the combined voltage of the batteries.

If you wanted to fully charge the capacitor, would it take twice as long as it would to halfway charge the capacitor? Why?

It would take more than twice as long because the graph starts to level off as the rate of charge being added to the capacitor decreases.

What would a graph of current versus voltage look like for the charging and discharging capacitor?

The graph would start out steep and then level off for both cases. The shape is the same as that of the discharging voltage graph.

4 Use a free wire to fully discharge the capacitor. To do this, touch one end of the wire to one terminal of the capacitor and the other end of the wire to the other terminal of the capacitor. Close switch 1 and measure the time it takes the capacitor to charge and reach a voltage of 1.5 V. Once you record the time, use the wire to discharge the capacitor.

Make sure students carefully discharge the capacitor before going on.

Remove the 47 kΩ resistor and replace it with a 22 kΩ resistor. Then repeat with a 100 kΩ resistor. Make sure you discharge the capacitor each time.

Make sure all capacitors are discharged before the equipment is put away.

What effect did changing the resistor have on the charging time and the current?

The greater the resistance, the greater the time to charge the capacitor. The current was less when the resistance was greater, so it took longer for the charges to build up on the capacitor.

3 **4** **Example answers**

3a. Graphs:

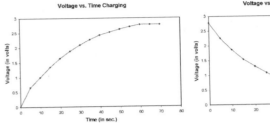

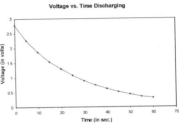

3 Charging and discharging the capacitor

Collecting data for this Investigation requires that you pay close attention and act quickly. Read the instructions below BEFORE you close the switch so you know exactly what you are doing.

1. Set your Timer to stopwatch mode and make sure switches 1 and 2 are both open.

2. Close switch 1 and start the Timer at the same time. Use Table 1 to record the voltage across the capacitor every 5 seconds for 60 seconds. Open switch 1 at the end of the 60 seconds and take two more data points at 5 and 10 seconds after opening the switch.

3. Reset the Timer. Close switch B to discharge the capacitor and start the Timer at the same time you close the switch. Use Table 2 to record the voltage across the capacitor every 5 seconds for 60 seconds. Open switch B once the capacitor's voltage reaches zero.

Table 1: Charging Data

Time (sec)	Voltage (V)

Table 2: Discharging Data

Time (sec)	Voltage (V)

a. Use Tables 1 and 2 to make a graph of voltage versus time for charging and discharging the capacitor.

b. Describe the shape of the graphs. Are they linear?

c. If you were to continue charging the capacitor for a long time, would the voltage reach a maximum value or continue to climb steadily? Your graph should help you answer this question.

d. Suppose you wanted to charge your capacitor to the full battery voltage. Would this take twice as long as the time to reach half the battery voltage? Why or why not?

e. Imagine you had measured the current in the circuit while charging or discharging the capacitor. Would the current have been constant or would it have changed over time? Sketch the shape of the current versus time graphs you think you would have measured during charging and discharging.

f. (Challenging) Both a capacitor and a battery can create voltage differences and drive electric current. Give at least three electrical differences between a capacitor and a battery.

4 The effect of changing the charging or discharging current

1. Touch a wire across the terminals of the capacitor with both switches open. This drains any charge immediately and restores the capacitor voltage to zero. Close switch 1 and use the Timer to measure the time it takes the capacitor to charge up to 1.5 volts. Record the time in Table 3.

2. Remove the 47 kΩ resistor and replace it with a 22 kΩ resistor. Repeat step 1.

3. Remove the 22 kΩ resistor and replace it with a 100 kΩ resistor. Repeat step 1.

Table 3: Capacitor charging times

Resistance (Ω)	Time to reach 1.5 V (sec)

a. Describe the effect of changing the resistor in the circuit.

b. How does the current compare for the three different resistors?

c. Explain why the time it took the capacitor to reach 1.5 volts was different for each of the three resistors. Use your knowledge of current, resistance, and capacitors.

151

3b. These graphs are not linear, they are curves.

3c. The capacitor can only gain the maximum voltage of the battery or batteries charging it. If our capacitor was allowed to charge for a little while longer, it would have reached a full charge eventually equal to the voltage of our batteries.

3d. It would take longer. The rate at which the capacitor gains charge decreases as its voltage increases. The time it would take to reach the first half of the battery voltage would be less than for the second half, because it would be charging at a faster overall rate for the first half.

3e. The current would not be constant. In the charging process the current in the circuit reduces quickly as the voltage gained by the capacitor increases. In the discharging process the current also reduces quickly because the voltage provided by the capacitor drops as current flows out of it. Both graphs would look basically the same.

3f. (1)Batteries are used to supply energy for use over a long period of time while capacitors are used for quick bursts of energy. (2) Batteries use chemical reactions inside them to store charge while most capacitors use metal plates that are charged from an external source. (3) Adding a fully charged capacitor to a circuit will reduce current to zero, while adding a fully charged battery will increase current.

Table 3: Capacitor charging times

Resistance (Ω)	Time to reach 1.5 V (sec)
47	18.31
22	8.64
100	37.6

4a. The greater the resistance of the resistor used in the circuit, the longer it takes for the capacitor to charge.

4b. The greater the resistance of the resistor used in the circuit, the less current available to charge the capacitor.

4c. The greater the resistance, the less current reaching the capacitor. Since current is a measure of charge flowing per second, a lower current means there is less charge per second available to charge the capacitor. When there is less charge available, it takes longer to charge the capacitor up to a specific voltage.

22.1 Properties of Magnets

Key Question: How do magnets interact with each other?

Almost every student has played with magnets many times in their life. However, few students have done any quantitative measurement with magnets. In this Investigation, students explore the effects of magnets on each other and determine quantitatively how far the magnetic force reaches. A compass is then used to sketch the magnetic field around a small ceramic magnet. Comparisons are made between electric fields and magnetic fields.

Reading Synopsis

Students read Section 22.1 Properties of Magnets after the Investigation.

If a material is magnetic, it has the ability to exert forces on other magnets or magnetic materials. All magnets have common properties. For example, they always have two opposite "poles," called north and south. If divided, each part of a magnet has both north and south poles—we never see an unpaired north or south pole.

When near each other, magnets exert magnetic forces on each other. The forces between magnets depend on the distance between them and the relative orientation of their poles. Two unlike poles attract each other and two like poles repel each other. The strength of the force between magnets decreases rapidly as the distance between the magnets increases.

Magnetic forces are carried through a magnetic field, similar to electrical forces. A magnet creates a magnetic field then the field exerts forces on other magnets. Magnetic field lines point from north to south and are drawn to show the shape of the magnetic field in a region.

The Investigation

Leading Questions
- What are the characteristics common to all magnets?
- How far does the magnetic force reach?
- How do you tell which direction a magnet will be pushed or pulled when it is near another magnet?
- What is magnetic force and how can it be measured?
- What is the magnetic field?

Learning Goals

By the end of the Investigation, students will be able to:
- Describe the properties of a permanent magnet.
- Describe and measure the forces that magnets exert on each other.
- Describe and sketch magnetic fields.

Key Vocabulary   magnet, magnetic force, north pole, south pole, compass, magnetic field

Setup and Materials

Students work in groups of four or five at tables.

Each group should have:

- 10 ceramic magnets (from the electric motor set)
- Navigational compass

Details

Time  One class period

Preparation Practice making magnetic field drawings using a compass

Assignments Section 22.1 Properties of Magnets in the **Student Edition** after the Investigation.

Skill Sheets Skill Builder: Significant Digits

Teaching the Investigation

1 Describing the forces that two magnets exert on each other
2 Determining how far the magnetic force reaches
3 Magnetic field lines
4 Interpreting the diagram

Introduction

Magnetism has fascinated people since earliest times. Until the period of the Renaissance, many people thought magnetism was a form of life because it could make rocks move. We know that magnets stick to refrigerators and pick up paper clips or pins. They are also part of electric motors, computer disk drives, burglar alarm systems, and many other common devices. but then anyone defined for me what it means to be magnetic?

If a material is magnetic, it has the ability to exert forces on other magnets or magnetic materials. If a material is magnetic, it has the ability to exert forces on magnets or other magnetic materials. Some materials are actively magnetic, and we call them magnets. Other materials are attracted to nearby magnets but do not show magnetism otherwise. Iron and steel are in the second category because they are attracted by magnets but are not themselves magnetic. A magnet on a refrigerator is attracted to the magnetic material (steel) that makes up the refrigerator's door. A permanent magnet is a material that keeps its magnetic properties, even when it is not close to other magnets. Bar magnets, refrigerator magnets, and horseshoe magnets are good examples of permanent magnets.

Describing the forces that two magnets exert on each other

1 In today's Investigation you're going to carefully observe and measure the interactions between two permanent magnets. The magnets we're going to use are small ceramic magnets that are very strong. This part of the magnet is the north pole, and this part, the south pole.

Show students the red, north face of the magnet, and the white, south face. Make sure that students have Investigation copies and two magnets per group.

Take two of the magnets and follow the instructions in Part 1 in the Investigation. Write down what you see happening.

The students should discover that the magnets repel each other when they have the same poles (N-N or S-S) facing each other, and that they attract when they have opposite poles (N-S) facing. A common student technique is to put two magnets on the table and slowly move one toward the other. For repelling poles, the loose magnet will usually spin around so that the opposite pole faces the approaching magnet. The students must be watchful when this happens, and note that the first effect is repulsion, followed by attraction only when the facing poles have become opposite. The experiment works better if both magnets are held in the fingers of opposite hands. The repulsion force is quite strong and easily felt.

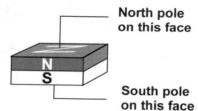

North pole on this face

South pole on this face

What did you observe?

Have several volunteers describe the interactions between the two magnets.

You can see that each magnet experiences a push or a pull. This means that there is a force exerted by each magnet on the other. This force, called the magnetic force, is much stronger than the force of gravity—as you can see because a very small magnet will pick something up even though Earth is pulling it down! Question 1(a) on the Investigation sheet asks you to write down a rule that clearly describes how magnets exert force on each other. Your rule should take into account your observations, and should use at least two of the following words: attract, repel, north, south, and pole.

Write a rule that describes how magnets affect each other.

Use at least two of the following words: attract, repel, north, south, pole

Two north poles will repel each other. Two south poles will repel each other. A north and a south pole will attract each other.

Permanent magnets

There are several materials that are used to make permanent magnets. Regular iron or steel can become a permanent magnet by being rubbed by another permanent magnet. This process is called magnetization. As you might guess, making a magnet this way does not produce a very strong magnet. Iron or steel magnets can also be the magnetized by forcing like pulls together. Not all alloys of steel can be magnetized. Stainless steel is not magnetic. Stainless steel contains elements like vanadium mixed in with iron and carbon. Vanadium atoms are larger than iron atoms and disrupt the structure of the steel in a way that leaves the steel non magnetic.

Many industrial magnets are made from at material known as Alnico. The letters stand for Aluminum-Nickel-Cobalt, the three elements used in Alnico. Alnico magnets are stronger than steel or iron magnets and harder to demagnetize. Alnico magnets are found in electric motors and also in electric guitar pickups.

The magnets used in the lab are made from a ceramic material. Ceramic magnets are much stronger than steel magnets and also much more difficult to de-magnetize. It takes a very strong magnetic field or high temperature to de-magnetize a ceramic magnet.

UNIT 7: Electricity and Magnetism

22.1   Properties of Magnets

Question: How do magnets interact with each other?

In this Investigation, you will:

1. See how two magnets affect each other.
2. Determine how distance affects magnetic forces.
3. Draw magnetic field lines around a bar magnet.

In this Investigation, you will experiment with permanent magnets to learn more about magnets, magnetic forces, and magnetic fields. The magnets you will use may not look like other magnets you have seen. The poles are on the opposite faces as shown in the picture at right.

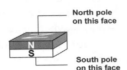

North pole on this face

South pole on this face

1   **Describing the forces that two magnets exert on each other**

1. Hold two magnets 1 centimeter apart with their south poles facing each other. What force do you observe between the magnets—attractive or repulsive?

2. Hold two magnets 1 centimeter apart with their north poles facing each other. What force do you observe between the magnets—attractive or repulsive?

3. Hold two magnets 1 centimeter apart so one north pole and one south pole face each other. What force do you observe between the magnets—attractive or repulsive?

a. Write down a rule that describes how magnets exert forces on each other. Your rule should take into account your observations from steps 1 through 3.

152

---

1   **Example answers**

1a. Two north poles repel each other. Two south poles repel each other. A north pole and a south pole attract each other.

Determining how far the magnetic force reaches

Students quantify the magnetic force by measuring distance.

2 In Part 2 of the Investigation, we are going to determine the distance over which the magnetic force acts. This is an important factor for machines that use magnets.

Following the instructions on your Investigation, hold one magnet next to the zero on the printed ruler, and place the other magnet on the right-hand side of the ruler. Slide the second magnet toward the first. When you see the first magnet move, stop sliding the second magnet and see how far apart they are by using the ruler. Be as precise as possible, and record the distance to the nearest 0.5 millimeter. Try the three orientations, N-S, N-N, and S-S, and determine if the force is the same or different for the different orientations. Try to use the same technique each time you measure the interactions between magnets.

Circulate among groups as they work on this part of the Investigation.

What did you observe? Was the distance the same in all three combinations?

Students should observe that the force is about the same for all three orientations, and therefore the magnetic force is the same strength whether the force is attractive or repulsive. Students sometimes have difficulty determining whether two measurements are significantly different from each other. If all of their averages are not the same, students may jump to the conclusion that one of the combinations of magnet poles yields a stronger force. You may wish to record each group's data on the board and compare the data, prompting a discussion of the technique used and the sources of the small differences in the measurements.

Suppose the magnet you move with your fingers causes the stationary magnet to move when the two are 33 millimeters apart. Now you place the magnets 35 millimeters apart and nothing happens. Do you think there is a magnetic force present? How would you explain what's going on?

There is still a magnetic force between the magnets, but it is too small to be detected. You may want to start a discussion on exactly what is being measured in this Investigation. Students should recall what they learned about friction forces in Section 6.2. The stationary magnet begins to move when the magnetic force exceeds the force of static friction between the magnet and the paper. If the Investigation were done on another surface, the distance measurements would be different.

22.1 Properties of Magnets

Determining how far the magnetic force reaches

How far does the magnetic force of a magnet reach? This is an important question concerning machines such as motors and generators that use magnets.

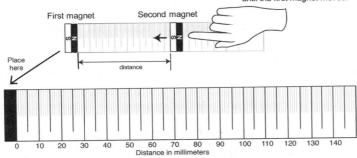

1. Place one magnet on the solid rectangle on the ruler above and slide a second magnet closer and closer until the first magnet moves. Practice the technique several times before recording data.

2. In Table 1 below, record the distance between the magnets when you first see movement. Measurements that are *precise* are exactly stated. For example, a single measurement of 32.5 millimeters is more *precise* than a measurement of 32 millimeters. Move the magnet slowly enough to make your distance measurements precise to 0.5 millimeters. Try each of the combinations of poles—north-north, south-south, and north-south.

3. For each combination, complete three trials, and average your three distances. Record the averages in Table 1.

a. When referring to many measurements of the same quantity, *precision* describes how close the measurements are to each other. Estimate the precision (in millimeters) of your measured magnet interaction distance using the largest difference between any one measurement and the average.

b. Look at your results and compare the average distances for the three combinations of poles. Are the attract and repel distances *significantly* different? In science, "significantly" means the differences are large compared to the precision of your measurement.

Table 1: Magnetic forces between two magnets

	North-South	South-South	North-North
Distance 1 (mm)			
Distance 2 (mm)			
Distance 3 (mm)			
Average distance (mm)			

153

2 Example answers

Table 1: *Magnetic forces between two magnets*

	North-South	South-South	North-North
Distance 1 (mm)	34.0	34.0	34.0
Distance 2 (mm)	33.0	33.0	32.5
Distance 3 (mm)	33.5	34.0	33.0
Average distance (mm)	33.5	33.7	33.2

2a. The precision is 0.8 mm.

2b. The distances are not significantly different. The largest difference between the averages is 0.5 mm. This is less than the precision of 0.8 mm.

Magnetic field lines

A compass can be used to determine the direction of the magnetic field.

Interpreting the diagram

Magnetic field lines point away from the north pole and toward the south pole of a magnet.

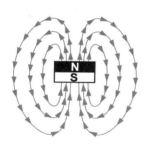

3 In this part of the Investigation, you will be drawing magnetic field lines. All magnets create a magnetic field in the space around them, and the magnetic field exerts forces on other magnets. A compass can be used to determine the direction of the magnetic field at any location around a magnet. A compass needle is simply a tiny bar magnet that is free to rotate. The magnetic field exerts a torque on the compass needle and causes it to turn until it points in the direction of the magnetic field. Moving the compass needle to different locations allows you to get an overall picture of the magnetic field in the region around the magnet. Stack 10 magnets to make a bar magnet. Follow the procedure in Part 3 of the Investigation to draw the magnetic field around the bar magnet.

Circulate around the room and assist students in getting started if necessary. Each group should position their compass at many locations (at least 50) to get a very accurate drawing of the magnetic field lines.

4 You should have seen a pattern emerge as you moved the compass around the paper. What pattern did you find?

The magnetic field points away from the north pole and toward the south pole. It is parallel to the bar magnet along the side and curves at the top and bottom.

How are magnetic field lines similar to electric field lines? How are they different?

Magnetic field lines exist in the space around magnets. Electric field lines exist in the space around charges. Magnetic field lines point away from the north pole and toward the south pole. Electric field lines point away from positive charges and toward negative charges. Magnetic field lines always form closed loops while electric field lines do not. This is due to the fact that magnetic poles always are present in pairs, while electric charges can exist in isolation. Both types of field lines are closer together where the field is stronger and farther apart where the field is weaker.

What configuration of electric charges would create field lines similar to those you drew for the bar magnet?

A positive charge next to a negative charge would create field lines of the same shape as the bar magnet. The north pole of the bar magnet corresponds to the positive charge (field lines pointing away) and the south pole corresponds to the negative charge (field lines pointing toward).

22.1 Properties of Magnets

3 Magnetic field lines

In this part of the Investigation, you will use a compass to discover the direction of the magnetic field around a permanent magnet. A compass is simply a small bar magnet mounted on a support that allows it to rotate. When placed near a magnet, a compass lines up with the magnetic field at that location.

1. Stack 10 magnets on top of each other with alternating poles touching each other. When you join magnets in this way, you create one large magnet with a north pole at one end and a south pole at the other end. A long narrow magnet of this shape is called a bar magnet.

2. Place the stack of magnets in the center of a blank sheet of paper as shown in the diagram at right. Trace the outline of the magnets and label the north and south poles.

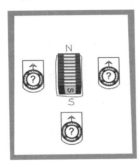

3. Place the compass on the paper beside the magnets as shown. The compass will turn until it is lined up with the magnetic field around the stack of magnets. Remove the compass and then make a small line (1 to 1 ½ centimeter long) on the paper in the location where the compass needle had been. Draw a small arrowhead on the end of the line where the red end of the compass needle points. You may want to set your compass on top of the line to check whether it was drawn accurately.

4. Repeat step 3, putting the compass in a different location on the paper. Do this in many locations (at least 50) all around the stack of magnets. You should see a pattern emerge among the lines you draw.

4 Interpreting the diagram

a. The pattern you drew shows the shape of the magnetic field around the stack of magnets. Connecting the small arrows together forms magnetic field lines. Describe the shape of the magnetic field around the stack of magnets.

b. Do the magnetic field lines point toward or away from the north pole of the stack of magnets?

c. You learned about *electric* field lines when studying positive and negative charges. How are magnetic field lines similar to electric field lines? How are they different?

d. Which of the following has electric field lines shaped similar to the magnetic field lines for a bar magnet?

- One positive charge.
- One negative charge.
- A pair of positive charges.
- A pair of negative charges.
- A positive charge next to a negative charge.

3 4 Example answers

Part 3 drawing:

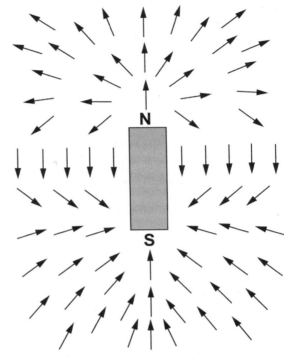

4a. The magnetic field points away from the north pole and toward the south pole of the magnet. The field lines are parallel to the magnet along the sides and curve at the ends.

4b. The field lines point away from the north pole of the stack of magnets.

4c. Magnetic field lines can be drawn around magnetic poles. Electric field lines can be drawn around electric charges. Magnetic field lines point away from the north pole and toward the south pole. Electric field lines point away from a positive charge and toward a negative charge.

4d. The magnetic field lines around a bar magnet are similar in shape to the electric field lines around a positive charge next to a negative charge.

22.2 Magnetic Properties of Materials

Key Question: How do magnets interact with different materials?

Many materials affect, and are effected by magnets. Other materials do not respond to magnets at all, at least in any way that is obvious to someone holding a magnet in their hand. In this Investigation, students study the interactions between magnets and various other materials. They determine which materials are affected by magnetic forces and learn whether nonmagnetic materials placed between two magnets change the strength of the force.

Reading Synopsis

Students read Section 22.2 Magnetic Properties of Materials after the Investigation.

The source of magnetic effects in matter is the motion of electrons. Diamagnetic materials contain equal numbers of electrons spinning in each direction, which results in a net magnetic field of zero. Individual atoms in paramagnetic materials are magnetic, but atoms are randomly arranged so the overall field is zero.

Ferromagnetic materials such as iron, nickel, and cobalt are highly magnetic. Individual atoms are magnetic and form groups called magnetic domains. Magnetic domains contain atoms with their fields oriented in the same direction. When placed in an external magnetic field, the domains grow and the object becomes magnetized.

Ferromagnetic materials that make good permanent magnets are called hard magnets. Domains in these materials tend to remain aligned. Materials that lose their magnetism quickly are called soft magnets. Both hard and soft magnets can become demagnetized through vibration or with heat.

The Investigation

Leading Questions
- What materials are affected by magnets?
- What do magnetic materials have in common?
- If a material is magnetic, how does it interact with a magnet?
- How do materials affect the force between two magnets? Does the force change as it passes through materials?

Learning Goals

By the end of the Investigation, students will be able to:
- Describe how a magnet is used to test between magnetic and nonmagnetic materials.
- Describe common magnetic materials.
- Describe the effect of nonmagnetic materials on the force between magnets.

Key Vocabulary   magnet, magnetic force, ferromagnetism, magnetic domain

Setup and Materials

Students work in groups of four or five at tables.

Each group should have:

- Two ceramic magnets (use the magnets from the electric motor set)
- An assortment of materials to test, such as a plastic spoon, wooden pencil, steel paper clip, fabric, scissors, aluminum foil, coins, a nail, or chalk

Details

Time ⏲ One class period

Preparation ✏ Prepare kits of materials to test for magnetic properties

Assignments 📖 Section 22.2 Magnetic Properties of Materials in the **Student Edition** after the Investigation.

Teaching the Investigation

1 Testing materials to see if they are affected by magnets
2 Ferromagnetism
3 Do nonmagnetic materials affect the magnetic force?

Introduction

Magnetism is caused by magnetic properties common to the particles in all atoms.

Testing materials to see if they are affected by magnets

1

Objects containing iron are attracted to magnets.

Ferromagnetism

2

Iron is a ferromagnetic material.

Ferromagnetism is caused by the ability of atoms of certain metals to align themselves in response to an externally applied magnetic field.

It seems unusual that magnets can attract and repel other magnets but can only attract objects such as steel paper clips and nails. This is true because magnetism is a property of the particles inside the atoms that make up matter. The source of nearly all magnetism in matter is the electrons in atoms. There are two ways in which electrons create magnetism. First, the electrons move around the nucleus and their motion makes the entire atom a small magnet. Second, electrons themselves act as though they were magnets. All atoms have electrons, so you might think that all materials should be magnetic. In fact, there is great variability in the magnetic properties of materials. The variability comes from the arrangement of electrons within atoms of different elements. The electrons in some atoms align to cancel out one another's magnetic field. In other atoms, the electrons align themselves so they strengthen the magnetic field.

In this Investigation we are going to examine a number of materials to see if they show magnetic properties. Some materials, although not magnets, are affected by magnets. These materials are called magnetic materials. Materials that are not affected by magnets are called nonmagnetic materials.

> Hand out the set of test materials. Remind students to identify the material the objects are made of as well as the name of the object itself. Students may need help in identifying materials from which their objects are made. For example, a paper clip looks silver but is actually made from steel.

What kinds of materials are affected by magnets?

> Help students to conclude that only the iron and steel (which has iron in it) objects tested are affected by magnets.

Look at your results again. Is any material repelled by a magnet?

> Students will have observed that only attraction occurs if one of the materials is not a magnet.

Why do you think this is so? Does anyone have a theory that might explain this result?

> Encourage students to come up with ideas that may explain this result. Students may recall the concept of charge polarization from Section 21.1 which explains why charged objects are attracted to neutral objects (such as a charged balloon sticking to a wall).

A small group of metals (iron, nickel, and cobalt) have very strong magnetic properties. These metals are called ferromagnetic materials. The magnetic fields of the electrons in the atoms of ferromagnetic materials do not all cancel. Atoms in these materials do not act independently, but line up with neighboring atoms in small groups called magnetic domains. The atoms in each domain are oriented so their magnetic fields point in the same direction, and each domain acts like a tiny magnet.

> Students will read about this topic in Section 22.2 and will further study the magnetic field of moving charges in Section 23.1.

Try the following experiment. Set one magnet up so it's north pole is facing sideways. Slowly slide another magnet toward the first magnet with its north pole facing the north pole of the first magnet. Carefully observe what happens to the first magnet has the second magnet approaches. Do not hold the first magnet. leave it free to slide around on the desktop.

> The two north poles normally repel each other however, if the first magnet is allowed to move, students should see that it spins around and becomes attracted to the second magnet.

This is essentially what happens inside a ferromagnetic material like iron. Iron atoms move around in response to the field of an external magnet. If a north pole is brought near iron, the atoms spin so their south poles face the external magnet. The iron is attracted to the magnet. If a south pole is brought near, the atom spin so their north pole faces the external magnet and again, the iron is attracted.

22.2　Magnetic Properties of Materials

Question: How do magnets interact with different materials?

In this Investigation, you will:

1. Determine the kinds of materials are affected by magnets.
2. Determine whether the magnetic force can be blocked by nonmagnetic materials.

In this Investigation, you will test various materials to determine how each is affected by a magnet. You will also test how nonmagnetic materials affect the strength of the force between permanent magnets.

1　Testing materials to see if they are affected by magnets

Some materials are affected by magnetic forces and some are not. You will test various materials to determine which of them respond to a magnet. Use one of your permanent magnets to test each object. An object is magnetic if you feel a perceptible force that attracts or repels either pole of your test magnet. An object is non-magnetic if you do not feel any perceptible force on your test magnet. If the object is magnetic, test it against both poles. Determine whether the object is always attracted, always repelled, or both attracted and repelled depending on whether you use the north or south pole of your test magnet. Record your data in Table 1.

Table 1: How different objects are affected by magnets

Object	Material composition	Attract	Repel	No effect

a. The word *magnetic* is used to describe things that are affected strongly by magnets. What common property do you see in the materials you observed to be magnetic?

b. Do the terms *repulsive* and *nonmagnetic* mean the same thing?

2　Ferromagnetism

The diagram at right shows a microscopic view inside a piece of iron. Iron is an example of a *ferromagnetic* material. The atoms in iron arrange themselves in magnetic domains. Each magnetic domain acts like its own tiny magnet. This occurs because the individual magnetic fields of atoms are aligned within a single domain.

In normal (unmagnetized) iron or steel, the magnetic orientation of domains varies randomly. On average, as many point one way as another way. When a magnet is brought near a ferromagnetic material, the domains close to the external magnet realign themselves as if they were each small magnets.

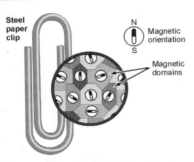

Steel paper clip

N ⬍ S Magnetic orientation

Magnetic domains

155

1　Example answers

Table 1: How different objects are affected by magnets

Object	Material composition	Attract	Repel	No effect
pencil	wood			×
paper clip	steel	×		
foil	aluminum			×
penny	copper			×
chalk	don't know			×
nail	iron	×		
spoon	plastic			×
key	brass			×
fabric	cotton			×

1a. The magnetic materials were steel and iron. Steel contains iron, so iron was present in both of the magnetic materials.

1b. Repulsive and nonmagnetic do not mean the same thing. The nonmagnetic materials did not feel a force at all from the magnet. If two objects repel, there is a force pushing them apart.

Do nonmagnetic materials affect the magnetic force?

3

In this part of the Investigation, we are going to see if nonmagnetic materials affect the magnetic force. Suppose I have two magnets and I measure the distance at which one can move the other to be 33 millimeters, as you did in Investigation 22.1. If I place a plastic ruler between the two magnets, do you think the ruler will affect the magnetic force? Will the distance be the same, more, or less? Or will the ruler completely block the force? What do you think?

> Students will have a wide variety of answers. Some will think the ruler will decrease the force or even totally block it. Students may have played with magnets by placing one on top of a table and moving it with a magnet held below the table. This may cause them to realize the force is not totally blocked by a nonmagnetic material.

Now you will answer this question. First measure the distance at which one magnet can move the other with nothing between the two. Then measure the distance with various nonmagnetic materials between the two magnets.

> Students should repeat the experiment testing the distance at which magnets interact but this time placing materials in between the magnets to see if the presence of a material affects the force between the magnets.

What could you tell about the force between two magnets as it passed through the non magnetic material? Did the force get stronger? Did the force get weaker? Was the force unchanged?

> Students should observe that nonmagnetic materials do not affect the distance at which one magnet can move the other. This supports the conclusion that the magnetic force passes through non-magnetic materials without being affected. The students should see some variability in the interaction distance however, the variability will not be consistently related to materials placed between the magnets. If they try many different magnets they will see that the variability is within the magnets theselves. The ceramic magnets used in these experiments typically have a magnetic field that varies by as much as 30 percent from magnet to magnet.

Actually, all materials show some kind of magnetic effect, but the magnetism in most materials is too weak to detect without highly sensitive instruments. In diamagnetic materials, there are equal numbers of electrons spinning in each direction. So while each individual electron is magnetic, the net magnetic field of each atom is zero. When placed in a region with a magnetic field, the motion of the electrons is disturbed, and these materials become very slightly magnetic. In paramagnetic materials, individual atoms are magnetic because the electron spins do not all cancel. However, the atomic magnets are randomly arranged so the overall magnetic field is zero. An external magnetic field causes the atoms to become partially aligned, and a paramagnetic material becomes weakly magnetic when near another magnet.

22.2 Magnetic Properties of Materials

③ Do nonmagnetic materials affect the magnetic force?

You may know that you can make a magnet move on the top of a table by moving a second magnet underneath the table. Maybe you wondered whether the table affects the strength of the magnetic force. In this part of the Investigation, you will find out if magnetic forces get weaker or stronger when they pass through nonmagnetic materials.

1. Choose three nonmagnetic materials from Table 1. List the names of these materials in the column headings of Table 2.

2. Place one magnet on the black rectangle on the ruler below and slide a second magnet closer and closer until the first magnet moves. When you first see movement, record the distance in the first column of Table 2. Repeat for a total of three trials and calculate the average distance.

3. Place each nonmagnetic material between the two magnets as shown in the diagram below and repeat the experiment.

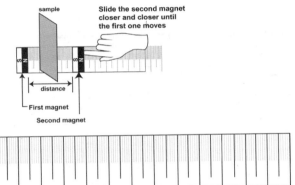

Table 2: Testing nonmagnetic materials

	No material between magnets	material: _____	material: _____	material: _____
Distance 1 (mm)				
Distance 2 (mm)				
Distance 3 (mm)				
Average (mm)				

a. Examine your results in Table 2. Does the strength of the magnetic force diminish by passing through any of the materials you tested?

---

③ Example answers

Table 2: *Testing nonmagnetic materials*

Object	No material between magnets	material: paper	material: plastic	material: wood
Distance 1 (mm)	33.0	32.5	33.0	32.5
Distance 2 (mm)	33.5	33.0	33.0	33.0
Distance 3 (mm)	33.0	33.0	33.5	33.5
Average (mm)	33.2	32.8	33.2	33.0

3a. The strength of the magnetic force does not diminish when a nonmagnetic material is placed between the magnets.

22.3 The Magnetic Field of the Earth

Key Question: How do we use Earth's magnetic field to tell direction?

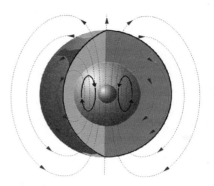

Like many other planets, Earth has a magnetic field, as if its core contained a huge magnet. In this Investigation students use a compass to explore the magnetic field of the Earth. They observe how the magnetized needle of a compass aligns with the north-south orientation of the Earth's magnetic field. The magnetic field of the Earth is not exactly aligned with the geographical north and south poles. Students research the magnetic declination in their area. Students also investigate how materials containing iron can shield out the magnetic field of the Earth, making a compass unreliable for telling direction.

Reading Synopsis

Students read Section 22.3 The Magnetic Field of the Earth after the Investigation.

Like many other planets, Earth has a magnetic field, as if its core contained a huge magnet. Magnetite and lodestone are naturally occurring magnetic rocks. A compass works because a magnetized needle that is free to rotate will align itself with the magnetic field of the Earth. The geographic north pole of the Earth is actually a south magnetic pole.

The magnetic field of the Earth comes from the circulation of electric currents deep in the molten iron core of the planet. Over the history of the planet, the magnetic field has reversed itself on average every 500,000 years. The magnetic poles of Earth do not align exactly with the geographic poles. The difference between the orientation of the Earth's magnetic field and the geographic direction of north is called declination. In North America, the declination may be up to 16 degrees, with magnetic north slightly west of geographic north.

The Investigation

Leading Questions
- In which direction does a compass needle point?
- What is magnetic declination?
- Can any other materials affect a compass?

Learning Goals
By the end of the Investigation, students will be able to:
- Explain how a compass works.
- Read and use a compass.
- Explain how magnetic declination affects a compass.
- Identify materials that will affect a compass magnetically.

Key Vocabulary
magnet, magnetic field, north pole, compass, south pole, magnetic field lines, magnetic declination

Setup and Materials

Students work in groups of four or five at tables.

Each group should have:

- Navigational compass
- A magnet (from the electric motor set)
- A steel bucket or baking pan

Details

Time 🕐 One class period

Preparation ✏️

Assignments 📖 Section 22.3 The Magnetic Field of the Earth in the **Student Edition** after the Investigation.

Skill Sheets 22.3 Magnetic Earth
Skill Builder: Internet Research Skills

Teaching the Investigation

1 Introduction
2 Why a compass works
3 Reading a compass
4 Declination
5 The effect of magnetic materials on a compass

Introduction

Compass - has a magnetized needle that aligns with the magnetic field of the Earth.

Why a compass works

[1]

Earth's magnetic field is created by electric currents that are driven by its rotation as it revolves around the sun.

Reading a compass

Compass bearing - a direction referenced to north.

Can anyone described to me how a compass works?

    Distribute the compasses and review the parts and the use of a compass.

A compass works because it contains a magnetized needle that is free to rotate. The needle rotates in such a way as to align with the magnetic field of the Earth. The north pole of a magnet is actually defined as the end that points north when the magnet is made into a compass. Today's Investigation has two parts. One part is to review how a compass works and test situations in which a compass may not work reliably. The other part of the Investigation is research and could save your life if you are ever lost in the wilderness and need to use a map and compass to find your way to safety.

Can anyone suggest an experiment which proves that the action of a compass is based on magnetism?

    Get a dialog going. The suggestion you wish to capitalize on is to use a magnet and see if a compass responds to a magnet in the same way that it responds to the Earth. If a magnet deflects a compass needle, then it is a reasonable proof that the magnetism of the Earth is the force that causes a compass needle to point north. Have the students do the experiment to see that the compass needle follows an external magnet. They should quickly determine that the north-pointing needle of a compass points toward the south pole of an external magnet.

The magnetic field of the Earth is created by electric currents, not by a giant magnet in the core of the planet. The electric currents are driven by the Earth's motion through space as it orbits the sun. A tremendous flow of electrical particles is constantly streaming away from the sun. As Earth moves through this giant electrical current, some of the current is intercepted by the planet itself. This electrical current is what ultimately powers the magnetic field of the planet.

It has been a while since we used a compass so let's review how it works. The base of your compass has an arrow that is used to tell direction. On the dial of the compass is a rotating ring that can be turned to align the degree marks on the ring with the north-pointing needle of the compass. To find the direction to anything, like the door, start by pointing the arrow at the object.

    Students should rotate their compasses until the arrow points to the door

Rotate the adjustable ring until the N mark at 0 degrees is aligned with the north pointing tip of the compass needle, which is painted red or black. You should hold the compass firmly to keep the arrow on the base pointing at the door while you rotate the adjustable ring.

    Students should hold their compass so the arrow on the base remains pointing at the door while they adjust the ring to align north on the ring with the north tip of the compass needle.

You can now use the arrow on the base of the compass to read the compass bearing to the door. A direction in degrees referenced to north is called a compass bearing.

    Have students read the compass bearings they measure. They all will be slightly different because the students are in different places relative to the door. Help groups who have gotten compass bearings that do not seem possible. Repeat the exercise choosing a distant object, such as a tree or building you can see through the window.

UNIT 7: Electricity and Magnetism

22.3 The Magnetic Field of the Earth

Question: How do we use Earth's magnetic field to tell direction?

In this Investigation, you will:

1. Research the local magnetic declination and use it to determine true north from a compass.
2. Determine the sensitivity of a compass to nearby magnets and magnetic materials.
3. Explain why compasses do not work near the north and south poles.

Like many other planets, Earth has a magnetic field. Earth behaves as if its core were a huge magnet. The planet's magnetic field is not strong compared with the magnetic field near a small permanent magnet. However, Earth's magnetic field fills a tremendous volume of space around and within the planet. This Investigation explores some useful characteristics of Earth's magnetic field.

1 Why a compass works

A compass needle is a magnet that is free to spin until it lines up with the local magnetic field. The origin of the terms "north pole" and "south pole" of a magnet come from the direction in which a compass needle points. The end of the needle that pointed to the geographic north was called the north pole of the magnet and the end that pointed to the geographic south was called the south pole. The names were decided before people understood fully why a compass needle worked.

a. If the magnetic north pole of a compass needle points toward Earth's geographic north pole, what is the orientation of Earth's magnetic field? Is the geographic north pole of the planet a magnetic north or a magnetic south pole?

b. The north pole of a compass needle always points toward which pole of a permanent magnet?

2 Reading a compass

Around the needle of the compass is a rotating scale that has degrees marked clockwise from zero to 360. Zero degrees is straight north. Straight south is 180 degrees. East is 90 degrees, and west is 270 degrees. A compass *bearing* means direction in degrees relative to north. For example, a *bearing* of 45 degrees is a direction northeast of where you are.

The arrow on the base of the compass indicates the direction to go when you know the compass bearing. With the compass in your hand, rotate the base until the arrow aligns with the bearing you want to travel. Next, rotate the entire compass until the north end of the needle is aligned with the north arrow *inside* the compass dial. The arrow on the base now points in the direction you wish to go.

Using a compass

Arrow on base
Adjustable ring
North arrow in dial
Compass needle

Set your bearing
Rotate the compass until its needle aligns with north arrow in dial
The arrow on the base points in the direction to go

157

Teaching tip

The earliest written description of the properties of magnets to point direction comes from Chinese literature. Stories written in 220 B.C. tell of Chinese "magicians" who carved the magnetic mineral lodestone into a spoon with a large bowl and a thin handle. By balancing the spoon on the round part of its bowl, the handle was free to rotate and point to the north. Compasses appeared in Europe much later, and by 1200 A.D., the property of a compass needle to point north was widely used for navigation. But why? What influence acted to turn a compass needle to the north? People used compasses for another 400 years before a brilliant and clever fellow named William Gilbert demonstrated that the Earth was a magnet.

A compass needle is free to rotate in only one plane. When held horizontal, a compass shows the horizontal component of the magnetic field. A compass held vertically will show that the field also points down in the northern hemisphere and up in the southern hemisphere (Figure 22.14, page 449 of the text). At the north pole, a compass needle points straight down, and at the south pole, the needle points straight up. By the seventeenth century this was known to explorers who traveled the Earth.

In 1600, William Gilbert, physician to Queen Elizabeth I of England, published a remarkable book titled *De Magnete*. In his book, Gilbert demonstrated by careful experiment and rigorous analysis that the Earth itself was a large magnet and that magnetism was the force that motivated compass needles. Gilbert carved a magnetic lodestone into a sphere and demonstrated that the behavior of a compass around his spherical lodestone was exactly the same as a compass around the sphere of Earth. You can achieve a similar result with your students by embedding a powerful ceramic magnet in a Styrofoam sphere you can purchase from a hobby store. A ceramic magnet two cubic inches in volume gives excellent results with a sphere that is six inches in diameter.

1 Example answer

1a. The south magnetic pole of the Earth's magnetic field is at the north geographic pole.

1b. The north pole of a compass needle always points toward the south pole of a permanent magnet.

Declination

Declination - the amount of misalignment between magnetic south and geographic north.

Declination depends on where you are located on Earth's surface.

The effect of magnetic materials on a compass

It is helpful to try magnets of differing strengths so students can observe a range of effects.

Ceramic magnets work well and are relatively easy to obtain.

Old speakers contain strong magnets that can produce dramatic effects on the compass.

"Rare-earth" magnets like those made of neodymium-iron-boron can be expensive but extremely powerful.

3

In many references, magnetic south pole is referred to as 'magnetic north pole' because it is located at the geographic north pole. This terminology can be confusing because we know that opposite poles attract. The north pole of a compass needle is in fact the north end of a bar magnet. Therefore, it is best to use the term magnetic south pole as the point to which the north end of a compass needle is attracted. The magnetic field of the Earth changes over time and is not exactly aligned with the geographic north-south axis of the planet. The amount of misalignment between "magnetic" south and "geographic" north is called declination. The declination can be as great as 30 degrees! A declination of 30 degrees east means the north-pointing needle of a compass points 30 degrees east of true north. Declination also depends on where you are. Some areas on the Earth's surface have high concentrations of magnetic rock that create deviations in the magnetic field.

4

For homework, research the magnetic declination for our area. You will need this information to answer question 3b of the Investigation.

You already discovered that a magnet can affect the reading of a compass. For the next part of the Investigation, I want you to determine how far away from a magnet the compass must be before you can trust it to point north.

> Help the students to design and set up experiments that test the interaction between the compass and one of the small permanent magnets that comes with the electric motor. Students may also wish to see if combining two or more magnets causes the magnetic field to extend farther, and affect a compass at a greater distance.

I have a steel bucket that is magnetic, which you can see because it sticks to this magnet. I also have a plastic bucket that is not magnetic.

> Demonstrate that the steel bucket is magnetic and the plastic bucket is not magnetic.

Suppose I were to put the compass in each of these buckets. Do you think the compass will still be able to point north?

> Start a dialog. Most students recognize that the plastic bucket should not affect the needle of the compass because plastic is a nonmagnetic material and they tested materials in a previous Investigation.
>
> The steel bucket is magnetic and therefore can respond to a magnetic field, such as the field of Earth.

Let's do a test. I think the deeper in the bucket I hold the compass, the more of the Earth's magnetic field is blocked. There must be a certain depth below which the compass cannot feel enough of the Earth's magnetic field to maintain its north-pointing orientation.

> Help groups to do the experiment.

If the bucket shields out the magnetic field of the Earth, do you think it can also shield out for the effect of a permanent magnet? Propose an experiment to test this hypothesis.

> Discuss with students how to do such an experiment. The experiment is easy to do and should be done by each group of students. Have students document the procedure they used to make the test and also record their observations carefully.

22.3 The Magnetic Field of the Earth

3   Declination

Earth's magnetic field is not lined up perfectly along the north-south axis of the planet. That means a compass does not point directly to the geographic north pole. Depending on where you are, a compass will point slightly east or west of true north. The difference between the direction a compass points and the direction of true north is called *magnetic declination*. Magnetic declination is measured in degrees and indicated on topographical maps.

a.   Research the magnetic declination for your area.

b.   If the magnetic declination were zero, straight east would be a bearing of 90 degrees on a compass. What compass bearing will you set if you wish to go straight east but need to correct for the local magnetic declination?

4   The effect of magnetic materials on a compass

The needle of a compass aligns itself with the magnetic field in its vicinity, whether the field comes from a nearby magnet or from Earth. For this reason, magnets and magnetic materials can interfere with navigation when you are using a compass. In the next part of the Investigation, you will determine how sensitive a compass is to external magnets and magnetic materials.

1.   Place the compass on a large flat surface such as a floor or table. Rotate the ring on the compass to a bearing of zero degrees (north). Rotate the whole compass until the direction arrow and compass needle are both aligned with north.

2.   Obtain one of the small permanent magnets that come with the electric motor experiment. How close can you bring the permanent magnet before the compass needle is deflected from north? You should try the experiment with several different orientations of the magnet to see which one has the largest effect on the compass needle.

3.   Obtain a steel bucket or baking pan. The bucket should be magnetic steel (you can test it with your permanent magnet). Orient the compass so that it is aligned with north and slowly lower it into the bucket. As you lower the compass, rotate it gently back and forth to see whether the needle stays aligned with north. At some point the steel will shield out enough of Earth's magnetic field that the compass will no longer be able to stay in alignment with north.

5   Reflecting on your observations

a.   How close did the magnet have to be before it affected the compass? There are magnets in many devices such as television sets, electric motors, and computers. How far away from these devices must you be before you can trust the reading from a compass?

b.   The bodies of automobiles are made of magnetic steel yet you can buy a compass for your car. Some cars even have electronic compasses built in. Based on your observations, would you believe the directions from a compass inside a car?

c.   A compass does not work close to Earth's geographic north or south poles. Draw a sketch showing the Earth's magnetic field and use the drawing to explain why compasses have this limitation.

3a. Boston, MA -16°/Washington, DC -11°/Atlanta, GA -4°/Chicago, IL -3°/Dallas, TX +5°/San Diego, CA +13°/Seattle, WA +20°

3b. Boston, MA 106°/Washington, DC 101°/Atlanta, GA 94°/ Chicago, IL 93°/Dallas, TX 85°/San Diego, CA 77°/Seattle, WA 70°

5a. The magnet was about 20 centimeters away when it began to affect the compass. Since this wasn't a very strong magnet it would seem safe to double this distance to at least 40 centimeters to keep the compass reading from being altered by more powerful magnets in appliances.

5b. It would seem the metal may affect the compass, but the compass would not be completely shielded from Earth's magnetic field like in the baking pan.

5c.

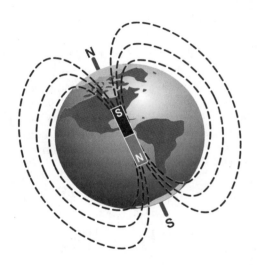

The needle of a compass aligns with the magnetic field lines of Earth's magnetic field. At the poles, there are no lines of force to align with. Since there is not enough magnetic force to move the compass' needle, it will not point in any direction that is useful.

23.1 Electric Current and Magnetism

Key Question: Can electric current create a magnet?

Magnetism is fundamentally created by moving charge, which is electric current. Even the magnetism of a permanent magnet comes from moving electrons inside an atom. An electromagnet is a device that creates magnetism with electric current, usually in a coil of wire. A simple electromagnet can be made with a coil of wire, a nail, and a battery. In this Investigation, students build their own electromagnets and compare them to permanent magnets. They test the strength of their electromagnets by picking up paper clips, and determine the effect of changing the current and the number of turns on the electromagnet's strength.

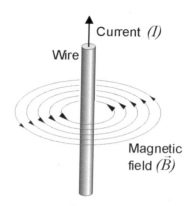

Current *(I)*

Wire

Magnetic field *(B)*

Reading Synopsis

Students read Section 23.1 Electric Current and Magnetism after the Investigation.

A wire carrying current creates a magnetic field that circles the wire in a direction given by the right hand rule. Parallel wires carrying current in the same direction attract each other. Parallel wires carrying current in opposite directions repel each other. Atomic-scale electric currents create the magnetism in permanent magnets.

Magnetic fields exert forces on moving charges. The force on a moving charge, or current flowing in a wire is perpendicular to both the direction of current and to the direction of the magnetic field. The unit of magnetic field strength is the tesla (T). A magnetic field of one tesla exerts a force of one newton on one meter of wire carrying a current of 1 amp. The direction of the force is given by the right-handed rule. Formulas are presented for the magnetic field near a wire and at the center of a coil.

The Investigation

Leading Questions
- How it is magnetism created?
- Do magnets exert forces on moving currents?
- What is the unit of magnetic field and what does it mean?
- What is the relationship between current and magnetic field?
- Do permanent magnets and electromagnets create the same kind of magnetism or is there a difference?

Learning Goals
By the end of the Investigation, students will be able to:
- Build an electromagnet.
- Explain how electric current affects the strength of the magnetic field in an electromagnet.
- Compare permanent magnets and electromagnets.

Key Vocabulary   permanent magnet, current, electromagnet, right-hand rule

Setup and Materials

Students work in groups of three to five at tables

Each group should have:

- Two ceramic magnets (from the electric motor set)
- Three meters of magnetic wire, 24 gauge
- Sandpaper
- Two galvanized nails 7 centimeters long
- Electric circuits kit
- Two D-cells
- The assortment of magnetic and nonmagnetic materials used in Investigation 22.2
- Multimeter with red and black leads
- 100 steel paper clips
- Graph paper
- Pencils
- Ruler or straightedge

Teacher should have:

- A working electromagnet

Details

Time	⏰	Two class periods
Preparation	🖊	Cut pieces of magnet wire for each group
	🖊	Prepare a demonstration electromagnet
Assignments	📖	Section 23.1 Electric Current and Magnetism in the **Student Edition** after the Investigation.
Skill Sheets		23.1 Magnetic Fields and Forces

Teaching the Investigation

1. Build an electromagnet
2. Compare electromagnets and permanent magnets
3. The right-hand rule
4. What happens to the strength of an electromagnet when you increase the current?
5. What did you learn?

Introduction

For a long time, people thought electricity and magnetism were unrelated. What does the current flowing in a wire have to do with a magnet attracting or repelling another magnet? The breakthrough discovery was made in front of a class of students. In 1819, Hans Christian Oersted, a Danish professor, placed a compass needle near a wire through which he could make electric current flow. When the switch was closed, the compass needle moved just as if the wire were a magnet. We now know that magnetism is created by the motion of electric charge and that electricity and magnetism are really two forms of the same basic force.

Sketch the drawings in figures 23.1 and 23.2 on page 456 of the text.

Wires carrying electric current create magnetic fields. Consider the following experiment. A long straight wire is connected to a battery with a switch. The wire passes through a board with a hole in it. Around the hole are compasses. When the switch is off, the compasses all point north. When the switch is closed, the compasses point in a circle. The compasses stay pointing in a circle as long as electric current is flowing in the wire. If the current stops, the compasses return to pointing north again. If the current is reversed in the wire, the compasses again point in a circle, but in the opposite direction. Actually, it takes a lot of current to make a compass needle move however we can use less current by making the same wire go round and round in a coil. Today's investigation is about making magnets with electricity using coils of wire.

Build an electromagnet

Electromagnet: a magnet that is created when there is current in a coil of wire.

1

An electromagnet is a device that creates magnetism with electric current, usually in a coil of wire. Electromagnets normally have the wire wrapped around a core of iron or steel. Can anyone guess why hired or steel is important?

Define electromagnet on the board. Discuss with students that iron and steel, as they previously determined, are magnetic materials. The presence of iron ore steel amplifies the magnetic field created by the coil of wire. The magnetic amplification permits lower currents to make higher magnetic fields.

The first step of our Investigation is to build a simple electromagnet. Each group will make an electromagnet following the instructions in the Investigation guide. Work carefully so your coil is neat and tightly wound. You can make more than one layer of wire on top of the nail.

Show students the demonstration electromagnet you prepared ahead of time.

After you make the coil, sand the ends of the wire. It has a coating on it that needs to be removed so that you can have a good electrical connection. Do not connect the batteries yet.

Check on each group's work.

How can an electric current create a magnet?

Students perform tests to show that an electromagnet acts like a permanent magnet.

2

This coil certainly doesn't look much like the permanent magnets we used in other Investigations. Determine two tests you can do to show that the electromagnet acts like a permanent magnet. Work on this assignment with your group. Then perform your tests and record your data. When you are ready to use your electromagnet, you will have to connect the wires to the battery. The electromagnet will get hot quickly, so only leave the battery connected for short periods of time.

Students may choose to study interactions of the coil of wire with a permanent magnet, with another electromagnet, or with magnetic and nonmagnetic materials. Students may also wish to test the coil to see how it acts with the current on and off. They should demonstrate that the coil exerts magnetic forces on another magnet, that it has both a north and a south pole, and that it attracts magnetic materials, such as a paper clip. If an electromagnet is not working, make sure that the ends are sanded well enough to get a good connection. Make sure students disconnect their batteries as soon as they are done using their electromagnet.

23.1 Electric Current and Magnetism

UNIT 7: Electricity and Magnetism

Question: Can electric current create a magnet?

In this Investigation, you will:

1. Build an electromagnet.
2. Determine the location of the north and south poles of an electromagnet.
3. Measure the electromagnet's strength as the current is varied.

A magnet that creates its magnetic field from the flow of electric current is called an *electromagnet*. The simplest electromagnet uses a coil of wire often wrapped around a piece of iron or steel. The iron or steel concentrates the magnetic field created by the current in the coil.

By controlling current, you can easily change the strength of an electromagnet or even turn its magnetism on and off. Electromagnets can also be much stronger than permanent magnets when there is a great deal of electric current. For these reasons, electromagnets are widely used. Stereo speakers, toasters, doorbells, car alternators, and power plant electrical generators are just a few of the many devices that use electromagnets.

◆**Safety Tip: Disconnect your electromagnet when not in use as the wire and batteries get hot quickly.**

1 Build an electromagnet

1. Wrap a nail tightly with wire as shown at right. Leave 30 centimeters of uncoiled wire on each end of the nail. Count the number of turns you wrap and write the result here.

   Turns: _____

   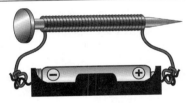

   Make sure your wire turns are neat, tight, and evenly spaced or the electromagnet may not work efficiently. This is your electromagnet coil.

2. Remove any insulation or varnish from the two free ends of the wire.
3. Do not connect the wires to the battery yet.

2 Compare electromagnets and permanent magnets

a. The electromagnet certainly does not look much like the permanent magnets you are familiar with. Using what you know about magnets, think of at least two tests to show that your electromagnet acts like a permanent magnet. Describe your two proposed tests.

b. Connect your electromagnet to the battery and perform the two tests you described in the previous step of the Investigation. Record your observations.

   ◆**Safety Notes: Do not leave the battery connected for an extended period of time because the wire will get hot.**

a. Does the electromagnet act like a permanent magnet? Explain.

159

---

2 3 Example answers

2a. Test one: Hold a permanent magnet up to each end of the electromagnet. The permanent magnet and electromagnet should sometimes attract and sometimes repel, depending on which poles are positioned toward each other.

Test two: Hold various magnetic and nonmagnetic materials up to the electromagnetic. The magnetic materials should be attracted and the nonmagnetic materials should show no effect.

2b. Test one: The north pole of the permanent magnet attracted the right end of the electromagnet and repelled the left end. The south pole of the permanent magnet attracted the left end of the electromagnet and repelled the right end.

Test two: A paper clip was attracted to both ends of the electromagnet. A pencil and a plastic spoon showed no effect.

2c. The electromagnet does act like a permanent magnet. It can both attract and repel a permanent magnet and it attracts magnetic materials.

3a. The north end of the electromagnet is attracted to the south pole of the permanent magent.

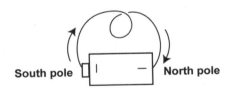

South pole   **North pole**

3b. Reversing the current reversed the poles.

3c. The right-hand rule gave the same result as using the permanent magnet.

The right-hand rule

N

What happens to the strength of an electromagnet when you increase the current?

How many paper clips can the electromagnet pick up?

What did you learn?

How did the current affect the strength of the electromagnet?

How did the number of turns of wire affect the strength of the electromagnet?

3 You may have already identified which end of your electromagnetic coil is the north pole and which end is the south pole. If you have not already done this, use a permanent magnet to determine the location of your electromagnet's poles.

The north pole of the electromagnet is the end that is attracted to the south pole of the permanent magnet.

Reverse the current through your electromagnet by switching the locations where the ends of the electromagnet wire connect to the battery. Determine the locations of your electromagnet's poles now.

The poles are reversed.

You can easily predict the location of the poles of an electromagnet if you know the direction of the current in the wire. If your fingers curl in the direction of the current, your thumb points in the direction of the north pole. This method is called the right-hand rule. Use this rule to determine the locations of the poles of your electromagnet.

The right-hand rule will yield the same result students found by testing the poles with a permanent magnet.

When might this rule be useful?

It is useful when you don't have access to a permanent magnet with the poles marked on it.

4 In this part of the Investigation, you're going to vary the current through the electromagnet and see how current affects the magnetic strength. You will vary current by using first one, then two, then three batteries. For each number of batteries, measure the current with the meter and then measure how strong the magnet is by seeing how many paper clips it can pick up. Then you will unwrap half of the wire from the nail, reducing the number of turns of wire to half the original amount. You will repeat the measurements with one, two, and three batteries.

Circulate among groups as they work on varying current and measuring the strength of their electromagnets. Since each group has only two battery holders and batteries, have groups share.

4 Now you will make a graph showing how the number of paper clips picked up by the magnet changes as the current is increased. Graph the data for the electromagnet with all of the coils of wire wrapped around it. Who can tell me which variable goes on the *x*-axis? Which variable goes on the *y*-axis?

Students should be able to tell you that current, the independent variable, goes on the x-axis, and the number of paper clips, the dependent variable, goes on the y-axis.

What is your conclusion about the relationship between current and strength of the electromagnet?

Students should see that magnetic strength increases as current is increased.

How did changing the number of turns affect the strength of the electromagnet?

The electromagnet is stronger when the number of turns is greater.

Now, go look at everyone's results. Look at the data and see if some electromagnets picked up more paper clips. Look at the electromagnets and write down anything you notice that might explain differences in performance.

Examine each group's work yourself. Electromagnets that are made more neatly and that have more coils of wire will be stronger. Some batteries may have been newer than others, resulting in more current in those electromagnets.

3 **The right-hand rule**

a. Use a permanent magnet or compass to determine the location of the north and south poles of your electromagnet. Explain your method and include a diagram showing the direction of the current from the positive battery terminal, around the nail, and into the negative battery terminal.

b. Reverse the direction of the current through your electromagnet by switching the locations where the electromagnet wires' ends connect to the battery. Test for the locations of the north and south poles. What effect did reversing the current have on the locations of the poles?

c. The polarity of an electromagnet can be predicted easily if you know the direction of the current in the coil. When the fingers of your right hand curl in the direction of the current, your thumb points toward the electromagnet's north pole. This method of finding the magnetic poles is called the *right-hand rule*. Use the right-hand rule to find the locations of the poles of your electromagnet.

The right-hand rule

Electric current

4 **What happens to the strength of an electromagnet when you increase the current?**

1. Measure the current through your electromagnet when it is connected to one battery. Test how many paper clips it can pick up and record your results in Table 1.

2. Increase the current through the electromagnet by connecting it to two batteries. Again measure the current and test how many paper clips it can pick up. Record your results.

3. Repeat step 2 using three batteries.

4. Remove half the turns by unwrapping some of the wire from the nail. Leave the total length of wire the same.

5. Repeat steps 1-3 with the "new" electromagnet which has only half as many turns of wire.

⬥**Safety Note: Keep the batteries connected for only a short time or the electromagnet will get hot.**

Table 1: Current and magnet strength

Turns	No. of batteries	Current (A)	No. of paper clips picked up

5 **What did you learn?**

a. Draw a graph showing how the number of paper clips picked up by the magnet varies as the current increases. Label your axes and title your graph.

b. How did changing the number of turns affect the strength of the electromagnet?

c. What is your conclusion about the relationship between current and the strength of the electromagnet?

d. Look at other groups' electromagnets, data tables, and graphs. Did some electromagnets work better than others? Write down anything you notice that might explain differences in performance.

4 5 Example answers

Table 1: *Current and magnet strength*

Turns	No. of batteries	Current (A)	No. of paper clips picked up
54	1	4.1	18
54	2	5.3	23
54	3	5.8	26
27	1	4.1	10
27	2	5.3	14
27	3	5.8	16

5a. Graph:

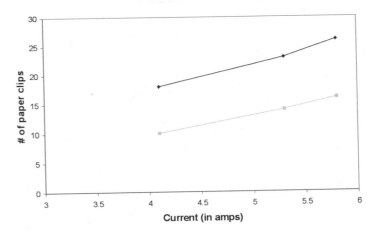

# of paper clips vs. Current

5b. The electromagnet was stronger when there were more turns.

5c. The greater the current, the stronger the electromagnet.

5d. Electromagnets that are more neatly wound and that have more turns are stronger.

23.2 Electromagnets and the Electric Motor

Key Question: How does a motor work?

The electric motor revolutionized human technology. With an electric motor power could easily be transferred through electricity from one place to another. The electric motor is based on the principals of electricity and magnetism. In this Investigation, students build a simple electric motor. They apply what they learned about electromagnets in Investigation 23.1 to explain why the motor spins. Various motor designs are tested and the current and voltage are measured for the different configurations. The power used by the motor is determined both when the motor is spinning and when it is stopped and comparisons are made.

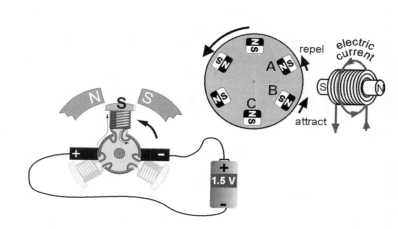

Reading Synopsis

Students read Section 23.2 Electromagnets and the Electric Motor after the investigation

Electromagnets depend on electric current to create their magnetism. The most efficient design for an electromagnet is a coil of wire wrapped around a core of iron or steel. The magnetic field of an electromagnet is proportional to the current and to the number of turns of wire in the coil.

An electric motor converts electrical energy to rotating motion. One type of motor has a rotating spindle (the armature) that contains permanent magnets. These permanent magnets are alternately attracted and repelled by stationary electromagnets. Electromagnets are used because they can be switched from north to south by reversing the current through them. The commutator is the part of the motor that switches the electromagnets from attract to repel at the right time to keep the armature spinning.

The Investigation

Leading Questions
- How is an electromagnet made?
- How does an electric motor work?
- How can a motor be designed for optimum performance?
- How much electric power does a motor use?

Learning Goals
By the end of the Investigation, students will be able to:
- Build a working electric motor.
- Explain how permanent magnets and electromagnets interact to make a motor spin.
- Measure the motor's current and voltage.
- Calculate the power used by various motor designs.

Key Vocabulary
motor, electromagnet, permanent magnet, voltage, current, commutator, power

Setup and Materials

Students work in groups of four or five at tables.

Each group should have:

- Electric motor set with four D-cell batteries
- Multimeter with red and black leads

In addition, the teacher should have:

- Extra D-cell batteries

Details

Time ⊙ Two class periods

Preparation 🖊 Practice building the different configurations of the motor

Assignments 📖 Section 23.2 Electromagnets and the Electric Motor in the **Student Edition** after the Investigation.

Skill Sheets 11.2 Power
19.3A Ohm's Law

Teaching the Investigation

1   Introduction
2   Getting the rotor to spin
3   Making a four-pole electric motor
4   Why does it work?
5   Designing and testing different electric motors
6   Measuring current
7   Measuring voltage
8   Collecting the data
9   Analyzing the data

Introduction

Getting the rotor to spin

Magnets

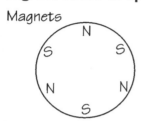

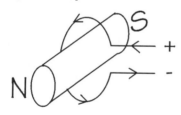

Making a four-pole electric motor

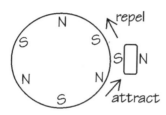

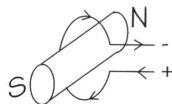

1

In previous Investigations, you experimented with permanent magnets and electromagnets. Today we are going to examine how these two types of magnets can be used together to create an electric motor. The electric motors that you use every day—in a washing machine, in an electric drill, or in a hair dryer—run on the same principle as the motor you will build in the lab today.

First, remove the nut from the center of your motor and then remove the plastic disk underneath it. You will see 12 magnets in the slots that line the edge of the spinning part, which we call the rotor. Remove all 12 magnets from the rotor.

> Allow students time to complete these steps.

Put six magnets back in the rotor so they alternate north and south poles facing out. Use every other hole so the magnets are evenly spaced. If you take a NORTH and push on a SOUTH like this (draw), the rotor will turn a little. When the next magnet comes by, switch the magnet in your fingers to make it repel and attract the next magnet in the rotor. If you do it right, you can make the rotor spin! Try it for yourself!

> Circulate among the groups, making sure that each student is an active participant in the lab. If students have trouble making the disk spin, suggest that they hold the stack of magnets slightly above the rotor magnets and push downward until the rotor magnet is repelled. Then they must quickly pull the magnet stack backward as the rotor spins. Otherwise, they may pull the next magnet right out of the motor! The secret is to keep reversing the magnet in your fingers to push and pull each magnet in the rotor as it passes by. With a little practice, each student should be able to spin the rotor.

When each person in your group has spun the rotor, discuss questions 1a and 1b. What do you have to do with the magnet in your fingers to make the rotor spin? How do you make the rotor spin the other way? Record your answers.

> Circulate and encourage students to repeat what they did to make the rotor turn while carefully observing exactly what they do with the magnet they are holding. They should recognize that they need to reverse the magnet in their fingers just as each magnet in the rotor comes by. This way their magnet first attracts the rotor magnet in, then switches to repel it away and attract in the next magnet.

2

Turning a motor using magnets is fun and helps us see how a motor works. But if the only way to turn a motor was to stand there and flip magnets all day, it wouldn't be a great invention. With an electromagnet, we can switch the magnet from north to south with electricity instead of our hands. Now you will see how an electromagnet can turn the rotor much faster than we turned it by flipping magnets in our fingers. What determines the location of the north and south poles of an electromagnet?

> Prompt a discussion of electric current and the right-hand rule.

To make the rotor spin, you had to flip the magnet in your fingers each time a rotor magnet passed by. If we use an electromagnet instead of a permanent magnet, what can we do to achieve the same effect?

> Reversing the direction of the current will reverse the north and south poles of the electromagnet.
> Stress that you need to switch the electromagnet's poles every time a rotor magnet comes by, just as before.

When you were using the permanent magnet to spin the rotor, you used your eyes to see when to flip the magnet. How do you suppose the electromagnet will know when to reverse the current?

> Encourage students to examine the motor and come up with possible ideas.

UNIT 7: Electricity and Magnetism

23.2 · Electromagnets and the Electric Motor

Question: How does a motor work?

In this Investigation, you will:

1. Learn the principles and design of the electric motor.
2. Measure the electric current, voltage, and power for an electric motor.

Electric motors are everywhere. You find them in fans, washing machines, automobiles, tools, spacecraft—anywhere that we use powered machines. All electric motors use permanent magnets and/or electromagnets. Permanent magnets are useful because they create a magnetic field without needing any electricity. Electromagnets have the advantage of being able to reverse their poles when the direction of current is changed.

1 Getting the rotor to spin

Electric motors use magnetism to spin. Try to get the rotor to spin by manipulating permanent magnets as follows:

1. Take the motor apart and put six magnets in the rotor so they are evenly spaced and alternate north-south poles facing outward.
2. Bring a stack of two or three magnets close and try to repel one of the magnets in the rotor. The rotor should spin a little.
3. As soon as the rotor spins a little, flip the magnet in your fingers to attract and then repel the next magnet on the rotor.
4. By sequentially flipping the magnet in your fingers, try to push and pull on the magnets in the rotor to get the motor to spin.

You will see that reversing the poles of the magnet in your fingers is the key to making the rotor spin.

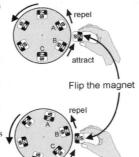

a. When is the right time to reverse the magnet in your fingers? Think about where the magnets are in the rotor.

b. How could you make the rotor spin the other way?

2 Making a 4-pole electric motor

All electric motors use some kind of switch to change the orientation of the poles of the magnet at the right time. You accomplished this by flipping the permanent magnet. An easier way to do this is with an electromagnet. The locations of the north and south poles of an electromagnet depend on the direction of the current through it. Reversing the current through an electromagnet has the same effect as flipping a permanent magnet. A device called a *commutator* is used to switch the orientation of the north and south poles of the electromagnet. In the electric motor you are building, the commutator is a plastic disk and it uses a beam of light to tell it when to switch the location of the poles.

161

1 Example answers

1a. The magnet must be flipped each time one of the magnets in the rotor passes by.

1b. The motor would spin the other way if the permanent magnet were held with the opposite pole facing the rotor. This would cause it to attract the rotor magnets that it had been repelling and vice versa.

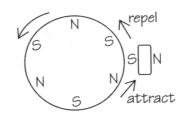
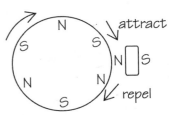

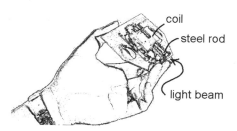

Point out the parts of the electromagnet module.

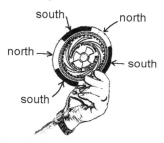

The students should understand that the electromagnet switches polarity when the commutator disk changes from clear to black or black to clear. They should be able to determine the number of switches per revolution of each disk.

The run button disconnects the power supply as soon as it is released. This is to conserve batteries. The motor will drain the batteries in about 15 minutes if used continuously. It is a good idea to keep extra batteries on hand during this Investigation.

2 Examine one of the electromagnets. Notice there is a coil of wire around a steel rod. This electromagnet has a special switch that uses an infrared light beam to reverse the positive and negative ends of the coil. The light beam is between the end of the steel rod and the green circuit board (hold up and demonstrate). When the beam is not blocked, the end of the electromagnet is a north pole. When the beam gets blocked, the end switches to a south pole.

Have students find the electromagnet in their kit. The students should pass it around the group. Each person should have an opportunity to locate the infrared beam and the LEDs.

The thing that makes the electromagnet switch in a motor is called the commutator. Since our electromagnet uses light to switch, our commutator needs to block and unblock the light beam. Find one of the plastic commutator disks. Notice the edges have areas that are clear and areas that block the light beam. Where will the commutator switch the magnet from north to south?

Have each student look at one of the commutator disks. They should see how the black sections on the commutator disk are used to block the infrared beam. Prompt them to remember that the end of the electromagnet (facing the rotor) is north when the light beam is not blocked. The electromagnet switches to south when the commutator blocks the beam. The edge between clear and black is where the switching happens.

Now follow steps 1-5 at the bottom of the page. Use the pink commutator disk and put four magnets in the rotor so they alternate north and south. Remember that the electromagnet switches polarity when the commutator disk changes from clear to black or black to clear. The border between a clear and black section on the disk should be lined up with a magnet in the rotor so that the switch happens in the right place. The diagrams in the center of your Investigation page will help you line everything up. You need to push and hold the RUN button to make the motor work. You also have to give the rotor a little push to get it going.

Circulate around and help each group make their motor work.

Suggest that students try keeping their hand on the rotor as it goes around so that they can feel the push and pull of the electromagnets. They should notice how this push-pull corresponds to the change in magnetism that is indicated by the green LEDs on the electromagnets. The LEDs tell where the north pole is. They switch back and forth as the commutator disk breaks the light beam.

If things don't work, try the following
1) Check the batteries. Is one of the green lights on when you hold the RUN button down? Sometimes the battery holders are tight and prevent the batteries from touching in the center. Rolling them around usually works to fix this problem.
2) Check that the electromagnet is not touching the rotor. If it is, slide it back a smidgen.
3) Check that the thumb nuts on the electromagnet are making a good connection to the circuit board.
4) Check that the commutator disk is lined up so the edges from clear to black are aligned with the centers of the four magnets in the rotor.

23.2 Electromagnets and the Electric Motor

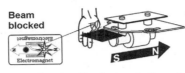
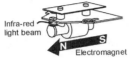

Beam unblocked — Infra-red light beam — Electromagnet — N S

Beam blocked — Electromagnet — S N

When the light is not blocked (see diagram above), the current flows in a direction to make the north pole at the front of the electromagnet. When the light is blocked, the current flows in the opposite direction, making the north pole at the back of the electromagnet. There are two green lights on the electromagnet. The illuminated light shows which end is the north pole.

The commutator disks have alternating black and clear sections around the edge that switch the direction of current in the electromagnets by blocking the light beam. Align the clear and black edges with the centers of the magnets.

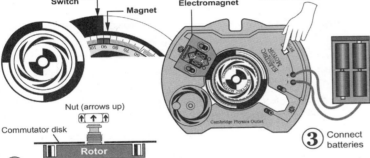

(1) Find the pink 4-switch commutator disk and adjust it so the switch aligns with magnet

Switch — Magnet — Electromagnet

(2) Fasten the commutator disk down with the nut (finger tight)

Nut (arrows up) — Commutator disk — Rotor

(3) Connect batteries

(4) Slide in an electromagnet and push (and hold) the run button

The following steps explain how to set up the electronic motor:

1. Find the pink four-pole commutator disk shown in the picture.
2. Arrange four magnets so the north or south poles alternate. Be sure the disk is aligned so the border between clear and black is centered on each of the four magnets. The border is where the electromagnet will switch from north to south. Finger-tighten the big nut to secure the disk once you have it aligned with the magnets.
3. Connect the battery pack matching the red (+) and black (-) wires to their corresponding terminals on the motor.
4. Attach the electromagnet to position A or B. To make the electrical connections, push the electromagnet forward, and gently tighten the thumb-nuts. Do not overtighten them.
5. Push and hold the RUN button. You may need to give the motor a small push to start it.

Real-world applications

As an assignment, have each student identify 10 things in his or her home that use an electric motor. Some examples are:

1. clock
2. washing machine
3. electric can opener
4. VCR
5. vacuum cleaner
6. sump pump or well pump
7. electric drill
8. electric saw
9. clothes dryer
10. hair dryer
11. fan
12. air conditioner
13. kitchen mixer
14. food processor
15. refrigerator (in the compressor)
16. computer (disk drives, cooling fans)
17. cassette tape player
18. CD player
19. humidifier
20. oil burner for furnace
21. circulating pump for hot-water heating system
22. toys such as radio-controlled cars or boats

Why does it work?

Start

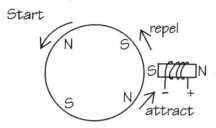

Switch

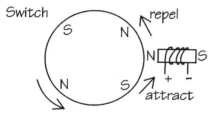

Designing and testing different electric motors

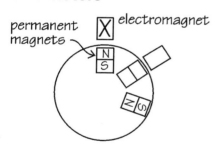

permanent magnets — electromagnet

Students will design and test motors using four new magnet configurations. They should record their successful designs on the Investigation sheet.

If there is time, ask students to find the most efficient way to reverse the direction of the motor.

Can anyone explain why the electromagnets have to switch at the right place? Where is the right place?

> Prompt the class to discuss that the electromagnets have to switch just as a magnet passes by so that they attract the rotor magnet and then repel it once it passes. The commutator disk is what does the switching.

We are going to call this design a four-pole motor because there are four magnetic poles in the rotor, two north and two south. Now I want you to design motors with various numbers of magnets. You need to build a working motor using each of the five commutator disks. You may have to experiment with different configurations of magnets until you are able to get the motor to spin.

> Show the students the five disks. Point out that the green one is tricky and should be saved for last. (See the side notes.)

Once you get the motor to spin, record the location and direction of each magnet and the position of the electromagnet. There are charts on the sheet for you to make your diagrams. Let's record our magnet configuration for the pink disk together now.

> Guide the students as they fill out the diagram. You may wish to draw a large version on the board in order to show them how to record their work.

Now you are free to try each disk. I would suggest starting with the orange disk. It will help you design the magnet configurations for the other disks.

> The orange and blue disks are straightforward. The blue requires all twelve magnets. Because it has the highest number of magnets and switches, it will cause the motor to turn fastest. The yellow disk has only two switches. Students may need to borrow an extra electromagnet to get the rotor to make a full turn. The green disk is the most challenging. It is impossible to evenly space eight magnets in twelve slots. Therefore, another approach is required. Only four magnets are used. Because a polarity switch occurs between each magnet, the existing magnets must all face the same direction (north out or south out). If the magnets alternate (as they do with the other disks), the rotor won't turn.

If you finish early, try this challenge: How many ways can you discover to get the motor to spin in the opposite direction?

> Students will probably start by flipping all the magnets over. They may discover that there is an easier way: If they rotate the disk one segment, they will change the initial polarity of the electromagnet. This causes the motor to reverse. Rotating the disk is essentially the same as reversing each magnet since the reference is how each magnet faces relative to the disk.

> If you are doing this Investigation over two days, this is a natural stopping point for the first day.

23.2 Electromagnets and the Electric Motor

3 **Designing and testing different electric motors**

Design and test a working electric motor for each of the commutator disks. Use the design charts to record each design, including the direction (north and south) and position of all magnets. Put an X where you placed the electromagnet. Record only the designs that work. Try different arrangements until you get a design that works for each commutator disk. The green disk requires you to think creatively.

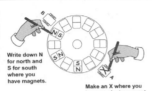

Write down N for north and S for south where you have magnets.

Make an X where you have an electromagnet.

4 **Measuring current**

When you push the RUN button on the motor, it connects an electric circuit that allows current to flow through the electromagnet. The current flows from the red (+) terminal to the black (-) terminal of the battery pack. For you to measure the current in the motor, it must travel through the meter on its path from the batteries, through the motor, and back to the batteries again.

1. Make a working motor with the orange disk, six magnets, and the electromagnet. Remember to alternate the north-south orientation of the magnets.
2. Connect the battery pack so the current flows through the meter before (or after) flowing through the electric motor. Look at the diagram below to make sure you are connecting the wires properly.
3. Set the data collector to measure DC current.

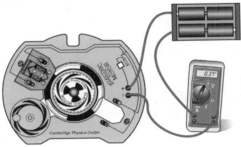

a. How much current is the motor using when it is spinning? Record your answer in Table 1.
b. Now, measure the current with the rotor stopped (use your finger to stop it). How much current is the motor using when the rotor is stopped? Record your answer in Table 1.

Table 1: Amount of current used by the motor

Current with rotor stopped (amps)	Current with rotor spinning (amps)

Extension activity

Challenge students to try to build the fastest motor in the class. The speed of the motor can be measured by connecting a photogate to the motor. The rotation speed can then be calculated from the frequency shown on the timer.

The motor's speed can be optimized by rotating the commutator disk so that the border between the black and clear segments is not at the center of each magnet. Students can experiment with the position of the switching point to find the location that yields the fastest motor.

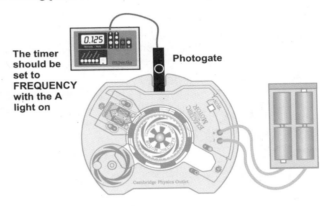

The timer should be set to FREQUENCY with the A light on

Photogate

$$\text{Rotation speed (rpm)} = \frac{\text{frequency}}{\text{Number of black segments}} \times 60 \frac{\text{sec}}{\text{min}}$$

3 **4** **Example answers**

Table 1: Amount of current used by the motor

Current with rotor stopped (amps)	Current with rotor spinning (amps)
0.76	0.45

Measuring current

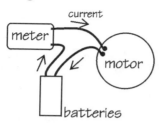

Measuring current with the meter in series

Measuring voltage

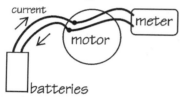

Measuring voltage with the meter in parallel

Collecting the data

Analyzing the data

The motor uses more power when it is stopped than when it is spinning.

5

When you push the RUN button on the motor, it connects an electric circuit that allows current to flow through the electromagnet. You use an electrical meter to measure the current. Build a working motor with the orange disk, six magnets, and the electromagnet. You will measure the current when the motor is running, and then when the rotor is held so that it can't spin (with the RUN button held down).

Make sure students press the RUN button while measuring the current in the stopped motor.

6

Now you will measure voltage. First measure the voltage of the battery pack when the motor is off and the RUN button is not pressed. This is called the no-load voltage, which means nothing is drawing current from the batteries.

Students may also wish to disconnect the battery pack from the motor and measure the voltage. The result will be the same as when it is connected but the motor is off.

Now that you are familiar with building the motor and measuring current and voltage, you will be comparing the electricity used by various motor designs. Choose four designs that use different numbers of permanent magnets. Measure the current and voltage for each design when the motor is spinning and when it is held in place with the RUN button pressed.

Students should be comfortable working with the equipment by now and should need very little assistance. The students should discover that the voltage is about the same when the motor is stopped or when it is turning. The current is different. When the motor is stopped it draws more current than when it is running. The faster the motor turns, the less current it uses.

7

Now you will determine the power used by the motor in each case. How do we calculate electrical power?

Prompt students to remember that power is current multiplied by voltage. Power is measured in watts.

Calculate the power used by the motor when it is spinning and also when you hold it stopped. How do the numbers compare?

Have the students multiply voltage and current to get power. The motor uses more power when it is stopped than when it is running free. The power is also related to the number of permanent magnets. The greater the number of magnets, the less the power.

We said energy can never be created or destroyed. When the motor is turning, most of the energy is going to overcoming friction and speeding up the rotor. When you hold the motor stopped, where does the energy go? Is this good or bad?

If the rotor is stopped, the energy is going to heat. The coils get warm. This is usually bad and motors can burn out if they try to move too heavy a load and, as a result, stop turning with the power still on. When a motor burns out, the insulation between the wire in the coil melts and the coil becomes a block of copper (short circuit) and may melt. The wire in the electromagnet looks like plain copper, but it is painted with a clear insulating varnish. When a motor overheats you can smell the varnish melting.

23.2 Electromagnets and the Electric Motor

5　Measuring voltage

Measure and record the battery pack's voltage when the motor is off. This is called the *no-load voltage*, meaning nothing is drawing current from the battery pack. The battery voltage changes when current is flowing. In the next part of the Investigation, you will measure and compare the no-load voltage of the battery pack with its voltage under load while the motor is running.

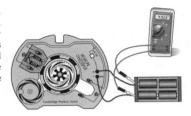

6　Collecting the data

Measure the current and voltage of the motor for four different motor designs using different numbers of permanent magnets. Record the current and voltage both with the rotor spinning and with the rotor held in place while the RUN button is held down.

Table 2: Current and voltage for different motor designs

Number of permanent magnets	Current with rotor spinning (amps)	Current with rotor stopped (amps)	Voltage with rotor spinning (volts)	Voltage with rotor stopped (volts)

Use the data from Table 2 to calculate the power consumed by the motor.

Table 3: Power used by the motor

Number of magnets	Power with rotor spinning (W)	Power with rotor stopped (W)

7　Analyzing the data

a. How does the no-load voltage of the battery pack compare with the voltage when the motor is connected and running? How does it compare when the motor is connected but stopped?

b. How does the motor's voltage when it is on but stopped compare to the voltage when it is running?

c. How does the current when the motor is on but stopped compare to the current when it is running?

d. How is the number of permanent magnets used related to the power consumed by the motor?

e. Does the motor use more power when it is running or when it is stopped? Use your observations to explain why electric motors in machines often burn out if the machine jams and the motor is prevented from turning although the electricity is still on.

f. When the motor is running, most of the energy from the battery goes to overcoming friction and adding kinetic energy to the rotor. Where does the energy go when the motor is stopped from turning?

g. How much power does your motor use compared with a 100-watt light bulb? Your answer should show a calculation of how many motors you could run using the electricity used by the 100-watt bulb. Base the calculation on the power used when the rotor is spinning (use any motor configuration).

164

6　7　Example answers

Table 2: Current and voltage for different motor designs

No. of permanent magnets	Current with rotor spinning (amps)	Current with rotor stopped (amps)	Voltage with rotor spinning (amps)	Voltage with rotor stopped (amps)
12	0.29	0.77	5.79	5.18
6	0.45	0.76	5.55	5.17
4	0.58	0.76	5.40	5.16
2	0.73	0.75	5.17	5.16

Table 3: Power used by the motor

No. of magnets	Power with rotor spinning (W)	Power with rotor stopped (W)
12	1.7	4.0
6	2.5	3.9
4	3.1	3.9
2	3.8	3.9

7a. The no-load voltage is greater than the voltage when the motor is running. The voltage is greater when the motor is running than when it is stopped.

7b. The voltage is greater when the motor is spinning.

7c. The current is greater when the motor is stopped.

7d. The power is greater when fewer magnets are used.

7e. The motor uses more power when it is stopped because it is trying to spin but cannot. Electric motors burn out when they are stopped because all the energy goes into heating the wires instead of turning the rotor.

7f. When you stop the rotor, all of the energy is transformed into heat.

7g. The motor uses much less power than a light bulb. Using the 2-magnet motor: 100 watts per bulb/3.8 watts per motor = 26.3 motors that could be powered.

23.3 Induction and the Electric Generator

Key Question: How does a generator produce electricity?

Physics demonstrates a strong tendency toward symmetry. In physics, symmetry means that a process that goes one way can also go the opposite way. If electric current can create moving magnets than moving magnets must also be able to create electric current. In this Investigation, students learn how moving magnets can be used to create electricity by building and testing an electric generator. By changing the design and speed of the generator, students discover the principle of electromagnetic induction. The amount of electricity generated is proportional to the speed at which the magnetic field in a coil of wire alternates back and forth from north to south.

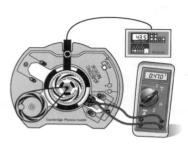

Reading Synopsis

Students read Section 23.3 Induction and the Electric Generator after the Investigation.

A changing magnetic field can generate voltage and create electric current in a coil of wire. Using moving magnets to create electric current is called electromagnetic induction and is the principle behind the electric generator.

Faraday's law of induction says the induced voltage (or current) is proportional to the number of turns of wire in a coil and to the rate of change of the magnetic field through the coil. Because the magnetic poles switch back and forth, generators produce alternating current (AC) electricity. This is the type of electricity produced by power plants and used in homes.

A transformer is another electrical device based on induction. A transformer changes AC electricity at one voltage to AC electricity at a different voltage keeping the total power constant. Transformers are used to step down high voltage electricity from power transmission lines to 120 VAC electricity used in homes and businesses.

The Investigation

Leading Questions
- How is the electricity you use in your home or business created?
- How does an electric generator work?
- What is the relationship between electricity and magnetism?

Learning Goals

By the end of the Investigation, students will be able to:
- Explain how an electric generator works.
- Build and test several electric generator designs.
- Use Faraday's law of induction to explain why the amount of electricity generated depends on the speed and number of magnets in the generator.

Key Vocabulary

generator, electromagnetic induction, Faraday's law of induction, voltage, current, alternating current

Setup and Materials

Students work in groups of four or five at tables.

Each group should have:

- Electric motor kit with generator coil
- Timer with one photogate, AC adapter (or 9-volt battery), and a cord to connect the photogate to the timer
- Multimeter with red and black leads
- Graph paper

In addition, the teacher should have:

- Extra rubber bands

Details

Time One to two class periods

Preparation Practice working with the generator

Assignments Section 23.3 Induction and the Electric Generator in the **Student Edition** after the Investigation.

Skill Sheets 23.3 Michael Faraday

Teaching the Investigation

1. Faraday's law of induction
2. Observing the induced current in a coil
3. Building the generator
4. Gathering data
5. Analyzing data for the alternating poles generator
6. Changing the orientation of the magnets

Introduction

Faraday's law of induction

Induced voltage is proportional to the number of turns of wire and to the rate at which the magnetic field through the coil changes. The polarity of the voltage depends on the direction of the magnet's motion relative to the coil.

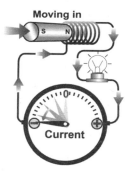

Moving in

Current

Moving out

Current

Electric motors transform electrical energy into mechanical energy. Electric generators do the opposite. They transform mechanical energy into electrical energy. Many laws in physics display an elegant kind of symmetry. An excellent example of symmetry is seen in with magnetism and electricity. A current running through a wire creates a magnetic field. The reverse is also true. If you move a magnet near a coil of wire, a current will be produced. This process is called electromagnetic induction, because a moving magnet induces electric current to flow. Just about all the electricity you use is produced using electromagnetic induction in power generators. In today's investigation, you are going to build an electric generator and see how it works.

Electric generators convert kinetic energy into electrical energy. In the generator we are going to build moving permanent magnets in the rotor induce current to flow in a coil of wire.

1   Draw a schematic showing the rotor and magnets and a coil of wire similar to the illustrations on page 470 of the text.

As a magnet moves past the coil, it creates a magnetic field passing through the coil. The amount of magnetic field crossing through the coil is called the magnetic flux. For our generator, the magnetic flux is the strength of the magnetic field times the area of the coil. Faraday's law of induction says the voltage that appears at the terminals of the coil is proportional to the rate of change in the magnetic flux. The voltage is not proportional to without flux itself. You will see that holding a magnet right up to the coil produces no voltage. The magnet must be moving. The magnet must move because the voltage is proportional to the rate at which the magnetic flux in the coil changes, not to the amount of magnetic flux itself.

2   The concept of electromagnetic induction may seem complicated to students at this point. It will become much clearer to them as they experiment with the generator. Refer them to the diagram in Part 1 of the Investigation. Stress that a changing magnetic field is needed to induce current, not simply a magnetic field.

As a magnet enters a coil of wire, the current flows in one direction. As it exits the coil, the current flows in the opposite direction. Which type of current is generated in this case?

Alternating current is generated.

Alternating current is what we use for electricity in our homes and other buildings. Generators that produce electricity for our homes use electromagnetic induction. Now you will create electricity using induction. You need the generator coil, one permanent magnet, and an electrical meter for this activity. The generator coil is just like the electromagnet coil, but it lacks the infrared beam. Make sure your meter is set to measure AC voltage. Read the instructions in Part 2 and experiment with moving the permanent magnet near the coil. Record your observations.

Students may be surprised that they can generate voltage simply by shaking the magnet. The faster the magnet is moved, the greater the voltage. The voltage is also affected by the distance between the coil and the permanent magnet. As the magnet is moved farther away, the voltage decreases. If the magnet is simply held near the coil, no voltage is generated because there is not a changing magnetic field through the coil.

2 Example answers

2. The electrical meter shows that there is voltage across the ends of the coil.

3. The voltage increases when the magnet is moved at a faster rate.

4. The voltage decreases as the magnet is moved away.

5. There is no voltage if the magnet is held in place.

UNIT 7: Electricity and Magnetism

23.3 Induction and the Electric Generator

Question: How does a generator produce electricity?

In this Investigation, you will:

1. Build and test several designs of an electric generator.
2. Measure the voltage produced by the generator.
3. Use Faraday's law of induction to explain how a generator works.

Electric generators convert mechanical energy into electrical energy. This Investigation explores the design, operation, and principles of an electric generator that works by rotating magnets past a coil of wire. The passing of the magnets causes a magnetic field to change in the coil of wire. The changing magnetic field produces electricity.

1 Faraday's law of induction

A changing magnetic field near a coil of wire can induce current to flow in the wire. Current flows because the changing field creates a *potential difference* (also called *voltage*) across the ends of the wire. The effect of this voltage is similar to what happens when a battery is connected to the ends of the wire. This process is called *electromagnetic induction*.

Faraday's law of induction states that the voltage is proportional to the number of turns of the wire and to the rate at which the magnetic field through the coil changes. The faster the magnetic field changes, the greater the voltage induced in the coil. The polarity of the voltage depends on the direction of the magnet's motion relative to the coil.

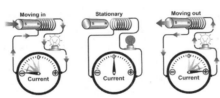

2 Observing the induced current in a coil

1. Remove the coil from the generator (or motor). Attach the leads of the digital multimeter to the positive and negative terminals of the coil. Set the multimeter to measure AC volts.

2. Move a permanent magnet back and forth very close to the coil. Watch the multimeter. What do you notice?

3. Move the magnet at a faster rate. What happens to the voltage?

4. Slowly move the permanent magnet away from the coil while continuing to shake it at a fast rate. What happens to the voltage?

5. Place the magnet on the coil. What voltage is induced when the magnet is not moving?

165

Building the generator

Gathering data

One turn per second, 2 magnets

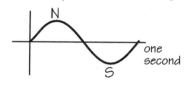

Two turns per second, 2 magnets

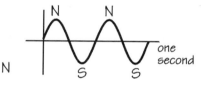

One turn per second, 4 magnets

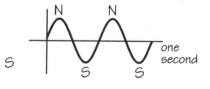

Two turns per second, 4 magnets

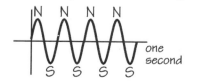

3 Now you will use the electric motor equipment to build a generator. You will turn the rotor manually, using the hand crank. You will be able to demonstrate that when you move the magnets past a coil of wire, you generate electricity. For this activity, you will need both the electrical meter and the timer with one photogate. You will be using the generator coil in place of the electromagnet. Follow the directions in Part 3 and assemble the generator.

Circulate around the room and help students set up. You may wish to provide a sample setup for students to follow.

Wrap a rubber band around the crank and the spindle on the rotor. Connect the meter to measure voltage between the plus and minus terminals of the coil. Since the generator produces AC voltage, you should set the meter to measure AC volts.

Have the groups turn the crank and observe the voltage increasing as they spin faster.

4 Now connect the photogate to the generator. Plug the photogate into the timer and set it to frequency mode. When the motor spins, the timer will display the number of times the photogate beam is broken each second. Because you are using the blue disk, the photogate beam is broken six times for each complete turn of the rotor. This is true no matter how many magnets are in the rotor. For now, put two magnets in the rotor. One should have a north pole facing out, and the other should have a south pole facing out.

Allow students to connect the photogate and timer and to observe how it measures the frequency.

The next part is tricky. Have one person watch the timer and try to spin the crank to keep the frequency steady at 20 Hz. Another person should watch the meter and try to read the average voltage made by the generator. A third person should record the voltage in the right place in the data table. Then repeat for 40 Hz and 80 Hz.

Have the students measure the voltage with two magnets for 20, 40, and 80 Hz speeds. The exact number of rotations per minute is not important; only the relative speeds matter.

Try the experiment with four, six, and 12 magnets. The magnets should always have alternating poles facing out. Record all the measurements in the data table.

This will take considerable time. It is hard to hold the speed constant while the voltage is being measured. Don't worry that the results are not exact. The pattern will come out clearly. Doubling the speed doubles the voltage. Doubling the number of magnets also doubles the voltage. Tripling the number of magnets triples (roughly) the voltage.

When you have finished this portion of the Investigation, answer questions a and b in your lab notebook.

Allow time for the students to answer these questions independently.

What happened to the voltage as you increased the speed of the rotor?

Students should have found that doubling the speed doubles the voltage.

What happened to the voltage as you increased the number of magnets?

Doubling the number of magnets also doubles the voltage.

Your results confirm what is called the law of induction. This law states that the amount of electricity produced by a generator is proportional to how fast the coil sees a change from north to south and back. If you spin the rotor faster, the change from north to south happens faster and you get more voltage. If you increase the number of magnets you also make the coil see a faster alternation of north and south, so the voltage also increases. The faster the polarity switches, the more electricity you produce.

23.3 Induction and the Electric Generator

3   Building the generator

A generator uses induction to convert the mechanical energy of the spinning rotor into electrical energy. When the rotor spins, the permanent magnets pass by the coil. This causes current to flow in the coil. When a north pole passes the coil, current flows in one direction; when a south pole passes it, current flows in the opposite direction. If the magnets are arranged so alternating poles face outward, the current in the coil moves back and forth as the rotor spins, creating alternating current, or AC.

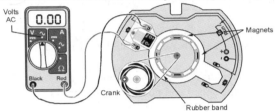

1. Place four magnets in the rotor on opposite sides of the rotor with alternating poles facing out.
2. Slide the generator coil over the thumb screws in either the A or B position. Slide the generator coil toward the rotor and tighten the screws to hold it in place.
3. Stretch a rubber band around the crank and the spindle of the motor. You can spin the rotor by turning the crank. The meter will measure the AC voltage produced.

a. Describe the relationship you observe between the speed of the rotor and the voltage produced.

4   Gathering data

There are two main variables that affect the performance of the generator: the number of magnets and the rate at which the rotor spins. The photogate Timer can be used to measure the spin rate.

1. Place the blue disk on the rotor and fasten it with the nut. It does not matter how you align the disk since it is only being used to break the light beam to measure the speed of the rotor. No matter how many magnets are used, you will use the blue disk for the entire Investigation.
2. Attach a photogate and set the Timer to measure frequency.
3. With two magnets in the rotor, spin the motor at frequencies of 40, 60, and 80 hertz as displayed by the Timer. It may take some practice to keep the rotor spinning at the correct frequency long enough to read the voltage. Measure and record the voltage you generate in Table 1.
4. Repeat the last step with 4, 6, and then 12 magnets in the rotor. The magnets should always have alternate north and south poles facing outward. If you loosen the generator coil, make sure you slide it back toward the rotor and tighten the thumbscrews before collecting data.

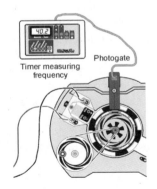

Timer measuring frequency   Photogate

3 4 5 Example answers

3a. The faster the rotor spins, the greater the voltage generated.

Table 1: *Generator data with alternating poles facing out*

Rotation frequency	Voltage with 2 magnets	Voltage with 4 magnets	Voltage with 6 magnets	Voltage with 12 magnets
40 Hz	0.089	0.177	0.275	0.468
60 Hz	0.135	0.263	0.410	0.705
80 Hz	0.175	0.347	0.536	0.929

5a. Graph:

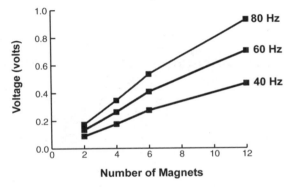

Voltage vs. Number of Magnets with Alternating Poles Facing Out

5b. The greater the number of magnets, the greater the voltage. Doubling the number of magnets roughly doubles the voltage.

5c. The voltage would approximately quadruple.

5d. The voltage would be approximately 0.55 V for 40 Hz, 0.9 V for 60 Hz, and 1.15 V for 80 Hz.

5e. Both increasing the speed and increasing the number of magnets increases the rate at which the magnetic field changes through the coil. Faraday's law states that the voltage induced is proportional to the rate of change of the magnetic field.

5f. The magnetic field is weaker if the magnets are farther from the coil. This results in a lower voltage.

Analyzing the data for the alternating poles generator

5 Use your data from Table 1 to make a graph of voltage versus number of magnets for each frequency. Plot all three sets of data on the same graph. Label each one to indicate the frequency.

> Students should plot the number of magnets on the *x*-axis and the voltage on the *y*-axis.

Describe your graph. What does it show about the relationships between the speed of the rotor, the number of magnets, and the voltage?

> The faster the speed, the greater the voltage. The greater the number of magnets, the greater the voltage.

If you were to double the number of magnets and double the speed, what would happen to the voltage generated?

> The voltage would approximately quadruple.

Imagine that you were to use a generator with a rotor that could hold 16 magnets. Use your graph to predict the voltage for each frequency.

> Students should extrapolate the lines on their graphs to predict the voltages.

How does Faraday's law explain why the speed and number of magnets affected the voltage?

> Faraday's law states that the change in the magnetic field through the coil creates the voltage. The faster the rate of change, the greater the voltage. The magnetic field changes more quickly if either the rotor spins more quickly or if more magnets are used.

6 Why must the coil be close to the rotor?

> The magnetic field decreases as distance increases. The voltage would be less if the rotor and coil were not close to each other.

Changing the orientation of the magnets

Now you will experiment with a different generator design. Flip the magnets so they all have a north pole facing outward. Repeat the experiment, measuring the voltage at all three frequencies and with two, four, six, and 12 magnets.

> Circulate around the room as students work.

Make a graph using your new data. How does it compare with the other graph you made?

> The voltages are lower, especially for the design with 12 magnets.

Alternating magnets

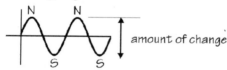

Magnets in the same direction

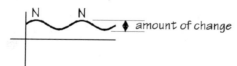

Why do you think there is a difference?

> With the alternating design, the current is forced to completely switch directions each time a magnet passes by because the poles alternate. With the non-alternating design, the current is not forced to switch each time a new magnet passes by. The current drops when there is no magnet nearby, but if the magnets are close together there is not enough time for this to occur. In the 12 magnet, non-alternating design, the generator coil constantly has a north pole near it, so there is not much change in the strength of the magnetic field. And the change in the field is what creates the voltage.

Suppose you had positioned the magnets so all of the south poles were facing out. How would your results compare?

> The results would be the same as when the north poles all faced out. The direction of the current at any instant will vary depending on whether a north or south pole is approaching, but the overall voltage generated is the same.

5 Analyzing the data for the alternating poles generator

Table 1: Generator data with alternating magnetic poles facing out

Rotation frequency	Voltage with 2 magnets	Voltage with 4 magnets	Voltage with 6 magnets	Voltage with 12 magnets
40 Hz				
60 Hz				
80 Hz				

a. Use the data from Table 1 to make a graph of voltage versus number of magnets for each frequency. Plot all three sets of data on the same graph. You should have three separate lines on your graph. Clearly label each one to indicate the frequency.

b. How does changing the number of magnets affect the voltage generated? If you double the number of magnets, how much does the voltage change?

c. If you doubled both the number of magnets and the speed, what change would you expect in the voltage?

d. Suppose you had a rotor with a different magnet slot spacing. If you used 16 magnets, what would you expect the voltage to be for each frequency? You should use your graph to answer this question.

e. Why do increasing the rotor speed and changing the number of magnets have a similar effect on the voltage generated? You should mention Faraday's law in your answer.

f. Why is it important for the generator coil to be positioned close to the rotor? If you loosen the generator coil screws and slide the coil away from the motor, what happens to the voltage generated?

6 Changing the orientation of the magnets

Flip the magnets so they all have a north pole facing outward. Repeat the experiment measuring speed and voltage for a range of rotation frequencies. Record your measurements in Table 2.

Table 2: Generator data with north poles facing out

Rotation frequency	Voltage with 2 magnets	Voltage with 4 magnets	Voltage with 6 magnets	Voltage with 12 magnets
40 Hz				
60 Hz				
80 Hz				

a. Make a graph of voltage versus number of magnets for each frequency.

b. Compare the voltage generated with all north poles facing out to the voltage of the generator with alternating poles facing out. Which design produced the greater voltage overall?

c. Is the difference between the voltage of the two motor designs more noticeable at low or high speeds? Why do you think this is?

d. Compare the voltage created by each design using 12 magnets. Why do you think the generator with all north poles facing out did not work well with 12 magnets?

e. How could you improve the design of the generator? Discuss three improvements you could make that would increase the voltage generated.

6 Example answers

Table 2: *Generator data with north poles facing out*

Rotation frequency	Voltage with 2 magnets	Voltage with 4 magnets	Voltage with 6 magnets	Voltage with 12 magnets
40 Hz	0.088	0.173	0.236	0.139
60 Hz	0.134	0.253	0.347	0.194
80 Hz	0.162	0.331	0.449	0.242

6a.

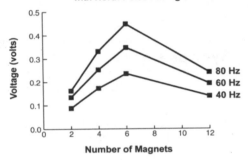

Voltage vs. Number of Magnets with North Poles Facing Out

6b. The voltage was greater when the magnets had alternating poles facing out.

6c. The difference is more noticeable at high speeds. When the motor spins at a low speed, the current in the coil in the non-alternating design has time to decrease after a magnet passes by. When the rotor spins quickly, there isn't enough time between magnets for the current to drop. With the alternating design, the current is forced to completely switch directions each time a magnet passes by because the poles alternate.

6d. The generator with all north poles facing out did not work well because there was not enough time for the current to drop after each magnet passed by.

6e. The number of turns of wire on the coil could be increased. Stronger permanent magnets could be used. The generator coil could be moved closer to the rotor. Additional generator coils could be added.

24.1 Semiconductors

Key Question: What are some useful properties of semiconductors?

Electronic devices are in telephones, computers, video games, cars, watches; a virtually endless list. Diodes are a basic element of electronics and are used to control the direction of current flowing in a circuit. This investigation will introduce students to the properties of a diode. Students first learn to use the solderless breadboard, a platform for building electronic circuits. They then measure the current vs. voltage curve for a diode in both the forward bias and reverse biased direction. They observe that a diode only allows current to flow in one direction and only when the voltage is greater than a minimum value. The same experiment is repeated for an LED.

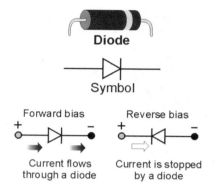

Diode

Symbol

Forward bias — Current flows through a diode

Reverse bias — Current is stopped by a diode

Reading Synopsis

Students read Section 24.1 Semiconductors after the Investigation

Diodes are a basic building block of all electronics. A diode is a one way valve for electric current. A transistor is a control valve for electric current.

The conductivity of semiconductor materials lies between conductors and insulators and depends on the number of free charge carriers. An n-type semiconductor is created when a phosphorus impurity is added to silicon. Each phosphorus atom contributes an extra electron to the silicon crystal, increasing its conductivity. A p-type semiconductor is created when atoms of boron are added to silicon. Each boron atom captures an electron from the silicon crystal. The resulting "hole" in the crystal acts like a positive charge which can move and carry current. A p-n junction is formed where n-type and p-type semiconductors meet. The p-n junction is the fundamental operating structure of electronic devices. A p-n junction allows current to flow only in one direction. A diode contains a single p-n junction and a transistor contains two p-n junctions back to back.

The Investigation

Leading Questions
- How are semiconductor electronic devices different from resistors and capacitors?
- How is the direction of electric current controlled?
- What does a diode do?

Learning Goals
By the end of the Investigation, students will be able to:
- Describe the electrical behavior of a diode.
- Describe how a diode is different from a resistor in terms of its current and voltage characteristics.

Key Vocabulary
diode, semiconductor, forward bias, reverse bias, bias voltage, breadboard, bus

Setup and Materials

Students work in groups of four or five at tables.

Each group should have:

- Solderless breadboard
- 2 D batteries
- An assortment of small 22 gauge solid core wires to use for making connections on the breadboard.
- A small flat bladed screwdriver used for prying parts off the breadboard
- A small pair of needle nose pliers for bending small wires
- A wire stripping tool (or use pre-stripped wire)
- Electric Circuits experiment with battery holder and potentiometer.
- Two jumper wires with alligator clips to bring 3V and 0V from the Electric Circuits to the breadboard.
- Several diodes to test. Rectifier diodes and signal diodes work well. Zener diodes may not work so you should avoid these.
- A multimeter

Any Radio Shack™ will carry these parts, as will most hobby electronics stores. hobbyengineering.com and Kelvin Electronics (kelvin.com) are also excellent source used to serving schools.

Details

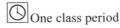

Time	One class period

Preparation If you have time, prepare the jumper wires by cutting and stripping the ends. Each student will use the following in the electronics experiments. All lengths are approximate.

10 pcs. 1/2" long

6 pcs 1" long

4 pcs 4"long

2 pcs 8" long

Note, you can buy jumper wire kits pre-cut, and pre-stripped in organized little plastic boxes from any of the three sources listed on the left.

Assignments Section 24.1 Semiconductors in the **Student Edition** after the Investigation.

Skill Sheets 3.2 Making Line Graphs
19.3A Ohm's Law

Teaching the Investigation

1 Introduction
2 Building circuits on a breadboard
3 Testing a diode
4 The current vs. voltage curve for a diode
5 LED's
6 Preparing for next class

Introduction

What are diodes?

Diodes are a basic element of electronics, which are used to control the direction of current flowing in a circuit.

Building circuits on a breadboard **1**

A breadboard is used as a test version of an electronic circuit.

Testing a diode **2**

How does current flow in a diode?

Current flows in only one direction in a diode; from the positive end to the negative end.

So far with our experiments on circuits we have learned about current, voltage, resistors, power and energy. Today we are going to start learning about electronics. Electronics applies the basic concepts in electricity in the design of complex electrical devices such as computer chips, stereos, and control systems. Electronic circuits may contain hundreds or thousands of electrical components including resistors, capacitors and semiconductor devices. Today, we are going to experiment with a diode which is the simplest sort of semiconductor device. More advanced devices like transistors, and computer chips are fundamentally made by connecting many diodes, so diodes are a good place to start.

The first step to learning electronics is figuring out how to connect all of a tiny components to make a circuit. In a finished electronic device the components are soldered to a circuit board. If you look at a circuit board you see that there are silver traces which are the wires. There are so many wires that they are etched onto the board. Connections are made when the component is soldered into the circuit board.

Obtain a few old circuit boards and passed them around so students can see the construction. These can often be obtained at computer repair places or from any electronic device which someone has thrown away.

Unfortunately, soldering everything together is time-consuming and makes it difficult to change anything. To design and test circuits engineers use a device called a solderless breadboard, usually referred to as just a breadboard. The breadboard has a pattern of holes which accept wires and components such as resistors, capacitors, diodes, etc. Underneath the holes are many conducting pieces of metal that electrically join the holes in a pattern. You put electronic components into the holes and the conducting metal strips underneath make the connections for you.

Pass out the breadboards so students may examine them.

To use a breadboard correctly you need to know how the holes are connected underneath. All five holes in a short row are connected to each other. All the holes in a long row are similarly connected together. The long rows along the edge are called busses and are used for power and ground. Connect the +3V from a pair of batteries to one bus and 0V from the negative terminal of the batteries to the other bus.

Demonstrate for students how to make connections between batteries and the breadboard. Also demonstrate how to insert electronic components such as resistors. The first circuit I usually build is with one battery, a 100Ω resistor, and an LED connected in series (see sidebar).

A common diode looks like a small cylinder with a stripe on one end. A diode is a one way valve for electric current. Current can flow one direction through a diode and is blocked from flowing in the other direction. The stripe indicates the negative end of the diode. Since current flows from positive to negative, current flows toward the end with the stripe. Current is blocked if it tries to flow the other way. The symbol for a diode is a arrow with a line crossing the tip. The arrow indicates the direction current is allowed to flow. The line shows that current cannot flow in the other direction.

Draw the symbol for a diode on the board.

Connect the circuit shown in step 2 of your Investigation. Use two batteries, a switch, the potentiometer, and a diode. Be careful to put the diode in so current flows toward the stripe. Close the switch and turn the potentiometer so the bulb lights. Next, open the switch, remove and reverse the diode in the circuit. Close the switch and try to light the bulb. What happens.

Students should see that the bulb lights when the diode is in the forward biased direction but does not like if the diode is in backwards

24.1 Semiconductors

Question: What are some useful properties of semiconductors?

In this Investigation, you will:

1. Show how a diode acts like a one-way valve for electric current.
2. Measure the current versus voltage curve for an LED.

It is almost impossible to do anything today without being affected by electronics. Electronic devices are in telephones, computers, video games, cars, and watches, a virtually endless list. Diodes, a basic element of electronics, are used to control the direction of current flowing in a circuit. Diodes are also the building blocks for transistors. This Investigation explores the properties of diodes.

1 Building circuits on a breadboard

Many experimental circuits are built on a device called a solderless breadboard, usually referred to as just a breadboard. The breadboard has a pattern of holes that accept wires and components such as resistors, capacitors, and diodes. Underneath the holes are many conducting pieces of metal that electrically join the holes in a pattern. For example, all five holes in a short row are connected to each other. All the holes in a long row are similarly connected together.

Breadboard

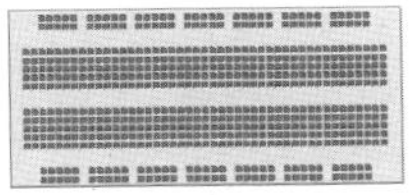

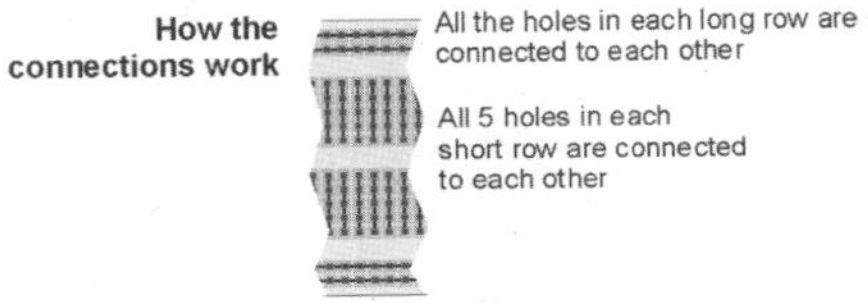
How the connections work
All the holes in each long row are connected to each other
All 5 holes in each short row are connected to each other

The long rows along the edge are called *busses* and are used for power and ground. For these experiments, you will connect the +3V from a pair of batteries to one bus and 0V from the negative terminal of the batteries to the other bus.

2 Testing a diode

A common diode looks like a small cylinder with a stripe on one end A diode is a one-way valve for electric current. Current can only flow one way through a diode and not the other way.

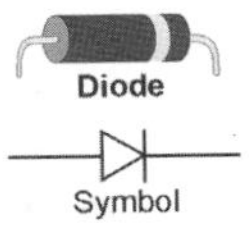
Diode
Symbol

1. Connect the circuit below using two batteries, a switch, the potentiometer, and a diode.

Build this circuit

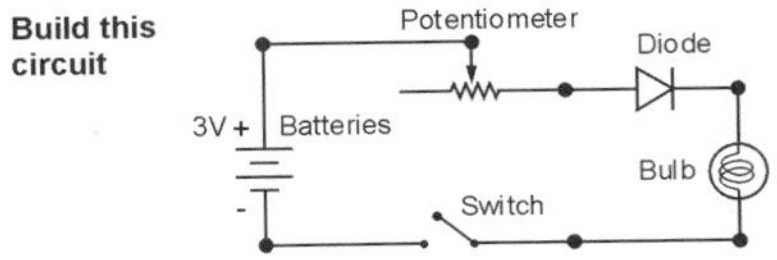
Potentiometer
Diode
3V +
Batteries
-
Bulb
Switch

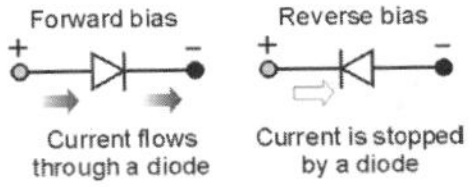
Forward bias
+
-
Current flows through a diode
Reverse bias
+
-
Current is stopped by a diode

2. Close the switch and turn the potentiometer so the bulb lights. Next, open the switch and remove and reverse the diode in the circuit. Close the switch and try to light the bulb.

2 3 Example answers

2.2 When the diode is reversed in the circuit, the bulb will not light.

Table 1: *Positive Voltage vs. Current*

Potentiometer setting	Current (A)	Voltage (V)
Setting 1	0.0949	0.96
Setting 2	0.0731	0.93
Setting 3	0.0477	0.87
Setting 4	0.0367	0.85
Setting 5	0.0266	0.82

Table 2: *Negative Voltage vs. Current*

Potentiometer setting	Current (A)	Voltage (V)
Setting 1	0	-4.88
Setting 2	0	-4.88
Setting 3	0	-4.88
Setting 4	0	-4.88
Setting5	0	-4.88

3a. Graph:

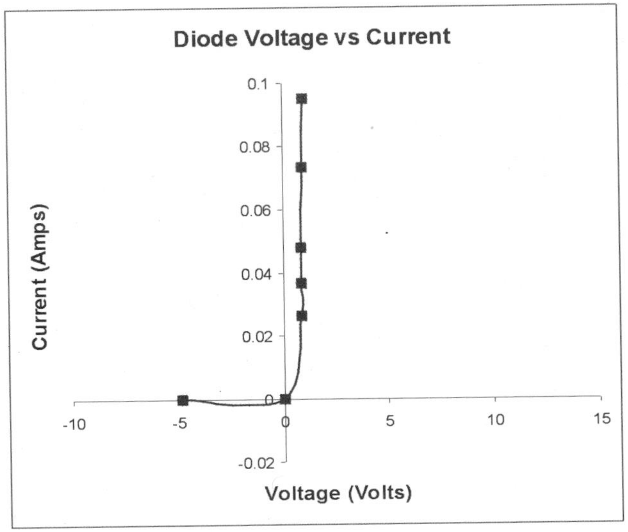
Diode Voltage vs Current
Current (Amps)
0.1
0.08
0.06
0.04
0.02
0
-0.02
-10
-5
0
5
10
15
Voltage (Volts)

The current vs. voltage curve for a diode

Forward bias: when a diode is connected in a circuit so that current flows through it

Reverse bias: when the diode is reversed so that it blocks the flow of current

Bias voltage is the energy difference needed to open the diode.

LED's

What is a LED?

LED stands for Light Emitting Diode. LEDs are energy-efficient diodes used as indicator lights on electronics equipment.

Preparing for next class

Semiconductors are solid, crystalline materials whose electrical resistance is temperature dependent and can be controlled or changed.

When we studied resistors, we made a graph of current vs. voltage to determine their resistance. We are now going to make them that same graph for a diode. The graph will look quite different. Follow the instructions in step three of the investigation. Use the potentiometer to adjust the current in the circuit. To measure the current set the meter to amps DC and touch the leads across the terminals of the switch with the switch open. This causes the current to flow through the meter to complete the circuit. Measure the voltage drop across the diode with the meter set to volts DC. Measure at least 5 points of current and voltage. Record the data in Table 1 under "Positive Voltage vs. Current". We called this positive because the current is flowing from the positive side of the diode toward the negative side. This is called the forward bias direction in electronics.

Students make voltage and current measurements of the diode in the forward biased direction.
Now remove the diode and turned it backwards. The diode is now reverse biased because the positive voltage in the circuit is trying to force current to flow into the negative end of the diode. Measure voltage and current and enter the results in table 2 under the heading "Negative Voltage vs. Current". We call these values negative because the positive end of the diode (away from the stripe) is seeing a lower (more negative) voltage than the negative side.

Students make voltage and current measurements of the diode in the forward biased direction. They should find that the current is zero no matter what voltage appears across the diode.
Draw the current vs. voltage graph for the diode. Set the vertical and horizontal axes in that center of the page so you can plot both positive and negative values for both current and a voltage. Plot both current and voltage values in table 1 as positive and values in table 2 as negative.

Students make the current versus a voltage graph for the diode.
Does anyone know what the acronym LED stands for?

At least one student is likely know that LED stands for Light Emitting Diode.
If it is a diode, how do you think the voltage and current behave?

Students should discuss this can't recognize that and LTD acts just like an ordinary diode with respect to voltage and current. Current can't flow in the forward biased direction and is blocked from flowing into the reverse unbiased direction.
With an LED there is not a stripe to determine which side is the negative side. Look for a small flattened part of the rim on a round LED, that is the negative side. The negative lead is also made a little shorter than the positive lead. Repeat the voltage and current measurements for the LED. At what value of current do you start to see light?

Students measure voltage and current in both the forward biased and reverse biased directions for the LED.
Now that we see what a diode does, it is time to discuss how it works. Diodes are made from silicon which is a semiconductor material. Like carbon, each atom of silicon has can bond with four neighbors. Pure silicon forms a crystal in which each silicon atom is bonded to four neighboring atoms. The electrons are bonded so only a very few are free to move and carry current. That is why silicon is a semiconductor. Anything that contributes more electrons that are mobile greatly changes the conductivity of silicon. Read section 24.1 on semiconductors and be prepared to discuss what you learned next class.

Students read section 24.1 after the investigation and prior to doing Investigation 24.2.

3   24.1 Semiconductors

The current versus voltage curve for a diode

The next part of the experiment measures the current versus voltage curve for a diode. You will first measure positive voltage and current with the diode forward biased. You will then reverse the battery connections to measure negative voltage and current.

1. Replace the diode in the proper direction in your circuit so current flows through the diode toward the striped end.
2. Turn the potentiometer all the way to the left to make the bulb as bright as possible.
3. Set the meter to DC volts. Close the switch and measure the voltage across the diode by touching the leads of the meter to the terminals of the diode. Record the value in Table 1.
4. Set the meter to DC amps. Measure the current by opening the switch and inserting the leads of the meter between the terminals of the switch.
5. Turn the potentiometer down and repeat the voltage and current measurements for at least five settings of the potentiometer across its full range.
6. Reverse the battery connections so the diode is now biased in the reverse direction. Relative to the diode, all voltage and currents are now negative.
7. Measure voltage across the diode and current in the circuit for at least five settings of the potentiometer. The bulb will not light because the diode is blocking all the current. Record the values in Table 2.

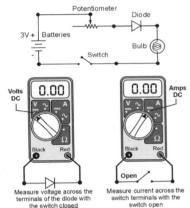

Measure voltage across the terminals of the diode with the switch closed

Measure current across the switch terminals with the switch open

Table 1: Positive Voltage vs. Current

Potentiometer Setting	Current (A)	Voltage (V)

Table 2: Negative Voltage vs. Current

Potentiometer Setting	Current (A)	Voltage (V)

a. Showing both positive and negative voltages and currents, draw the current versus voltage graph for the diode.

b. Explain how the graph shows that the resistance of the diode changes with the direction of current.

4 ### LED's

The acronym LED stands for Light Emitting Diode. Repeat the experiment in Part 3 except use an LED instead of an ordinary diode and replace the bulb with a 100Ω resistor.

---

3 **4** ## Example answers

3b. According to Ohm's law, the resistance equals voltage divided by current. At any point on the diode graph, the resistance is the inverse of the slope of the graph. For the negative voltages, the slope is zero and the resistance is infinite. For the positive voltages, once you get past the forward bias voltage, the slope goes up very quickly and the resistance of the diode drops rapidly to close to zero.

4. Data for LED experiments:

Table 3: *Data for LED experiments*

Pot. Setting	Positive		Negative	
	Current	Voltage	Current	Voltage
1	0.0214	2.02	0	-4.93
2	0.0167	1.98	0	-4.93
3	0.0141	1.97	0	-4.93
4	0.0129	1.95	0	-4.93
5	0.0112	1.94	0	-4.93

Graph:

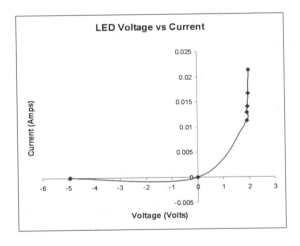

24.2 Circuits with Diodes and Transistors

Key Question: What are some useful properties of transistors?

The electronic age we live in began with the invention of the transistor. A transistor is an electronic control valve for voltage and current. Transistors are the basic element in computers, stereos, video cameras, and almost every other electronic device you can think of. In this investigation, students use a transistor as an on-off switch for an electric motor. The transistor senses a current from a solar cell. The current from the solar cell is not enough to run the motor. But, the solar cell makes enough current to turn on a transistor which controls the motor. After makning the motor control work, students use their circuit to measure the electrical characteristics of a transistor.

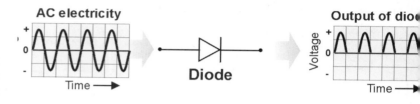

Reading Synopsis

Students read Section 24.2 Circuits with Diodes and Transistors before the Investigation

This section is an introduction to simple circuits using diodes and transistors. A very common diode circuit is a rectifier. A rectifier circuit uses diodes to convert AC electricity into DC.

A transistor may be used as an electronic switch. A small voltage or current applied to the base of a transistor causes the collector-emitter resistance to drop from >100,000Ω to less than 10Ω A transistor may also be used as an amplifier. An amplifier takes a small signal and multiplies its voltage without changing the time dependent shape of the signal. The section introduces the concept of input and output voltage as applied to electronic circuits.

Transistors are also used to construct electronic logic circuits. A logic circuit makes a decision based on evaluation of a number of conditions. An example is given of a three input AND function constructed with three transistors.

The Investigation

Leading Questions
- What is a transistor and what does it do?
- How are the electrical characteristics of a transistor different from electrical components such as resistors and capacitors?
- How is a transistor used in a circuit?

Learning Goals By the end of the Investigation, students will be able to:
- Describe the three terminals of a transistor and their functions.
- Describe how to make a transistor work as a switch.
- Connect a circuit using a transistor as a switch.

Key Vocabulary transistor, based, collector, emitter, diode, terminal

Setup and Materials

Students work in groups of four or five at tables.

Each group should have:

- Solderless breadboard
- 2 D-batteries
- An assortment of small 22 gauge solid core wires to use for making connections on the breadboard.
- A small flat bladed screwdriver used for prying parts off the breadboard
- A small pair of needle nose pliers for bending small wires
- A wire stripping tool (or use pre-stripped wire)
- Electric Circuits experiment with battery holder and potentiometer.
- Two jumper wires with alligator clips to bring 3V and 0V from the Electric Circuits to the breadboard.
- A 1.5 V to 3V DC electric motor
- A solar cell of 4-10 cm^2 area.
- Several npn transistors to test. Do not use pnp transistors as these require a slightly different circuit than the one shown in the Investigation.
- An assortment of resistors with values from 100Ω to 100 kΩ. These may be 1/8 watt or 1/4 watt size.
- A multimeter

Any Radio Shack^{TM} will carry these parts, as will most hobby electronics stores. hobbyengineering.com and Kelvin Electronics (kelvin.com) are also excellent source used to serving schools.

Details

Time ⊙ One class period

Preparation 🖊 If you have time, prepare the jumper wires by cutting and stripping the ends. Each student will use the following in the electronics experiments. All lengths are approximate.

10 pcs. 1/2" long

6 pcs 1" long

4 pcs 4" long

2 pcs 8" long

Note, you can buy jumper wire kits pre-cut, and pre-stripped in organized little plastic boxes from any of the three sources listed on the left

Assignments 📖 Section 24.2 Circuits with Diodes and Transistors in the **Student Edition** after the Investigation.

Skill Sheets 19.3A Ohm's Law

Teaching the Investigation

1 Introduction
2 The physics of semiconductors
3 Connections and circuits for a transistor
4 A transistor switch circuit

Introduction

A transistor is a semiconductor device with three terminals for controlling current.

The physics of semiconductors

Conductivity is a measure of how well a substance conducts electricity.

Substances, like metals, with high conductivity are called conductors. Insulators, like rubber, have low conductivity.

The conductivity of semiconductors lies between that of conductors and insulators.

Connections and circuits for a transistor

Transistors have three terminals: the collector, the emitter, and the base.

The main path for current is between the collector and the emitter.

The base controls how much current flows.

In the last investigation we learned how a diode worked in a circuit. Today we are going to discuss the physics of what goes on inside a diode, then build some circuits with a transistor. A transistor is really two diodes back-to-back in a single device. In order to understand how a transistor works, we need to dig deeper into the physics of the p-n junction.

The relative ease at which electrical current flows through a material is known as conductivity. The conductivity of a material comes from electrons. A conductor, like copper has many electrons that are free to move because they are not bonded to individual atoms. Copper has a very high conductivity because the high density of mobile electrons makes it easy for electrical current to flow. The opposite is true for rubber. All the electrons in a molecule of rubber are tied up in chemical bonds and cannot move. If the electrons cannot move, there is nothing to carry any electric current and therefore the conductivity is low. Rubber is a good insulator, because it has a very low conductivity.

Semiconductors are in between conductors and insulator. The electrons in a semiconductor are bound to atoms only the bonds are relatively weak. The energy from a battery or heat is enough to free a few electrons which can move and carry moderate amounts of current. However, the conductivity of a semiconductor can change dramatically. Anything that changes the number of free electrons has a huge effect on conductivity. For example, adding an impurity of 1 phosphorus atom per 10 million silicon atoms increases the conductivity by 20,000 times!

Diodes and transistors are made from silicon with impurity elements such as boron and phosphorus added. Boron atoms tend to trap free electrons. Phosphorus atoms tend to donate free electrons. To make a diode, silicon containing boron is mated to silicon containing phosphorus. The region where they two types touch can have many free electrons or none, depending on the direction of the voltage. When the voltage goes one way, the free electrons given up by phosphorus atoms are trapped by boron atoms and the junction becomes an insulator. When voltage goes the other way, free electrons are pushed away from the boron atoms and the junction is a conductor. A diode only allows current to flow one way, in the direction that pushes electrons away from the boron side of the junction.

1

A transistor allows you to control the current, not just block it in one direction. A transistor is like a variable flow valve for current. A good analogy for a transistor is a pipe with an adjustable gate. When the gate is closed the pipe has very high resistance and not much water flows. When the gate is open the pipe has low resistance and water flows easily. The adjustable gate is a control for the flow through the pipe.

Sketch a diagram like the one on page 479 of the text.

A standard silicon transistor has three terminals, called the collector, the emitter, and the base. The main path for current is between the collector and emitter. The base controls how much current flows. Very tiny amounts of current flowing into the base of the transistor change the conductivity by many orders of magnitude. You can think about a transistor like a resistor which has a resistance that depends on the amount of current flowing into the base. When there is no base current, the resistance between the collector and the emitter is very high, often $100,000\Omega$ or more. A base current of ten millionths of an amp can drop the collector-emitter resistance to 10Ω or lower. In some ways a transistor acts like a potentiometer that can be electrically controlled using the base current. You have to turn a dial to change the resistance of an ordinary potentiometer. Transistors are the building blocks of electronics. A computer CPU contains more than a million tiny transistors.

Why electronic devices are made from silicon

Atoms of silicon have 16 electrons. Twelve are bound tightly inside the atom. Four are near the outside of the atom and only loosely bound. In pure silicon the atoms are arranged so each of the four outer electrons is paired with another electron from each of four neighboring atoms. At room temperature a small fraction of the electrons in silicon have enough energy to break free from their pairs and carry electric current. The small population of free electrons are what makes silicon a semiconductor.

Sketch figure 24.5 from page 480 of the text.

Phosphorus atoms have five outer electrons compared to silicon's four. When a phosphorus atom tries to fit in with four silicon atoms, four of its five outer electrons pair up with the neighboring silicon atoms. The extra electron does not pair up and is free to carry current. Adding a phosphorus impurity to silicon increases the number of electrons that can carry current.

Sketch figure 24.6 from page 481 of the text.

When a small amount of boron is mixed into silicon the opposite effect happens. A boron atom has three outer electrons, one less than silicon. When a boron atom tries to fit into silicon it needs another electron so it can pair up with its four neighbors. The boron atom captures an electron from a neighboring silicon atom.

When an electron is taken by a boron atom, the silicon atom is left with a positive charge. The silicon atom with the missing electron is called a hole because it needs to be filled with another electron. The positive silicon atom attracts an electron from one of its neighbors, and the hole moves. The new hole takes an electron from its neighbor and the hole moves again. In fact, as electrons jump from atom to atom, the positive hole moves in the opposite direction and can carry current! Silicon with a boron impurity is a p-type semiconductor. The current in a p-type semiconductor is carried by holes with positive charge.

Sketch the diagram from the bottom of the page and figure 24.7, both from page 481 of the text.

UNIT 7: Electricity and Magnetism

24.2 Circuits with Diodes and Transistors

Question: What are some useful properties of transistors?

In this Investigation, you will:

1. Measure the voltage and current characteristics of a transistor.
2. Use a transistor to switch a small motor on and off.

A transistor allows you to control the current, not just block it in one direction. A transistor is like a variable flow valve for current. A good analogy for a transistor is a pipe with an adjustable gate. When the gate is closed, the pipe has very high resistance and not much water flows. When the gate is open, the pipe has low resistance and water flows easily. The adjustable gate is a control for the flow through the pipe.

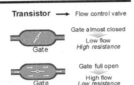

Transistor → Flow control valve
Gate almost closed
Low flow
High resistance

Gate full open
High flow
Low resistance

1 Connections and circuits for a transistor

A transistor has three terminals. The main path for current is between the *collector* and *emitter*. The *base* controls how much current flows. You can think about a transistor like a potentiometer that can be electrically controlled. The effective resistance of a transistor is changed by altering the current flowing into the base.

When used as a switch, the current needed to "turn on" a transistor is very small. A few millionths of an amp is typical. In a circuit, the current into the base is limited by a resistor with a resistance that is large, often 100 kΩ or more.

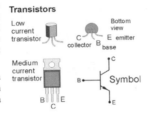

Transistors

Low current transistor

Bottom view

C collector B base E emitter

Medium current transistor

B — C

Symbol

B | E

E

2 A transistor switch circuit

Transistor switches are often used when small input signals control larger output currents used to drive motors, lights, or other electrical devices. A good example is a light-controlled fan. In this circuit, a fan goes on when there is light. The solar cell does not produce enough electricity to drive the fan motor directly. However, it does produce enough current to turn the transistor on. The transistor switches the motor on by allowing current to flow from the battery.

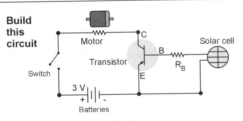

Build this circuit

Motor

Transistor

Switch

C

B

E

R_B

Solar cell

3 V
Batteries

1. Connect the circuit shown in the diagram.
2. You will need to try different values for the base resistor R_B until the motor switches on and off when light reaches or is blocked from the solar cell.

170

A transistor switch circuit

An ordinary switch can be seen as a device which changes from very low resistance to a very high resistance when you move a mechanical part.

Describe how the base of a transistor controls the resistance between the collector and emitter with small amounts of electric current.

2 One of the basic uses for a transistor is an electronic switch. There are many circuits in which a small voltage or current controls a much larger voltage or current using a transistor. Many of the controls in your appliances at home are based on transistors. When you push a button, it sends a low voltage signal which turns on a transistor that controls a much larger current and voltage to the motor or other component. When used as a switch, a transistor needs only a very tiny current to turn "on". Today we are going to use a transistor to make a light-controlled motor, such as might operate a fan on sunny days. The solar cell only makes a very small amount of current, not enough to turn the motor. However, the solar cell does make enough current to switch the transistor from high resistance to low resistance. Take a few minutes and build the circuit from step 2 of your Investigation. Do not apply power yet, just build the circuit.

Students make the circuit of step 2 with the solar cell, motor, and transistor.

3 Before we make the circuit work, lets talk about how it works. The base of not transistor is connected to the solar cell through a resistor. Current from the solar cell can flow through the basic resistor and out of the emitter to ground. Remember, a solar cell makes current from light. When there is no light falling on the solar cell how much current flows into the base of the transistor? Is about resistance of the transistor high or low? How much current flows through the circuit including the motor?

When there is no light falling on the solar cell, the current into the base of the transistor is zero. This means of the transistor is in its high resistance state. If the transistor has high resistance, very little current flows through that circuit because the transistor is in series with the motor.

Now what happens when light is allowed to fall on the solar cell? Does current that flow into the base of the transistor? How much current flows in the circuit?

When light falls on the solar cell current flows into the base of the transistor. If the current is large enough, the transistor changes to a low resistance state. Current can now flow in the circuit because the largest resistance in the circuit is the motor with has a resistance of only a few ohms. The motor turns on.

What is the significance of the base resistor?

The base resistor limits how much current flows into the base of the transistor. This resistance must be low enough so that the solar cell can turn the transistor fully on at the desired light level. The resistance of the base resistor determines the level of light which turns on the motor.

You may now turn on the power to your circuit. Use a piece of cardboard to cover and uncover the solar cell to test your circuit. You may need to adjust the base resistor until the circuit works as it is supposed to.

Students work on their circuits until they function correctly. This may take 5 pr 10 variations of the base resistor. Make sure students turn off the power when the date change in the resistor. Electronic components should never be changed with power on.

While you are working on your circuit, answered the questions in part three of the investigation. You will need to use the meter to measure current and voltage at several places in the circuit to answer the questions.

Students complete the investigation making the measurements required for part 3.

Ohm's Law

$$I = \frac{V}{R}$$

3 Analyzing the circuit

24.2 Circuits with Diodes and Transistors

a. What size resistor did you use for the base of the transistor?

b. Measure the voltage across the base resistor when the transistor is switched on (low resistance). Use Ohm's law to calculate how much current flows into the base of the transistor when it is turned on.

c. Break the circuit at the battery and connect your meter in series to measure the current through the motor when the transistor is turned on.

d. Cover the solar cell and measure the current through the circuit when the transistor is turned off. This current may be too small for your meter to measure; in this case you can only estimate what the maximum current through the circuit could be. The meter rounds measurements to the nearest 0.001 amps. For example, if the meter reads 0.000 A, the maximum current that can be flowing is 0.0005 amps.

e. Reconnect the circuit and measure the voltage across the transistor when it is turned on. Also, measure the voltage across the transistor when it is turned off.

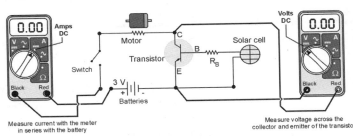

Measure current with the meter in series with the battery

Measure voltage across the collector and emitter of the transistor

f. Use Ohm's law to calculate the resistance of the transistor in its "on" state, and record your answer in Table 1.

g. Use Ohm's law to calculate the resistance of the transistor in its "off" state and record your answer in Table 1. If your meter read 0 A, your calculation is really only telling you the *minimum* resistance the transistor could have. The actual resistance could be much higher, making the current through the circuit even smaller than your estimate.

Table 1: Transistor voltage and current measurements

	Motor on	Motor off
Current (A)		
Collector - emitter voltage (V)		
Transistor effective resistance (Ω)		

171

3 **Example answers**

3a. 10-ohm resistor

3b. With 0.25 volts across the base resistor:
  I = V/R
  I = (0.25 volts)/10 ohm = 25 milliamps.

3c through 3g data:

Table 1: *Transistor voltage and current measurements*

	Motor on	Motor off
Current (A)	0.325	0.004
Collector + emitter voltage (V)	0.85	2.72
Transistor effective resistance (Ω)	2.6	680

24.3 Digital Electronics

Key Question: How do you construct electronic logic circuits?

Computers are based on logic circuits. A logic circuit compares two or more input signals and adjusts its output to reflect the state of the inputs. Students learn that in digital circuits YES, TRUE, and 1 are represented by 5 volts. NO, FALSE, and 0 are represented by 0 volts. In the first part of the investigation students use integrated circuit chips to build an AND logic circuit. The AND circuit returns 5 V (TRUE) only if both inputs are also 5 V (TRUE). Students build AND and OR circuits then are given a two level design problem to build a circuit to evaluate (A AND B) OR C.

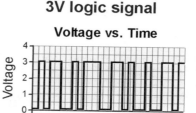

3V logic signal

Voltage vs. Time

Reading Synopsis

Students read Section 24.3 Digital Electronics before the Investigation.

A signal is a stream of information, often in the form of voltage, current, or light. The information in an analog signal is represented by a continuous value such as a voltage. A digital signal is not continuous, and can only be on or off. Information in a digital (binary) signal is encoded as a sequence of on-off transitions. Several codes exist for representing numbers and letters in binary (ASCII, BCD).

Chapters 19-23 have dealt with analog circuits. Analog circuits are built to do a specific function. Computers are digital circuits. Computers are able to do many functions with the same circuit by changing a program. Different programs instruct the electronic hardware to do different functions. Logic circuits are the building block of computers. The four basic logic gates are called AND, OR, NAND, and NOR. An integrated circuit (chip) may contain hundreds or thousands of individual transistors to implement one or more logic functions.

The Investigation

Leading Questions
- What is the difference between an analog and a digital circuit?
- How are logical decisions represented so they can be understood by an electronic device such as a computer?
- How can electronic devices like computers evaluate information and make logical decisions?
- What are the basic types of logic circuits?
- What is an integrated circuit?
- Why is a logic circuit useful?

Learning Goals
By the end of the Investigation, students will be able to:
- Describe how electronic logic functions in terms of circuits and voltages.
- Use the AND and OR logical functions to solve a logic problem with 2-4 inputs and one output.
- Connect a logic integrated circuit chip into a circuit.
- Interpret a truth table for a logical function.

Key Vocabulary   AND, OR, NAND, NOR, logic, gate, integrated circuit, chip, LED, breadboard

Setup and Materials

Students work in groups of four or five at tables.

Each group should have:

- Solderless breadboard
- 3 D-batteries
- An assortment of small 22 gauge solid core wires to use for making connections on the breadboard.
- A small flat bladed screwdriver used for prying parts off the breadboard
- A small pair of needle nose pliers for bending small wires
- A wire stripping tool (or use pre-stripped wire)
- Electric Circuits experiment with battery holder and potentiometer. (you may need to combine Electric Circuit sets to get enough battery holders to stack 3 batteries to get 4.5 volts needed for some logic circuits)
- Two jumper wires with alligator clips to bring 4.5V and 0V from the Electric Circuits to the breadboard.
- A 1.5 V to 3V DC electric motor
- A solar cell of 4-10 cm^2 area.
- Several logic integrated circuits, at least AND and OR. These are typically 4 circuits per 14-pin chip. DO NOT get the "open collector" type as these require extra resistors not shown in the circuit. TTL chips are not as sensitive to static electricity as CMOS chips. Also, many chip families will work at 3V even though the specification is for 5V.
- An half dozen 330Ω resistors. These may be 1/8 watt or 1/4 watt size.
- A multimeter

Hobby electronics stores such as hobbyengineering.com and Kelvin Electronics (kelvin.com) are a good source for logic chips.

Details

Time 🕐 One class period

Preparation 🖊 If you have time, prepare the jumper wires by cutting and stripping the ends. Each student will use the following in the electronics experiments. All lengths are approximate.

10 pcs. 1/2" long

6 pcs 1" long

4 pcs 4"long

2 pcs 8" long

Note, you can buy jumper wire kits pre-cut, and pre-stripped in organized little plastic boxes from any of the three sources listed on the left

Assignments 📖 Section 24.3 Digital Electronics in the **Student Edition** after the Investigation.

Skill Sheets 24.3 Binary Number Problems

Teaching the Investigation

1   Introduction
2   Digital logic
3   Building a logic circuit
4   Designing and building some logic circuits

Introduction

Digital logic

Explaining the basic concepts. 5 V - true, 1, or yes. OV = false, 0, or no.

Electronic logic is also called binary logic since there are only two states for each decision: yes or no.

1 Many science fiction writers describe future machines that are able to think like a human. What does it mean to think? How could thinking be represented in a way that it could be done by a machine? We already know one piece of the solution. That piece involves a special part of thinking call the logic. Logic is a process by which one reaches a decision by evaluating information that relates to the decision. Computers are based on electronic logic. Today's investigation is about electronic logic and is the first step to understanding the basic principles underlying how computers work.

Logic involves making decisions. Suppose you are deciding whether to buy a new car. Your decision can be represented by yes or no. The output of your decision-making process will be a yes or a no. Your decision will be based on input knowledge, such as whether you have the money, whether you really need the car, whether you like the car, and other factors. Logically, these three factors can be also be represented by a yes or a no.

Draw a table with the three input states corresponding the three question and one output state corresponding to the decision.

The first two logic functions are called AND and OR and they are just what the definition of the English words imply. The AND function has an output that is TRUE only if all its inputs are TRUE also. The decision to buy a car can be represented logically by an AND function with three inputs. The logical construction says it is TRUE that you will buy the car if you like it AND you have the money AND you need a new car. With an AND function, the output is true only if all the inputs are true. The output of the OR function is TRUE if one OR the other of its inputs are TRUE. Logical functions can be combined to create complex decisions. Suppose there are three input questions A, B, and C. Can anyone give me a function that is TRUE if A is true but also if B and C are both true?

This takes some thinking. The solution is A OR (B AND C).

With electronics, the values of TRUE and FALSE are represented by voltages. In the most common system, 5 volts represents TRUE and 0 volts represents FALSE. Actually, the circuits are designed so any voltage greater than 2.4 volts is TRUE and any voltage less than 0.8 volts is FALSE. The range of voltages makes digital signals much less sensitive to electrical noise or fluctuations. In digital circuits the decisions are represented by voltages on different electrical terminals.

Draw the table 2.4 - 5 V = TRUE, YES, or 1 and 0 - 0.8 V = FALSE, NO, or 0

Since here are only two allowed states, electronic logic is called binary. A binary number has only two possible digits, 0 and 1. Your textbook has some examples of binary numbers, but for now it is enough to know that it is possible to do any math with binary numbers and logic circuits. Think about doing multiplication, there are rules for what you do with each digit. Any set of rules can be broken down into logical steps and therefore represented by electronic logic. To make this convenient, engineers have designed special integrated circuits, also called IC's or chips to perform electronic logic. An integrated circuit has many transistors all printed on a tiny piece of silicon the size of a pinhead. The inputs and outputs are connected to the pins of the chip. The chip I am handing out has four AND circuits. Each AND circuit has two inputs and **2** one output. The circuit diagram is given at the top of step 2 in your investigation book.

Hand out some chips so students can examine them.

Notice that one end of the chip has a little notch. This is how you tell what the pins do. The pins are numbered counterclockwise starting from the pin to the left of the notch. For this chip, pin 1 and pin 2 are inputs to the first AND gate and pin 3 is the output.

24.3 Digital Electronics

Question: How do you construct electronic logic circuits?

In this Investigation, you will:

1. Build circuits using electronic logic to evaluate inputs and make a decision (output).
2. Practice using integrated circuits ("chips").

Digital electronics use voltages to represent numbers and decisions. The word *digital* means that only two possibilities are allowed. For example, 5 V can mean YES and 0 V can mean NO. When representing a number, 5 V can mean one and 0 V can mean zero. A decision can either be yes or no. A number can either be 1 or 0. There is no in-between or "maybe" allowed. At first glance, it might seem you could not do much when the only possibilities are yes/no or 0/1. However, by combining millions of yes/no decisions or 1/0 numbers, it is possible to build computers, CD players, and all the other complex electronic devices we use. In this Investigation, you will build some basic decision-making circuits with electronic logic.

1 Digital logic

Circuits called *logic gates* are the building blocks of almost all digital systems. The fundamental logic gates are called AND, OR, NAND, and NOR. As their names imply, these gates compare two input voltages and produce an output voltage based on the inputs. The diagram below shows the output of each of the four logic gates for every combination of inputs. The NAND gate is named for the combination Not AND, which is the opposite of AND. The NOR gate is the opposite of OR.

Basic logic circuits

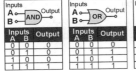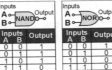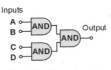

Combination circuit

The basic logic gates can be combined to make more complex decisions. For example, the outputs of two AND gates can be connected to the inputs of a third AND gate. The output of this circuit is 1 only if all four of the inputs are also 1. Electrically, the output is 5 V only when all four inputs are also 5 V. If *any one* of the inputs goes to 0 V, the output also goes to 0 V.

2 Integrated circuits

Logic gates are built from many transistors in *integrated circuits* commonly known as "chips." The diagram at right shows a picture of a chip that has four AND circuits. This chip operates with 5V signals and must be supplied with 5 V to pin 14 and 0 V to pin 7. Inputs and outputs are connected to pins 1-6 and 8-13.

Integrated circuit (chip)

Circuit diagram

Signals and information

A signal is anything that carries information. Today the word signal usually means a voltage, current, or light wave that carries information. In electronics, signals are usually voltages and the information is contained in the way the voltages vary with time. For example, a voice is a sound wave. A microphone converts the variations in air pressure from the sound wave into variations in voltage in an electrical signal.

The voltage versus time graph from a microphone is an example of an analog signal. The voltage in an analog signal can have continuous values. For example, a particular microphone might produce a voltage from -0.1 V to +0.1 V. The signal from the microphone could be a voltage that covered the whole range, including voltages in between + 0.1 V and -0.1 V. The information in an analog signal is contained in both the value and the way the signal changes with time.

A digital signal can only be on or off. For the digital signals in many computers, on is 3 V, off is 0 V. A 5 V digital signal has only two values: 0 V or 5 V. A digital signal is very different from an analog signal. The information in a digital signal is coded in the sequence of changes between 0 V and 5 V. For example, a voltage of 2.5 volts might be represented by the binary number 00100101 where each bit (1) represents 0.1 volts.

Digital signals are resistant to errors caused by electrical fluctuations. If the voltage of a power supply varies, an analog signal may also vary. For example, if the voltage should be 2.5 volts and is 2.6 volts than the circuit may not function correctly. A digital circuit does not care if the voltage representing a 1 is 4.9 volts or 5 volts. A long as the voltage is above 2.4 volts, the circuit will function correctly and recognize the value of 2.5.

Digital signals can also carry more information per wire than analog signals. A digital network wire can send billions of ones and zeros per second, carrying more information than a whole cable full of analog signals. Digital signals are also easier to store, process and reproduce than analog signals.

Building a logic circuit

3

The hole spacing on a breadboard is designed to accept standard integrated circuits. The diagram in step e of your investigation shows the AND chip on the breadboard with power and ground connected. The power busses are connected to 5V and 0V (ground). Notice the notch on the chip is on the left. Pin 7 must be connected to 0 volts and pin 14 must be connected to 5 volts for the chip to work. Notice the small wire jumpers than connect pins 7 and 14 to the correct power busses.

Circulate around and assist students to connect the chip in their breadboard. It helps to have some small needle nose pliers to pull and push wires in the breadboard. Also useful is a small flat-head screwdriver for removing chips without bending the pins. Pry a chip out by slipping the blade of the screwdriver under the chip in the center channel of the breadboard.

How will you know if your circuit works? When testing circuits it is useful to attach LED's to the outputs of the logic gates. The LED's light up when the output is 5 V. The 330W resistors limit the current that must be supplied by the chip to drive the LED. The circuit diagram shows LED's and resistors attached to the outputs of an AND gate. When building the circuit remember, LED stands for Light Emitting Diode, and diodes only allow current to flow in one direction. If you connect the LED backwards it will never light up! To supply inputs, you can connect wires from the 5 V supply line to the inputs of the chip. The diagram shows both inputs of an AND gate connected to 5 V, and the LED lights up.

Students should complete the circuit diagrammed in step 3 of the investigation. The LED should light up when the power is applied.

Designing and building some logic circuits

4

Construct a circuit with two inputs (A and B) and one output. The output should be 5 V when either A or B input is at 5 V. This is an OR function and here is another chip that contains four OR circuits. Use an LED to indicate the output. See what happens when you connect one or both of the input wires to 0 V instead of 5 volts. What happens to the output LED?

Students should apply 5 V and 0 V to each of the inputs (4 combinations) and note which combination makes the output LED light. The LED should light when either or both inputs are connected to 5 V.

Construct the four input AND circuit shown on the previous page. The output should be 5 V only when all four inputs are 5 V. Use an LED to indicate the output. This circuit will use three of the four AND circuits on the chip.

To connect this circuit students must wire the output of two AND circuits to the inputs of a third AND circuit. The logic for building a four-input AND function from two-input AND circuits is Output = (A and B) AND (C AND D).

Design and construct a circuit that has an output described by the table in step 4 of the Investigation. This kind of table is called a truth table. This truth table describes a function with three inputs, A, B, and C. The table gives the output state for every possible combination of the inputs. Logically the function can be written Output = (A AND B) OR C. Your circuit should use an LED to indicate what the output is 5 V.

Assist students to build and test this circuit.

4 **Example answers**

3 **Building a logic circuit**

The hole spacing on a breadboard is designed to accept standard integrated circuits. The long rows are connected to 5 V and 0 V (ground). The diagram at right shows the AND chip on the breadboard with power and ground connected. The notch on one end is how you find pin 1. Pin 1 is to the left of the notch and the pins are numbered counterclockwise around the chip.

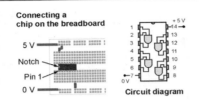

Connecting a chip on the breadboard

Circuit diagram

How will you know if your circuit works? When testing circuits, it is useful to attach light-emitting diodes (LEDs) to the outputs of the logic gates. The LEDs light up when the output is 5 V. The 330Ω resistors limit the current that must be supplied by the chip to drive the LED. The diagram below shows LEDs and resistors attached to the outputs of an AND gate. When building the circuit, remember the *diode* in light-emitting diode: diodes allow current to flow in only one direction. If you connect the LED backward, it will never light!

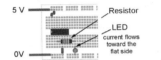 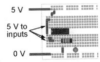 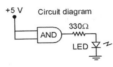

To supply inputs, you can connect wires from the 5V supply line to the inputs of the chip. The diagram shows both inputs of an AND gate connected to 5 V so the LED lights up.

Designing and building some logic circuits

1. Construct a circuit with two inputs (A and B) and one output. The output should be 5 V when either A or B input is at 5 V. Use an LED to indicate the output.

2. Construct the four input AND circuit shown on the previous page. The output should be 5 V only when all four inputs are 5 V. Use an LED to indicate the output.

3. Design and construct a circuit that has an output described by Table 1. This kind of table is called a *truth table*. This truth table describes the function OUTPUT = (A AND B) OR C. Your circuit should use an LED to indicate that the output is 5 V.

Table 1: Truth table for (A AND B) OR C

Inputs			Output
A	B	C	
0	0	0	0
0	0	1	1
0	1	0	0
0	1	1	1
1	0	0	0
1	0	1	1
1	1	0	1
1	1	1	1

Circuit #1

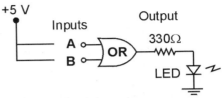

A OR B circuit

Circuit #2

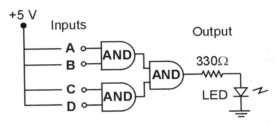

(A AND B) AND (C AND D) circuit

Circuit #3

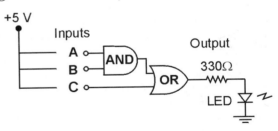

(A AND B) OR C circuit

25.1 Matter and Atoms

Key Question: What are the properties of different elements?

All the elements are made of atoms containing the same three basic particles: protons, electrons, and neutrons. Although they are made of the same particles, elements can have very different properties. In this Investigation, student groups will research one element that they select or that is assigned to them. The group will collect information about their element such as the element symbol, melting point, and density and summarize the information on a poster. On the back of the poster, students will include a bibliography of the resources they used to research the element.

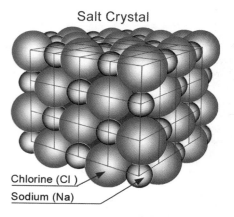

Salt Crystal

Chlorine (Cl)
Sodium (Na)

Reading Synopsis

Students read Section 25.1 Matter and Atoms

There is a tremendous variety of matter in the universe. A simple list of matter in the home includes: wood, plastic, glass steel pots, leaves, and even the air. This section begins with three questions for students to think about: What is the smallest piece of matter? Does matter have different forms? and Can one type of matter transform into another type with different properties?

Democritus a Greek philosopher proposed that matter is made up of small particles called atoms. In 1803, John Dalton revived the idea of atoms, but lacked proof. Albert Einstein finally proved that matter was made of tiny particles by explaining Brownian motion. These particles of matter are atoms and molecules. A molecule is a group of two or more atoms than are joined. Matter can be made of atoms, molecules, or mixtures of these. Nearly all the matter in the world is made from 92 different elements which are arranged on the periodic table. Each of the 92 elements has a unique type of atom and all atoms of a given element are similar to each other.

The Investigation

Leading Questions
- Are the diverse forms of matter actually made from a smaller number of basic substances?
- How many elements are there?
- What makes elements different from each other?
- What are the characteristics of a pure element?
- How do elements combine to make different forms of matter?
- What are elements used for?

Learning Goals

By the end of the Investigation, students will:

- Explain the observed diversity of matter in terms of elements, compounds, and mixtures.
- Describe the properties of a pure element, such as its atomic number, mass, boiling point, melting point, and density.
- Describe examples of where an element is found, in what types of matter, and in what forms.
- Understand how to research elements to learn about their properties.

Key Vocabulary

Brownian motion, atoms, molecular, mixtures, elements, periodic table, compound

---

Setup and Materials

Students work in groups of four or five at tables.

Each group should have:

- A copy of the periodic table
- Access to the library, internet, and/or science resource materials
- Poster board
- Colored markers
- Glue and tape
- Any additional supplies for creating the poster such as old magazines, construction paper, and rulers

Details

Time ⏲ One class period

Preparation ✎ Gather materials and information for students about the elements prior to class.

Assignments 📖 Section 25.1 Matter and Atoms in the **Student Edition** after the Investigation.

Teaching the Investigation

1   Introducing the Investigation
2   Motivating questions: What is the smallest quantity of matter that can exist?
3   How do we explain the phases of matter?
4   How do we explain the observation that matter can change from one kind into a completely different kind?
5   Elements, atoms, and the periodic table
6   Elements and compounds
7   Atoms and molecules
8   Mixtures
9   Researching an element for the Investigation

Introducing the Investigation

Elements are the basic constituents of matter.

Motivating questions:
What is the smallest quantity of matter that can exist?

The smallest particles of matter are electrons and quarks.

How do we explain the phases of matter?

Matter can exist as a solid, liquid, gas, or plasma. A phase changes is an example of a physical change.

How do we explain the observation that matter can change from one kind into a completely different kind?

The elements that comprise matter can be rearranged through chemical reactions.

Elements, atoms, and the periodic table

Atoms are arranged on the periodic table in order of increasing atomic number.

Steel and Wood are both matter, so is the water and the air. But matter has different properties. How many different kinds of matter can we name in this room?

> Student name different types of matter, examples might be plastic, silver, gold, copper, wood, paper, ink, floor tiles, glass, rubber, pencil lead, wax crayon, etc.

We could name millions of different types of matter if we had the time. One of the goals of science is to find the simplest underlying explanations for the diversity of what we see in the universe. It begs the question: are the many millions of kinds of matter really made of a few simpler substances? For example, are there common substances in rocks and glass? Or rocks and water? The Greeks thought so, and they called the basic constituents of matter elements. The different kinds of matter are made from different combinations of the basic elements, just like bread is made from different combinations of eggs, flour, and other ingredients.

I have three questions to ask that will guide our study of the fundamental nature of matter:

1   What is the smallest piece of matter that can exist?

> Discuss with the students what the smallest piece of matter is called. It may be useful to review the concept of matter as having mass and taking up space. Students may know that an atom is a small piece of matter. Students may also know that there are smaller particles within the atom such as electrons, protons, and neutrons. And, some students may even know that quarks are within protons and neutrons. Today, we believe quarks and electrons are the smallest particles of matter that exist.

2   Why can the same kind of matter assume different forms such as water and ice?

> Discuss the forms, called phases, matter may take, which are solid, liquid and gas. Ask students to identify types of matter for which they have seen more than one phase. For example, most students have seen candle wax in both liquid and solid phases. Nearly everyone is familiar with steam, liquid water, and ice. Dry ice and carbon dioxide (CO_2) gas are also two phases of the same type of matter.

3   How can one type of matter turn into a completely different type of matter? For example, when you burn candle wax the result is smoke and ash. This result has very different properties from the candle wax you started with.

> Discuss the concept of matter that is made of different fundamental elements. By changing the combination of the elements we can explain the changing of matter from one type to another. Chemistry which is the branch of science which describes how matter and energy combine and interact.

1

Today, we know that nearly all the matter around us is made from 92 basic elements. The periodic table arranges the elements from the lightest to the heaviest starting with the first element, hydrogen. Hydrogen is a gas and is a rarely found as a pure element. Most of the hydrogen you see around you is combined with oxygen in water. A single atom is the smallest quantity of any element that there can be.

> Introduce the periodic table by having students identify different elements by name and number. For example, the seventh element is nitrogen. The fifteenth element is phosphorus. Ask students if they know anything about each element. For example, nitrogen is found in the atmosphere. Phosphorus is found in glow-in-the-dark materials. An atom is the smallest particle of matter that maintains the properties of the bulk matter. For example, an atom of gold is the smallest particle of gold that you can have. If you divide one atom of gold the result is no longer gold but a different type of matter

UNIT 8: Matter and Energy

25.1   Matter and Atoms

Question: What are the properties of different elements?

In this Investigation, you will:

1. Research an element to learn about its properties.
2. Construct a poster summarizing what you learned about the element.
3. Share your poster with your class.

All the elements are made of atoms containing the same three basic particles: protons, electrons, and neutrons. Although they are made of the same particles, elements can have very different properties. In this Investigation, you will research one element.

1   Atoms and elements

Nearly all the matter in the world is made from 92 different elements. Water is made from the elements hydrogen and oxygen. Air contains mostly nitrogen and oxygen. Steel is mostly iron and carbon with a few exotic elements like vanadium and chromium mixed in. Rocks are mostly silicon and oxygen. We get different kinds of matter by using different combinations of the 92 basic elements.

Each of the 92 elements has a unique type of atom. All atoms of a given element are similar to each other. If you could examine a million atoms of carbon, you would find them all to be similar. However, carbon atoms are different from iron atoms or oxygen atoms. The atoms of an element are similar to atoms of the same element but different from atoms of other elements. One single atom is the smallest particle of an element. Since atoms of the same element are similar, every atom of carbon has the properties of carbon. Similarly, every atom of gold has all the properties of gold.

Periodic Table of the Elements 1-92

Early theories of the elements

The ancient Greeks are credited with the first written theory of matter that proposed the idea of elements. Their theory proposed that all matter was made of four fundamental elements: air, fire, water, and earth. According to the Greek theory of matter, everything could be made by combining different amounts of the four elements. For example, wood contained certain proportions of water, earth, air, and fire. When wood was burned, the smoke was the fire and air. The ash left over was earth. Gold was a different mixture with more earth and less water. The theory was based on simple observations.

In the Greek theory, each element sought its natural place. Fire rose because its natural place was in the sky with the sun. Earth fell because its natural place was on the ground. According to the theory, smoke rose because smoke had a percentage of fire mixed in with the air. Rocks fell because they were mostly earth, with very little fire. Despite being wrong, the greek theory was important because it was based on a few simple observations that everyone could make. Like most scientific knowledge, the or more and sophisticated the observations and that people made, the more refined brew of the theory until it eventually became the atomic theory of matter that we believe today.

Between the time of the Greeks and the invention of modern chemistry, many variations on the theory of matter were believed. Chinese and arabian experimenters at various times proposed theories that included more than a dozen elements. Early research into the elements was often directed along two lines of inquiry. One was the use of chemicals as medicines. The other was the search for a method to make gold from other metals. For example, if gold were just a different mixture of the same basic elements in lead, then it would be possible to turn lead into gold by adjusting the proportions of the elements! The quest for the process by which lead could be turned into gold was the basis of alchemy the medieval practice which was the predecessor of modern chemistry.

Elements and compounds

Both elements and compounds are pure substances; however elements are made up of only one kind of atom. Compounds are composed of two or more different elements.

Atoms and molecules

An atom is the smallest particle of an element.

Molecules are groups of atoms held together by bonds.

Mixtures

Although mixtures may contain many different compounds, they are not pure substances.

Researching an element for the Investigation

The discovery of the true elements was difficult because nearly all matter is made from compounds, and not pure elements. A compound is a substance that contains more than one element. Can anyone tell me whether water is an element or a compound?

Students should answer that water is a compound because it contains the elements hydrogen and oxygen.

An atom is the smallest particle of a element. A molecule is the smallest particle of a compound. A molecule is a collection of atoms that are bonded together. The properties of a substance are determined more by the molecules than by the elements in the molecules. For example, if I combine one carbon atom with four hydrogen atoms, it makes a molecule of methane. Methane is a colorless, explosive gas that people use to heat their homes and cook. If I take ten carbon atoms and 22 hydrogen atoms, I get a molecule of decane, which is charcoal lighter fluid. I can also make plastic, the solvent benzene, or paraffin wax from just carbon and hydrogen. The important thing to remember is that the properties of matter are determined mostly by the molecules, and not by the elements that are in the molecules.

Draw a methane and decane molecule on the board.

Can someone give me an example of a substance and tell me whether it is an element or compound?

Prompt the class for examples, water is one example of a compound, as is rubber. Gold, copper, and neon are some elements that can either be found in their pure form in nature or have been refined to be pure by human technology.

To scientists, a mixture is matter that contains more than one compound. Most of the matter around this room is mixtures. For example, wood contains hundreds of different compounds. Some compounds give wood its characteristic color, some like cellulose give wood its strength. Can anyone name a common substance that is NOT a mixture?

Water is one, others include oxygen gas you get from a gas bottle, or some forms of sugar. The sugar you buy actually contains more than one kind of sugar molecule. Pure compounds are relatively rare and often take much refining to produce.

2 Investigation 25.1 asks you to select an element from the periodic table and find some of its properties and uses. For example, suppose you chose the element hydrogen. The symbol for hydrogen is a capital letter H. Hydrogen has atomic number 1 and its average atomic mass is 1.007 amu. The boiling point of hydrogen is -259°C and the melting point is -253°C. The density depends on its phase. At room temperature and pressure, hydrogen is a gas with a density of 0.09 kg/m^3, which is about ten times lighter than air which has a density of about 1 kg/m^3. Hydrogen is colorless as a gas. The name comes from the Greek *hydro* for water and *genes* for forming. Pure, elemental hydrogen was identified as a component of water. Water is one compound that includes hydrogen and the chemical formula for a water molecule is H_2O. Orange juice is a mixture than contains water, and therefore hydrogen. In the future, some people predict that cars will run on liquid hydrogen fuel instead of gasoline.

Either assign, or let students choose their element for the periodic table. The Investigation contains a list of the information students should research.

2 Research your element

Each group will select or be assigned a different element. Research your element to determine the information below. Record the bibliographic data for all of the sources you use in your research.

- Symbol
- Atomic number
- Average atomic mass
- Melting point
- Boiling point
- Density
- Color
- Origin of the element's name
- One compound that contains the element and state its molecular formula
- One mixture that contains the element
- One use for the element
- Three interesting facts about the element

3 Sharing your information

Make a one-page poster that neatly displays the information you found for your element. Include a bibliography on the back of the poster.

4 Characterizing the element and comparing it with other elements

Answer the following questions regarding the element you researched:

a. Name three other elements with similar chemical properties. Where on the periodic table are elements with similar properties located in relation to each other?

b. How many atoms are in 1 kilogram of your element?

c. At 500°C, is your element a solid, liquid, or gas?

d. At 1,500°C, is your element a solid, liquid, or gas?

e. Does your element play a role in living organisms such as being in your body's chemistry or being recommended in food for nutrition or health reasons?

175

---

2 4 Example answers

2. Copper's symbol is Cu
   Atomic number: 29
   Average atomic mass: 63.546 amu
   Melting point: 1084.62 C (at 1 atmosphere pressure)
   Boiling point: 2562 C (at 1 atmosphere pressure)
   Density: 8.2 g/cm³ (liquid density at the melting point)
   Color: reddish brown
   Origin of the element's name: from the Latin word *cuprum*, meaning the Greek island of Cyprus, famous for its copper mines
   One compound that contains the element: copper chloride (CuCl)
   One mixture that contains the element: brass (an alloy)
   One use for the element: Due to its high electrical conductivity, copper is extensively used in the electrical industry
   Three interesting facts about the element: (1) All American coins are made from copper alloys, (2) Copper was discovered in prehistoric times and has been used for at least 10,000 years, and (3) 65% of the copper used in the United States is mined in Arizona.

   Bibliographic References:
   Lide, David R. (Editor-in-Chief). CRC Handbook of Chemistry and Physics, 77th Edition. Boca Raton: CRC Press, Inc, 1996.
   Phelps Dodge Corporation. Fun Facts about Copper [Online]. Available: http://www.phelpsdodge.com/products/copper/ [5 December 2002]
   Faculty of Chemical Technology, KTF-Split, Croatia. Periodic Table of the Elements: Cu. [Online]. Available: http://www.ktf-split.hr/periodni/en/cu.html [5 December 2003]
   Northwestern University Northwesternutrion. Available: http://www.feinberg.northwestern.edu/nutrition/factsheets/copper.html [5 December 2003]

4a. Three similar elements are: Silver (Ag), Nickel (Ni), and Zinc (Zn)
   Elements with similar properties are located close to each other on the periodic table of the Elements, usually in the same column or group with similar energy levels. Copper is one of the transition metals, including the elements in groups 3 to 12, which have similar energy levels and chemical properties.

4b. 1 atom of Cu $= 63.546$ amu $\times 1.66 \times 10^{-27}$ kg/amu $= 1.0549 \times 10^{-25}$ kg/atom
   1 kg of Cu $\div 1.0549 \times 10^{-25}$ kg/atom $= 9.48 \times 10^{24}$ atoms

4c. At 500°C, copper is a solid.

4d. At 1,500°C, copper is a liquid.

4e. Copper is a necessary component of different enzymes, acts as a catalyst for different chemical reactions in the human body, and has a key role in energy metabolism. Copper is found naturally in many of Earth's minerals and is absorbed by plants, making it available in many fruits, vegetables and meat.

25.2 Temperature and the Phases of Matter

Key Question: What is temperature?

The concepts of warm and cold are familiar to everyone. What causes ice to feel cold and fresh coffee to feel hot? The simple answer is temperature. Temperature is related to energy and determines whether matter takes the form of solid, liquid, or gas. In this Investigation, students explore the change of phase between ice, liquid water, and steam. The students confine a fixed mass of water in a plastic bottle. Some of the water changes phase as the bottle is immersed in boiling water or ice water. The students observe that the volume changes dramatically from the liquid to the gas phase. Students also observe that water expands when it goes from liquid to solid.

Reading Synopsis

Students read Section 25.2 Temperature and the Phases of Matter after the Investigation

Temperature is measured in Fahrenheit and Celsius. Thermometers, thermistors, and thermocouples measure temperature. Temperature describes the average kinetic energy of atoms in random motion.

It is not possible for objects to be colder than absolute zero (-273°C), the temperature at which the motion of atoms reaches a minimum. The Kelvin temperature scale starts at absolute zero. Ordinary matter exists as solid, liquid, and gas. Solid has the lowest energy per atom, and the lowest temperature. Atoms in the gas phase have the most energy and the highest temperature of the three common phases. Plasma is a fourth phase of matter that occurs at greater than 10,000 K. The melting point is the transition temperature from solid to liquid, and the boiling point is the transition temperature from liquid to gas. Phase changes use or give off energy, even though the temperature does not change. Evaporation and condensation describe phase changes at temperatures other than the melting or boiling point.

The Investigation

Leading Questions
- Why can the same substance exist as a solid, liquid, or gas?
- How is temperature related to the phase of matter?
- How do properties such as density, mass, and volume change during phase changes in matter?

Learning Goals
By the end of the Investigation, students will be able to:
- Observe and identify phase changes of water from liquid to solid or gas.
- State evidence that mass does not change during a phase change.
- Measure the temperature at which phase changes occur.
- Demonstrate that phase changes are physical changes because they are reversible.

Key Vocabulary
Fahrenheit scale, Celsius scale, thermometer, thermistor, themocouple, random motion, temperature, Kelvin, solid, liquid, gas, plasma, ionized, melting point, heat of fusion, boiling point, heat of vaporization, evaporation, condensation, relative humidity

Setup and Materials

Students work in groups of four or five at tables.

Each group should have:

- A clear, flexible plastic water bottle with cap (500 mL volume or smaller)
- Stove or hot plate
- Pan of water with a lid (large enough to submerge two-thirds of the bottle)
- Thermometer
- A graduate cylinder
- A timer or stopwatch
- Second pan or bowl with ice water (large enough to submerge two-thirds of the bottle)
- Tongs to hold the bottle
- Mitts to hold hot material
- Safety goggles

Safety note: Be sure that students are careful around the hot plates and hot water. Have safety materials nearby throughout the Investigation. Instruct students to handle hot material with tongs and/or insulating mitts. You may also wish to have students wear safety goggles. However, be sure to alert students that they should avoid getting the mitts wet by the boiling water.

Details

Time One class period

Preparation You will need to have tongs, insulating mitts, a supply of soft plastic bottles, and assorted pots and hot plates ready to do these experiments. Check that your safety equipment is adequate and accessible.

Assignments Section 25.2 Temperature and the Phases of Matter in the **Student Edition** after the Investigation.

Skill Sheets 25.2 Temperature Scales
Skill Builder: Safety Skills (review)

Teaching the Investigation

1 Introduction
2 Relating changes in temperature to phase changes of water
3 Setting up the experiment
4 Observing the change of phase
5 Thinking about what you observed
6 The solid phase of water

Introduction

In what phases of matter can water exist?

Water can exist as a solid, liquid, or gas.

Relating changes in temperature to phase changes of water

Water undergoes phases changes as its temperature is altered.

As the temperature of water molecules increases, they move faster and spread farther apart.

Water molecules have more energy at higher temperatures than at lower temperatures.

Setting up the experiment

SAFETY PRECAUTION: Hot plates and boiling water can cause serious burns. Handle hot objects with tongs and insulating mitts. Wear goggles throughout the Investigation.

Before we begin today's Investigation, let's review what we already know about the phases of water. Can anyone describe what happens when an ice cube is removed from the freezer and placed in a drinking glass?

The ice melts and becomes water.

What would happen to the water in a pot if you boiled it?

Steam would rise from the pot as the water is changed from liquid to gas.

In what phases can water exist?

Water can exist as a solid in the form of ice, a liquid, or in the gaseous phase as steam.

Water can exist as a solid, liquid, or gas. How is each of these phases different?

Solids have a definite shape and volume. The molecules in ice are constantly vibrating but they are not able to switch positions with other molecules.

Liquids have a definite volume but they take the shape of the container in which they are held. Molecules in a liquid move faster than in a solid and are able to slip out of position. The molecules in a liquid are farther apart than in a solid. Water flows because its molecules can move.

Neither the shape or volume of a gas is definite. A gas expands to fill its container. Water molecules are very far apart in the gaseous state.

I need three students to volunteer to be water molecules.

Choose three students and have them come up to the front of the class. Each student will act out the assigned role that follows.

Each of these students is a water molecule. Student A is in a freezer. Student B is in a swimming pool, and student C is above the liquid surface in a kettle of boiling water. How is the motion of each different?

Student A is still, while student B moves. Student C moves very fast.

What causes the difference in the motion of each water molecule?

The low temperature in the freezer limits student A's motion. It is warmer in the swimming pool than in the freezer, so student B can move faster. The highest temperature is in the kettle so student C moves the fastest.

How does a change in temperature alter the phase in which water exists?

Adding heat to the water molecules causes them to move faster, spread apart, and eventually change state. Removing heat causes the water molecules to move slower and closer together.

Which water molecule has the most energy?

Molecules at higher temperatures (student C) possess more energy than those at lower temperatures.

1 Today, you are going to observe the phase changes of water. In the first part of this Investigation, you will look at what happens to water in its liquid and gaseous phases. Gather the materials that are needed to complete the Investigation and bring them to your lab station.

Allow students time to gather materials listed in the Set up and Materials section of this document.

Put on your goggles and leave them on throughout the Investigation. Hot plates and boiling water can cause serious burns. Use tongs and insulating mitts to handle hot objects.

Complete Part 1 of the Investigation. Be sure to record your data in Table 1.

UNIT 8: Matter and Energy

25.2 Temperature and the Phases of Matter

Question: What is temperature?

In this Investigation, you will:

1. Observe the phase change of water from liquid to solid or gas.
2. Measure the temperature at which phase changes occur.
3. Demonstrate that phase changes are physical changes because they are reversible.

The concepts of warm and cold are familiar to everyone. What causes ice to feel cold and fresh-brewed coffee to feel hot? The simple answer is temperature. Ice feels cold because its temperature is lower than the temperature of your skin. Coffee feels hot because its temperature is higher than your skin's temperature. Temperature is related to energy and determines whether matter takes the form of solid, liquid, or gas. This Investigation is about temperature and its effect on materials.

1 Setting up the experiment

Water is an all-important substance on the planet Earth. Many processes, including life, depend on how water behaves at different temperatures. In the first part of this Investigation, you will look at what happens to water in its liquid and gaseous phases.

1. Obtain a small, clear, flexible plastic water bottle with a cap. A volume of 500 milliliters is ideal although similar volumes will also work. Record the volume in Table 1.

2. On a stove or hot plate, bring a pan of water to a boil. The pan should be large enough to submerge at least 2/3 of the plastic bottle. The lid should be on the pan while the water is heating up. Use a thermometer to measure the temperature of the boiling water. Record the temperature in Table 1.

3. Prepare a second pan or bowl with ice water. Measure and record the temperature of the ice water in Table 1.

4. Put 20 milliliters of water in the plastic bottle and loosely put the cap on. It is important that air can escape during the first phase of the experiment.

Safety Note: Hot plates and boiling water can cause serious burns. Have safety materials nearby. Handle hot objects with tongs and insulating mitts. DO NOT allow mitts to be wetted by boiling water.

Lid
Boiling water
Pot
Hot plate

Cap
Clear plastic water bottle 0.5 liters
Bottle must be flexible, soft plastic
20 milliliters of water
DO NOT USE GLASS OR HARD PLASTIC

Table 1: Temperature and volume data

Volume (ml)	
Hot temp. (°C)	
Cold temp. (°C)	

---

1 Example answers

Table 1: *Temperature and volume data*

Volume (mL)	500.0
Hot temp. (°C)	100.0
Cold temp. (°C)	5.0

Observing the change of phase

As the temperature of a gas increases, the energy of its particles also increases.

Gases are expandable and compressible.

2 Complete Part 2 of the Investigation. Be sure to record your observations in steps 3 and 4.

> Give the students time to complete this part of the Investigation.

How did the sides of the bottle change as the steam inside cooled down?

> As the steam inside the bottle cooled down, the sides of the bottle "caved in". Some students may have heard a popping sound. Others may have observed water collecting on the sides of the bottle.

Why do you think this happened?

> As the steam collected in the bottle, the gas expanded to fill the container. As the steam cooled and changed phase (to water), the molecules moved slower, the temperature was reduced, and the gas was compressed.

What happened to the bottle after it was immersed in the pan of ice water?

> The bottle became rigid.

Did your bottle return to its original shape after being replaced in the boiling water?

> Yes, the bottle returned to its original shape.

Thinking about what you observed

The density of water decreases as its temperature increases.

3 Now that you have completed Part 2 of the Investigation, review your observations and answer questions 3a through 3d.

> Allow students time to answer these questions. Refer students to reference books like the CRC Handbook of Chemistry and Physics, or other sources, in order to obtain density values for water and steam.

Density is the ratio of the mass of a substance to its volume.

> Write the formula for calculating density on the chalkboard.

How does the density of water change as its phase changes from liquid to gas?

> The density of water decreases as its temperature increases.

Since steam is less dense than liquid water, how do you think that the volume of equal masses of water and steam would compare.

> The volume occupied by steam would be greater than that of water.

The solid phase of water

Water expands as it freezes.

Ice is less dense than liquid water.

4 Retrieve your plastic bottle. Complete steps 1-3 of Part 4 of the Investigation. Write your name on the plastic bag before placing it in the freezer. We will continue this portion of the Investigation tomorrow.

> The plastic bags containing the student's bottles should remain in the freezer overnight.

Go to the freezer and recover your plastic bag. Record your observations and answer questions 4a and 4b.

> Allow students time to answer these questions.

Which is more dense, solid ice or water?

> Water expands when it freezes, therefore ice is less dense than water.

In cold climates, living species that reside in large bodies of water do not die. Why so you think this is so?

> Ice is less dense than water. Consequently, ice floats in liquid water. Fortunately for living organisms, the low density of ice prevents these bodies of water from freezing solid and killing them.

Do you think that the density pattern exhibited by the phases of water is the norm for all substances?

> Encourage students to research different substances and compare the effect of temperature on their densities.

2 Observing the change of phase

1. Using a pair of tongs, hold the bottle in the pan of boiling water for 1 minute. You may hear some air escaping from under the cap as the water in the bottle heats up and becomes steam. Steam is water in the gaseous phase. As the water in the bottle boils, steam displaces air until the bottle is mostly filled with steam instead of air.

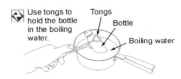

Use tongs to hold the bottle in the boiling water.   Tongs   Bottle   Boiling water

2. When the bottle is filled with steam, you need to seal the cap to keep air from getting back in. Have one person ready with oven mitts to take the bottle from the tongs and tighten the cap quickly. Place the lid back on the pan of boiling water and turn the heat down but keep the water boiling.
3. Watch the sides of the bottle as the steam inside cools down. Record your observations.
4. Immerse the bottle in the pan of ice water. Record your observations of what happens to the bottle.
5. Remove the bottle from the ice water and use the tongs to immerse it back in the pot of boiling water. The cap should still be tightly closed. After a minute or so in the boiling water, the bottle should expand back to its original shape.

3 Thinking about what you observed

a. Why was it important to keep the cap loose during step 1 above?
b. Explain why the bottle changed its volume when it was immersed in the ice water.
c. Explain why the bottle regained its original volume when it was reheated.
d. Research the ratio of the volume of 100 grams of water at 100°C compared with 100 grams of steam at 100°C. Note that the temperature is the same but that water is a liquid phase and steam is a gas phase.

4 The solid phase of water

1. Take the same plastic water bottle and fill it completely with water—right up to the top, leaving no air space.
2. Place the cap on the bottle tightly and put the capped bottle in a sealable plastic bag.
3. Place the bagged bottle in the freezer overnight.
4. Remove the bottle after it has frozen and answer the following questions.

a. Is the density of solid water (ice) about the same as, greater than, or less than the density of liquid water? Use the observations from this experiment to justify your answer.
b. Most solid materials have a density that is greater than the same material in its liquid phase. Suppose the density of ice were greater than the density of water. What would happen to a body of water such as a lake in the winter when the temperature is well below freezing for a long period of time?

177

2 3 4 Example answers

2.3 As the steam cools down, the sides of the bottle contract inward.
2.4 When the bottle is immersed in ice water, the bottle contracts and the steam turns into liquid water.

3a. You need to allow all the air to escape so the bottle can completely fill with steam.
3b. Liquid water has less volume than the same mass of steam.
3c. Steam has a greater volume than the same mass of liquid water.
3d. The ratio of the volume of 100 grams of water compared with 100 grams of steam at 100°C is 1/1700.

4a. The density of solid water is less than the density of liquid water. The volume of the ice was greater than the volume of the water because it expanded out of the bottle. Since density is the ratio of mass to volume, if you keep the mass constant and increase the volume, the density decreases.
4b. If the density of ice were greater than the density of water, a lake in winter would freeze from the bottom up instead of the top down.

25.3 Heat and Thermal Energy

Key Question: What is the relationship between heat, temperature, and energy?

To change the temperature of matter, energy is added or subtracted in the form of heat. This Investigation explores the connection between temperature, heat, and energy. In the Investigation, students prepare equivalent masses of steel, oil, and water at the same temperature. They observe the different thermal energy stored in each sample by adding each to a fixed mass of water and measuring the change in temperature of the water. Students use the heat equation and their observations to prove that different amounts of thermal energy are stored by different substances, even when mass and temperature are the same. The concept of specific heat is introduced.

Reading Synopsis

Students read Section 25.3 Heat and Thermal Energy after the Investigation

This reading describes heat, thermal energy, and temperature. Temperature measures the random kinetic energy of each atom and is an average measurement of this energy. Thermal energy is the total amount of random kinetic energy for all atoms in a substance. It takes 400 J of thermal energy to heat a cup of coffee to 100°C, but 400,000 J to heat 1,000 cups of coffee to 100°C. Heat is moving thermal energy that flows from high to low temperatures. Units of heat (and thermal energy) are joules, calories, or BTUs (British thermal unit). One calorie equals 4.184 joules. One BTU equals 1,055 joules.

The heat equation is used to calculate how much heat it takes to make a temperature change. The equation relates mass, temperature, and specific heat. Specific heat is the quantity of heat it takes to raise the temperature of one kilogram of material by 1°C. Different substances have different specific heats because of differences in the mass of their atoms.

The application reading is on the refrigeration cycle.

The Investigation

Leading Questions
- How much energy does it take to change the temperature of a material?
- How is the temperature of a substance related to its thermal energy?
- Do the same amounts of different substances at the same temperature have the same thermal energy?

Learning Goals
By the end of the Investigation, students will be able to:
- Explain the connection between temperature, heat, and thermal energy.
- Use the specific heat equation to calculate thermal energy.
- Observe that different amounts of thermal energy are stored by different substances even when they are at the same temperature and have the same mass.
- Explain the meaning of the specific heat of a substance.

Key Vocabulary   specific heat, temperature, heat, thermal energy

Setup and Materials

Students work in groups of four or five at tables.

Each group should have:

- Hot water baths at about 50°C with a thermometer and a cup for removing water
- A cold water bath with ice cubes at about 0°C with a thermometer and a cup for removing water
- Another Celsius thermometer
- 15 steel washers held together with a small piece of string or wire (from the ropes and pulleys kit)
- A balance
- Tongs
- Stirring rod
- A timer or stop watch
- About 300 grams of vegetable oil
- Three 16-ounce foam cups
- Three 8-ounce plastic cups
- Paper towels for cleaning up
- Simple calculator

Details

Time	⊙ One class period
Preparation	✎ none required
Assignments	▭ Section 25.3 Heat and Thermal Energy in the **Student Edition** after the Investigation.

Teaching the Investigation

1 Introduction

2 Demonstrating temperature and heat

3 Thermal energy, Part 1: Steel and water

4 Thermal energy, Part 2: Oil and water

5 Thermal energy, Part 3: Water and water

6 Specific heat and energy

7 Summary

Introduction

Heat: Moving thermal energy.

Temperature: A measurement that is related to the average kinetic energy of particles in a substance.

Thermal energy: Energy stored in substances due to differences in temperature.

Demonstrating temperature and heat

Have one student group represent a substance at a high temperature.

Have another student group represent a substance at a low temperature.

Thermal energy, Part 1: Steel and water

Ask students: If you had equal amounts of hot steel, oil, and water and three equal amounts of cold water, which substance do you think would heat the cold water the fastest?

In this Investigation, you will observe how substances change of temperature. You will use these observations to determine how heat, temperature, and thermal energy relate to each other. To get started let's define each of these terms.

Write the definitions of heat, temperature, and thermal energy on the board.

What do you think about these definitions? Is temperature the same as heat? Is thermal energy the same as temperature?

Guide students in discussing that each definition is unique, but that each concept depends on the other concepts. Energy connects each of these terms.

To illustrate these terms, let's do a demonstration. First, we will demonstrate temperature. I need two small groups of students to come to the front of the room.

Have one group of students move quickly in place while another group of students moves slowly in place or not at all. Encourage the students within each group to move differently from each other. Then, ask the class to identify which group represents a higher temperature and ask them to explain their response.

This demonstration is further described on the facing page under the heading, Demonstrating Temperature and Heat. Use the demonstration to explore understanding how substances heat up or cool down, and how a thermometer works. Also, explore concepts like average kinetic energy (temperature) and total kinetic energy of particles (thermal energy).

We have demonstrated important concepts that will be used in the Investigation. Let's begin.

1

In this Investigation, you will observe how three different substances change the temperature of a certain amount of water. The three different substances are steel, oil, and water. If you had equal amounts of hot steel, oil, and water and three equals amounts of cold water, which substance do you think would heat the cold water the fastest?

Have students discuss this question in their groups. Illustrate the question on the board so that the students better understand what you are asking.

Let's hear what everyone thinks. I will write up your responses on the board. Then, let's pick one as a class that will serve as a hypothesis for the Investigation.

If your students have not read the text, they will have a variety of responses. Also, because specific heat is a challenging concept, they may not realize how the specific heat of a substance relates to its ability to change temperature. For example, a high specific heat means a higher resistance to a change in temperature. Information to share with your students later on: Water takes a long time to heat up and cool down. By comparison, steel heats up and cools down quickly.

Now, let's work through Part 1 together so that you understand the procedures of the Investigation.

At your stations, you have a hot water bath and a cold water bath. You will use the hot water bath to heat up the steel and the oil. During Part 3, you will take some of the water from this bath. The water that you will heat up in Parts 1 - 3 will come from the cold water bath. What are the temperatures of the hot water bath and the cold water bath?

Have students read the temperatures and record them in their notebooks.

25.3 Heat and Thermal Energy

Question: What is the relationship between heat, temperature, and energy?

In this Investigation, you will:

1. Learn the physical significance of specific heat.
2. Observe that different amounts of thermal energy are stored by different substances even when they are at the same temperature.

To change the temperature of matter, you need to add or subtract energy in the form of heat. When you want to warm your house in winter, you add heat. If you want to cool your house in summer, you remove heat. *Thermal energy* is energy stored in materials due to differences in temperature. *Heat* is what we call thermal energy that is moving. Heat naturally flows from hot to cold and carries thermal energy from higher temperatures to lower temperatures. This Investigation explores the connection between temperature, heat, and energy.

1 Thermal energy, Part 1: Steel and water

In this part of the Investigation, you will measure the energy content of different materials by comparing how much they each raise the temperature of a known mass of water.

1. Prepare two containers of water that hold at least two liters each. One container should be cold water with ice cubes in it to maintain the temperature at very close to 0°C. The second container should be filled with water as hot as it can be from the faucet. A temperature of at least 50°C is desirable.

2. Measure the temperature of both containers of water with a thermometer. Stir them well before measuring the temperature to even out any differences in temperature.

3. Measure the mass of 15 steel washers. Place the washers in the hot water bath with tongs so that they come to the same temperature as the water. Record the temperature of that hot water in Table 1.

4. Measure 100 grams of cold water into a large foam cup. Measure and record the temperature of the cold water in Table 1.

5. Remove the hot steel washers with tongs and add them to the cup of cold water. Swirl the water around to allow the temperature to come to equilibrium. After about a minute, measure the temperature of the water containing the steel washers. Record that temperature in Table 1.

Table 1: Temperature and mass data

| | Hot substance | | Cold water | | Mixture |
	Mass (kg)	Temp (°C)	Mass (kg)	Temp (°C)	Temp (°C)
Steel			0.1		
Oil			0.1		
Water			0.1		

Demonstrating temperature and heat

Heat, temperature, and thermal energy are easily confused. To help your students better understand these concepts, you may want to have them participate in a demonstration in which students act like atoms or molecules of a substance.

Temperature: Have one small group of students move quickly in place while another small group of students moves slowly in place or not at all. Encourage the students within each group to move differently from each other. Ask your students which group represents the higher temperature substance. Guide students to using the term, kinetic energy, in answering your question. Then ask them what happens to a thermometer if it is placed within the group of students that represents the hotter temperature. See how many concepts can be illustrated about temperature (increasing, decreasing, and measuring with a thermometer) using the groups of students.

Heat: Ask the students, "Since we have a temperature difference between these two groups, in which direction do you think heat will flow?" Use a large paper arrow with the word, "HEAT," written on both sides to illustrate heat going from the hotter group to the colder group. To illustrate the role of molecules in heat, you may want to have the groups move close enough to each other to cause faster moving individuals influence the slower moving individuals.

1 Example answers

Table 1: *Temperature and mass data*

| | Hot substance | | Cold water | | Mixture |
	Mass (kg)	Temp (°C)	Mass (kg)	Temp (°C)	Temp (°C)
Steel	0.0626	60	0.1	5.3	9.7
Oil	0.0626	57.4	0.1	5.7	16.8
Water	0.0626	54.9	0.1	5.7	24.1

Thermal energy, Part 1: Steel and water (continued)

1

Now, you take the group of 15 washers and find the mass. Record the mass on the first line of Table 1. Place the washers in the hot water bath. While the temperature is stabilizing in the hot water bath, follow step 4 of Part 1.

Have students place the foam cup on their balance and zero it. Then, they should carefully pour water into the foam cup until they have collected 100 grams. Point out that another way to collect 100 grams of water is to measure 100 mL of water. One milliliter of pure water equals 1 gram. Have your students write the mass and the temperature of the water in the cup in the first line of Table 1.

When the temperature stabilizes in the hot water bath, record the temperature in the first row of the second column of the table. This is the temperature of the "hot substance" (the steel washers). Now, carefully place the steel washers in the cup of cold water. Use your stopwatch to time one minute. After one minute, record the temperature of the mixture in Table 1.

The temperature of the hot water bath with the steel washers should stabilize quickly.

Thermal energy, Part 2: Oil and water

2

Now, you are ready to observe how the same mass of oil affects temperature of the same mass of cold water. Follow the directions in Part 2. Place your plastic cup on the balance, zero it, and then pour oil into the cup until the mass equals the mass of the washers.

It will take about 30 minutes to heat the oil to the temperature of the hot water bath. Be sure to circulate around the room to make sure that your students are following the procedures and to answer questions. Make sure the students stir the oil-water mixture before recording the temperature.

Thermal energy, Part 3: Water and water

3

Now, complete Part 3. Here, you are performing the experiment with hot water.

It will not take long for the temperature to stabilize for the water-water mixture.

SAFETY PRECAUTION: Hot water can burn the skin.

Specific heat and energy

$E = mC_p(T_2 - T_1)$

E = heat energy (J)
m = mass (kg)
C_p = specific heat (J/kg C)
$T_2 - T_1$ = change in temperature

4

Part 4, includes an equation called the specific heat equation. We can use this equation to calculate the amount of thermal energy in each of our hot substances. Do these three calculations right now and then answer question 4(a). The specific heat values for each substance are given to you. T1 is the temperature of the final mixture. T2 is the temperature of the hot substance.

The thermal energy values for each substance are: E_{steel} = 1,480 J; E_{oil} = 4,829 J; and E_{water} = 8,067 J.

Now, answer the remaining questions in Part 4. You may discuss your answers with your group.

Alternatively, you can have each student answer the questions independently. However, question 4(d) is challenging. Students will benefit from discussing and working on this problem together. You may need to illustrate how to get started on the problem on the board.

Now that we have completed, why do you think substances have different thermal energies?

Thermal energy is a measure of the random kinetic energy of all the atoms or molecules in a substance. Whereas, temperature is an average value of the kinetic energy of the particles in a substance. Also, it takes more thermal energy to heat up a large quantity of a substance to a certain temperature, than to heat up a smaller quantity of a substance to that same temperature.

How can we demonstrate the difference between temperature and thermal energy?

Example demonstration: The normal body temperature of each person in your classroom is about 98.6°F. In theory, everyone is the same temperature. However, the thermal energy of a group of students, each one at the same temperature, would be higher than the thermal energy for a single student. Also, the taller a student is, the more thermal energy he or she has.

Summary

Heat, temperature, and energy are all related. Adding heat to a substance causes its temperature to increase. As its temperature increases, the atoms or molecules that comprise the substance gain energy.

25.3 Heat and Thermal Energy

2   **Thermal energy, Part 2: Oil and water**

1. Weigh a mass of vegetable oil equal to the mass of the steel washers and pour it into a thin-walled plastic cup. Hold the cup in the hot water with tongs and swirl it gently until the oil in the cup is at the same temperature as the hot water. Record the temperature of the oil in Table 1.

2. Measure 100 milliliters of cold water into a large foam cup. Measure and record the temperature of the cold water in Table 1.

3. Pour the hot oil into the cup of cold water. Swirl the mixture to allow the temperature to come to equilibrium. After about a minute, measure the temperature of the oil/water mixture. Record that temperature in Table 1.

3   **Thermal energy, Part 3: Water and water**

1. Weigh a mass of hot water equal to the mass of the steel washers and pour into a thin-walled plastic cup. Record the temperature of the warm water in Table 1.

2. Measure 100 milliliters of cold water into a large foam cup. Measure and record the temperature of the cold water in Table 1.

3. Pour the hot water into the cup of cold water. Swirl the mixture around to allow the temperature to come to equilibrium. After about a minute, measure and record that temperature in Table 1.

4   **Specific heat and energy**

Heat is a form of energy measured in joules, the same units used for other forms of energy. The amount of energy that can be obtained from an object depends on three things: the mass of the object, its temperature, and the material the object is made of. Different types of material can store different amounts of energy even at the same temperature. The amount of thermal energy stored in an object is given by the heat equation:

Heat equation

$$\text{Heat energy (J)} \quad E = mC_p(T_2 - T_1)$$

Mass (kg), Specific heat $\left(\frac{J}{kg°C}\right)$, Change in temperature (°C)

The specific heat (C_p) is the quantity of heat it takes to raise the temperature of 1 kilogram of material by 1 degree Celsius. Water is an important example; the specific heat of water is 4,184 J/kg°C. It takes 4,184 joules to raise the temperature of 1 kilogram of water by 1 degree Celsius. The specific heat of steel is 470 J/kg°C and oil has a specific heat of 1,900 J/kg°C (depending on the type of oil).

a. Do equal masses of steel, oil, and water at the same temperature contain the same amount of thermal energy? Explain the physical reasoning behind your answer.

b. Examine the data in Table 1. Were the final temperatures about the same, or was each final temperature different for each of the three cases—steel/water, oil/water, water/water?

c. Explain how the concept of specific heat explains the observed final temperatures.

d. (Challenging) Use the heat equation to derive a prediction for the final mixture temperature based on the mass, specific heats, and starting temperatures of the materials in the mixture. HINT: Let T_f be the final temperature and set the energy lost by the hot material equal to the energy gained by the cold material. Compare the prediction with the actual final temperatures.

179

4   **Example answers**

4a. Equal masses of steel, oil and water at the same temperature do not contain the same amount of thermal energy. These materials have different specific heats and hold different amounts of thermal energy.

4b. Each final temperature was different for each of the three cases.

4c. If you look at how temperature changed for the steel, oil, and hot water, you see that the steel changed the most (60°C - 9.7°C = 50.3°C) and water changed the least (55°C - 24.1°C = 30.8°C). This observation agrees with the fact that steel had the lowest specific heat value and water had the highest value. One way to think of specific heat is as a resistance to change in temperature. The cold water increased in temperature only 4.4°C when steel was added. In this case, the cold water resisted changed in temperature more than the steel. Among all three mixtures, the changes in temperature for the hot and cold water mixture in Part 3 were the closest in value (30.8°C for the hot water and 18.4°C for the cold water).

4d. heat lost = heat gained

$$(m_1 c_1(T_{i1} - T_f) = m_2 c_2(T_f - T_{i2}))$$

$$T_f = \frac{m_1 c_1 T_{i1} + m_2 c_2 T_{i2}}{m_1 c_1 + m_2 c_2}$$

For steel washers and cold water, actual final temperature was 9.7°C and predicted is 8.8°C.

$$T_f = \frac{m_1 c_1 T_{i1} + m_2 c_2 T_{i2}}{m_1 c_1 + m_2 c_2}$$

$$T_f = \frac{(0.0626 \text{ kg})(470 \text{J/kg°C})(60°C) + (0.1 \text{ kg})(4184 \text{J/kg°C})(5.3°C)}{(0.0626 \text{ kg})(470 \text{J/kg°C}) + (0.1 \text{ kg})(4184 \text{J/kg°C})}$$

$$T_f = 8.8°C$$

26.1 Heat Conduction

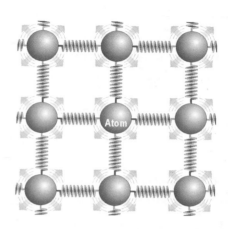

Key Question: How does heat pass through different materials?

Heat flows from hot too cold. However, different materials transmit heat different rates. In this Investigation, students investigate the thermal insulating or conducting properties of common materials by measuring the rate of heat flow between two different temperatures. Students use the data collected to explain which materials are better conductors or insulators. Students apply the heat equation to compare the amount of energy required to raise and lower the temperature of a constant mass of water.

Reading Synopsis

Students read Section 26.1 Heat Conduction after the Investigation.

Thermal energy travels as heat from a material at a higher temperature to a material at a lower temperature. This general process is called heat transfer. One of the three mechanisms of heat transfer is conduction. Conduction is heat transfer by the direct contact of particles of matter. It occurs between two materials at different temperatures when they are touching each other. The atoms in the hotter material have more kinetic energy. This energy is transferred to the cooler material by the collisions of atoms until thermal equilibrium is reached and both materials have the same temperature.

Materials that conduct heat easily are called thermal conductors, and those that conduct heat poorly are thermal insulators. Thermal conductors tend to be dense, metallic, and can conduct electricity (due to having free electrons). Thermal insulators tend to be less dense. The degree to which something can conduct heat is measured as a value called thermal conductivity.

The Investigation

Leading Questions
- How fast does heat flow from one material to another?
- Does heat flow differently in different materials?
- What property of a material describes its ability to conduct heat?
- How does temperature influence the flow of heat?

Learning Goals

By the end of the Investigation, students will be able to:
- Describe how thermal energy is transferred by conduction.
- List what kinds of materials are thermal conductors or insulators.
- Describe a technique for measuring the thermal conductivity of a material.

Key Vocabulary

conduction, thermal conductor, thermal insulator, thermal conductivity, specific heat

Setup and Materials

Students work in groups of two or three at tables.

Each group should have:

- One shallow baking pan
- Two thin plastic cups
- Two foam cups
- Four copper nails
- One metric ruler
- One permanent marker
- Two Celsius thermometers
- One small pot
- One hot plate
- One timer or stopwatch
- Ring stand
- Clamps (to hold thermometers in place)
- Crushed ice
- Water
- Digital or triple beam balance (accuracy to at least 0.1 gram)

Details

Time ⏱ Two class periods

Preparation ✎ Gather materials and practice the Investigation ahead of time. Be sure to read the additional notes about the Investigation beforehand.

Assignments 📖 Section 26.1 Heat Conduction in the **Student Edition** after the Investigation.

Skill Sheets Skill Builder: Safety Skills (review)

Teaching the Investigation

1 Introduction
2 Heat flowing from a cup
3 Heat flowing into a cup
4 Analyzing the data

Introduction

Heat energy results from the random motion of molecules. Heat flows naturally from hot to cold.

Heat and temperature are related.

Conduction is the transfer of kinetic energy when particles collide.

Solids are usually better conductors than liquids, and liquids are better than gases.

Heat flowing from a cup

The rate of heat flow varies with different materials.

Insulators (such as styrofoam) are poor conductors of heat.

Metals (like copper and aluminum) are excellent thermal conductors.

Before we begin today's Investigation, let's review what we already know about heat. What is heat?

Heat is the form of energy that results from the random motion of molecules. Some students may respond by saying that heat is a measure of "hotness" or "coldness". Remind them that this is actually related to temperature and that temperature and heat are not the same.

How does heat energy flow?

Heat flows from hot to cold.

How are heat and temperature related?

Heat is thermal energy that is moving. Heat naturally flows from hot to cold and moves thermal energy from higher temperatures to lower temperatures.

Suppose you are boiling water in order to cook pasta. You accidentally touch the pot of boiling water without using a mitt. What do you feel?

You might burn your hand because the pot feels hot.

Why does the pot feel hot?

The pot feels hot because heat flows from the pot into your skin, causing the temperature of your skin to rise very quickly.

Because your hand was in direct contact with the hot pot, heat was transferred. This process of heat transfer is called conduction. A requirement for conduction to occur is that substances are in direct contact with each other. Can you think of some other examples of conduction?

Students may give a variety of examples. Encourage students to explain how particles of matter are in direct contact with each other in each example cited.

Do all materials conduct heat?

All materials conduct heat. However, the rate at which materials conduct heat varies.

What are some factors that might influence the rate of conduction?

The ability of a material to conduct heat depends on factors like its state of matter, and the structure of the material.

Which would you expect to be a better conductor, a solid, a liquid, or a gas?

Solids are usually better conductors than liquids or gases because the particles in solids are closer together. Although particles are close together in liquids, they do not conduct heat as well as solids. Gases don't conduct heat very well because their particles are spread very far apart.

1 Today you are going to measure the rate of heat flow through different materials by the process of conduction. In the first part of the Investigation, you will observe the flow of heat from a cup of hot water to cold water in a pan. Gather the materials that are needed to complete the Investigation, and bring them to your lab station.

Allow students time to gather materials listed in the Set up and Materials section of this document. Now that you have gathered the necessary materials, you may complete Part 1 of the Investigation. Be sure that the temperature of your hot water is at least 60°C. Use the same starting and final temperatures for all variations of the experiment. Remember to gently swirl your cup constantly as you are monitoring the temperature. Record your data in Table 1.

Walk around the laboratory and verify that the students' initial water temperature is at least 60°C, and that they are recording the data for each trial in the appropriate section of Table 1.

26.1 Heat Conduction

Question: How does heat pass through different materials?

In this Investigation, you will:

1. Compare the thermal insulating or conducting properties of materials.
2. Measure the heat flowing between two different temperatures.

Conduction is the transfer of heat through materials by the direct contact of matter. All materials conduct heat at some rate. Solids usually are better heat conductors than liquids and liquids are better conductors than gases. The *thermal conductivity* of a material describes how well the material conducts heat. Materials with high thermal conductivity such as copper, aluminum, and other metals are good thermal *conductors*. Materials with low thermal conductivity like fiberglass and foam are *insulators*. This Investigation explores how different materials conduct heat.

1 Heat flowing from a cup

This experiment will investigate how quickly heat moves from hot water in a cup to cold water in a pan through different substances. Fill a shallow baking pan with 2 centimeters of water and crushed ice. You will also need a container of water that has a temperature of at least 60°C. Record your data in the top section of Table 1.

Ice water

1. Measure the depth of water in the cold pan. Mark the depth on a thin plastic disposable cup with a marker. Fill the cup with hot water to the mark.

2. Hold the cup of hot water in the pan of cold water and swirl it gently with the thermometer in the water. Measure the time it takes for the temperature to drop from 50°C to 40°C and from 30°C to 20°C. Use the same starting and final temperatures for all variations of the experiment.

Thermometer
Hot water
Mark depth on the cup

3. Measure the temperature of the cold water bath and record it under T_c in Table 1.

4. Repeat the same experiment except use a foam cup to hold the hot water. Use the plastic cup to transfer the hot water so the volume of water stays constant.

5. Prepare another foam cup by pushing four copper nails through the bottom as shown in the diagram. Repeat the experiment again with the hot water in the cold pan of water. Remember to swirl the cup constantly as you are monitoring the temperature.

6. Use the plastic cup to measure the mass of water used in the experiment. Enter the mass in all three rows of Table 1 since it is the same for each trial.

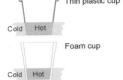
Thin plastic cup
Cold   Hot

Foam cup
Cold   Hot

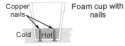
Copper nails
Foam cup with nails
Cold   Hot

Additional notes about the Investigation

- It is extremely important that students use the same mass of water in each part of the Investigation. Have students obtain the mass of water in grams and convert to kilograms. Students should record this mass in Table 1 for all six trials.
- Have students keep one thermometer in the cup and one thermometer in the beaker or pan. This will help students to obtain more accurate data and maintain the temperature as needed throughout the Investigation.
- Review the heat equation with students before the Investigation, as they will need to use it in order to answer questions on Part 3.

Heat flows from the hot water through the Styrofoam and raises the temperature of the cold water in the top. The amount of the heat that flows depends on the properties of the Styrofoam, and also on the thickness and area through which the heat flows. In physics, power is the flow of energy per second. The power transferred by heat (P_H) depends on four factors.

- The area through which the heat flows (A).
- The length the heat has to travel (L).
- The temperature difference ($T_1 - T_2$).
- The thermal conductivity of the material (κ)

Heat conduction equation

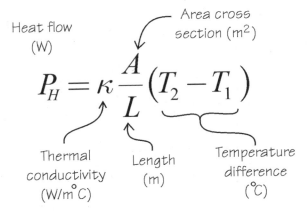

Heat flow (W)

Area cross section (m²)

$$P_H = \kappa \frac{A}{L}\left(T_2 - T_1\right)$$

Thermal conductivity (W/m°C)

Length (m)

Temperature difference (°C)

Heat flowing into a cup

Heat flows rapidly from metals because they are good conductors.

Analyzing the data

Thermal conductivity describes how well a material conducts heat. Materials with high thermal conductivity, like metals, are good thermal conductors. Materials with low thermal conductivity are insulators.

Diamond and the metal screw are examples of conductors. Wood, fiberglass, and air are examples of insulators.

Although objects are at the same temperature, they sometimes "feel" differently. The thermal conductivity of a substance determines whether it feels warm or cold when touched.

2 Now that you have observed the heat flow from the three different cups to the pan, let's see what will happen if the circumstances are reversed. In this part of the Investigation, you will observe what happens when heat flows from hot water in the beaker to cold water in the cup.

> Remind students that in this part of the Investigation, they will record the time required to raise the temperature of the water in each of the three cups as heat flows from the water in the pan into the cup.

3 Now that you have completed Part 2 of the Investigation, use the data in Table 1 to answer questions 3a through 3f.

> Give students adequate time to complete these questions. Write the heat equation on the board for students to use in order to answer questions 3e and 3f. It is always a good idea to do an example problem. Have one of the lab teams volunteer to use some of their data to review the calculation with classmates.

Has everyone completed the questions?

> Verify that students have answered all questions.

Let's discuss your data. What is a thermal conductor?

> A thermal conductor is a material through which heat can easily flow.

What is an thermal insulator?

> A thermal insulator does not allow heat to flow easily.

Identify each of the following as an example of either a conductor or an insulator.

> Have students respond to each object described in the list: a metal screw, wood, fiberglass, air, diamond.

What does your data tell you about the thermal conductivity of each of the materials used in this Investigation?

> Plastic and foam are insulators. Adding the copper nails to the foam cup increases its thermal conductivity. Metals have high thermal conductivity and insulators have low thermal conductivity.

We know that different substances have distinctive thermal conductivities. Each of the objects placed on the table are at room temperature. Briefly touch each object and record whether it feels cold, cool, or room temperature. Why do the items "feel" differently when they are actually at the same temperature?

> Place a plastic bottle, metal box, a styrofoam cup, and a ceramic mug on the table. Students should note that the styrofoam cup feels like it is at room temperature, while both the metal box and the ceramic mug are feel cold. The plastic bottle is cool. Have students use this data to rank the thermal conductivity of each item. The items feel differently because they have different thermal conductivities.

Why does the metal box feel cold?

> The quick transfer of heat from the students' hands to a substance with high thermal conductivity (like the metal box) causes that substance to feel cold.

Why does the styrofoam cup feel warmer than the other objects?

> The styrofoam cup feels warmer than the other objects because it has low thermal conductivity. Heat does not leave the students' hands quickly when touching the styrofoam cup, therefore the cup feels warm.

2 Heat flowing into a cup

26.1 Heat Conduction

For this part of the Investigation, set up the opposite circumstance. Heat will flow from the hot water in the pan to the cold water in the cup. Fill the pan with two centimeters of hot water that is at least 60°C. You may need to add hot water from time to time to keep the water temperature within 3-4 degrees of 60°C. Fill a second container with crushed ice and enough water, enough to refill the cup several times.

1. Repeat the same three experimental variations you did in Part 1 except this time the heat will flow *into* the cup. Measure the time it takes for the temperature of the water in the cup to go from 20°C to 30°C and from 40°C to 50°C. Again, be sure to gently swirl the cup around the bottom of the pan to mix the water and even out the temperature. Keep the thermometer in the cup.

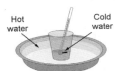
Hot water Cold water

2. Record the temperature of the water in the pan and the mass of water in the cup in the appropriate row with the times using the bottom part of Table 1.

Table 1: Temperature and mass data

Heat flowing cup to pan	Cold temp (T$_c$, °C)	Mass (kg)	50°C to 40°C (time in sec)	30°C to 20°C (time in sec)
Plastic cup				
Foam cup				
Foam cup, nails				

Heat flowing pan to cup	Hot temp (T$_h$, °C)	Mass (kg)	20°C to 30°C (time in sec)	40°C to 50°C (time in sec)
Plastic cup				
Foam cup				
Foam cup, nails				

3 Analyzing the data

a. Use the concept of thermal conductivity to explain the differences between the measurements for the plastic cup, the foam cup, and the foam cup with the nails pushed through the bottom.

b. Based on your observations, is the copper in the nails a thermal insulator or a thermal conductor?

c. Compare the time it took the water in the cup to cool down from 50°C to 40°C with the time it took to cool down from 30°C to 20°C. Explain the difference using what you know about how heat flows.

d. Compare the time it took the water in the cup to heat up from 20°C to 30°C with the time it took to heat up from 40°C to 50°C. Explain the difference using what you know about how heat flows.

e. The specific heat of water is 4,184 J/kg°C. Use the heat equation to calculate how much energy was used to change the temperature of the water from 20°C to 30°C.

f. Compare the amount of energy used to heat the water from 20°C to 30°C with the amount of energy used to heat the water from 40°C to 50°C. Is the energy the same? Do the same comparison for the energy removed to cool the water from 50°C to 40°C, and from 30°C to 20°C.

181

Table 1: *Temperature and mass data*

Heat flowing cup to pan	Cold temp. (T$_c$, °C)	Hot temp. (T$_h$, °C)	50°C to 40°C (time in sec)	30°C to 20°C (time in sec)
Plastic cup	2	0.50	33	71
Foam cup	2	0.50	261	720
Foam cup, nails	2	0.50	111	240

Heat flowing cup to pan	Hot temp. (T$_h$, °C)	Mass (kg)	20°C to 30°C (time in sec)	40°C to 50°C (time in sec)
Plastic cup	63	0.50	34	68
Foam cup	63	0.50	364	1583
Foam cup, nails	63	0.50	125	460

3a. Both plastic and foam are both thermal insulators (have low thermal conductivity). However, the foam cup is a better insulator than the plastic cup, therefore the heat flow occurred faster in the plastic cup. Adding the copper nails to the foam cup increased the heat transfer because copper has a much higher thermal conductivity than foam.

3b. The copper in the nails is a thermal conductor.

3c. In each of the experimental samples, less time was needed to cool the water in the cup from 50°C to 40°C. Heat flows naturally from hot to cold. The water temperature in the baking pan was only 2 degrees C. The greater temperature difference supports the faster heat flow.

3d. Less time is needed to raise the temperature of the water in the cup from 20°C to 30°C.

3e. 21 J of energy was used.

3f. The amount of energy needed to heat the water from 40°C to 50°C was 21 J. Since the same mass of water was used in each sample, the amount of energy removed to cool the water at both temperatures is also 21 J

26.2 Convection

Key Question: Can moving matter carry thermal energy?

In this Investigation, students set up systems to observe free and forced convection. An ice cube that is dyed with food coloring is briefly placed in a glass that is filled with hot tap water, removed and then placed in an identical glass of cold water. The cold water melting off the ice cube flows differently in hot and cold water. Students observe free convection in water and compare the motion of water melting off the colored ice cube in both systems. Students then dip the colored ice cube into two identical glasses of hot water. They then simulate forced convection by stirring the water in one glass. Students use their observations to compare the rate of heat flow between free and forced convection.

Reading Synopsis

Students read Section 26.2 Convection after the Investigation.

Convection is a type of heat transfer that occurs only in fluids (liquids and gases). This process of heating occurs because warmer fluids are less dense and rise. Cooler fluids are denser and sink. This temperature-based motion of fluids causes fluid currents and circulation.

There are two types of convection: free (natural) and forced. Free convection causes global weather patterns and ocean currents. In cooking, free convection is essential for heating pots of liquid. Free convection occurs when less dense, warm fluid displaces denser cool fluid and vice versa so that fluid circulation results. In forced convection, a mechanical device (like a fan or pump) forces the air or liquid to move. Warm fluids can carry heat to cooler regions. Likewise, forced convection can be used for cooling. Moving cool fluids can take heat from hot regions. Most homes are heated and cooled using a combination of free and forced convection.

The Investigation

Leading Questions
- When matter moves, such as wind blowing, thermal energy moves with the moving matter. How is this kind of heat transfer described?
- Why are fans used to blow air around in heating and cooling?
- Why do you stir up a pot when heating it? What does the stirring accomplish?

Learning Goals
By the end of the Investigation, students will be able to:
- Describe free and forced convection and give an example of each.
- Explain how thermal energy is be transferred by convection.
- Describe what causes motion in liquid or gas during free convection.

Key Vocabulary
convection, heat transfer, free convection, forced convection, density, buoyancy

Setup and Materials

Students work in groups of two or three at tables.

Each group should have:

- Two clear identical glasses
- One colored ice cube
- Uncolored ice cubes
- Tongs
- One Celsius thermometer
- Metric ruler
- Stirring rod
- Hot tap water

The teacher needs:

- Food coloring
- Access to a freezer
- Six or more ice cube trays for making ice cubes

Details

Time ⏰ One class period

Preparation ✏️ Prepare the ice cubes a day before doing the Investigation.

Assignments 📖 Section 26.2 Convection in the **Student Edition** after the Investigation.

Teaching the Investigation

1 Introduction
2 Observing free convection in water
3 Reflecting on what you observed
4 Forced convection
5 Observing forced convection

Introduction

What is convection?

Convection is the flow of heat in liquids or gases.

How many of you have lit a candle before?

> Most students will respond by saying that they have done so.

If you placed your hand one half meter above the flame, would it get hot?

> Yes, it would.

How about if you placed your hand one half meter to the side of the flame?

> No, my hand would not get hot when placed to the side of the flame.

Why do you feel heat above the flame but not at the same distance to the side of the flame?

> You feel heat directly above the flame because hot air rises after being heated by the flame. Since the hot air rises above the flame, no heat is felt to the side of the flame.

The heat rising above the candle flame is an example of convection. Can anyone explain what convection is?

> Convection is the transfer of heat by the motion of liquids and gases.

Now use the example of the candle flame to explain how convection occurs in a gas.

> Convection in a gas occurs because gases expand when heated. When a gas expands, the mass is spread out over a larger volume so the density decreases. Hot gas with a lower density is lighter than surrounding cooler gas and floats upward. Convection occurs because currents flow when hot gas rises and cool gas sinks.

Suppose you were going to cook pasta for dinner. What would be your first step in preparing the pasta?

> You must have a pot of boiling water.

Which method of heat transfer is responsible for boiling the water in your pot?

> Convection is the method of heat transfer.

Who can explain how this happens?

> Convection in liquids occurs because of differences in density. Hot water is less dense than cold water.
> The hottest water rises from the bottom of the pot while cooler water near the surface sinks. This circulating flow transfers heat from the bottom of the pot to the surface.

Observing free convection in water **1**

Use caution when handling hot water.

Free convection occurs because of differences in density and temperature.

In Part 1 of today's Investigation, you will observe one type of convection: free or natural convection. Free convection occurs when the flow of gas or liquid results from differences in density and temperature. Both the examples of heat rising above the candle flame and water circulating in a pot of boiling water are examples of free convection. Gather the materials that are needed and bring them to your lab table.

> Allow students time to gather the materials listed in the Set up and Materials.

Let's begin. Read steps 1-6 carefully. Record any observations that you make. Use the tongs to handle your colored ice cube. Be sure to return your colored ice cube to the freezer once you have completed step 6.

Reflecting on what you observed **2**

The colored ice cube helps students to see the convection currents in each glass.

Now that you have completed Part 1 of the Investigation, let's reflect on what you observed. Take a moment to read and answer questions 2a and 2b.

> Allow students a few minutes to read and answer these questions.

What was the purpose of the colored ice cube?

> The colored ice cube made the convection currents visible in each glass.

How was the motion of the cold water melting off the colored ice cube different when it was partially immersed in the hot water as compared to the cold water?

> The cold water melting off the ice cube quickly moved downward in the glass of hot water, unlike in the glass of cold water, which had very little movement.

26.2   Convection

Question: Can moving matter carry thermal energy?

In this Investigation, you will:

1. Observe the currents created by free convection in water.
2. Observe the rapid exchange of thermal energy in forced convection.

Convection is the transfer of heat by the motion of liquids and gases. Free (or natural) convection occurs whenever there is a temperature difference in a gas or liquid. Free convection in a gas occurs because gas expands when heated. Hot gas with lower density is lighter than surrounding cooler gas and floats upward, carrying heat along with it. Convection in liquids also occurs because of differences in density. Hot liquid is less dense than cold liquid. Therefore, hot liquid rises and cold liquid sinks. The resulting current transfers heat from hotter regions of liquid to cooler regions. This Investigation demonstrates an example of convection in a liquid.

1   👆 Observing free convection in water

1. This experiment requires preparation a day ahead of time. Make a colored ice cube by mixing five drops of food coloring in enough water to fill 1 pocket of an ice cube tray. Fill the rest of the tray with clear water and place the tray in the freezer overnight.
2. Obtain two clear drinking glasses that are the same size and shape. Fill one with hot water from the faucet, as hot as it can get.
3. Fill the other glass with water and a few ice cubes that are not colored. Stir the water and ice well until the temperature of the water is close to 0°C.
4. Remove the colored ice cube from the tray. Handle the colored ice cube with tongs because the color may stain your clothes or fingers.
5. Using the tongs, dip about 2 centimeters of the colored ice cube into the hot water and observe what happens. You should see melting water flow away from the colored ice cube.
6. Remove the ice cubes from the glass of cold water so they do not interfere with observing. Using the tongs, dip about 2 centimeters of the colored ice cube into the cold water and observe what happens. Remove the colored ice cube and put it back in the freezer.

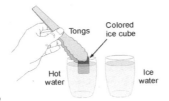
Tongs   Colored ice cube   Hot water   Ice water

2   Reflecting on what you observed

a. Describe the motion of the cold water melting off the colored ice cube when it was partially immersed in hot water. Did the melting colored water move upward, downward, or to the side? Explain what you observed using the concepts of density and buoyancy of hot and cold liquids.

b. Compare the motion of the water melting off the colored ice cube when it was partially immersed in cold water. Did the melting colored water move upward, downward, or to the side? Was the motion faster or slower than it was in the hot water? Explain what you observed using the concepts of density and buoyancy of hot and cold liquids.

Teaching tip

Create a graphic organizer to help students visualize the two types of convection and where these processes occur. Challenge students to come up with uncommon uses of free and forced convection. Some examples are provided in the table below.

Free Convection	Forced Convection
Home heating	Home heating
Heating water in a pot	Home cooling
Heating an aquarium	Mixing very hot water into a bathtub full of warm water to make it hotter
Lava lamps	Using a hair dryer
Ocean currents	Water pump in a radiator
Sea breezes	A hot tub with water jets

2   Example answers

2a. The cold water melting off the colored ice cube moved downward as it was partially immersed in the hot water. Hot water is less dense than cold water. The cold water melting from the ice cube is more dense than the hot water therefore it sinks toward the bottom of the glass. A convection current is created as the cold water sinks forcing hot water to rise.

2b. There was very little movement of the cold water melting off the ice when it was partially immersed in the cold water. Convection is driven by differences in density. There was little to no temperature difference between the ice and the water bath. Therefore, the water melting off the ice cube had about the same density as the surrounding water. With no difference in density, there was nothing to cause flow.

Forced convection

What is forced convection?

Forced convection occurs when the flow of gases or liquids is circulated by pumps, fans, or anything other than natural buoyancy forces.

Observing forced convection

Use caution when handling hot water.

Forced convection transfers heat at a faster rate than free convection.

3 The second type of convection is forced convection. What does using the word, *forced*, imply about this type of convection.

Using the word, *forced*, implies that this type of convection is stimulated or encouraged, unlike free or natural convection.

Forced convection occurs when the flow of gas or liquid is circulated by pumps, fans, or anything other than natural buoyancy forces. Since forced convection is stimulated, which would you expect to have the faster rate of heat flow: free or forced convection?

Forced convection would have the faster rate of heat flow.

Let's take a moment to read Part 3 of the Investigation.

Allow students time to read this section.

4 Now we are ready to observe forced convection. In this part of the Investigation, you will need to fill both glasses with hot tap water. Be extra careful while filling your glasses with hot water. You will also need to retrieve your colored ice cube from the freezer.

Allow students time to retrieve the colored ice cube from the freezer.

Use your tongs to dip the colored ice cube into one cup of the hot water. Since the temperature of the water in both glasses is the same, you want to pay special attention to the rate at which the liquids mix. Let's dip the ice cube into the first glass of hot water.

Each lab team should dip the ice cube into the hot water at your prompting.

Is this an example of free or forced convection?

This is an example of free convection.

This time, one person will dip the ice cube into the hot water while your partner stirs the water. One person on each Investigation team should have a stirring rod.

Check to ensure that each team has a stirring rod.

Now, dip the colored ice cube into the glass of hot water while your partner continues to stir the water.

What do you notice about the rate at which the colored water mixes with the clear, hot water while stirring?

Stirring encourages faster mixing of the colored and clear water.

Stirring is a form of forced convection because water is circulated by forces other than free convection.

Carefully read and answer questions 4a and 4b.

Students should be able to answer these questions easily from the observations made during Part 4 of the Investigation.

Pour out any remaining water. Return the colored ice cubes to the freezer. Clean all equipment and return it to its proper place.

26.2 Convection

3 🔥 Forced convection

When the flow of gas or liquid is circulated by pumps, fans, or anything other than natural buoyancy forces, the heat transfer is called *forced convection*. Using a fan on a hot day is an example of forced convection. The breeze blowing over your skin carries away heat much faster than natural convection would in still air. Forced convection is used in many human technologies.

To see why forced convection is so effective, consider a warm surface in the air. Heat flows from the surface to the air by conduction because the molecules in the air contact the molecules of the surface. The air near the surface gets slightly warmer and rises, carrying the heat with it by natural convection.

The rate at which heat flows depends on the difference in temperature between the surface *and the air right near the surface*. Natural convection circulates cooler air against the surface only slowly. After a while, the rate of heat flow drops because the air near the surface is not much cooler than the surface itself. The diagrams below show how the temperature changes with distance away from the surface.

Now consider the situation with a fan. Cool air is forcefully blown against the surface, displacing the warmer air right near the surface. The difference between the air temperature and the surface temperature is much greater. Heat flows faster because the temperature difference is greater. The temperature difference remains great because the fan constantly replaces air that has been warmed by the surface with cooler air from farther away.

Free convection

Forced convection

Observing forced convection

The effect of forced convection can be demonstrated using the colored ice cube. With the ice cube, the color allows you to see the mixing of low and high temperature that would normally be detectable only with sensitive probes.

1. Prepare two glasses with hot water from the faucet.
2. Using the tongs, dip the colored ice cube into one cup of water and observe the rate at which the colored water mixes with the clear water. The rate at which the liquids mix reflects the rate at which heat is being carried by convection from the water farther from the ice cube to the ice cube itself.
3. Have a partner stir the hot water in the other glass. Dip the colored ice cube in the glass with the stirred water (and keep stirring). Observe the rate at which the colored water mixes with the clear water while stirring.

Stirring is a form of forced convection because the water is circulated by forces other than natural convection.

a. Which situation mixed the colored water more rapidly into the clear water: free convection or forced convection?

b. In which situation would you expect more rapid flow of heat: free convection or forced convection?

183

4 Example answers

4a. Forced convection mixed the colored water more rapidly into the clear water.

4b. More rapid flow of heat is expected by forced convection.

Free convection and the Earth

Currents caused by convection are responsible for much of our weather. Warm air rises off the surface of the Earth. As the warm air rises higher it cools. The cooler air sinks back down, creating a circulation pattern.

The sea breezes that form near coastlines are a good example of circulation patterns created by convection. During the day, the land is warmed by the sun more than water because rocks and earth have a lower specific heat than water. Warm air over land rises because of convection and is replaced by cooler air from the ocean. A daytime sea breeze blows from the ocean inward. In the evening the circulation pattern reverses. At night the ground cools rapidly but the ocean remains warm because water has a high specific heat. Warm air rises over the water and is replaced with cooler air from over the land. The nighttime breeze blows from the land out to the sea.

Much of the Earth's climate is regulated by giant convection currents in the oceans. Dense, cold water from melting ice near the poles sinks to the ocean floor and flows toward the equator. Warmer water from the equator circulates back toward the poles near the ocean surface. The weather pattern known as El Niño causes heavy storms in some years. El Niño is caused by an oscillation in the flow of convection currents in the Pacific Ocean

26.3 Radiant Heat

Key Question: How does heat from the sun get to Earth?

Thermal energy can be carried by light. In fact, this is how the Earth receives its energy from the sun. Radiant heat transfer is the transfer of thermal energy by light and other forms of electromagnetic radiation, such as infrared. In this Investigation, students construct a focusing mirror from aluminum foil in order to observe radiant energy from the sun. From their observations, students infer how heat is transferred through space and the properties of an object that make it either a good absorber or emitter of radiation. Students finish the Investigation by using a spectrometer to observe the blackbody spectrum from an incandescent bulb at different settings of a dimmer switch.

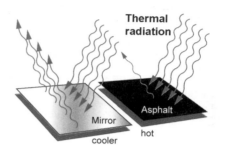

Reading Synopsis

Students read Section 26.3 Radiant Heat after the Investigation.

Radiation is heat transfer by electromagnetic radiation that occurs in the presence or absence of matter. Radiation is the only way that heat can travel through space (a vacuum) from the sun to Earth. Heat transfer by convection and conduction occurs only in the presence of matter.

Objects emit radiation according to their thermal properties or internal energy. radiation is in the form of visible light or invisible forms of light such as infrared or ultraviolet. A color-temperature relationship exists for objects that emit visible light. For example, the temperature of stars is determined by their spectral diagrams. Warm stars have peaks of blue in their spectral diagrams, while cold stars have peaks of red.

Radiation is reflected or absorbed by varying degrees from objects. Objects that are good reflectors are shiny and metallic, or light colored. Good absorbers are dark colored. Objects can re-emit heat by radiation, conduction, or convection.

The Investigation

Leading Questions
- How do we describe the heat we receive from the sun as light?
- What is the source of thermal radiation?
- How is heat transfer by radiation different from conduction and convection?

Learning Goals

By the end of the Investigation, students will be able to:
- Explain how sunlight carries heat.
- Describe how the spectrum of light emitted by hot objects changes with their temperature.
- Describe the properties that make an object a good absorber or emitter?

Key Vocabulary thermal radiation, blackbody spectrum, spectrometer

Setup and Materials

Students work in groups of four or five at tables.

Each group should have:

- Two 8.5" x 11" pieces of cardboard
- Double sided tape
- One Celsius thermometer
- One incandescent lamp with a dimmer switch
- One spectrometer
- Scissors
- Glue
- Aluminum foil
- Metric ruler
- Pencil
- Timer or stopwatch
- Thermometer

Details

Time ⏱ Two class periods

Preparation ✏ This investigation has students build a simple solar oven using cardboard and foil. You should build it yourself before trying to build it with students. Try out the experiment prior to class to anticipate student questions or problems.

Assignments 📖 Section 26.3 Radiant Heat in the **Student Edition** after the Investigation.

Skill Sheets 26.3 Heat Transfer

Teaching the Investigation

1 Introduction
2 Creating a focusing mirror for collecting radiation
3 Observing radiant energy in action
4 Reflecting on what you observed
5 The blackbody spectrum
6 Observing the blackbody spectrum

Introduction

> Radiation is the transfer of heat by electromagnetic radiation.

> Radiation can occur in the presence or absence of matter.

Creating a focusing mirror for collecting radiation

1

In today's Investigation, you will observe a different method of heat transfer called radiation. What is radiation?

> Radiation is heat transfer by electromagnetic waves. It can occur in the presence of absence of matter.

How is this different from conduction or convection?

> Both conduction and convection require the presence of matter.

Are you familiar with any types of radiation?

> Some examples of different types of radiation are sunlight, ultraviolet, microwaves, and infrared.

In order to observe radiant energy in action, each team will need to construct a parabolic focusing mirror. The materials that you will need to build the focusing mirror are on the supply table. Gather the materials that are needed to begin constructing the mirror.

> Allow students time to gather the materials listed in the Setup and Materials section.

Let's begin with one of the pieces of cardboard. Place the cardboard on the table in front of you. Use your ruler to draw lines parallel to the short side of the cardboard. The lines should be two centimeters apart.

> Hold up one of the cardboard pieces and point to the short side. It is a good idea to already have a few of the parallel lines drawn on the cardboard. Draw one or two more lines with the students emphasizing that the lines are two centimeters apart.

Continue to draw parallel lines until the entire piece of cardboard is filled.

> Walk around to ensure that students are doing this correctly. Stress the importance of the lines being exactly two centimeters apart.

Use your metric ruler to plot the points given in Table 1 of the Investigation onto your piece of cardboard. Once you have completed your first piece of cardboard, repeat the exact procedure with the second piece of cardboard. Use your pencil to connect the points on both pieces of cardboard with a smooth curve.

> Monitor students to ensure that they are not connecting the points in straight lines.

Cut out the shape as shown on your Investigation handout. Now, cut 2-centimeter square notches out of the two bottom corners.

> Demonstrate this to students. Point to the corners where the notches ate to be cut. Show students that they must measure 2-centimeters in both directions. Advise them to use a pencil to draw lines that can be easily followed to cut the notches.

You can now connect to the two pieces of cardboard together as shown on your handout.

> Show students how to fold the bottom and sides of each piece of cardboard. Place the two pieces of cardboard together so that the folded flaps overlap. Instruct them to use the double sided tape to fasten the tabs.

Use the remaining cardboard scraps to measure two pieces of cardboard that measure three centimeters by fourteen centimeters. Apply double-sided tape to each of the cardboard rectangles. Use your scissors to cut pieces of foil that can be folded over the sides of the cardboard. Place the foil on the cardboard rectangles shiny side up.

> Remind students not to wrinkle the foil because it is the reflective surface for the mirror.

Use glue to affix the two foil-covered cardboard strips to your mirror.

> Show students what the finished product looks like. Allow time for the glue to dry on the students' mirrors before moving on to the next section.

Why don't we see thermal radiation?

All objects with a temperature above absolute zero give off thermal radiation. Thermal radiation comes from the thermal energy of atoms. The power in thermal radiation increases with higher temperatures because the thermal energy of atoms increases with temperature.

Thermal radiation is also absorbed by objects. An object constantly receives thermal radiation from everything else in its environment. Otherwise all objects would eventually cool down to absolute zero by radiating their energy away. The temperature of an object rises if more radiation is absorbed. The temperature falls if more radiation is given off. The temperature adjusts until there is a balance between radiation absorbed and radiation emitted.

We do not see room temperature thermal radiation because it occurs at infrared wavelengths invisible to the human eye. Up to a few thousand degrees Celsius most of the energy in thermal radiation is in invisible infrared light.

As objects heat up they start to give off visible light, or glow. At 600°C objects glow dull red, like the heating element on an electric stove. You can see the heating element glow in the dark and that means it gives off light of its own. The amount of energy in visible light is very small however. More than 99.9% of the heat from a hot stove element is radiated as infrared light.

As the temperature rises, thermal radiation produces shorter-wavelength, higher- energy light. At 1,000°C the color is yellow-orange, turning to white at 1,500°C. If you carefully watch a bulb on a dimmer switch, you see its color change as the filament gets hotter. The bright white light from a bulb is thermal radiation from an extremely hot filament, near 2,600°C.

Between room temperature and 600°C the power of thermal radiation increases more than a hundred times. You may have had a doctor look in your ear with a thermometer that measured your temperature. Ear thermometers work by measuring the power of infrared thermal radiation.Add text

---

UNIT 8: Matter and Energy

26.3 Radiant Heat

Question: How does heat get from the sun to Earth?

In this Investigation, you will:

1. Demonstrate that sunlight carries heat.
2. Observe how the spectrum of light emitted by hot objects changes with their temperature.

Thermal radiation is electromagnetic waves (including light) produced by objects because of their temperature. All objects with a temperature above absolute zero give off thermal radiation. Thermal radiation comes from the thermal energy of atoms. Power given off as thermal radiation increases with higher temperatures because the thermal energy of atoms increases with higher temperatures. This Investigation explores some of the properties of thermal radiation both from the sun and from an electric light.

1 Creating a focusing mirror for collecting solar radiation

Radiation carries energy through the vacuum of space—93 million miles between the sun and Earth. One way to collect solar power is to use a mirror that concentrates the radiation from the sun on a small area. A parabolic mirror reflects parallel rays of light to a point at the focus. Solar collectors use parabolic mirrors because they are the most efficient shape for concentrating radiation from the sun.

1. To create a parabolic mirror, start with an 8 1/2 × 11-inch piece of cardboard. Draw lines parallel to the short side 2 centimeters apart across the cardboard. Using a ruler, plot the points in Table 1 on the cardboard, working left to right. The points describe the surface of a parabola with two flat sections on either side.

2. Connect the points with a smooth curve and cut out the shape as shown in the diagram at right. Also cut 2-centimeter-square notches out of the corners.

3. Make a second, identical cardboard shape and fasten the two shapes together with tape or glue by folding and overlapping the tabs on either side as shown at right.

4. Cut two more pieces of cardboard that measure 3 × 14 centimeters. Apply three strips of double-sided tape to each of the cardboard rectangles. Carefully lay aluminum foil shiny side up on the cardboard so it sticks to the tape. Cut the foil a little wider than the cardboard and fold it around the edges. Be careful not to wrinkle the foil because it is the reflective surface for your parabolic mirror.

5. Carefully lay the two strips of foil-covered cardboard on the parabolic shape and glue them in place. (Hot melt glue works well for this purpose. Safety precautions must be taken!) The completed mirror should look like the diagram at right.

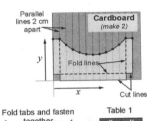

Parallel lines 2 cm apart

Cardboard (make 2)

Fold lines

Cut lines

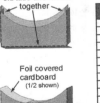

Fold tabs and fasten together

Foil covered cardboard (1/2 shown)

Glue mirror surface to edges

Table 1

x (cm)	y (cm)
0	13.0
2	13.0
4	11.2
6	9.8
8	8.8
10	8.2
12	8.0
14	8.2
16	8.8
18	9.8
20	11.2
22	13.0
24	13.0

Observing radiant energy in action

2

Now that you have constructed your focusing mirror, we are ready to observe radiant energy in action. We will be going outside to do Part 2 of the Investigation. Take a few moments to carefully read through Part 2 of the Investigation.

Allow time for students to become familiar with the procedure.

Each team needs the Investigation handout, a focusing mirror, a Celsius thermometer, a small piece of aluminum foil, a timer or stopwatch, and a pencil. Gather these materials and let's proceed outside so that we can collect data.

Verify that students have all the needed materials before going outside.

Each team will collect temperature data using the mirror. When holding your mirror toward the sun, be sure not to look directly at the sun. Carefully follow each step of the Investigation. Record your data in Table 2 on your handout.

Demonstrate the proper way to hold the mirror to the class before students collect their own data. Each lab team should have one person designated to keep time, one to hold the mirror, and one to hold the thermometer at the focus of the mirror.

Now that everyone has completed Part 2 of the Investigation, collect your materials and let's return to the classroom.

SAFETY PRECAUTION: Never look directly at any bright light source, especially the sun!

Reflecting on what you observed

3

Take a few minutes to read and answer questions 3a and 3b on Part 3 of the Investigation.

Give students time to answer each question.

Let's discuss the data you collected and your responses to the questions. Compare the temperature reading when the thermometer was in sunlight outside of the mirror to the temperature you recorded when the thermometer was placed at the focus of the mirror.

The temperature was higher when the thermometer was placed in the focus of the mirror. In the event that students did not notice a temperature increase, have them hypothesize about what might have gone wrong. For instance, maybe the thermometer was not properly placed at the focus of the mirror or the thermometer might be defective.

Why do you think that the temperature increased when the thermometer was held at the focus?

Students may have a variety of suggestions as to the cause of the elevated temperature. Heat from the sun is reflected off the shiny foil surface. Because the thermometer bulb is held at the focus of the mirror, it lies in the direct path of the reflected heat waves which accounts for the temperature increase.

Placing the thermometer bulb at the focus of the mirror causes the temperature to increase.

Good answer. What happened to the temperature when the thermometer bulb was covered in aluminum foil?

The temperature decreased.

That's right. What do you suppose caused this temperature decline?

Heat from the sun is reflected off the surface of the mirror as well as the foil-covered thermometer bulb. This reduces the amount of heat absorbed by the thermometer bulb and results in a lower temperature.

Covering the thermometer bulb with foil reduces the amount of heat it absorbs, resulting in a reduced temperature.

Can you suggest ways to improve the construction of the mirror?

Students may suggest a variety of improvements. Encourage all responses. Some students might actually want to reconstruct the mirror with improvements.

2 Observing radiant energy in action

1. Hold a thermometer in open air and sunlight until it comes to thermal equilibrium. Record the temperature in Table 2.

2. Hold the mirror so its axis faces the sun. Hold the thermometer in the focus of the mirror. The focus is 5 centimeters above the lowest point and along the axis. Hold the thermometer by its stem with the bulb at the focus of the mirror. Observe the rate of rise in the temperature at the focus of the mirror. Record the temperature after the thermometer has been in the focus of the mirror for 30 seconds. Remove the thermometer from the focus to prevent it from being damaged. Let the thermometer cool down to the temperature measured in step 1.

3. Wrap a small amount of aluminum foil around the bulb of the thermometer. Repeat step 2, holding the foil-wrapped bulb of the thermometer at the mirror's focus. Again, hold the thermometer at the focus for 30 seconds and record its temperature in Table 2. Remove the thermometer from the focus and let it cool down again.

◆**Safety Tip: Never look directly at any bright light source, especially the sun!**

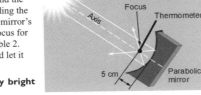

Table 2: Temperature data

	Temp (°C)
In sunlight, outside of mirror	
After 30 seconds at focus	
After 30 seconds at focus, covered with aluminum	

3 Reflecting on what you observed

a. Explain why the thermometer at the focus of the mirror measured a much higher temperature than the same thermometer in sunlight outside the mirror. Your explanation should make use of the concepts of radiant heat and intensity.

b. Explain why the thermometer wrapped in aluminum foil measured a lower temperature rise than when the thermometer was not wrapped. Your answer should use the concepts of absorbed and reflected radiant energy.

185

---

2 3 Example heading

Table 2: *Temperature data*

	Temp (°C)
In sunlight, outside of mirror	4
After 30 seconds at focus	7
After 30 seconds at focus, covered with aluminum	5

3a. The thermometer at the focus of the mirror measured a higher temperature than the same thermometer in sunlight outside the mirror because the shiny (foil) mirror reflected most of its thermal radiation. Since the thermometer bulb was in the direct path of these reflected waves, it absorbed more heat, and registered a higher temperature.

3b. The thermometer wrapped in aluminum foil measured a lower temperature rise than the unwrapped thermometer because the foil around the thermometer reflected most of its radiation, limiting the amount of radiant energy absorbed by the thermometer bulb.

The blackbody spectrum

All objects with temperatures above absolute zero emit thermal radiation.

What is a blackbody?

A blackbody is an ideal surface that reflects nothing, completely absorbs all radiant energy falling on it, and emits pure thermal radiation.

The blackbody spectrum can be expressed in graphical form by plotting relative power versus wavelength.

Observing the blackbody spectrum

4 When objects are heated, they can emit visible light. Cool objects still emit electromagnetic radiation, but it is not visible radiation. What kind of radiation am I emitting as I stand before you?

Students should reply infrared radiation.

That is correct. The warmer an object is, the higher the energy of the radiation it emits. High energy radiation has high frequency but short wavelength. Which color of visible light has the most energy?

Violet light has the most energy, the highest frequency, and the shortest wavelength.

As temperature rises, thermal radiation produces shorter-wavelength, higher-energy light. At room temperature, we do not see objects by their thermal radiation. We see objects by the light they reflect from other sources. We do not see the thermal radiation because it occurs at infrared wavelengths invisible to the human eye.

How can you tell if an object is perfectly black?

Students may offer a variety of responses.

To a physicist, an object is perfectly black when it absorbs all the light that falls on its surface. Is all light is absorbed, any light coming off the surface can only be from thermal radiation. A surface that reflects nothing and absorbs only thermal radiation is a perfect blackbody.

Write this definition on the board and give students time to copy it into their notes.

Go to Part 4 of the Investigation. The graph on the right shows the relationship between power and wavelength. The power versus wavelength graph for a perfect black body is called the blackbody spectrum. Notice how the wavelength increases as energy of the light emitted decreases in the visible region.

Give students time to study this trend on the graph. They should already be familiar with the relationships between energy, frequency, and wavelength from previous discussions of the electromagnetic spectrum.

As objects heat up, they start to give off visible light, or glow. Look at the graph. Notice that the curve for 600°C shows some power emitted in red and orange visible light. At 600°C, objects glow dull red like a burner on an electric stove. As the temperature rises, thermal radiation produces shorter-wavelength, higher-energy light. At 1,000°C, the color is yellow-orange and turns to white at 1,500°C.

5 Carefully read through the procedure in Part 5 of the Investigation.

Give students time to read the procedure.

Obtain a halogen lamp and spectrometer from the supply table. In this part of the Investigation, you will observe changes in the colors of the spectrum as the intensity of the light changes.

Demonstrate how students are to position the spectrometer in order to see the colors of the spectrum.

Now complete steps 1 and 2. Use your observations to help you answer questions 2a through 2c.

Give students time to complete these tasks. Walk around the classroom to assist students who might have problems. Be sure that the spectrometer is properly positioned so that the spectrum can be viewed.

26.3 Radiant Heat

4   The blackbody spectrum

To a physicist, an object is perfectly *black* when it absorbs all light that falls on its surface. If all light is absorbed, any light coming off the surface can only be from thermal radiation. A perfect *blackbody* is a surface that reflects nothing and emits only thermal radiation. To a physicist, the white-hot filament of a bulb is a good blackbody. All light from the filament is thermal radiation; almost no light is reflected from other sources.

The power versus wavelength graph for a perfect blackbody is called the *blackbody spectrum*. The blackbody spectrum changes with the temperature of the surface emitting the radiation. Near room temperature (20°C), the spectrum does not extend into visible light. Therefore, we cannot "see" objects by their own light. We see ordinary objects by reflected light. Up to a few thousand degrees Celsius, most of the energy in thermal radiation is invisible infrared light. As objects heat up, they start to give off visible light, or glow. The curve for 600°C at right shows some power emitted in red and orange visible light. At 600°C, objects glow dull red like a burner on an electric stove. As the temperature rises, thermal radiation produces shorter-wavelength, higher-energy light. At 1,000°C, the color is yellow-orange and turns to white at 1,500°C.

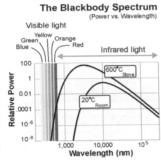

The Blackbody Spectrum
(Power vs. Wavelength)

5   Observing the blackbody spectrum

If you carefully watch a bulb on a dimmer switch, you can see the color of the bulb change as the filament gets hotter. The bright white light from an incandescent bulb is thermal radiation from a very hot filament—near 2,600°C.

1. Obtain a halogen lamp that has a dimmer switch. Halogen bulbs operate at very high temperatures. An ordinary incandescent lamp with a dimmer switch also will work but a fluorescent light will not work.

2. Look at the light through the spectrometer as you adjust the dimmer switch. Remember, to use the spectrometer, point the slit at the light and look left to see the spectrum.

a. Describe the relative amount of red, green, and blue light in the spectrum when the bulb is at its brightest setting.

b. Describe how the relative amounts of red, green, and blue light change as the bulb is turned to lower and lower brightness. The brightness diminishes but try to separate out the color changes from the change in overall brightness.

c. Explain your observations using the blackbody spectrum.

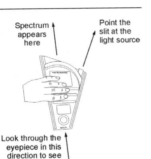

4 5   Example answers

5a. When the bulb is at its brightest setting, more blue and green is visible than red. At higher temperatures, shorter wavelength, higher-energy light is produced.

5b. As the bulb is turned to lower and lower brightness, the amounts of red, blue, and green light change. As the temperature is lowered, the energy of the light is reduced. This lower energy light has longer wavelengths. More red light is visible than green or blue light.

5c. A blackbody emits a certain spectrum of light depending on its temperature. At higher temperatures, light has higher energy and shorter wavelengths. However, as the temperature is reduced, the energy of this light is lowered, resulting in longer wavelengths.

27.1 Properties of Solids

Key Question: How do you measure the strength of a solid material?

In this Investigation, students measure the tensile strength of a solid material: modeling clay. They use a spring scale to determine the breaking force of three samples of modeling clay, each having the same length but a different diameter. After measuring the breaking force of each clay cylinder, students calculate its cross-sectional area and stress. Students use this data to determine the strength of the modeling clay, the stress the clay can take before breaking, and the force required to break the clay.

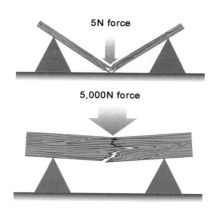

5N force

5,000N force

Reading Synopsis

Students read Section 27.1 Properties of Solids after the Investigation.

Solids have a definite shape and volume. The atoms or molecules of a solid occupy fixed positions, therefore, solids do not flow. The density of common solids ranges from 100 kg/m^3 (cork) to 21,000 kg/m^3 (platinum).

Not all solid materials have equal strength. Stress is force per unit area. The breaking strength of a material is the maximum amount of stress the material can take before it breaks, or bends irreversibly.

Solid materials deform (strain) under stress. The strain is the percent change in a linear dimension. Hooke's law for solids says the strain equals the applied stress multiplied by the modulus of elasticity. Solid materials also expand and contract with changes in temperature. The coefficient of thermal expansion describes how much a material changes in any linear dimension per degree change in temperature.

A wide range of mechanical properties exist in solids. For example, the tensile strength is very different for plastic, wood, aluminum, and steel.

The Investigation

Leading Questions
- How is the strength of a material described and measured?
- How are things designed so they do not break?
- Rubber is a solid but is stretchy. Steel is a solid that does not seem to stretch at all. How is the "stretchiness" of a solid material described and measured?
- How do we describe the fact that the size of solid objects changes when their temperature changes?
- What types of solid materials exist?

Learning Goals

By the end of the Investigation, students will be able to:
- Describe the terms stress and strain as applied to the strength of a material.
- Measure the tensile strength of a material.
- Explain the relationship between force, strength, and stress.

Key Vocabulary   tensile strength, stress, breaking force, cross-section area

Setup and Materials

Students work in groups of two or three at tables.

Each group should have:

- Modeling clay (one cup)
- Metric ruler
- One 5-Newton spring scale
- Graph paper
- Packaging tape
- Calculator

Details

Time ⏲ One class period

Preparation ✎ Try out the Investigation prior to class to anticipate student questions or problems.

Assignments 📖 Section 27.1 Properties of Solids in the **Student Edition** after the Investigation.

Skill Sheets 27.1 Stress and Strain

Teaching the Investigation

1 Introduction

2 Force, strength, and stress

3 Measuring the tensile strength

Introduction

What are solids and how do they differ from liquids and gases?

Solids have a definite shape and volume. The atoms or molecules of a solid are in fixed positions. Solids, unlike liquids or gases, do not flow.

Solids have many different properties. They may be dense, elastic, ductile, hard, or brittle.

Force, strength, and stress

The strength of an object depends upon how much it bends or deforms under applied force, and how much force the object can take before it breaks.

Stress (N/m^2) = Force (N) ÷ Area (m^2)

$$\sigma = \frac{F}{A}$$

Notice on this table that I have placed two glasses. The first glass contains only ice cubes. The second glass contains only liquid water. How are the substances in both glasses alike?

Both substances are water, with the chemical formula, H_2O. Each water molecule in both the ice cubes and liquid water has two hydrogen atoms for each atom of oxygen present.

Are there any differences between the water in the solid state and the liquid water?

Yes, the shape and the volume of the ice cubes is definite. Because the ice cubes are solid, its water molecules exist in fixed positions. The ice cubes can not flow. The liquid water have a definite volume but it has adopted the shape of the glass in which it is contained. Unlike the ice cubes, the liquid water can flow.

Do you think that all solids have the same properties?

No, the properties of solids may vary.

Suppose you wanted to build your dream home. Would you consider building your home out of wax?

No way.

Why not?

Although wax is a solid, it is not strong enough to build a home.

What type of solids would you consider using, and why?

Wood or brick would be good for building a home because they are strong.

1   We know that not all solids have the same strength. In order to determine the strength of a solid, we must consider two factors. First, one must know how much the object will bend or change shape when force is applied. The second factor is that one must know how much force the object can withstand before it breaks. The strength of an object can be broken down into considerations of *design* and *materials*.

Although wax is a weak solid, do you think that it could support a car?

Yes, the wax could support a car if it is a solid block that is the same size as the car.

What is the significance of the wax being a solid block the same size as the car?

This is significant because the size and shape of a material can influence the strength of the material.

When scientists or engineers consider using solid materials, they are concerned with the stress in a material. The stress in a material is the ratio of the force acting through the material divided by the cross-section area through which the force is carried.

Write the formula for calculating stress on the board. Label each variable and provide the appropriate units with each.

Suppose you wanted to know the stress in a material that has a force equal to 68N and a cross-section are of 7.5 m^2. How would you calculate the stress?

Demonstrate how to use the formula by substituting the given data into the equation. The correct answer is 9.1 N/m^2.

Soft solids, like wax, break at a low value of stress. Materials like steel break at a higher stress level. The tensile strength is the stress at which a material breaks under a tension force. Tension forces are stretching forces. Which would you expect to have higher tensile strength, steel or wax?

Steel has higher tensile strength than wax because steel is a stronger material than wax.

Teaching tip

Gather a variety of solid substances with different strengths. Place the solids on a table before your students. Allow them to touch each of the solid materials and discover its properties. For example, students might describe each of the materials as elastic, brittle, expandable, bendable, or dense. Use some of examples provided below, or add others that you may find interesting.

SOLID MATERIALS

Rubber band	Wooden block
Aluminum foil	Glass mirror
Plastic straw	Sandstone rock
Wax	Nylon stocking
Metal block	Cork stopper

UNIT 8: Matter and Energy

27.1 | Properties of Solids

Question: How do you measure the strength of a solid material?

In this Investigation, you will:

1. Measure the breaking strength of a material.
2. Calculate the tensile stress at fracture.
3. Observe the deformation of a material as it breaks in tension.

The concept of physical strength means that an object has the ability to hold its form even when force is applied. Solid materials vary widely in strength and we often choose a material for a given application based on the strength of the material. For example, steel is good for building bridges because it is solid and strong. You would not build a bridge from wax even though wax is a solid.

The strength of an object (such as a bridge) depends on the answers to two questions:

1. How much does the object bend or deform under applied force?
2. How much force can the object take before it breaks?

This Investigation explores how scientists and engineers find the answers to these two questions.

1 **Force, strength, and stress**

The strength of an object can be broken down into considerations of *design* and *materials*. Design means the size and shape of an object. Even a weak material like wax can support a car if the wax is a solid block the size of the car. A thin steel cable can support the same car but with much less material. To properly assess the strength of a material itself, the effects of size and shape must be separated out.

The *stress* in a material is the ratio of the force acting through the material divided by the *cross-section* area through which the force is carried. The cross-section area is the area perpendicular to the direction of the force. Dividing force by cross-section area (mostly) separates out the effects of size and shape from the strength properties of the material itself. The Greek letter sigma (σ) is used as the symbol for stress. Stress (σ) is force (F) divided by cross-section area (A).

$$\text{Stress (N/m}^2\text{)} \quad \sigma = \frac{F \quad \text{Force (N)}}{A \quad \text{Area (m}^2)}$$

Imagine a force F stretching a thick wire

Imagine cutting the wire, all the force must pass through this area (cross section)

Materials break when the stress within them reaches the limit the material can take. Soft solids like wax break at a low value of stress. Materials like steel break at a much higher stress level. The *tensile strength* is the stress at which a material breaks under a tension force. Tension forces are "stretching" forces. Strong materials like steel have high tensile strength. Weak materials like wax and rubber have low tensile strength. Materials like wood and plastic have tensile strength between rubber and steel.

187

Measuring the tensile strength

2

Tensile strength is the stress at which a material breaks under a tension force.

In this Investigation, you will measure the tensile strength of a soft material: modeling clay. Each group should have one cup of the modeling clay, tape, a metric ruler, and a 5-Newton spring scale.

Circulate to confirm that each group has the necessary materials.

Work the clay with your hands until it is smooth. Be sure that it has no cracks or voids inside. Cracks and voids can cause your clay to fail at low stress values. You will know that the clay is ready to be used when you can shape it easily.

Demonstrate this to your students. Manipulate your own clay sample until it is ready to be used.

You need a total of nine clay cylinders. Each of your cylinders will be 10 centimeters long but will vary in diameter. Three of your cylinders will have a diameter of 0.5 centimeter, three with a diameter of 1.0 centimeter, and three that measure 1.5 centimeters in diameter. Use your metric ruler to measure the length and diameter of each clay cylinder.

Be sure that your students are correctly measuring the diameter of each clay cylinder.

Now let's ensure that your spring scale is calibrated. Be sure that the pointer on your scale reads 0 N when it is held horizontally.

Walk around the classroom with a scale that is correctly calibrated in hand. Show students that the pointer must read 0 N.

Use the tape to make a hook at the end of each cylinder. Attach the scale to the tape and slowly pull the clay until it stretches and breaks. As one person pulls the clay, your partner should watch the scale carefully. Once the clay starts to stretch rapidly, it has failed. Record the force reading on the scale when the stretching occurs.

Demonstrate the breaking force test to the students. Remind them that they will need to repeat this test for each cylinder several times in order to obtain accurate data. Each cylinder will have to be remade for each test.

Record your force measurements for each cylinder in Table 1. Use this data to answer questions 5a through 5e. In order to calculate the stress for each of your cylinders, you must convert your centimeter measurements to meters. Then you can apply the formula.

Allow students time to answer these questions. Some students may need help with the calculations. Be sure that the formula for calculating stress is on the board and that each variable is labeled with proper units.

27.1 Properties of Solids

2 Measuring the tensile strength

In this Investigation, you will measure the tensile strength of a soft material: modeling clay. Although the clay breaks at a relatively low value of stress, the technique used for measuring the tensile strength is exactly the same as used for stronger materials such as steel and aluminum.

1. Get about 1 cup of modeling clay. Work the clay with your hands until it is smooth and uniform with no voids or cracks inside. Any cracks or voids in the clay will cause it to fail at a much lower value of stress.

2. Roll the clay into three cylinders as shown in the diagram at right. The cylinders should be 10 centimeters long and have diameters of 1, 1.5, and 2 centimeters.

3. The breaking force for each of the cylinders will be measured with a 5-newton spring scale. Adjust the calibration of the scale so that the pointer reads 0 N when held horizontal.

4. Use a small length of tape to make a hook on one end of each clay cylinder. You have to thicken the ends of the smallest sample with additional clay to attach the tape. Attach the spring scale to the tape and slowly pull the clay until it stretches and breaks. You will watch the scale carefully. The breaking force is the reading the scale has *just as the clay starts to stretch and break*. Once the clay starts to stretch, it will keep stretching rapidly if you keep a constant force applied. A material is considered to have failed as soon as it starts to stretch rapidly.

5. Repeat the breaking force measurement for all three samples of clay. You have to remake each clay sample several times to get consistent measurements. Practice your technique and try to be consistent about identifying the force at which the clay just begins to stretch toward failure. Record your most consistent results in Table 1.

Table 1: Breaking force data

Diameter (cm)	Breaking force (N)	Cross sec. area (cm²)	Stress (N/cm²)

a. Calculate the cross-section area and stress for each of the clay cylinder samples.

b. Compare the force required to break each sample with the stress in each sample. Which is a better measure of the strength of the clay as a material: the breaking force or the stress?

c. Plot a graph showing the breaking force versus the cross-section area. What mathematical property of the graph is the tensile strength? Which is the maximum stress the clay can take before breaking?

d. Use your data to estimate the force required to break a cylinder of clay that is 3 centimeters in diameter.

e. Suppose you could keep a constant force applied as the clay stretches. What happens to the stress in the clay once it starts stretching?

2 Example answers

Table 1: *Breaking force data*

Diameter (cm)	Breaking force (N)	Cross sec. area (cm²)	Stress (N/cm²)
0.5	2.0	0.2	10
1.0	3.2	0.79	4.1
1.5	4.3	1.8	2.4

5a. The cross section area of a clay cylinder with a diameter of 0.5 cm is 2.0×10^{-5} m². Cross section area in each of the samples is calculated by first converting each cylinder's diameter to meters from centimeters. Then the area is calculated using πr^2 (where r is the radius). Using $\sigma = F/A$, a clay cylinder with a 0.5 cm diameter has a stress (σ) equal to 2.0 N ÷ 2.0×10^{-5} m². The stress on this cylinder is 1.0×10^{5} N/m².

5b. The stress is a better measure of the strength of the clay as a material.

5c. The tensile strength is represented by the slope. The breaking force is the maximum stress the clay can take before breaking.

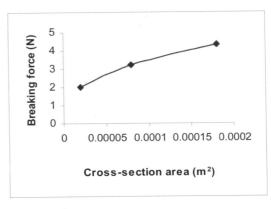

5d. Approximately 8.0 N of is required to break a cylinder with a 3 cm diameter.

5e. As the clay starts stretching, the stress in the clay increases.

27.2 Properties of Liquids and Fluids

Key Question: What are some implications of Bernoulli's equation?

Energy conservation applies to fluids just as it does to all other forms of matter. However, with fluids the variables are different and applying energy conservation takes some new tricks. In this Investigation, students review Bernoulli's equation, which is energy conservation for a moving fluid. They use a simple demonstration to show that as air speed increases, the air pressure decreases. Next, they build their own device to measure the pressure difference when air flows from a larger to a smaller diameter tube. They use their pressure measurements to calculate the speed of the air in the large and small tubes.

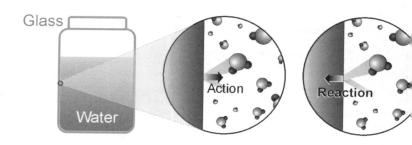

Reading Synopsis

Students read Section 27.2 Properties of Liquids and Fluids

Buoyancy is an important property of fluids. An object submerged in a fluid feels a buoyant force equal to the weight of the liquid displaced by the object.

Pressure is created when force is applied to a fluid. Pressure acts in all directions and is measured in force per unit area. The metric unit is N/m^2, the pascal.

Gravity is one cause of pressure because fluids have weight. Dense fluids (water) create more pressure than light fluids (air) at the same depth. Pressure in a fluid still fluid is equal to density times gravitational acceleration times depth.

Fluids flow because of differences in pressure. Moving fluids have different speeds in different places.

The law of conservation of energy applies to fluids. The total energy of a small mass of fluid is equal to its potential energy from gravity plus potential energy from pressure plus kinetic energy. This is known as Bernoulli's equation.

The Investigation

Leading Questions
- ow do you measure the speed of moving air?
- How are stress and pressure alike? How are they different?
- How do aircraft wings generate lift?
- If air is flowing through a pipe that has a reduction in diameter, what happens to the speed of the air? What happens to the air pressure?

Learning Goals
By the end of the Investigation, students will be able to:
- Demonstrate how the movement of a fluid creates pressure differences.
- Build a device for measuring the speed of moving air and describe how it works.
- Use Bernoulli's equation to determine the speed of moving air from a pressure difference.

Key Vocabulary   Pressure, stress, Bernoulli's equation, manometer

Setup and Materials

Students work in groups of four or five at tables.

Each group should have:

- Plastic straw with flexible "elbow" (one for each student)
- 3-by-3 inch sticky note (one for each student)
- 8-inch length of 3/4-inch pvc pipe with pre-drilled hole
- 8-inch length of 1/2-inch pvc pipe with pre-drilled hole
- Coupling to join the two pipes
- 0.5-meter length of 1/4-inch clear flexible plastic tubing
- Red food coloring
- Water
- Paper cup
- Clear tape
- Meter stick

Details

Time 🕐 One class period

Preparation ✏️ The pvc pipes, couplings, and flexible plastic tubing can be purchased at a home improvement store. Cut materials to the correct lengths and drill the holes prior to the start of class. The pipes and couplings can be reused year after year.

Assignments 📖 Section 27.2 Properties of Liquids and Fluids in the **Student Edition** before the Investigation.

Skill Sheets 27.2 Archimedes

Teaching the Investigation

1   Introduction
2   Bernoulli's equation
3   Demonstrating Bernoulli's equation
4   Using Bernoulli's equation to measure the speed of moving air
5   Building the air speed tester
6   Calculating the air speed

Introduction

Bernoulli's equation

1

Discuss E = PV, energy is pressure times volume, pressure is energy density in joules per cubic meter. (p 552 of textbook)

Go over the derivation of Bernoulli's equation similar to the text pages 552-553.

$$\rho gh + P + \frac{1}{2}\rho v^2 = constant$$

Today's Investigation takes a look at what happens when forces are applied to fluids. You will learn more about Bernoulli's equation, which can take some of the mystery out of how airplanes can actually fly, even though some of the largest ones can weigh up to 360 metric tons when fully loaded.

The Investigation involves some complicated-looking equations. We will take them step by step, and it really only takes an understanding of basic algebra to follow them. It's sometimes tempting to skim over the equations when you're reading, but if you take the time to work through them you will gain a much deeper understanding of how forces in fluids work.

Part One begins with the statement "Pressure and energy are related." Who can define pressure for me?

Students learned in the reading that pressure is created when forces are applied to fluids. Pressure, unlike stress, acts in all directions—not just the direction of the applied force. Pressure is measured in force per unit area. The metric unit of pressure, N/m^2, is known as the pascal.

The pressure that is created when you have fluid in a container can do work. Therefore, where you have pressure, you have potential energy. We can calculate the potential energy if we know the amount of pressure and the volume of fluid, using the equation $E = PV$, where energy is measured in joules, pressure in pascals, and volume in cubic meters.

Let's say you have a container of water, like the one pictured in Part one of your Investigation. There's a hole in the side. The water that is streaming out can do useful work. For example, you could have it turn a turbine to generate electricity or operate a machine. The pressure energy of the water inside the tank is converted to kinetic energy of the water squirting out the hole. The law of conservation of energy applies to this system as it does to any other. What is the law of conservation of energy?

The law of conservation of energy states that energy is neither created or destroyed. In a closed system, energy can be changed from one form to another, but the total amount of energy stays the same.

Let's follow a small mass of fluid as it travels from point A, inside the container, to point B, outside the container. At point A, its total energy is equal to potential energy from gravity (mgh) plus potential energy from pressure (PV) plus its kinetic energy ($^1/_2mv^2$). Now take a look at this equation. What are the three variables that could change as the mass of water moves from point A to point B?

Height, pressure, and velocity could change. Label them h_1, P_1, and v_1.

The law of conservation of energy tells us that the total energy outside the container will be equal to the total energy inside the container.

Write the equation at left on the board.

There are three variables in your equation that won't change as our small mass of water moves from the inside to the outside of the container. What are they?

They are mass, volume, and acceleration due to gravity.

We can simplify this equation by dividing each of the terms by volume. In the first and third terms, we can rewrite "mass divided by volume" as density. We use the Greek letter rho to indicate density.

Now you have the standard form of Bernoulli's equation. It shows that height, pressure, and speed are related—in order to keep the equation balanced, if one of those variables increases, at least one of the others must decrease. We often use a shortcut when writing Bernoulli's equation. Rather than writing out both sides, we write just the left side, eliminate the subscripts, and add "= constant." This means that the sum of the three terms has to stay the same. If one variable increases, another decreases to compensate.

UNIT 8: Matter and Energy

Properties of Solids

Question: How do you measure the strength of a solid material?

In this Investigation, you will:

1. Measure the breaking strength of a material.
2. Calculate the tensile stress at fracture.
3. Observe the deformation of a material as it breaks in tension.

The concept of physical strength means that an object has the ability to hold its form even when force is applied. Solid materials vary widely in strength and we often choose a material for a given application based on the strength of the material. For example, steel is good for building bridges because it is solid and strong. You would not build a bridge from wax even though wax is a solid.

The strength of an object (such as a bridge) depends on the answers to two questions:

1. How much does the object bend or deform under applied force?
2. How much force can the object take before it breaks?

This Investigation explores how scientists and engineers find the answers to these two questions.

1 Force, strength, and stress

The strength of an object can be broken down into considerations of *design* and *materials*. Design means the size and shape of an object. Even a weak material like wax can support a car if the wax is a solid block the size of the car. A thin steel cable can support the same car but with much less material. To properly assess the strength of a material itself, the effects of size and shape must be separated out.

The *stress* in a material is the ratio of the force acting through the material divided by the *cross-section* area through which the force is carried. The cross-section area is the area perpendicular to the direction of the force. Dividing force by cross-section area (mostly) separates out the effects of size and shape from the strength properties of the material itself. The Greek letter sigma (σ) is used as the symbol for stress. Stress (σ) is force (F) divided by cross-section area (A).

$$\text{Stress (N/m}^2) \quad \sigma = \frac{F \quad \text{Force (N)}}{A \quad \text{Area (m}^2)}$$

Imagine a force F stretching a thick wire

Imagine cutting the wire, all the force must pass through this area (cross section)

Materials break when the stress within them reaches the limit the material can take. Soft solids like wax break at a low value of stress. Materials like steel break at a much higher stress level. The *tensile strength* is the stress at which a material breaks under a tension force. Tension forces are "stretching" forces. Strong materials like steel have high tensile strength. Weak materials like wax and rubber have low tensile strength. Materials like wood and plastic have tensile strength between rubber and steel.

Streamlines

Bernoulli's equation is constant *along a streamline*. This is an important qualification for your students to grasp. The principle is really quite simple. A streamline is an imaginary line following the path of a small mass of fluid. If the speed at v_2 was measured below the streamline, we wouldn't be measuring the speed of the same individual mass of fluid that we measured in v_1. The speed would be slower due to friction created by the edge of the container's opening. Students can learn more about why the speed of a fluid is different along different streamlines under the heading "Motion of fluids" in section 27.2 of the student text.

Demonstrating Bernoulli's equation

Using Bernoulli's equation to measure the speed of moving air

Group 1: Show

$$\rho g h_1 + P_1 + \tfrac{1}{2}\rho v_1^{2} = \rho g h_2 + P_2 + \tfrac{1}{2}\rho v_2^{2}$$

$$\downarrow$$

$$P_1 - P_2 = \frac{\rho}{2}\left(v_2^{2} - v_1^{2}\right)$$

Group 2: Derive

$$v_2^{2} - v_1^{2} = v_2^{2}\left(1 - \frac{A_2^{2}}{A_1^{2}}\right)$$

Group 3: Show

$$v_2^{2} - v_1^{2} = v_2^{2}\left(1 - \frac{A_2^{2}}{A_1^{2}}\right) \quad \text{and}$$

$$P_1 - P_2 = \frac{\rho}{2}\left(v_2^{2} - v_1^{2}\right)$$

$$\downarrow$$

$$v_2 = \frac{\sqrt{P_1 - P_2}}{\sqrt{\dfrac{\rho}{2}\left(1 - \dfrac{A_2^{2}}{A_1^{2}}\right)}}$$

2 Now you will have a chance to see for yourself what happens to pressure as you increase the airspeed. Each of you will get a flexible straw and a sticky note. Follow the directions in Part two on your own.

> Students will see that the paper curls upward. The air speed is greater above the paper, so the air pressure above the paper is lower than the pressure below. For an interesting discussion of how this principle creates lift under an airplane wing, see the heading "Applying Bernoulli's equation" in Section 27.2 of the student text.

3 Part three asks you to consider a pipe that has a reduction in diameter, like a water pipe that comes into your house from the main line at the street. Where do you think the water would travel faster, in the large pipe or the small one?

> If students have trouble answering correctly, ask them what happens when they attach a nozzle to the end of a hose. Does the water come out faster with or without the nozzle? The water comes out fast because the pressure decreases passing through the nozzle opening therefore the velocity of the water goes up.

When the cross-sectional area of the pipe decreases, the speed increases. Area and speed are inversely proportional.

> Write the equation on the board. Then have students practice a few problems so they can see for themselves how it works. Be sure to have them solve for v2, since they will need to do that later.

With your group, answer the following question: If the area of the pipe decreases from 9 cm^2 to 3 cm^2, and the air speed in the larger pipe was 2 m/sec, what is the air speed in the smaller pipe?

> The answer is 6 m/sec.

Would someone please read the last paragraph in Part three out loud?

> After reading the paragraph together, show them the apparatus they will use in Part four and five. Blow through the pipe so they can see the pressure difference.

You are going to use Bernoulli's equation to find the speed of your air in the larger pipe. But first we must figure out how to transform the equation to solve for v$_1$. The graphic at the bottom of the page summarizes the steps. In Part one, I walked through the algebra with you. This time I want each group to take a piece of the transformation and figure out the algebraic steps. Then you will present the steps to your classmates.

> Assign one group the transformation from Bernoulli's equation (left). A second group should explain the steps involved in the transformation in the gray box entitled "Relationship between areas and speeds." A third group should explain the transformation from to the final result in the box at the end of Part three.

This formula looks complicated but all the variables except the h are things we know. We only have to calculate them once.

> Show how plugging in the numbers results in v2 = 115 times the square root of the height difference. You will have to show how the density of water and the factor under the square root reduces to 9,800h (step 5)

27.2 Properties of Liquids and Fluids

2   Demonstrating Bernoulli's equation

For this experiment, you will need a plastic straw and a sticky note that is about 3-by-3 inches.

1. Cut a strip of the sticky note about 2 centimeters wide. Stick the note on a desk as shown at right.

2. With the straw, blow air across the sticky note from the stuck side toward the free side. Position the straw so the air blows parallel to the paper. The end of the straw should not overlap the paper by more than 1 centimeter.

3. Observe what happens to the paper as the moving air blows across its upper surface.

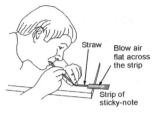

Straw   Blow air flat across the strip

Strip of sticky-note

a. Does the paper curl up into the moving air or down away from the moving air?

b. Use the relationship between speed and pressure to explain the direction in which the paper moves.

3   Using Bernoulli's equation to measure the speed of moving air

Bernoulli's equation gives us a simple way to measure the speed of air moving in a pipe. Consider air flowing in a pipe that has a reduction in its diameter. When air flows through the pipe, the speed is greater in the smaller pipe than in the larger pipe. The difference in speed creates a difference in pressure that you can measure.

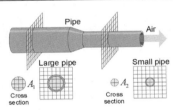

Pipe   Air

Large pipe   Small pipe

A_1 Cross section A_2 Cross section

Relationship between speeds

$$\frac{v_1}{v_2} = \frac{A_2}{A_1}$$

Imagine cutting a cross-section across the pipe in two places. The same amount of air must cross each place in equal amounts of time. That means the speed of the air increases by the inverse of the ratio of the areas. If the area of the larger pipe is twice the area of the smaller pipe, the speed of the air in the smaller pipe is twice the speed of the air in the larger pipe.

If the speed goes up, the pressure must go down. Because we know the ratio of speeds from geometry, the change in pressure allows us to measure the air speed. Applying Bernoulli's equation to the pipe gives the following relationship: since the variation in pressure is very small, the density of the air is nearly constant. If the pipe is horizontal, the height is also constant. The only unknowns are the speed and pressure difference. The speed is what you want and the pressure difference you can measure.

$P_1 \Rightarrow$ v_1 $P_2 \Rightarrow v_2$

Bernoulli's equation

Large pipe   Small pipe

$$\rho g h + P_1 + \tfrac{1}{2}\rho v_1^2 = \rho g h + P_2 + \tfrac{1}{2}\rho v_2^2$$

$$P_1 - P_2 = \tfrac{1}{2}\rho(v_2^2 - v_1^2) \quad P_1 - P_2 = \tfrac{1}{2}\rho v_2^2\left(1 - \frac{A_2^2}{A_1^2}\right)$$

Relationship between areas and speeds

$$v_2^2 - v_1^2 = v_2^2 - v_2^2\left(\frac{A_2}{A_1}\right)^2 = v_2^2\left(1 - \frac{A_2^2}{A_1^2}\right)$$

Final result

$$v_2 = \sqrt{P_1 - P_2}\sqrt{\frac{2}{\rho}\left(1 - \frac{A_2^2}{A_1^2}\right)}$$

2   Example answers

2a. The paper curls up into the moving air.

2b. As the speed of the air above the paper increases, the pressure decreases. Then the air pressure under the paper is greater than the air pressure above the paper, so the paper is pushed up. This is similar to the lift created by air moving across the upper surface of an airplane wing.

Group 1 presentation:

$$\rho g h + P_1 + \tfrac{1}{2}\rho v_1^2 = \rho g h + P_2 + \tfrac{1}{2}\rho v_2^2$$

Since h is the same on both sides, the term $\rho g h$ cancels from both sides, leaving:

$$P_1 - P_2 = \tfrac{1}{2}\rho v_2^2 - \tfrac{1}{2}\rho v_1^2$$
$$= \tfrac{1}{2}\rho(v_2^2 - v_1^2)$$

Group 2 presentation:

$$v_2 = \frac{A_2}{A_1}v_1$$

Therefore,

$$v_2^2 - v_1^2 = v_2^2 - v_2^2\left(\frac{A_2}{A_1}\right)^2$$
$$= v_2^2\left(1 - \frac{A_2^2}{A_1^2}\right)$$

Building the air speed tester

Students follow the procedure to assemble the air speed tester from pre-cut parts prepared ahead of time.

Students blow into the larger pipe and see that the water is forced toward the smaller pipe by the pressure differential.

We are going to build our own air-speed tester from plastic pipes. For the large pipe, use an 8-inch length of 3/4-inch plastic pipe. This pipe has an inner diameter of 0.75 inches (.019 meter). We will use a similar length of 1/2-inch plastic pipe for the smaller pipe. This pipe has an inner diameter of 0.5 inches, or .012 meter). There are two holes in the centers of both pipes drilled to fit plastic tubing. Connect the two pipes with a coupling. You do not need to glue the coupling; the pipes will fit tightly enough without it.

Students put the pipes together

To measure the pressure difference, we will use the difference in height of a water-filled tube. A water-filled tube used to measure pressure differences is called a manometer. Make your manometer from a half-meter length of 1/4-inch, clear, flexible plastic tubing. I have put food coloring in this water so it is easier to see. Very slowly fill the tube about 1/4 full of colored water so that there are no air bubbles in the filled section of the tube.

Filling the tubes takes some patience. If they get bubbles they can slowly turn the tube upside down and back again, while keeping the ends covered with a finger. It is very important that there be no bubbles in the filled portion. If there are bubbles, the height difference will not correspond the true pressure difference.

Hold up the tube and the water in both sides should come to the same level. What does this mean?

The air pressure in both sides of the tube is the same.

Squeeze the tube into the holes so that the tube ends are nearly flush with the inner wall of the pipe. Use tape to fasten the tubes as shown. The completed air speed tester should look like the diagram at right. When you blow through the larger pipe, you will see the water level in the tube change as the pressure changes. You can measure the difference in height with a meter stick. The greater the height difference, the greater the difference in pressure.

Students should try their air speed testers.

Where in the tube is the pressure the greatest? How do you know?

The pressure is greater in the larger section of the tube. They can tell because the water is forced up toward the smaller tube. The water is forced by the higher pressure in the low-speed part of the tube.

How is this predicted by Bernoulli's equation?

Bernoulli's equation says that the pressure along any streamline must go down when the speed goes up.

How can you tell the pressure difference is caused by flowing air and not by something else?

The water goes back to the same level on both sides of the manometer when we stop blowing through the pipe.

Calculating the air speed

The water moves up and down very fast because you cannot keep an constant air flow for very long with your lungs. To get the measurements, this is what we will do.

• One person will hold the air speed tester and blow through the tube.
• One person will hold a meter stick behind the vertical part of the manometer.
• One person will read the high point reached by the water on the meter stick.
• One person will read the low point from the other side of the tube on the meter stick

You can subtract the high and low readings to get the height.

Students follow the procedure in parts 4 and 5 to calculate the speed of the air.

Group three presentation:

$$P_1 - P_2 = \tfrac{1}{2}\rho(v_2^2 - v_1^2)$$

$$= \tfrac{1}{2}\rho v_2^2\left(1 - \frac{A_2^2}{A_1^2}\right)$$

$$\frac{P_1 - P_2}{\dfrac{\rho}{2}\left(1 - \dfrac{A_2^2}{A_1^2}\right)} = v_2^2$$

$$v_2 = \frac{\sqrt{P_1 - P_2}}{\sqrt{\dfrac{\rho}{2}\left(1 - \dfrac{A_2^2}{A_1^2}\right)}}$$

5

Example data

We did a series of tests, each with slightly different results. This is expected since it was difficult to blow with the same strength every time.

Test 1:
h = 67.5 cm - 63.5 cm = 4 cm = 0.04 m
v_2 = 28 m/sec

Test 2:
h = 69.0 cm - 67.5 cm = 1.5 cm = 0.015 m
v_2 = 17 m/sec

27.2 Properties of Liquids and Fluids

4

Building an air-speed tester

Construct an air-speed tester from plastic pipes. For the large pipe, use an 8-inch length of 3/4-inch plastic PVC pipe that has an inner diameter of 0.75 inches (.019 meter). Use a similar length of 1/2-inch plastic pipe for the smaller pipe (with an inner diameter of 0.5 inches, or .012 meter). Drill two 31/32-inch holes in the centers of both pipes for plastic tubing. Connect the two pipes with a coupling. You do not need to glue the coupling; the pipes will fit tightly enough without it.

20 cm (8")
3/4" PVC pipe
31/32" holes
1/2" PVC pipe
Coupling fitting

To measure the pressure difference, you will use the difference in height of a water-filled tube. A water-filled tube used to measure pressure differences is called a *manometer*. Make your manometer from a half- meter length of 1/4-inch, clear, flexible plastic tubing. Mix some food coloring in a 1/4 cup of water. Slowly fill the tube about 1/4 full of colored water so that there are no air bubbles in the filled section of the tube. Squeeze the tube into the holes so that the tube ends are nearly flush with the inner wall of the pipe. Use tape to fasten the tubes as shown. The completed air speed tester should look like the diagram at right.

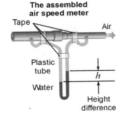

The assembled air speed meter
Tape
Air
Plastic tube
Water
h
Height difference

When you blow through the larger pipe, you will see the water level in the tube change as the pressure changes. You can measure the difference in height with a meter stick. The greater the height difference, the greater the difference in pressure.

5

Calculating the air speed

At standard atmospheric pressure and temperature, the density of air is 1.22 kg/m^3. At low speeds, the density of air remains constant as it passes through the pipe. The ratio of areas between the large and small pipe is 2.25, meaning the speed in the smaller pipe is 2.25 times the speed in the larger pipe. That means the complicated factor under the square root reduces to a simple value:

$$\sqrt{\frac{\rho}{2}\left(1 - \frac{A_2^2}{A_1^2}\right)} = \sqrt{\frac{(1.22\ \text{kg/m}^3)}{2}\left(1 - \frac{1}{2.25^2}\right)} = 0.6996$$

One further simplification is needed. The difference in pressure is related to the height difference in the water in the tube by the equation $P_1 - P_2 = \rho gh$ where ρ is the density of water (1,000 kg/m^3).

$$v_2 = 1.15\sqrt{P_1 - P_2} \qquad P_1 - P_2 = \rho gh = 9{,}800h$$

If we substitute the values for ρ and g into the formula for the speed, we get a nice, simple result. The speed of the air in the small pipe (v_2) is 142 × the square root of the height difference in meters!

$$v_2 = 142\sqrt{h}\ \ \text{m/sec}$$

Blow through the tube, measure the water's height difference, and use the relationship above to calculate the speed of the air in the large and small pipes.

191

27.3 Properties of Gases

Key Question: How much matter is in a gas?

Air may seem like nothing but air is a gas and it has mass. The mass in a fixed volume of gas depends on the type of gas and on the pressure. If you squeeze more mass in the same volume, the pressure goes up because the atoms are packed tighter together. In this Investigation, students use a bicycle pump to increase the pressure in a fixed volume of air. They measure the mass of the air at different pressures. After converting their pressure measurements to absolute pressure in pascals, students graph pressure vs. mass and describe the mathematical relationship between the two. Next, students submerge their apparatus in ice water. They measure and describe how lowering the temperature affects the pressure of the gas.

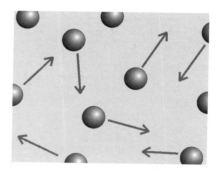

Reading Synopsis

Students read Section 27.3 Properties of Gases after the Investigation

Gases are fluids because like liquids, they can change shape and flow when force is applied. However, while liquids and solids undergo only small density changes, the density of a gas can vary greatly because gases easily expand and contract.

Buoyant forces apply to gases as well as liquids. A helium balloon, for example, floats because it weighs less than the air it displaces.

Boyle's law explains that at constant temperature, the pressure of a gas is inversely proportional to its volume. If you double the pressure, the volume is halved.

Charles' law states that the pressure of a gas is directly proportional to temperature when volume and mass are constant. If you double the temperature, the pressure is doubled as well.

The ideal gas law, $PV=mRT$, relates pressure, volume, and temperature of a gas in one equation. R is a constant unique to each gas, and m is mass in kg.

The Investigation

Leading Questions
- What proof exists that a gas such as air has mass?
- What is the relationship between pressure and mass?
- How can you describe the relationship between mass, density and pressure in a gas?
- How does lowering the temperature of a gas affect its pressure and mass?

Learning Goals

By the end of the Investigation, students will be able to:
- Describe experimental evidence that gas contains mass.
- Explain why changing the pressure of a fixed volume of gas changes its mass.
- Describe what happens to mass and pressure of a fixed volume of gas when its temperature is reduced.

Key Vocabulary

gauge pressure, absolute pressure, pounds per square inch (psi), pascals

Setup and Materials

Students work in groups of four at tables.

Each group should have:

- 1-liter plastic soda bottle
- 100-milliliter graduated cylinder
- Water source
- Bottle cap with valve stem attached (see directions below)
- Good quality tire pressure gauge with dial readout (available at automotive supply stores) Please note: the "ballpoint pen" style pressure gauge with a movable stick readout is not accurate enough for this Investigation.
- Electronic balance
- Calculator
- Graph paper
- Bucket of ice water

Optional material for lesson extension:

- 10-milliliter oral syringe commonly used to dispense liquid cough syrup to small children (many retail pharmacies will donate these)
- Petroleum jelly
- Candle
- Kitchen matches

Directions for preparing bottle caps:

You will need:

- Cap from 1-liter plastic bottle for each group
- Valve stem for each group (available for purchase at automotive supply stores)
- Electric drill, large drill bits
- Household silicone adhesive/sealant

Drill a hole in the center of the bottle cap large enough to accommodate the black neck and shoulder of the valve stem. Test-fit the valve stem, then remove it. Place a bead of silicone sealant around the hole inside the bottle cap. Replace the valve stem. Allow the silicone to cure 24 hours before using the cap.

Details

Time One class period

Preparation The bottle caps must be prepared at least 24 hours in advance. Directions are found in the lower left column of this page. The modified bottle caps can be reused year after year.

Assignments Section 27.3 Properties of Gases in the **Student Edition** after the Investigation.

Skill Sheets 27.3 Gas Laws

Teaching the Investigation

1 Introduction
2 Observing the mass of a gas
3 Analyzing the data
4 The effect of temperature on pressure
5 Extension: Boyle's law demonstration

Introduction

How are liquids and gases alike? How are they different?

Today we are going to investigate some of the physical properties of gases. What are some of the properties that gases and liquids share?

> Both are fluids—they can change shape and flow when forces are applied. Students may also mention that buoyant forces apply to both liquids and gases.

What is an important difference in the physical properties of liquids and gases?

> The density of a liquid changes only slightly (with temperature). The density of a gas can vary greatly because gas can be compressed. You can squeeze different amounts of molecules into the same volume of a gas.

In this Investigation, you will explore the relationship between the pressure, mass, volume, and temperature of a gas.

Observing the mass of a gas　　**1**

While students don't use the volume of the bottle in their calculations, taking time to find and record the volume helps students recognize that the volume will remain constant.

You may wish to discuss why the bottle actually holds more than one liter. The extra space at the top helps prevent the liquid from spilling over when the pressurized gas of a carbonated beverage is released upon opening. (You may also wish to discuss why a chilled soda bottle is less likely to overflow than a warm one—cold water holds more dissolved gas than warm water.)

Emphasize the variables: pressure, mass, volume, and density. Which values will increase? Decrease? Remain the same?

Read the introduction to part one of the Investigation. The last sentence reads, "Pressurized gas stores energy." Can you think of an example of pressurized gas being used to do work?

> There are many examples students could mention. The release of pressurized gas is used to push pistons, to turn turbines, and to move rockets. It is used to spray cooking oil, hair spray, shaving cream, and paint out of cylindrical containers. It is used to deliver oxygen to SCUBA divers. Allow students time to come up with their own examples.

Now follow steps one through five. Step two asks you to measure the volume of the bottle. Make sure you fill the bottle all the way to the top. Be careful not to squeeze the full bottle as you begin to pour the water into the graduated cylinder. If even a small amount of water spills, empty the graduated cylinder, refill the bottle, and try again. It may take several attempts before you get an accurate measurement.

> Allow students time to take the volume measurements.

When you are ready for step three, take a look at the modified bottle cap. There is a silicone seal between the valve stem and bottle cap so that air can't leak out. Take care not to twist the valve stem roughly or you may break that seal.

> You may wish to have several extra modified bottle caps on hand to replace any leaky seals.

Before you start increasing the pressure in the bottle, think about the relationship between pressure, mass, volume, and density of gases. Answer these questions with your group: Which of these values will stay the same? Which will increase? Which will decrease?

> Students should recognize that the volume will remain the same throughout. Pressure is obviously increasing. Because they are adding more air molecules to the bottle, the mass will increase. Density is mass divided by volume, so the density will increase as well.

Measure the mass of the bottle at 0, 10, 20, 30, 40, and 50 psi. If you can get 60 or 70 psi in the bottle, you may take those measurements as well. Do not exceed 80 psi!

27.3   Properties of Gases

Question: How much matter is in a gas?

In this Investigation, you will:

1. Measure the mass of a volume of gas.
2. Measure the relationship between mass, density, and pressure for a gas.
3. Demonstrate the relationship between pressure and temperature for a gas.

Gases are fluids because they can change shape and flow when forces are applied. Gases are different from liquids because they can expand and contract, greatly changing their density. Depending on the pressure and temperature, the density of a gas can vary from near zero (outer space) to densities greater than solids. This Investigation explores the relationship between the pressure, temperature, and density of a gas.

1   **Observing the mass of a gas**

For this part of the Investigation, you will use a digital balance to measure the difference in mass of a volume of gas at different pressures. The gas will be contained in a 1-liter plastic soda bottle. The cap of the bottle has been modified to include an air valve to which a bicycle pump may be attached. The pump can be used to raise the pressure of the gas (in this case, air) in the bottle. Pressurized gas stores energy.

⬧**Safety Note: Be careful with the bottle, and DO NOT exceed 80 pounds per square inch (psi) of pressure.**

1. Use the balance to measure and record the mass of the bottle (and air) at ordinary atmospheric pressure. Record the mass in Table 1.
2. Fill the bottle to the very top with water. Empty the water into a graduated cylinder to measure the volume of the bottle. Record the volume in Table 1.
3. Use the bicycle pump to increase the pressure of gas in the bottle to 10 psi. You should take the pressure a little higher than 10 psi and use the valve to let some air out, adjusting the pressure until it equals 10 psi. Check the pressure with your gauge as the gauge on most bicycle pumps is not accurate enough for this experiment.
4. Use the balance to measure and record the mass of the bottle (and air) at 10 psi pressure. Record the mass in Table 1.
5. Repeat the pumping and mass measurement for pressures between 10 psi and 80 psi. Record all data in Table 1. DO NOT exceed 80 psi!

Valve cut-away view

Pin push to open the valve

Cap

Plastic soda bottle

Table 1: Pressure and mass data

Gauge pressure (psi)	Mass (g)	Volume (ml)

 Example answers

Table 1: Pressure and mass data

Gauge pressure (psi)	Mass (g)	Volume (ml)
0	50.0	1075.0
10	51.2	1075.0
20	51.9	1075.0
30	52.8	1075.0
40	53.6	1075.0
50	54.5	1075.0

Lesson Extension: Boyle's law demonstration

The modified bottle can also be used to demonstrate Boyle's law. You will need a 10-milliliter medicine syringe (commonly used for dispensing cough syrup to small children), a candle, matches, and petroleum jelly. Remove the plunger from the syringe. Use the candle flame to seal the narrow end of the syringe. Coat the rubber gasket on the syringe plunger with petroleum jelly.

Put the plunger back into the syringe. Notice that if you push in the plunger, it will slide back. Place the syringe into the soda bottle. Place the cap on the bottle and tighten. Attach the bicycle pump to the valve stem.

Ask the students: What is the current air pressure in the bottle? In the syringe? How do you know? What do you think will happen to the volume of air in the syringe when you add pressure to the bottle?

Now let the students add pressure to the bottle. They will see the plunger move further into the syringe. The volume of air in the syringe decreases as the pressure increases.

If you wish to have students measure and record the pressure and volume, it works best to pump up the bottle and then slowly release pressure until the syringe plunger is on an exact volume mark. Then measure the air pressure with the gauge. Release pressure again until the plunger reaches the next volume mark, then measure the pressure again.

Analyzing the data

Make sure students understand the difference between gauge pressure and absolute pressure.

If students have difficulty figuring out how to estimate the mass of the air in the bottle at a gauge pressure of 0 psi, ask them how much the mass increased between 10 and 20 psi, 20 and 30 psi, and so on. Then give them time to independently recognize how that information can help them estimate the mass at 0 psi.

The effect of temperature on pressure

Extension: Boyle's law demonstration

2 In Part two of the Investigation, you will find the total pressure in the bottle. Why isn't that the same as the pressure measured by the gauge?

> The gauge reads zero before air is pumped into the bottle. But the bottle doesn't contain a vacuum—it's full of air at atmospheric pressure. We need to account for those air molecules.

Next, convert total pressure to the metric measurement, pascals.

Part 2c asks why the balance doesn't measure the mass of the air in the bottle at zero psi. Discuss this with your group and write your answer in the space provided.

Now find the mass of the air *that you added* to the bottle by subtracting the mass of the bottle from the total mass.

The next step asks you to estimate the mass of the air in the bottle before you added pressure. How can you do that?

> Students should look at how much the mass changed each time they added 10 psi. In the sample data, the average change was 0.8 grams. Subtracting 0.8 grams from the mass of air at a gauge pressure of 10 psi (1.2 grams) gives us a reasonable estimate of 0.4 grams at atmospheric pressure.

In the fourth column of the table, write the total mass of the air in the bottle. This is the mass of the air you added *plus* the mass of the atmospheric air.

Now you are ready to make your graph. Remember to put the dependent variable on the *y*-axis. Because the pascal is such a small unit, the values are very large. You may wish to use 100,000 pascals as your unit so that the values are easier to graph.

> Allow students time to graph their results and to answer the question in Part 2g. If time permits, have students find the equation for their line using the slope-intercept form $y = mx + b$.

3 In Part 3, you will look at how a temperature change affects the pressure in the bottle. Follow the directions as written.

> Allow students to complete this portion independently. Use whatever you have on hand to submerge the bottle. For example, an inverted coffee cup can be placed on top of the bottle and used to push it into the ice water. Students will find a small but noticeable (3-5 psi) drop in the pressure.

> If time permits, conclude with the optional Boyle's law demonstration outlined on the previous page. Compare and contrast this with their first activity. In both cases, we increase the pressure. In the Boyle's law demonstration, we are observing the change in volume of the air inside the syringe. The mass of the air in the syringe remains constant, since the air added to the bottle does not enter the syringe. Instead, it pushes the plunger. Because the mass stays constant but the volume decreases, the density of the gas inside the syringe increases as pressure increases.

27.3 Properties of Gases

2   Analyzing the data

The pressure gauge you use measures pressure relative to the pressure of the atmosphere outside the gauge. This type of pressure is called *gauge* pressure. The *absolute* (total) pressure inside the bottle is equal to the gauge pressure *plus* the pressure of the atmosphere. On average, the atmosphere has a pressure of 14.7 psi. To calculate the absolute pressure, you need to add 14.7 psi to each pressure you measured on the gauge.

In metric units, pressure is measured in pascals (Pa). One Pa equals 1 newton of force per square meter of area (1 Pa = 1 N/m2). To convert between pounds per square inch and pascals (psi and Pa), you need to use the relationship 1 psi = 6,895 Pa.

a. Calculate the first column of Table 2 (absolute pressure) by adding 14.7 psi to the gauge pressures from Table 1.

b. Calculate the second column of Table 2 by converting the absolute pressures in psi to Pa.

c. To calculate the mass of air, you need the mass of the bottle so that you can subtract it from the total mass you measured in Table 1. However, when the gauge reads zero pressure, there is still 14.7 psi of air in the bottle. Fortunately, *the balance measures only the mass of the bottle itself* and is not sensitive to the mass of air in the bottle as long as the pressure inside and outside the bottle is the same. Explain why this is true.

d. Calculate the third column of Table 2 by subtracting the mass of the bottle from the total mass.

e. Estimate the mass of air in the bottle at an absolute pressure of 14.7 psi (when the gauge measured zero pressure). Use the measurements you have to make the estimate.

f. Calculate the fourth column of Table 2 by adding the result from (e) above to the masses in column 3. The result is the total mass of air in the bottle as a function of the absolute (total) pressure in the bottle.

g. Make a graph showing the pressure of air versus the mass of air in the bottle. Describe a mathematical rule that the graph shows. For example, is the graph a straight line, demonstrating that the pressure is a linear function of the mass?

Table 2: Calculated pressure and mass data

1 Absolute pressure (psi)	2 Absolute pressure (Pa)	3 Mass increase (g)	4 Total mass (g)

3   The effect of temperature on pressure

1. Pump the bottle up to a pressure of exactly 60 psi (gauge).

2. Immerse the pressurized bottle in a bucket of ice water. Hold the bottle under water for at least five minutes (using something other than your hand) so the temperature of the air in the bottle has time to reach the same temperature as the ice water. Measure the pressure of the cold air.

a. What happens to the pressure in the bottle when the temperature is reduced?

b. Does reducing the temperature change the total mass of air in the bottle?

c. Give a physical reason the pressure should depend on the temperature.

193

---

2 3   Example answers

2c. The balance is tared so that when there is nothing but a column of air above the balance, it reads 0.0 grams. We ignore the mass of the atmospheric air molecules, but when pressurized air is added to a container, the "extra" air molecules can be measured.

2e. Each time 10 psi was added to the bottle, the mass of air increased by an average of 0.8 grams. When the gauge pressure was 10 psi, the mass of the air in the bottle was 1.2 grams. To estimate the mass of air in the bottle when the gauge pressure was 0 psi, I subtracted 0.8 grams from 1.2 grams. I estimate there was 0.4 grams of air in the bottle.

2g. Graph, right:
The graph is a straight line. As the pressure in the bottle increases, the mass of the air in the bottle also increases. This is because we are pumping more air molecules into the bottle.

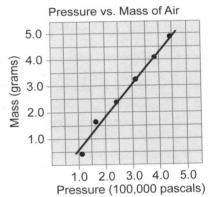

Pressure vs. Mass of Air

Table 2: *Calculated pressure and mass data*

1 Absolute pressure (psi)	2 Absolute pressure (Pa)	3 Mass increase (g)	4 Total mass (g)
14.7	101,000	0.0	0.4
24.7	170,000	1.2	1.6
34.7	239,000	1.9	2.3
44.7	308,000	2.8	3.2
54.7	377,000	3.6	4.0
64.7	446,000	4.5	4.9

3a. The pressure went down 3 psi.

3b. No. The bottle is sealed so no air molecules can escape.

3c. When the temperature is reduced, the air molecules have less kinetic energy. They bounce off the walls of the container with less force so the pressure decreases.

28.1 The Nucleus and Structure of the Atom

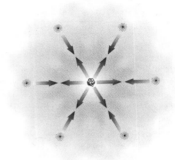

Key Question: What is inside an atom?

In this Investigation, students build models of atoms using the Atom Building Game. Students come to understand how the particles in an atom are arranged, and what makes the atoms of one element different from the atoms of another element. They also learn the difference between stable isotopes and radioactive isotopes in terms of the number of protons and neutrons in the nucleus. Students use the Atom Building Game to play a game that provides practice and facility with the periodic table, atomic numbers, mass numbers, and the concepts of atomic structure.

Reading Synopsis

Students read Section 28.1 The Nucleus and Structure of the Atom after the Investigation.

The atom is made from three basic particles: electrons, protons, and neutrons. The protons and neutrons have 99.97 percent of the mass and are in the nucleus. The electrons are outside the nucleus and define the size of an atom. All of the elements are made from different combinations of protons, neutrons, and electrons.

The atomic number is the number of protons in the nucleus. The periodic table shows the elements in order of increasing atomic number. Elements may have several isotopes, which differ from one another in the number of neutrons. The atomic mass is an average including all naturally occurring isotopes of an element. Some isotopes are not stable, and are called radioactive. A nucleus with too many protons is not stable because the electromagnetic repulsion between protons overcomes the attraction of the strong nuclear force. Chemical reactions rearrange atoms into different molecules. Nuclear reactions may change atoms of one element into atoms of a different element.

The Investigation

Leading Questions
- What makes atoms of one element different from atoms of another element?
- What is inside an atom?
- What is radioactivity and how does it relate to the structure of the atom?

Learning Goals
By the end of the Investigation, students will be able to:
- Describe the structure of the atom.
- Identify what makes elements different from each other.
- Recognize the differences between stable and unstable isotopes.

Key Vocabulary
atom, mass number, atomic number, element, isotope, radioactivity, proton, neutron, electron

Setup and Materials

Students work in groups of four at tables.

Each group should have:

- Atom building game
- Marbles representing subatomic particles that come with the model
- A copy of the periodic table that comes with the model

Nucleus   Electron levels

● Neutrons *(blue)*

● Protons *(red)*

○ Electrons *(yellow)*

Details

Time ⏱ One class period

Preparation Become familiar with the Atom Building Game and atomic challenge game before class.

Assignments 📖 Section 28.1 The Nucleus and Structure of the Atom in the **Student Edition** after the Investigation.

Skill Sheets 28.1A The Structure of the Atom
28.1B The Periodic Table
28.1C Lise Meitner

Teaching the Investigation

1 Introduction and setup
2 Building a model of a lithium atom
3 Isotopes
4 Adding electrons to complete the atom
5 The rules for building a correct atom
6 Building a beryllium atom
7 Stable and unstable isotopes
8 The game of atomic challenge
9 Assessing what was learned

Introduction and setup

Democritus proposed that atoms existed.

Atoms contain three kinds of particles: protons, neutrons, and electrons.

Building a model of a lithium atom

Atomic number = number of protons

Mass number = protons + neutrons

Protons and neutrons are located in the nucleus of the atom.

Isotopes

Isotopes are different forms of the same element. The number of protons is constant; only the number of neutrons changes.

^7_3Li ^6_3Li

Adding electrons to complete the atom

Electrons are located in the energy levels of an atom.

Energy levels are around the atom's nucleus.

Take out the Atom Building Game and have each student take 6 blue marbles and 5 red and 5 yellow marbles and place them in their corner of the model. Up to 4 students can play using one game.

Students should have their Investigation manuals open to the periodic table in Investigation 28.1.

In the beginning, people believed atoms were the smallest bits of matter, and were themselves unbreakable. A gold atom was a tiny sphere of gold that could not be divided into anything smaller. That is how Democritus first proposed the atomic idea and how people thought about atoms until almost the end of the 19th century. The puzzle of radioactivity was the first crack in the theory of the unbreakable atom. If energy and particles could get out of an atom, clearly there had to be something inside an atom, there had to be structure in the atom.

We are now sure that the atom is made from three particles. We are going to use these red marbles to represent protons. The blue and yellow marbles will represent neutrons and electrons. Can anyone guess which are the neutrons and which are the electrons?

Students should guess the yellow marbles are electrons because they are smaller.

1 The periodic table lists the elements in order from hydrogen with one proton to uranium with 92 protons. The atomic number is the number of protons and appears below the symbol for each element. For example, lithium has three protons. Each group should place 3 red marbles in the atom. Where do you put them?

Students should place the 3 red marbles (protons) in the center, answering that protons go in the nucleus.

Above the symbol for lithium are two numbers, 6 and 7. These are the mass numbers for lithium. The six means there are six particles in the nucleus of a lithium atom. If there are three protons, what are the other three?

Students answer that the other three are neutrons and they should place 3 blue marbles in the nucleus.

How many neutrons are in the nucleus when the mass number is 7?

Students answer that there are 4, and may add another blue marble to the nucleus.

Natural lithium occurs in two forms, called isotopes. An atom of lithium-6 has three protons and three neutrons in its nucleus. An atom of lithium-7 has four neutrons. Both isotopes are lithium because they both have three protons. The number of protons determines the element. The number of neutrons determines which isotope of the element.

There is one thing still missing from the lithium atom in the model. What is it?

Students answer that the electrons are missing.

How many are there and where do they go?

Students answer that there are three, to match the three protons and that they go outside the nucleus.

The model has five levels around the nucleus with pockets for electrons. Each pocket can hold one electron. The first two electrons in lithium go in the two pockets in the first level above the nucleus. The third electron goes into the second level.

Students should add 3 electrons (yellow marbles) to the lithium atom.

About the atomic structure model

The model of the atom used in this activity is based on both the Bohr atom and the more modern quantum description of the atom. The activities are designed to teach the basic ideas behind the structure of the atom. Those ideas include:

- Protons and neutrons are in the nucleus while electrons are outside the nucleus.
- The atomic number is the number of protons in the nucleus and determines which element an atom is.
- The mass number is the total number of particles in the nucleus and determines the isotope.
- Isotopes may be stable or unstable. Unstable isotopes are radioactive.
- Radioactivity occurs because the nucleus changes.
- The electrons in atoms are arranged in well-defined energy levels.
- The rows of the periodic table correspond to electrons filling the energy levels in the atom. For example, the first row of the periodic table has two elements (H and He) because the first energy level can fit only two electrons.

While the model of the atom is quite effective at illustrating these concepts, there are limits to how realistic the model is with respect to other aspects of atomic structure. For example, you may wish to point out to the students:

- The nucleus in an atom is far, far smaller in relation to the overall size of the atom than it is in the model. If the atom were the size of the model, the nucleus would have a diameter about 1/2 the thickness of a single sheet of paper.
- The mass difference between the yellow marbles and the red and blue marbles does not accurately represent the true mass difference between electrons, protons, and neutrons. Protons and neutrons have almost 2,000 times the mass of an electron. For the protons (or neutrons) to be in scale, the red or blue marbles would be 6 inches in diameter compared with the 1/2-inch yellow marbles.

In an atom, electrons do not exist in fixed locations as shown by the pockets in the energy levels. The electrons in atoms are described by quantum wave functions which spread the "location" of any electron over the entire atom. There is no definite location for any electron in an atom.

UNIT 9: The Atom

28.1 The Nucleus and Structure of the Atom

Question: What is inside an atom?

In this Investigation, you will:

1. Describe the structure of the atom.
2. Identify what makes elements different from each other.
3. Recognize the differences between stable and unstable isotopes.

The atoms of all the known elements are made from three kinds of particles: electrons, protons, and neutrons. Protons are particles with positive electric charge. Electrons are particles with negative electric charge. Neutrons are neutral and have zero charge. The neutrons and protons are grouped together in the nucleus, which is at the center of the atom. The electrons are found outside the nucleus. In this Investigation, you will use The Atom model to learn about atomic structure.

1 Modeling an atom

In the atomic structure model, colored marbles represent the three kinds of subatomic particles. Red marbles are protons, blue marbles are neutrons, and yellow marbles are electrons. The positions on the model show where the particles are in the structure of an atom. The neutrons and protons are in the nucleus (center of the board) and the electrons are arranged in levels around the nucleus

The variety of matter we find on Earth is made from 92 different types of atoms called *elements*. All atoms of the same element have the same number of protons in the nucleus. For example, every atom of helium has two protons in the nucleus. The *atomic number* of each element is the number of protons in the nucleus.

The periodic table arranges the elements in increasing atomic number. Atomic number one is hydrogen with one proton. Atomic number 92 is uranium with 92 protons.

There are different ways to form the nucleus of a particular element. Each form is called an *isotope*. For example, all the isotopes of lithium have 3 protons but they have different numbers of neutrons. The *mass number* is the total number of particles (protons and neutrons) in the nucleus. Different isotopes of the same element have different mass numbers. For example, there are two natural isotopes of lithium. Lithium-6 (Li^6) has a mass number of 6 with three protons and three neutrons in the nucleus. Lithium-7 (Li^7) has a mass number of 7 with three protons and four neutrons in the nucleus.

Nucleus   Electron levels

⬤ Neutrons *(blue)*
◯ Protons *(red)*
◯ Electrons *(yellow)*

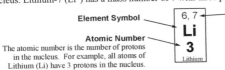

Element Symbol

Atomic Number

Li
3
Lithium

6, 7

Mass Number
The mass number is the total number of protons plus neutrons in the nucleus. For example, lithium has two stable isotopes, Li^6 with three protons and three neutrons, and Li^7 with three protons and four

The atomic number is the number of protons in the nucleus. For example, all atoms of Lithium (Li) have 3 protons in the nucleus.

194

The rules for building a correct atom

> Red marbles = atomic number= protons
> Red marbles + blue marbles = mass number = protons + neutrons
> Yellow marbles = red marbles = electrons

Building a beryllium atom

> A beryllium (Be) atom has 4 protons, 5 neutrons, and 4 electrons.

Stable and unstable isotopes

> Unstable isotopes are radioactive.

The game of atomic challenge

2

Assessing what was learned

3

> Review the definition of isotope: same number of protons but different number of neutrons.

> Mass numbers that don't appear in the periodic table are unstable.

You now have a perfect model of a lithium atom. This model satisfies the three rules.
1) The number of protons (red marbles) matches the atomic number.
2) The number of protons and neutrons (blue and red marbles) together matches one of the mass numbers.
3) The number of electrons equals the number of protons (red marbles = yellow marbles).
    Put the three rules on the board.

Can anyone find an element that has only one isotope and an atomic number less than 10?
    Students find beryllium.
How many neutrons are in a beryllium nucleus? Build a model of a beryllium atom.

    There are 5 neutrons (and 4 protons) students should build a model of beryllium, including 4 red marbles, 5 blue marbles, and 4 yellow marbles. Walk around the room and check, helping as necessary.
We now know how to build models of the stable atoms found in nature. This periodic table shows only stable atoms. A stable atom is one that stays together. An unstable atom comes apart. For example, you can make an isotope of beryllium that has a mass number of 11. But this isotope is unstable and the nucleus undergoes a reaction that turns the extra neutron into a proton and an electron. That's what we call radioactivity. Unstable atoms are radioactive. This periodic table shows all the isotopes that are NOT radioactive. For the next part we are going to play a game with the atom. Everyone should empty the atom building board and take back their marbles so they have 6 blue, 5 red and 5 yellow.
    Students do this.
The objective of the game is to lose all your marbles. Each person takes a turn and can add up to 5 marbles to the atom. The added marbles build on marbles already in the atom. The catch is that each player must create a stable isotope. If you can not make one of the isotopes on this periodic table, the player must take back their marbles and lose the turn. (Read the rules to the game.)

    Students play the atomic challenge game described in the Investigation book. Walk around the room and note when the first student has only a few marbles left. At this point you need to stop the class and explain the marble bank.
I notice that some of you have reached the point where you cannot make a stable isotope with the marbles you have left. Instead of taking a turn, you need to trade marbles with the bank. (Explain rules for the marble bank.)

    Class resumes playing the game. The game should take about 30 minutes. Groups that finish early could answer the questions in the Investigation.

    After students have completed one game, it is useful to ask some questions to make sure the concepts of atomic structure have been learned.
What do we call atoms that have the same number of protons but different numbers of neutrons?
    Students should answer "isotopes."
Suppose you were able to make an atom of carbon with an atomic mass of 15. How many neutrons are in the nucleus? Is the atom stable or will it be radioactive?
    Carbon has atomic number 6; therefore, carbon-15 has 9 neutrons in the nucleus. It is not stable because 15 is not listed as a stable mass number for carbon in the periodic table.

28.1 The Nucleus and Structure of the Atom

2 The Atomic Challenge

Atomic Challenge is a game that simulates the periodic table of elements. Each player starts with a certain number of marbles of each color. These are the raw materials for building atoms. Each player takes a turn adding marbles to the atom. The objective of the game is to be the first player to use all your marbles. The challenging part is that the marbles added to the model in any turn must result in the model showing a real atom, one that matches one of the isotopes listed on the periodic table.

1. Each atomic structure model can have four players. Each player uses one of the four pockets at the corners. Each player should start with the following marbles: 6 blue marbles (neutrons), 5 red marbles (protons), and 5 yellow marbles (electrons). The remaining marbles in the containers are the "bank." Players may need to trade marbles with the bank later in the game.

2. Each player takes turns adding from 1 to 5 marbles to the atom. The marbles may include any mixture of electrons, protons, and neutrons. The marbles played in a turn are added to the marbles already in the atom.

3. Marbles must be added according to the three rules for building atoms. If a player completes a turn and any of the rules have been broken, that player must take the marbles they added back out of the atom and they cannot add any more until their turn comes around again.

4. A player can trade marbles with the bank INSTEAD of taking a turn. At some point in most games, a player will not be able to take a turn and still create a real atom. That player may exchange marbles with the bank. The player can take as many marbles, and of as many colors as they need but must take at least as many total marbles as put in. For example, a player can trade 2 yellows for 1 yellow, 1 blue, and 1 red.

Example of a good move

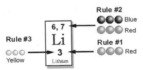

$Li^7 + p + n + e = Be^9$

The Three Rules

Rule #1: The number of protons matches the atomic number

Rule #2: The total number of protons and neutrons equals a stable mass number

Rule #3: The number of electrons matches the number of protons

Rule #2 ●●● Blue / ●●● Red

Rule #3 ○○○ Yellow

6, 7 / **Li** / 3 / Lithium

Rule #1 ●●● Red

3 Reflecting on what you learned

Atoms which are not on the periodic table shown may exist in nature but they are radioactive and unstable. For example, carbon-14 (C^{14}) is unstable and is not listed although C^{12} and C^{13} are stable.

a. What do you know about an atom if you know its atomic number?

b. What do you know about an atom if you know its mass number?

c. How many stable isotopes does oxygen have?

d. Find one element on the chart that has no stable isotopes.

e. What element has atoms with 26 protons in the nucleus?

195

3 Example answers

3a. You know the number of protons if you know the atomic number of an atom.

3b. If you know an atom's mass number, you know the number of subatomic particles it has in its nucleus.

3c. Oxygen has three stable isotopes.

3d. Radon (Rn) has no stable isotopes.

3e. Iron (Fe) has 26 protons in its nucleus.

28.2 Electrons and Quantum States

Key Question: How do atoms create and interact with light?

Electrons inside atoms are limited to discrete energy states. The most convincing evidence for this unusual behavior is that atoms only emit light of certain specific energies. In this Investigation, students use the Atom Building Game in conjunction with "pump" and "laser" cards that simulate photons of different colored light. By using this model and playing the game of photons and lasers, students simulate the absorption and emission of light from an atom. As they reflect on this activity, students learn that quantum physics is the branch of science that deals with extremely tiny systems such as how electrons behave inside of an atom.

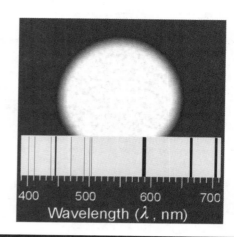

Reading Synopsis

Students read Section 28.2 Electrons and Quantum States after the Investigation.

Quantum theory is the branch of physics that deals with extremely small systems such as an atom. The wavelengths of light given off by particular atoms show discrete spectral lines. For hydrogen the wavelengths of the lines are predicted by the Balmer formula. Neils Bohr proposed that electrons in the atom were limited to having certain energies corresponding to being in discrete *quantum* states.

The energy of an electron depends on which quantum state it is in, and the quantum states in an atom are grouped into energy levels. Bohr explained that characteristic spectral lines (that show up when atoms of elements are energized) are produced by electrons moving between different energy levels. Two electrons cannot occupy the same quantum state at the same time. The rows of the periodic table correspond to the number of quantum states in each energy level. The "shape" of quantum states (orbital shapes) of the atoms that make up a molecule determine the ultimate structure of the molecule.

The Investigation

Leading Questions
- What is a quantum state?
- How do energy levels explain spectral lines?
- What is stimulated emission?
- How do atoms absorb and emit light?

Learning Goals
By the end of the Investigation, students will be able to:
- Describe qualitatively how atoms absorb and emit light.
- Model how lasers work, using the Atom Building Game.

Key Vocabulary
quantum physics, spectrum, spectral line, spectrometer, quantum states, quantum numbers, energy levels, Pauli exclusion principle

Setup and Materials

Students work in groups of four or five at tables.

Each group should have:

- Atom building game
- A copy of the periodic table that comes with the game
- For Part 4 of the Investigation, two groups will combine so that they have two atom building games.

Details

Time One class period

Preparation

Assignments Section 28.2 Electrons and Quantum States in the **Student Edition** after the Investigation.

Skill Sheets 28.2 Niels Bohr

Equipment Setup Atom Building Game

Teaching the Investigation

1   Introduction
2   Classical versus quantum physics
3   Modeling the absorption of light
4   Emitting light
5   The ground state
6   Stimulated emission
7   The photons and lasers game

Introduction

In many circumstances, the laws of physics can not provide thorough explanations to all of man's questions.

Predictions are an integral part of explaining scientific phenomena.

Classical versus quantum physics

Quantum physics arose out of the need for physicists to explain behavior of within atoms and interactions between atoms.

Modeling the absorption of light

Quantum states provide a complete description of electrons in an atom.

Electrons move to a higher energy level in order to absorb and store energy.

It may surprise you but the laws of physics you learned in this course are only approximations! For nearly every circumstance you are likely to encounter, they are very good approximations. But that does not mean they always give the correct description of what happens in all circumstances. For example, the universal law of gravitation will allow you to calculate the orbit of a planet around the sun to better than 99.99 percent accuracy. But near the sun itself, or near a black hole, the law of gravitation does not describe all of what happens. For example, the orbit of the planet Mercury is slightly elliptical and the ellipse rotates. The rotation of the ellipse is due to the warping of space by the sun's gravity. Newton's law of gravitation does not say anything about warping of space. Another theory, Einstein's theory of general relativity, describes the warping of space and accurately predicts the rotation of Mercury's orbit.

Newton's law of universal gravitation is part of classical physics. Classical physics includes the laws of motion, the wave theory of light, and the laws describing electricity and magnetism. By the late 1800's scientists started to uncover evidence that the laws of classical physics did not correctly describe what happens inside atoms, or between atoms. Gradually, a new theory was created that is called quantum mechanics. Quantum mechanics is the physics of small systems and describes in detail the processes that occur inside an atom. Today we are going to play a game that illustrates one of the stranger predictions of quantum mechanics. The game involves electrons and light, and will show you how a laser works. A laser is a device that uses quantum mechanics to operate.

1 Set up the isotope neon-20 in your atom
    Students build neon-20 with 10 protons, 10 electrons, and 10 neutrons.
According to quantum mechanics, electrons in an atom can only exist in certain states. In the model, the states are represented by the pockets in the levels around the nucleus. Each quantum state can hold only one electron. In your neon atom all the quantum states in the first two rows are completely filled. That means the atom has the lowest energy it can have, like when a ball has rolled to the bottom of a valley.
    Draw a valley on the board and show a ball at the top as being higher energy than a ball at the bottom.
    Discuss the idea that systems in nature tend to move toward the lowest energy.
Now suppose the atom was to get some energy, for example by absorbing some light. One of the electrons moves up to absorb and store the energy. The electrons in an atom store energy, like a battery. They do it by moving up to higher energy levels.
    Take out the can of cards that says photons and lasers.
Open the photons and lasers cards and find a red card that says pump one. This card represents a single photon of red light. If a red photon is absorbed then you can move one electron up by one level, to any empty state. It does not matter which electron you move.
    Students first find a pump-1 card, then move one electron from the second level to the third level, simulating the absorption of a photon of red light.

28.2 Electrons and Quantum States

Question: How do atoms create and interact with light?

In this Investigation, you will:

1. Describe how atoms absorb and emit light.
2. Model how lasers work, using the atomic structure model.

Quantum physics is the branch of science that deals with extremely tiny systems such as how electrons behave inside of an atom. When scientists look at light emitted by an atom they see a few very specific colors. The colors are different for atoms of different elements. The energy of light depends on the color. The fact that atoms emit only certain colors of light means that the process of emitting light from an atom must only work for certain special amounts of energy. In this Investigation, you will simulate the absorption and emission of light from an atom using the atomic structure model.

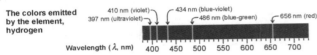

The colors emitted by the element, hydrogen — 410 nm (violet), 397 nm (ultraviolet), 434 nm (blue-violet), 486 nm (blue-green), 656 nm (red)

Wavelength (λ, nm)   400   450   500   550   600   650   700

1 Modeling the absorption and emission of light

The Investigation uses colored and numbered cards to represent the absorption and emission of different colors of light by the atom. For example a red "Pump 1" card represents a photon of red light absorbed by the atom. When the atom absorbs one red photon, one electron moves up one energy level. There are yellow (2), green (3), and blue (4) cards that raise an electron 2, 3, and 4 levels. The word 'pump' comes from the technology of lasers. In the first lasers, the process of injecting energy into the atoms in the laser was compared to pumping water into a bucket with a hand pump. Each stroke of the pump puts an equal amount of water into the bucket as each photon puts an equal amount of energy into the atom.

Electron moves up one level

An atom with one or more electrons above the ground state is said to be in an *excited state*. Atoms in an excited state can be triggered to release the energy of the elevated electrons. The trigger is a photon of light that is that same color as the light the atom would release if the electron were to come down from its higher level. This process is called *stimulated emission* because photons are used to stimulate the excited atom to emit more photons of matching color. The word *laser* is really an acronym standing for Light Amplification by Stimulated Emission of Radiation.

Laser cards represent the trigger photons that stimulate the atom to emit matching light. The emitted photons are emitted by the atom as electrons fall to lower energy levels. For example, if an atom has an excited electron that *can* move down, a red Laser 1 card represents a photon of light that triggers the electron to move down. Laser cards allow all the electrons on a particular level to move down, if there are any empty levels for them to move down to.

Electron moves down one level

Energy levels and quantum numbers

Many introductory textbooks confuse the issue of quantum numbers and energy levels. Quantum numbers are mathematical parameters of solution to the quantum wave equations. Energy levels are real, physical phenomena and follow the rows of the periodic table. They are not the same thing. An electron with quantum number n = 3 may not be in the third energy level.

The confusion stems from a collision between two perspectives. One perspective is purely mathematical. The second perspective is based on patterns deduced from observation. Scientists knew that atoms emitted spectral lines of discrete and categorized the lines into groups labeled *s*, *p*, *d*, and *f*. The groups were later associated with energy levels and quantum states. The periodic table groups elements by similar chemical properties. The 2-8-8-18-18 organization of the rows of the periodic table is based on observed chemical reactions and was deduced by Mendeleev long before Bohr's model of the atom was conceived.

When quantum physics finally provided a mathematical solution to the structure of the hydrogen atom, each electron was found to be described by four numbers. These are the quantum numbers n, l, m, and s. Each unique combination of the four numbers (n, l, m, s) represents one solution of the quantum wave equation that can represent one electron in the atom.

There were now three sets of patterns that needed to be reconciled: the *s-p-d-f* pattern from spectroscopy; the 2-8-8-18-18 pattern from the periodic table; and the four quantum numbers (n, l, m, s).

The first energy level corresponds to the first row of the periodic table and also to all the states with quantum number n = 1, of which there are only two.

The second energy level corresponds to the second row of the periodic table and also to all the states with quantum number n = 2, of which there are 8.

The third energy level corresponds to the third row of the periodic table and also to the first 8 of the 18 possible states with quantum number n = 3. Ten of the states with quantum number n = 3 belong in the fourth energy level because they have energies that are close to the states that have quantum number n = 4.

Emitting light

Electrons change quantum state as they gain or lose energy.

The ground state

Atoms whose electrons are at the lowest energy are in ground state.

As these electrons gain energy, they become "excited".

Stimulated emission

Stimulated emission happens when a photon triggered from one atom provokes another atom to emit a photon.

The photons and lasers game

According to quantum theory and the particle concept of light, a photon is the smallest discrete packet of energy that makes up light.

2

3

4

5

The atom now has more energy that it did before. The energy is stored in the elevated electron, which can give the energy back by moving back down to the lower state it started in. What do you think happens when the electron eventually moves back down to its original level?

Students should answer that the atom gives off energy when the electron falls back down. Discuss the idea that the emitted light has the same color (energy) as the photon that was absorbed in the first place, because of conservation of energy.

Find one of the red cards that says "Laser 1." This card represents a photon of red light that is emitted by an atom. Move the electron back down, simulating the release of red light.

Students move the electron back down after they find the red laser 1 card.

The atom has now returned to its lowest energy. In physics the lowest energy configuration of the atom is called the ground state, because it is like a ball on the ground that is lower in energy than it would be up in the air. An atom with one or more electrons ABOVE the ground state is said to be in an excited state. When light is absorbed by an atom, an electron is elevated to an excited state. The electron falls back down, and the light is re-emitted by the atom. This is the quantum description of how reflection works on the atomic level.

Most of the time, the process of emission occurs immediately after an atom has absorbed light. Certain atoms (and certain quantum states) can absorb light and hold on to the energy for an extended period of time. Remember, this is how the glow-in-the-dark material was able to continue glowing for a long time. Suppose now that a photon of a certain energy strikes an atom that has an electron in an excited state with the same energy. The first photon stimulates the excited atom to release a photon. There are now two photons moving in the same direction with the same color. When emission of a photon from an atom is triggered by another photon, the process is called stimulated emission. Stimulated emission is how lasers work. In a laser, a large number of atoms are pumped up to excited states. The first atom that emits a photon triggers its neighbors to also emit photons. The second generation of photons trigger even more photons. The result is a cascade of emitted photons that are all moving in the same direction.

We are now going to have fun playing a game that simulates how atoms absorb and emit light, like they do in a laser. Take the photons and lasers cards and deal five cards to each player. Leave the atom set up as neon-20. In this game the electrons will move up and down, but the atom will not change otherwise.

Someone in each group should deal the cards. Review the rules of the game with students.

The objective of this game is to win by scoring 10 points. You score points by playing laser cards that stimulate any excited electrons in the atom to fall one or more levels and give off light.

Review the rules for the photons and lasers game. You will have to carefully repeat the rules for how many electrons can be "lasered" in any given turn. Players can move electrons from only one level in any turn. If there are three excited electrons on a level, then all three can be moved in the same turn, scoring three times as many points as a single electron. This is a strategy game; players must decide how "excited" the atom is allowed to get before they play their laser cards and score points.

28.2 Electrons and Quantum States

2 Playing the game

The game of photons and lasers is a simulation of the processes that go on inside atoms of a material that is absorbing and emitting light. Although the game is played using one model, real atoms only absorb a single photon at a time. Think of the single model as representing a collection of many atoms.

The objective of the game is to win by scoring ten points. Points are scored by playing laser cards when the atom has electrons that are above the ground state (excited). One point is scored for each electron for each level it moves down. Of course, an atom in the ground state has no excited electrons. Players must play pump cards to excite electrons before points can be scored. The strategy of playing involves balancing the use of pump and laser cards to make points.

1. Set up the atomic structure model to represent neon-20 (10 protons, 10 neutrons, and 10 electrons). The electrons should be in the lowest possible energy levels. When electrons are in the lowest energy levels, we say the atom is in its *ground state*.

2. Each player is dealt a hand of five cards. A player chooses one card to play per turn, and draws a replacement card from the deck to maintain a hand of five.

3 Pump cards

1. Each pump card played allows the player to move *any single electron* up the number of levels corresponding to the card. For example, a pump 2 (yellow) card allows one electron to go up 2 levels. A move cannot be divided among more than one electron.

2. Electrons cannot be moved to places where there are already electrons. The quantum rules forbid more than one electron in any given quantum state. The pockets in each level represent the electron states that exist in all atoms. The first level has two states, and can hold two electrons. The second level has 8 states and can hold 8 electrons, and so on.

4 Laser cards and scoring

Points are scored by playing laser cards. The following rules apply to laser cards.

1. The number of points scored = the number of electrons moved × the number of levels moved. For example, playing a laser 2 card can score 6 points by moving 3 electrons down 2 levels each.

2. A laser card may only move electrons from *one* level during any given turn. For example, suppose there are two excited electrons on level 5 and two more on level 4. A laser card can move only two electrons, from either level 5 or level 4 but not electrons from both levels in the same turn.

3. There must be open states for an electron to be moved into. Electrons are not allowed to pile up in the same state or be placed into the nucleus.

5 Reflecting on what you learned

a. Research additional sources of information about lasers to find out more about how they work. Using that information, think of an application for a laser that has not been thought of before. Describe your new application of a laser.

b. Write a a short paragraph that describes how fireworks work. Use what you learned from playing the Photons and Lasers game and research additional sources of information to write your paragraph.

c. What is a photon? What do photons have to do with lasers and fireworks?

5 Example answers

5a. A new application for a laser could be an appliance to replace the microwave oven, using the concentrated energy of a laser to cook food. If you wanted to get really fancy, you could combine that with a laser that cuts the food, making an appliance that both prepares and cooks your dinner.

5b. The loud bang of fireworks are caused by black powder exploding when burned. The different colors of fireworks are created by using different metal salts, which when heated, excite electrons to emit energy at specific levels, which appear as the different colors of light.

5c. Photons are the smallest discrete bundles of energy that make up light. The different levels of energy released as different colored lights in fireworks are composed of different energy photons. The single color of light produced by a laser consists of a single frequency and wavelength of photons, aligned in phase.

28.3 The Quantum Theory

Key Question: How can a system be quantized?

In quantum theory, all matter and energy has both wave-like properties and particle-like properties. It is difficult to see the wave-like properties of matter because the wavelength is very small. This Investigation uses a vibrating string to model different aspects of the quantum theory. The students first observe that the patterns on the string only occur at integer multiples (harmonics). This behavior is like the quantized wavelength of the electron in an hydrogen atom. Students determine a "Planck's constant" for their vibrating string can calculate the energy of each harmonic using the relationship between energy and frequency ($E = hf$). In the last activity of the investigation, students calculate the DeBroglie wavelength of a steel ball and show that it is far too small to observe.

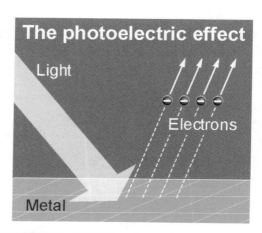
The photoelectric effect
Light
Electrons
Metal

Reading Synopsis

Students read Section 28.3 The Quantum Theory after the Investigation.

Quantum theory was invented to explain the photoelectric effect and blackbody radiation, to phenomenon which could not be explained by classical physics. In the quantum theory, matter and energy exist in tiny bundles called quanta. Light, which was previously believed to be a way, was shown to have particle like properties. A particle of light is known as a photon. Matter particles were also shown to have a wave like properties.

The uncertainty principle places a fundamental limit on how well certain variables such as a position and momentum can simultaneously be measured for the same particle. Quantum theory is based on probability. When systems to get very small, such as inside an atom, it is not possible to predict the exact location or the value of any measurable quantity. The best that can be done is to predict the probability that a quantity will have a specific value. Quantum theory only becomes exact when applied to the average behavior of a very large number of atoms or particles.

The Investigation

Leading Questions
- What does it mean that a system is quantized?
- What do quantum numbers mean?
- What does Plank's constant have to do with energy?
- Why don't we see the quantum wavelengths of ordinary objects?

Learning Goals
By the end of the Investigation, students will be able to:
- Show how a vibrating string has similar properties to a quantum system.
- Identify the "quantum states" of a vibrating string.
- Calculate the energy of a quantum from Planck's constant and the frequency.
- Calculate the wavelength of a particle from its mass, speed and Planck's constant.

Key Vocabulary
photoelectric effect, photons, Planck's constant, quantum, uncertainty principle, probability, wave function,

Setup and Materials

Students work in groups of four or five at tables.

Each group should have:

- Sound and waves equipment module
- Timer with the AC adapter and a cord
- Physics stand
- Calculator

Details

Time	⊙	One class period
Preparation	✎	
Assignments	📖	Section 28.3 The Quantum Theory in the **Student Edition** after the Investigation.
Skill Sheets		13.1 Harmonic Motion
Equipment Setup		Sound and Waves

Teaching the Investigation

1. Introduction and setup
2. The meaning of "quantum" and the quantum-like behavior of the vibrating modes of a string
3. Wave energy and Planck's constant
4. Calculating the energy of the "quantum states" of the string
5. The "classical" orbiting electron
6. Quantum mechanics and resonance
7. Why we don't see the quantum wavelength of ordinary objects?

Introduction and setup

Matter has both wave properties and particle properties.

1 According to the quantum theory all matter has both wave properties and particle properties. For example, an electron can act like a particle when it is traveling far outside of an atom. This means the electron can be described by speed, acceleration, position, kinetic energy and other variables common to classical physics. When an electron is confined between boundaries in a small system such as an atom, the situation changes. The electron is dominated by its wave-like behavior. Energy levels in atoms come from the wave properties. To see how this works, set up the sound generator to make waves on a vibrating string. We will use the string to represent an electron wave trapped inside an atom.

> Students set up the sound generator attached to the wiggler and string. The timer is set on frequency mode. Students should adjust the frequency until they get a wave typically the second or third harmonic.

The meaning of "quantum" and the quantum-like behavior of the vibrating modes of a string

Quantum is the smallest quantity of energy absorbed or released in a process.

2 To a physicist the word quantum means that something only occurs in whole units. That means you can have one or two or three but not 1 1/2. The vibrating string is a good example of a system that shows quantum-like behavior. Quantum number 1 would be a pattern with a single bump, which is the first harmonic. Quantum No. 2 is a pattern with two bumps, or the second harmonic. Try to find the frequencies that result in the first eight "quantum numbers" for the vibrating string. Each quantum number corresponds to a specific wave pattern for the string. Notice that each wave pattern only occurs at a certain frequency.

> Students do the experiment and write down the frequency of each harmonic of the vibrating string.
> You may wish to review the concepts of frequency and wavelength once students get started and have made some waves.

Wave energy and Planck's constant

$E = hf$

E = energy (J)
h = Planck's constant
6.626×10^{-34} J-sec
f = frequency (Hz)

3 The energy of a wave depends on its frequency. If you think about it, this should make sense. It takes more energy to shake the string back and forth at high frequency than it does to shake it at low-frequency. In the quantum mechanics the relationship between frequency and energy is given by the formula $E = hf$, where E is the energy, f is the frequency, and h is Planck's constant. Planck's constant tells you how much energy a quantum wave has at any frequency.

Assume the vibrating string is the wave of an electron trapped inside an atom. The actual energy of the vibrating string depends on how much the string stretches and how fast the string is moving. For the purpose of our model, assume the energy on the first harmonic, or quantum No. 1, is equal to one joule. Use the frequency you measured for the first harmonic to calculate a value of Plank's constant for your vibrating strength from the relationship E = hf.

> Students calculate $h = E/f$. Discuss the units (joule-sec) with them.

Use your value of Planck's constant for the strength to calculate the energies of the different harmonics. Remember, our model is that each harmonic represents a different quantum state of the electron with a quantum number equal to the harmonic number.

> Students complete Table 1 by multiplying the frequency of each harmonic by their value of Planck's constant for their strength. Each group will have a different value of Planck's constant because the tension in the string is likely to be different for each group.

Calculating the energy of the "quantum states" of the string

Imagine the electron is in a circular orbit around the nucleus. The attraction between the negative electron and positive nucleus holds the electron in orbit around the nucleus much as the gravitational attraction between the earth and moon holds the moon in orbit around Earth. This was the model that Niels Bohr first proposed to describe the structure of the atom.

28.3 The Quantum Theory

Question: How can a system be quantized?

In this Investigation, you will:

1. Show how a vibrating string has similar properties to a quantum system.
2. Identify the "quantum states" of a vibrating string.

To a physicist, if something is quantized it can only exist in whole units, not fractions of units. A *quantum* of something is the smallest amount that can exist. For example, light is quantized and one photon is the smallest unit, or quantum of light. In the quantum theory, all matter and energy has both wave-like properties and particle-like properties. Light acts like a wave from far away. However, up close, light acts "particle-like" because the wave is made of individual photons. An electron acts like a particle when it is free to move and far from other electrons. However, if an electron is confined in a small space (like an atom) it behaves like a wave. This Investigation uses a vibrating string to model different aspects of the quantum theory.

1 | Setting up the experiment

Connect the Timer to the Sound and Waves Generator as shown in the diagram. The telephone cord connects the Timer and wave generator. The black wire goes between the wave generator and the wiggler.

1. Attach the fiddle head to the top of the stand, as high as it goes.
2. Attach the wiggler to the bottom of the stand, as low as it goes.
3. Stretch the elastic string a little (5-10 cm) and attach the free end to the fiddle head. Loosen the knob until you can slide the string between any two of the washers. GENTLY tighten the knob just enough to hold the string.
4. Turn on the Timer using the AC adapter.
5. Set the wave generator to WAVES using the button. The wiggler should start to wiggle back and forth, shaking the string.
6. Set the Timer to measure FREQUENCY. You should read a frequency of about 10 Hz. Ten hertz means the wiggler is oscillating back and forth 10 times per second.
7. Try adjusting the frequency of the wiggler with the frequency control on the wave generator. If you watch the string, you will find that interesting patterns form at certain frequencies.

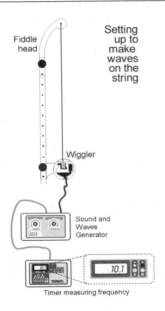

Setting up to make waves on the string

Fiddle head

Wiggler

Sound and Waves Generator

10.1

Timer measuring frequency

Teaching quantum mechanics

Quantum mechanics is not an intuitively obvious subject, even for physicists. It is unlikely many students will grasp the essential concepts at the level of this course. That being said, it IS important that students are aware that there is a branch of physics that deals with the realm of the very small, and that quantum mechanics has the following tenets:

- Matter has both wave-like and particle-like properties. Whether the wave or particle behavior dominates depends on the energy and the scale of the system under consideration.
- The energy levels in an atom arise because of a resonance condition on the quantum wavelength of the electron. The material previously learned about waves and resonance has application far beyond the scope of the context in which it was first introduced.
- Quantum effects are noticeable when the size of a system is comparable to the DeBroglie wavelength of any particles in the system.
- We don't see quantum effects in ordinary matter because the quantum wavelength of ordinary objects is incredibly tiny, much smaller than the dimensions of the objects themselves.

The vibrating string is a good analogy for a system that shows quantum-like behavior. But, the analogy is not exact. The approximation that the energy of the first mode is one joule is made for convenience rather than accuracy. Also, the energy of a string wave depends on the amplitude as well as the frequency.

Because the wiggler itself has a limited energy output, the amplitude of the higher harmonics decreases as the frequency goes up. This can be explained by noting that the energy of a wave depends on both the amplitude and frequency. If the energy is fixed, increasing the frequency results in a decrease in amplitude.

The "classical" orbiting electron

Classical physics suggests that accelerating a charged particle always results in the emission of light energy.

Quantum mechanics and resonance

Quantum mechanics explains that electrons exist in resonant states around the atom rather than orbits.

Why we don't see the quantum wavelength of ordinary objects?

DeBroglie formula: a particle's wavelength (λ) depends on its mass(m) and speed (v).

$$\lambda = \frac{h}{mv}$$

Units for variables:
λ = meters
h = J-sec
m = kg
v = m/sec

The problem with Bohr's first model is that circular motion always requires acceleration. To keep an electronic moving in a circle there must be constant centripetal acceleration. According to classical physics, any time a charged particle is accelerated energy is given off as light. This happens because the electron zipping around and around causes oscillation in the electric field. The oscillation travels as a lightwave. If light is carrying energy away from the electron, then the electron must be slowing down. Eventually its energy must be completely depleted and the electron should then fall into the nucleus! When physicists did the calculation it appeared that atoms should self-destruct almost immediately as all their electrons fell into the nucleus giving off bursts of light. Of course this does not actually happen and therefore classical physics must not be the right way to think about electrons in an atom.

The solution to the dilemma was the new physics of quantum mechanics. According to quantum mechanics if an electron is in a resonant state then it does not lose energy. To see how this works in an atom, consider the following situation. Suppose we assume the electron moves in a circular orbit around the nucleus. The length of one complete cycle of its motion is the circumference of the orbit. If we 'unwrap' the orbit, the resonance condition means that the electron wave must have a node at the two 'ends' in the same way as the vibrating string has a node at each of its two ends. If the electron wave has a wavelength that is equal to 1/2 the circumference, this condition is met, and gives the first quantum state of the electron. The first state has the lowest energy. The second state has the wavelength equal to the circumference, and has higher energy because the shorter wavelength means higher frequency.

We now believe electrons do not actually move in orbits, but the analogy is still qualitatively correct. Electrons do not lose energy because they are in states of resonance around the atom. The resonance condition requires that the wavelength of the electron wave have specific values that correspond to the size of the atom. Since wavelength and frequency are related, each allowed wavelength has a specific frequency. Each frequency in turn, has a specific energy given by Plank's formula (E = hf). The result is that electrons in an atom only exist in specific energy levels.

Ordinary matter also has energy levels, but the energies are so incredibly close together that there is no observable consequence of them. For example, the energy of a moving steel ball can have any value depending on the mass and speed of the ball. If we devise an experiment to measure the energy of the ball, we do not find quantized values.

As an exercise, calculate the quantum wavelength of the steel ball we used in our motion experiments. Assume the ball is moving at 45 m/sec, which is about 100 miles per hour.

Students calculate the wavelength of the steel ball using the Debroglie formula on the Investigation.

The find a value that is extremely small, 5×10^{-34} meters. This is a billion, billion times smaller than even the nucleus of an atom! Any dimension of a system that confines the ball is huge compared with the quantum wavelength and therefore quantum physics is not necessary for describing the behavior of the steel ball. Newton's laws (classical physics) work just fine!

28.3 The Quantum Theory

2. Waves on the vibrating string

The first five harmonics of the vibrating string

1   2   3   4   5

At certain frequencies the vibrating string will form wave patterns called *harmonics*. The first harmonic has one bump, the second harmonic has two bumps, and so on. The harmonic number is like the *quantum number* for the electron wave in an atom. The first harmonic (fundamental) has quantum number 1. The second harmonic has quantum number 2 and so forth.

Adjust the frequency to obtain the first 8 "quantum numbers" for the string and record the frequency for each one in Table 1. You should fine-tune the frequency to obtain the largest amplitude before recording the data for each harmonic.

Table 1: Frequency and energy data

Quantum # (harmonic #)	Frequency (Hz)	Energy (joules)
1		
2		

The energy of a wave is proportional to the frequency of the wave. In quantum physics, the constant of proportionality is Planck's constant, *h*, which has the value $h = 6.626 \times 10^{-34}$ J-sec. The energy of the wave is its frequency times Planck's constant, $E = hf$.

a. Suppose the energy of the fundamental wave on the string (quantum # 1) is one joule. Use your data to determine a 'Planck's constant' for the vibrating string.

b. What are the units for your string's Planck's constant?

c. Use your string's Planck's constant to calculate the energies of the other harmonics. Record your calculations in the last column of Table 1.

3. The wavelength of a particle

The wavelength of a particle (λ) depends on its mass (*m*) and speed (*v*) according to the DeBroglie formula. The wavelengths of particles tend to be extremely small. An electron moving at a million m/sec has a wavelength of only 7×10^{-10} meters. The short wavelength is why an electron looks like a particle most of the time. Its wave properties only become apparent when the electron is confined to a space near the size of its wavelength such as an atom.

Classical concept:
Electron is a particle described by mass (*m*) and speed (*v*)

Electron

Quantum concept:
Electron 'particle' is spread out into a wave

DeBroglie's formula

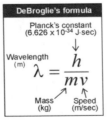

Planck's constant (6.626×10^{-34} J-sec)

Wavelength (m)

$$\lambda = \frac{h}{mv}$$

Mass (kg)   Speed (m/sec)

a. Calculate the wavelength of a steel ball with a mass of 28 grams that is moving at 45 m/sec (100 mph).

b. Is the wavelength you calculated a large or small number compared to the size of the ball?

c. Suppose the ball is confined to a box that has a width of 10 cm. Do you think you need quantum mechanics to describe the motion of the ball in the box? Base your answer on the comparison between the wavelength of the ball and the size of the box.

200

2 3 Example answers

Quantum # (harmonic #)	Frequency (Hz)	Energy (joules)
1	12.7	1.00
2	25.0	1.97
3	38.3	3.01
4	51.4	4.05
5	63.8	5.02
6	76.7	6.04
7	89.6	7.05
8	101.1	7.96

2a. E = hf
1 j = 12.7 hz x f
1 j/12.7 hz = 0.0787 j-s or 7.87×10^{-2} j- s

2b. The units are joule - sec.

3a. λ = h/mv
λ = $(6.626 \times 10^{-34})/(0.028$ kg x 45 m/s)
λ = 5.26×10^{-34} m

3b. Even though we don't know the exact size of the ball, anything with a mass of 28 grams would be gigantic compared to the incredibly small size of the wavelength.

3c. The wavelength is so small that a 10 cm box would be enormous compared to it. Quantum mechanics would not be needed to describe the motion of the ball.

29.1 Chemistry

Key Question: What techniques are used to separate heterogeneous mixtures?

Physics is the concerns the most basic properties of matter, energy and interactions. The next level of complexity is chemistry which concerns the large-scale behavior of matter and energy organized into in structures such as molecules. In this Investigation, students receive a mixture of four components: sawdust, sand, iron filings, and salt. Each group receives a different percent composition. Students must use what they know about the physical properties of each material to devise a method for separating the four components. Using a procedure of their own design, students separate the mixture and then find the percent composition of their sample.

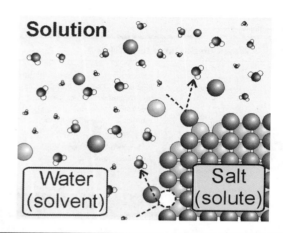

Solution

Water (solvent)   **Salt (solute)**

Reading Synopsis

Students read Section 29.1 Chemistry after the Investigation.

Chemistry is the science of how atoms and elements create the world that we experience. Chemists classify matter into substances and mixtures. A substance is made up of one kind of element or compound. It can't be separated by physical means. Each particle of a substance is like every other. Mixtures contain more than one substance. In a homogeneous mixture, the substances are evenly distributed. In a heterogeneous mixture, different samples may have different amounts of each substance.

A physical change does not make one substance into another; instead it may change the phase of the substance between solid, liquid, or gas, or change the physical form in another way. Chemical changes turn one substance into a different substance or substances. Chemical changes rearrange atoms into new molecules. A solution is a mixture in which solute molecules move freely among solvent molecules. Solubility tells how much solute will dissolve in a given amount of solvent at a given temperature.

The Investigation

Leading Questions
- Which branches of science and/or industry routinely separate complex mixtures?
- What physical properties of materials may be used to separate a mixture?
- How can you determine percent composition of a sample?

Learning Goals

By the end of the Investigation, students will be able to:
- Separate a heterogeneous mixture using their own procedure.
- Calculate the percent composition of their sample.
- Evaluate their procedure and suggest ways to make it more efficient.

Key Vocabulary

substance, mixture, element, compound, homogeneous, heterogeneous, physical change, chemical change, solution, solute, solvent, solubility

Setup and Materials

Students work in groups of two or three at tables.

Each group should have:

- One 100 mL vial containing a mixture of sawdust, colored sand, salt, and iron filings (see preparation instructions below)

Access to tools for separating the mixture. These are not automatically provided to students. They must request specific tools in their equipment list.

Preparation

You will need to mix a vial containing unique proportions of sawdust, colored sand, salt, and iron filings for each group. Record the mass of each component in grams for your own records. Label the vial with the total mass of the mixture but do not reveal the mass of each component.

Hints:

- Do not use more than 4 grams of sawdust because it is the most time-consuming to separate.
- The solubility of salt is 37.7 grams per 100 mL H_2O at 25°C. The solubility changes very little with temperature. To reduce the time used to recover the salt, do not use more than 10 grams.
- Colored sand can be purchased inexpensively at most discount and/or craft stores. Bright colors make it much easier for students to detect impurities in their separation.

You will also need separation tools for each group.

Suggestions:

- magnets
- small paintbrushes and plastic spoons
- coffee filters
- strainers or screens of varying mesh
- water and clear plastic disposable cups
- goggles, aprons, and hot mitts
- ring stand, bunsen burner, and crucible or small aluminum pans and electric burner
- paper towels
- electronic balance accurate to 0.1 gram

Details

Time Two class periods

Preparation Prepare vials of mixture for each group. Record mass of each component in each mixture. Provide students with total mass of mixture only. Gather separation tools but do not distribute unless they are requested on students' equipment lists.

Assignments Section 29.1 Chemistry in the **Student Edition** after the Investigation.

Skill Sheets Skill Builder: Safety Skills (review)
Skill Builder: Lab Report Format

Teaching the Investigation

1   Introduction
2   Designing the procedure
3   Separating the materials
4   Finding percent composition
5   Discussing the results
6   Follow-up discussion

Introduction

Review types of mixtures discussed in the reading, and help the students connect this Investigation to real-world science.

In your reading you learned how chemists classify different types of mixtures. Can you describe them?

Homogeneous mixtures have the same proportions throughout. A heterogeneous mixture is one in which different samples may have different proportions. A solution is a special kind of homogenous mixture. It contains no "clumps" of molecules. Instead, it is homogeneous down to the molecular level.

Separating mixtures into their components is an important part of scientific work. Can you think of any industries and/or occupations that involve separation of mixtures?

Oil refineries separate petroleum into various useful components, including fuel, oils, asphalt, and waxes. Medical researchers try to isolate substances in plants that may help heal diseases. Forensic scientists try to match evidence from the scene of a crime with substances found on a suspect. Nutritionists evaluate the amount of carbohydrates, fats, proteins, vitamins, and minerals in various foods.

Today you are going to take on the role of a team of scientists who need to separate a mixture. You will devise your own method using what you know about the physical properties of the materials you are separating. Your method should be as cost-efficient and time-efficient as possible.

Designing the procedure   **1**

Go over the instructions given on the Investigation sheet. If necessary, review percent composition with students so they clearly understand their final goal.

Each group will receive a vial containing a mixture of sawdust. colored sand, iron filings, and salt. The total mass of your mixture is printed on your vial. Your group's vial will not have the same proportion of ingredients as any other group's. It is up to your group to determine the mass of each individual component of the mixture, and then the percent composition of your sample. Can someone explain how you will find percent composition?

Have a student work out a quick sample problem on the board. For example, if the total mass of the mixture was 50 grams and 10 grams of iron filings are recovered, the mixture is 10/50ths, or 20 percent iron filings by mass.

Read and follow the directions on your Investigation sheet. Use what you know about the physical properties of these materials to design a separation process. You will submit an equipment list and a procedure for separating the mixture. If I can't provide one of your equipment requests, your group will have to modify your plans. Remember, no plans can be accepted without safety measures.

Separating the materials   **2**

Allow students to work as independently as possible. Remind them to keep notes of any changes they made to their procedure, and any changes they would make if they were to do the Investigation a second time.

Hand out labeled vials to each group. Remind students that professional scientists have to consider time and equipment costs when they design a procedure. The more equipment requested, the higher the cost—unless the equipment saves significant amounts of time.

Remember that you may have to modify your procedure as you go. That's okay, as long as you keep detailed notes as you go. Another group should be able to perform the separation exactly as you did by following your lab write-up. If you later think of a more efficient way you could have performed a specific step, write that down too.

Give the students time to carry out their procedure. Allow them to work as independently as possible, and help them realize that mistakes are part of the learning process.

Now that you have completed the separation, we will leave the materials to dry undisturbed overnight. We will find the mass of each component and the percent composition during your next lab period.

If you have one extended block of lab time, the materials can be dried under a strong lamp or in a warm (not hot) oven.

Example answers and data

Investigation page

UNIT 9: The Atom

29.1 **Chemistry**

Question: What techniques are used to separate heterogeneous mixtures?

In this Investigation, you will:

1. Develop techniques to separate a four-component heterogeneous mixture.
2. Determine the percent composition of each component in your mixture

Separating heterogeneous mixtures is an important part of scientific research. Biochemists try to isolate the substances in plants that may help heal diseases. Forensic scientists try to match evidence from the scene of a crime with substances found on a suspect. Recycling centers separate various types of plastics so that they can be melted and formed into new products. In this Investigation, you will develop some of the same techniques used by professional scientists to separate a mixture into its components.

Mixture

Separated components

Water   Salt   Ink

1 **Designing your procedure**

Your group will be given a vial containing a mixture of four components: sawdust, iron filings, sand, and salt. Each group will receive the same four components but the amount of each will vary from group to group. Your task is to use what you know about physical properties of matter to create a procedure to separate the mixture. You will find the mass of each material at the end of the lab, and report the percent composition by mass of your mixture.

Mystery mixture

1. Begin by discussing what you know about the physical properties of each material. Can you identify a unique property that may help you separate each material from the others?
2. Determine what equipment you will need for separating the mixture.
3. Discuss the order in which the materials should be separated.

a. Make a list of equipment you will need to carry out your procedure. Submit the list to your instructor. If any items are unavailable, determine an alternative method and resubmit your list.
b. Write out your procedure, step by step. Be sure to include appropriate safety instructions throughout. Remember, your final step is to find the percent composition by mass of your mixture. Show the procedure to your instructor before you proceed.

201

---

1 **2** **Example answers**

1a. Equipment list:
1 strong magnet, 1 small artist's paintbrush, 1 permanent marker, 200 mL distilled water, 4 clear 10-ounce plastic cups, 2 plastic spoons, 1 strainer with window-screen sized mesh, 8 coffee filters, 1 bunsen burner, 1 ring stand, 1 crucible, 1 cafeteria tray, 1 electronic balance with weighing boats, and goggles, aprons, and hot mitts for each group member.

1b. Procedure:
1. Pour the mixture into a plastic cup.
2. Label a second cup "Iron Filings."
3. Use the magnet to lift the iron filings out of the mixture. Brush off any clinging sawdust, sand, or salt with the paintbrush. Put the iron filings in the second cup and set aside.
4. Add 100 mL water to the mixture cup. The density of wood is less than that of water so the sawdust will float. Skim the sawdust off the top of the water with a spoon.
5. Place the strainer on another cup. Put all of the sawdust into the strainer.
6. Pour 50 mL of water over the sawdust in the strainer to wash out any sand or salt. Gently squeeze the sawdust mixture with a spoon.
7. Spread the sawdust on a coffee filter on the cafeteria tray to dry. Make sure to get all of the sawdust out of the strainer.
8. Pour the water under the strainer back into the mixture cup.
9. Put a coffee filter in the strainer and put the strainer on a clean cup. Pour the sand, salt, and water mixture through the coffee filter. The sand will stay in the filter but the dissolved salt will pass through in the water.
10. Put the coffee filter with the sand on the tray to dry.
11. Put on goggles and aprons.
12. Put the salt water in the crucible. Heat with the bunsen burner to boil off the water.
13. Scrape the salt into a clean plastic cup. Set aside.
14. When all components are dry, find their mass.

2a. Some of the sawdust became waterlogged and sank. We swirled the mixture cup and poured off the water into another cup. The less dense sawdust reached the lip of the cup before the sand. We scraped the sawdust into the strainer, poured the water back, and repeated until all the sawdust was out.

2b. Using less water in step 4 (40 mL instead of 100) would mean there would be less water to boil away in step 12, saving time and energy.

Finding percent composition

Percent composition is based on the mass of the original sample.

Discussing the results

Ask students to evaluate where missing material might have been lost. Have them devise means of improving the results.

Follow-up discussion

Reveal the original percent composition only after the Investigations are graded. Lead a follow-up discussion to compare original and final composition of each sample.

3 Now it's time to determine the percent composition of your sample. The total mass of your original sample is printed on your vial. You will find the mass of each component of your sample and calculate its percent composition. Follow the directions in Part 3 of your Investigation.

> Some students may wonder why we are using the original mass rather than the sum of the recovered masses to calculate percent composition. Explain that in many industrial applications, some components are discarded, or may be allowed to evaporate. Calculating percent composition based on the original sample mass gives us a better picture of what the original sample was like, before any material was discarded or lost due to experimental error.

When you found the sum of your percentages in Part 3a, how many groups had 100 percent?

> It is improbable any did, given the equipment and time frame of the Investigation.

How many groups had a value between 85 and 100 percent?

> Most of the class will probably fall in this range.

What happened to the missing material?

> Some could be lost to spills or other experimental error. Dissolved salt was retained in the wet sawdust and remained behind as the water evaporated. Some salt remained behind in the wet sand and filter paper as well.

Name some ways you would modify your procedure if you had an opportunity to do it again.

> Allow students time to brainstorm ideas. Make a list on the board. Emphasize that this type of evaluation is a vital part of scientific work.

> After the Investigations are graded, have students return to their groups as you hand back their papers. At this time, reveal the original percent composition of their sample.

Are there any surprises as you compare the original to the final percent composition?

> Many students may be surprised to find that their final sawdust mass was MORE than the original mass.

How could you end up with a greater mass of one component than you started with?

> There must be impurities in the sawdust that was collected. It might be retained water, salt left behind when the water evaporated, or sand that was clinging to the sawdust.

How many of you lost a higher percentage of salt than any other ingredient?

> Most of the groups will probably raise their hands.

How could you minimize salt loss in this experiment?

> Have the students brainstorm ways to reduce sources of experimental error. They may discuss the pros and cons of using more or less water, or ways to reduce the amount of salt water left in the sand, sawdust, and filter paper.

29.1 Chemistry

2   Separating the materials

Follow your procedure step by step to separate the four components. Keep detailed notes as you work. Be sure to save all of the material. You will need it for step 3.

a. Did you make any changes to your procedure as you went along? If so, describe the changes and why they were made.

b. If you were to separate another batch of this material, would you modify your procedure further? Are there ways you could make it less time-consuming or less expensive? Explain.

3   Finding the percent composition of your sample

Finding percent composition is a vital skill in many scientific fields, including toxicology. A toxicologist works quickly to identify a sample of a poisonous substance swallowed by a child. He or she must also determine the concentration of the substance in the child's body, often by analyzing the percent composition of a blood sample. Once such determinations are made, doctors can prescribe appropriate life-saving treatment.

In this section, you will find the percent composition by mass of your mixture.

1. Find the mass of each component to the nearest 0.1 gram. Record your results in Table 1.
2. Record the original mass of your mixture (labeled on the vial) in the third column of Table 1.
3. Divide each component's mass by the total mass to find the percent composition. Record this information in column four.

Table 1: Percent composition of the mixture

Component	Mass (grams)	Total mass of sample (grams)	Percent composition
Sawdust			
Iron filings			
Sand			
Salt			

a. Find the sum of the percentages in column four. Do they add up to 100 percent? If not, explain why not.

b. Identify at least two sources of experimental error in your procedure. How could you minimize them if you were to repeat the experiment?

202

3   Example answers

3a. The sum of the percentages is 93.4%. This means we must have lost 6.6% of the original mass during our experiment. I think we probably lost some of the salt. The salt dissolved in the water we added during our second step. After we separated the sawdust and the sand, we placed those two materials on filter paper to dry. The filter paper absorbed some of the water, and I think some salt remained behind when the water evaporated.

3b. The sawdust and the sand were both clumpy when we measured their mass. This makes me wonder if they were still a tiny bit damp. Next time, I would try putting them under a strong light bulb or other heat source to try to dry them further.
Some salt water dripped on the floor while we were separating the sawdust and sand. I would be more careful to save every drop of water possible.

Teaching tips

The original composition of the sample data mixture was: 3.5 g or 10.0% sawdust, 12.5 g or 35.7% iron filings, 12.5 g or 35.7% sand, and 6.5 g or 18.6% salt.

Typically, the final sawdust mass will be slightly greater than the original because of absorbed water and small amounts of sand and salt clinging to it.

Students should be able to get very close to the original percent composition of iron filings and sand if they perform their separations carefully.

This group lost two-fifths, or 40 percent of its salt. Students should be able to retain approximately 75 percent of the salt with common classroom separation techniques carefully administered.

It is helpful to keep the original percent composition secret until after the Investigation has been graded and returned to the students. Otherwise students may succumb to the temptation to "fudge" their data to match what they believe the teacher expects. After the papers are returned, you may wish to have students meet to compare and discuss the original and final percent composition.

29.2 Chemical Bonds

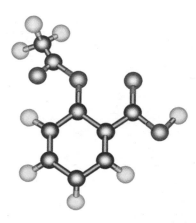

Key Question: Why do atoms form chemical bonds?

Most of the matter we interact with does not consist of pure elements. Most matter is made of compounds and molecules. In a molecule, many atoms are bonded together. In this Investigation, students are introduced to how and why atoms combine to form molecules. Concepts like valence electrons, the octet rule, and bond types are discussed. These concepts are challenging because the students can't see the atoms. The use of the Atom Building Game in the Investigation provides students with a fun and engaging way to conceptualize the parts of an atom and the arrangement of electrons in an atom. By using two atom models, they are be able to visualize how and why atoms form chemical bonds.

Reading Synopsis

Students read Section 29.2 Chemical Bonds after the Investigation.

Almost every atom in the matter you experience in life is bonded to at least one other atom. For example, the oxygen in the air is not in the form of single atoms, but molecules made from two oxygen atoms bonded together. There are two major types of chemical bonds that form between atoms (ionic, covalent).

A chemical bond forms when atoms exchange or share electrons. The electrons that participate in chemical bonds are called valence electrons. Two atoms that are sharing one or more electrons are chemically bonded together. Chemical bonds form because the constituent atoms are able to lower their total energy by being combined in a molecule. In a covalent bond the electrons are shared between atoms.

Atoms in the same group of the periodic table have the same number of valence electrons and similar bonding properties. Acids and bases are solutions that contain ions. Organic chemistry is the chemistry of the element carbon, and is the basis for living things on Earth.

The Investigation

Leading Questions
- Why do atoms form molecules?
- How do chemical bonds form between atoms? What parts of the atom are involved?
- What are the different types of chemical bonds?
- How can you tell what kind of bonds a molecule has?

Learning Goals

By the end of the Investigation, students will be able to:
- Build models of atoms showing the arrangement of electrons.
- Identify how atoms form chemical bonds
- Explain the role of electrons in bonding.

Key Vocabulary energy levels, valence electrons, chemical bond, oxidation number, ionize, ion

Setup and Materials

Students work in groups of four at tables.

Each group should have:

- Atom building game
- A copy of the periodic table that comes with the game
- For Part 4 of the Investigation, two groups will combine so that they have two atom game boards.

Details

Time	⊙ One class period
Preparation	If you have not used it before, become familiar with the Atom Building Game equipment and its components.
Assignments	📖 Section 29.2 Chemical Bonds in the **Student Edition** after the Investigation.
Skill Sheets	28.1A The Structure of the Atom 28.1B The Periodic Table
Equipment Setup	Atomic Building Game SE

Teaching the Investigation

1   Introduction

2   Reviewing atomic structure

3   Building atoms and determining unoccupied spaces

4   Introducing valence electrons

5   Modeling a chemical bond

6   Determining oxidation numbers

Introduction

In this Investigation, you will use the atomic structure model to show how electrons are involved in the formation of chemical bonds.

Reviewing atomic structure

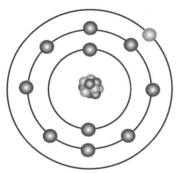

SODIUM ATOM

A sodium atom has two electrons in the first energy level, eight in the second, and only one in the third level.

Building atoms and determining unoccupied spaces

1

2

Have you ever left an object made of iron (a nail, a skillet, a bicycle chain) out in the rain? What happens to it?

> Students should respond that it rusts.

What is rust? How does it form?

> Students may or may not know that rust is a chemical compound that is made out of iron atoms and oxygen atoms. Explain to them that when it rains, the iron metal gets wet and this allows the oxygen in the air to form a chemical bond with the iron metal to form rust.

When the iron atoms react with oxygen in the air to form a compound, a chemical bond is formed. Does anyone know what happens at an atomic level when a chemical bond is formed between two atoms?

> Students will probably not have any ideas about this yet. Give them a hint that it has to do with electrons.

In this Investigation, you are going to use the atom building game to answer the question: Why do atoms form chemical bonds with other atoms? You will build models of atoms and discover how electrons are involved in the formation of chemical bonds.

Let's review what you already know about atoms. Let's use the example of a sodium atom to review. How many protons does a sodium atom have in its nucleus?

> Students should know that the atomic number of sodium is 11, and this means that sodium has 11 protons.

How many neutrons does a sodium atom have in its nucleus?

> Students should remember that the mass number is the number of protons plus neutrons. Have them look at the periodic table that came with their models. If the mass number of a sodium atom is 23, then the atom will have 12 neutrons.

How many electrons does a sodium atom have?

> Students should remember that a sodium atom has the same number of electrons as protons. Therefore, it has 11 electrons.

Do you remember how these electrons are arranged around the nucleus?

> Students should remember that electrons fill energy levels around the nucleus. Draw the nucleus of a sodium atom on the board. Then, draw the first energy level as a ring. It holds two electrons. Have a student come up and draw in the two electrons. Draw the next level. It holds eight electrons. Have another student come up and add eight electrons. The total so far should be 10 electrons.

Where does the last electron go?

> Students should respond that it goes in the next energy level which holds eight electrons. Draw another energy level and add the electron.

How many empty spaces are there in the third energy level? Remember, it holds eight electrons.

> Students should answer that there are seven empty spaces in the third energy level.

Now I want you to build models of the atoms in question 2 on your Investigation sheet. Remember that blue marbles are neutrons, red are protons, and yellow are electrons. Fill in the table as you go.

> Supervise groups as they work and review as necessary.

UNIT 7: Changes in Matter

29.2 Chemical Bonds

Question: Why do atoms form chemical bonds?

In this Investigation, you will:

1. Build models of atoms to gain an understanding of the arrangement of electrons.
2. Identify how atoms form chemical bonds and the role of electrons in bonding.

Most of the matter on Earth is in the form of compounds. Even when a substance exists as a pure element, it tends eventually to combine with other elements. For example, if you leave an iron nail outside in the rain, it will quickly combine with the oxygen in the air to form iron oxide, better known as rust. In this Investigation, you will build models of atoms and discover one of the fundamental ideas in chemistry: how electrons are involved in the formation of chemical bonds.

1 Reviewing atomic structure

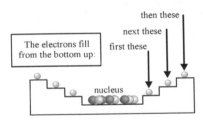

The electrons fill from the bottom up:

then these
next these
first these

nucleus

Let's review what you already know about atoms:

- A neutral atom has the same number of electrons and protons.
- The electrons occupy energy levels surrounding the nucleus.
- Since electrons are attracted to the nucleus, they fill the lower energy levels first.

Once a given level is full, electrons start filling the next level.

2 How many electrons are in the outermost level?

Using the atom building game, build each element in the table. For each element, record the number of electrons in the outermost energy level and the number of unoccupied spaces in the outermost energy level.

element	atomic number	electrons in outermost level	unoccupied spaces in outermost level
hydrogen			
helium			
lithium			
fluorine			
neon			
sodium			
chlorine			
argon			
potassium			

203

Dot diagrams

After the Investigation, you may wish to introduce dot diagrams, also known as Lewis Dot Structures, after the chemist G.N. Lewis, who developed this system. The number of dots placed around the symbol of the element is equal to the number of valence electrons. This is helpful in visually representing why atoms combine with other atoms in certain ratios as in the example of sodium and chlorine. Here is a dot diagram of sodium, before and after ionization:

$$\text{H}\cdot \qquad \text{Mg}\cdot$$

$$\cdot\overset{\cdot}{\text{C}}\cdot \qquad \cdot\overset{\cdot\cdot}{\underset{}{\text{O}}}\text{:}$$

$$\cdot\overset{\cdot\cdot}{\underset{\cdot\cdot}{\text{F}}}\text{:} \qquad \text{:}\overset{\cdot\cdot}{\underset{\cdot\cdot}{\text{Ar}}}\text{:}$$

$$\text{Na}\cdot \; -\cdot \longrightarrow \text{Na}^+$$

Here is a dot diagram of chlorine, before and after ionization:

$$\cdot\overset{\cdot\cdot}{\underset{\cdot\cdot}{\text{Cl}}}\text{:} \; + \; \cdot \longrightarrow \text{:}\overset{\cdot\cdot}{\underset{\cdot\cdot}{\text{Cl}}}\text{:}^-$$

Here is a dot diagram of sodium chloride showing the electrons involved in the chemical bond:

$$\text{Na}\text{:}\overset{\cdot\cdot}{\underset{\cdot\cdot}{\text{Cl}}}\text{:}$$

Introducing valence electrons

3

Valence electrons: The electrons in the outermost level that are involved in chemical bonding.

Sodium, potassium, lithium all have one valence electron.

The groups on the periodic table tell you how many valence electrons the elements have. Elements in Group 1 all have one valence electron. Elements in group 17 all have seven valence electrons.

After students have finished building their models, have them answer questions 3(a) - 3(c) of the Investigation. Then go over the answers with the entire class.

You found that sodium, potassium, and lithium all had one electron in their outermost level, and seven empty spaces. Do you think this is important?

Students should respond that they all need seven more electrons to fill their outermost levels.

The electrons in the outermost level of an atom are called valence electrons. Lithium, potassium, and sodium all have one valence electron. Now look at the periodic table. Where are these elements found?

Students should see that they are all found in Group 1 on the periodic table. Review questions 3(b) and 3(c) and show students where these elements are found on the periodic table.

So you can tell how many valence electrons an element has by looking at where it is found (which group it is in) on the periodic table. Stable atoms have eight valence electrons. Which group of the periodic table has eight valence electrons?

Students should see that Group 18, the noble gases, all have eight valence electrons.

Atoms will gain or lose electrons in order to have eight valence electrons in their outermost level. Which atoms need to lose electrons to have eight valence electrons in their outermost level?

You may need to build a sodium atom to review this. Show that a sodium atom has one valence electron. If it loses that electron, it will have a full outermost level because the lower level holds eight.

Show students that lithium is an exception to this rule because the first energy level only holds two electrons before it is full. Also review a chlorine atom and show how it will gain one electron instead of lose seven in order to complete its set of valence electrons.

Modeling a chemical bond

4

Now combine two groups so that each double group has two atomic structure models. I would like each group to build a model of a sodium atom and a model of a chlorine atom. Then, discuss questions 4(a) through 4(c) on your Investigations sheets and record your answers.

Supervise the double groups of students. Make sure that all students are actively involved in building the models and answering the questions. Go over the answers to the questions and make sure that all students understand that sodium loses one electron while chlorine gains one. This is why they will form a chemical bond.

Determining oxidation numbers

5

When sodium loses one electron, it becomes an ion with a charge of +1.

Sodium's oxidation number is 1+.

When sodium loses its electron, what happens to its electrical charge?

Students should answer that when sodium loses one electron, it has 10 electrons and 11 protons, so its charge becomes +1.

When sodium loses its electron, it becomes an ion with a positive charge. Its charge is positive one. An element's oxidation number is equal to its charge when it ionizes. What is sodium's oxidation number?

Make sure that all students understand how its oxidation number is positive 1 (1+). Review the oxidation numbers of other elements on the periodic table.

Why do sodium and chlorine combine in a one-to-one ratio?

Students should understand that it is because the sum of their oxidation numbers is zero.

29.2   **Chemical Bonds**

3   What are valence electrons?

Examine the table you just completed and record the answers to the following questions:

a.   What do lithium, sodium, and potassium have in common?

b.   What do fluorine and chlorine have in common?

c.   What do neon and argon have in common?

The electrons in the outermost energy level of an atom are called **valence electrons**. These are the electrons involved in chemical bonds. Lithium, sodium, and potassium each have one valence electron.

4   Modeling a chemical bond

Atoms that have a complete outermost energy level are stable. If there are empty holes, an atom will either gain, lose, or share electrons with another atom in order to complete its outermost level and become stable. When atoms gain, lose, or share electrons with another atom, they form **chemical bonds**.

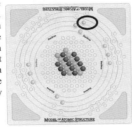 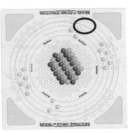

Using two atom building games, build a sodium atom and a chlorine atom. Put them next to each other and answer the questions below.

a.   In order to complete its outermost energy level, do you think sodium will tend to lose its only valence electron, or gain seven? Explain your answer.

b.   In order to complete its outermost energy level, do you think chlorine will tend to lose all of its valence electrons or gain one electron? Explain your answer.

c.   Why might these two atoms bond together to form a molecule? In your answer, describe what you think might happen when sodium and chlorine form a chemical bond.

5   Determining oxidation numbers

An element's *oxidation number* is equal to the charge an atom has when it **ionizes**, that is, gains or loses electrons.

Use your models of sodium and chlorine to answer the questions below.

a.   Remove the valence electron from sodium. What has happened to the balance of positive and negative charges? What is sodium's oxidation number?

b.   Move the electron you took from sodium into the chlorine. What happens to chlorine's charge when it gains the electron from the sodium atom? What is chlorine's oxidation number?

c.   When sodium and chlorine form a chemical bond, what is the overall charge of the molecule? Why do you think sodium and chlorine combine in a 1:1 ratio?

3 4 5 Example answers

3a. They all have 1 electron in their outermost levels. They also have 7 unoccupied spaces in their outermost levels.

3b. They each have 7 electrons in their outermost levels and 1 unoccupied space in their outermost levels.

3c. They each have 8 electrons in their outermost levels and no unoccupied spaces in their outermost levels.

4a. Sodium will tend to lose its only valence electron. It is easier to lose 1 electron than to gain 7. When sodium loses its valence electron, it will become more stable because its outermost level will be full.

4b. Chlorine has 7 valence electrons. By gaining 1 electron, chlorine will have 8 valence electrons and will become more stable

4c. When sodium loses 1 electron, it will become positively charged, because it will have more positively-charged protons than negatively-charged electrons. When chlorine gains 1 electron, it will become negatively charged, because it will have more negatively-charged electrons than positively-charged protons. Sodium and chlorine will bond together because opposite electrical charges cause an attraction.

5a. When the valence electron was removed, there were 11 protons (positive charges) and 10 electrons (negative charges). This means that there was one more positive charge than negative. Sodium's oxidation number is therefore 1+.

5b. When I moved the electron from sodium to chlorine, chlorine gained an extra negative charge. It had 17 protons (positive charges) and 18 electrons (negative charges). Chlorine's oxidation number is therefore 1-.

5c. If sodium has a charge of 1+ and chlorine has a charge of 1-, their overall charge is neutral. This is because the charges add up to zero. Sodium and chlorine combine in a 1:1 ratio because the sum of the charges of 1 sodium atom plus 1 chlorine atom is equal to zero.

29.3 Chemical Reactions

Key Question: How can you predict the yield of a chemical reaction?

In this Investigation, students discover an important mathematical relationship that is useful in predicting the mass of the products in a reaction. They carry out a simple reaction involving baking soda and vinegar. The students measure the mass of the baking soda (the limiting reactant) and, through subtraction, the mass of the carbon dioxide produced in the reaction. Finally, they organize and analyze their data to discover the relationship between the coefficients in the balanced equation, the formula mass, and the actual mass of the limiting reactant and products.

$$C_6H_{12}O_6 \longrightarrow 6\,CO_2$$
$$+\,6\,O_2 \qquad +\,6\,H_2O$$

Reading Synopsis

Students read Section 29.3 Chemical Reactions after the Investigation.

Chemical reactions rearrange atoms into different molecules. In a chemical reaction, reactants are changed into products. For example, iron and oxygen react to form rust. Through chemical reactions, chemical bonds between atoms in the reactants are broken and re-formed to make new products. Energy is required to break chemical bonds and energy is released when new bonds are formed. In an exothermic reaction, more energy is given off when new bonds are formed than the energy required to break the original bonds. Endothermic reactions are the opposite.

A chemical equation is a way of writing a chemical reaction. The chemical equation for a reaction must have the same number of atoms on the reactants side as are found on the products side. A balanced chemical equation tells you how many of each molecule or atom the reaction uses and produces. In a chemical reaction, the total mass of the reactants is always equal to the total mass of the products.

The Investigation

Leading Questions
- What is a chemical reaction?
- How are chemical reactions described?
- How can you predict the amount of product in a reaction?
- How can you tell how much of each chemical you need for a chemical reaction?
- What stops a chemical reaction from continuing?

Learning Goals
By the end of the Investigation, students will be able to:
- Write a balanced equation for a simple chemical reaction with only a few products and reactants.
- Use a balanced equation to calculate the quantities of required reactants in grams.
- Use a balanced equation to predict the yield of one of the products in a chemical reaction.
- Measure the amount of product produced in the reaction and compare predicted yield with actual yield.

Key Vocabulary limiting reactant, excess reactant, percent yield

Setup and Materials

Students work in groups of three to five at lab tables.

Each group should have:

- Electronic scale or triple-beam balance
  NOTE: The Investigation works best if the scale is accurate to 0.01 gram. If a 0.1 gram balance is used, have students round their predicted masses to the nearest 0.1 gram.
- 250 mL glass beaker
- 250 mL plastic beaker
- 200 mL of 0.1M hydrochloric acid solution (provided to students in a 500 mL bottle)
- 5 strips of magnesium ribbon (approximately 2.0 grams per strip)
- Forceps
- Thermometer
- Calculator
-
-

SAFETY PRECAUTION: Hydrochloric acid can cause burns. Handle it with extreme caution! Wear gloves, goggles, and an apron during the entire Investigation.

Details

Time One class period

Preparation Cut strips of magnesium ribbon before the lab. Each strip should have a mass of approximately 2.00 grams. Fill beakers with 200 mL of 0.1 M hydrochloric acid solution before the lab. Students will use the same solution for each trial.

Assignments Section 29.3 Chemical Reactions in the **Student Edition** after the Investigation.

Skill Sheets Skill Builder: Safety Skills (review)

Teaching the Investigation

1. Introduction
2. Discussing the relationship between coefficients and formula mass
3. Balancing the equation for the magnesium and hydrochloric acid reaction
4. Discussing the balanced equation
5. Observing the reaction
6. Predicting the amount of hydrogen gas produced
7. Doing the experiment
8. Calculating percent yield
9. Applying what we have learned

Introduction

What does this balanced, chemical equation tell you?

$2H_2 + O_2 \rightarrow 2H_2O$

2 parts of hydrogen gas to 1 part of oxygen gas yields 2 parts of water.

The coefficients in a balanced equation tell you the ratios of reactants and products.

Discussing the relationship between coefficients and formula mass

$2H_2 + O_2 \rightarrow 2H_2O$

$2 \times (2.02 \text{ amu}) + (32.00 \text{ amu})$
$= 2 \times (18.02 \text{ amu})$

$36.04 \text{ amu} = 36.04 \text{ amu}$

Balancing the equation for the magnesium and hydrochloric acid reaction

Before we begin today's Investigation, let's review what we already know about chemical equations. What does this balanced chemical equation tell you?

> Write the following chemical equation on the board:
> $2H_2 + O_2 \rightarrow 2H_2O$
> The chemical formulas tell you the reactants and the products in the reaction.
> The coefficients tell you the ratios of each of the reactants and products in the reaction.
> The subscripts tell you how many atoms of each element there are in each of the products and reactants.
> The arrow separates the reactants from the products and its direction tells you which are the reactants and which are the products (it points toward the products).
> The plus signs tell you how many reactants and products there are.

You could say that a chemical equation is a lot like a recipe. Have you ever made frozen orange juice? The recipe is simple: 1 can of frozen juice concentrate plus 3 cans of water makes 1 quart of juice. What is the ratio of concentrate to water to in this recipe?

> The ratio is 1 can of juice to 3 cans of water, or 1:3

If the chemical equation on the board was a recipe for making water, what are the ratios of the reactants and products?

> 2 parts of hydrogen gas to 1 part of oxygen gas yields 2 parts of water.

The coefficients tell you the ratios in the balanced chemical equation.

Calculate the formula masses of the reactants and products in the water reaction on the board. What is the formula mass for H_2? For O_2? For H_2O?

> The formula masses are 2.02, 32.0 and 18.02.

Now, if you apply the ratios in the balanced equation to the formula masses of the reactants and products, what is the total formula mass for H_2 in the balanced equation?

> Coefficient of $2 \times$ formula mass for H_2 (2.02) = 4.04 amu

What is the total formula mass for O_2 in the balanced equation?

> Coefficient of $1 \times$ formula mass for O_2 (32.00) = 32.00 amu

What is the total formula mass for H_2O in the balanced equation?

> Coefficient of $2 \times$ formula mass for H_2O (18.02) = 36.04 amu

Add the masses of the reactants up. Does the sum equal the mass of the product? Does this agree with the law of conservation of mass?

> Yes. The total mass of the reactants is equal to 36.04 amu and the total mass of the products is equal to 36.04 amu.

1

Today you are going to carry out a simple reaction using magnesium and hydrochloric acid to produce magnesium chloride and hydrogen gas. Balance the equation for this reaction in Part 1 on the Investigation sheet.

> Give students a few moments to complete this task.

29.3   Chemical Reactions

Question: How can you predict the yield of a chemical reaction?

In this Investigation, you will:

1. Use a balanced equation to predict the yield of one of the products in a chemical reaction.
2. Measure the amount of product produced in the reaction and compare predicted yield with actual yield.

A balanced chemical equation tells you how many of each molecule the reaction uses and produces. You can use the equation to predict the mass of the products if you know the mass of the reactant used up in the reaction. In this Investigation, you will predict how much product will be formed in a reaction, measure the actual amount produced, and compare the amounts.

1   Writing the balanced equation for the reaction

In this experiment, you will react magnesium metal (Mg) with hydrochloric acid (HCl) in solution to produce magnesium chloride ($MgCl_2$) and hydrogen gas (H_2). The equation for this reaction is written below. Balance the equation by writing the correct coefficients in the boxes in front of the reactants and products.

$$\Box Mg \;+\; \Box HCl \longrightarrow \Box MgCl_2 \;+\; \Box H_2$$

2   Determining the masses of reactants and products

The atoms in this equation are magnesium (atomic mass = 24.31 amu), hydrogen (atomic mass = 1.01 amu), and chlorine (atomic mass = 35.45 amu). Use this information, and the balanced equation above to complete Table 1 below.

1. Calculate the mass, in atomic mass units, for each reactant and product. Record your calculations in the "Mass (amu)" column of Table 1. Remember that subscripts indicate the number of atoms of an element in a compound. Multiply the atomic mass of an element by its subscript.
2. From the balanced equation, write the coefficient in the correct column of the table.
3. Multiply the mass of each molecule by its coefficient in the balanced equation. This will give you the total mass, in atomic mass units, of each substance in the balanced equation.

Table 1: Masses of reactants and products in atomic mass units

Reactants				Products			
Substance	Mass (amu)	Coefficient	Total mass (amu)	Substance	Mass (amu)	Coefficient	Total mass (amu)
Mg				MgCl₂			
HCl				H₂			
Total mass of reactants (amu):				Total mass of products (amu):			

a. Does the information in the table support the statement that chemical reactions conserve mass? Explain your answer.

b. What is the importance of coefficients in the equation?

205

---

1 2 Example answers

1. Balanced equation:
   $$1Mg + 2HCl \rightarrow 1MgCl_2 + 1H_2$$

Table 1: Masses of reactants and products in amu

Reactants				Products			
Substance	Mass (amu)	Coeff.	Total mass (amu)	Substance	Mass (amu)	Coeff.	Total mass (amu)
Mg	24.31	1	24.31	MgCl₂	95.21	1	95.21
HCl	36.46	2	72.92	H₂	2.02	1	2.02
Total mass reactants:			97.23	Total mass products:			97.23

2a. Yes, the total mass, in amu, of the reactants is equal to the total mass, in amu, of the products.

2b. Coefficients tell you the correct ratio in which the atoms and molecules in the reactants combine to produce the correct ratio of atoms and molecules of products.

Discussing the balanced equation

$$Mg + 2HCl \rightarrow$$
$$MgCl_2 + H_2$$

1 part magnesium + 2 parts hydrochloric acid yields 1 part magnesium chloride + 1 part hydrogen gas

Observing the reaction

Limiting reactant - the reactant that is used up in the reaction. It limits the amount of products produced.

Excess reactant - the reactant that is left over (in excess).

③

Write the equation for mixing magnesium and hydrochloric acid on the board.

In the Investigation, you will add a small piece of magnesium ribbon (Mg) to a dilute solution of hydrochloric acid (HCl). How did you balance this equation on your Investigation sheet?

Under each side of the equation, begin listing the numbers of each atom. There is one magnesium atom, one hydrogen atom, and one chlorine atom on the reactants side. There is one magnesium atom, two chlorine atoms, and two hydrogen atoms on the products side. Once you have tallied the atoms with the class, have them figure out how to balance the equation. It should look like this:

Mg	+	2HCl	$\rightarrow$	$MgCl_2$	+	H_2
magnesium		hydrochloric acid		magnesium chloride		hydrogen gas

Has everyone figured out how to balance the equation? What is the ratio of reactants and products in the reaction?

The ratio is 1:2:1:1. In other words, for every one atom of magnesium reacted with two molecules of hydrochloric acid, you will get one molecule of magnesium chloride and one molecule of hydrogen gas.

Now, complete Part 2 of the Investigation by filling in Table 1. After you complete the table, answer questions 2a and 2b.

Give the students some time to complete the table and answer the questions.

Does the information in the table support the statement that chemical reactions conserve mass?

Yes, the total mass of the reactants in amu is equal to the total mass of the products in amu.

Why are coefficients important in a balanced equation?

Coefficients tell you the ratio in which the reactants combine and the ratio of the products produced in a given chemical reaction.

Put on your goggles, apron, and gloves. You should wear these during the entire Investigation. Hydrochloric acid can burn your skin if you are not careful. Gather your materials and bring them to your lab station.

Allow students time to gather the materials listed in the Setup and Materials section in this document.

Complete Part 3 of the Investigation and answer the questions.

Allow students to complete Part 3, then discuss the questions.

How do you know a gas is being produced?

The solution bubbles when the magnesium is added. Bubbling indicates a gas is being formed.

The magnesium ribbon completely disappeared in the reaction. What does this tell you?

Magnesium is completely used up in the reaction. Hydrochloric acid is left over.

Because magnesium is completely used up, we call it the limiting reactant. This is because the amount of hydrogen gas produced is limited by the amount of magnesium reacted. Because hydrochloric acid is left over after the reaction, we call it the excess reactant.

Is the reaction exothermic or endothermic?

The reaction is exothermic because heat is given off.

How could you measure the mass of the hydrogen gas produced?

You could obtain the mass of the beaker plus magnesium before the reaction, and the mass of the beaker after the magnesium has disappeared. Through subtraction, you could obtain the mass of the hydrogen gas produced.

3   Observing the reaction

Safety Tip: Hydrochloric acid can cause burns. Handle it with extreme caution! Wear gloves, goggles, and a lab apron at all times during the Investigation.

1. Put on your goggles, gloves, and apron.
2. Gather the following materials: one 250-milliliter beaker containing 100 mL of hydrochloric acid solution, one strip of magnesium metal, a thermometer, a pair of forceps.
3. Use the thermometer to measure the temperature of the hydrochloric acid. Record the results and keep the thermometer in the liquid.
4. Using the forceps, carefully drop the strip of magnesium strip into the beaker of acid. Record your observations, including any changes in temperature. Answer the questions below.

a. What evidence did you observe that a gas was produced in the reaction?
b. What evidence did you observe that the magnesium metal was completely used up in the reaction?
c. Is this reaction endothermic or exothermic? Explain your answer.
d. Describe a simple method for measuring the mass of the hydrogen gas produced in the reaction.

4   Predicting the amount of product

Suppose you add exactly 2.0 grams of magnesium to a beaker containing hydrochloric acid in solution. The magnesium metal is completely used up in the reaction. How many grams of hydrogen gas will be produced?

You can use the information from Table 1 to predict the answer to this question.

1. You are asked for the mass of hydrogen gas, in grams.
2. You know the mass of magnesium metal, in grams, and atomic mass units. You also know the mass of hydrogen gas in atomic mass units.
3. Since the magnesium is completely used up in the reaction, the amount of magnesium used is directly proportional to the amount of hydrogen gas produced. Therefore, you can set up the following proportion:

$$\frac{\text{total mass of Mg in balanced equation(amu)}}{\text{mass of Mg used in the reaction (g)}} = \frac{\text{total mass of } H_2 \text{ in balanced equation (amu)}}{\text{mass of } H_2 \text{ produced by the reaction (g)}}$$

4. Since you know three out of the four variables in the relationship, you can plug in the numbers and solve the problem.

$$\frac{24.31 \text{ amu}}{2.00 \text{ g}} = \frac{2.02 \text{ amu}}{x}$$

Rearrange the variables and solve for x:

$$x = \frac{(2.00 \text{ g})(2.02 \text{ amu})}{24.31 \text{ amu}} = 0.17 \text{ g}$$

5. If 2.00 g of Mg reacts completely with HCl, 0.17 g of H_2 gas will be produced.

a. Suppose you reacted 3.5 grams of magnesium with enough hydrochloric acid so that the magnesium was completely used up. Predict how many grams of hydrogen gas would be produced.
b. How many grams of magnesium would be required to react completely with hydrochloric acid to produce 5.00 grams of hydrogen gas?

3 4   Example answers

3a. When the magnesium ribbon was placed in the solution, bubbles formed. This is evidence that a gas was formed.

3b. The magnesium ribbon completely disappeared. This indicates that all of the magnesium atoms were used to make another substance.

3c. The reaction is exothermic because the temperature increased.

3d. Step 1: Find the mass of the beaker with hydrochloric acid.

Step 2: Find the mass of the magnesium ribbon.

Step 3: Add the results of steps 1 and 2. This is the mass before the reaction.

Step 4: Add the magnesium to the beaker and allow the reaction to occur.

Step 5: Find the mass of the beaker after the reaction.

Step 6: Find the mass of the hydrogen gas by subtracting step 5 from step 3.

4a. Solution:

$$\frac{24.31 \text{ amu}}{3.5 \text{ g}} = \frac{2.02 \text{ amu}}{x}$$

$$x = \frac{3.5 \text{ g} \times 2.02 \text{ amu}}{24.31 \text{ amu}} = 0.29 \text{ g of } H_2$$

4b. Solution:

$$\frac{24.31 \text{ amu}}{x} = \frac{2.02 \text{ amu}}{5.00 \text{ g}}$$

$$x = \frac{24.31 \text{ amu} \times 5.00 \text{ g}}{2.02 \text{ amu}} = 60.17 \text{ g Mg}$$

Predicting the amount of hydrogen gas produced

mass of Mg (amu)/mass of Mg (g) = mass of H_2 (amu)/mass of H_2 (g)

$$\frac{24.31\ amu}{2.00\ g} = \frac{2.02\ amu}{x}$$

Rearrange the variables and solve for x:

$$x = \frac{(2.00\ g)(2.02\ amu)}{24.31\ amu} = 0.17\ g$$

Doing the experiment

Calculate your predicted yield for each trial using the equation above. The mass of the magnesium will vary for each trial.

4 Suppose you add exactly 2.0 grams of magnesium to a beaker containing excess hydrochloric acid. The magnesium is completely used up in the reaction. Can we predict the mass of the hydrogen gas that will be produced?

Students should agree that this is possible because the coefficients in a balanced equation show the ratios of reactants and products.

What information do we need in order to make this prediction?

We need the information in Table 1 from Part 2 of the Investigation. This table has the total mass, in amu, of the reactants, and the total mass, in amu, of the reactants. Using this information, we can set up a proportional relationship.

Since the magnesium is completely used up (it's the limiting reactant), and we know the actual mass of magnesium, we can predict the actual mass of the hydrogen gas produced using the following proportional relationship:

$$\frac{\text{total mass of Mg in balanced equation (amu)}}{\text{mass of Mg used in the reaction (g)}} = \frac{\text{total mass of } H_2 \text{ in balanced equation (amu)}}{\text{mass of } H_2 \text{ produced by the reaction (g)}}$$

The quantity we are looking for is the mass, in grams, of hydrogen gas. We are given the other quantities. To solve, simply plug in the known values:

$$\frac{24.31\ amu}{2.00\ g} = \frac{2.02\ amu}{x}$$

Rearrange the variables and solve for x:

$$x = \frac{(2.00\ g)(2.02\ amu)}{24.31\ amu} = 0.17\ g$$

Try questions 4a and 4b on your own.

Make sure all students can solve the problems correctly.

5 Now complete Part 5 of the Investigation. The goal of the experiment is to obtain accurate measurements of the mass of the magnesium, and the mass of the hydrogen gas produced. You will conduct four trials of the experiment. Be sure to read the procedures very carefully before you begin.

Allow students plenty of time to complete the experiment. Visit each group briefly to ensure that accurate measurements are being taken. The experiment works best if students tap the beaker gently after the reaction to release as many bubbles as possible before taking the final measurement.

The predicted yield will vary for each trial based on the mass of the magnesium ribbon used.

5 **Doing the experiment**

You have learned how to predict the yield of a chemical reaction using the information in the balanced equation. Now you will test your prediction.

The goal of this experiment is to accurately measure the mass of the magnesium before the reaction, and the mass of the hydrogen gas produced by the reaction. Measuring the mass of the magnesium is easy—just place the strip on a balance and read the value. You will measure the mass of the hydrogen gas *indirectly* through subtraction. Follow the procedures below and record your data in Table 2. You will conduct four trials.

1. Gather the following materials: one clean, 250-milliliter plastic beaker, one 500-milliliter bottle of hydrochloric acid solution, four strips of magnesium metal, an electronic or triple-beam balance (accurate to 0.01 g), a forceps.

2. Obtain the mass of one magnesium strip and record in the first row of Table 2.

3. Use the method you learned in Part 4 to calculate the predicted mass of hydrogen gas that will be produced. This is your *predicted yield*. Record your result in the last row of Table 2.

4. Pour about 100 mL of hydrochloric acid into the beaker.

5. Obtain the mass of the beaker with acid and record in the second row of Table 2.

6. Add the mass of the magnesium to the mass of the beaker plus hydrochloric acid. This is the mass *before* the reaction. Record in the third row of Table 2.

7. Using the forceps, carefully drop the magnesium strip into the beaker. Observe the reaction until the bubbling stops. Gently tap the sides of the beaker with a pencil to disperse any remaining bubbles. Try to get rid of as many bubbles as you can.

8. Obtain the mass of the beaker after the reaction and record in the fourth row of Table 2.

9. Subtract the mass of the beaker after the reaction from the mass of the beaker before the reaction. This will give you the mass of hydrogen gas produced. This is the *actual yield* of the reaction. Record in the fifth row of Table 2.

10. Repeat steps 2-9 for the remaining magnesium strips.

Table 2: Data from the experiment

Measurements (g)	Trial 1	Trial 2	Trial 3	Trial 4
Mass of magnesium strip:				
Mass of beaker with hydrochloric acid:				
Mass of beaker *before* the reaction:				
Mass of beaker *after* the reaction:				
Mass of hydrogen gas produced (**actual yield**):				
Predicted mass of hydrogen gas (**predicted yield**):				

Using ratios

A good way to reinforce the concept of ratios in equations is to compare a chemical equation to a recipe. Section 20.4 in the Student Edition compares the "recipe" for the formation of water to a recipe for chocolate cake. Here is another recipe to discuss with your class:

Salad dressing

Olive oil

1/2 as much vinegar as olive oil

1/4 as much water as vinegar

1/16 as much salt as water

1/16 as much chopped basil as water

Ask students how this recipe is different from the one for chocolate cake in section 20.4 of the Student Edition.

Ask them how it is similar to the recipe for water.

Help your students reach the conclusion that a recipe for chocolate cake provides actual amounts of the ingredients needed. A balanced equation (and the recipe above) does not. Students should understand that the coefficients in a balanced equation provide information on the proportions of reactants and products. The balanced equation does not provide the specific amount of each substance that you would use if you were trying to perform a reaction in the lab.

5 **Sample data**

Table 2: *Data from the experiment*

Measurements (g)	T1	T2	T3	T4
Mass of Mg strip	1.97	2.45	2.20	2.15
Mass of beaker with HCl	165.50	167.37	169.63	171.68
Mass of beaker before the rxn	167.47	169.82	171.83	173.83
Mass of beaker after reaction	167.37	169.63	171.68	173.70
Mass of H2 gas produced	0.10	0.19	0.15	0.13
Predicted yield	0.16	0.20	0.18	0.18

Calculating percent yield

$$\text{percent yield} = \left(\frac{\text{actual yield}}{\text{predicted yield}} \right) \times 100$$

6 Let's see how close to our prediction your actual results are. You can do this by calculating the percent yield for each trial. To do this, enter your actual yield and predicted yield for each trial into the first and second columns of Table 3. Use the equation given in Part 6 to calculate percent yield for each trial and enter your results in the last column of Table 3.

> Give students enough time to complete the calculations, then have different groups compare their results. If students were careful with the experiments, they should get a good percent yield.

Do you think the percent yield for a reaction is always 100 percent?

> Students may not know the answer to this question. They will probably think that all reactions work out perfectly.

In reality, reactions rarely have a 100 percent yield. Why do you think this might be true?

> There are lots of factors involved in reactions which affect the final yield. Mistakes in procedures and measuring mass are not the only reasons for a less than 100 percent yield. Some reactions naturally do not finish completely.

What if your percent yield came out to be more than 100 percent? Could this actually happen? How can you explain this result?

> This could not happen because of the law of conservation of mass. There would have to be some error in measurement.

Applying what we have learned

7 Chemists use balanced equations to predict the yield of a reaction. Because most reactions do not yield 100 percent, one of the reactants is used as a limiting reactant, and the others are in excess. Which factors would help a chemist choose which substance to use as the limiting reactant?

> Cost is a major factor. The least expensive substance would be used as the limiting reactant if readily available. Availability would be another factor.

The reaction in Part 7 is used to extract pure aluminum from aluminum ore (aluminum oxide). Notice that aluminum oxide is the only reactant, so it is the limiting reactant. Balance the equation and solve the problems in Part 7 on your own.

> Allow students some time to complete these problems. If some of your students are struggling with the math in this Investigation, have them work with another student who has a good grasp of the math. The calculations are fairly straightforward. Some students, however, have trouble with the concept of ratios and proportions.

6   Calculating percent yield

The predicted yield of a reaction is rarely exactly equal to the actual yield. Use the formula below to calculate the *percent yield* of each of your trials. Record your results in Table 3. Then answer the questions below

$$percent\ yield = \left(\frac{actual\ yield}{predicted\ yield}\right) \times 100$$

Table 3: Percent yield

Trial	Actual yield	Predicted yield	Percent yield
1			
2			
3			
4			

a.   How do your actual yields compare with your predicted yields?

b.   Explain why there are usually differences between the predicted yield and the actual yield. Give as many reasons as you can.

7   Applying your knowledge

You use products made from aluminum every day, but do you ever wonder where this metal comes from? To obtain pure metal, aluminum ore is treated with large amounts of heat. Oxygen gas is another product of this reaction.

a.   Balance the equation for the reaction by placing the correct coefficients in the boxes.

$$\square Al_2O_3 \xrightarrow{\ heat\ } \square Al + \square O_2$$

b.   If you heat 50.0 grams of aluminum ore, and the reaction is completed, how many grams of oxygen gas will be released?

c.   How many grams of aluminum ore would you need to produce 1.0 kilogram of pure aluminum?

---

6 7 Example answers

Table 3: *Percent yield*

Trial	Actual yield	Predicted yield	Percent yield
1	0.10	0.16	62.50%
2	0.19	0.20	95.00%
3	0.15	0.18	83.33%
4	0.13	0.18	72.22%

7a. Balanced equation:
$$2Al_2O_3 \rightarrow 2Al + 3O_2$$

7b. Solution:

$$\frac{203.93\ amu}{50.00\ g} = \frac{96.00\ amu}{x}$$

$$x = \frac{50.00\ g \times 96.00\ amu}{203.93\ amu} = 23.54\ g\ of\ O_2$$

7c. Solution:

$$\frac{203.93\ amu}{x} = \frac{53.96\ amu}{1,000.00\ g}$$

$$x = \frac{203.93\ amu \times 1,000.00\ g}{53.96\ amu} = 3,779.28\ g\ of\ Al_2O_3$$

30.1 Radioactivity

Key Question: How do we model radioactivity?

In this Investigation, students simulate the radioactive decay of an isotope. Students first predict what they think a graph showing radioactive decay over time looks like. A set of 100 pennies is used to represent 100 atoms of a radioactive element which undergoes "decay" when they are heads up. Students are able to plot their data to determine whether or not they were correct in their prediction of what this graph looks like. Because the field of nuclear chemistry has controversial aspects that are debated in the media and politics, students may be particularly curious about this subject. The last part of the Investigation gives students the opportunity to reflect on (and discuss) how radioactive elements can be used, managed and stored.

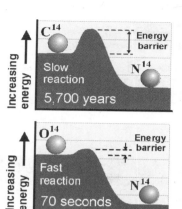

Reading Synopsis

Students read Section 30.1 Radioactivity after the Investigation.

The nuclei of radioactive atoms are unstable. Over time, radioactive nuclei spontaneously turn into nuclei of other elements, releasing energy and/or particles in the process. Radioactivity occurs because matter tends to move toward lower energy and nuclei may achieve lower energy by reorganizing their protons and neutrons into different nuclei.

The three most common forms of radioactivity are alpha, beta, and gamma. In alpha decay the nucleus ejects two protons and two neutrons. In beta decay one neutron becomes a proton, an electron, and a neutrino. In gamma decay the nucleus emits high energy electromagnetic radiation but does not change the number of neutrons or protons.

The half-life is the time it takes for one half the atoms in any sample of radioactive atoms to decay. The half lives of different isotopes vary from fractions of a second to billions of years. Carbon-14 has a half life of 5,700 years.

The Investigation

Leading Questions
- What is radioactivity?
- What causes radioactivity?
- What types of radioactivity exist in nature?
- How fast does radioactivity happen?

Learning Goals
By the end of the Investigation, students will be able to:
- Describe the three different types of radioactive decay (alpha, beta, and gamma decay).
- Calculate the fraction of a radioactive sample that remains in its original isotope after an integer number of half lives.
- Explain how probability and half life are related concepts.

Key Vocabulary   fission, fusion, half-life, radioactive decay, isotope

Setup and Materials

Students work in groups of three to five at tables.

Each group should have:

- 100 pennies in a jar or paper cup
- A tray or box to collect the pennies when they are poured out
- Graph paper

Details

Time   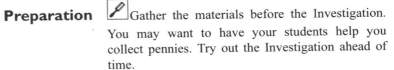One class period

Preparation   Gather the materials before the Investigation. You may want to have your students help you collect pennies. Try out the Investigation ahead of time.

Assignments   Section 30.1 Radioactivity in the **Student Edition** before the Investigation.

Skill Sheets   30.1A Radioactivity
30.1B Marie and Pierre Curie

Teaching the Investigation

1   Introduction
2   Probability and chance
3   Simulating the process of radioactive decay
4   Recording the data
5   Graphing your data
6   Wrapping up

Introduction

What is radioactivity?

Radioactivity is the result of an unstable atom emitting radiation in the form of particles until it either disintegrates or becomes stable.

Isotopes have the same number of protons but a different number of neutrons.

Radioactive nuclei decay in order to achieve a lower energy state.

Probability and chance

Half-life is the timed needed for one-half of the atoms in any sample to decay.

Where have you heard the term "radioactivity" before?

> Students will have a variety of responses. Many responses will have to do with nuclear power or nuclear arms.

Where does radioactivity come from?

> Students should know from the reading that radioactivity comes from the nucleus of the atom. When an atom is radioactive, it emits radiation in the form of alpha, beta, and/or gamma particles.

If the nucleus of an atom has too many neutrons, or is unstable for any other reason, the atom undergoes radioactive decay. The word "decay" means "to break down" and when this happens, the nucleus breaks down and forms a different nucleus. Almost all elements have some isotopes that are radioactive and other isotopes that are not radioactive.

What is an isotope? Can you name an example?

> Isotopes are atoms that have the same number of protons, but different numbers of neutrons. Carbon has 6 protons. There are three naturally-occurring isotopes of carbon. Carbon-12 has 6 protons and 6 neutrons. Carbon-13 has 6 protons and 7 neutrons. Carbon-14 has 6 protons and 8 neutrons.

Do you know which one of the carbon isotopes is radioactive?

> Carbon-14 is radioactive. Have the students look at a periodic table and name radioactive isotopes that are used by scientists or in medicine. Students may be familiar with iodine being used to treat diseases such as thyroid conditions. Point out that some elements exist only as radioactive isotopes such as uranium and technetium.

If the nucleus of an atom has too many neutrons, the atom is radioactive. For example, both carbon-12 and carbon-13 have stable nuclei and are not radioactive. Carbon-14 has one too many neutrons and is radioactive. Because of its unstable nucleus, carbon-14 decays into stable nitrogen-14, giving off radiation in the process.

Radioactivity occurs because everything in nature tends to move toward lower energy. A ball rolls downhill to the lowest point. A hot cup of coffee cools down. Both are examples of systems that move from higher energy to lower energy over time. The same is true of the nucleus. A radioactive nucleus decays because the neutrons and protons have lower overall energy in the final nucleus than in the original.

1

Not all of the atoms in a sample of a radioactive isotope decay at the same time. Which atoms undergo radioactive decay at a certain time depends on chance. It is possible to predict the average behavior of lots of atoms, but impossible to predict when any one atom will decay. The half-life is the time it takes for one half of the atoms in any sample to decay. In today's Investigation, you will simulate radioactive decay by flipping coins. Why is flipping a coin a good analogy for radioactive decay?

> You cannot predict whether a specific toss will come up heads or tails. But, you can make a good prediction of the average outcome of 10,000 tosses. Since the chances are 50/50, out of 10,000 coin tosses you expect about 5,000 to be heads and about 5,000 to be tails. Since even small samples of ordinary materials contain many more then 10,000 atoms, it is possible to accurately predict the average rate of decay.

Will someone read page 1 of the Investigation out loud?

> Have someone read the first page of the Investigation. This will help students make the connection between tossing coins, and determining the half-life of an atom.

30.1 Radioactivity

Question: How do we model radioactivity?

In this Investigation, you will:

1. Learn about chance and probability.
2. Simulate the radioactive decay and half life of a radioactive isotope using coin tosses.
3. Explore the statistical nature of random processes such as coin tosses and radioactive decay.

Radioactivity is the release of energy and/or particles from the nucleus of an atom. If the nucleus has too many neutrons or is unstable for any other reason, the atom becomes radioactive and may spontaneously change into another kind of atom. For example, if you leave a carbon-14 (C^{14}) atom alone, it eventually changes into a nitrogen-14 (N^{14}) atom. The most common form of radioactivity is called *radioactive decay*. The word *decay* means to break down. In radioactive decay, the nucleus breaks down and forms a different nucleus. This Investigation simulates some of the properties of radioactive decay.

1 **Probability and chance**

We cannot predict when a specific atom will decay and give off radioactivity. What you can know is the *probability* that any atom will decay in a certain interval of time. For example, atoms of the isotope sodium-25 (Na^{25}) have a 50 percent probability of decaying into magnesium-25 (Mg^{25}) every minute. If you had a sample of Na^{25} and waited one minute, half of it would have changed into Mg^{25}.

Radioactive decay of Na^{25} into Mg^{25}

○ Sodium-25 (Na^{25})
● Magnesium-25 (Mg^{25})

0:00	1:00	2:00
36 sodium atoms 0 magnesium atoms	18 sodium atoms 18 magnesium atoms	9 sodium atoms 27 magnesium atoms

In mathematics, the word *chance* means the likelihood that a particular outcome will occur. For example, a 40 percent chance of rain means that it will rain on 40 out of 100 days. Probability and chance are related. Probability describes the likelihood of a single event occurring. Chance describes the outcome of a whole system which may be dependent on many single events.

Radioactive decay depends on chance. It is possible to accurately predict the average rate of decay of lots of atoms although the decay of a single atom is impossible to predict. One very useful prediction is the *half life*. The half life is the time it takes for one half of the atoms in any sample to decay. For example, the half-life of sodium-25 is 1 minute. If you start out with 36 grams of Na^{25}, one minute later only 18 grams will still be Na^{25}. The rest will have decayed to Mg^{25}. Wait another minute and half of the remaining 18 grams of Na^{25} will decay, leaving 9 grams of Na^{25} and 27 grams of Mg^{25}. Wait a third interval of a minute, and you will be down to 4.5 grams of Na^{25}. *One half of the radioactive atoms decay during every time interval of one half life.*

209

Radioactive isotopes in medicine

One of the most commonly used radioactive isotopes in medicine is technetium-99m. The m stands for metastable, which means that it releases energy and becomes a more stable form of the isotope without changing its atomic number or mass number. Medical professionals use technetium-99m because it has a short half-life (about six hours) which minimizes the radiation dose to the patient. It also does not emit harmful particles that could further damage cells. It is used to obtain images of and locate tumors in organs such as the heart, lungs, liver, and kidneys.

Many isotopes of iodine are also used in nuclear medicine. For example, iodine-123 is used in imaging and is becoming more widely used in the diagnosis of thyroid function; and iodine-125 is used for prostate and brain cancer therapy. Iodine-131 is used in both imaging of the thyroid and treatment of thyroid cancer. The thyroid gland is responsible for regulating your growth and maintaining your metabolism.

2 **Sample student data:**

Table 1: *Coin toss decay simulation*

	Heads	Tails	Na^{25} Atoms	Mg^{25} Atoms
Start			100	0
First toss	55	45	55	45
Second toss	30	25	30	25
Third toss	16	14	16	14
Fourth toss	9	7	9	7
Fifth toss	6	3	6	3
Sixth toss	4	2	4	2
Seventh toss	2	2	2	2
Eighth toss	2	0	2	0
Ninth toss	1	1	1	1
Tenth toss	0	1	0	1

Simulating the process of radioactive decay

Today, we will simulate the radioactive decay of sodium-25 into magnesium-25. Each group has 100 "sodium-25 atoms." To simulate decay, you will spill the atoms out onto a tray. Spread the atoms so that all are lying flat. Let the heads-up coins represent sodium-25 atoms and tails-up coins represent magnesium-25 atoms. Remove and count these at each sample time and then record the number in the Table 1. Return the heads-up coins (sodium-25 atoms) to the jar. Repeat the procedure until all your atoms have decayed.

Have the students start the experiment. As they work, make sure they record their data correctly on their answer sheets.

Recording the data

As you record your data, think about what a graph of this data would look like. The number of decayed atoms (magnesium-25 atoms) will be plotted on the *y*-axis and the time will go on the *x*-axis. Let each toss of the coins represent one minute of time.

The 100 pennies should have all decayed by sample number 10 or 11.

Graphing your data

Your graph needs:

1. a title
2. axis labels
3. smooth curve or best-fit line

Use your piece of graph paper to plot the data from Table 1. Be sure to title the graph and label the axes. Use the entire graph to plot your data. First plot the points and then draw a line or smooth curve that best fits the points.

Allow students time to make their graphs. When they are finished, have them share the graphs with the entire class.

Now let's try to improve our data. We can combine the data from the entire class. Why is this better than just graphing your own data?

If we combine data from all groups, we increase the size of our data set.

I'll make a table on the board and I want everyone to come up and put their data on the table. Then, I want you to graph the class data and compare the graph with the first one you made.

Allow students time to put up their data and make new graphs. The second graph should have a smoother curve than the first.

Did anyone predict what their graph would look like? This particular type of graph can be described as an exponential curve. If you were to plot population increases, they often exhibit exponential curves. How is half-life like population growth?

Both population and half-life data change by factors of two (doubling or halving). If we are talking about bacteria, two bacteria produce four and four produce eight, etc. Radioactive decay occurs by halves.

Wrapping up

What are some uses for radioactive elements?

What are the pros and cons for using radioactive elements?

What are some uses for radioactive elements? What are the pros and cons for using radioactive elements?

You can have students complete 7(b) on their own or you may want to have them brainstorm the answer in class as a class. The Internet or your school library may have a great deal of information about the uses of radioisotopes.

2 Simulating radioactive decay

Tossing a coin is a good example of a process that is described by probability. There is a 50 percent probability of any single toss coming up heads or tails. You cannot predict whether a specific toss will come up heads or tails. However, you can make a good prediction of the average outcome of many tosses. For example, the graph on the right shows the chance of getting a certain number of heads out of 100 tosses. According to the graph, if you repeated the experiment of tossing 100 coins you could expect 55 out of every 1,000 experiments to come up exactly 50 heads. Most experiments would come up with 40 to 60 heads out of every 100 tosses. The graph also shows that very few experiments would have less than 30 heads or greater than 70 heads per 100 tosses.

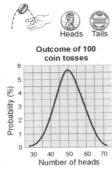

Heads   Tails

Outcome of 100 coin tosses

Since coin tosses are based on chance, an experiment of tossing 100 coins can simulate the radioactive decay of 100 atoms. Let a heads-up coin represent one atom of Na^{25}. If the coin lands tails-up, the atom it represents has decayed and become Mg^{25}. Each toss of the coins represents one half life since 50 percent of the coins can be expected to "decay" with every toss.

1. Place 100 pennies in a large paper cup so they can be shaken and dumped on a table.
2. Shake the cup and dump the pennies on the table. Separate and count the number of pennies that land heads-up and the number that land tails-up. Record the counts in Table 1 in the row for the first toss, which represents one half life. The number of heads represents the number of remaining Na^{25} atoms, and the number of tails represents the number of Mg^{25} atoms.
3. Place all the pennies that landed heads-up back in the cup. Do not reuse the pennies that landed tails-up since they represent atoms that have already decayed. Shake the cup again and dump the pennies on the table. Record the number of heads and tails in the row for the second toss, which represents two half lives. The number of heads represents the number of Na^{25} atoms remaining. The number of Mg^{25} atoms is the number of (new) tails plus the previous number of Mg^{25} atoms.
4. Repeat the experiment using only the pennies that landed heads-up. Keep going until you have one or no pennies left.

Table 1: Coin toss decay simulation

	Heads	Tails	Na^{25} Atoms	Mg^{25} Atoms
Start			100	0
First toss (1 half life)				
Second toss (2 half lives)				

a. Make a graph showing the number of Na^{25} atoms and the number of Mg^{25} atoms on the vertical axis. Put time on the x-axis, with each toss of the coins representing one minute.

b. Add the data from your entire lab or class for each toss. For example, if there are six groups, the class data set would represent the decay of 600 atoms. Make the same graph with the class data.

c. How does the class graph compare with any single group graph for 100 atoms? Sketch what the graph would look like for 10^{20} atoms, a typical number of atoms in a sample of matter.

2 Example answers

3a. Graph:

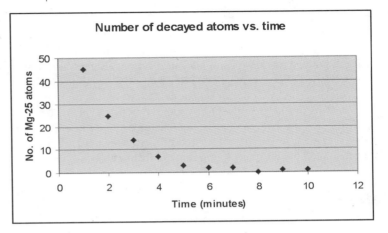

3b. Graph:

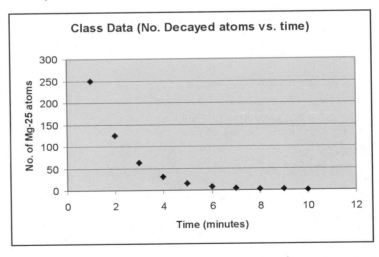

3c. The graph of the class data was a more perfect curve. A graph of 10^{20} atoms would be a perfect curve.

30.2 Radiation

Key Question: What is speed and how is it measured?

Many people mistakenly think of radiation as only associated with nuclear reactions. However. the term "radiation" generally means the flow of energy through space by any process, not just radiation from nuclear reactions. Light, radio waves, microwaves, and x-rays are forms of electromagnetic radiation. Alpha and beta radiation come from moving particles given off by nuclear reactions. Ultrasound is radiation of sound energy through the air. This investigation explores some sources and characteristics of radiation found in the daily environment. Students calculate the decrease in intensity from the inverse square law. They then research sources and properties of ionizing radiation, including how it is detected and how it affects living things (dosimetry).

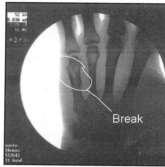

Break

X-ray

Reading Synopsis

Students read Section 30.2 Radiation

Radiation describes the flow of energy through space. Intensity is measured in watts per square meter. The intensity from a point source of radiation diminishes the according to the inverse square law. The inverse square law is a property of geometry.

Radiation is harmful when it has enough energy to remove electrons from atoms (ionizing radiation). X-rays, gamma rays and ultraviolet light are examples of ionizing radiation. The energy absorbed by living tissue from radiation (dose) is measured in rems.

The two largest sources of ionizing radiation in your environment are background and medical procedures such as x-rays. Background radiation includes cosmic rays (21%), radon gas (20%), natural radioactivity in rocks and soil (57%) and fallout from nuclear weapons testing (2%).

A medical procedure typically results in a dose equal to 10% of the yearly background dose. Medical procedures that use ionizing radiation include x-rays, and CAT scans. A geiger counter is one of many types of radiation detectors.

The Investigation

Leading Questions
- What is a radiation?
- What types of radiation exist in the environment?
- What types of radiation are created by human technology?
- How is radiation described and measured?
- How does radiation spread out from a source?

Learning Goals

By the end of the Investigation, students will be able to:

- Calculate radiation intensity and show it diminishes with the inverse square of the distance.
- Describe at least three types and sources of radiation experience by the average person.
- Describe at least one radiation detector.
- Explain the term "dose" in the context of radiation.

Key Vocabulary

intensity, inverse square law, ionization, nonionizing, ultraviolet, ionizing, shielding, rem, dose, background radiation, fallout, CAT scan, detectors, Geiger counter

Setup and Materials

Students work in groups of four or five at tables.

Each group should have:

- Calculator
- Access to the Internet or library for research

Details

Time One class period

Preparation

Assignments Section 30.2 Radiation in the **Student Edition** after the Investigation.

Skill Sheets Skill Builder: Internet Research Skills

Teaching the Investigation

1   Introduction, defining radiation
2   Energy, power, and intensity
3   Moving away from radiation sources lowers the danger
4   The inverse square law
5   Ionizing radiation
6   Energy versus intensity, electromagnetic radiation
7   Energy carried by moving particles
8   Detecting radiation
9   Radiation dosimetry and rems

Introduction, defining radiation

Radiation is the process of energy flow through space.

The word radiation means the transport of energy through space. Many people associate radiation with nuclear processes, but radiation comes from many sources. Some types of radiation are harmful, like gamma rays. Some types of radiation are beneficial, like ordinary light. Can anyone name a form of radiation they are familiar with?

> Students name forms of radiation that are listed on the board. Some typical examples are: x-rays, cosmic rays, ultraviolet light, infrared light, ultrasound, and microwaves. This list is not complete as there are many other forms of radiation as well.

Since radiation is energy traveling through space, it makes sense to ask how much energy moves per second. What unit in physics have we met before that describes the flow of energy per second?

> Students should answer "power." To reinforce the concept, write power equals energy flow per unit of time on the board, along with the formula $P = \Delta E / \Delta t$, and the units 1 watt = 1 joule/second.

Energy, power, and intensity

Power (in watts) is the rate of energy transfer (J) in a given interval of time (sec).

$$P = \frac{\Delta E}{\Delta t}$$

$$I = \frac{P}{A}$$
Intensity (W/m^2)
Power (W)
Area (m^2)

Another important characteristic of radiation is its intensity. Intensity measures how much power crosses a given area. For example, suppose all light from a 1-watt bulb could be made to shine on a surface of one square meter. The intensity of light would be one watt per square meter. This is a fairly low intensity. The intensity of light in this classroom is probably 10 - 50 times greater. In fact, we can estimate the intensity of light fairly easily. How many bulbs are there lighting this room? What is the power of each bulb? What is the approximate floor area of the room?

> Go through the calculation of intensity on the board. A typical classroom might have 40 fluorescent tubes that are 40 watts each. This makes a total of 1,600 watts. If the measurements of the room were 5 meters by 8 meters, the floor area is 40 square meters. The intensity of irradiation is therefore 40 watts per square meter, 1,600 W ÷ 40 m^2. To be accurate, fluorescent tubes are only 70 percent efficient at converting electrical power to light, so 40 watts of electrical power gives 28 watts of light power.

Suppose you knew there was a source of dangerous radiation nearby. What should you do first?

> Students answer that they would get away, the most direct thing to do. Notifying the proper authorities is also a good thing to do, after you get away from the source of the radiation.

Moving away from radiation sources lowers the danger

SAFETY PRECAUTION: If you are near a source of dangerous radiation, get away from the source and immediately notify the proper authorities.

Why does moving away from a source of radiation lessen the danger?

> Discuss with students that the energy of radiation spreads out from its source. The farther you are from the source, the smaller fraction of the energy you receive. It helps to draw a diagram on the blackboard similar to the diagram on page 619 of the text.

The inverse square law

Radiation spreads out as it travels, lowering the intensity.

$$I = \frac{P}{4\pi r^2}$$

1

Moving away from a concentrated source of radiation lowers the intensity because the energy is spread out over a larger area the farther away .you get from the source. If the source of radiation is small and uniform, then the energy is distributed over the inside surface of a sphere of radius r. From geometry, you know that the area of a sphere is $4\pi r^2$. If the source of irradiation has a power (P) in watts, then the intensity at a distance R is equal to $P \div 4\pi r^2$. This important rule is known as the inverse square law because the intensity decreases like the inverse square of the distance. If you move 10 times farther away, the intensity decreases by a factor of 100. The inverse square law is the reason that moving away from a radiation source is a very effective way to lessen the danger.

> It is worth sketching the sphere of radius, r, on the blackboard along with the equations $I = P/A$ and $I = P \div 4\pi^2$.

30.2 Radiation

Question: What are some types and sources of radiation?

In this Investigation, you will:

1. Calculate radiation intensity and show it diminishes with the inverse square of the distance.
2. Research types and sources of radiation.
3. Learn about radiation detectors and dosimetry through research.

The word *radiation* means the flow of energy through space. There are many forms of radiation. Light, radio waves, microwaves, and x-rays are forms of electromagnetic radiation. The energy in alpha and beta radiation comes from moving particles. Ultrasound is radiation of sound energy through the air. Many people mistakenly think of radiation as only associated with nuclear reactions. This Investigation explores some sources and types of radiation you may experience.

1 Intensity and energy

The intensity of radiation measures how much energy flows per second per unit of area. In metric units, intensity is power per square meter or watts per square meter (W/m^2).

When radiation comes from a single point, the intensity decreases by one over the square of the distance. This is called an *inverse square law*. If you get two times farther away from a radiation source, the intensity goes down by one-fourth, which is one divided by the square of two ($1 \div 2^2$). If you get 10 times farther away, the intensity goes down by a factor of 100, which is $1 \div 10^2$.

a. A bright lamp emits a power of 100 watts of light and infrared radiation. Calculate the intensity of radiation from the lamp at a distance of 1 meter and at a distance of 10 meters.

b. How far would you have to be from a source of radiation for the intensity to decrease by a factor of 1,000 compared with the intensity at a distance of 1 meter?

c. The intensity of radiation from the sun is about 1,000 W/m^2 at Earth's surface. Use the inverse square law to estimate the intensity of solar radiation on the planet Mercury.

2 Types of radiation

Radiation becomes harmful when it has enough energy to remove electrons from atoms. The process of removing an electron from an atom is called *ionization*. Ultraviolet (UV) light is harmful because an ultraviolet photon has enough energy to eject an electron from an atom. UV light is an example of *ionizing radiation*. The diagram below shows a few forms of ionizing radiation. The energy in the radiation can come from matter particles or from waves such as electromagnetic waves.

Three typical forms of ionizing radiation		
Charged particles	**Neutral particles**	**Energy**
Alpha radiation Beta radiation	Neutrons	Gamma radiation & x-rays
Example		
Helium 4 nuclei or electrons moving at high speed	Neutrons moving at high speed	Electromagnetic waves (photons)
Description		

211

1a. For a distance of 1 meter:

$$I = \frac{P}{A}$$

$$A = 4\pi r^2 = 12.56 \text{ m}^2$$

$$I = \frac{P}{4\pi r^2} = \frac{100 \text{ watts}}{12.56 \text{ m}^2} = 7.96 \text{ W/m}^2$$

For a distance of 10 meters:

$$I = \frac{P}{A}$$

$$A = 4\pi r^2 = 1256 \text{ m}^2$$

$$I = \frac{P}{4\pi r^2} = \frac{100 \text{ watts}}{1256 \text{ m}^2} = 0.0796 \text{ W/m}^2$$

1b. For the intensity to decrease by a factor of 1,000:

$$I = \frac{P}{A}$$

$$A = \frac{P}{I} = 4\pi r^2$$

$$r^2 = \frac{P}{4\pi I}$$

$$r = \sqrt{\frac{P}{4\pi I}} = \sqrt{\frac{100 \text{ watts}}{4\pi(0.00796 \text{ W/m}^2)}} = 31.6 \text{ m}$$

1c.

$$I = \frac{P}{A}$$

$$P = I_E A_E = (1000 \text{ W/m}^2)4\pi(1.5 \times 10^{11})^2 = 2.8 \times 10^{26} \text{ W}$$

$$I_M = \frac{P}{A_M} = \frac{2.8 \times 10^{26} \text{ W}}{4\pi(5.8 \times 10^{10})^2} = 6600 \text{ W/m}^2$$

Ionizing radiation

2

Radiation is harmful when it has enough energy to remove electrons from atoms. When an electron has been removed from an atom, we say that the atom is ionized. Since electrons are bound to atoms, it takes energy to remove one. Remember, in the photon theory of light, that electromagnetic radiation comes in bundles of energy called photons. An atom becomes ionized if it absorbs a single photon with more energy than the minimum required to remove one electron.

Energy versus intensity, electromagnetic radiation

3

Photon energy and intensity are different. High-energy photons can be dangerous even when the intensity is fairly low. This is because photons with enough energy to remove electrons also have enough energy to break chemical bonds between atoms in molecules. Biological processes depend on specific molecules, such as proteins. Breaking the molecules apart disrupts their normal function, and is therefore harmful to the body. Ultraviolet light, x-rays, and gamma rays are examples of electromagnetic radiation carried by ionizing, high-energy photons. On the other hand, if the photon energy is low, even high-intensity radiation is not harmful. For example, bright green light is not harmful even at high intensity because the photon energy is low.

Energy carried by moving particles

Radiation can also come from energy transmitted by moving particles. Alpha and beta radiation are charged particles. Alpha radiation is helium nuclei that are moving very fast. Alpha radiation comes from radioactive decay and is one way that unstable nuclei get rid of excess protons and neutrons. Beta radiation is electrons. The energy in alpha and beta radiation is kinetic energy of moving charged particles. Charged particles interact strongly with other matter, and therefore both alpha and beta radiation can be stopped by shielding more easily than electromagnetic radiation such as x-rays or gamma rays. Moving neutrons can also carry energy and are an example of radiation from neutral particles. Because they have no charge, neutrons are harder to stop than protons or electrons.

4

Despite being associated with nuclear energy or weapons, radiation is not something created only by humans. The environment also contains many sources of radiation. Natural nuclear reactions and other processes in distant stars and galaxies create a constant background of radiation called cosmic rays.

5

Detecting radiation

Visible light, infrared light (heat), and sound are the only forms of radiation that humans can sense directly. These types of radiation have relatively low energy, too low to be ionizing. To measure other forms of radiation, scientists have developed many kinds of detectors. A radiation detector uses the physical response of a material to sense the presence of radiation. For example, film is a radiation detector. When radiation strikes film, it initiates a chemical change that causes the film to change color. The color change is how we recognize that radiation is present. Radiation detectors have also been constructed from crystals, water, dry cleaning fluid, capacitors, alcohol vapor, and other things. What all radiation detectors have in common is that they sense the presence of radiation by some physical process that converts some of the energy of the radiation into a form that we can detect and measure.

6

Radiation dosimetry and rems

One of the most dangerous aspects of radiation is that you cannot feel when you are being hurt by it until long after the damage is done. Doctors and others who work around radiation have strict guidelines for how much exposure they may safely get. The amount of energy absorbed by the body from radiation is called a dose, like a dose of medicine. Radiation dosage in people is measured in "rems." Rem stands for roentgen equivalent man. The roentgen is a unit of energy. The "equivalent" comes from the fact that the body is damaged more by some forms of radiation than by others. For example, gamma rays are 20 times more damaging per watt than alpha particles. That means the same amount of energy in gamma rays delivers 20 times the dose in rems as an equivalent amount of energy in alpha particles.

30.2 Radiation

3 Sources and risks from ionizing radiation

a. Name one form of nonionizing radiation you experience every day.
b. Identify one source of ionizing radiation that is charged particles.
c. Identify one source of ionizing radiation that is neutral particles.
d. Identify one source of ionizing radiation that is electromagnetic radiation.
e. If all three forms of ionizing radiation had the same energy and intensity, which would be most difficult to stop: charged particles, neutral particles, or electromagnetic radiation?

4 Cosmic rays

Earth is constantly bathed by radiation from space. The term cosmic rays describes all forms of radiation that come from beyond our solar system. Research cosmic rays and answer the following questions.

a. List three types of radiation present in cosmic rays.
b. Give the intensity of at least one form of cosmic ray radiation in W/m^2.
c. Identify two sources of cosmic rays.
d. Are cosmic rays ionizing or nonionizing radiation or do cosmic rays include both types?

5 Radiation detectors

Since we cannot see most forms of ionizing radiation, we need to use detectors. Detectors are instruments or materials that respond to radiation in a way that we can measure. For example, photographic film is a very sensitive detector of radiation.

a. Research and identify a detector of radiation.
b. What physical principle does the detector use to sense the radiation?
c. What forms of radiation can the detector sense?
d. What forms of radiation cannot be sensed by the detector?
e. Where is the detector used?

6 Dosimetry

Ionizing radiation absorbed by people is measured in a unit called the *rem*. The total amount of radiation received by a person is called a *dose*, just like a dose of medicine. Radiation doses in people are measured in rems instead of watts because different kinds of radiation are absorbed differently by body tissues.

a. If a person were to receive the same energy from neutrons, alpha particles, and gamma rays which would have the highest dose in rems?
b. What is the average annual dose in rems you receive from background radiation in the environment?
c. What is the average dose limit allowed for people who work in nuclear reactors?

212

3 4 5 6 Example answers

3a. Infrared or visible light are forms of nonionizing radiation.
3b. Radon decay is a source of ionizing radiation that is charged particles.
3c. Neutrons are a source of ionizing radiation that is neutral.
3d. X-rays are a source of ionizing radiation that is electromagnetic radiation.
3e. Electromagnetic radiation would be the most difficult to stop.

4a. Gamma rays, alpha particles, and beta particles are present in cosmic rays.
4b. Galactic cosmic ray particles have an intensity of approximately 10^{-5} W/m^2.
4c. Two sources of cosmic rays are interstellar wind and supernova explosions.
4d. Cosmic rays are ionizing radiation.

5a. Geiger counter.
5b. The Geiger counter uses a Geiger-Mueller tube, which is a sealed tube filled with a special gas with a voltage across it. Normally, the gas insulates and no current is drawn. When a particle of ionizing radiation passes through the tube, it triggers the gas to ionize and create a current impulse that is amplified and made audible as a clicking noise. The gas then returns to its nonionized state. This allows each radioactive particle to register separately and be counted.
5c. Depending on the type of tube, a Geiger counter senses gamma rays, alpha particles, and beta particles.
5d. A Geiger counter cannot sense nonionizing radiation.
5e. Geiger counters are best used for determining the presence of ionizing radiation, for the detection of cosmic rays, or in demonstrations.

6a. Gamma rays would give the highest dose in rems.
6b. 0.3 rem per year
6c. 5 rem per year.

30.3 Nuclear Reactions and Energy

Key Question: How do we describe nuclear reactions?

A nuclear reaction is a process that changes of the nucleus of an atom. Because the nucleus is changed, nuclear reactions often change atoms of one element into atoms of another element. In this Investigation, students will use the Atom Building Game to simulate nuclear reactions and learn about isotopes. Fusion reactions combine light nuclei to form heavier nuclei. Fission reactions split heavy nuclei into lighter nuclei. Both types of reactions may release energy or may use energy depending on the isotopes involved. Students model nuclear reactions that conserve the number and type of particles. For example, the number of neutrons, protons, and electrons before the reaction equals the number of neutrons, protons, and electrons after the reaction.

Reading Synopsis

Students read Section 30.3 Nuclear Reactions and Energy after the Investigation.

A nuclear reaction is a process that affects the nucleus of an atom. Radioactive decay is a type of nuclear reaction. Nuclear reactions are represented by equations similar to chemical reactions. Mass may not be conserved in a nuclear reaction because some of the mass is often converted to energy in the reaction.

Nuclear reactions occur when protons and neutrons can lower their total energy by reorganizing into a different nucleus. Fusion reactions combine small nuclei to form larger nuclei. Fission reactions split up large nuclei into smaller nuclei. Nuclear reactions follow rules that allow some reactions and not others. Energy and momentum must be conserved in nuclear reactions, although energy may be in the form of mass. Nuclear reactions create particles other than neutrons, protons, and electrons. Muons, pions, and neutrinos are a few of the other subatomic particles. Each particle of ordinary matter also has a antimatter partner with opposite electric charge.

The Investigation

Leading Questions
- What is a nuclear reaction?
- How are nuclear reactions different from chemical reactions?
- How does the nucleus of an atom change during fission?
- How is a fusion reaction different from a fission reaction?

Learning Goals
By the end of the Investigation, students will be able to:
- Describe the processes of fission and fusion.
- Write the equation for a simple nuclear reaction.
- Describe at least two fundamental differences between nuclear reactions and chemical reactions.

Key Vocabulary
radioactive, radioactive decay, isotope, fusion reaction, fission reaction, neutron

Setup and Materials

Students work in groups of four or five at tables.

Each group should have:

- Atom building game
- A copy of the periodic table of stable isotopes that comes with the game
- The Nuclear Reaction cards that come with the game

Details

Time	One class period
Preparation	For hints on how to use the Atom Building Game II, read the **Reference Guide**.
Assignments	Section 30.3 Nuclear Reactions and Energy in the **Student Edition** after the Investigation.
Skill Sheets	30.3 Ernest Rutherford
Equipment Setup	Atom Building Game

Teaching the Investigation

1   Introduction
2   Nuclear reactions
3   An example reaction
4   Energy from nuclear reactions
5   Playing nuclear reactions
6   Scoring points

Introduction

Where did the elements come from?

Scientists believe hydrogen, helium, and lithium were created as a result of the Big Bang.

Other elements with atomic numbers less than 92 were created by nuclear reactions in the cores of stars and by supernovas.

Nuclear reactions

Fission and fusion are two types of nuclear reactions.

Fission is splitting of an atom's nucleus.

Fusion in the combining of atomic nuclei.

An example reaction

Fusion Reaction: Creating boron from the fusion of helium-4 and lithium-6

$$^4_2He + \,^6_3Li \rightarrow \,^{10}_5B + 5p^+ + 5n^0$$

Energy is either absorbed or released when nuclear reactions occur.

Most scientists believe that the universe began with hydrogen, helium, and a small amount of lithium. Where did the other elements come from? Can anyone name some elements that are present in your body other than hydrogen, helium, and lithium?

> **Start a discussion about how the human body contains large amounts of carbon, hydrogen, nitrogen, and oxygen, and smaller amounts of other elements, including all 92 naturally occurring elements.**
> **Even uranium and gold are present in trace amounts in the human body.**

Today's Investigation will look at nuclear reactions. Nuclear reactions are how atoms of one element can be turned into patterns of other elements. Nuclear reactions in the core of stars created all popped the elements heavier than lithium. That means all of the carbon or nitrogen in your body was once in a star that exploded billions of years ago. The remnants of exploded stars condensed into our solar system more than 4 billion years ago.

1

There are two basic kinds of nuclear reactions. Fusion reactions combine nuclei to make a larger nucleus. Fusion reactions split up a nucleus into smaller parts. A nuclear reaction is written in the form of an equation, much like a chemical reaction. Like a chemical reaction, all of the parts of the reactant side of the equation must appear on the product side of the equation.

> **Sketch the two reactions as examples of fusion and fission reactions.**
> **Fusion: C12 + C12 > Mg24 + energy**
> **Fission: n + U235 > Mo99 + Sn135 + energy**

Notice that I wrote down which isotope appears. In nuclear reactions the isotope is very important. Notice also that the fusion reaction begins with 24 protons and 24 neutrons organized into two carbon-12 nuclei. The reaction rearranges the same number of protons and neutrons into one magnesium-24 nucleus. All of the reactions we will simulate today obey a rule that the number and type of particles is conserved by the reaction. This is not always true however. Some nuclear reactions convert a proton and an electron into a neutron or vice versa.

Build a lithium-6 atom with your model. How many protons and neutrons are there in the nucleus?

> **Students build an atom with three protons and three neutrons in the nucleus. 3-D electrons should also be present in the shell around the nucleus.**

Suppose I were to have a reaction where we add a helium-4 atom to the lithium-6 atom you just built. This could occur if both the lithium and helium were very hot. When atoms are very hot, their electrons are stripped away, exposing the bare nucleus. If the temperature is hot enough, the thermal kinetic energy is high enough to overcome the repulsion between the positive charges. This allows two nuclei to come close enough together for the strong nuclear force to pull them into a single nucleus. How many protons and neutrons are in a single helium-4 nucleus?

> **Students answer that there are two protons and two neutrons.**

Add the protons and neutrons from the helium-4 nucleus to the lithium-6 atom. What isotope do you get? Is this a fusion reaction or a fission reaction?

> **Students add two protons and two neutrons to the atom to form boron-10 with five protons and five neutrons. This is an example of a fusion reaction. Write the reaction on the board and have students copy it to see how a nuclear reaction is written.**

What do you get when you fuse a lithium-6 nucleus and a boron-11 nucleus together?

> **Students combine eight protons and nine neutrons to get oxygen-17.**

UNIT 9: The Atom

30.3 Nuclear Reactions and Energy

Question: How do we describe nuclear reactions?

In this Investigation, you will:

1. Simulate and describe fusion and fission reactions.
2. Play an interesting game that explores the stable isotopes of the periodic table.

A nuclear reaction is any process that changes the nucleus of an atom. Radioactive decay is one form of nuclear reaction. Because the nucleus is affected, a nuclear reaction can change one element into another. The ability to change elements is one important way nuclear reactions are different from chemical reactions. This Investigation will simulate several nuclear reactions using The Atom model in a challenging game that builds the stable isotopes of elements on the periodic table.

1 **Nuclear reactions**

There are two general types of nuclear reactions, *fusion* and *fission*. Fusion involves the combination of two elements with small mass numbers to make an element with a larger mass number. Fission involves splitting the nucleus of an element with a large mass number into elements with smaller mass numbers. Both nuclear reactions can release energy or absorb energy, depending on the specific isotope and reaction.

A fusion reaction **A fission reaction**

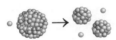

$$C^{12} + C^{12} \rightarrow Mg^{24} + energy \qquad n + U^{235} \rightarrow Mo^{99} + Sn^{135} + 2n + energy$$

Nuclear reactions are written in a way similar to chemical reactions. The mass number of each isotope is written next to the element symbol. Individual particles such as electrons (e-), protons (p), and neutrons (n) may also appear in a reaction.

a. Demonstrate the fusion reaction $Li^6 + He^4 = ?$, using the Atomic Building Game board. What element is represented on the model after the reaction?

b. Collect enough marbles (signifying protons, neutrons, and electrons) to build Li^6. Then collect enough marbles to build B^{11}. Place all the marbles in the correct places on the model. What element is represented? Was this activity an example of fusion or fission?

c. An impact with a fast neutron can cause fission even in elements that have low mass numbers. Use the Atom Building Game board to figure out six different ways the fission reaction $n + O^{16} = ?$ can divide the oxygen-16 nucleus. Each reaction must use up all the protons, electrons, and neutrons, including the extra neutron you added to start the reaction. Write down the six possible fission reactions you found.

d. Suppose you split a uranium-238 atom. If you have to break it into two pieces, name isotopes of two elements that could be formed. Be sure that your two isotopes use up all the neutrons and protons in the uranium. Use the periodic table to determine if either of the two isotopes are stable, or are one or both radioactive?

213

1 **Example answers**

1a. $Li^6 + He^4 = B^{10}$

1b. $Li^6 + B^{11} = O^{17}$

1c. There are only four reactions that yield two stable product nuclei. They are:

$$n + O^{16} = H^2 + N^{15}$$
$$n + O^{16} = He^4 + C^{13}$$
$$n + O^{16} = Li^6 + B^{11}$$
$$n + O^{16} = Li^7 + B^{10}$$

Any other combination that includes 9 neutrons and 8 protons is acceptable, including $n + O^{16} = n + O^{16}$ in which the oxygen nucleus ejects the neutron back out again.

1d. Any isotope on the periodic table can be formed. However, there are rules that prevent many from being very probable. An example would be:

$$U238 = Zr97 + Te141$$

Both of the product isotopes are neutron-rich and radioactive themselves. They decay into other isotopes.

The fission of U-238

The fission yield of uranium-238 can be represented by a graph called a fission yield curve. The fission yield curve shows the probability of the outcome of a fission reaction versus the atomic mass of the product nuclei. The graph typically has two humps which show that the most probable reactions split the uranium nucleus into two uneven pieces. The graph below shows that product nuclei with mass numbers of 95 or 136 are most probable.

Fission Yield Curve

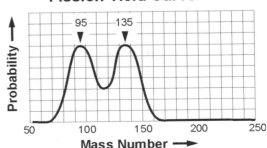

Energy from nuclear reactions

A chain reaction occurs when one nucleus triggers fission of many other nuclei.

Playing nuclear reactions

2

Scoring points

The Three Rules
1. Number of protons = atomic number
2. Protons + neutrons = stable mass number
3. Number of electrons = number of protons

Uranium-238 has a half-life of 4.5 billion years. Uranium-235 with a half-life of 700 million years is not much faster. Because of the long half-life, natural radioactive decay is far too slow a process to create energy in a power plant. However, if a uranium nucleus is struck by a neutron, it is likely to split almost immediately in a fission reaction. When a uranium-238 nucleus undergoes fission, all of the products have too many neutrons. That means the reaction is quite likely to release one or more neutrons that are not confined in a nucleus. These free neutrons are capable of causing a nearby uranium nucleus to fission, releasing more neutrons. If each fission reaction frees two additional neutrons that cause two more fissions, you can see what happens. One neutron frees two more, which cause reactions that free four more, then eight, and so on. This multiplication of neutrons is called a chain reaction and is how nuclear power plants are able to increase the reaction rate of uranium to release energy. The energy released by the fission of one kilogram of uranium is the same as 600,000 gallons of gasoline. The reaction is controlled by adjusting the amount of other elements that absorb neutrons, such as cadmium. If a neutron is absorbed by a cadmium nucleus it is no longer available to cause fission. The control rods in a nuclear reactor contain cadmium. The rate of reaction is controlled by sliding the control rods into or out of the reactor core.

Draw a chain reaction diagram on the board similar to Figure 30.20 on page 631 of the text.

For the next part of the Investigation we are going to play a game. The game is called nuclear reactions. The objective of the game is to win by being the first person to score 10 points. In order to score points, you must build stable atoms with the correct number of protons, neutrons, and electrons. Each group of four4 people should have one Atom Building Game and a deck of the nuclear reactions cards. Each player should have six of each color marble (red, blue, yellow) in the pocket on their corner of the board. Shuffle the cards and deal each player a hand of five cards. One card is played each turn, after which the player draws a new card from the deck to maintain a five-card hand.

Go through the rules to the game listed in step 2 of the Investigation.

When a more massive nucleus is built up from lighter nuclei, what type of nuclear reaction is it?

Students should answer that this is a fusion reaction.

3

Points are scored depending on how many of the three rules are matched after you have completed your turn. You get three points if your turn creates a perfect atom that obeys all of the rules for a stable isotope. The atomic number and mass numbers of the stable nuclei are on the periodic table in Investigation 28.1 on page 195 of your Investigation book. Even if the protons and electrons are not equal, you still can get one point if your turn creates a stable nucleus. You also can get one point if you add an electron or proton that makes the number of electrons and protons equal, even if the nucleus is unstable. If the nucleus is unstable and the electrons and protons are not equal, then you get no points. This is a game of strategy. You must decide which card to play to make the most points in each turn. Or, you may play a card to block another player from scoring points.

Students play the nuclear reactions game. In this game they may take extra marbles at any time if they need them. Make sure each player draws a new card after playing a card in his or her turn.

The purpose of the game

The nuclear reactions game is an excellent way to provide students with a concrete activity that reinforces the concepts of atomic structure. It was designed to teach the following specific concepts:

1. The meaning and significance of the atomic number.

2. The meaning and significance of the mass number.

3. The overall structure of the atom with neutrons and protons in the nucleus and electrons outside the nucleus.

4. How the elements of the periodic table are built up from the three elementary particles: neutron, proton, and electron.

5. How basic nuclear reactions are written and how they work in terms of rearranging protons and neutrons.

6. That atoms of the same element can differ in the number of neutrons in the nucleus (isotopes).

7. That there are stable and unstable isotopes.

8. That nuclei with higher atomic numbers can be assembled by combining nuclei with lower atomic numbers (nucleosynthesis).

Like any introductory teaching activity for an advanced concept, the model makes many simplifications, some of which are not physically realistic. You may wish to point out the following:

1. The actual nucleus is far, far smaller compared with the size of the atom. To scale, the nucleus would be smaller than a speck of sand if the atom were the size of the model.

2. Compared with electrons, the relative masses of neutrons and protons are much larger than the size difference between the yellow and red or blue marbles suggests.

3. Actual nuclear reactions may not conserve the number of protons or neutrons. For example, in beta decay, a neutron is transformed into a proton, an electron, and another particle called an electron antineutrino.

4. The quantum states of electrons are not as simple as pockets arranged in geometrical rings around the nucleus.

5. The model only shows five levels outside the nucleus, when there are actually an infinite number. The model can be used to build elements from hydrogen up to xenon, atomic number 54.

---

2   Playing Nuclear Reactions

Now you and your group will play Nuclear Reactions using the Atom Building Game board, marbles, and the Nuclear Reactions cards. Before you begin, read the instructions below carefully. Good luck!

1. The first player to reach 10 points wins the game.

2. Each player starts with at least six neutrons, protons, and electrons in their corner of the board.

3. Each player is dealt five cards from the Nuclear Reactions deck. These cards are held and not shown to anyone else.

4. Players take turns, choosing which card to play each turn, and adding or subtracting particles from the atom as instructed on the card. For example, playing an "Add 2 Electrons" card would mean you place two yellow marbles in the atom. Players may get additional marbles without penalty if they need them.

5. After playing a card, each player draws a new one from the deck so as to maintain a hand of five cards. Played cards can be shuffled and reused as needed.

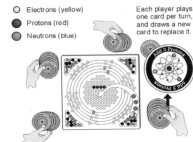

- ○ Electrons (yellow)
- ● Protons (red)
- ● Neutrons (blue)

Each player plays one card per turn, and draws a new card to replace it.

3   Scoring points

Points are scored depending on the atom that is created after a turn is played. Players should use the periodic table of stable isotopes as a reference to figure out which card to play in order to score the most points. Try anticipate the plays of others and develop strategies for scoring as many points as possible. Points are scored based on how a turn satisfies the three rules for building a stable atom.

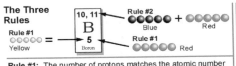

The Three Rules

Rule #1: The number of protons matches the atomic number

Rule #2: The total number of protons and neutrons equals a stable mass number

Rule #3: The number of electrons matches the number of protons

Scoring:

3 points if all three rules are met

1 point if rule #1 and #2 are met, but not #3

1 point if rule #3 is met but not #2

0 points if rules #2 and #3 are not met

4   Additional rules

1. When it is your turn, you must either play a card and add or subtract marbles from the atom, or trade in your cards for a new set of five.

2. You may trade in all your cards at any time by forfeiting a turn. You have to trade all your cards in at once. Shuffle the deck before taking new cards.

3. All players need a periodic table of the isotopes to play the game.

Chapter 2 Review Answer Key

Vocabulary review

Set One	Set Two	Set Three
1. c	1. e	1. a
2. a	2. a	2. e
3. b	3. c	3. f
4. e	4. b	4. b
		5. d

Concept review

1. Units are important when measuring quantities because units allow people to communicate amounts uniformly in a way that can be understood by others.

2. The two common systems of units are the English system and the metric system.

3. Because both sets of units, English and metric, are commonly used in everyday life, understanding them both enables us to comprehend what others mean.

4. Students may use many common examples. Some examples are:
   a. Grams are often used on nutrition facts labels.
   b. Miles are commonly used to indicate the distance between two cities.

5. The units of the fish tank volume are calculated by Volume = length × width × height, the units of volume should be $cm \times cm \times cm = cm^3$, instead of cm^2.

6. One means the time at a specific moment; the other means a quantity of time, or the time interval between two events.

7. When making a graph, time is usually plotted on the x-axis.

8. Precision means how close several measurements are to each other. Accuracy means how close each measurement is to the actual value.

9. Her measurements were precise, because each measurement was the same. Her measurements were not accurate, because they were not close to the actual value.

10. Iron is an element, oxygen molecules are in the air, and oil is a mixture of several molecules.

11. Atoms move more freely in gases.

12. Answers are:
    a. 500 laps

b. 100 km/h
c. 7 ft. 2 in.
d. 65 mph
e. 29 inches, 32 inches

13. mixture, molecules

14. Answers are:
    a. meters
    b. millimeters
    c. centimeters
    d. kilometers

15. Kilograms and grams are commonly used for measuring mass.

16. A kilogram is the mass of 1 liter ($1,000 \ cm^3$) of water.

17. Very large and very small numbers are often expressed in scientific notation.

Problems

1. First convert all the lengths into the same units:
   a. 17.4 mm × 1 m/1,000 mm = 0.0174 m
   b. 24 km × 1,000 m/1 km = 24,000 m
   c. 31 ft × 2.54 cm/1 ft × 1 m/100 cm = 0.787 m
   d. 8.1 cm × 1 m/100 cm = 0.081 m
      Because 0.0174 m < 0.081 m < 0.787 < 24,000 m
      a) 17.4 mm < d) 8.1 cm < c) 31 ft < b) 24 km

2. Answers are:
   a. 25 km × 0.6215 mi/1 km = 15.54 mi
   b. 3 mi × 5,280 ft/1 mi = 15,840 ft
   c. 400 cm × 1 m/100 cm = 4 m
   d. 7 in. × 1 m/39.37 in. × 1,000 mm/1 m = 177.8 mm

3. Answers are:
   a. Surface Area = $2hw + 2hl + 2wl$
      Surface Area = $(2 \times 0.5 \times 1) + (2 \times 0.5 \times 0.8) + (2 \times 1 \times 0.8)$
      Surface Area = $3.4 \ m^2$
   b. Surface Area = $3.4 \ m^2 \times 10,000 \ cm^2/m = 34,000 \ cm^2$
   c. Volume = $hwl = 0.5 \times 1 \times 0.8 = .4 \ m^3$

4. Answers are:
   a. Surface Area = $2\pi r^2 + 2\pi rh = 2 \times 3.14 \times (3 \ cm)^2 + (2 \times 3.14 \times 3 \ cm \times 15 \ cm) = 339.12 \ cm^2$
   b. Volume = $\pi r^2 h = 3.14 \times (3 \ cm)^2 \times 15 \ cm = 423.9 \ cm^3$

5. 60 min/hr × 24 hr/day × 365 days/yr = 525,600 min/yr

6. Answers are:
   a. 1×10^4
   b. 5.2×10^2
   c. 3×10^8
   d. 1×10^{-6}
   e. 2.3×10^{-5}
   f. 4.44×10^{-3}

7. Answers are:
   a. 2,330,000
   b. 99,999
   c. 913
   d. 0.13
   e. 0.0000005
   f. 0.00801

Chapter 3 Review Answer Key

Vocabulary review

Set One	Set Two	Set Three
1. c	1. c	1. d
2. f	2. d	2. e
3. b	3. b	3. a
4. d	4. a	4. f
5. a	5. e	5. b

Concept review

1. The distance the object moves and the time required for the movement.

2. Answers are:

Distance	Time	Speed	Abbr.
meters	seconds	meters per second	m/s
kilometers	hours	kilometers per hour	km/h
centimeters	seconds	centimeters per second	cm/s
miles	hours	miles per hour	mph
inches	seconds	inches per second	in/s, ips
feet	minutes	feet per minute	ft/min, fpm

3. Answers are:
   a. $v = d/t$
   b. $d = vt$
   c. $t = d/v$

4. Answers are:
   Step 1: Identify what you are asked to find.
   Step 2: Identify the given information with units of measurements.
   Step 3: Identify relevant relationships
   Step 4: Substituting numbers and units of measurements in the equation, solve for the mathematical answer.

5. There is no confusion over which variable caused the change.

6. *Experimental variable:* size of the ball *Control variables:* angle, initial speed, mass, internal structure (hollow or solid), starting position

7. The independent variable, which is generally graphed on the *x*-axis, is changed at the discretion of the experimenter. The dependent variable, which is generally graphed on the *y*-axis, changes in response to the independent variable's changes.

8. Graphs are used to show the exact relationship between two variables by using a picture; pictures are generally easier to interpret than tables of data.

9. Answers are:
   a. Label each axis with the proper variable and its units of measurement.
   b. Make a properly sized scale for each axis and number the axes.
   c. Plot the data points.
   d. Draw a smooth, best-fit line.
   e. Give the graph a title.

10. Answers are:
    a. Time is the independent variable.
    b. Angular position is the dependent variable. It is placed on the *x*-axis.
    c. Time is on the *x*-axis and angular position is on the *y*-axis.

11. Possible answers include:
    a. The distance a moving object travels in a given time.
    b. The amount of candy eaten by teenagers compared to their report card grades.
    c. A student's favorite color compared to the student's age.
    d. When the distance traveled is constant, the time required to travel the distance is inversely proportional to the speed.

603

12. Position is the instantaneous location of an object. Distance is the total length of movement without regard to direction from the initial position to the final position. Displacement is the length of the straight line drawn from the initial position to the final position.

13. Choose two points on the line. Read and record the x- and y-coordinates of each point. To calculate the slope, divide the difference between the first and second y-values by the difference between the first and second x-values. The quotient is the slope.

14. Since slope is the change of the y-values divided by the change of the x-values, the slope of the position vs. time graph represents speed in a certain direction.

15. Because the slope of a curving line is not constant, it indicates that the speed is not constant; it is changing.

16. Answers are:
    a. A horizontal line
    b. A straight line sloping up from left to right
    c. A curved line whose slope decreases to zero; the line becomes horizontal.

17. It represents the distance traveled by the object.

18. Answers are:
    a. A horizontal line coincident with the x-axis passing through the origin
    b. A horizontal line at some point above the x-axis
    c. A line sloping down to the right which meets the x-axis

Problems

1. $v = d/t = 4.80 \times 10^3 \text{ m}/3.20 \text{ s} = 1{,}500 \text{ m/s} = 1.5 \times 10^3 \text{ m/s}$

2. $d = vt = (3.00 \times 10^8 \text{ m/s})(500 \text{ s}) = 1.50 \times 10^{11} \text{ m}$

3. $t = d/v = 110/22 \text{ mi/hour} = 5.0 \text{ hrs}$

4. Answers are:
    a. $d_t = d_{65} + d_{55} + d_{47}$
       $d_t = (65 \text{ mph} \times 1 \text{ hr}) + (55 \text{ mph} \times 1 \text{ hr}) + (47 \text{ mph} \times 3 \text{ hr})$
       $d_t = 261 \text{ mi}$
    b. $v = d/t = 261 \text{ mi}/5 \text{ hrs} = 52.2 \text{ mph}$

5. $v = d/t = 1 \text{ mi}/3.81 \text{ min} = 0.262 \text{ mi/min} \times 60 \text{ min/hr} = 15.7 \text{ mi/hr}$

6. The speed of the cart is equal to the slope of the line, 2 m/s.

7. Answers are:
    a. From 0 s to 4.0 s, the line is curving, so the slope is changing.
    b. After 4.0 s, the slope of the graph is zero, or 0.0 m/s.

8. Answers are:
    a. Interval C-D
    b. Intervals B-C and D-E

9. Sample answer:

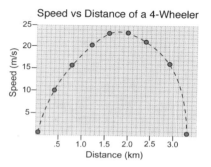

10. Answers are:
    a. An object is accelerating away from the observer
    b. An object is sitting motionless at a distance from the observer
    c. An object is moving at constant speed toward the observer

11. Answers are:
    a. Strong
    b. None
    c. Weak

Chapter 4 Review Answer Key

Vocabulary review

Set One	Set Two
1. b	1. b
2. d	2. e
3. e	3. d
4. c	4. f

Concept review

1. Average speed is the ratio of the distance traveled to the time. The speed may not be the same over the entire time. Instantaneous speed is the speed an object has at a specific position during its motion.

2. The instantaneous speed is found by calculating the slope of the line at a point on the line of the graph.

3. The initial speed (V_i), the final speed (V_f) and the elapsed time (Δt).
   $a = (V_f - V_i) \div \Delta t$

4. Answers are:
   a. *Positive:* Acceleration in the direction of motion: pedaling, coasting downhill. *Negative:* Acceleration in the direction opposite to motion (deceleration): braking, wind resistance.
   Zero: When positive forces (pedaling and gravity) are balanced by negative forces (wind resistance and braking force)
   b. If the acceleration is positive, the speed increases. If the acceleration is negative, speed decreases. If the acceleration is zero, speed remains the same.

5. Answers are:
   a. The graph is a straight line sloping up from left to right.
   b. The car's acceleration is equal to the slope of the line of the graph.

6. The distance traveled can be found by calculating the area between the slope line and the x-axis of the graph.

7. Answers are:
   a. A triangle whose area equals the distance required for the car to stop
   b. A rectangle whose area equals the length of the pool table

8. While the coin is traveling up, its velocity is positive, and its acceleration is negative. At the top, velocity is zero, but acceleration is still negative. As it starts down, the velocity is negative, and the acceleration is negative.

9. The negative sign indicates a direction toward the Earth.

10. Both hit the ground at the same time because the acceleration due to gravity is the same for both.

11. Since the rhino has a greater surface area, it has a greater force applied to it by the air molecules.

12. The jumper continues to fall downward in both cases. The apparent upward motion in the movie is due to the motion of the camera on which the scene is filmed. It continues to fall and accelerate at a rate that is greater than that of the person and parachute; they approach a terminal velocity.

Problems

1. Answers are:
   a. Speed = Δdistance ÷ Δtime = 600 km ÷ 2 hrs = 300 km/hr
   b. Speed = Δdistance ÷ Δtime = 800 km ÷ 5 hrs = 160 km/hr
   c. Speed = Δdistance ÷ Δtime = 1,400 km ÷ 7 hrs = 200 km/hr

2. Answers are:

a. The speed of car A is 50 m/s; the speed of car B is 30 m/s.
b. Find the area under the curve for each car.
   A = 30 m/s × 60 s = 1,800 m
   B = ½(60 m/s × 60 s) = 1800 m
c. The velocity of A is constant for time $t = 0$ to $t = 70$ s; car B from $t = 60$ s to $t = 70$ s
d. The slope of the line is zero for car A. Therefore, the acceleration of car A is zero. The slope of line for car B is 1 m/s/s; the acceleration is 1 m/s^2.
e. Choice 2. Finding the area under the slope line, car A travels 1,350 meters from $t = 30$ to $t = 60$ s.

3. $a = \Delta v \div \Delta t = (V_f - V_i) \div \Delta t$
   Since Seth starts from rest, $V_i = 0$
   $V_f = a\Delta t = (0.40 \text{ m/s}^2)(12\text{s}) = 4.8$ m/s

4. Answers are:
   a. $V_{av} = \Delta d \div \Delta t = 30 \text{ cm}/0.0066 \text{ s} = 4,500$ cm/sec
   b. $V_{av} = (V_f + V_i) \div 2$
      Since $V_i = 0$, $V_f = 2(V_{av})$, $V_f = 2(4,500 \text{ cm/sec}) = 9,000$ cm/sec.
   c. $a = \Delta v \div \Delta t = (V_f - V_i) \div \Delta t$
      Since $V_i = 0$, $a = V_f \div \Delta t = (9,000 \text{ cm/sec}) \div (0.0066 \text{ sec}) = 1.4 \times 10^6 \text{ cm/s}^2$.

5. Answers are:
   First question: $a = \Delta v \div \Delta t$
   $\Delta t = \Delta v \div a$
   $\Delta t = (8.00 \times 10^3 \text{m/s}) \div 20 \text{ m/s}^2 = 4.0 \times 10^2$ s, or about 6.7 min.
   Second question:
   $s = \frac{1}{2} at^2 = \frac{1}{2}(20 \text{ m/s}^2)(4.0 \times 10^2 \text{ s})^2 = 1.6 \times 10^6$ m

6. Answers are:
   a. 9.8 m/s^2
   b. Area = $(39.2 \times 4) + \frac{1}{2}(39.2 \times 4) = 156.8\text{m} + 78.4 \text{ m} = 235.2$ m
   c. Slope = 0.33 m/s^2

7. 5 miles

8. Answers are:
   a. *A-B:* The cart accelerates away from the garage.
   b. *B-C:* The cart travels with constant velocity (3.5 m/s) away from the door.
   c. *C-D:* The cart continues away from the door at a lower constant velocity (1 m/s).
   d. *D-E:* The cart is stopped.

605

e. *E-F:* The cart accelerates toward the garage.

f. *F-G:* The cart travels toward the door at constant velocity (9 m/s).

g. *G-H:* The cart decelerates as it approaches the garage.

9. Choice 1

10. Answers are:

   a. 25 m

   b. A-B and C-D

   c. $7.5 m/s^2$

11. $V = V_0 + gt = 114$ m/s $+ (-9.8 m/s^2)(8$ s$)$

   $V = 114$ m/s $- 78.4$ m/s

   $V = 35.6$ m/s up

12. $X = X_0 + V_0 t + \frac{1}{2}gt^2$

   $X = 0 + (58.8$ m/s$)(7.2$ s$) + \frac{1}{2}(-9.8$ m/s2$)(7.2$ s$)^2$

   $X = 170$ m

Chapter 5 Review Answer Key

Vocabulary review

Set One	Set Two
1. b	1. d
2. f	2. b
3. a	3. e
4. e	4. a
5. c	5. c

Concept review

1. Newtons are used by scientists, and pounds are used more commonly by non-scientists. One pound is equivalent to 4.48 newtons. One newton equals 0.22 pounds.

2. Answers are:

   a. False. A force has the ability to cause movement but may not. For example, pushing on the walls of most buildings causes no motion.

   b. False. If there is no friction, a moving object continues to move. For example, a cannon ball launched into frictionless space from a spaceship continues to move with no additional force.

   c. True. An object continues to move in a straight line unless a force is applied. For example, to change the direction of a bicycle, the road must apply a force on the wheels.

3. The massive head remains in motion, pushing it farther onto the handle.

4. The inertia of an object is proportional to its mass. Since mass is a measure of the amount of matter in an object, a bowling ball with more mass cannot be rolled as fast down the lane. That is, it cannot be accelerated (its velocity cannot be changed) as rapidly.

5. Answers are:

   a. seat belts, air bags – apply forces to overcome your inertia as the car stops

   b. cup holders – apply forces to overcome inertia of the cup/can as the car stops, starts, and changes direction

   c. brakes – adapted to apply force to overcome the inertia of the moving car

   d. seat backs – apply forces to overcome your inertia as the car starts

   e. steering wheel – adapted to apply force to change the direction of the motion

6. The acceleration of an object is directly proportional to the force applied and inversely proportional to the mass of the object. ($F = ma$)

7. A newton is the force required to cause the acceleration of a 1-kilogram mass at a rate of 1 meter per second per second (1 N $= 1$kg-m/s^2)

8. Use a spring to accelerate the object and one of a known mass. Since the force applied by the spring is the same for both objects, the products of mass $\times$ acceleration for each is the same.

9. Mass is a measure of the matter in an object. It is commonly measured in grams and kilograms. Weight is a measure of the effect of the force due to gravity on an object. It is commonly measured in newtons and pounds.

10. A force is, simply stated, a push or a pull on an object. Objects may have many forces exerted on them at one time. Net force is the one force that, when applied, could replace the effect on the object of all of the applied forces. (It is the result of the vector addition of all the forces applied at one time.)

11. Positive and negative values differ in their direction by 180°. For example, a positive force may be exerted up; therefore, a negative force would be down, in the opposite direction.

12. It should always be given the same sign because the direction is the same.

13. Both are in equilibrium, meaning all forces exerted on the objects (the net force) add up to zero.

14. Dynamic problems involve objects in motion such as solving for the acceleration of an object to which an unbalanced force is applied. Static problems involve motionless objects such as solving for the value of support forces in a pulley system.

606

15. The forces are the same size but in opposite directions. Because you have more mass than your cousin, your cousin accelerates at a higher rate.

16. Answers are:
    a. first law – To move, the inertia of each body must be overcome. The inertia of each body is proportional to its mass. The Earth has so much inertia it will not move as easily.
    b. second law – The acceleration that takes place is inversely proportional to the mass and directly proportional to the force. The acceleration of the Earth is imperceptible due to its huge mass.
    c. third law – Forces occur in pairs. The Earth applies a force on you. You apply an equal force on the Earth in the opposite direction.

17. You push on the water. It moves back. At the same time, the water pushes on you in the opposite direction; you move forward.

Problems

1. Answers are:
    a. $(16.0 \text{ N})/(4.48 \text{ N/lb.}) = 3.57 \text{ lb.}$
    b. $(7.00 \text{ lb.}) (4.48 \text{ N/lb.}) = 31.4 \text{ N}$
    c. $(3.00 \text{ kg})/(.454 \text{ kg/lb.}) \times (4.48 \text{ N/lb.}) = 29.6 \text{ N}$
    d. $(12.0 \text{ N})/(4.48 \text{ N/lb.}) \times (.454 \text{ kg/lb.}) = 1.22 \text{ kg}$

2. The 400 kg object has twice as much inertia as the 200 kg object. (Mass and inertia are directly proportional.)

3. Its rate of acceleration is reduced to 1/3 of its initial value.

4. It triples. Force and acceleration are directly proportional.

5. $W = mg$; $m = W/g = 800 \text{ N}/8.86 \text{ m/s}^2 = 90.29 \text{ kg}$, or 90.3 kg

6. $F = ma = (72 \text{ kg})(3.25 \text{ m/s}^2) = 234 \text{ N}$

7. Answers are:
    a. $F = ma$; $a = F/m = 75 \text{ N}/30 \text{ kg} = 2.5 \text{ m/s}^2$
    b. $F = ma$; $a = F/m = 75 \text{ N}/7.0 \text{ kg} = 10.7 \text{ m/s}^2$, or 11 m/s^2

8. $W = mg$; $g = W/m = 280 \text{ N}/75 \text{ kg} = 3.7 \text{ m/s}^2$

9. Answers are:
    a. 500 newtons. Action and reaction forces are equal.
    b. $F = ma$; $a = F/m = 500 \text{ N}/0.15 \text{ kg} = 3.3 \times 10^3 \text{ m/s}^2$
    c. $v = at = (3.3 \times 103 \text{ m/s}^2)(0.2 \text{ s}) = 6.6 \times 10^2 \text{ m/s}$

10. B-C, D-E

11. $a = \Delta v/\Delta t = (15 \text{ m/s})/4\text{s} = 3.75 \text{ m/s}^2$
    $F = ma = (1,500 \text{ kg})(3.75 \text{ m/s}^2) = 5,625 \text{ N}$

12. $F_{net} = F_R - F_L = 8.0 \text{ N} - 2.0 \text{ N} = 6.0 \text{ N}$ to the right
    $F = ma$; $a = F/m = 6.0 \text{ N}/2.0 \text{ kg} = 3.0 \text{ m/s}^2$ to the right

13. The mass is the ratio of the change in force to the change of acceleration:
    $mass = \Delta F/\Delta a = 3 \text{ N}/6 \text{ m/s}^2 = 0.5 \text{ kg}$

14. The force must be applied opposite in direction to the motion to stop the woman, that is, in the negative direction:
    $F = ma$, $a = \Delta v/t$, $F = m\Delta v/t$
    $F = (50 \text{ kg})(-10 \text{ m/s})/(0.50 \text{ s}) = (-500 \text{ kg-m/s})/(0.50 \text{ s})$
    $F = -1,000 \text{ N}$, or $-1.0 \times 10^3 \text{ N}$

Chapter 6 Review Answer Key

Vocabulary review

Set One	Set Two	Set Three
1. d	1. f	1. e
2. b	2. d	2. f
3. f	3. c	3. b
4. e	4. e	4. c
5. a	5. a	5. a
	6. b	6. g

Concept review

1. Weight equals the object's mass times the acceleration due to gravity. At the same position in the universe, the larger the mass, the larger the weight. Weight is directly proportional to mass.

2. Weight would be less because the acceleration due to gravity is less, but the mass stays the same. Mass does not depend on gravity.

3. One is to get away from gravity; the other is to be in free fall.

4. Answers are:
    a. The backpack sits on the floor.
    b. The backpack sits on the floor.
    c. The backpack moves upward with acceleration.

5. It is caused by the contact between two surfaces moving relative to each other.

6. The force of friction is to the left. It is the sliding friction.

7. Answers are:
    a. Difference: Static friction does not have one specific value for a pair of objects. The amount of static friction depends on the forces exerted on the objects. It has a maximum value that can be calculated if the coefficient of friction is known.
    b. Similarity: There are coefficients of friction assigned to static friction as well as the other types of friction. The maximum force of static friction is calculated by the same formula as calculating other friction forces.

8. Answers are:
    a. rolling friction
    b. sliding friction
    c. air friction
    d. static friction
    e. viscous friction

9. 0, 1

10. The coefficient of static friction is greater because it requires more force to break the surfaces loose than to maintain the sliding motion.

11. 250 N in a direction opposite the direction of the applied force.

12. Apply a lubricant, use ball bearings, or separate the surfaces by magnetic levitation.

13. Answers are:
    a. Friction enables us walk; without friction we would not be able to grip the road.
    b. A baseball pitcher uses friction to rotate the ball when he / she throws it.
    c. Pencils leave marks on paper due to friction, which allows us to write.

14. Answers are:
    a. False
    b. False
    c. True

15. to the left

16. The force of a spring is directly proportional to the distance it is stretched or compressed.

17. The negative sign indicates that the direction of the force exerted by the spring is opposite the direction of deformation.

18. The one with a spring constant of 10 N/m would be easier to stretch.

Problems

1. Answers are:
    a. $F_w = mg = (60 \text{ kg})(9.8 \text{ N/kg}) = 588 \text{ N}$
    b. $F_w = mg = (4 \text{ kg})(9.8 \text{ N/kg}) = 39.2 \text{ N}$
    c. $F_w = mg = (30 \text{ kg})(23 \text{ N/kg}) = 690 \text{ N}$

2. Answers are:
    a. $m = F_w/g = (15,000 \text{ N})/(9.8 \text{ N/kg}) = 1,530.6 \text{ kg}$
    b. $m = F_w/g = (12 \text{ N})/(23 \text{ N/kg}) = 0.52 \text{ kg}$

3. $F_w - F_n = ma$
    $mg - F_n = ma$
    $(75 \text{ kg})(9.8 \text{ N/kg}) - F_n = (75 \text{ kg})(4.9 \text{ N/kg})$
    $735 \text{ N} - F_n = 367.5 \text{ N}$
    $F_n = 367.5 \text{ N}$

4. $F_n = F_w = mg = (55 \text{ kg})(9.8 \text{ N/kg}) = 539 \text{ N}$
    $F_f = \mu F_n = (0.80)(539 \text{ N}) = 431.2 \text{ N}$

5. $\mu = F_f/F_n = (200)(500) = 0.40$

6. $F_n = F_w = mg = (50 \text{ kg})(9.8 \text{ N/kg}) = 490 \text{ N}$
    $F_f = \mu F_n = (0.10)(490 \text{ N}) = 49 \text{ N}$
    $F - F_f = ma$
    $100 \text{ N} - 49 \text{ N} = (50 \text{ kg})a$
    $a = 1.02 \text{ m/sec}^2$

7. Answers are:
    a. $F_w = mg = (1 \text{ kg})(9.8 \text{ N/kg}) = 9.8 \text{ N}$
        $F_n = F_w = 9.8 \text{ N}$

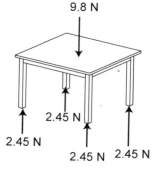

9.8 N

2.45 N

2.45 N

2.45 N 2.45 N

b. Ignoring friction:

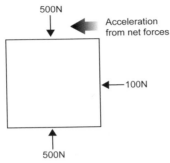

c. $F_w = mg = (20\ \text{kg})(9.8\ \text{N/kg}) = 196\ \text{N}$
$F_n = F_w = 196\ \text{N}$

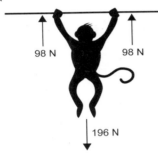

8. $F = 20\ \text{N} - 15\ \text{N} = 5\ \text{N}$
$a = F/m = 5\ \text{N}/2.5\ \text{kg} = 2\ \text{m/sec}^2$

9. Answers are:
   a. $F = -kx = -(20\ \text{N/m})(0.5\ \text{m}) = -10\ \text{N}$, so the magnitude of the force is 10 N.
   b. $F = -kx = -(3\ \text{N/m})(0.1\ \text{m}) = -0.3\ \text{N}$, so the magnitude of the force is 0.3 N.
   c. $F = -kx = -(5 \times 10^7\ \text{N/m})(1 \times 10^{-5}\ \text{m}) = -5 \times 10^2\ \text{N}$, so the magnitude of the force is 5×10^2 N.

Chapter 7 Review Answer Key

Vocabulary review

Set One	Set Two	Set Three
1. e	1. e	1. c
2. f	2. c	2. a
3. c	3. d	3. b
4. d	4. a	4. d
5. b	5. f	

Concept review

1. A scalar quantity only has magnitude, while a vector quantity has both magnitude and direction.

2. Answers are:
   a. scalar
   b. vector
   c. vector
   d. scalar

3. Sample answer:

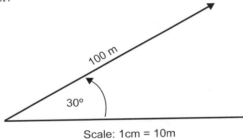

Scale: 1cm = 10m

4. Your displacement is zero because your starting and ending locations are the same.

5. Maximum resultant is a 5-centimeter vector. This results when both of the vectors are in the same direction. The minimum resultant is a 3-centimeter vector. This results when the vectors are in opposite directions.

6. When a vector is expressed in Cartesian coordinates, each coordinate is a vector quantity. When a vector is expressed in polar coordinates, each coordinate is a scalar quantity.

7. The magnitudes of its components are equal because $\cos 45° = \sin 45°$.

8. Adding vectors using components is more accurate, faster, and easier than making a scale drawing.

609

9. The only force that affects a projectile is the force of gravity.

10. The vertical component of a projectile's velocity changes as it moves through the air as the projectile is affected by gravity; the horizontal component does not change.

11. The initial vertical velocity is zero.

12. Answers are:
    a. At the top of its path, the ball's velocity is entirely horizontal because its vertical velocity equals zero.
    b. At the top of its path, the ball's acceleration is entirely vertical. The only acceleration is the acceleration due to gravity, and its direction is downward.

13. 45° results in the maximum horizontal distance.

14. 65°; the pair of angles adds up to 90°.

15. Equilibrium means the net force acting on the object is zero. The sum of all the forces acting on the object is zero.

16. Students may use many common examples. A car moving down a hill, a skier skiing down a hill, and a package sliding down a ramp are examples of objects moving along an inclined plane.

17. Answers are:
    a. The force of gravity, the normal force, and friction act on the sled.
    b.

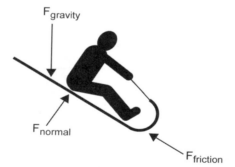

18. The force of gravity causes an object on an inclined plane to accelerate.

19. The force of friction decreases the acceleration of an object on an inclined plane.

20. If an object is in equilibrium, the net force in the x-direction is zero and the net force in the y-direction is zero.

Problems

1. Answers are:
   a. $(0, 2)$ cm + $(-7, 0)$ cm = $(-7, 2)$ cm
   b. $(0, -500)$ cm + $(0, 8)$ cm = $(0, -492)$ cm
   c. $(-30, 0)$ m/s + $(0, -50)$ m/s = $(-30, -50)$ m/s
   d. $(0, 5)$ cm + $(-7, 0)$ cm + $(0, -9)$ cm = $(-7, -4)$ cm

2. $x = r \cos \theta = 6 \cos 25° = 5.43$ cm
   $y = r \sin \theta = 6 \sin 25° = 2.54$ cm

3. $v_x = v \cos \theta = 40 \cos 55° = 22.9$ m/s
   $v_y = v \sin \theta = 40 \sin 55° = 32.8$ m/s

4. $\sin \theta = V_y/V_r$
   $\theta = \sin^{-1}(30 \text{ m/s})/(100 \text{ m/s}) = 17.5°$

5. $t = x/v_{paddle} = 100$ m/(1 m/s) = 100 s
   $d = v_{current}\, t = (2 \text{ m/s})(100 \text{ s}) = 200$ m
   The time to cross the river is not affected by the current.

6. Answers are:
   a. $x = v_{0x}\, t = (7 \text{ m/s})(1.5 \text{ s}) = 10.5$ m
   b. $y = v_{0y}\, t - \frac{1}{2}gt^2 = 0 - \frac{1}{2}(9.8 \text{ m/s}^2)(1.5 \text{ s})^2 = -11.0$ m
   The height of the diving platform is 11.0 meters.

7. Answers are:

Table 2.1

Time (s)	Horizontal speed (m/s)	Vertical speed (m/s)
0	20.0	39.2
1	20.0	29.4
2	20.0	19.6
3	20.0	9.8
4	20.0	0
5	20.0	-9.8
6	20.0	-19.6
7	20.0	-29.4
8	20.0	-39.2

8. $y = v_{oy}t - \frac{1}{2}gt^2$; $v_{oy} = 0$; $y = -\frac{1}{2}gt^2$

$$t = \sqrt{\frac{(2y)}{g}} = \sqrt{\frac{2 \times 10 \text{ m}}{9.8 \text{ m/sec}^2}} = 1.43 \text{ s}$$

$$v_{ox} = \frac{x}{t} = \frac{5 \text{ m}}{1.43 \text{ s}} = 3.50 \text{ m/s}$$

9. Answers are:
   a. $v_x = v \cos \theta = 35 \cos 40° = 26.8$ m/s
      $v_y = v \sin \theta = 35 \sin 40° = 22.5$ m/s
   b. $v_y = v_{ox} - gt$; $v_y = 0$; $v_{ox} = gt$
      $t = v_y / g = (22.5 \text{ m/s})/(9.8 \text{ m/s}^2) = 2.30$ s
   c. Time in the air equals time to reach maximum height times 2
      $T = 2t = 2 \times 2.30$ s = 4.60 s
   d. $y = v_{0y}t - \frac{1}{2}gt^2 = (22.5 \text{ m/s})(2.30 \text{ s}) - \frac{1}{2}(9.8 \text{ m/s}^2)(2.30 \text{ s})^2 =$
      25.83 m
   e. $x = v_{ox}T = (26.8 \text{ m/s})(4.60 \text{ s}) = 123.3$ m

10. Answers are:
   a. $T = F_y \cos \theta = (200 \text{ N})(\cos 10°) = 197$ N
   b. This tension is less than the tension in the vertical rope.

11. Answers are:
   a. $N = F_w \cos \theta = (500 \text{ N})(\cos 22°) = 463.6$ N
   b. $F_{wx} = F_w \sin \theta = (500 \text{ N})(\sin 22°) = 187.3$ N
   c. $m = F_w/g = (500 \text{ N})/(9.8 \text{ N/kg}) = 51.0$ kg
      $a = F_{wx}/m = (187.3 \text{ N})/(51.0 \text{ kg}) = 3.67 \text{ m/s}^2$
   d. $F_{wx} = F_w \sin \theta = (500 \text{ N} + 200 \text{ N})(\sin 22°) = 262.2$ N
      $m = F_w/g = (500 \text{ N} + 200 \text{ N})/(9.8 \text{ N/kg}) = 71.4$ kg
      $a = F_{wx}/m = (262.2 \text{ N})/(71.4 \text{ kg}) = 3.67 \text{ m/s}^2$
   e. The acceleration of the object on a frictionless inclined plane is independent of the object's mass.

12. Answers are:
   a. $a = g \sin \theta = (9.8 \text{ m/s}^2)(\sin 30°) = 4.9 \text{ m/s}^2$
   b. $a = g \sin \theta = (9.8 \text{ m/s}^2)(\sin 60°) = 8.5 \text{ m/s}^2$
   c. The steeper the slope, the greater the acceleration.

13. Answers are:
   a. increased acceleration
   b. no change
   c. decreased acceleration

Chapter 8 Review Answer Key

Vocabulary review

Set One	Set Two
1. c	1. f
2. a	2. c
3. e	3. b
4. b	4. a
5. f	5. g
6. g	6. e

Concept review

1. Answers are:
   a. rotates
   b. revolves
   c. revolves
   d. revolves

2. Answers are:
   a. yes
   b. no
   c. yes

3. 2π

4. They have the same angular speed, but the ant at point B has a greater linear speed, since it is further from the center.

5. The cyclist's velocity at points A, B and C is tangent to the circle. The directions of the centripetal force and centripetal acceleration are both toward the center of the circle.

6. Answers are:
   a. centripetal force increases as velocity increases
   b. centripetal acceleration increases as velocity increases

7. Some examples are:
   a. The friction between the tires and road when the car is going around a bend keeps the car moving in a circular path.
   b. The force of gravity between the Earth and sun keeps the Earth in orbit.
   c. The force of your arm pulling on a bucket of water as you swing it around in a circle holds the water in the bucket.

8. We feel centrifugal force on our bodies when we move in a circle. It feels like a true force pulling outward, but is actually inertia making us want to move in a straight line.

9. The gravitational force increases if the objects are moved closer together.

10. The force doubles when the mass of one object is doubled.
The force quadruples when the masses of both objects are doubled.
$F = Gm_1m_2/r^2$

11. Because the distance between you and the center of the Earth increases, the gravitational force acting on you gets smaller as you go higher. The force is inversely proportional to the square of the distance.

12. The force of gravity is the only force involved in both projectile motion and orbital motion.

Problems

1. 34 cm = 0.34 m; $v = \omega r$
   a. $\omega = v/r = (8 \text{ m/s})/(0.34 \text{ m}) = 23.5 \text{ rad/s}$
   b. 23.5 rad/s × 60 s/min × 10 min × (1 revolution/2π radian) = 2,244 revolutions

2. Answers are:
   a. $C = 2\pi r = 2\pi (30 \text{ m}) = 188 \text{ m}$
   b. $d = 5 \times C = 5 \times 188 \text{ m} = 940 \text{ m}$
   c. $\omega = \theta/t = 5 \times 2\pi/220 \text{ s} = 0.14 \text{ rad/s}$
   d. $v = d/t = 940 \text{ m}/220 \text{ s} = 4.27 \text{ m/s}$

3. Answers are:
   a. $30° \times 1 \text{ rad}/57.3° = 0.524 \text{ rad}$
   b. $220° \times 1 \text{ rad}/57.3° = 3.84 \text{ rad}$
   c. $2 \text{ rad} \times 57.3°/1 \text{ rad} = 114.6°$
   d. $4.25 \text{ rad} \times 57.3°/1 \text{ rad} = 243.5°$
   e. 2 revolutions × 2π rad/1 revolution = 12.56 rad

4. $v = \omega r = 25 \text{ rad/s} \times 3 \text{ cm} = 75 \text{ cm/s}$

5. $v = d/t; v = \omega r; \omega = \theta/t$
   $d = \theta r = 10,250 \text{ rad} \times 33 \text{ cm} \times (1 \text{ m}/100 \text{ cm}) = 3,382.5 \text{ m}$

6. $F_c = mv^2/r = (50 \text{ kg})(7 \text{ m/s})^2/(5 \text{ m}) = 490 \text{ N}$

7. Answers are:
   a. $a_c = v^2/r = (6 \text{ m/s})^2/(6.5 \text{ m}) = 5.5 \text{ m/s}^2$
   b. $T = F_c = ma_c = (0.30 \text{ kg})(5.5 \text{ m/s}^2) = 1.65 \text{ N}$

8. $F = Gm_1m_2/r^2 = (6.67 \times 10^{-11} \text{ N m}^2/\text{kg}^2)(55 \text{ kg})(55 \text{ kg})/(0.25 \text{ m})^2 = 3.23 \times 10^{-6} \text{ N}$

9. Answers are:
   a. Let M be the mass of Pluto and m be the mass of an object on its surface.
   $GmM/r^2 = mg$
   $g = GM/r^2 = (6.67 \times 10^{-11} \text{ N} \times \text{m}^2/\text{kg}^2)(1.5 \times 1,0^{22} \text{ kg})/(1.15 \times 10^6 \text{ m})^2 = 0.76 \text{ m/s}^2$
   b. $F_w = mg = (70 \text{ kg})(0.76 \text{ N/kg}) = 53.2 \text{ N}$
   A person on Earth weighs (70 kg)(9.8 N/kg) = 686 N.
   A person on Pluto weighs 7.76% of his/her weight on Earth.

Chapter 9 Review Answer Key

Vocabulary review

Set One	Set Two
1. b	1. a
2. f	2. d
3. a	3. f
4. d	4. e
5. c	5. b

Concept review

1. Torque and force are similar in that they can both create acceleration and change the motion of an object. The differences between torque and force are that torque creates angular acceleration while force creates linear acceleration, and although a force can act alone, torque requires both the force and the length of the lever arm to change the motion of an object.

2. Translation is motion in which the entire object moves. If the center of mass is in motion, then the object is in translational motion. Rotation is motion in which an object spins. If various parts of an object are in motion but the center of mass remains fixed, the object is rotating.

3. Since a long-handled wrench has a long lever arm, it requires less force to achieve the same torque.

4. The torque is at its maximum when one foot is in front of the other because the lever arms are perpendicular to the forces provided by your feet. The torque is zero when both of your feet are in a vertical line, because the lever arms are parallel to the forces.

612

5. Suppose the lever arm of the shovel is L meters long:
For a force at an angle,

$$\tau_1 = r_1 \times F_1 \cos\theta = L \times 60\cos 45° = 42.4L \text{ N}$$

$$\tau_2 = r_2 \times F_2 = 50L \text{ N}$$

The torque created by F_2 is greater.

6. Wally has the greater weight. The seesaw is in rotational equilibrium, so the magnitude of the torque exerted by Holly is the same as that exerted by Wally. Since the lever arm on Wally's side is shorter, his weight must be greater for $\tau = rF$.

7. An object is in rotational equilibrium if the net torque on an object is zero.

8. The center of mass is the point that an object will rotate around. The center of gravity is the point the object will "balance" on. They are at the same location when the acceleration due to gravity is the same at every point on an object.

9. Point C is correct for the pyramid because it has more mass at the bottom than at the top. Point B is correct for the horseshoe because it has an opening at the bottom.

10. The pole increases the person's rotational inertia. This makes it more difficult for the person to fall if he or she gets off balance.

11. When you stop the egg, the inside keeps spinning. When you release the egg, the inside is still spinning, so the entire egg starts to turn. This will not happen if the egg is hard-boiled because the whole egg will stop when you stop the shell.

12. Suspend the object from one point. Hang a plumb line from that point. Trace the path of the string along the object. Suspend the object and plumb line from another point, and trace the string again. The two lines intersect at one point, and that point is the center of gravity.

13. The first and the third ones (tall box and tall pyramid) will topple. If you draw a straight line from the center of gravity of the object to the center of Earth, and the line passes outside the base of the object, the object will topple because their centers of gravity are not over their bases.

14. An object's mass and how the mass is distributed determine its rotational inertia.

15. The bowling ball would be easier to spin. The barbell has most of its mass at the ends of the bar, further away from the axis of rotation. The bowling ball has more of its mass near the axis of rotation, so the mass has to move a smaller distance when the object spins.

16. Torque equals rotational inertia times angular acceleration.

Problems

1. $\tau = r \times F = (0.3 \text{ m})(250 \text{ N}) = 75 \text{ N-m}$

2. $r = \tau/F = (60 \text{ N-m})/(15 \text{ N}) = 4 \text{ m}$
A 15-newton force can create the same torque by acting on a 4-meter level arm.
To balance, the seesaw must be in rotational equilibrium:

$$\tau_1 + \tau_2 = 0$$
$$\tau_1 = m_1 g r_1 = (30 \text{ kg})(9.8 \text{ m/s}^2)(2 \text{ m}) = 588 \text{ N-m}$$
$$\tau_2 = m_2 g r_2 = (45 \text{ kg})(9.8 \text{ m/s}^2)(-r) = 441 \text{ N-m}(-r)$$
$$\tau_1 + \tau_2 = 0 = 588 \text{ N-m} + 441 \text{ N-m}(-r)$$
$$r = 1.33 \text{ m}$$

Helena should sit 1.33 m from the center of the seesaw.

3. To balance, the rod must be in rotational equilibrium
$$\tau_1 + \tau_2 + \tau_3 = 0$$
$$\tau_1 = m_1 g r_1 = (2 \text{ kg})(9.8 \text{ m/s}^2)(4 \text{ m}) = 78.4 \text{ N-m}$$
$$\tau_2 = m_2 g r_2 = (4 \text{ kg})(9.8 \text{ m/s}^2)(2 \text{ m}) = 78.4 \text{ N-m}$$
$$\tau_3 = m_3 g r_3 = m_3(9.8 \text{ m/s}^2)(-3 \text{ m}) = -29.4 m_3 \text{ N-m}$$
$$\tau_1 + \tau_2 + \tau_3 = 0 = 78.4 \text{ N-m} + 78.4 \text{ N-m} + -29.4 m_3 \text{ N-m}$$
$$m_3 = 5.33 \text{ kg}$$

4. Answers are:
a. $I = \frac{2}{5}(mR^2) = \frac{2}{5}(2 \text{ kg})(0.10 \text{ m})^2 = 0.008 \text{ kg-m}^2$
b. $I = mR^2 = (1 \text{ kg})(0.15 \text{ m})^2 = 0.0225 \text{ kg-m}^2$
c. $I = \frac{1}{12}ml^2 = \frac{1}{12}(0.3 \text{ kg})(1.0 \text{ m})^2 = 0.025 \text{ kg-m}^2$
d. $I = mR^2 = (4 \text{ kg})(0.25 \text{ m})^2 = 0.25 \text{ kg-m}^2$

5. $\tau = I\alpha = (2.5 \text{ kg-m}^2)(5 \text{ rad/s}^2) = 12.5 \text{ N-m}$

6. $I = \dfrac{\tau}{\alpha} = \dfrac{3,000 \text{ N-m}}{10 \text{ rad/s}^2} = 300 \text{ kg-m}^2$

7. $\alpha = \dfrac{\tau}{I} = \dfrac{15,000 \text{ N-m}}{60,000 \text{ kg-m}^2} = 0.40 \text{ rad/s}^2$

613

Chapter 10 Review Answer Key

Vocabulary review

Set One	Set Two	Set Three	Set Four
1. d	1. f	1. f	1. d
2. c	2. d	2. d	2. b
3. f	3. e	3. e	3. f
4. a	4. a	4. a	4. c
5. b	5. b	5. c	5. a

Concept review

1. Answers are:
   a. Measure the length of input arm and length of output arm and then divide; $MA = L_i/L_o$
   b. Measure the input force needed to lift the load and the output force, which is the weight of the load and then divide; alternatively, simply count supporting ropes; $MA = F_o/F_i$
   c. Measure the radius of the wheel and radius of the axle and then divide; $MA = R_{wheel}/R_{axle}$
   d. Measure the ramp length and ramp height and divide; $MA = \text{length}_{ramp}/\text{height}_{ramp}$

2. Mechanical advantage does not have a unit, because it is a ratio of output force to input force and the units cancel.

3. The major difference among the three classes of levers is the location of the fulcrum. In a first class lever, the fulcrum is located between the input force and the output force. In a second class lever, the output force is located between the fulcrum and the input force. In a third class lever, the input force is located between the fulcrum and the output force.

4. In a rope and pulley system, force is multiplied by pulling a long length of rope through the pulleys to lift the weight only a small distance; you can apply a smaller input force to obtain a larger output force by trading a larger motion for a smaller motion.

5. Work is defined as force multiplied by the distance over which the force acts. Since the wall does not move when a force of 1,000 N is applied to a brick wall, the distance is zero and so is the work.

6. The joule is used to measure both work and energy because work is the action of changing things and energy is the ability to change things; work is a form of energy—energy is transformed through the action of work.

7. A perpetual motion machine can never be invented because friction is present in all machines. Since energy is conserved, the output energy is always less than the input energy by an amount equal to the energy converted to other forms of energy through friction.

8. Nuclear energy of the sun is converted to radiant energy, which is converted in the process of photosynthesis into chemical energy in the corn; chemical energy from the cereal is converted to mechanical and thermal energy as Stacy pedals the bike; mechanical energy is converted to electrical energy in the generator; electrical energy is converted to light and thermal energy as the light turns on and flashes.

9. The kinetic energy formula tells us that the kinetic energy of the car is proportional to the square of its speed. As the result, the car has four times as much kinetic energy when it goes twice as fast, so it requires four times as much stopping distance.

10. Harold has the highest gravitational potential energy when he reaches his maximum height above the trampoline. He has the highest kinetic energy as he just touches the trampoline on the way down, and again when he just leaves the trampoline on the way up, because these are the points in the motion when his speed is the greatest and all his potential energy has been converted to kinetic energy. As he sinks down into the trampoline, the springs in the trampoline store potential energy which is then converted to kinetic energy as he leaves the trampoline on the way up.

11. If there is an angle between the force and the distance, the work equals force multiplied by the distance and the cosine of the angle. For example, when you are pulling a wheeled suitcase, you are applying a force at an angle to the motion of the suitcases. Only your horizontal force component does work while the vertical force component doesn't. Thus the work done by you on the baggage equals the horizontal force component times the distance.

614

Problems

1. Sample answer:

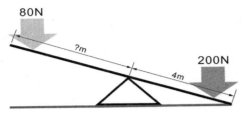

$F_iL_i = F_oL_o$
$(80 \text{ N})L_i = (200 \text{ N})(4 \text{ m})$
$L_i = 10 \text{ m}$

2. Answers are:
   a. $F_t = 400 \text{ N}/4 \text{ ropes} = 100 \text{ N}/ \text{ rope}$
   b. $L_i = 3 \text{ m} \times 4 \text{ ropes} = 12 \text{ m}$
   c. $MA = 4 =$ the number of ropes

3. Sample answer:

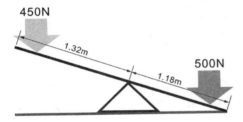

$F_i = 450 \text{ N}$
$F_o = 1000 \text{ N}/2 = 500 \text{ N}$
$L_i = 2.5 \text{ m} - L_o$
For a first class lever, $F_iL_i = F_oL_o$
$(450 \text{ N})(2.5 \text{ m} - L_o) = (500 \text{ N})L_o$
$L_o = 1.18 \text{ m}$
The fulcrum should be placed 1.18 m from the edge of the refrigerator.

4. $W = F_wh = (50 \text{ N})(2 \text{ m/flight} \times 3 \text{ flights}) = 300 \text{ J}$

5. $W = F_wh = (100,000 \text{ N})(1.5 \text{ m}) = 150,000 \text{ J}$
   Students should understand that the distance covered in work against gravity is equal to the height differential, which is 1.5 m.

6. Answers are:
   a. First, convert feet to meters; 50 feet $\times$ 0.304 m/1 foot = 15.2 m
      $E_p = mgh = (136 \text{ kg})(9.8 \text{ N/kg})(15.2 \text{ m}) = 20,300 \text{ J}$
   b. By conservation of energy, $E_k = E_p$:

$$\frac{1}{2}mv^2 = mgh$$

$$v = \sqrt{2gh} = \sqrt{(2(15.2 \text{ m})(9.8 \text{m/s}^2))} = 17.3 \text{ m/s}$$

   17.3 m/s $\times$ (0.4470 m/s)/mph = 38.7 mph

Chapter 11 Review Answer Key

Vocabulary review

Set One	Set Two	Set Three	Set Four
1. b	1. b	1. f	1. e
2. e	2. f	2. c	2. f
3. c	3. a	3. a	3. a
4. a	4. e	4. e	4. c
5. d	5. c	5. d	5. f

Concept review

1. An ideal machine has an efficiency of 100%, and a real machine has an efficiency of less than 100%.

2. Answers are:
   a. It is a product with a high energy efficiency. i.e. It has a large ratio of output to input energy.
   b. An energy efficient product takes less input energy to do the same amount of output work. In addition, it produces less pollution because it uses less fuel (gas, oil, coal, etc.) to do the same amount of work.

3. A plant's leaves only absorb one third of the energy that reaches them from the sun. Much of the energy produced during photosynthesis is used for growth and to transport water in the plant. The small remaining amount of energy is used to create food.

4. The remaining 15% of energy is not lost. It is converted into heat, sound, and other forms of energy.

615

5. The efficiency of a motorcycle is lower than the efficiency of a bicycle. In a motorcycle, chemical energy from the gasoline is converted into mechanical energy and this process has a low energy efficiency. In a bicycle, mechanical energy from the motion of the rider's feet is converted into the mechanical energy of the bike; this process has higher energy efficiency.

6. The efficiency of animals is low because they must use most of their energy to generate body heat. Plants use most of their energy for growth and to move water to their leaves.

7. Power is the rate of energy flow. It is determined by the amount of energy and also the duration of time.

8. One interpretation is that power is the rate at which work is done; the other interpretation is that power is the rate of energy flow from one place to another. Power can be calculated by dividing energy by time or by multiplying force by velocity.

9. People have used the horsepower unit for many years and are resistant to changing the way engine power is measured. Manufacturers would have to convert their measurements from horsepower to watts and this costs money.

10. Both Erik and Patsy do the same amount of work, because they both lift 50-pound barbell 10 times. But Erik delivers the most power because he lifts the barbell in a shorter time.

11. The heavier mountain lion does the most work, but they both deliver the same amount of power. This is because the smaller lion runs twice as fast as the heavier one.

12. Air conditioners and electric heaters have high power ratings. They use large amounts of electrical energy to cool or warm rooms. Fluorescent light bulbs have relatively low power ratings. They only have to convert a small amount of electrical energy into light.

13. His power is less on the moon because the gravity on the moon is less than on Earth. The work he does depends on the force of gravity

14. Answers are:
    a. Secondary carnivores.
    b. Since it takes more corn (producer) to make beefsteak (herbivore), it is reasonable for the beefsteak to cost more.

15. Answers are:
    a. There is no energy storage device on the car. Solar panels do not store energy, they only convert it.
    b. The solar panel converts radiant energy from the sun into electrical energy. The motor converts the electrical energy into mechanical energy.

c. Power is transmitted from the solar panel to the motor through the wires. The motor transmits car motion through the motor shaft, gears, and wheels.

d. The output is the mechanical energy of the car that results in its motion.

Problems

1. $\varepsilon = \dfrac{E_o}{E_i} = \dfrac{20 \text{ J}}{200 \text{ J}} = 0.10 = 10\%$

2. Answers are:

   a. $E_p = mgh = (75 \text{ kg})(9.8 \text{ N/kg})(3.0 \text{ m}) = 2205 \text{ J}$

   $P = \dfrac{E}{t} = \dfrac{2205 \text{ J}}{3 \text{ s}} = 735 \text{ W}$

   b. $P = \dfrac{735 \text{ W}}{746 \text{ W/hp}} = 0.99 \text{ hp}$

   c. $W = mgh = (75 \text{ kg})(9.8 \text{ N/kg})(3.0 \text{ m}) = 2205 \text{ J}$

   d. $E_o = (10 \text{ food cal})(4187 \text{ J/food cal}) = 41870 \text{ J}$

   $E_i = 2205 \text{ J}$

   $\varepsilon = \dfrac{E_o}{E_i} = \dfrac{41870 \text{ J}}{2205 \text{ J}} = 0.053 = 5.3\%$

3. $P = E/t$
   Matt's car has 9.375 times the power of Robert's car, so it will take $1 \div (9.375)$ the time to reach the same speed.
   $16 \div 9.375 = 1.71 \text{ sec}$

4. Answers are:
   a. $2 \text{ hp} \times 746 \text{ W/hp} \times 24 \text{ hr} \times 3{,}600 \text{ sec/hr} = 1.29 \times 10^8 \text{ J}$
   b. a 1.0 horsepower engine will need to spend 48 hours to do the same amount of work.

5. Answers are:
   a. $800 \text{ J} \times 85\% = 680 \text{ J}$ available to raise the car

   b. $W = F_w h$

   $h = \dfrac{W}{F_w} = \dfrac{800 \text{ J}}{13600 \text{ N}} = 0.0588 \text{ m} = 5.88 \text{ cm}$

6. Answers are:
   a. $P = Fv = (200 \text{ N})(2 \text{ m/sec}) = 400 \text{ W}$
   b. $P = Fv = (200 \text{ N})(1 \text{ m/sec}) = 200$, or half of the power in part a

7. Answers are:
  a. $m = 20 \text{ people} \times 70 \text{ kg/person} = 1400 \text{ kg}$
     $E = mgh = (1400 \text{ kg})(9.8 \text{m/s}^2)(5 \text{ m}) = 68600 \text{ J}$

  b. $P = \dfrac{E}{t} = \dfrac{68600 \text{ J}}{5 \text{ s}} = 13720 \text{ W}$

  c. $P = \dfrac{3000 \text{ food cal} \times 4187 \text{ J/food cal}}{24 \text{ hr} \times 3600 \text{ s/hr}} = 145 \text{ W}$

8. Answers are:

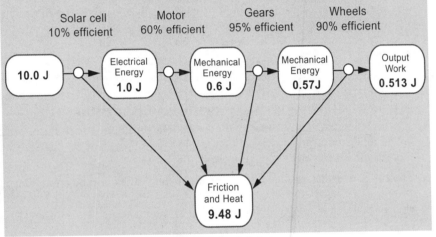

Energy Flow Diagram for Model Solar Car

  a. electrical energy = 10% × 10.0 J = 1.0 J
  b. mechanical energy = 60% × 1.0 J = 0.60 J
  c. mechanical energy = 95% × 0.60 J = 0.57 J
  d. output work = 90% × 0.57 J = 0.513 J
  e. friction and heat = 10.0 J − 0.513 J = 9.487 J

Chapter 12 Review Answer Key

Vocabulary review

Set One	Set Two
1. c	1. b
2. b	2. c
3. a	3. a
4. e	4. d
	5. e

Concept review

1. Kinetic energy and momentum both depend upon mass and velocity. They differ in that kinetic energy is a scalar while momentum is a vector and therefore depends on direction.

2. Momentum is considered a vector quantity because it depends upon direction. For example, two balls with the same mass and speed have opposite momentum if they are moving in opposite directions.

3. Answers are:
  a. The total momentum of a system is conserved in the absence of outside forces.
  b. All objects with mass and velocity have momentum.
  c. Correct
  d. Momentum is measured in kg-m/s
  e. An object moving at a constant speed has momentum.
  f. The momentum of two objects with equal mass will be equal if their velocity is equal.
  g. If two objects of different mass move at the same speed, they will have different momentum.
  h. Correct
  i. The momentum of an accelerating object changes proportionally to the acceleration.
  j. The momentum of a faster object will always be greater than the momentum of a slower object. This occurs if the product of the faster object's mass and velocity is greater than the product of the slower object's mass and velocity.
  k. Correct for object with mass. Light also carries momentum even through it is pure energy with no mass. The momentum of light depends on the energy of the light.

4. Answers are:
    a. The bulldozer has the greater mass.
    b. The hockey player has the greater velocity; the bulldozer's velocity is zero since it is at rest.
    c. The hockey player has greater momentum because he has velocity. The bulldozer's velocity is zero and therefore its momentum is zero.

5. The magnitude of her momentum doubles when her speed doubles, because the scalar component of momentum is directly proportional to speed.

6. The law of conservation of momentum is a consequence of Newton's third law of motion, the law of action and reaction.

7. The system of Howard and the rowboat conserves momentum. As Howard increases his momentum toward the dock by exerting a force to push off, the rowboat increases its momentum away from the dock. Not only does Howard probably fall into the water, but the boat drifts away.

8. The plane moves forward because the exhaust jet carries away momentum in the negative direction (assuming the plane is moving in the positive direction). The force exerted on the plane in the forward direction is equal to the rate at which the exhaust jet carries away momentum in the backward direction. The total momentum of the jet going forward is built up over time from the total of all the momentum of the exhaust jet going backward. Since there is friction however, the total accumulated momentum of the exhaust jet is always greater than the forward momentum of the plane. In fact, when flying at constant speed the momentum of the exhaust jet creates just enough force to overcome air friction, and the momentum of the plane remains constant.

    The exhaust jet typically (although not always) has a much greater speed than the plane going forward. The plane has a much greater mass than the exhaust jet. When applying momentum conservation, the greater mass of the plane compared to the exhaust jet means that the plane changes its speed less than the exhaust jet.

9. Answers are:
    a. Due to conservation of momentum, the total momentum of the system is the same before and after the collision.
    b. Since a minimal amount of kinetic energy is lost in the collision, as illustrated by the balls not changing shape or sticking together, the collision is more elastic.
    c. The cue ball has kinetic energy before the collision when it is moving. The cue ball does not have kinetic energy after the collision when it stops.

    d. Assuming the collision is completely elastic, the velocity of the numbered ball after the collision is proportional to the ratio of the mass of the cue ball to the mass of the numbered ball.
    e. If the cue ball hit the numbered ball at an angle, rather than head-on, both the cue ball and the numbered ball would continue moving at angles to each other after the collision. Momentum will be conserved.

10. Impulse is the product of a force and the time the force acts and represents a change in momentum. Impact is a collision at a specific moment.

11. Yes, the units used to represent impulse and momentum are equivalent. Momentum is measured in kg-m/s, and impulse is measured in N-s.
    N-s = $(kg$-$m/s^2) \times sec = kg$-m/s

12. Yes, the net impulse is the product of the force and the time the force acts. Force is the rate of change of momentum.
    $F = m\Delta v \div \Delta t$ where $m \times \Delta v = \Delta p$, so $F = \Delta p \div \Delta t$
    $\Delta p = F \times \Delta t$

13. The force of the impact is reduced by the padding, dissipating the momentum over a longer time. The padding also increases the area on which the force acts, lowering the force per unit area on an area of the body.

14. The secret to catching a water balloon without breaking it is to move your hands along with the water balloon to slow its impact and spread out the momentum change over a longer period of time.

15. The car body is designed to absorb the momentum of a crash by crumpling as slowly as possible to reduce the force of the impact by spreading out the change in momentum over a longer period of time.

16. Linear momentum is due to the momentum of an object's linear motion. Angular momentum is due to the momentum of an object's rotational motion. An object can have both linear and angular momentum at the same time if it is spinning and moving linearly at the same time. An example is Earth's motion as it spins about its axis while it moves in orbit around the sun.

17. The solid cylinder will roll faster. The solid cylinder's moment of inertia (I) is lower than the hollow cylinder since more of its mass is concentrated near its center of rotation.

18. The acceleration down the ramp is independent of the mass, depending only on the angle of the ramp and the geometry of the cylinder. The linear and angular acceleration of the rolling cylinders are independent of mass as follows, where ΔP is the linear momentum, ΔL is the angular momentum and θ is the angle of the ramp:

$$F = \frac{\Delta P + \Delta L}{\Delta t} = \frac{m\Delta v + \frac{1}{2}mR^2\Delta\omega}{\Delta t}$$

$$F = ma = mg\sin\theta = \frac{m\Delta v + \frac{1}{2}mR^2\Delta\omega}{\Delta t}$$

$$a = g\sin\theta = \frac{\Delta v + \frac{1}{2}R^2\Delta\omega}{\Delta t}$$

Problems

1. First, find the mass of 1 ton:
   1-ton = 2,000 lbs = (2,000 lb)(4.448 N/lb) = 8896 N
   8896 N ÷ 9.8 m/s^2 = 908 kg
   $p_{elephant} = mv = (908 \text{ kg})(0.5 \text{ m/s}) = 454 \text{ kg-m/s}$
   For the momentum of the baseball to be less than the elephant,
   $p_{ball} < 454 \text{ kg-m/s}$; $v_{ball} > p \div m$
   $v_{ball} > (454 \text{ kg-m/s}) \div (0.15 \text{ kg}) = 3,026 \text{ m/s}$
   $v_{ball} > (3,026 \text{ m/s})(2.237 \text{ mi/hr per m/s})$
   $v_{ball} > 6,771 \text{ mi/hr}$
   Even a major league pitcher can't pitch a ball that fast.

2. They have the same momentum:
   $p_{boat} = mv = (1,200 \text{ kg})(50 \text{ m/s}) = 60,000 \text{ kg-m/s}$
   $p_{truck} = mv = (6,000 \text{ kg})(10 \text{ m/s}) = 60,000 \text{ kg-m/s}$

3. Answers are:
   a. $m = 0.040$ kg; $v = (50 \text{ mi/hr}) \times (0.447 \text{ m/s per mi/hr}) = 22.35 \text{ m/s}$
      $p = mv = (0.40 \text{ kg})(22.35 \text{ m/s}) = 0.894 \text{ kg-m/s}$
   b. $v = p/m = (0.894 \text{ kg-m/s})/(0.15 \text{ kg}) = 5.96 \text{ m/s}$
      (5.96 m/s)(2.237 mi/hr per m/s) = 13.3 mi/hr

4. Answers are:
   a. The collision is inelastic since the cars stick to each other.
   b. Momentum of the system is conserved. The total momentum before the collision equals the total collision after the collision.

c. $m_1 = 1200$ kg; $m_2 = 1000$ kg; $v_1 = 12$ m/s; $v_2 = -16$ m/s
   Momentum, before and after the collision, is conserved, so
   $p_1 = p_2$
   $m_1v_1 + m_2v_2 = (m_1 + m_2)v_3$
   $v_3 = (m_1v_1 + m_2v_2) \div (m_1 + m_2)$
   $m_1v_1 = 1200 \text{ kg} \times 12 \text{ m/s} = 14{,}400 \text{ kg-m/s}$
   $m_2v_2 = 1000 \text{ kg} \times (-16 \text{ m/s}) = -16{,}000 \text{ kg-m/s}$
   $v_3 = 14{,}400 \text{ kg-m/s} - 16{,}000 \text{ kg-m/s} \div (1200 \text{ kg} + 1000 \text{ kg})$
   $v_3 = -0.72$ m/s (in the direction of the second car)

5. $m_1 = 75$ kg; $m_2 = 70$ kg; $v_1 = 3$ m/s; $v_2 = -2$ m/s, East is positive and West is negative
   $m_1v_1 + m_2v_2 = (m_1 + m_2)v_3$
   $v_3 = (m_1v_1 + m_2v_2) \div (m_1 + m_2)$
   $m_1v_1 = 75 \text{ kg} \times 3 \text{ m/s} = 225 \text{ kg-m/s}$
   $m_2v_2 = 70 \text{ kg} \times (-2 \text{ m/s}) = -140 \text{ kg-m/s}$
   $v_3 = (225 \text{ kg-m/s} - 140 \text{ kg-m/s}) \div (75 \text{ kg} + 70 \text{ kg})$
   $v_3 = 0.59$ m/s moving East

6. $m_1 = 45$ kg; $m_2 = 50$ kg; $v_1 = 5$ m/s; $v_2 = -7$ m/s; $v_3 = -8.5$ m/s
   $m_1v_1 + m_2v_2 = m_1v_3 + m_2v_4$
   $v_4 = (m_1v_1 + m_2v_2 - m_1v_3) \div m_2$
   $m_1v_1 = 45 \text{ kg} \times 35 \text{ m/s} = 1575 \text{ kg-m/s}$
   $m_2v_2 = 50 \text{ kg} \times (-7 \text{ m/s}) = -350 \text{ kg-m/s}$
   $m_1v_3 = 45 \text{ kg} \times (-8.5 \text{ m/s}) = -382.5 \text{ kg-m/s}$
   $v_4 = \{1575 + -350 - (-382.5)\} \div 50$
   $v_4 = 32.15$ m/s

7. Answers are:
   a. Impulse $= F\Delta t = (20 \text{ N})(2.0 \text{ sec}) = 40 \text{ N-s}$
   b. Change in momentum $= \Delta p = m \Delta v = F\Delta t = 40 \text{ kg-m/s}$

8. Answers are:
   a. $F = \Delta p \div \Delta t = m\Delta v \div \Delta t$
      $F = (65 \text{ kg})(30 \text{ m/s} - 0 \text{ m/s}) \div (0.400 \text{ sec}) = 4.88 \times 10^3 \text{ N}$
   b. $F = \Delta p \div \Delta t = m\Delta v \div \Delta t$
      $F = (65 \text{ kg})(30 \text{ m/s} - 0 \text{ m/s}) \div (0.001 \text{ sec}) = 1.95 \times 10^6 \text{ N}$

9. Answers are:
   a. Moment of inertia of a sphere $= I = \frac{2}{5}(mR^2)$
      $I = \frac{2}{5}(0.5 \text{ kg})(0.1 \text{ m})^2 = 0.002 \text{ kg-m}^2$
   b. Angular momentum $= L = I\omega = Iv/R$
      $L = (0.002 \text{ kg-m}^2)(3.0 \text{ m/s}) \div (0.1 \text{ m}) = 0.06 \text{ kg-m}^2/\text{s}$
   c. Linear momentum $= p = mv = (0.5 \text{ kg})(3.0 \text{ m/s}) = 1.5 \text{ kg-m/s}$

10. Answers are:
   a. Angular momentum $= L = I\omega = (1.5 \text{ kg-m}^2)(10 \text{ rad/s})$
      $L = 15 \text{ kg-m}^2/\text{s}$
   b. Due to conservation of angular momentum, $L_1 = L_2$
      $L_1 = I_2\omega$
      $\omega = L_1 \div I_2 = (15 \text{ kg-m}^2/\text{s}) \div (3 \text{ kg-m}^2) = 5 \text{ rad/s}$

Chapter 13 Review Answer Key

Vocabulary review

Set One

1. f
2. d
3. g
4. a
5. c
6. e

Set Two

1. d
2. c
3. f
4. b
5. g
6. e

Concept review

1. Answers are:
   a. linear
   b. harmonic
   c. harmonic
   d. linear
   e. harmonic

2. Graphs of linear motion do not represent cycles. Harmonic motion graphs show oscillation and cycles

3. The two balls are at the same height and moving in the same direction at the same instant.

4. If the amplitude of harmonic motion increases dramatically when small periodic forces are applied at the natural frequency of a body, the behavior is known as resonance. You apply a small periodic force to the swing at the instant after it reaches its maximum amplitude on each swing, causing the swing to reach increasingly larger amplitudes. This is resonance.

5. Answers are:
   a. the time required for the swing to travel all the way over and back
   b. the number of times that the swing goes over and back in one unit of time (generally one second; in this case, one minute is more appropriate).
   c. a complete swing all the way over and back

   d. the maximum distance or angle from a line perpendicular to the ground

6. Sample answer:

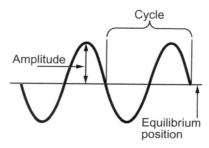

7. The radio station applies a signal with this frequency to an antenna whose natural frequency is 106.7×10^6 Hz.

8. Any change that affects the restoring force or the mass of the string causes a change in the natural frequency. Stretching the string increases the restoring force, increasing the frequency. Using a thicker (more massive) string results in a lower frequency.

9. Examples of oscillators include musical instruments as well as the speakers through which the music is played. Oscillators are used to keep time, from the simple pendulum to cesium atom oscillators. Cellphones and radio stations use oscillators.

10. Damping is a gradual loss of amplitude of an oscillator due to frictional forces. A restoring force is one that acts in the direction of the equilibrium position.

11. Oscillation is caused by a disturbance of the system followed by the interaction of inertia and a restoring force.

12. When disturbed, a body in stable equilibrium moves back toward the equilibrium position. Harmonic motion is often established. A body in unstable equilibrium moves away from the equilibrium position after any disturbance and harmonic motion generally does not result. *Stable:* pendulum at rest, chairlift hanging from its cable *Unstable:* girl on stilts, snowboarder at the top of a hill

13. Since the frequency of vibration for an oscillator is inversely proportional to mass, the period of vibration is directly proportional. By attaching known masses to an oscillator and measuring and recording the period of oscillation, the mass of an unknown may be determined by measuring its period by comparison to a graph of the data for known masses. (The apparatus is sometimes called an inertial balance).

14. The acceleration of mass is at a maximum when the amplitude is at its maximum and is directed toward the equilibrium position. At the equilibrium position, acceleration is zero. Acceleration increases while velocity decreases.

15. Potential energy is continually converted to kinetic energy and back again as a pendulum swings through its cycle. At maximum angular amplitude, all energy is transformed to PE since the bob has no motion and is at a maximum height above equilibrium. At the equilibrium position, the height is zero, but velocity is at a maximum, so all energy is transformed to KE. The KE diminishes to zero as the bob moves to maximum amplitude…and so on.

16. The goblet has a natural frequency. It is matched by the vibration of your finger as it "sticks and releases" (vibrates) on the rim of the goblet. This small periodic force causes the goblet to vibrate with increasing amplitude until the vibrations are audible. The phenomena is called resonance.

17. Steady state; as energy is added to the system, the resonant frequency changes slightly reducing the efficiency and limiting the amplitude. Friction in the system also limits the amplitude. When the friction force and the inefficiency match the energy input, the steady state is reached and the amplitude is constant.

Problems

1. Answers are:
   a. A and GB and XC and ID and J
   b. A and DB and EC and FD and G
      (note that other answers for b. are possible)

2. Answers are:
   a. A and C
   b. A and B AND B and C

3. Frequency = 1/Period
   Period = 1/70 hz, or 0.014 seconds

4. Answers are:
   a. Revolution of the Earth around the sun is 365.25 days, or 1 year.
   b. The rotation of the Earth on its axis is 24 hours, or 1 day.
   c. The revolution of the moon around the Earth is 27.5 days, or about 1 month.

5. High to Low KE: 4, 3, 5,2, 1, 6, 7

6. High to Low PE: 7, 6, 1, 2, 5, 3, 4

7. 1-C, G
   2-D, H
   3-A, E
   4-B, F

8. Answers are:
   a. 15 centimeters
   b. 2 seconds
   c. 0.5 hertz
   d. 8

9. $E_T = PE + KE$
   $PE = mgh$
   $KE = \frac{1}{2}mv^2$
   PE is completely converted to KE at the lowest point of the cycle.

   $$mgh = \frac{1}{2}mv^2$$

   $$v^2 = 2gh$$

   $$v = \sqrt{2(9.8\,\text{m/sec}^2)(0.25\ \text{m})}$$

10. $v^2 = 2gh$
    $h = v^2/2g$
    $h = (7.5 \text{ m/s})^2 \div 2(9.8 \text{ m/s}^2) = 2.87$ m
    Distance above the ground is 2.87 m + 0.42 m = 3.29 m

11. Frequency = 1/period.
    Period = 1/frequency = 1/(0.286 Hz) = 3.50 seconds. From the graph, the mass is about 8.75 kg.

12. Since $f_n \approx F/m$,
    then $f_{n1}(m_1) = f_{n2}(m_2)$
    23 hz(1.4 kg) = f_{n2}(6.4 kg)
    $f_{n2} = 5.0$ hz.

13. Period = 1/frequency = $1/1.67 \times 10^{-3}$ seconds = 600 hz.

621

Chapter 14 Review Answer Key

Vocabulary review

Set One	Set Two
1. d	1. c
2. a	2. e
3. g	3. b
4. e	4. a
5. b	5. g
6. f	6. f

Concept review

1. The velocity of a wave equals the product of the frequency multiplied by the wavelength.

2. A pulse is generally a single disturbance or oscillation of a medium away from the equilibrium position. A wave is the periodic oscillation of a medium away from the equilibrium at a certain frequency measured in hertz.

3. Amplitude is the maximum distance a medium is moved from its equilibrium position. A wavelength is the distance energy travels in one cycle.

4. The period of a wave is the reciprocal of the frequency ($f = 1/T$).

5. velocity = wavelength /period, or $v = \lambda/T$

6. Sample answer:

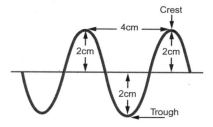

7. Answers are:
    a. reflection – waves bounce off the boundary and go in a new direction
    b. refraction – waves enter the medium and may change direction
    c. diffraction – waves pass around the edges or through openings in a boundary
    d. absorption – energy of the wave is absorbed by the medium after crossing the boundary

8. Answers are:
    a. absorption
    b. reflection (internal reflection)
    c. refraction
    d. diffraction

9. For a standing wave to form, a wave must be reflected and confined between two boundaries. If the resonant frequency of the vibrating object is matched, the amplitude of the standing wave can be very large.

10. Like a pendulum, when the string is at its greatest amplitude, it has its maximum PE; at its equilibrium position, it has maximum KE.

Problems

1. $v = f\lambda = (4.33 \times 10^{14} \text{ hz}) \times (4.17 \times 10^{-7} \text{ m}) = 1.81 \times 10^{8} \text{m/s}$

2. $v = f\lambda$
    $\lambda = f/v = (256 \text{ hz})/340 \text{ m/s} = 7.5 \times 10^{-1} \text{ m}$

3. $v = f\lambda = (512 \text{ hz}) \times (2.99 \text{ m}) = 1{,}531 \text{ m/s}$
    $s = v\Delta t \ (\Delta t = 0.25 \text{ s}/2) = (1{,}531 \text{ m/s})(0.125 \text{ s}) = 191 \text{ m}$

4. $T = 1/f = 1/225 \text{ hz} = 4.44 \times 10^{-3} \text{ s}$

5. Answers are:
    a. longitudinal
    b. Three answers are correct responses: A-C, C-E, and B-D.
    c. horizontally

6. Answers are:
    a. diffraction
    b. refraction
    c. reflection
    d. reflection

7. Answers are:
    a. A
    b. D

8. Answers are:
    a. A and C
    b. B
    c. C and D

9. Answers are:
    a. The composite wave should have an amplitude of 0.3 m and a wavelength of 1.0 m and be in phase with A and B.

b.   0.3 m

c.   1.0m

10. The cork is moving toward point B.

11. Answers are:

a. $T = 1/f = 0.050$ s

b. $\lambda = 4.88$ cm/6.0 waves $= 0.81$cm

c. $v = \lambda/T = 0.81$ cm/0.05 s $= 16$cm/s

Chapter 15 Review Answer Key

Vocabulary review

Set One	Set Two	Set Three
1. c	1. e	1. c
2. e	2. d	2. a
3. a	3. b	3. d
4. d	4. f	4. e
5. b	5. a	

Concept review

1.   The restoring forces in molecules cause the propagation of sound. The magnitude of the restoring force is directly proportional to the speed of the sound in a medium. Since solids are in general more elastic than liquids which, in turn, are more elastic than gases, sound travels fastest through solids, slowest between gas molecules, and at an intermediate rate in liquids.

2.   Sound is an oscillation of the pressure applied by one molecule on another. That is, a medium is required to transmit sound. In the space station, the sound of the collision would be transmitted through the air; outside there is no air or other media to transmit the sound to the workers.

3.   While the pitch of a note is directly proportional to the frequency, pitch is also affected by an individual's brain and ear. The pitch one hears is determined, in part, by the sounds that precede and follow the sound in question.

4.   According to the text, music is a combination of sound and rhythm that an individual finds pleasant. That which is pleasing to you may not be to your parents, but if it has both rhythm and sound and is pleasing to you, it is considered music.

5.   Beats occur when two notes being played simultaneously are very close to the same frequency. Alternating constructive and destructive interference between superposed waves cause the beats. If you listen to the frequency to which you are to "tune" your instrument and adjust your clarinet so that no beats are heard, the two frequencies are the same.

6.   The sound produced by most sources is a combination of many frequencies. While the fundamental note produced by each source is an "A," each source produces its own combination of harmonics that also differ in rise and fall times from one instrument to the next. Each combination is characteristic of a specific instrument.

7.   The string is attached to the body of an acoustic guitar. The vibrating string causes the body to vibrate at the same frequency that moves a greater volume of air than the string by itself. Also, the hollow body of the guitar produces louder sound through resonance with the many frequencies produced by the vibrating strings.

8.   As the steel string vibrates, it passes through the magnetic field of the pickup, inducing an oscillating electric current whose frequency is that of the vibrating string. The current is amplified to produce a loud sound.

9.   For each increase of 20 dB on the decibel scale, there is a corresponding ten-fold increase of amplitude in the pressure wave.

10. Answers are:

a.   Sound has a frequency we can hear and a wavelength we can verify by experiment.

b.   The speed of sound can be calculated as the product of frequency and wavelength.

c.   Sound shows evidence of diffraction and interference, characteristic of wave motion.

d.   Resonance can be demonstrated for sound.

11. If the instrument is closed on one end (has a closed boundary), the instrument will produce resonance for a wave that is approximately four times as long as the instrument.

12. Sounds coming from an instrument may be reflected from several surfaces in a concert hall. If the path length difference from the points of reflection to the patron is an odd number of half wavelengths, the reflections arrive out of phase at her location, destructive interference will occur, and the sound may be much quieter at that spot.

623

13. Table 15.1 summarizes pressure changes that accompany sounds of various intensities. A change in pressure of 2×10^{-9} atmospheres can be detected as a 20 dB sound. In fact, a loud sound of 120 dB represents an increase of pressure to only 2×10^{-4} atmospheres. That even loud sounds represent only small pressure changes suggests that the structure of the ear is a delicate mechanism. Continued exposure to loud sounds can damage it.

14. The sun is spinning on its axis. One edge is moving toward the observer while it spins while the other moves away. The Doppler shift causes the observer to see a higher frequency (more violet) light coming from the edge moving toward the observer. Light from the other edge is shifted toward the red as it moves (spins) away.

15. Because the sound from a source usually travels slightly different path lengths to each ear, the signals arrive at different times slightly out of phase. Interpretation of the phase difference by the brain provides a directional sense. Since sound travels 4½ times faster underwater, the arrival of the signals are more nearly simultaneous, and the brain cannot distinguish the phase difference and direction as certainly. In other words, the direction of the source is harder to determine.

16. It will increase slightly. As the temperature increases, the speed of sound increases. Since the instrument maintains a nearly constant length, the wavelength reinforced remains constant. The frequency must increase in proportion to the increased velocity.

17. Two frequencies of sound occurring simultaneously in the same medium cause beats. If the frequencies are nearly the same, the beats are obvious, and the sound produced is generally irritating, or dissonant. If the frequencies are quite different, the beats are not discernible, and the sound is, in general, pleasing or consonant.

Problems

1. The tube must be approximately ¼ of the wavelength of the fundamental. To find the wavelength, divide the speed of sound by frequency. ($\lambda = (340$ m/sec$) \div (264$ hz$) = 1.29$ m; the tube is ¼ of this length, or 0.323 m)

2. It takes 1.2 seconds for the sound to travel to the object and 1.2 seconds back. Distance is velocity $\times$ time, or $d = vt = 344$ m/s $\times 1.2$ s $= 413$ m

3. The wavelength is $4 \times$ pipe length or 4×2.46 m; $\lambda = 9.84$ m; frequency equals the speed of sound divided by the wavelength; $f = 345$ m/s / 9.84 m = 35.1 hz

4. Answers are:
   a. about 3,500 hz
   b. about 110-5,500 hz
   c. about 36-76 dB
   d. about 3,500 hz

5. Answers are:
   a. toward B
   b. at B
   c. It would increase.

6. The signal is reflected as an echo. It travels 2,000 meters in 1.31 seconds. $v = d/t = 2,000$ m/1.31 s $= 1,528$ m/s

7. Since the speed of sound calculated using this data is 384 m/s, it indicates that the temperature of the air is greater than 20°C since the speed of sound increases with an increase in temperature.

8. Pair A

9. Answers are:
   a. beats
   b. 0.20 sec
   c. 5 hz

10. Answers are:
    a. A < speed of sound B > speed of sound
       C has no motion D = speed of sound
    b. The Doppler effect occurs for A and D; a shock wave occurs with B.

11. Answers are:
    a. 264 hz, 528 hz, 792 hz, 1,056 hz, 1,320 hz, 1,848 hz
    b. 792 hz, 264 hz, 528 hz, 1,848 hz, 1,056 hz, 1,320 hz

Chapter 16 Review Answer Key

Vocabulary review

Set One	Set Two	Set Three	Set Four
1. d	1. a	1. e	1. c
2. c	2. e	2. d	2. e
3. e	3. b	3. a	3. d
4. b	4. f	4. b	4. b
	5. d		

Concept review

1. An incandescent bulb generates light and also a great deal of heat. A fluorescent bulb generates light and only a small amount of heat.

2. Light intensity is measured in watts per square meter (W/m^2).

3. You can read with the desk lamp because it is closer to the book than the ceiling light is. Even though the desk light has less power, the intensity of the light on the book is great because it is a small distance away.

4. Television, lasers, and fiber-optic cables use light for communication.

5. We see lightning before we hear thunder because light travels much faster than sound.

6. Reflection is the bouncing of incident light off a surface. Refraction is the bending of light when it moves from one material into another material.

7. White light is the combination of all colors of light.

8. A blacksmith uses color of the fire as a reference to determine the temperature. When the fire appears red, it is at a relatively low temperature; when the fire appears blue, it is at a relatively high temperature.

9. Cone cells in our eyes respond to color. They are not as sensitive as rod cells, so the cones do not work well in a dimly lit room. Therefore, it is difficult to distinguish among different colors.

10. Our eyes can see many colors because all colors of light are combinations of red, green, and blue light. Depending on its color, light can stimulate more than one type of cone. Our brains receive these combined signals and perceive different colors.

11. Answers are:
    a. Magenta
    b. Cyan
    c. Yellow
    d. White

12. Mixing pigments is called color subtraction because pigments absorb some colors and reflect others. When pigments are mixed, they subtract more colors of light.

13. White

14. Answers are:
    a. True
    b. True
    c. True
    d. False

15. A white shirt reflects most of the light and keeps the person cool on a hot sunny day while a black shirt absorbs all of the light and makes the person hot.

16. Chlorophyll in a plant reflects green light, so the plant will not absorb enough energy if placed in green light. But chlorophyll absorbs light of other colors, so it grows faster if placed in white light.

17. A television's three types of pixels give off red, green, and blue light. By turning on the different color pixels in different amounts, the TV mixes the three colors and produces pictures of many colors.

18. One way to make high intensity light is to have high-energy photons; the other is to have a large number of low-energy photons.

19. When the glow-in-the-dark plastic is exposed to light, phosphorus atoms absorb the energy from the photons they receive. Then those atoms slowly release the stored energy and the plastic glows.

Chapter 17 Review Answer Key

Vocabulary review

Set One	Set Two	Set Three	Set Four
1. b	1. d	1. c	1. b
2. f	2. e	2. e	2. c
3. c	3. b	3. d	3. a
4. d	4. f	4. a	4. e
5. a	5. a		5. f

Concept review

1. Angle of reflection equals to the angle of incidence. This law holds true for specular reflection but not refraction.

2. Answers are:
   a. Incident ray
   b. Normal line
   c. Reflected ray
   d. Angle of incidence
   e. Angle of reflection

3. Answers are:
   a. Virtual image
   b. Line 2-3
   c. Line 3-4
   d. 8 cm

4. Diamond has the greatest ability to bend light because it has the greatest index of refraction.

5. Answers are:
    a. C
    b. D
    c. E

6. Fiber optic cables are made of thin glass fibers. When light enters a glass fiber with an angle greater than the critical angle, it repeatedly reflects off the wall due to total internal reflection. The beam of light then travels from one end of the fiber to the other.

7. Green light refracts more because it has a greater index of refraction.

8. positive, negative

9. virtual, real

10. Answers are:
    a. ABG
    b. ACF
    c. ADE

Problems

1. Sample answer:

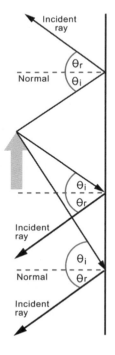

2. The angle of incidence is 30 degrees.

3. You see MOM YM. The word MOM doesn't look backwards because the letters are symmetric.

4. $n_i \sin\theta_i = n_r \sin\theta_r$
    $(1.00) \sin 40 = (1.66) \sin\theta_r$
    $\sin\theta_r = 0.387$
    $\theta_r = \sin^{-1}(0.387) = 22$ degrees
    The angle of refraction is 22 degrees.

5. $n_i \sin\theta_i = n_r \sin\theta_r$
    $(1.00)(0.6427) = n_r (0.4726)$
    $n_r = 1.36$
    The index of refraction for ethyl alcohol is 1.36.

6. $n_i \sin\theta_i = n_r \sin\theta_r$
    $(1.00) \sin\theta_i = (1.46) \sin 30$
    $\sin\theta_i = 0.73$
    $\theta_r = \sin^{-1}(0.73) = 47$ degrees
    The angle of incidence is 47 degrees.

7. $^1/d_o + {}^1/d_i = {}^1/f$
    $^1/d_i = {}^1/f - {}^1/d_o$
    $^1/d_i = {}^1/6 - {}^1/10$
    $^1/d_i = {}^1/15$
    $d_i = 15$ cm
    The image is located 15 cm to the right of the converging lens.

Chapter 18 Review Answer Key

Vocabulary review

Set One	Set Two	Set Three
1. f	1. b	1. e
2. a	2. e	2. b
3. b	3. d	3. a
4. e	4. a	4. f
5. c		5. c

Concept review

1. Magnetic fields, electric fields and gravitational fields are examples of energy fields. Gravitational fields are an example of a potential energy field.

2. An electromagnetic wave consists of oscillating electric and magnetic waves that travel together perpendicular to each other at the speed of light, 90° out of phase, and at the same frequency and wavelength.

3. Some of the spectrum of electromagnetic waves, ranked from highest to lowest energy, are:
gamma rays
x-rays
visible light
microwaves
radio waves

4. The color with the highest frequency is violet, and the color with the lowest frequency is red.

5. True.

6. $c = f\lambda$

$f = \dfrac{c}{\lambda}$

$\lambda = \dfrac{c}{f}$

7. Energy from the microwaves inside a microwave oven is absorbed by food molecules, causing the molecules to vibrate and heat up. Absorption of microwaves is strongest at the surface of the food, but microwaves can penetrate several centimeters into the food.

8. Light slows down due to the absorption and emission of the light in atoms of the glass. In between the glass atoms, light moves at normal speed. As the light exits the glass, it again moves at its normal speed because no more absorption and emission slows it down.

9. The frequency must be the same, regardless of the material, because frequency is related to the number of waves passing through in a second. If the frequency changed at the boundary between materials, waves would start interfering with each other at the boundary as they moved from one material to another, therefore it is the wavelength that changes.

10. Thomas Young demonstrated the wave nature of light with the double-slit experiment. The experiment consists of a beam of light passing through a pair of very thin, parallel slits in a piece of metal. When the light passes through the slits onto a screen behind the piece of metal, a pattern of bright and dark bands appears, instead of the expected two bright stripes. This interference pattern indicates that light has the properties of waves. The alternating bands illustrate the constructive and destructive interference patterns created by the addition of the light waves.

11. Waves that are exactly one wavelength out of phase cause the first order bright spot in the interference pattern from a diffraction grating.

12. A diffraction grating spreads out white light into its component rainbow of colors because each point on the screen is a point of constructive interference for a different wavelength, or color, of light.

13. A wave is polarized when it is limited in its orientation.

14. A polarizer absorbs light energy and re-emits it from the other side of the polarizer in a single orientation. A polarizer completely transmits the portion of the incoming light that is aligned with the polarizer and completely blocks the portion of the light that is perpendicular to the alignment of the polarizer. A percentage of the incoming light that is at an angle to the alignment of the polarizer is transmitted. This percentage depends on the resolution of the angle of transmission into its component waves, with the component that is aligned with the polarizer being transmitted and the component that is perpendicular to the polarizer being blocked.

15. An LCD display is very inefficient due to the first polarizer blocking half the light.

16. Time dilation was proven by synchronizing two precise atomic clocks, one of which was put on a plane and flown around the world, and the other left on the ground. After the flight, the clocks were compared, and the difference in time between them proved the predictions of the theory of special relativity.

17. Twins are born on Earth. They grow up and one becomes an astronaut. The astronaut twin goes on a mission in space, traveling close to the speed of light. Because of the high speed, time on the ship runs slower than time on Earth. When the mission returns to Earth after a few years, the astronaut twin is much younger than the twin left on Earth.

Problems

1. $f = \dfrac{c}{\lambda} = \dfrac{3\times10^{8}\text{ m/s}}{6.5\times10^{-7}\text{ m}} = 4.62\times10^{14}\text{ Hz}$

627

2. $f = \dfrac{c}{\lambda} = \dfrac{3 \times 10^8 \text{ m/s}}{1.5 \text{ m}} = 2 \times 10^8 \text{ Hz}$

3. $f = \dfrac{c}{\lambda}$

$f_1 = \dfrac{3 \times 10^8 \text{ m/s}}{1 \times 10^{-5} \text{ m}} = 3 \times 10^{13} \text{ Hz}$

$f_2 = \dfrac{3 \times 10^8 \text{ m/s}}{1 \times 10^{-8} \text{ m}} = 3 \times 10^{16} \text{ Hz}$

4. $\lambda = \dfrac{v_{lucite}}{f} = \dfrac{2 \times 10^8 \text{ m/s}}{6.4 \times 10^{14} \text{ hz}} = 3.13 \times 10^{-7} \text{ m}$

5. $n = \dfrac{c}{v} = \dfrac{3 \times 10^8}{1.239 \times 10^8} = 2.42$

6. $v = \dfrac{c}{n} = \dfrac{3 \times 10^8 \text{ m/s}}{1.92} = 1.56 \times 10^8 \text{ m/s}$

7. $v = \dfrac{c}{n} = \dfrac{3 \times 10^8 \text{ m/s}}{1.66} = 1.8 \times 10^8 \text{ m/s}$

$v = \dfrac{d}{t}$

$t = \dfrac{d}{v} = \dfrac{10,000 \text{ m}}{1.8 \times 10^8 \text{ m/s}} = 5.5 \times 10^{-5} \text{ sec}$

8. $\dfrac{\lambda}{d} = \dfrac{x}{L}$

$\lambda = \dfrac{xd}{L} = \dfrac{(2.5 \times 10^{-4} \text{ m})(0.25 \text{ m})}{2.0 \text{ m}} = 3.13 \times 10^{-5} \text{ m}$

Chapter 19 Review Answer Key

Vocabulary review

Set One	Set Two	Set Three	Set Four
1. c	1. f	1. f	1. d
2. d	2. d	2. d	2. a
3. e	3. a	3. b	3. e
4. f	4. e	4. a	4. b
5. a	5. c	5. e	

Concept review

1. Water and electric current are similar in their ability to carry power and energy as they flow and in their ability to do work. They are different in that electric current flows in solid metal wires and is not visible.

2. Electrical symbols are used when making circuit diagrams because they are quicker and easier to draw than realistic pictures and provide a shorthand method of describing a circuit. In addition, electrical symbols standardize circuit diagrams so anyone familiar with electricity can understand a diagram.

3. Answers are:

    a.

    resistor

    b.

    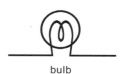

    bulb

    c.

    battery

    d.

    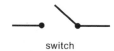

    switch

e.

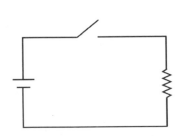

wire

4. Sample answer:

5. An open circuit is a circuit with a break in it, as when a switch is open. An open circuit has no current flow, because the electricity cannot flow through the break. A closed circuit has a complete and unbroken path between the current source and the return to the source through which current can flow.

6. The function of a circuit breaker or fuse is to protect a circuit from too much current by creating a break in the circuit and stopping the current flow once the current exceeds design limits.

7. Voltage differences are what makes current flow.

8. Voltage is a measure of electric potential energy. Energy differences represent energy that can be used to do work. The way to get the work is to let the voltage cause current to flow through a circuit.

9. The flashlight will not work because the potential difference across the two batteries is zero. The negative/positive cancels out the positive negative.

10. The energy supplied by a battery is supplied by chemical reactions.

11. Materials with high electrical resistance, known as insulators, include: glass, plastic, paper, air, rubber, and others. Materials with low electrical resistance, known as conductors, include most metals, salty water, and others.

12. A multimeter measures voltage, current, and resistance.

13. You cannot use this meter to measure current because you need two probes to complete the circuit through the meter to measure the current. You cannot use this meter to measure voltage because you need two probes to measure the potential difference across two points.

14. Answers are:
    a. The current will decrease with a higher resistance bulb, because resistance is inversely proportional to current according to Ohm's law.
    b. The current will increase with a lower resistance bulb.

    c. The current will increase as voltage increases, because voltage is directly proportional to voltage according to Ohm's law.

15. Answers are:
    a. Current is measured in amperes
    b. Voltage is measured in volts
    c. Resistance is measured in ohms

16. Ohm's law states that $V = IR$, therefore $I = V \div R$. Current is inversely proportional to resistance and directly proportional to voltage.

17. Wet skin has much lower resistance than dry skin. The lower resistance causes more current to pass through your body for a given amount of voltage. The 120 volts of a household electrical outlet is enough to possibly cause a fatal current to flow through your body.

18. A resistor's value does not change when voltage is varied. A light bulb has very low resistance when cold or when the voltage is low, but gets higher as the filament heats or the voltage increases.
    • If you were to measure the resistance of a cold 60 W light bulb, it would be approximately 30 Ω. When hot, the same light bulb has a resistance of approximately 240 Ω.
    $P = IV$; $I = P/V = (60 \text{ W})/(120 \text{ V}) = 0.5 \text{ A}$
    $V = IR$; $R = V/I = (120 \text{ V})/(0.5 \text{ A}) = 240 \text{ Ω}$
    • If the resistance did not change, the 60 W light bulb would actually burn 500 W. The low resistance heats the light bulb quickly.
    $P = V^2/R = (120 \text{ V})^2/(30 \text{ Ω}) = 500 \text{ W}$

19. A conductor has high conductivity and low resistance; conductors allow current to flow easily. An insulator has low conductivity and high resistance; current does not flow easily through an insulator.

20. Answers are:
    a. semiconductor
    b. conductor
    c. insulator
    d. conductor
    e. insulator

21. A material with low resistance has high conductivity.

22. Covering the electrical wires in homes with plastic keeps conductors separated so they don't short or cause a fire.

23. A potentiometer can be adjusted for a range of resistance; a fixed resistor has a resistance that cannot be changed.

629

24. Some possible uses for a potentiometer are: a dimmer switch, a volume control.

25. Fixed resistors often contain colored stripes as a standardized way of identifying their resistance. The color bands are used so the value can be read in any orientation the resistor is installed.

Problems

1. $R = \dfrac{V}{I} = \dfrac{120 \text{ V}}{10 \text{ A}} = 12 \ \Omega$

2. $I = \dfrac{V}{R} = \dfrac{1.5 \text{ V}}{2 \ \Omega} = 0.75 \text{ A}$

3. $V = IR = (0.25 \text{ A})(48 \ \Omega) = 12 \text{ V}$

4. $V_T = IR = (0.3 \text{ A})(15 \ \Omega) = 4.5 \text{ V}$

    $(4.5 \text{ V}) \div (1.5 \text{ Volts per battery}) = 3 \text{ batteries}$

5. $V = (2 \text{ batteries}) \times (1.5 \text{ volts per AA alkaline battery}) = 3.0 \text{ V}$

    $I = \dfrac{V}{R} = \dfrac{3.0 \text{ V}}{6 \ \Omega} = 0.5 \text{ A}$

6. $R = \dfrac{V}{I} = \dfrac{120 \text{ V}}{15 \text{ A}} = 8 \ \Omega$

Chapter 20 Review Answer Key

Vocabulary review

Set One	Set Two
1. f	1. c
2. e	2. d
3. b	3. a
4. c	4. e
5. d	5. b

Concept review

1. Series circuits contain only one current path, with the amount of current being the same at all points in the circuit. An example of a series circuit is an inexpensive set of holiday lights. When one light burns out, all the lights go out.

2. Both bulbs turn off because the circuit has been broken.

3. The total resistance increases because each resistor in a series circuit adds to the total.

4. In a parallel circuit, if one bulb goes out, the other bulb continues to burn.

5. series, parallel

6. As more parallel paths are added, the total resistance can only decrease.:

$$\frac{1}{R_T} = \frac{1}{R_1} + \frac{1}{R_2} + \frac{1}{R_3} + \dots$$

7. R_1 and R_2 are in series; R_3 and R_4 are in parallel.

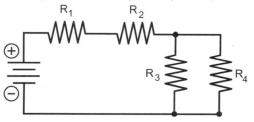

8. A short circuit is a parallel path in a circuit with zero or very low resistance created by accidently connecting a wire between two other wires at different voltages.

9. Ohm's law, $I = V/R$, relates current, voltage and resistance in a circuit. Kirchhoff's Current law states that the total current flowing into any junction in a circuit equals the total current flowing out of the junction. Kirchhoff's Voltage law states that the total of all voltage drops and voltage gains around any loop of a circuit must be zero.

10. lower

11. joules, second

12. Some units of measuring power are: watts, joules/second, kilowatts, and horsepower.

13. The electrical energy used by a fan is converted to mechanical energy in turning the fan and in heat losses.

14. energy

15. Your home has a meter measuring how many kilowatt-hours used. By multiplying the kilowatt-hours used by the cost per kilowatt-hour, the electric company can determine your bill.

16. AC current alternates polarity regularly. DC current flows in one direction only.

17. power factor, less

Problems

1. Answers are:
   a. $R_T = R_1 + R_2 + R_3 = 4\ \Omega + 4\ \Omega + 4\ \Omega = 12\ \Omega$
   b. $R_T = R_1 + R_2 = 5\ \Omega + 2\ \Omega = 7\ \Omega$
   c. $\dfrac{1}{R_T} = \dfrac{1}{R_1} + \dfrac{1}{R_2} = \dfrac{1}{4} + \dfrac{1}{4}$

   $R_T = 2\ \Omega$

   d.
   $\dfrac{1}{R_T} = \dfrac{1}{R_1} + \dfrac{1}{R_2} = \dfrac{1}{6} + \dfrac{1}{9}$

   $R_T = 3.6\ \Omega$

2. $R_T = 2\ \Omega + 4\ \Omega = 6\ \Omega$

   $I = \dfrac{V}{R} = \dfrac{3\ V}{6\ \Omega} = 0.5\ A$

3. $V = 12\ V \qquad I = 2\ A$

   $R_T = 3 + 1 + R = \dfrac{V}{I}$

   $3 + 1 + R = \dfrac{12\ V}{2\ A}$

   $R = 2\ \Omega \qquad R_T = 6\ \Omega$

4. Answers are:
   a. $\dfrac{1}{R_T} = \dfrac{1}{4} + \dfrac{1}{4}$

   $R_T = 2\ \Omega$

   $I_T = \dfrac{V}{R_T} = \dfrac{3\ V}{2\ \Omega} = 1.5\ A$

   $I_{4\ \Omega} = \dfrac{V}{R} = \dfrac{3\ V}{4\ \Omega} = 0.75\ A$

b. $\dfrac{1}{R_T} = \dfrac{1}{1} + \dfrac{1}{2}$

   $R_T = 0.67\ \Omega$

   $I_T = \dfrac{V}{R_T} = \dfrac{1.5\ V}{0.67\ \Omega} = 2.25\ A$

   $I_{1\ \Omega} = \dfrac{V}{R} = \dfrac{1.5\ V}{1\ \Omega} = 1.5\ A$

   $I_{2\ \Omega} = \dfrac{V}{R} = \dfrac{1.5\ V}{2\ \Omega} = 0.75\ A$

5. Kirchhoff's voltage law states that the total voltage drop is zero
   If $R_1 = 12\ \Omega$ and $R_2 = 6\ \Omega$

   $V_i = 24\ V$

   $V_o = \left(\dfrac{R_2}{R_1 + R_2}\right)V_i = \left(\dfrac{6\ \Omega}{12\ \Omega + 6\ \Omega}\right)24\ V = 8\ V$

   If $R_1 = 6\ \Omega$ and $R_2 = 12\ \Omega$

   $V_i = 24\ V$

   $V_o = \left(\dfrac{R_2}{R_1 + R_2}\right)V_i = \left(\dfrac{12\ \Omega}{6\ \Omega + 12\ \Omega}\right)24\ V = 16\ V$

6. $\dfrac{1}{R_T} = \dfrac{1}{R_1} + \dfrac{1}{R_2}$

   $R_1 = 1 + 3 = 4\ \Omega$
   $R_2 = 2 + 6 = 8\ \Omega$

   $\dfrac{1}{R_T} = \dfrac{1}{4} + \dfrac{1}{8}$

   $R_T = 2.67\ \Omega$

   $I = \dfrac{V}{R_T} = \dfrac{12\ V}{2.67\ \Omega} = 4.5\ A$

7. $P = VI$

   $I = \dfrac{P}{V} = \dfrac{1{,}000\ W}{120\ V} = 8.33\ A$

631

8. $P = VI = (120 \text{ V})(0.8 \text{ A}) = 96 \text{ W}$

9. Answers are:
   a. $10 \text{ W} \times \dfrac{1 \text{ kW}}{1,000 \text{ W}} = 0.01 \text{ kW}$

   $0.01 \text{ kW} \times 24 \text{ hrs} = 0.24 \text{ kW per day}$

   b. $0.24 \text{ kWh/day} \times 365 \text{ days/yr} = 87.6 \text{ kWh/yr}$

   $87.6 \text{ kWh/yr} \times \$0.15/\text{kWh} = \$13.14 \text{ per year}$

Chapter 21 Review Answer Key

Vocabulary review

Set One	Set Two	Set Three
1. c	1. e	1. f
2. e	2. a	2. b
3. d	3. b	3. a
4. a	4. c	4. c
5. b	5. f	5. d

Concept review

1. We don't usually notice the electric charge in everyday objects because most objects contain exactly the same number of positive and negative charges, so the net charge is zero.

2. When an object contains equal amounts of positive and negative charges, the total charge on an object is zero, and it is electrically neutral.

3. If a neutral object loses negative charge, its net charge will be positive.

4. repel; repel; attract

5. Sample answer:

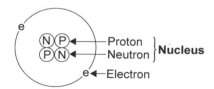

6. The electroscope leaves will be charged negatively, because that charge is driven away from the top and into the leaves.

7. Answers are:

a. 2 C
b. 10 C
c. 120 C

8. The electrons are free to move in metals.

9. positive; negative

10. Electrons have random motion. The voltage across the wire causes a drift in the electrons through the wire toward the positive voltage.

11. The positively charged balloon approaches the neutral electroscope which is connected by a wire to a large object. The positive charge on the balloon drives away the positive charge from the electroscope through the wire. The wire is disconnected, leaving the electroscope negatively charged. When the balloon is removed, the electroscope remains negatively charged.

12. charges; distance between the charges

13. The force is reduced by the square of the distance between the protons; since the distance is doubled, the force will be reduced by a factor of 4.

14. The strength of the electric field grows weaker as you move farther away from the source of the field.

15. positive

16. Electric fields can be measured in newtons per coulomb (N/C) or volts per meter (V/m).

17. Gravitational and electrical fields are both force fields. In a gravitational field, mass creates a force field that exerts a force on other masses. In an electrical field, charge creates a force field that exerts a force on other charges.

18. Electrical forces are much stronger than gravitational forces. The gravitational force between two 1-kg objects would be 6.7×10^{-11} N, and the electrical force between two 1-kg objects of opposite charge would be 1.8×10^{25} N.

19. Because charges are free to move under the influence of an electric field inside a conductor, negative charges will move within the conductor to neutralize the field.

20. A parallel plate capacitor is a simple type of capacitor made of two conductive metal plates placed close together with a sheet of insulating material between them. When the capacitor is charged, one plate is positive and one plate is negative.

21. Answers are:

a. The plate connected to the positive end of the battery will become positive and the plate connected to the negative end of the battery will become negative.

b. The positive plate will lose electrons; the protons do not move.

c. The negative plate will gain electrons; the protons do not move.

22. As a capacitor discharges, current flows for a short time with an exponential decay until the capacitor's charge is gone.

23. A 3 F capacitor can store 3 C if it is connected to a 1 V battery.

24. The three factors that affect a capacitor's ability to store charge are: the size of the capacitor, the distance between the plates, and the type of insulator between the plates.

Problems

1. $I = \dfrac{q}{t} = \dfrac{20\ C}{30\ sec} = 0.67\ A$

2. $F = K\dfrac{q_1 q_2}{r^2} = 9\times 10^9\ N\text{-}m^2/C^2 \dfrac{(1\ C)(1\ C)}{(0.01\ m)^2} = 9\times 10^{13}\ N$

3. $F = K\dfrac{q_1 q_2}{r^2} = 9\times 10^9\ N\text{-}m^2/C^2 \dfrac{(2\ C)(-3\ C)}{(0.5\ m)^2} = -2.16\times 10^{11}\ N$ An attractive force of:

4. For identical charges,

$F = K\dfrac{q^2}{r^2}$

$q = \sqrt{\dfrac{Fr^2}{K}} = \sqrt{\dfrac{(0.1\ N)(0.2\ m)^2}{9\times 10^9\ N\text{-}m^2/C^2}} = 6.7\times 10^{-7}\ C$

5. If the four batteries are in series

$q = CV$

$C = \dfrac{q}{V} = \dfrac{0.015\ C}{4\times 1.5\ V} = 0.0025\ f = 2500\ \mu f$

If the four batteries are in parallel,

$q = CV$

$C = \dfrac{q}{V} = \dfrac{0.015\ C}{1.5\ V} = 0.01\ f = 10000\ \mu f$

6. Answers are:

a. $C = \dfrac{q}{V} = \dfrac{0.06\ C}{9\ V} = 0.0067\ f = 6667\ \mu f$

b. $V = \dfrac{q}{C} = \dfrac{2\ C}{0.0067\ f} = 300\ V$

Chapter 22 Review Answer Key

Vocabulary review

Set One	Set Two
1. c	1. a
2. b	2. f
3. d	3. c
4. a	4. e
	5. d

Concept review

1. paper clips, straight pins, metal clothes hangers (objects made from iron, cobalt and nickel)

2. A north pole repels another north pole; a south pole repels another south pole; a north pole attracts a south pole.

3. As the distance increases, the force between the poles decreases but more rapidly than the force between charges.

4. The field strength is greater in areas where the lines are closer together. If arrows are drawn on the field lines, the arrows point away from the north pole of a magnet and toward the south pole

5. The direction is determined by placing a test magnet in the field. The direction is described as the direction of the force applied to the north pole of the test magnet.

6. Answers are:
   a. Both poles and charges can exert attractive and repulsive forces depending upon the type of pole and sign of charges next to one another.
   b. Poles may not be separated into single poles; charges may be isolated as positive or negative.

7. Electrons are the source of nearly all magnetic effects in matter. Electrons moving around the nucleus can make the atom a small magnet. Each electron acts as a tiny magnet.

8. Answers are:

a. Diamagnetic materials are made from atoms containing electrons of equal numbers with opposite spin. The magnetic field of each atom is zero. Diamagnetic materials may become very slightly magnetic when their electrons are disturbed by a strong magnetic field. (Diamagnetic materials oppose the field by which they are surrounded.)

b. Paramagnetic materials contain atoms that are magnetic because the electron spins do not cancel out but the atoms are randomly arranged so their overall magnetic field is zero. Paramagnetic materials become weakly magnetic when placed near another magnet.

c. Ferromagnetic materials contain atoms whose electrons are aligned and the atoms themselves are arranged in groups called magnetic domains which grow or shrink in response to a magnetic field. Ferromagnetic materials can be strongly magnetized.

9. The magnetism of most electrons is cancelled by the random arrangement of individual magnetic atoms or by the pairing of electrons with opposite spin orientations within each atom.

10. Magnetic domains are groups of neighboring atoms with similar magnetic orientation.

11. Hard magnets are difficult to magnetize but, once magnetized, are not easily demagnetized. Soft magnets can be easily magnetized and demagnetized. It makes soft magnetic material ideal for making computer discs.

12. A magnetic material may be stroked by another magnet or placed in a strong magnetic field to cause it to become a permanent magnet.

13. If a permanent magnet is vibrated, continually struck or heated it may lose its magnetism.

14. The north magnetic pole is actually located in the southern hemisphere. The north geographic pole is located north of that point to which the north seeking end of a compass points but actually has a south magnetic polarity; the poles of magnets were named for the direction in which they pointed before the magnetic field of the Earth and its polarity were clearly understood.

15. The angular direction between true north and the direction your compass points, called magnetic declination, is indicated on topographic maps of an area. A correction for the declination of the area allows you to travel in the correct direction.

16. The motion of the Earth's molten metal core creates electric currents which, scientists believe, results in the production of a magnetic field similar to that made by an electromagnet.

17. Studies of magnetized rock in the Earth's crust provide evidence that the poles have reversed many times. The magnetic patterns in the rock of the ocean's floor are particularly helpful.

18. The angular difference between true north and the direction your compass points is called magnetic declination.

Problems

1. Sample answer:

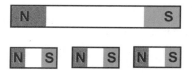

2. B

3. B

4. D and H

5. D

6. The triangle formed by the two 10 km legs has angles of 16°, 82°, and 82°. Using the law of sines:

$$\frac{D}{\sin 16°} = \frac{10.0 \text{ km}}{\sin 82°}$$

$$D = \frac{10 \text{ km} \times \sin 16°}{\sin 82°} = 2.78 \text{ km}$$

7. C

Chapter 23 Review Answer Key

Vocabulary review

Set One	Set Two	Set Three
1. c	1. e	1. a
2. a	2. b	2. e
3. e	3. c	3. f
4. b	4. a	4. d
		5. b

Concept review

1. A magnetic field

2. conventional electric current; magnetic field

3. attract; repel

4. in the center of the coil

5. the strength of the magnetic field, the velocity of the charge and the size of the charge

6. Pointing the fingers of your right hand in the direction of the magnetic field, when your thumb is pointing in the direction of the current, your palm faces the direction in which force will be applied to the current. (There are slight variations to this rule depending upon the parts of the right hand you orient to the moving charge, magnetic field direction, and force.)

7. circle; spiral

8. Tesla and gauss; the tesla is 1×10^4 times bigger than the gauss.

9. a magnet created when an electric current flows in coil of wire

10. The strength of an electromagnet can be more easily controlled than the strength of a permanent magnet.

11. Speakers, toasters, and motors are three common examples.

12. Wrapping the fingers of your right hand around the coil of the electromagnet in the direction of the current, your thumb points in the direction of the north pole of the electromagnet. Also, the north pole of an electromagnet repels the north-seeking pole of a compass.

13. Sample answer:

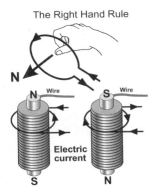

The Right Hand Rule

14. Answers are:
   a. increase the current flowing in the coil by the applying higher voltage
   b. increase the number of turns of wire used in the coil
   c. insert a magnetically permeable material in the coil

15. electrical; mechanical

16. rotor, field magnet, and commutator

17. The polarity changes periodically; this causes the armature to rotate as it is continually attracted and repelled.

18. the process of causing a current to flow by moving a coil of wire past a magnet

19. Current flows in the wire.

20. Current will not flow in the wire because there is no relative motion between the magnetic field and the wire.

21. Orient the loop perpendicular to the magnetic field, increase the number of turns in the coil, and increase the size of the coil.

22. mechanical; electrical

23. A transformer uses electromagnetic induction to increase or decrease the voltage of an alternating current.

Problems

1. clockwise

2. into the page

3. The size of the magnetic field is 4.0×10^{-6} tesla:

$$\vec{B} = (2 \times 10^{-7})\frac{I}{R} = 2 \times 10^{-7}\left(\frac{1\ A}{0.05\ m}\right)$$

4. The size of the magnetic field is 2.35×10^{-3} tesla:

$$\vec{B} = (2\pi \times 10^{-7})\frac{NI}{R} = 2\pi \times 10^{-7}\left(\frac{25\ turns \times 3.00\ A}{0.02\ m}\right)$$

$$\vec{B} = 2.35 \times 10^{-3}\ T$$

5. counterclockwise

6. The toothbrush is charged using a current produced by electromagnetic induction.

7. The primary voltage is 36,000 V:

$$\frac{\text{\# of primary turns}}{\text{\# of secondary turns}} = \frac{\text{primary voltage}}{\text{secondary voltage}}$$

$$\frac{9,000 \text{ turns}}{30 \text{ turns}} = \frac{\text{primary voltage}}{120 \text{ V}}$$

$$\text{primary voltage} = \frac{9,000 \text{ turns} \times 120 \text{ V}}{30 \text{ turns}} = 36,000 \text{ V}$$

Chapter 24 Review Answer Key

Vocabulary review

Set One	Set Two	Set Three	Set Four
1. d	1. e	1. c	1. e
2. c	2. c	2. a	2. f
3. b	3. d	3. f	3. a
4. a	4. b	4. e	4. b
5. f	5. f	5. d	5. c

Concept review

1. When a diode is connected in a circuit so current flows through it, it is called forward biased. When a diode is reversed so it blocks the flow of current, the diode is reverse biased.

2. The voltage needs to reach the bias voltage before a forward biased diode will open.

3. The current vs. voltage graph for a resistor is a straight line with a constant slope. The current vs. voltage graph for a diode stays a zero until the bias voltage is reached, then rises in a straight line with a constant slope.

4. The base connection on a transistor controls how much current flows through the between the collector and emitter.

5. A semiconductor acts like an insulator at low temperatures and low voltages.

6. The density of free electrons is what determines the conductivity of a semiconductor. If there are many free electrons to carry current, the semiconductor acts more like a conductor. If there are few electrons, the semiconductor acts like an insulator.

7. Impurities change the number of free electrons and are added to semiconductors to adjust conductivity.

8. In an n-type semiconductor, current is carried by electrons with negative charge. In a p-type semiconductor, current is carried by holes with positive charge.

9. The *n* side of a p-n junction becomes positively charged as negative electrons from the *n* side flow over to the *p* side and combine with the positive holes.

10. The depletion region acts as an insulator because movable charges are driven out, making the region incapable of conducting current.

11. The size of the depletion region can be changed by voltages across the region. The depletion region is affected by both the magnitude and the polarity of the voltage differential.

12. A half-wave rectifier passes only the positive values of AC voltage, using only half the AC signal. The negative values are held to zero. A full-wave rectifier converts the AC signal to its absolute value, using the entire AC signal.

13. *Differences:* A transistor switch has no moving parts, and a mechanical switch has moving parts. A transistor switch works electronically and mechanical switch physically disconnects wires. Mechanical switches are always either open or closed. A transistor switch can be partly on and partly off. *Similarities:* Both transistor and mechanical switches turn the current on and off.

14. Some examples of devices that use logic circuits are computers and microprocessors, home security alarms, three-way light switches, and the ABS brakes in a car.

15. Digital

16. Letters other characters, such as punctuation, are coded in ASCII. Standard ASCII has 8 bits, which allows for 256 different characters to be represented. Numerals can be represented as symbols in ASCII. Numbers are typically represented in base 2, which allows the computer to manipulate the value of the number. Binary Coded Decimal (BCD) is a way to represent a single digit in base 10 with four bits of binary data. The four bits have 16 possible combinations and six of them are not used.

17. The main components of a computer are: (1) the memory system, which stores information digitally, (2) the central processing unit, which manipulates the data, and (3) the input-output (I/O) system, which interacts with the outside world.

18. The four main types of logic gates are AND, OR, NAND, and NOR.

Problems

1. Answers are:
   a.
   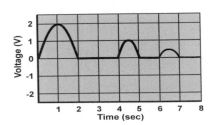

   b.
   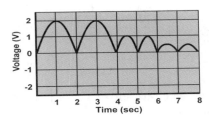

2.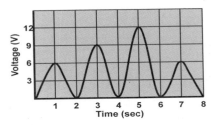

3. Answers are:
   a. 1
   b. 2
   c. 7

4. C

5. D

Chapter 25 Review Answer Key

Vocabulary review

Set One	Set Two	Set Three	Set Four
1. b	1. e	1. f	1. f
2. c	2. a	2. c	2. b
3. e	3. b	3. b	3. d
4. a	4. c	4. e	4. a
5. b		5. a	5. c

Concept review

1. A tiny speck of ash is struck by individual molecules of air as they move irregularly, buffeting the smoke particle this way and that.

2. A compound is made from at least two different kinds of atoms (two or more elements); a molecule is made by combining two or more atoms but not necessarily different elements.

3. An element is one of 92 naturally-occurring materials, combinations of which form all other substances. A single atom is the smallest particle of an element. All atoms of the same element have similar properties.

4. In the U.S., the Fahrenheit scale is commonly used to measure temperature. Europe and most other countries of the world use the Celsius scale. On the Fahrenheit scale, "the 20's" is cold. On the Celsius scale, "the 20's" is warm; it's in the 70's on the Fahrenheit scale. The German student dressed for Celsius temperatures to which he was accustomed.

5. Answers are:
   a. A thermistor is a device that changes its electrical resistance as its temperature changes. The temperature scale of the thermometer using the thermistor is calibrated to record the correct temperature value as the resistance changes.
   b. A thermocouple is an electrical device in which a small potential difference is created as two metals of different elements touch. The voltage depends on the temperature. Thermometers using a thermocouple convert the voltages to a temperature reading.
   c. Some liquids such as alcohol expand and contract a certain amount per degree of temperature change. In conventional thermometers, the liquid expands up a thin tube calibrated to give the correct temperature reading.
   d. Certain chemicals undergo predictable color changes as the temperature changes. A strip containing these chemicals can be made to indicate the temperature.

6. The Celsius degree measures a greater temperature change. Consider the change in temperature from the freezing point to the boiling point of water: The difference on the Fahrenheit scale is divided into 180 degrees while on the Celsius scale it is divided into 100 degrees. Therefore, the Celsius degree must represent a change 180/100, or 9/5 times the Fahrenheit change.

7. Temperature is a measure of the random motion of the molecules in a body.

8. The Celsius degree and the Kelvin represent the same change of temperature, but the Kelvin scale represents temperatures that are 273 units lower than the same numerical reading in Celsius degrees. Zero on the Celsius scale represents the freezing point of water while zero on the Kelvin scale represents absolute zero, a point measuring the lowest possible temperature in nature, approximately -273 Celsius.

9. The change of phase depends upon a change in the thermal energy of the molecules. As the individual molecules acquire more thermal energy, the bonds holding molecules together and even the forces holding electrons in place are insufficient to maintain the molecules in a certain phase.

10. More heat energy will be required to change 2 kilograms of water at its boiling point to steam than to change 10 kilograms of ice to liquid water. The heat of vaporization of water is more than 6 times the heat of fusion of ice.

11. Since temperature is the average of the random motion of the molecules, when a higher energy molecule is able to escape the surface of the liquid, it takes with it some of the energy of the liquid, resulting in lower average random motion and a lower temperature.

12. Answers are:
   a. D
   b. B
   c. C
   d. A

13. Answers are:
   a. A is a gas; indefinite shape and volume
   b. B is a solid; definite shape and volume
   c. C is a liquid; definite volume, indefinite shape

14. Steam would cause a more serious burn at 100°C. Per kilogram, steam contains much more thermal energy than liquid water at the boiling point of water.

15. Relative humidity is an expression that indicates how close the air is to saturation. At high relative humidity, the air is nearly saturated. Water will not evaporate rapidly. If humidity is high, vigorous exercise will be uncomfortable because evaporation, which normally cools our body as we perspire, does not occur.

16. The bathtub contains more thermal energy (heat); temperature is not the same as heat. Thermal energy depends on the temperature and also on the amount of water.

17. Specific heat is the heat required to raise the temperature of 1 kilogram of a material 1 Celsius degree. Temperature is a measure of the random kinetic energy of each atom. Because gold atoms are heavier than aluminum atoms, there are fewer atoms of gold in one kilogram of gold. Therefore, more heat is added to each gold atom. Each atom of gold acquires more kinetic energy and its temperature rises more rapidly.

18. When air is added to the tire, the air is compressed. Compression is a heating process.

19. As heat is withdrawn from the inside of the refrigerator, it is exhausted into the room. Due to the unavoidable inefficiency of the refrigerator, the room will actually get warmer.

20. Graph C; (-273°C.)

Problems

1. Heat required is 5,400 joules

$$E = mc(T_2 - T_1) = (0.5 \text{ kg})(900 \text{ J/kg°C})(37°C - 25°C)$$
$$E = 5,400 \text{ J}$$

2. Since gold has a specific heat of 129 J/kg°C, the material is probably gold.
$$E = mc(T_2 - T_1)$$
$$c = \frac{E}{m(T_2 - T_1)} = \frac{322.5 \text{ J}}{0.25 \text{ kg}(30°C - 20°C)} = 129 \text{ J/kg°C}$$

638

3. heat lost = heat gained

$$m_g c_g (T_{ig} - T_{fg}) = m_w c_w (T_{fw} - T_{iw})$$

$$T_{ig} = \frac{m_w c_w (T_{fw} - T_{iw})}{m_g c_g} + T_{fg}$$

$$T_{ig} = \frac{0.10 \text{ kg}(4184 \text{ J/kg°C})(24°C - 20°C)}{0.15 \text{ kg}(800 \text{ J/kg°C})} + 24°C$$

$$T_{ig} = 38°C$$

4. Answers are:

a. Since the substance changes from a liquid to a solid at 70°C, the heat of fusion is determined at this plateau. Since 5 minutes is required to remove enough heat to change the substance to a solid, the heat dissipated is 1,000 kilojoules.
$E = mh_f$; $h_f = E/m$
$h_f = (1000 \text{ kJ})/(10 \text{ kg}) = 100 \text{ kJ/kg}$

b. Specific heat is the heat removed per kilogram of substance per degree of change of temperature. As a liquid, the substance cools from a temperature of 160°C to 70°C in 8 minutes, losing 1,600 kilojoules of heat energy.
$$E = mc(T_2 - T_1)$$
$$c = \frac{E}{m(T_2 - T_1)} = \frac{1600 \text{ kJ}}{10 \text{ kg}(120°C - 70°C)} = 3.2 \text{ kJ/kg°C}$$

c. The melting point is the same temperature as the freezing point, 70°C. In Kelvins, this is a temperature numerically 273 Kelvin units higher, or 343 K.

d. The boiling point (and the temperature at which the gas changes to a liquid) is 120°C.

e. The freezing point is 70°C. To convert to Fahrenheit:
$T_f = (9/5)T_c + 32$
$T_f = (9/5)(70) + 32$
$T_f = 158°C$

f. 1 BTU = 1,055 joules, or 1.055 kilojoules. Since 7 minutes elapse in the change, 1,400 kJ of heat energy, or 1,327 BTU's, are liberated.

g. The difference measured in Celsius degrees is 50°C.

h. Since a Celsius degree represents the same change in temperature as a Kelvin, the change is 50 Kelvins.

Chapter 26 Review Answer Key

Vocabulary review

Set One	Set Two	Set Three
1. e	1. b	1. e
2. d	2. c	2. d
3. f	3. a	3. f
4. a	4. e	4. a
5. b	5. f	5. b

Concept review

1. Answers are:
   a. Heat transfer is proportional to temperature difference.
   b. Between two bodies of different temperature, heat is transferred from the body at higher temperature to the body of lower temperature.
   c. Thermal equilibrium occurs when bodies are at the same temperature. It prevents heat transfer.

2. Diagram 4

3. The floor is made of tile, a much better conductor than the mat. The floor tile conducts the heat of your feet away more quickly than the mat, which is a poor conductor.

4. The glass fibers contain trapped air, a very poor conductor.

5. Solids are generally the best conductors and gases are generally the poorest. Liquids are intermediate in their ability.

6. Since the cross-sectional area is quadrupled, the rate of heat transfer increases by 4 times.

7. Because all objects constantly receive thermal radiation from all other objects in their environment

8. First, convert the temperature to Fahrenheit
   $T_f = (9/5)T_c + 32 = (9/5)(-33°C) + 32 = -27.4°F$
   From the chart, 0°F at nearly 40 mph.

9. During the day, the land is hotter; air rises over the land, causing a convection current that results in an onshore breeze. At night, warmer air rises over the water, causing the breeze to blow offshore.

10. At body temperature, because there is no flow of heat into or out of your body due to the contact.

11. It may be a real time saver. The dark ashes absorb the heat from the sun much faster than white snow. It may melt enough snow so that you will not have much left to shovel.

12. As candles burn, they produce CO_2. Since they are orbiting in "zero g," no convection current is established to move the CO_2 away from the candles. They are extinguished.

13. The power of the UV light from the sun is between 1000 and 100,000 times greater than that from a bulb.

Problems

1. Change both temperatures to the Kelvin scale. $100°C = 373$ K, $1,592°C = 1865$ K
   Change in Thermal Radiation (ΔTR) is proportional to ΔT^4, $\Delta TR \sim (1,865$ K$/373$ K$)^4$
   $\Delta TR \sim 625$ times

2. $P = \sigma AT^4; A = \pi DL; P = \sigma(\pi DL)T^4$
   $D = P/(\sigma \pi LT^4)$
   $D = (100$ watts$)/(5.67 \times 10^{-8}$ W/m^{2}K$)\pi(0.05$ m$)(2,800$ K$)^4$
   $D = 5.7 \times 10^{-4}$ m, or 0.57 mm

3. Since the area to thickness ratio is the same for each and the rate of conduction for each must be the same, the conduction formulae simplify to:
   $\kappa_{cu}(T_2 - T_i) = \kappa_{al}(T_i - T_1)$ where T_i = their interface temperature.
   $\kappa_{cu}T_2 - \kappa_{cu}T_i = \kappa_{al}T_i - \kappa_{al}T_1$
   $T_i = (\kappa_{cu}T_2 + \kappa_{al}T_1)/(\kappa_{cu} + \kappa_{al})$
   $T_i = [(401)(20°C) + (226)(80°C)]/(401 + 226)$
   $T_i = 41.6°C$

4. The equation $P_H = \kappa(A/L)(T_2 - T_1)$, becomes
   $P_H = A(T_2 - T_1)/$R-value
   Therefore, if the R-value is increased by 4 times, the rate of thermal energy loss is reduced to ¼ of its previous value.

5. The rate of flow is directly proportional to the temperature difference. The change in the rate is equal to the ratio of the final temperature difference to the initial temperature difference. As the temperature of the hot water decreases by 20°C, the cold water increases by 20°C. The ratio of differences then is 40:80, or 1:2. The rate decreases by half.

6. $P_H = \kappa(A/L)(T_2 - T_1)$ where $A = \pi r^2/L$
   $P_H = 226$ W/m°C$(4.42 \times 10^{-5}$m$^2/0.25$ m$)(100°C-20°C)$
   $P_H = 3.2$ watts

7. $P_H = hA(T_2 - T_1) = 200$W/m^2-°C$(0.08$ m$^2)(37°C - 20°C)$
   $P_H = 272$ watts
   This is about 10 times the heat transfer rate for air. We lose body heat very rapidly in water. As long as it is below our body temperature, we are in danger of exposure if we remain in the water too long even when the water temperatures are not "extreme."

8. Find the area of the window: 0.335 m^2
   Find the temperature of the window: The window temperature is approximately the average of the inside and outside temperature, or 0°C.
   The rate of heat transfer to the inside of the glass is given by the formula:
   $P_H = hA(T_2 - T_1)$ where $A = (0.67$ m$)(0.50$ m$) = 0.335$ m^2
   $P_H = (5.0$ W/m^2-°C$)(0.335$ m$^2)(20°C - 0°C) = 33.5$ watts

9. The rate of heat transfer through the window by conduction must equal the rate of heat transfer to the window by convection when the transfer reaches a steady state value. The rate of conduction is given by the equation:
   $P_H = \kappa(A/L)(T_2 - T_1)$
   $(T_2 - T_1) = P_H(L/A\kappa)$
   $(T_2 - T_1) = (33.5$W$)(0.0025$ m$)/(0.335$m$^2)(0.82$ W/m^2-°C$)$
   $(T_2 - T_1) = 0.30°C$
   The inside temperature of the glass is +0.30°C, and outside temperature is -0.30°C.

10. All objects above absolute zero radiate heat. They also absorb heat from the surroundings. To calculate the NET heat lost due to radiation the term for temperature difference has to be introduced into the equation. The equation becomes: $P = \sigma A(T_2^4 - T_1^4)$ where T is measured in Kelvins. $37°C = 310$ K and $5°C = 278$ K. The net energy (E) is Power (P) × Time (t) so:
    $P = \sigma A(T_2^4 - T_1^4)$
    $E = \sigma A(T_2^4 - T_1^4)t$
    $E = 5.67 \times 10^{-8}$W/m^2-°C$(1.5$ m$^2)[(310$ K$)^4 - (278$ K$)^4](3,600$sec/hr$)$
    $E = 9.99 \times 10^5$ joules

Chapter 27 Review Answer Key

Vocabulary review

Set One	Set Two	Set Three
1. d	1. e	1. d
2. a	2. c	2. b
3. e	3. a	3. e
4. f	4. b	4. c
5. b	5. f	5. f

Concept review

1. Both have the same density. The ratio of mass to volume for the needle is the same as the mass to volume ratio for the bar.

2. All materials from the list will float, except platinum, which has greater density than mercury.

3. Answers are:
   a. How much is a material deformed under load?
   b. How much force is required to break the material?

4. Stress is the ratio of the force applied perpendicular to a certain cross-sectional area of the solid material. Pressure is the force applied to an area of a fluid but it acts in all directions.

5. While concrete is difficult to compress, it is brittle, meaning it has low tensile strength. Steel reinforcement is added to increase the tensile strength of the structure. Steel is elastic.

6. A safety factor is designed into the bridge. Consequently, a structure is built that is a number of times stronger than the normal (stated acceptable) load. Over time, the value of the safety factor may decrease for a variety of reasons such as rust and metal fatigue.

7. Rubber is very elastic; it can sustain a large strain. Glass is very brittle and will shatter if a small amount of stress is applied.

8. While both are quite elastic, steel has a much higher modulus of elasticity, meaning it can sustain higher stress with little strain. It will not "flex" as easily. Also, rubber has little tensile strength compared to steel. It will break under a relatively low tensile load.

9. The glass marble is heated to a high temperature. When dropped into cold water, the outermost glass cools faster than the internal portion. The relatively high coefficient of thermal expansion for glass means that stress will occur in the marble that exceeds the tensile strength of the glass. Multiple cracks occur in the marble. WARNING: This should not be attempted without proper eye protection!

10. Concrete that is heated and cooled as it is exposed to extremes of temperature change soon cracks due to its brittle nature and the thermal stress caused by linear expansion.

11. A. Wood is most easily broken along the grain as pictured in A.

12. Steel ships are not solid steel. Much of the ship's hull encloses air. The average density of enclosure we identify as "the ship" is less than the density of water. Therefore, the ship floats.

13. pressure is to density

14. Pressure is directly proportional to depth in a fluid. Since his average depth is greater in the prone position, the average pressure is greater in that position.

15. Loose sand does not apply as much force per unit of area as harder surfaces. To prevent a vehicle's wheels from sinking in the sand, the air pressure in the tire is reduced so that the surface area of the tire will increase. This allows the sand to apply its smaller reaction force to a bigger area which supports the weight of the vehicle.

16. B. Since the fluid moves over the airfoil (wing) with greater speed, the internal pressure is reduced on the top of the wing. The greater internal pressure of the air at B, applying a force in all directions, applies an upward force on the airfoil.

17. The inflated portion of the Goodyear blimp is filled with helium gas which, by itself, has low density. Since the gondola is small, the average density of the blimp is less than the density of air. This establishes a buoyant force that supports the Goodyear blimp.

18. On the left side. Since container A and B have the same volume and temperature, B contains a greater mass of air at higher pressure. Therefore, container A is on the left side of the balance.

Problems

1. Yes. The density of water is 1,000 kg/m^3. Since 1 milliliter has a volume equivalent to 0.000001 m^3, the volume is 0.000355 m^3.
   $\rho = m/V = 0.349$ kg/0.000355 m^3 = 983 kg/m^3
   The average density is less than the density of water.

641

2. The mass must be converted to the force due to gravity in newtons and area to square meters.
$F = ma = (2.45 \text{ kg})(9.8 \text{ m/s}^2) = 24.01 \text{ N}$
Then $\sigma = F/A = (24.01 \text{ N})/0.0002 \text{ m}^2 = 1.20 \times 10^5 \text{ Pa}$

3. A $5 \times$ safety factor $\times 7$ tons = 35 tons

4. From Table 27.2, the tensile strength of steel alloy is $8.25 \times 10^8 \text{ N/m}^2$. The cross-sectional area of the wire is found using
$A = \pi r^2 = 0.442 \text{ mm}^2 = \pi(\frac{1}{2}(0.75 \text{ mm})^2 = 4.42 \times 10^{-7} \text{m}^2$
Applying the formula, $\sigma = F/A$,
$F = \sigma(A) = (8.25 \times 10^8 \text{ N/m}^2)(4.42 \times 10^{-7} \text{m}^2) = 3.6 \times 10^2 \text{ newtons}$

5. The coefficient of linear expansion for steel is 1.2×10^{-5}. The temperature change for the day is 10°C.
Applying the formula $\Delta l = l\alpha(\Delta T)$,
$\Delta l = 1,280 \text{ m}(1.2 \times 10^{-5})10°C = 1.5 \times 10^{-1} \text{ m}$

6. Since lead is more dense than oil, it sinks in oil displacing its own volume in oil. Its weight in oil = weight in air – weight of oil displaced
To find the volume of oil displaced, the mass of oil displaced, and then the weight of oil displaced, first, the volume of the lead must be found.
From Table 27.1, the mass density of lead is 11,340 kg/m^3.
The weight density of lead is (11,340 kg $\times$ 9.81m/s^2)/m^3, or $1.11 \times 10^5 \text{ N/m}^3$
The volume of the lead = weight/weight density =
45.2 N/1.11 $\times 10^5 \text{ N/m}^3 = 4.07 \times 10^{-4} \text{m}^3$
From Table 27.5, the mass density of oil is 888 kg/m^3.
Mass of oil displaced = mass density $\times$ volume
Mass of oil displaced = 888 kg/m$^3 \times 4.07 \times 10^{-4} \text{m}^3 = 3.62$ x 10^{-1}kg, Weight of oil displaced = mg = 3.62 x 10^{-1}kg $\times$ 9.8m/s^2 = 3.54 N.
Its weight in oil = weight in air – weight of oil displaced =
45.2 N - 3.54 N = 41.8 N

7. The pressure difference is 1 mm of Hg:
From Table 27., the mass density of mercury is 13,560 kg/m^3
$P = \rho g\Delta d = 13,560 \text{ kg/m}^3 \times 9.8 \text{ m/s}^2 \times 0.001 \text{ m} = 133 \text{ Pa}$

8. Since the sand exerts a reaction force approximately equal to the weight of your car, the following relationship may be assumed:
$P_1 \times A_1 = P_2 \times A$
35 lbs/in$^2 \times A_1$ = 20 lbs/in$^2 \times A_2$
A_2/A_1 = 35 lbs/in^2/20 lbs/in^2 = 1.75, or an increase in area of 175%

9. Assume the pressure of the water is converted entirely into kinetic energy which is converted to potential energy to reach the fire at 20 meters of height. The mass density of water, ρ = 1,000 kg/m^3

a. $\Delta P = \frac{1}{2} \rho v^2 = \rho gh$
$v^2 = 2gh = 2(9.8\text{m/s}^2)(20 \text{ m})$
$v = 19.8 \text{ m/s}$

b. $\Delta P = \rho gh = (1,000 \text{ kg/m}^3)(9.8 \text{ m/s}^2)(20 \text{ m}) = 1.96 \times 10^5 \text{ Pa}$, or about 1.94 atm.

10. First, find the pressure at 30 meters.
$P = \rho gh = (1,000 \text{ kg/m}^3)(9.8 \text{ m/s}^2)(30 \text{ m}) = 2.94 \times 10^5 \text{ Pa}$
Using Boyles' law,
$P_1V_1 = P_2V_2$, where $V_1 = P_2V_2/P_1$
$V_1 = (2.94 \times 10^5 \text{ Pa})(1.0 \text{ liters})/(1.01 \times 10^5 \text{Pa})$
$V_1 = 2.9 \text{ liters}$

11. Change Celsius temperatures to Kelvin temperatures:
25°C = 298 K, -40°C = 233 K

$$\frac{P_1V_1}{T_1} = \frac{P_2V_2}{T_2}$$

$$V_2 = \frac{P_1V_1T_2}{T_1V_2} = \frac{(1.01\times10^5\text{Pa})(0.25 \text{ m}^3)(298 \text{ K})}{(233 \text{ K})(1.01\times10^4 \text{ Pa})}$$

$$V_2 = 1.95 \text{ m}^3$$

12. In the equation for the ideal gas law given in the text ($PV = mRT$), P is measured in Pascals, V in cubic meters, m in kilograms, R in joules per kilogram-Kelvins and T in Kelvins. Substituting in the rearranged equation [$P = (mRT)/V$],
where m = 15 g = 0.015 kg,
R = 462 j/kg-K (for water vapor from Table 27.7)
T = 400°C = 673 K
V = 1.5 l = 1.5×10^{-3}m^3
$P = (0.015 \text{ kg})(462 \text{ j/kg-K})(673 \text{ K})/(1.5 \times 10^{-3}\text{m}^3)$
$P = 3.11 \times 10^6 \text{ Pa}$

13. Given the diameter of 2.00 mm (radius = 1.00 mm) and force of 2,200 newtons, the area of the line is ($A = \pi r^2$) = π mm^2.
$\sigma = F/A = 2,200 \text{ N}/\pi \text{ mm}^2 = 700 \text{ N/mm}^2$

14. Decreasing the diameter to 1.50 mm (radius 0.75 mm), decreases the area to 1.77 mm^2:
$F = \sigma A = (700 \text{ N/mm}^2)(1.77 \text{ mm}^2) = 1,240 \text{ newtons}$

Chapter 28 Review Answer Key

Vocabulary review

Set One	Set Two	Set Three
1. f	1. d	1. d
2. d	2. b	2. e
3. b	3. a	3. b
4. c	4. c	4. f
5. a	5. f	5. a

Concept review

1. Summarize the properties of the major atomic particles by completing the chart below:

Particle Name	Relative Charge	Relative Mass	Mass (kg)	Charge (C)
Electron	-1	1	9.109×10^{-31}	-1.602×10^{-19}
Proton	+1	1,835	1.673×10^{-27}	$+1.602 \times 10^{-19}$
Neutron	0	1,837	1.675×10^{-27}	0

2. The electric forces of the atom are very strong. The positive charge concentrated in the nucleus of the atom exerts a mutually strong electromagnetic force of attraction on electrons.

3. Neutrons in the nucleus act as a glue by exerting the strong nuclear force that is a mutually attractive force between protons and neutrons. An atom that contains the proper number of neutrons (generally at least one per proton) makes the nucleus stable.

4. Answers are:
   a. strong force; acts between neutrons and protons; holds the nucleus together
   b. electromagnetic force; acts between any charged particles; holds negatively charged electrons in orbit around the positively charged nucleus.
   c. weak force; acts within neutrons; causes single neutrons to disintegrate
   d. gravitational force; acts between all particles with mass; no known significance in the maintenance of the structures of the atom which has little mass.

5. Different isotopes of carbon have the same atomic number and different mass numbers.

6. The atomic mass of an atom is the weighted average of the mass numbers of the isotopes in a typical sample of the element. Magnesium, atomic number 12, has 3 common isotopes, Mg^{12}, Mg^{13}, Mg^{14}. Their weighted average mass is 24.31 amu.

7. According to the chart, carbon-14 is not stable because it has more neutrons than the number that causes stability of the carbon nucleus.

8. *nuclear* – the reaction between helium nuclei. *atomic* – the reaction between hydrogen and oxygen. Nuclear reactions create new atoms (elements); atomic reactions create new molecules.

9. The electron; their arrangement and interactions are responsible for color, chemical properties and the size of atoms.

10. Your clothing's color is the result of the combination of specific light waves emitted by electrons in the atoms after they have absorbed energy from incident light.

11. It is a complete description of an electron including its energy, motion, location and spin.

12. quantum numbers

13. loses energy

14. Each quantum state in a level has about the same energy, just as each parking spot is at about the same height above the ground. Each level has a limited capacity for electrons just as a parking garage has limited parking spaces. Each parking spot in the garage can hold one car, just as each quantum state can be occupied by only one electron.

15. Analyzing the spectrum, the indicated lines are found only in the helium spectrum.

16. The frequency of the incident light. This determines the energy of the incident photons.

17. They are inversely related according to the following equation:
    $E = hc/\lambda$

18. When confined to a space nearly the size of its wavelength (like in an atom), an electron takes on wave-like properties. Otherwise, it behaves like a particle.

19. Answers are:
    a. $l = 2$
    b. $l = 0$
    c. $l = 1$

20. To "locate" an electron, the means by which the electron could be located disturbs its very location. The uncertainly principle states that measuring one variable of the quantum state disturbs another.

21. The wave function mathematically describes how the probability for finding a quantum of matter is spread out in space.

22. Answers are:
   a. Johann Balmer: showed that the wavelengths of light given off by hydrogen atoms could be predicted by a mathematical formula; the number n in the Balmer formula is one of four quantum numbers that describe which quantum state an electron is in.
   b. Neils Bohr: proposed that electrons in an atom were limited to certain quantum states, between which electrons could move but could not "rest." He explained that spectral lines are caused by the movement of electrons as they "drop" from a higher to lower energy levels.
   c. Wolfgang Pauli: proposed the Exclusion Principle that states that no two electrons may occupy the same quantum state at the same time. The principle explains why all electrons do not fall to the lowest energy levels in an atom.
   d. Max Planck: proposed that light existed in small quantized bundles of energy called photons. The energy of a photon, according to Planck, is given by the formula $E = hc/\lambda$ where h is Planck's constant.
   e. Albert Einstein: proposed that the photoelectric effect occurs because atoms absorb energy one photon at a time. A photon with too little energy causes no emission while a photon with enough energy causes an electron to be emitted with KE proportional to the energy of the absorbed photon.
   f. Louis DeBroglie: proposed the idea of matter waves; that all particles can behave with wave properties under certain circumstances. Their wavelength is given by the following equation: $\lambda = h/mv$.

Problems

1. Answers are:
   a. Ti = titanium
   b. Kr = krypton
   c. Au = gold

2. A C^{12} atom has a mass of 12 amu. Each amu represents a mass of 1.661×10^{-27} kg. The mass of the $C^{12} =$
   12 nucleons $\times$ (1.661×10^{-27} kg/nucleon) = 1.993×10^{-26} kg.

3. From the periodic table, determine the atomic number of uranium, 92. The number of neutrons is the difference between the mass number and the atomic number.
   atomic mass – atomic number = number of neutrons; $235 - 92 = 143$.

4. Atomic mass is the weighted average of the mass numbers of the isotopes that occur in nature. The weighted average for pennium is $\{(8 \times 31) + (2 \times 25)\}/10$, or 29.8.

5. Answers are:
   a. H^1 and He^3
   b. 19 and 21
   c. Ca has 6 stable isotopes
   d. H^1
   e. $Ar^{36}, Ar^{38}, Ar^{40}$

6. Answers are:
   a. Sulfur has four stable isotopes, S^{32}, S^{33}, S^{34}, and S^{36}. Since the average atomic mass listed for sulfur is 32.06, a weighted average results in a mass number closest to the most common isotope. Therefore, S^{32} must be the most common isotope.
   b. Sulfur's atomic number is 16, the same as the number of protons. The difference between the atomic number and atomic mass is the number of neutrons, $(32 - 16) = 16$

7. $\lambda = 91.16/(1/2^2 - 1/n^2)$
   for n = 8, $\lambda = 91.16/(0.2344) = 389$ nm

8. Balmer's formula substituting 1/3 for 1/2:
   $(\lambda = 91.16/(1/3^2 - 1/n^2) = 1,875$ nm.
   This is in the infrared range. He was correct.

9. Answers are:
   a. $E = hc/\lambda = (6.63 \times 10^{-34}$ J-s)$(3.0 \times 10^8$ m/s$)/5.0 \times 10^{-7}$ m
      $E = 4.0 \times 10^{-19}$ J
   b. With the law of conservation of energy in mind, an electron that absorbs 4.0×10^{-19} J of energy has an amount of kinetic energy equal to that of the incoming photon minus the energy used to free it from the zinc metal or $KE = E_p - E_w$. E_p represents the energy of the incoming photon, and E_w represents the energy to free the electron from the zinc.
      $KE = E_p - E_w = (4.0 \times 10^{-19}$ J$) - (1.0 \times 10^{-19}$ J$) = 3.0 \times 10^{-19}$ J

10. $\lambda = h/mv$
    $\lambda = (6.63 \times 10^{-34}$ J-s$)/[(9.109 \times 10^{-31}$ kg$)(1.23 \times 10^6$ m/s$)]$
    $\lambda = 5.9 \times 10^{-10}$ m

11. $\lambda = h/mv$, where $v = (100$ km/hr$) \times (.0278$ m/s per km/hr$) = 27.78$ m/s
    $\lambda = (6.63 \times 10^{-34}$ J-s$)/[(2,000$ kg$)(27.78$ m/s$)]= 1.19 \times 10^{-38}$ m

12. Answers are:
     a. 1 in 4
     b. 3 in 4
     c. 2 in 4 (or 1 in 2)

Chapter 29 Review Answer Key

Vocabulary review

Set One	Set Two	Set Three
1. d	1. e	1. b
2. c	2. a	2. d
3. b	3. f	3. a
4. e	4. b	4. e
5. f	5. c	5. c

Concept review

1. A homogeneous mixture is uniform throughout. A heterogeneous mixture is one in which different parts are not necessarily the same. All spoonfuls of Jello® are the same. It is likely that two spoonfuls of Jello® with fruit would contain different types and/or amounts of fruit.

2. Possible answers are:
    a. color change
    b. precipitation of a solid
    c. temperature changed
    d. formation of bubbles
    e. change in solution clarity

3. Solutions are a combination of solvent and solute. Water, called the "universal" solvent, dissolves many substances. Oxygen, the solute, is one of many things that may be dissolved in a lake or pond. Together, the oxygen and water may be considered a solution.

4. Possible correct answers include:
    a. The combination of sodium (soft, shiny, very active metal) with chlorine (pale green, poisonous gas with a choking odor) to form table salt (sodium chloride)
    b. The combination of carbon (relatively inactive non-metal at room temperature; forms many compounds at higher temperatures) with oxygen (a non-metal, colorless, tasteless, odorless gas, reacts with many materials; called "burning" at high reaction rate) to form carbon dioxide (colorless, tasteless, odorless gas that will not support combustion but is necessary for photosynthesis).

5. Alkali metals all have single valence electrons. Noble gases have no valence electrons. The valence electrons form bonds. The bonds control how molecules form and, in turn, how the molecules interact with other molecules.

6. Gummium is very active because it has 7 valence electrons. Dimeum is quite stable, virtually inactive, since it has a 8 valence electrons.

7. Systems in nature tend to settle into a configuration of lowest energy. Atoms combined as molecules represent a lower energy state than free atoms.

8. Atoms that are close to having 8 valence electrons (those with 7 valence electrons having a strong tendency to acquire electrons; those with 1 valence electron a strong tendency to lose electrons) tend to form ionic bonds. Others with 2-6 valence electrons form more covalent bonds.

9. Answers are:
    a. Soap contains a base; it is slippery and tastes bitter. Lemonade contains an acid; it is sour.
    b. The pH of lemonade is less than 7; the pH of soap is more than 7.

10. Each atom of carbon atom has the capacity to make up to 4 bonds.

11. CH_4 (methane) and O_2 (oxygen) are the reactants; CO_2 (carbon dioxide) and H_2O (water) are the products.

12. Endothermic; heat must be constantly added to cause the baking to continue.

13. The products and reactants must contain the same number and types of atoms.

14. Answers are:
    a. Determine the mass of each atom or molecule that appears in the equation.
    b. Use the balanced equation to determine the number of molecules of each type needed.
    c. Multiply the number of each type of molecule or atom by its mass in kilograms.

15. Possible answers are:
    a. Absorption of energy from sunlight and storage of the energy as chemical bonds in molecules of glucose. Nearly all energy in living things can be traced to this source.
    b. Production of the majority of oxygen in the atmosphere. While oxygen is a common element in rocks and minerals, photosynthesis makes it available as a gas to support life.
    c. Removal of carbon dioxide from the atmosphere. With too much carbon dioxide present, the atmosphere traps heat, leading to dangerously high global temperatures.

16. In an actual gasoline engine, not all the fuel burns completely, producing poisonous carbon monoxide as a waste product. Additionally, sulfur and nitrogen from the air combine with the fuel to produce dangerous pollutants such as sulfuric acid and nitrogen oxides.

17. Activation energy

18. Molecules with long straight chains like n-heptane burn rapidly. Molecules like with branches burn more slowly and smoothly and are, because of their rate and nature of combustion, considered to have higher octane.

Problems

1. Answers are:
    a. $2Al + 3H_2SO_4 \rightarrow Al_2(SO_4)_3 + 3H_2$
    b. $Zn + 2AgNO_3 \rightarrow Zn(NO_3)_2 + 2Ag$
    c. $3Ag_2SO_4 + 2AlCl_3 \rightarrow 6AgCl + Al_2(SO_4)_3$
    d. $2C_2H_6 + 7O_2 \rightarrow 4CO_2 + 6H_2O$

2. For each, the answer is calculated by finding the mass of an atom in amu's, multiplying by the number of atoms and finding the sum of the masses for each molecule.
    a. $C_2H_6 = (2 \times 12.0$ amu$) + (6 \times 1.01$ amu$) = 30.0$ amu's
    b. $PCl_3 = (1 \times 31.0$ amu$) + (3 \times 35.5$ amu$) = 138$ amu's
    c. $N_2O_5 = (2 \times 14$ amu$) + (5 \times 16$ amu$) = 108$ amu's

3. 84.3 kilograms represents 1 "kilogram molecular mass" of MgCO3. Since one kilogram molecular mass of magnesium carbonate is used as the reactant, according to the equation, one kilogram molecular mass of magnesium oxide will be produced.
    One kilogram molecular mass MgO = 24.3 kg + 16 kg = 40.3 kg.

4. Using the balanced equation,
    $2C_3H_6 = 2(3 \times 12 + 6 \times 1) = 84$ kg
    $CO_2 = 6\{(1 \times 12) + (2 \times 16)\} = 264$ kg
    Solving the proportion: $792/264 = M/84$, $M = 252$ kilograms.

5. Answers are:
    a. substance
    b. heterogeneous mixture
    c. heterogeneous mixture
    d. solution (homogenous mixture)
    e. homogeneous mixture
    f. substance
    g. homogeneous mixture
    h. heterogeneous mixture
    i. solution (homogenous mixture)

6. Answers are:
    a. P
    b. P
    c. C
    d. C
    e. C
    f. P
    g. P
    h. P
    i. C

7. Answers are:

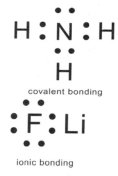

covalent bonding

ionic bonding

8. Answers are:
    a. O
    b. I
    c. O
    d. O

9. The law of conservation of mass is demonstrated.

Reactants		Products	
Ca(OH)$_2$ = 40.1 + (16.0 + 1.01)2	=74.12	CaCO$_3$ = 40.1 + 12.0 + (16.0)3	=100.1
CO$_2$ = 12.0 + (16.0)2	=44.00	H$_2$O = (1.01)2 + 16.0	=18.02
	118.12		118.12

10. Answers are:
    a. covalent
    b. ionic
    c. covalent

d. covalent

e. ionic

11. Answers are:

    a. #17

    b. #3→#12

    c. #18

    d. #1

    e. #14

12. Balance the equation below and use it to answer the questions that follow:
    $(4)NH_3 + (5)O_2 \rightarrow (4)NO + (6)H_2O$

    a. N = 4   O = 10
       H = 12   Total = 26

    b. N = 4   O = 10
       H = 12   Total = 26

    c. $4NH_3 + 5O_2 = 9$ molecules

    d. $4NO + 6H_2O = 10$ molecules

    e. The number of each kind of atom must be the same.

Chapter 30 Review Answer Key

Vocabulary review

Set One	Set Two	Set Three
1. f	1. c	1. c
2. a	2. d	2. d
3. d	3. e	3. e
4. b	4. f	4. f
5. c	5. a	5. b

Concept review

1. The nucleus of the atom is affected in radioactive materials. If the nucleus has too many neutrons or is unstable, the atom undergoes radioactive decay.

Decay	Protons	Neutrons	Ejected particle	Penetrating ability
Alpha	decrease by 2	decrease by 2	helium-4 (He^4) nucleus	1 sheet of paper
Beta	increase by 1	decrease by 1	beta particle (1 electron)	1/2 cm of water
Gamma	unchanged	unchanged	gamma ray (high energy proton)	6 cm of lead

2. Both chemical reactions and radioactivity change matter into different matter and both release energy. Chemical reactions rearrange atoms into different molecules, but the elements of those molecules remain the same. Radioactivity affects the nucleus of an atom, changing one element into one or more different elements.

3. Although scientists cannot predict the behavior of a small number of nuclei, is possible to predict the behavior of the nuclei in a sample, because even in small samples, there are many, many atoms. The average rate of decay can be accurately predicted because of the large number of atoms.

4. Carbon dating is accurate to about 57,000 years because after 57,000 years (or about 10 half-lives) there is not enough carbon-14 left to measure accurately.

5. As the distance to the screen increases, the intensity decreases as the square of the distance and the area increases as the square of the distance.

6. Radiation is harmful when it has enough energy to remove electrons from atoms (ionizing radiation), which allows it to break chemical bonds in important biological molecules. Some forms of harmful radiation include ultraviolet light, radiation from radon gas, cosmic rays, the radiation from fallout from nuclear weapons, x-rays.

7. X-rays can be used to destroy unhealthy cancer cells without killing healthy cells. Because a single beam of x-rays is not strong enough to cause damage on its own, multiple beams are aimed to overlap at the place where the diseased cells are to be destroyed. The beams are too weak on their own to damage healthy tissue, but when overlapping a specific area, they are strong enough to destroy the cancer cells.

8. CAT scans can yield 3-D pictures of the internal structure of the human body by taking multiple x-ray images from multiple angles, and combining the image information in a computer. The computer then constructs the finely detailed, 3-D pictures of the body.

9. It is difficult to avoid ionizing radiation because it is difficult to detect. You cannot feel or see the ionizing radiation in order to tell that damage is occurring.

10. No, the law of conservation of mass does not apply to nuclear reactions. Nuclear reactions convert mass to energy according to Einstein's formula ($E = mc^2$).

11. If you have equal masses of a nuclear reaction and a chemical reaction, the nuclear reaction will release much more energy. The energy of a nuclear reaction involves breaking the strong nuclear force of protons and neutrons in the nucleus, whereas the energy of a chemical reaction only involves breaking the much weaker force of the electrons.

12. Fission: Positive: easy to create and control the reaction
does not require burning nonrenewable fossil fuels.
creates new useful elements (plutonium)
Negative: creates dangerous nuclear waste products with long half-lives
Improperly designed reactors can be extremely dangerous
fissile material is difficult and hazardous to mine
Fusion: Positive: generates little nuclear waste
fusible material is easy to find and abundant
creates useful and non dangerous by-products
Negative: technically difficult to achieve due to high heat and density requirements
is prohibitively expensive to build and operate a plant

13. Answers are:
    a. iron (Fe) - 0
    b. krypton (Kr) - 10
    c. magnesium (Mg) - 48
    d. lead (Pb) - 95
    e. carbon (C) - 104
    f. lithium (Li) - 230

14. If a proton were to contact an anti-proton, they would both be converted to pure energy.

15. S^{34} could not be converted to He^3 and P^{31}, because both charge and number of protons and neutrons must be conserved. Although this reaction conserves the number of protons and neutrons ($3 + 31 = 34$), it does not conserve charge ($2 + 15$ does not equal 16).

16. In fusion, energy is released through mass conversion. In fission, energy is released as gamma rays and kinetic energy.

17. When beta decay was first discovered, the energy of the resulting proton and electron was less than the energy of the disintegrating neutron. The law of conservation of energy predicted that a neutrino was carrying away the missing energy. Neutrinos were later detected and proven to exist.

Problems

1. The explosion of TNT is a chemical reaction; no mass is converted to energy. Mass is only converted to energy in nuclear reactions. The answer is zero.

2. $E = mc^2 = 2(1.673 \times 10^{-27} \text{ kg})(3 \times 10^8 \text{m/s})^2 = 3 \times 10^{-10}$ J

3. You would have $1/2^5$ of the original mass left after 5 half-lives, where 5 is the number of half-lives. $(0.25 \text{ kg}) \div 32 = 0.0078$ kg.

4. 2 grams is 1/8 the amount of 16 grams
$1/8 = 1/2^3 = 3$ half-lives
3.8 days $\times$ 3 half-lives = 11.4 days

5. Answers are:
    a. The diameter (D) increases proportionally to the distance (d)

    $$\frac{D_{new}}{d_{new}} = \frac{D_{old}}{d_{old}}$$

    $$D_{new} = d_{new}\left(\frac{D_{old}}{d_{old}}\right) = 3 \text{ m}\left(\frac{0.25 \text{ m}}{1 \text{ m}}\right) = 0.75 \text{ m}$$

    b. The intensity decreases with the square of the distance according to the inverse square law. The distance increases from 1 m to 3 m, therefore the intensity decreases by $1/3^2$, or $1/9$.

6. Answers are:

    a. $A = 4\pi r^2 = 4\pi(0.25 \text{ m})^2 = 0.785 \text{ m}^2$

    $I = \frac{P}{A} = \frac{0.005 \text{ W}}{0.785 \text{ m}^2} = 6.37 \times 10^{-3}$ W/m^2

    b. $A = 4\pi r^2 = 4\pi(2 \text{ m})^2 = 50.27 \text{ m}^2$

    $I = \frac{P}{A} = \frac{0.005 \text{ W}}{50.27 \text{ m}^2} = 9.95 \times 10^{-5}$ W/m^2

    Alternatively,

    $\frac{I_1}{I_2} = \left(\frac{r_1}{r_2}\right)^2$

    $I_1 = I_2\left(\frac{r_1}{r_2}\right)^2 = 6.37 \times 10^{-3} \text{ W/m}^2\left(\frac{0.25 \text{ m}}{2 \text{ m}}\right)^2 = 9.95 \times 10^{-5}$ W/m^2

7. Answers are:
    a. Each watt of gamma radiation results in a dose of 1 rem.
        Each 20 watts of alpha radiation results in a dose of 1 rem.
        The environment gives everyone a dose of 0.3 rem per year.
        Her dose for the year is:
        35 $W_\alpha \div$ 20 W/rem+ 2 $W_\gamma \div$ 1 W/rem+ 0.3 rem = 4.05 rem
    b. The safe limit is 5 rem per year, therefore she should be permitted to
        return to work.

8. Answers are:
    a. Fusion
    b. Fission
    c. Fusion

9. Answers are:
    a. Radioactive beta decay
    b. Radioactive alpha decay
    c. Radioactive beta decay

10. Answers are:
    a. 25 kg, as read from the graph, or alternatively, $^1/_{16}$ of the original 400 kg
        (the half-life decay for 4 half-lives in 40 min).
    b. Since $^1/_2$ of the original mass decays in 10 minutes, the half-life must be
        10 minutes.

Additional Materials

The following pages list materials used in the Investigations in addition to the equipment kits provided. For ease of ordering and buying, the list is divided into the following subsections: office, household, and hardware supplies; laboratory equipment and science educational supplies; household chemicals; and specialty items. Quantities shown are the amounts needed for a class of 30 students with 6 lab groups. Consumable materials are indicated. Perishable, non-commercial, demonstration and optional items are not included in the list.

To familiarize yourself with the equipment and additional materials needed per Investigation, we recommend that you perform each Investigation during your teaching preparation time.

If you have concerns about the use or handling of chemicals, contact the manufacturer of the product with your questions and request a materials safety data sheet (MSDS) for the product. A phone number for the manufacturer is usually listed on the product label. Investigations that use these chemicals should be completed carefully, with safety in mind. Keep the volumes of liquids or powders that students use to a minimum and in small containers. Discuss safety concerns before each Investigation and continue to remind your students to be safe and careful throughout the Investigation. Have cleanup materials such as paper towels, sponges, and plastic trash bags (to collect paper towels with strong smelling chemicals) on hand for spills. Students should always wash their hands after any lab that uses chemicals.

Investigations	Office, household, and hardware supplies	Quantity	Consumable
multiple	simple calculators	6 - 30	
multiple	9-volt batteries (for the timer)	24; quantity depends on whether the timer is used with the AC adapter or batteries	
2.1, 3.3, 4.3, 6.3, 7.1, 7.2, 10.2, 10.3, 12.2, 14.1, 14.2, 14.3, 27.2	meter sticks	6	
2.1, 3.2, 5.1, 9.2, 10.1, 10.2, 11.2, 16.1, 17.1, 17.2, 17.3, 18.2, 21.1, 21.2, 23.1, 25.1, 26.3, 27.1	rulers (metric)	6	
2.1, 9.2, 25.1, 26.3, 27.1	scissors	6	
2.1, 21.1, 21.2, 25.1, 27.2	plastic tape (clear) or Scotch^{TM} brand magic tape (required for 21.1)	6 - 12 rolls	Yes
2.1, 12.2, 23.1	paper clips	600	
2.1, 2.3	1-liter soda bottles, empty	6	Yes
2.1	geometric compass (for drawing circles)	6	
2.1	construction paper	12 pieces	Yes
2.1	sand (enough to fill four 1-liter soda bottles)	1 large bag	

Investigations	Office, household, and hardware supplies	Quantity	Consumable
2.3, 11.2	bathroom scales	6	
2.3, 17.1	scientific calculators	6	
3.1, 3.2, 5.1	rulers, (English)	6	
3.2, 3.3, 4.1, 4.2, 6.3, 7.1, 7.3, 9.2, 10.3, 13.1, 13.3, 14.3, 15.1, 19.3, 21.3, 23.1, 23.3, 27.1, 30.1	graph paper	810 sheets	Yes
5.3, 16.2, 16.3	colored pencils	6 sets	Yes
5.3	drawing paper	30 sheets	Yes
7.2, 17.1	protractors	6	
7.2, 10.2, 10.3, 14.1, 14.3	metric measuring tape	6	
7.2	carbon paper	6 sheets	Yes
7.3, 9.2, 12.2, 12.3	string	~ 30 meters	Yes
7.3	key rings (metal)	6	
8.1, 11.2	masking tape	6 rolls	Yes
8.1, 26.1	permanent markers	6	Yes
9.2	cardboard	6 large pieces	Yes
9.2	hole punch (hand-held)	6	
12.2, 21.1, 27.1	modelling clay (2 x 2 x 4 cm)	9 - 27 sticks	Yes
12.2	wood blocks (5 x 10 x 25 cm)	6	
12.3, 21.1	flexible, drinking straws	30	Yes
12.3	washers	12	
13.2	oscillator supply kits (bowls, rubber bands, plastic rulers, elastic string, stiff wire, curved tracks, modelling clay, wood blocks, marbles, bolts)	6	Yes
14.2	flat pans with laminated grids on the bottom (such as deep cookie sheets) with two blocks of wood and straight edge that fit in the pan	6	
15.2	wine glasses	3 - 18 (depends on use for a demo or group work)	

651

Investigations	Office, household, and hardware supplies	Quantity	Consumable
15.2	glass bottles	3 - 18 (depends on use for a demo or group work)	
16.3	flashlight (optional)	6	
17.1	index cards (white, any size)	12	Yes
18.1, 25.1	poster board	12	Yes
19.1, 19.2, 19.3, 20.1, 20.2, 21.3, 23.1, 23.2, 24.1, 24.2, 24.3	D-cell batteries	48 or more	Yes
21.1, 21.2	thread or light string	3 meters	Yes
21.2	balloons (small)	12	Yes
22.2, 23.1	materials for testing magnets (an assortment of plastic, metal, wood objects)	6 kits	
22.3	steel bucket or baking pan	6	
23.1	wire, magnetic, 24 gauge	18 meters	Yes
23.1	sand paper (fine or medium)	6 sheets	Yes
23.1	nails, galvanized, 7-centimeters long	12	
23.3	rubber bands, large	12	
24.1	diodes (rectifier and signal diodes work best)	6	
24.2	transistors (several npn; do not use pnp transistors), assorted resistors (100 ohms to 100 kilo-ohms, 1/8 to 1/4 watts)	6 kits	
24.3	several logic integrated circuits (at least AND and OR); see notes in teacher's guide for 24.3), 6 330 ohm resistors (1/8 to 1/4 watt)	6 kits	
24.2,. 24.3	1.5 to 3-volt DC electric motor, solar cell (4-10 cm^2)	6 kits	
24.1, 24.2, 24.3	22-gauge solid core wire, small (an assortment)	6 - 12 spools	
24.1, 24.2, 24.3	solderless breadboard	6	
24.1, 24.2, 24.3	small flat-bladed screwdriver, small needlenose pliers, wire stripping tool, two jumper wires with alligator clips	6 tool kits	
25.1, 26.3 (if hot-melt glue is not available)	glue, white	6 bottles	Yes

Investigations	Office, household, and hardware supplies	Quantity	Consumable
25.1	colored markers	6 sets	Yes
25.1	old magazines	12 or more	Yes
25.2, 25.3, 26.2	tongs	6	
25.2, 25.3	stirring rods	6	
25.2	plastic bottles with caps (500 mL)	6	Yes
25.2	pans with lids (large enough to submerge a 500-mL bottle)	6	
25.2	bowls (large enough to submerge a 500-mL bottle)	6	
25.2	oven mitts	6 pairs	
25.3, 26.1, 30.1	foam cups (large)	30	Yes
25.3, 26.1	plastic cups (thin)	12	Yes
25.3	2-liter containers	12	
25.3	wire pieces (metal)	6 pieces	Yes
26.1	baking pans (shallow)	6	
26.1	copper nails (small)	24	
26.2	ice cube trays	6	
26.3	cardboard (8.5 x 11-inch pieces)	18	Yes
26.3	double-sided tape	6 rolls	Yes
26.3	aluminum foil	1 roll	Yes
26.3	hot-melt glue (or regular white glue)		Yes
27.1	packaging tape	6 rolls	Yes
27.2	drinking straws	30	Yes
27.2	office sticky notes	30	Yes
27.2	PVC pipe (8-inch length of 3/4-inch pipe with pre-drilled hole, 8-inch length of 1/2-inch pipe with pre-drilled hole, and coupling)	6 sets	Yes
27.2	plastic tubing (1/4-inch aquarium tubing)	6 meters	Yes

Investigations	Office, household, and hardware supplies	Quantity	Consumable
27.3	plastic bottle (1-liter, modified cap w/ air valve)	6	Yes
30.1	pennies	600	
30.1	cafeteria trays or other large trays	6	

Sections	Laboratory and science educational supplies	Quantity	Consumable
2.3, 5.2, 6.1, 6.2, 9.1, 9.3, 21.2, 21.3, 25.3, 26.1, 27.3, 29.1, 29.3	electronic balances or a triple-beam balances	6	
18.2	large springs	6	
18.2	polarizing filters	12	
19.2, 19.3, 20.1, 20.2, 23.1, 23.2, 23.3, 24.1, 24.2	digital mulitmeters with red and black leads	6	
25.2, 25.3, 26.1, 26.3, 29.3	thermometers	18	
25.2, 26.2, 29.3	beakers (250 mL), glass	12	
25.2, 27.3	graduated cylinders	6	
25.2	hot plates	6	
29.1	lab aprons	30	
29.1	goggles	30	
29.3	beakers (250 mL), plastic	6	
29.3	hydrochloric acid (0.1 M solution) provided in 500-mL bottles (200 mL per bottle)	1.2 liters; 6 bottles	Yes
29.3	magnesium strips (~ 2 grams each)	30	Yes
29.3	forceps	6	

Sections	Household chemicals	Quantity	Consumable
25.3	vegetable oil	2 liters	Yes
14.2, 26.2, 27.2	food coloring	3 packages	Yes
29.1	mixture kits (100-mL vials containing a mixture of sawdust, iron fillings, colored sand, and salt) plus equipment to facilitate separating the mixture	6	Yes

Sections	Specialty items	Quantity	Consumable
2.1	street maps of local area	6	
7.1, 22.1, 22.3	navigational compass	6	
8.1	basketballs	6	
12.2	rubber balls (small, 5-cm diameter)	6	
14.2	Slinky$^{(TM)}$ spring toy	6	
20.3	small appliances labeled with power ratings (iron, toaster oven, electric drill, desk lamp, hair dryer)	3 (for demo)	
21.1	charged materials (wool, glass, plastic comb)		
27.3	bicycle pumps	6	

Special notes:

1 Have on hand at all times enough lab aprons, goggles, and oven mitts for all 30 students. Some investigations require protective wear.

2 Plain, white copy paper (8.5 x 11 inches) is also useful during many investigations.

3 Stopwatches may be used in place of timers for Investigations 11.2, 13.2, 25.2, 25.3, and 26.3. One stopwatch is used per lab group.

4 Have extra 9-volt and D-cell batteries on hand at all times. The 9-volt batteries are used with the timer. When using the sound and waves generator with the timer, using the AC adaptor is recommended. Four D-cell batteries are needed to run each electric motor.

5 In Investigation 26.1, you will need to have access to ice. In Investigation, 26.2, you will need to have access to a freezer. For some Investigations, such as 27.2, you will need to have access to water.

655